BASIC FORMULAS

Class Width = Range/(# of classes) and roundup

Population Mean:
$$\mu = \frac{\Sigma x}{N}$$

Sample Mean: $\overline{x} = \dfrac{\Sigma x}{n}$

Population Variance
$$\sigma^2 = \frac{\Sigma (x-\mu)^2}{N}$$

Population Standard Deviation:
$$\sigma = \sqrt{\frac{\Sigma (x-\mu)^2}{N}} \quad ; \quad \sigma = \sqrt{\frac{\Sigma x^2 - \frac{(\Sigma x)^2}{N}}{N}}$$

Sample Standard Deviation:
$$s = \sqrt{\frac{\Sigma (x-\overline{x})^2}{n-1}} \quad ; \quad s = \sqrt{\frac{\Sigma x^2 - \frac{(\Sigma x)^2}{n}}{n-1}}$$

z Score Formula:
$$z = \frac{X-\mu}{\sigma} \quad ; \quad z = \frac{X-\overline{x}}{s}$$

Raw Score Formula:
$$x = \mu + z_x\sigma \quad ; \quad x = \overline{X} + z(s)$$

Percentile Rank Formula:
$$PR \text{ of } x = \frac{[B + (\tfrac{1}{2})E]}{N} (100)$$

PROBABILITY

Permutation Rule: $_nP_n = n!$

Permutation Rule for n objects taken s at a time:
$$_nP_s = n(n-1)(n-2) \cdots (n-s+1)$$

Permutation Rule of N objects with k alike objects
Given N objects where n_1 are alike, n_2 are alike, ... ,n_k are alike, then the number of permutations of these N objects is:
$$\frac{N!}{(n_1!)(n_2!) \cdots (n_k!)}$$

Number of Combinations of n objects taken s at a time:
$$_nC_s = \frac{n!}{s!\,(n-s)!}$$

Classical Probability Definition for Equally Likely Outcomes:
$$P(\text{Event E}) = \frac{\text{number of outcomes satisfying event E}}{\text{total \# of outcomes in sample space}}$$

Relative Frequency Approach to Calculating Probability:
$$P(\text{Event A}) = \frac{\text{number of times event A occurred}}{\text{total \# of times the experiment was repeated}}$$

The Addition Rule:
$$P(A \text{ or } B) = P(A) + P(B) - P(A \text{ and } B)$$

The Complement Rule:
$$P(E) + P(E') = 1$$

Multiplication Rule for:
Independent Events
$$P(A \text{ and } B) = P(A) \cdot P(B)$$

Multiplication Rule for:
Dependent Events:
$$P(A \text{ and } B) = P(A) \cdot P(B|A)$$

Conditional Probability Formula
$$P(A|B) = \frac{P(A \text{ and } B)}{P(B)}$$

Discrete Random Variable X:

MEAN: $\mu = \displaystyle\sum_{\substack{all\ possible \\ X\ values}} X \cdot P(X)$

Standard Deviation:
$$\sigma = \sqrt{\sum_{\substack{all\ possible \\ X\ values}} (X-\mu)^2 \cdot P(X)}$$

Binomial Probability Formula
$$P(s \text{ successes in } n \text{ trials}) = {_nC_s}\, p^s\, q^{(n-s)}$$

Binomial Distribution:
Mean: $\mu_s = np$

Standard Deviation: $\sigma_s = \sqrt{n \cdot p \cdot (1-p)}$

Sampling Distribution of the Mean:
Mean: $\mu_{\overline{x}} = \mu$

Standard Error: $\sigma_{\overline{x}} = \dfrac{\sigma}{\sqrt{n}}$

estimate of the standard error: $s_{\bar{x}} = \dfrac{s}{\sqrt{n}}$

Test Statistic Formula:

a) for normal distribution:

$$z = \frac{\bar{x} - \mu_{\bar{x}}}{\sigma_{\bar{x}}}$$

b) for t distribution:

$$t = \frac{\bar{x} - \mu_{\bar{x}}}{s_{\bar{x}}}$$

To find t_c, need to determine degrees of freedom using formula:

$$df = n-1$$

degrees of freedom: $df = n-1$

PROPORTION

population proportion: $p = \dfrac{X}{N}$

sample proportion: $\hat{p} = \dfrac{x}{n}$

Sampling Distribution of The Proportion:

Mean: $\mu_{\hat{p}} = p$

Standard Error: $\sigma_{\hat{p}} = \sqrt{\dfrac{p(1-p)}{n}}$

Test Statistic Formula is:

$$z = \frac{\hat{p} - \mu_{\hat{p}}}{\sigma_{\hat{p}}}$$

ESTIMATION:

POPULATION MEAN:
known population standard deviation

90% Confidence Interval:

$$\bar{X} - (1.65)\frac{\sigma}{\sqrt{n}} \text{ to } \bar{X} + (1.65)\frac{\sigma}{\sqrt{n}}$$

95% Confidence Interval:

$$\bar{X} - (1.96)\frac{\sigma}{\sqrt{n}} \text{ to } \bar{X} + (1.96)\frac{\sigma}{\sqrt{n}}$$

99% Confidence Interval:

$$\bar{X} - (2.58)\frac{\sigma}{\sqrt{n}} \text{ to } \bar{X} + (2.58)\frac{\sigma}{\sqrt{n}}$$

margin of error:
(known population standard)

$$E = (z)\left(\frac{\sigma}{\sqrt{n}} \right)$$

sample size:

$$n = \left[\frac{z\sigma}{E} \right]^2$$

POPULATION MEAN:
unknown population standard deviation

90% Confidence Interval:

$$\bar{X} - (t_{95\%})\frac{s}{\sqrt{n}} \text{ to } \bar{X} + (t_{95\%})\frac{s}{\sqrt{n}}$$

95% Confidence Interval:

$$\bar{X} - (t_{97.5\%})\frac{s}{\sqrt{n}} \text{ to } \bar{X} + (t_{97.5\%})\frac{s}{\sqrt{n}}$$

99% Confidence Interval:

$$\bar{X} - (t_{99.5\%})\frac{s}{\sqrt{n}} \text{ to } \bar{X} + (t_{99.5\%})\frac{s}{\sqrt{n}}$$

POPULATION PROPORTION:

90% Confidence Interval:

$$\hat{p} - (1.65)\, s_{\hat{p}} \text{ to } \hat{p} + (1.65)\, s_{\hat{p}}$$

95% Confidence Interval:

$$\hat{p} - (1.96)\, s_{\hat{p}} \text{ to } \hat{p} + (1.96)\, s_{\hat{p}}$$

99% Confidence Interval:

$$\hat{p} - (2.58)\, s_{\hat{p}} \text{ to } \hat{p} + (2.58)\, s_{\hat{p}}$$

margin of error:

$$E = (z)\left(\sqrt{\frac{\hat{p}(1-\hat{p})}{n}} \right)$$

sample size:

$$n = \frac{z^2 (\hat{p})(1-\hat{p})}{E^2}$$

conservative sample size formula:

$$n = \frac{z^2 (0.25)}{E^2}$$

Sampling Distribution of the Difference Between Two Means

mean: $\mu_{\bar{x}_1 - \bar{x}_2} = \mu_1 - \mu_2$

standard error: $\sigma_{\bar{x}_1 - \bar{x}_2} = \sqrt{\dfrac{\sigma_1^2}{n_1} + \dfrac{\sigma_2^2}{n_2}}$

estimate of the standard error:

$$s_{\bar{x}_1 - \bar{x}_2} = \sqrt{\frac{(n_1-1)s_1^2 + (n_2-1)s_2^2}{n_1+n_2-2} \cdot \left(\frac{1}{n_1} + \frac{1}{n_2} \right)}$$

t distribution with degrees of freedom given by: $df = n_1 + n_2 - 2$.

Test Statistic Formula is:

$$t = \frac{(\bar{x}_1 - \bar{x}_2) - \mu_{\bar{x}_1 - \bar{x}_2}}{s_{\bar{x}_1 - \bar{x}_2}}$$

difference between the two sample means: $d = \bar{X}_1 - \bar{X}_2$

CHI-SQUARE
Pearson's Chi-Square Statistic

$$X^2 = \sum_{all\ cells} \frac{(O-E)^2}{E} \quad ;$$

$$X^2 = \sum_{all\ cells} \left(\frac{O^2}{E}\right) - n$$

degrees of freedom: **df = (r-1)(c-1)**

expected cell frequency $= \dfrac{(RT)\ (CT)}{n}$

CORRELATION

Pearson's or Sample Correlation Coefficient:

$$r = \frac{n\sum(xy) - (\sum x)(\sum y)}{\sqrt{n(\sum x^2) - (\sum x)^2}\sqrt{n(\sum y^2) - (\sum y)^2}}$$

degrees of freedom: **df = n - 2**

Coefficient of Determination = r^2

Regression Line Formula: **y' = a + bx**

$$b = \frac{n\sum(xy) - \sum x\sum y}{n(\sum x^2) - (\sum x)^2} \quad ; a = \frac{\sum y - b\sum x}{n}$$

Sampling Distributions of the Difference Between Two Proportions

Mean: $\mu_{\hat{p}_1 - \hat{p}_2} = p_1 - p_2$

Standard Error:

$$s_{\hat{p}_1 - \hat{p}_2} = \sqrt{\frac{\hat{p}(1-\hat{p})}{n_1} + \frac{\hat{p}(1-\hat{p})}{n_2}} \quad \text{or}$$

$$s_{\hat{p}_1 - \hat{p}_2} = \sqrt{\hat{p}(1-\hat{p})\left(\frac{1}{n_1} + \frac{1}{n_2}\right)}$$

where $\hat{p} = \dfrac{X_1 + X_2}{n_1 + n_2}$ or $\hat{p} = \dfrac{n_1\hat{p}_1 + n_2\hat{p}_2}{n_1 + n_2}$

Test Statistic Formula is: $z = \dfrac{(\hat{p}_1 - \hat{p}_2) - \mu_{\hat{p}_1 - \hat{p}_2}}{s\hat{p}_1 - \hat{p}_2}$

ANOVA

Sums of Squares $SS = \sum(x - \bar{x})^2$

$SS_{(between\ treatments)} + SS_{(within\ treatments)} = SS_{(total)}$

$$SS_{(total)} = \sum x^2 - \frac{(\sum x)^2}{N}$$

$SS_{(between\ treatments)} =$

$$\left(\frac{(\sum T_1)^2}{n_1} + \frac{(\sum T_2)^2}{n_2} + \dots + \frac{(\sum T_i)^2}{n_1}\right) - \frac{(\sum x)^2}{N}$$

$$SS_{(within\ treatments)} = \sum x^2 - \left(\frac{(\sum T_1)^2}{n_1} + \frac{(\sum T_2)^2}{n_2} + \dots + \frac{(\sum T_i)^2}{n_1}\right)$$

Degrees of Freedom: $df_{(Between)} + df_{(within)} = df_{(Total)}$

Where: $df_{(Between)} = k - 1$
$df_{(within)} = N - k$
$df_{(Total)} = N - 1$

Mean Square, (denoted MS), formulas:

$$MS_{(Between)} = \frac{SS_{bet}}{df_{bet}}$$

$$MS_{(within)} = \frac{SS_{within}}{df_{within}}$$

Test statistic formula: $F = \dfrac{s_1^2}{s_2^2}$

test statistic: F-statistic

$$F = \frac{treatment\ sample\ variance}{within\ sample\ variance}$$

NONPARAMETRIC TESTS
SIGN TEST for MEDIANS

binomial mean: $\mu_s = np$

binomial std dev: $\sigma_s = \sqrt{np(1-p)}$

If the statistical result 0, is less than n/2,

then test statistic is: $z = \dfrac{(O - \frac{1}{2}) - \mu_s}{\sigma_s}$

If the statistical result 0, is greater than n/2,

then the test statistic is: $z = \dfrac{(O - \frac{1}{2}) - \mu_s}{\sigma_s}$

MANN-WHITNEY RANK-SUM TEST

When normal distribution can be applied, then test statistic, z, is:

$$z = \frac{w - \dfrac{n_1(n_1 + n_2 + 1)}{2}}{\sqrt{\dfrac{n_1 n_2 (n_1 + n_2 + 1)}{12}}}$$

KRUSKAL-WALLIS H TEST

Kruskal-Wallis H test statistic formula:

$$H = \frac{12}{N(N+1)} \left[\frac{(\sum R_1)^2}{n_1} + \frac{(\sum R_2)^2}{n_2} + \ldots + \frac{(\sum R_k)^2}{n_k} \right] - 3(N+1)$$

INTRODUCTION TO STATISTICS

Seventh Edition

INTRODUCTION
to STATISTICS

Carmine DeSanto • Michael Totoro

PEARSON

Custom
Publishing

Printed in the United States of America

10 9 8 7 6 5 4 3 2 1

ISBN 0-536-83612-4

2004360265

LH/LD

Please visit our web site at *www.pearsoncustom.com*

PEARSON CUSTOM PUBLISHING
75 Arlington Street, Suite 300, Boston, MA 02116
A Pearson Education Company

CONTENTS

4   Probability   221

5   Random Variables and Discrete Probabiliy Distributions   307

9 Introduction to Hypothesis Testing   577

10 Hypothesis Test Involving a Population Proportion   625

11 Hypothesis Test Involving a Population Mean   655

P R E F A C E

PREFACE TO THE SEVENTH EDITION

Today, mathematics education incorporates the use of all forms of technology. It is of no surprise that the teaching of elementary statistics incorporates these technological tools. Today's elementary statistics curriculum emphasizes the interpretation and presentation of data by using the technological tools readily available to the student. As a result, less time is being spent on computational skills while emphasis is being placed on statistical thinking. Most pedagogical approaches in mathematics education reform places data analysis as a high objective in most mathematics coursework. The proliferation and the use of technology in the home, classroom, business and industry have encouraged the student to use the technology both within, as well as, outside the classroom.

Furthermore, most high school curriculum now presents elementary statistics concepts as part of the high school coursework. In recent years, high school students have been encouraged to take an elementary statistics course as an elective to help fulfill their high school requirements.

In this seventh edition, we have continued to emphasize a step-by-step problem solving method while encouraging the student to understand concepts. Our writing style continues to "talk" to the student while developing the statistical concepts and ideas. You should find a decrease in computational emphasis. We have relied a lot on technological support with the hope that an in-depth analysis of the concepts and ideas will help develop a better understanding of statistics.

FEATURES OF THE SEVENTH EDITION

In this edition, the use of the TI-83 Plus calculator is ubiquitous. With the exception of Chapter one, Chapters two through eight have minor changes. In Chapter one we incorporated a presentation of sampling and sampling techniques. Chapters on hypothesis testing involving two proportions, ANOVA and nonparametric statistics have been added. Throughout the hypothesis testing chapters we changed the interpretations for decisions from an approach of a dependency on raw score, or critical score, to a standard score, and test statistic development. Furthermore, each chapter, where applicable, now has a section devoted to the p-value interpretation for hypothesis testing decisions. The seventh edition contains an extensive presentation on the use of the TI-83 Plus calculator in Appendix E.

As was first presented in the sixth edition, the exercises at the end of each chapter are keyed to the chapter sections. A chapter review and chapter test is also included. At the beginning of each chapter a table of contents outlines the chapter highlights. At the end of each chapter key terms are listed and include the pages within the chapter where the key terms appear.

ADDITIONAL FEATURES OF THE TEXT

- **Case Studies:** Appearing in all chapters are actual applications of statistical concepts. These case studies are presented as articles, statistical snapshots, or research articles that have been published in newspapers, magazines, or journals. All case studies are based on real data and allow the student to see the relevance of statistics and why a student should study statistics.
- **Using Technology:** At the end of every chapter is a section entitled Using Technology. These sections contain an example of software output such as MINITAB, or Microsoft EXCEL, or TI-83 Plus output screens. Along with each output screen is a brief interpretation of the statistics being represented.
- **What Do You Think?** Problems: Each chapter contains a What Do You Think? Section in the chapter exercises. This section provides the student with a set of realistic exercises which enable the student to explore diverse applications. In most cases, the problems will present applications which will require the student to analyze and interpret the information relating to some real practical situation.

- **Analyzing the DATABASE with Technology:** Within each chapter exercise section there is a section entitled Analyzing the Database Using Technology. The DATABASE referred to is included in the appendix. Students are encouraged to use a technological tool with the DATABASE to investigate the concepts presented in each chapter.
- **Projects:** Each chapter exercise section includes a section entitled Projects. Students are presented with suggestions for further exploration of the statistics presented within the chapter.

This text has been in production and revision for some thirty-five years. We believe that the features that distinguish it from other introductory statistics texts are:

- **Presentation of the Material:** Our informal "conversational" writing style thoroughly develops and explains all statistical concepts. The pedagogical approach of actively learning statistics through discovery and applications makes the subject relevant to the beginning student, and shows each student "the why" of studying statistics.
- **Design and Format:** All definitions, procedures, theorems, formulas, and other important concepts are highlighted with appropriate headings that include a two-color ink format with appropriate shading where applicable. Most procedures are carefully outlined and highlighted with this two-color enhancement to help students focus on the important aspects of each chapter.
- **Examples:** Every chapter contains an abundant number of examples which cover the concepts for each section. Relevant guided solutions are carefully developed.
- **Solutions:** The solution to every example is presented with a very clear and readable style. Our approach is built on the premise that each step is not trivial. Consequently, we have provided a step-by-step approach in solving each problem.
- **Numerous Diagrams:** The text uses many diagrams to picture many of the concepts visually. Most have been enhanced by using two-color highlighting.
- **Exercises:** The exercises are a special feature of this text. Each chapter contains numerous problems in each chapter section that cover a wide range of applications representing many diverse fields. The content of the problems will interest both the student and the instructor. Most of the problems use real data from periodicals, reports, newspapers, and journals. These problems provide an insight into the many diverse applications of the use of statistics. Exercise types include: fill-in the blank, multiple choice, true false questions, and word problems. The exercises are first keyed to the chapter sections. A chapter review follows along with What Do You Think?, database using technology and projects. In each chapter, a chapter test is presented summarizing all key chapter concepts.
- **Key Terms:** At the end of each chapter a glossary of key terms and concepts listing the appropriate page in which the term appears.
- **Database:** A database with 75 student records appears in the Appendix. Students are encouraged to use the database with a technological support hardware.
- **How to Use the TI-83 Plus Calculator:** In Appendix E is an extensive instruction section on the use of the TI-83 Plus calculator for most of the statistics procedures used in the text.

ACKNOWLEDGMENTS

We express our thanks to our colleagues at Nassau Community College who have made helpful criticisms and suggestions. We name some of them below as a sign of our gratitude but emphasize that they are not responsible for any weaknesses that may remain in the text. Special gratitude is reserved for Joe Altamura, Armen Baderian, James Baldwin, George Bruns, Mauro Cassano, Anthony Catania, Ron Cavallaro, Dennis Christy, Art Cohen, Kathleen Cramer, John Earnest, Les Frimerman, Ron Goodridge, Mark Gwydir, Larry Kaufer, Marcy Lerner, Zach Levy, Jack Lubowsky, Abe Mantell, Raphael Marino, George Miller, Tony Razziano, Gary Spelber, Richard Silvestri, Thomas Timchek, and Elaine Zseller.

We wish to express our indebtedness to Ken Lemp for his continual editing and helpful comments and suggestions.

We especially appreciate the editing contributions of Joan Tomaszewski who reviewed each chapter and section exercise for accuracy and content and provided valuable suggestions. In addition, we would like to express our heartfelt thanks to the late William Porreca whose years of contributions to this project are deeply appreciated and to Doug Brown, the chair of the Mathematics/Statistics/Computer Processing Department, for his continued encouragement and support.

Special thanks are extended to Chris Chiodo, Marisa Raffaele and Steve Welch for their guidance and dedication to this project. In addition, the technical support provided by Kristen Colman and Liane Hill has proven to be invaluable.

Finally, and most importantly, we would like to thank our wives Debbie and Kathleen, and our children Craig, Matthew, and Allison for their continuous support, understanding, patience, and encouragement during the preparation of this project, and for bringing love and happiness to our lives.

Carmine DeSanto
Michael Totoro

Introduction to Statistics

Contents

1.1 INTRODUCTION

What is Statistics?

Your life is a statistic!
    Can you describe a *typical day* in your life?
    For example:

- What do you have for breakfast?
  - eggs or egg beaters?
  - pastry or oat bran muffins?
  - coffee, tea or decaffeinated drink?
  - orange or grapefruit juice?
- Are you a full-time or part-time student?
- How many hours a week do you work?

    Consider the following fascinating facts that have been used to describe an "average" day in America.
    Did you know that on an average day in America . . .

- 9,077 babies are born. (1,282 are illegitimate.)
- 5,962 couples will wed; 1,986 will divorce.
- 56,000 animals are turned over to animal shelters.
- 3 million people will go to the movies.
- A car is stolen every 33 seconds.
- 2,466 children are bitten by dogs.
- 500 million cups of coffee are drunk.

- $54,794 is spent to fight dandruff.
- Amateurs take 19,178,000 snapshots.
- 679 million telephone conversations occur, of which 90 million are long distance.
- People drink 90 million cans of beer.
- 2,740 teenagers get pregnant.
- 438 immigrants become citizens.
- 10,930,000 cows are milked.
- Tobacco chewers chew up to 1.3 million packages of the stuff.
- The U.S. Postal Service sells 90 million stamps, handles 230 million pieces of mail and delivers 834,000 packages.
- The snack bar at Chicago's O'Hare Airport sells 5,479 hot dogs, covered with 12 gallons of relish and nine gallons of mustard, washed down with 890 gallons of coffee![1]

The previous statements represent statistical descriptions of a large collection of information or observations for phenomenon which can be described with a *numerical value* such as a person's height or *non-numerical value* like a person's hair color. Before these numerical and/or non-numerical value's of information or observations are arranged or analyzed in a useful manner they are called raw data values or simply **raw data**. The term **raw** is used because statistical techniques have not as of yet been applied to analyze the data.

DEFINITION 1.1
Statistics involves the procedures associated with the data collection process, the summarizing and interpretation of data, and the drawing of inferences or conclusions based upon the analysis of the data.

We will be primarily concerned with the application of statistical techniques to the collected raw data. The statistical techniques we will examine provides us with ways to summarize and describe the data, to search for patterns or relationships within the data, and to draw inferences or conclusions from the data. Essentially, statistics can be defined as follows.

After raw data is collected, we are usually confronted with a massive list of numbers, names, opinions, dates, measurements, percentages, etc. To make such a collection of raw data more meaningful and useful we need to examine the data set in a formal way.

A formal exploration of raw data may involve the use of:

- graphs to visually display the data, or
- numerical techniques to describe the main characteristics of the data.

These data explorations can also assist us in *discovering patterns or relationships within the data,* which will help *to generate hypotheses or to draw inferences* from the data set.

Essentially the study of statistics involves describing the main characteristics of raw data as well as drawing conclusions from the data based upon the analysis of the data. From this point of view, statistics can thus be subdivided into two branches: *Descriptive Statistics* and *Inferential Statistics.*

DEFINITION 1.2
Descriptive Statistics uses numerical and/or visual techniques to summarize or describe the data in a clear and effective manner.

Let us consider some case studies that illustrate the use of descriptive statistics.

---

[1] These facts appeared in *American Averages: Amazing Facts of Everyday Life,* by M. Feinsilber and W. B. Mead (Doubleday, New York).

CASE STUDY 1.1   NHL as a Growth Industry

The snapshot entitled "NHL a Growth Industry" is shown in Figure 1.1. This snapshot compares the size of the average NHL player of the 1971–72 season to the average NHL player of the 1994–95 season.

According to the snapshot, the *average NHL player* in 1971–72 was 5 feet 11 inches tall and weighed 184 pounds while the *average NHL player* in 1994–95 stands 6 feet 1 inch and weighs in at 196 pounds. The averages used to describe the height and weight of a typical hockey player for the indicated years were determined using a numerical formula. To appreciate the concise manner in which the average NHL player is described, realize that the data from which these averages were computed contained the weights and heights of **ALL** the NHL players for the years 1971–72 and 1994–95. If you were presented with this long data list rather than the average weight and height, you would not find this list helpful in visualizing a typical NHL player. However, presenting the *average weight and height of an NHL player, as shown in Figure 1.1, is a more concise way to numerically describe the "typical" NHL player* which helps us to comprehend the size of a professional hockey player.

Statistical Snapshot
NHL a Growth Industry

Source: NHL   **1971–72**   **1994–95**

FIGURE 1.1

CASE STUDY 1.2   The Cities of Charleston and Sarasota

The following statistical data describes the population, income and age of the people of the cities of Charleston, South Carolina and Sarasota, Florida.

TABLE 1.1   Statistical information for Charleston, South Carolina:

Population & Income:		Breakdown by Age:	
Population (metro area)	543,022	Under 6	10.7%
5-year projection	582,598	6–17	17.2%
Median household income	$37,680	18–24	12.3%
Median household wealth	$51,507	25–34	18.4%
Median age	30	35–44	15.7%
		45–54	10.0%
		55–64	6.6%
		65 & over	8.6%

CASE STUDY 1.2   The Cities of Charleston and Sarasota (continued)

FIGURE 1.2   **FIGURE 1.3**

TABLE 1.2   Statistical information for Sarasota, Florida:

Population & Income:		Breakdown by Age:	
Population (metro)	506,762	Under 6	6.3%
5-year projection	518,333	6–17	11.1%
Median household income	$30,130	18–24	6.2%
Median household wealth	$93,559	25–34	11.7%
Median age	47	35–44	12.6%
		45–54	10.1%
		55–64	11.3%
		65 & over	30.6%

The statistical information used to describe the population size, income, wealth and age of all the people living within these cities is very helpful in comparing Charleston and Sarasota. The statistical information uses both numerical and visual techniques to summarize the characteristics of both cities as shown in Tables 1.1 & 1.2, and Figures 1.2 & 1.3.

a) Interpret and compare the median income, median wealth and median ages of both these cities. In Chapter 3, we will discuss the concept of median. However, at this time, interpret the median value as the value having half of the data values lying below this median value while the remaining half of the data values lie above this median value.

b) Discuss how the graphs in Figures 1.2 and 1.3, which represent the ages of these two cities help explain the large difference in the median age of these cities.

c) Why would you expect Charleston's median income to be greater than Sarasota's median income? On the other hand, why would you expect Sarasota's median wealth to be greater than Charleston's median wealth?

Inferential statistics is the branch of statistics that involves drawing conclusions about a large group, a population, based on the analysis of a smaller group of data, a sample, collected from the population. Let's examine this concept in *Case Study 1.3.*

CASE STUDY 1.3   Time to Relax?

According to a *CNN/Gallup* nationwide telephone poll of 1,000 adults regarding leisure time, *52% of adults say they don't have enough free time.* This poll result is illustrated in Figure 1.4.

Statistical Snapshot

**CNN/Gallup Poll States: Most Adults Say
They Don't Have Enough Time For Leisure**

Enough   48%

Not Enough   52%

FIGURE 1.4

The *CNN/Gallup* pollsters are making an **inference** about the **typical American adult's** leisure time. A conclusion that can be drawn from this survey is that **most U.S. adults** *feel that they don't have enough time for leisure.* Since it is impractical for the pollsters to survey the response of ALL U.S. adults on leisure time, they used the response of only some (1,000) U.S. adults to infer about the leisure time of the majority of ALL U.S. adults. *This conclusion about the leisure time of the majority of ALL U.S. adults based on the response of only 1,000 adults is an example of inferential statistics.*

In Case Study 1.3, the pollsters based their inference about **all U.S. adults** on **the opinions of 1000 adults** during their telephone survey. This is the **essence of Inferential Statistics.** These pollsters are drawing **a conclusion or inference about *ALL* adults using the opinions of only a portion**, (i.e. the 1000 adults telephoned in their nationwide poll), **of U.S. adults.** The pollsters are really interested in the **opinions of ALL U.S. adults;** however it is impractical to poll every U.S. adult. In statistics the entire group of interest is referred to as the **population**, while the smaller group selected from the population for analysis is called the **sample.**

DEFINITION 1.3
The **population** is the entire collection of all individuals or objects of interest.

DEFINITION 1.4
The **sample** is the portion of the population that is selected for study.

In Case Study 1.3, the pollsters selected **a sample of 1,000 U.S. adults** to poll used this sample to obtain data regarding the opinions of **the population of ALL U.S. adults.** We may consider *the population to consist of all U.S. adults or the opinions of all U.S. adults.* The **opinions of all the U.S. adults** represent the **data values of the population**. The pollsters used the data values of the sample or opinions of 1,000 adults to draw a conclusion about the entire population. We will now use the notions of population and sample to define inferential statistics.

DEFINITION 1.5

Inferential Statistics is the process of using **sample information t**o draw inferences or conclusions about the **population.**

This concept plays an important role in our study of statistics so we present another case study on the use inferential statistics.

CASE STUDY 1.4   Cybercitizens

A pollster, Yankelovich Partners Inc, who has been tracking the lifestyles and values of Americans describes the profile of cybercitizens compared to the average U.S. citizen. Yankelovich randomly surveyed 414 on-line and internet users from their research database of 16,000 people representative of Americans 16 and older. Yankelovich identified a cybercitizen as anyone who regularly uses an on-line computer service or the internet.

   Their survey results describing the typical cybercitizen are shown in Figure 1.5. The margin of error for their survey results was stated to be *plus or minus 5 percentage points*.

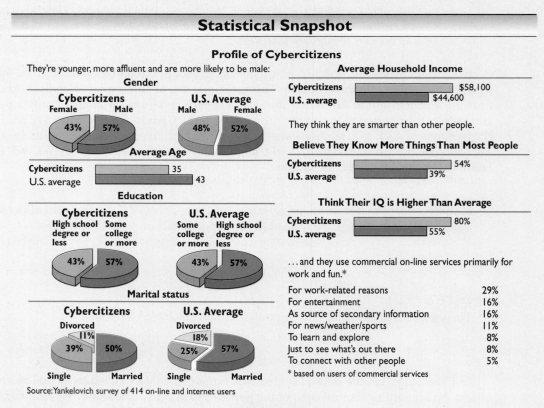

FIGURE 1.5

CASE STUDY 1.4   Cybercitizens (continued)

a) Name the populations being described in Figure 1.5.

b) Identity the sample used to define one of these populations? How was the sample selected and try to explain what that means to you? What is the sample size—i.e. the number of people selected for the sample?

c) State two conclusions that you can infer from the survey about each population. In each case, identify the data values of interest for the population.

d) Is the typical cybercitizen male or female? What about the typical U.S. citizen?

e) Who is older, the typical cybercitizen or the U.S. citizen? Can you explain why this might be the case?

f) Who has more college education—the cybercitizen or the U.S. citizen?

g) Is the cybercitizen more or less likely to be single? Married? Divorced?

h) Is the typical cybercitizen living in a household that makes more or less money than the average citizen?

i) Who thinks—the cybercitizen or the U.S. citizen—are smarter than the other?

j) Write a composite profile of the typical cybercitizen based upon the results of this survey. Begin the composite: "the typical cybercitizen is more likely to be male, . . .".

k) If I told you that I have a friend who is an active internet user and *she is a divorced 47 year old high school graduate with average intelligence making $45,000* would that surprise you based on the characteristics of a cybercitizen? Explain your answer.

l) Why is this case study an example of inferential statistics? Explain your answer.

m) If another random sample of 414 on-line and internet users was selected, do you believe the results of this new sample would be exactly the same as the results of the first sample? Or do you believe there would be a difference? Explain.

n) If we could do the improbable and survey every on-line and internet user in the U.S., do you think the results of this SAMPLE would be exactly the same as the results of ALL the users? Or do you believe there would a difference in the sample results and the population results? Explain.

o) Since inference statistics uses sample information to draw a conclusion about a population, based on your responses to the previous two questions do you believe an error can occur when drawing an inference from the sample to the population? What do you think is meant by the statement:

The margin of error for this survey is: plus or minus 5 percentage points?

Inferential Statistics is used to help researchers, pollsters and/or decision makers draw conclusions or inferences about a population. The following statements represent situations where sample information can be used to draw conclusions about a population.

- A medical researcher wants to determine if large doses of vitamin C are effective in combating colds.
- Pollsters want to estimate what percentage of the American public approve of the death penalty to curb crime.
- A quality control engineer for a video tape manufacturer must determine whether their high grade video tape meets the manufacturers' specifications before shipment.
- The Food and Drug Administration would like to determine if men who use Viagra have undesirable side effects.
- A market researcher wants to know in what quantities the American consumer is willing to purchase a new product.

In most applications of statistics researchers use a sample rather than the entire population because it is usually impractical or impossible to obtain all the population observations or measurements.

For example, suppose an electrical company wanted to determine the average life of their new 40 watt light bulb. All the 40 watt bulbs the company manufactures would constitute the population. To obtain the average life of the population of light bulbs it would be necessary to compute the life of each bulb. Obviously, this would be impractical since they would not have any bulbs left to sell! In such instances, it becomes necessary to select a *representative sample* (i.e., a sample with similar pertinent characteristics as all the new 40 watt light bulbs), that can be used to make inferences about the entire population.

Thus, the electrical company would try to design a procedure to select a representative sample of these new light bulbs and use this sample data to estimate the population average life of their new 40 watt light bulbs.

DEFINITION 1.6
Representative sample is a sample that has the pertinent characteristics of the population in the same proportion, as they are included in that population.

Since the **primary objective of inferential statistics** is to use sample information to estimate a population characteristic, it is imperative that the researcher try to design a procedure to select a **sample which is representative of the population**. For example, if a population has 60% defective light bulbs, then a representative sample of this population should also contain 60% defective light bulbs. If the sample is **not representative** of the population, then inferences about the population characteristics **may not** be reasonable. The idea of ensuring sampling representativeness is similar to the "toothpick" technique used to determine if a cake is completely baked. A toothpick is inserted in **several areas** of the cake, and if the toothpick comes out free of cake batter each time, we conclude that the **entire** cake is done.

In the previous example about the new 40 watt light bulb, a sample was selected and the **sample average** was used **to estimate** the **average life** for *all* **the new 40 watt light bulbs**. That is, a sample average was used to estimate the population average. Whenever a number is used to describe a characteristic of a sample, such as sample average, this number is called a **statistic**.

DEFINITION 1.7
A **statistic** is a number that describes a characteristic of a sample.

On the other hand, a number like the population average, which describes a characteristic of a population, is called a **parameter**.

DEFINITION 1.8
A **parameter** is a number that describes a characteristic of a population.

Thus, a population average is an example of a parameter while a sample average is an example of a statistic. The sample statistic (i.e., sample average for the 40 watt light bulb) is being used to estimate the population parameter (i.e., the average life of the population of new light bulbs). We can say that the concept of inferential statistics is to use a sample statistic to make inferences about a population parameter.

Examples 1.1 and 1.2 illustrate the difference between a parameter and a statistic.

EXAMPLE 1.1

A statistician computes the batting average of all American League players to be .285 and the batting average of 24 players randomly selected from all the American League players to be .267. If the population is defined to be all the baseball players in the American League, then determine which batting average represents a parameter and which one is a statistic?

Solution

Since the population is defined to be the baseball players in the American League, then the .285 batting average is an example of a parameter because it describes the batting average or characteristic of all American League players, the population. Since the 24 players randomly selected from the population is a sample of all American League players, then the .267 batting average is an example of a statistic because it describes the batting average of a sample of American League players. _____ ∎

EXAMPLE 1.2

A politician is interested in determining the proportion of 20,000 voters within her district who will vote for her in the upcoming election. An opinion poll of 1500 potential voters was taken to estimate how all the voters in her district will vote in the upcoming election. The results of the opinion poll indicate that 52% will vote for the politician in the upcoming election. Determine:
a) The population.
b) The sample.
c) Whether the result, 52%, is a parameter or statistic.

Solution

a) The 20,000 voters in her district comprise the population.
b) The 1500 potential voters polled represents the sample.
c) The value 52% is a statistic since it describes a characteristic of the sample of 1500 potential voters.

_____ ∎

CASE STUDY 1.5   Conducting Polls

The article in Figure 1.6 appeared in an edition of *The New York Times* explaining how a latest *New York Times*/CBS News Poll was conducted. As you carefully read this article notice how the pollsters took great care in selecting their sample.

How the Poll was Conducted

The latest *New York Times*/CBS News Poll is based on telephone interviews conducted Wednesday and Thursday with 944 adults throughout the United States. The sample of telephone exchanges was randomly selected by a computer from a complete list of more than 42,000 active residential exchanges across the country.

Within each exchange, random digits were added to form a complete telephone number, thus permitting access to both listed and unlisted numbers. Within each household, one adult was designated by a random procedure to be the respondent for the survey.

The results have been weighted to take account of household size and number of telephone lines into residence and to adjust for variations in the sample relating to geographic region, sex, race, age, and education.

FIGURE 1.6

(continued)

CASE STUDY 1.5   Conducting Polls (continued)

In theory, in 19 cases out of 20 the results based on such samples will differ by no more than three percentage points in either direction from what would have been obtained by seeking out all American adults.

For smaller subgroups the potential sampling error is larger. For example, for those adults who are between 18 and 44 years of age and single it is plus or minus about five percentage points.

In addition to sampling error, the practical difficulties of conducting any survey of public opinion may introduce other sources of error into the poll. Variations in question wording or the order of questions, for instance, can lead to somewhat different results.

FIGURE 1.6 (continued)

a) Identify the population and the number of people selected for the sample, that is, the sample size.
b) Describe the sampling techniques used by the pollsters in their attempt to obtain a representative sample.
c) What were the pollsters trying to accomplish by using a random procedure to decide who should be designated as the respondent to their poll?
d) In the article the following statement appears:

> In theory, in 19 cases out of 20 the results based on such samples will differ by no more than three percentage points in either direction from what would have been obtained by seeking out all American adults.

If a second sample were selected using this same procedure, do you believe the results of the second sample would be identical to the first? Explain your answer in relation to the previous statement.
e) This case study uses terms that identify some important concepts that will be studied in later chapters of this text. What do the terms **random digits** and **sampling error** mean to you?
f) After reading this article, list some areas you would need to address if you planned to take a survey in your town?

1.2   WHY SAMPLE?

Consider the following scenario.

A shopper, who is interested in purchasing a quart of nonfat yogurt, is debating whether to buy a new exotic flavor called "Hawaiian Pleasure" or the old reliable flavor "Simply Vanilla." Before making a decision, the shopper requests a spoonful of the new flavor from the salesperson. Based upon this small spoonful, the shopper decides to purchase the Hawaiian Pleasure.

This typical scenario represents the idea of **Inferential Statistics**. The shopper's decision to purchase the Hawaiian Yogurt was based only on a spoonful, or sample, of this yogurt. Obviously, it was not necessary for the shopper to buy and eat the entire quart of Hawaiian Pleasure Yogurt before determining whether or not this new flavor tasted good enough to purchase. This idea of selecting a portion, or sample, to determine the taste or characteristics of all the yogurt, or population, is the essence of inferential statistics. The process of selecting a sample from a population is called sampling.

DEFINITION 1.9
Sampling is the process of selecting a portion, or sample, of the entire population.

The information acquired from a sample is the basis of inferential statistics. A sample is merely a portion of a population, and, when we have only a portion of a population, any conclusion drawn about the characteristics of a population are inferred from the sample data.

Suppose the editors of a student newspaper at a large University are interested in determining the opinion of all U.S. college students on whether they favor some form of censorship of rock music. Is it necessary for the editors to ask "every" college student within the U.S. before drawing a conclusion about how college students feel about censorship of rock music? If the editors had access to the population of all college students, then they could obtain the opinions of all the college students. Such a survey is called a **census**.

> **DEFINITION 1.10**
> A survey that includes every item or individual of the population is called a **census**.

How practical would it be for the editors to take a census to determine the opinions of all the college students? Trying to interview every college student in the United States would become an impossible task in terms of time and money. In practice, a census is rarely taken because it requires an excessive amount of time and it is too costly to gather all the information about the entire population. In addition, it would be virtually impossible for the editors to try to identify each student of the population. The question then becomes: "Is it really necessary for the editors to interview the population of all college students before a valid conclusion can be drawn about the opinions of college students on censorship?" Statisticians are often faced with similar situations. In such situations, statisticians are forced to take a sample to obtain information about the population. However, if a conclusion or inference about a population is based on sample data, then a statistician must try to insure that the sample is representative of the population from which it is drawn. If conclusions are drawn about a population from a nonrepresentative sample, then these conclusions are likely to be incorrect. On the other hand, if the sample is representative, then inferences about the population based on the sample information are likely to be correct. Thus, the editors should try to select and interview a representative sample of college students about censorship of rock music. They could then use this sample information to draw a conclusion about the views of the population of all the college students.

Why Sample?

Samples are taken when it is either impossible or impractical to examine the entire population. Studying an entire population is impractical when the population is extremely large. For such large populations, trying to select every data value (item or individual) in the population would be costly, time consuming or just impossible.

For example:

1. The quality control department at G.E. must test the production of its light bulbs to determine if they meet company specifications regarding the mean life of the bulbs. To check the life of the bulbs produced, the quality control manager randomly selects 36 bulbs over the daily production of these bulbs and determines the life of each bulb.
2. The Gallup Poll randomly surveys 1500 registered voters within the U.S. to determine if presidential candidate Don Key will win the upcoming presidential election.
3. A Florida distributor of citrus fruits wants to determine the mean weight of Florida oranges to help estimate the cost of shipping the oranges. A sample of oranges are randomly selected and weighed.
4. A medical researcher wishes to determine the mean cholesterol level of men aged 40–59 years old living in a large Maryland community. She randomly selects 100 men aged 40–59 years old and determines their cholesterol levels.

In each of these previous situations, it would be extremely expensive, if not impossible, to test each bulb, to weigh each Florida orange, contact every registered U.S. voter or to measure the cholesterol level of every 40–59 year old man living within the community. In addition, if the G.E. quality control manager were to test every bulb produced, there would be no bulbs left to sell. This type of testing is called **destructive testing** and requires the use of a sample. Consequently, only a small portion of items or individuals is selected to study rather than the entire group. These examples illustrate the idea of using sample information to try to draw a valid conclusion about the population.

In this chapter, we discussed some common statistical terms such as a population, and a sample. Let's review these statistical terms using the previous examples. Recall, the word **population** is used to refer to the entire group that has been identified for study. A population can refer to items or individuals. A **sample** is a portion of items or individuals chosen from the population. The population for the previous examples was all the bulbs G.E. manufactured per day, all the registered U.S. voters, all the oranges the distributor will ship, and the cholesterol measurements of all the 40–59 year old men living within the community. Notice from these examples, the population can be items such as bulbs, oranges, or individuals like registered U.S voters. In each of these situations, a small portion or sample was selected from the entire group or population to draw a conclusion about the entire population. This is the objective of **Inferential Statistics**. For example,

The quality control manager might observe that the sample of 36 bulbs burn out very quickly. Thus, on the basis of this sample of 36 bulbs, the manager would probably conclude that *all* the G.E. bulbs manufactured during the production process were not satisfactory,

or

A Gallup Poll reports that 63% of the 1500 registered U.S. voters preferred presidential candidate Don Key. Based on the results of this sample of 1500 voters, we would expect the population of registered U.S. voters to elect candidate Don Key president, if the election were held today.

In each of these situations, it is virtually impossible to study the entire population. If we were to test every bulb to determine how many hours it will last before burning out, there would be no bulbs left to sell. Similarly, opinion polls conducted by such pollsters as the Gallup Poll are given to only a sample of people because it would be very time consuming and extremely expensive or impractical to interview everyone in the population. Consequently, we sample the population because it is frequently impossible to study all the individuals or items of a population.

Let's now summarize some of the reasons a sample is selected rather than study the entire population.

Since populations can rarely be studied completely, we must depend upon selecting a sample to draw a conclusion about the characteristics of the population. Thus, our interest is in making inferences from sample data concerning the characteristics of a population. In the example of the Gallup Poll, although the pollsters surveyed 1500 voters to determine how they intend to vote in the upcoming election, their primary interest is not how these 1500 people will vote, but, rather in estimating how the entire population of voters will vote in the upcoming election.

Some numerical characteristics of a population that we are usually interested in describing using sample information are the mean, or the standard deviation of a population. Recall from Section 1.1 that a numerical characteristic of a population such as the **population average** or **variability** is called a **parameter**. While a numerical characteristic of a sample such as the sample average or variability is an example of a **statistic**.

Suppose the average IQ of all the students attending a large community college in California is 112. This numerical value 112 is a population parameter because it represents a characteristic of the population of all students attending the community college. On the other hand, if we were to determine the average IQ of a class of statistics students attending this community college to be 114, then

Reasons for Sampling

1. A Census is Impossible
At times, a census may be impossible because obtaining information about every item in the population will eventually destroy all the items within the population. For example, a cigarette manufacturer would have to burn every cigarette they manufactured if they were interested in obtaining the average nicotine content of all their cigarettes.

A census may also be impossible because the population is so large or infinite that it is practically impossible to obtain information about all the items or individuals of the population. For example, a population may be defined to be all infants who have ever been born or will ever be born. Such a population is endless and would be impossible to study all the individuals.

2. Cost
The cost of studying all the items of a population or contacting all the individuals within a population is too expensive. For example, it would be too costly for the Gallup Poll to conduct a telephone survey or mail a questionnaire to the population of all U.S. registered voters regarding their opinions on a presidential race.

3. Time
One major reason of sampling is that it requires less time to take a sample than to study the entire population. Sample information can be processed much faster the population data. For example, the Gallup Poll can survey 1500 people and analyze the results of its survey much faster than the U.S. Census Bureau can analyze the results of its 10 year census.

4. Accuracy
The results of a sample may be more accurate than trying to study the entire population since gathering data from fewer items or individuals will probably result in fewer human errors when collecting and analyzing the sample data. A statistician surveying a small portion of the population will be able to do a complete and comprehensive job in gathering and analyzing sample data.

the numerical value 114 describes a characteristic of a sample of students. In this case, 114 would be a statistic since it describes the average IQ of a sample of students attending the community college.

Studying the entire population is usually impractical; consequently, we use sample information to estimate the characteristics of a population. That is, we would use a statistic such as the sample average to make inferences about the corresponding population parameter, the **population average**.

DEFINITION 1.11
Sample Size—The size of a sample, denoted by n, is the number of data values in the sample.

DEFINITION 1.12
Population Size—The size of a finite population, denoted by N, is the number of data values in the population.

One important aspect of Inferential Statistics is to select a representative sample of the population. Since a sample provides only partial information about the population, there is always a chance that any conclusion about the population, based upon sample information, can be subject to error. One way to minimize this error is to insure that you have selected a representative sample from the population. Let's now discuss ways to select a sample from a population.

1.3   SAMPLING TECHNIQUES

In this section, we will examine methods to select a sample from a population. One objective of statistical inference is to try to select a representative sample from the population. If 60% of a population is female, then a **representative sample** of this population should also contain 60% females.

> **DEFINITION 1.13**
> A **representative sample** is a sample containing similar characteristics of the population.

Selecting a **nonrepresentative** or **biased** sample from a population can lead to invalid inferences about the population. A **nonrepresentative** or **biased sample** is a sample that either under selects or over selects from certain groups within the population. For example, if a population consisted of 40% males and 60% females, then a representative sample would also contain 60% females. A sample containing 80% females would be a nonrepresentative or biased sample because the percentage of females within the sample is much greater than within the population.

Nonrepresentative or biased samples may yield results that may not be representative of the population and may lead to a distorted picture of the population. A famous example of a nonrepresentative or biased sample leading to an invalid inference is the 1936 *Literary Digest* Poll.

In 1936, a magazine entitled the *Literary Digest* conducted a poll to try to predict the winner of the presidential election between the incumbent President Franklin Delano Roosevelt and the Republican Governor of Kansas Alfred M. Landon. Most political analysts predicted President Roosevelt would win reelection.

However, the *Literary Digest* gained attention when they predicted Landon would win easily, 57% to 43%. The *Digest* mailed out 10 million questionnaires to prospective voters. However, a major flaw with their poll was that only 2.4 million people returned the questionnaires. Although a sample of over 2 million people may seem to be a reasonably large sample, the *Digest*'s sample was a nonrepresentative or biased sample of voters. Another flaw was the way the *Literary Digest* selected its sample of voters. The *Digest* selected its sample from lists of telephone numbers, automobile registrations and its own list of subscribers. The *Literary Digest*'s selection process for their sample was biased because it favored Republican voters and was nonrepresentative of the voting population. During the depression of 1936, phones, automobiles and magazine subscriptions were luxury items for many people. Most of the wealthy people who could afford these luxuries favored the Republican candidate Landon. Thus, the *Digest*'s sampling procedure led to the selection of a biased sample since it was not representative of the voter population. Although, the *Literary Digest* had correctly predicted the previous five presidential elections, their prediction for the 1936 election was completely inaccurate. In fact, President Roosevelt won reelection by a landslide margin of 62% to 38%. Thus, although, the *Literary Digest* had selected a very large sample their prediction was incorrect because their sampling procedure led to the selection of a nonrepresentative or biased sample. Not too long after their inaccurate prediction, the *Digest* went bankrupt.

The key to inferential statistics is to select a representative sample. We will now examine sampling techniques that are more likely to produce a representative sample. Notice we said "more likely to produce a representative sample." There is always a possibility that a sample selected by these sampling techniques may be a nonrepresentative or biased sample. The sampling procedures we will consider are referred to as **random** or **probability sampling techniques**. In random or probability sampling, every data value of the population has a chance of being chosen in the sample.

DEFINITION 1.14

A **random** or **probability sample** is a sample which is selected in such a manner that each data value of the population has a non-zero probability of being selected for the sample.

Random or Probability Sampling Techniques

In a random or probability sample, the items or individuals are selected by chance alone. Since each item or individual of the population has a chance of being selected for the sample, the probabilities can be calculated and used to make statistical inferences about the population. Such statements "we are 90% confident that Candidate Don Key will receive 62% of the votes, plus or minus 3.5 percentage points" can be made. There are four random sampling techniques we will consider. These sampling techniques are:

1. simple random sampling
2. systematic sampling
3. stratified sampling
4. cluster sampling

Simple Random Sampling or Random Sampling

A **simple random sampling** or **random sampling** is the most fundamental statistical method of selecting a sample. Simple random sampling is a procedure which provides each item or individual of the population an equal chance of being selected. In addition, every possible sample has the same probability of being selected.

DEFINITION 1.15

A **simple random sample** is a sample of data values selected from a population in such a way that every sample of size n has an equal probability of being selected and every data value of the population has the same chance of being selected for the sample.

EXAMPLE 1.3

Determine if each of the following sampling procedures will produce a random sample.

a) The population is all females between the ages of seventeen and thirty-five living in New York State. The sampling procedure is devised to select a sample of 100 female college students within New York State.

b) The population is defined to be all the people who shop at the Green Acres Mall during the week before Christmas. The sampling procedure is devised to select every 25th shopper who enters the Mall at only one of its ten entrances.

c) The population is all the faculty members teaching at the College of Bill and Mary. The sampling procedure will select a sample of 25 faculty members using the following procedure: The name of each faculty member is placed in a large drum. The drum is rotated several times before each of the 25 faculty names are selected.

d) An advertising agency decides to conduct a marketing poll of people living in a New England community. The sampling procedure will draw a sample of people living within this community by selecting the names of people from the community telephone directory.

Solution

a)   The sampling procedure of selecting 100 female college students within New York State is *not* a random sampling procedure because the females aged 17 to 35 years old who are not *college* students do not have a chance of being selected.

b)   The sampling procedure of selecting every 25th shopper who enters the Mall at only one of its entrances is not a random sampling procedure because the shoppers who use a different entrance to the Mall do not have a chance of being selected

c)   The sampling procedure of selecting the 25 faculty members *is* a random sampling procedure because every faculty member has an equal chance of being chosen and every possible sample of size 25 had an *equal* chance of being selected.

d)   The sampling procedure of selecting the names of the people from the community telephone directory is not a random sampling procedure because the people who have an unlisted telephone number will not have a chance of being selected.   ▬▬▬▬▬■

How can we choose a random sample? Let's illustrate some ways of selecting a random sample.

Suppose there are 200 students in a large lecture class and the instructor wants to select 10 students from this class for an experiment.

One way to select a random sample of 10 students from the population of 200 students is to write the name of each student on a slip of paper, put the 200 slips in a box, thoroughly mix the slips within the box, and select the first slip. Repeat this process until this sample of 10 students is selected. The names of the students on the chosen slips represent a random sample. This procedure is acceptable if the slips are the same size, the population size is reasonably small and the slips are mixed thoroughly. If the population size is extremely large, this procedure can be very tedious. A more convenient procedure of selecting a random sample is to use random numbers. These numbers can be generated either by a computer program such as MINITAB or by using a table of random numbers such as Table VI in Appendix D: Statistical Tables. Table VI contains a table of random numbers that have been generated by some random process in which each of the ten digits from 0 to 9 have the same probability of being selected. For example, the number 187 and 024 have the same chance of being selected using this table of random numbers.

To use a table of random numbers to select a random sample of 10 students, you must first assign an identifying number to each of the 200 students in the class. Suppose we assign every student in the class a 3 digit number from 000 to 199. The random number table, Table VI, can now be used to choose the sample of 10 students. Table VI in Appendix D has 50 rows and 10 columns of 5 digits each. Notice in Table VI the random numbers are recorded in blocks of 5 digits. To randomly select the 10 students we can start anywhere within the random number table. One way would be to close your eyes and place your finger anywhere on the page and start at this point. From this starting point, you can move in any direction, that is, to the left, to the right, up, down or even diagonally across the table. Suppose we start at the first block of random numbers in the 36th row from the top of Table VI. The random number in the 36th row and the first column is 04230. The 5 rows starting with the 36th row from Table VI are shown in Figure 1.7.

```
                    Portion of Random Number Table: Table VI
                             Starting with 36th Row

          1st student
               ↓      2nd student   etc.
 starting             ↓
 point     →04230   16831   69085   30802   65559   09205   71829   06489   85650   38707
            94879   56606   30401   02602   57658   70091   54986   41394   60437   03195
            71446   15232   66715   26385   91518   70566   02888   79941   39684   54315
            32886   05644   79316   09819   00813   88407   17461   73925   53037   91904
            62048   33711   25290   21526   02223   75947   66466   06232   10913   75336
```

FIGURE 1.7

Results of the Random Sampling Technique

3-digit number	outcome	3-digit number	outcome
042	*1st student selected*	413	skipped
168	*2nd student selected*	604	skipped
690	skipped	*031*	*6th student selected*
308	skipped	715	skipped
655	skipped	*152*	*7th student selected*
092	*3rd student selected*	667	skipped
718	skipped	263	skipped
064	*4th student selected*	915	skipped
856	skipped	705	skipped
387	skipped	*028*	*8th student selected*
948	skipped	799	skipped
566	skipped	396	skipped
304	skipped	543	skipped
026	*5th student selected*	328	skipped
576	skipped	*056*	*9th student selected*
700	skipped	793	skipped
549	skipped	*098*	*10th student selected*

FIGURE 1.8

Beginning with the random number 04230 as the starting point, we need to select 10 three digit numbers. Since each random number is a five-digit number, we will only use the first 3 digits of the random number to identify the first student from the population. Thus, the random number *04230* will be used to identify the student number 042 as the first student selected from the random sample. To continue selecting students, we can move in any direction. Suppose we decide to move to the right. The random number to the right of 04230 is *16831*. The first 3 digits of this second random number is 168. Thus, the student identified by number 168 will be the second student selected for our sample. The next random number to the right is *69085*. The first 3 digits of this third random number is 690. We cannot use 690 because the largest student number in the population is 199. This random number is skipped and we continue moving to the right to select our next random number. However, the next two random numbers *30802* and *65559* must also be skipped. The random number 09205 identifies the student with the number 092. We continue this process until the 10 students are randomly selected. This sample of 10 students is called a *simple random sample.* Figure 1.8 contains the 3 digit numbers observed in the random number table using our sampling procedure.

EXAMPLE 1.4

The Zoo, a New York FM radio station, decides to hold a contest to raffle 20 rock concert tickets. To enter the contest, each contestant must submit a postcard containing the answer to the Zoo's special music question. Each postcard the radio station receives with the correct response to their question is numbered. The postcards are numbered using a four digit number ranging from 0001 to 7126. Using the following portion of a 5-digit Random Number Table, starting at the random number 63271 and moving down each column, determine the five winning numbers which would be selected using this random sampling procedure.

Portion of Random Number Table

63271	59986	71744	51102	15141	80714	58683	93108	13554	79945
88547	09896	95436	79115	08303	01041	20030	63754	08459	28364
55957	57243	83865	09911	19761	66535	40102	26646	60147	15702
46276	87453	44790	67122	45573	84358	21625	16999	13385	22782
55363	07449	34835	15290	76616	67191	12777	21861	68689	03263

Solution

Beginning with the random number 63271 as the starting point, we need to select 20 *four* digit numbers. Since each random number is a five-digit number, we will only use the first 4 digits of the random number to identify the twenty winning numbers from the random number table.

Using this sampling procedure, the random number *63271* identifies the first winning postcard number 6327. To continue selecting winning numbers, we move down the column. The random number below the starting number is *88547*. The first 4 digits of this second random number is 8854. Since this second random number is outside the range of the postcard numbers 0001 to 7126, we skip this random number. The first four digits of the next random number 55957 is 5595. Thus, 5595 represents a winning number since it falls within the range of postcard numbers. Continuing with this sampling procedure, the twenty winning numbers are:

6327, 5595, 4627, 5536, 5998, 0989, 5724, 0744, 4479, 3483,
5110, 0991, 6712, 1529, 1514, 0830, 1976, 4557, 0104, 6653   ■

Systematic Sampling

The simple random sample method may be very tedious and time consuming when working with an extremely large population. For example, suppose that the population consisted of 20,000 households and we needed to select a sample of 2,000 households to participate in a survey. Using simple random sampling, we would first need to assign a 5-digit number to each household ranging from 00001 to 20000 and then use a random number table to select the sample of 2,000 households. A computer could also be used to generate the random numbers and select the 2,000 households.

An alternate procedure would be to use systematic sampling. Systematic sampling is usually used when the items or individuals of a population are already arranged in some type of order, such as alphabetical order or numerical order. A random sample is selected from this ordered list by selecting every kth item in order where the initial starting point of the first k items of the list is selected at random. For instance, if we want to select a sample of 2,000 households from a population of 20,000 households, then we need to determine the ratio of the population size to the sample size. This is the value of k. That is,

$$k = \frac{\text{population size}}{\text{sample size}} = \frac{20{,}000}{2{,}000}$$

$$k = 100$$

Here, k = 100; in other words, we would select every 100th household from the list of 20,000 households using a random number table to obtain our sample of 2,000 households. To accomplish this systematic sampling, we would first begin by arranging the households in alphabetical order. Since our objective is to randomly select one household from every 100 households, we begin by selecting a number from 1 and 100 for our starting point using a random number table. Using this randomly selected starting point, we would then select every 100th household from this starting point to determine the remaining households.

For example, suppose from the random number table, the starting point we select is 56. The first household selected would be the 56th household on our list of 20,000 households. We would then select every 100th household from this starting point of 56. Thus, the second household selected for our sample would be the 156th household, and the third household would be the 256th household. Continuing in this manner, our selected sample would include the following households:

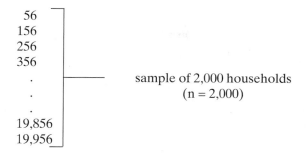

56
156
256
356
·
·
·
19,856
19,956

sample of 2,000 households
(n = 2,000)

> **DEFINITION 1.16**
> In a **systematic sampling**, the items or individuals of the population are ordered in some way such as alphabetically or numerically. A starting point is randomly selected from the first k positions, and then every kth number, including the first item or individual selected, is selected from the sample. Since k is the ratio of the population size to sample size, to find k use the formula: k = population size/sample size.

Using the systematic sampling procedure, each item or individual within the population has an equal chance of being chosen for the sample. However, systematic sampling differs from simple random sampling since each sample does not have an equal chance of being selected.

EXAMPLE 1.5

A psychology professor decides to select a sample of 10 students from her large lecture class containing 500 students to be part of a psychology experiment using the systematic sampling procedure.

If each student has an assigned number from 1 to 500 and she randomly selects 24 as her starting point, then:
a) Determine the ratio of the population size to the sample size, and
b) Identify the students selected for the experiment.

Solution

a) The value of k, the ratio of the population size to the sample size, is:

$$k = \frac{\text{population size}}{\text{sample size}} = \frac{500}{10}$$
$$k = 50.$$

b) For k = 50, a systematic sample would involve selecting one student out of the first 50 students, and then selecting every 50th student from the student list. Since the starting point is 24, then the first student selected is the 24th student on the list. The remaining students of the systematic sample are identified by selecting every 50th student starting from the 24th student. Thus, the sample of selected students are:

1st student:	24th	6th student:	224 + 50 = 274th
2nd student:	24 + 50 = 74th	7th student:	274 + 50 = 324th
3rd student:	74 + 50 = 124th	8th student:	324 + 50 = 374th
4th student:	124 + 50 = 174th	9th student:	374 + 50 = 424th
5th student:	174 + 50 = 224th	10th student:	424 + 50 = 474th

Stratified Sampling

In stratified sampling, the population is first divided into subgroups or subpopulations called **strata** such that each data value in the population belongs to one and only one strata. An attempt is made to define the strata such that the population of data values within each stratum are as much alike as possible. For example, suppose a Wall Street Brokerage House has a population of investors which can be divided into 3 different groups based upon their investment risks. These groups are defined as: low risk, medium risk and high risk. These three subgroups or subpopulations are called the strata. Notice that the investors within each stratum (or subpopulation) are all alike or homogeneous. Now, from each stratum (or subpopulation), a simple random sample is selected. These samples which were selected from each strata are combined to form the overall stratified sample.

> **DEFINITION 1.17**
> In **stratified sampling**, the population is first divided into subgroups or subpopulations called strata and a simple random sample is selected from each stratum. The stratified sample is the total collection of samples selected from all the *stratas*. Usually, the size of the samples selected from each different stratum corresponds to the proportion of data values within each stratum.

Stratified sampling is a sampling method that is usually used when you know the numerical value of some important characteristic of the population. For example, suppose within the population of investors, we know that 30% of the investors belong to the low risk group, 50% of the investors belong to the medium risk group, and 20% of the investors belong to the high risk group. The brokerage house would like to select a simple random sample of investors from each subpopulation or stratum which would reflect the proportion of investors found within each stratum. Thus, the total collection of investors selected from the three strata would represent the stratified sample where 30% of the total sample would reflect the proportion of low risk investors, 50% of the total sample would reflect the proportion of medium risk investors, and 20% of the total sample would reflect the proportion of high risk investors.

The advantage of stratified sampling is that the stratified sample reflects some important characteristic of the population where the percentages in the various strata are the same in the sample as in the population. The reason for stratifying a population is to increase your chances of selecting a representative sample from the population. Populations can be stratified on the basis of such characteristics as economic level, family size, location, income, age, race, gender or education.

EXAMPLE 1.6

The Student Government Association (SGA) of a large college is interested in obtaining the views of the student body concerning the textbook prices charged at the bookstore. To obtain a representative sample, the SGA decides to select a stratified sample and divides the population into 4 subgroups: freshman, sophomore, junior and senior.

a) What are these subpopulations of this stratified sample called?

b) What sampling procedure is used to select the students from the student body for the stratified sample and how is the overall stratified sample formed?

Solution

a) The subpopulations of this stratified sample are called the strata. The strata of this stratified sample are: freshman, sophomore, junior and senior.

b) The simple random sampling procedure is used to select a sample of students from each stratum. These random samples selected from the four strata would be combined to form the overall stratified sample.

————————— ∎

Cluster Sampling

In cluster sampling, the population is divided into separate groups called clusters. Each data value of the population belongs to only one cluster. A simple random sample of entire groups or clusters are selected. Every data value within the sampled cluster is included within the sample. The difference between clusters and strata is that the strata contain data values which are all alike, i.e., homogeneous, while the clusters contain data values which are not alike, i.e., heterogeneous. Ideally, we would like all the clusters to be similar and each cluster to be a representative small-scale version of the overall population. If each cluster is similar and representative of the entire population, then randomly sampling a few of the clusters will provide a representative sample of the population.

> **DEFINITION 1.18**
> In **cluster sampling**, the population is divided into groups or clusters, usually based upon geographic location. A simple random sample of the clusters is selected to represent the population. Ideally, the clusters should be similar and be a representative small-scale version of the overall population.

Cluster sampling is a sampling technique used primarily to minimize the cost of sampling a population that may be scattered across a large geographic area. If a simple random sample were selected, it would be very costly to travel to each selected individual of the population. In such instances, the population would be divided into different geographical areas called clusters. We assume that these clusters are similar and are small representative groups of the entire population. A random sample of k clusters is selected from the total number of clusters and every individual within the selected clusters is sampled. For example, suppose a large international corporation has 100 factories located in different parts of the world. The corporation would like to personally interview the employees within these factories to determine their opinions regarding some important company issues. If each of the factories is similar with respect to the employees and is representative of the population of all the employees within the corporation, cluster sampling can be used to minimize the cost of traveling to interview the employees selected for the interview. The factories will represent the clusters. Since these clusters are scattered across the world, we would want to randomly select a few of these clusters rather than visit all the factories. If we were to select only 5 clusters or factories, then we would only need to travel to these 5 factories and interview all the employees within each of these factories. All the employees interviewed at these 5 factories would represent our cluster sample.

Stratified and cluster sampling require that the population be divided into well-defined groups. Stratified sampling should be used when the data values of the group are similar but there are large differences between the groups or strata. On the other hand, cluster sampling is used when the data values within each group or cluster are very different but the clusters are essentially similar to each other.

Within this section, we presented different fundamental sampling methods that are most often employed. Simple random sampling, systematic sampling, stratified sampling and cluster sampling. The choice of which of these sampling techniques to use depends upon many factors such as the type of population, the characteristics of the population to be investigated, the difficulty in selecting a random sample, and the cost of sampling.

Even though we examined four sampling techniques that attempt to ensure the selected sample is representative of the population, *we will assume for all theory and problems for the remainder of the text that the sample data has been chosen using simple random sampling*. This assumption is necessary because the foundation of inferential statistics is based upon simple random sampling. Randomly selecting the data values of a population means that no characteristics of the data values make it more or less likely to be selected.

EXAMPLE 1.7

A statistician wants to determine the number of children per family in Los Angeles, California. To minimize the cost of selecting a sample the statistician decides to divide the city of Los Angeles into city blocks and use the cluster sampling procedure to select the sample.

a) What do the city blocks represent within this cluster sampling?
b) What assumptions are made about the city blocks or clusters of the sample?
c) How is the sample selected?

Solution

a) The city blocks represent the clusters or groups of the population.
b) In cluster sampling, each cluster or city block is assumed to be representative and a small-version of the entire city of Los Angeles.
c) A random sample of the city blocks are selected and every family on the block are interviewed to determine the number of children in the family.

In summary, Figure 1.9 compares the four random sampling procedures discussed in this section.

Summary of the Four Random Sampling Procedures

Sampling Technique	Procedure to Select Sample
Simple Random Sampling	Each population data value is assigned a number. Random numbers are selected using either a computer or a random number table to select the data values of the sample.
Systematic Sampling	Every kth data value is selected from an ordered list of the population data values, after a starting point has been selected at random.
Stratified Sampling	The population is divided into subgroups or subpopulations called strata where the data values are alike or homogeneous within each strata. A simple random sample is selected from each strata, and these samples are combined to obtain the overall sample.
Cluster Sampling	The population is divided into groups called clusters where the clusters are relatively similar and a representative small-scale version of the overall population. A simple random sample of the clusters is selected to represent the population.

FIGURE 1.9

CASE STUDY 1.6   Sample Universe

The article entitled "Statisticians Sample Universe" shown in Figure 1.10 appeared in the magazine *Purchasing*. This article discusses the importance of sampling in different applications.

Forecast Basics: Statisticians Sample Universe

Here's the fifth in a series titled "Forecast Basics" exploring the mathematical building blocks for strategic planning.

Without sampling, statistical analysis and forecasting would be impossible. Quality control people, who, on the basis of limited testing, decide whether to accept or reject a production lot are essentially sampling. So are government price collectors who study a limited number of transactions to come up with the nation's overall price trend. Sampling sometimes yields less-than perfect results, but the practice is indispensable for a variety of reasons:
- Cost: If sampling 5 or 10% of the data can give a reliable estimate of the population or universe, a tremendous saving can be achieved.
- Practicality: It is frequently impossible to collect the universe of data, even if money is available. For example, counting the total number of unemployed or every single price transaction each month is not physically feasible.
- Waste: It doesn't make sense to use data that are more precise than needed. It might make little difference to a soap producer whether 84, 85 or 86% of its customers like the product smell.
- Destruction: A sample is often necessary because the product is destroyed in the process of being tested. Case in point: light bulbs.
- Spurious accuracy: Count the number of marbles in a glass urn several times; the chances are that no two counts will agree. The same accuracy can be attained by counting the number of marbles in one-tenth of the urn (a sample) and then extrapolating the results to the entire urn.

Sampling can offer tremendous advantages, but it is not foolproof. There is no guarantee of 100% accuracy. Two challenges await anyone who samples.

The first is a matter of common sense: **A sample must represent the attributes of a given population or universe.**

A classic example of how a sample can go awry involves a poll conducted more than 50 years ago in the presidential contest between Franklin D. Roosevelt and Alfred M. Landon. The *Literary Digest* randomly samples telephone numbers. Their prediction: Landon by a landslide. The magazine was woefully wrong because its sample didn't accurately represent the electorate; at that time only the relatively wealthy had telephones. Inferring total votes on the basis of the wealthy was unjustified and the magazine was folded soon after the fiasco.

Beyond the problem of building a representative sample—no matter how much time and effort are devoted—the possibility remains that the sample will vary from the true population or universe on the basis of chance. So sampling results should always be couched in terms of probability or odds (see box).

This "chance" concept can be applied to a myriad of industrial sampling problems, for example, statistical quality control. The rationale is straightforward as described in the following steps:
- Measure a sample lot of some product (say, steel sheet) for some attribute like weight, width, or tensile strength.
- Calculate the difference between the sample result and the specifications for the given attribute.

CASE STUDY 1.6   Sample Universe (continued)

> **PROBABILITY: A SIMPLE SAMPLE**
>
> *Problem:* What is the most likely result if you toss two coins into the air? What are the odds of obtaining that result?
>
> *Answer:* One head and one tail is the most likely result. There is a 50% chance of obtaining that result.
>
> *Rationale:* The probability of obtaining one head when tossing the first coin is one-half. The odds of getting a head on the second coin is also one-half. The odds of two heads is then calculated by multiplying the odds together 50% x 50% = 25%. If there is a 25% chance of getting two heads, then there is an equal 25% chance of getting two tails. This leaves a 50% probability for one head and one tail.

• Calculate the probability of getting such a difference on the basis of pure chance.

Set acceptance-rejection limits. Example: If the probability of obtaining such a difference due to chance is (say 1%) then reject the sample lot, dubbing it "significantly different" from the population spec for the given attribute.

Such a rejection might not be warranted 1% of the time, but we could say with 99% confidence that we took the correct action. The business, in most cases, is willing to accept the 1% risk of making the wrong decision in return for the tremendous potential savings derived from being able to differentiate most of the time between good and bad lots.

Not every sampling procedure requires the same degree of accuracy. A parachute maker would want 100% precision. A bulb maker may settle for considerably less. And risk is not the only determinant of required accuracy. The amount of money riding on a decision is another key consideration.

FIGURE 1.10

a) Explain some reasons of how sampling is necessary and discuss an application for each reason.
b) Explain two problem areas that one should be aware of when using a sample to make an inference from a population.
c) Discuss an example on how a sample is used to determine whether to accept or reject a sample lot of a product.
d) Why do you think that a 1% chance is used in determining whether to reject the sample lot? Do you think that a 15% chance is practical to use in determining whether to reject the sample lot? Explain.
e) What does the statement "99% confidence that we took the correct action" mean to you?
f) What does the phrase "degree of confidence or accuracy" mean to you?

1.4   USES OF STATISTICS

The role of statistics in our lives is increasing and some may even find it disturbing. Statements such as, "Your family's socio-economic index is too high to qualify for financial aid," or "Your cholesterol level is too high, therefore you are advised to change your diet immediately," are all by-products of the advances in data collection and processing which occurred during the twentieth century.

Today, even at an elementary level, it is impossible to understand economics, finance, psychology, sociology, or the physical sciences without some understanding of the meaning and interpretation of *average, variability, correlation, inference, charts or tables.*

Extensive data collection and distribution activities are performed by the federal and other governmental and private agencies in areas such as education, employment, health, crime, prices, housing, medical care, manufacturing, agriculture, construction, transportation, etc.

Furthermore, the development of the electronic computer has led to a revolution in the area of data collection and analysis. Statistical analysis can now be applied to vast amounts of data accurately and quickly. Such diverse problems as weather forecasting, economic stabilization, and disease control are today being solved using statistical analysis.

The following examples represent some applications of statistics.

EXAMPLE 1.8   **"Supreme Court Rules Census Bureau Cannot Use Statistical Sampling For The 2000 Census"**

It is important for the Census Bureau to provide an accurate count of every person who lives in the United States. Census numbers are used to allocate billions of dollars in federal funds for schools, hospitals, highways, mass transit, etc. They are also used to draw political lines and apportion seats in Congress.

The Census Bureau begins a census by mailing out questionnaires to every household in the country. However, most households do not mail the forms back. The Census Bureau reported that the rate of nonresponse to their census forms has been increasing as shown by the graphic in Figure 1.11.

Statistical Snapshot

Census Form Returns Down

The percentage of households that return the Census questionnaires in the mail is dwindling.

Year	Percentage
1970	78%
1980	75%
1990	65%
2000	61%*

*Estimate

FIGURE 1.11

This increasing rate of nonresponse forces the Census Bureau to send interviewers to visit those households who didn't return the census form. In spite of the many attempts to count every person who lives in the United States, the census usually results in an undercounting of minorities, children and the poor. This is the reason the Census Bureau wanted to use a *statistical sampling method* to estimate these people who are too difficult to reach.

For the 2000 census, the Census Bureau planned to use a mail questionnaire to count 90% of the population followed by a 10% probability sample of the remaining 10% to complete the enumeration phase. However, the Supreme Court ruled that statistical sampling could not be used to apportion seats in Congress.

The census is an example of a vital descriptive statistic that may effect the disbursement of federal and state aid as well as the boundaries of the voting districts.   ∎

EXAMPLE 1.9   **"Dewey Defeats Truman"**

In the 1948 presidential election the Gallup Poll incorrectly predicted the defeat of Truman by Dewey. The Gallup Poll uses statistical methods in selecting samples for their public opinion surveys and applies inferential techniques to make predictions. Their method of sampling has produced presidential election predictions which have had an error averaging around 2% since 1948. (They failed to pick the winner in 1948 but have been correct ever since.)

Examples 1.10 and 1.11 discuss descriptive economic measures to reflect changes in the economy.

EXAMPLE 1.10   "This past month The Consumer Price Index (CPI) Rose 1.2%"

What does this mean? The Bureau of Labor Statistics uses a collection of over 400 goods and services called a *fixed market basket* to reflect changes in the purchasing power of the dollar. An increase of 1.2% in the Consumer Price Index indicates that prices for the 400 goods and services have increased 1.2% during the past month as compared to the prices for these goods and services in the base period (currently 1982–84).

EXAMPLE 1.11   "Dow Gains More Than 250 Points As The Stock Market Soars"

The Dow Jones Industrial Average(DJIA) is an index of stock prices that is used to reflect the movement of stock prices on the New York Stock Exchange. It is used by the media to indicate the level of stock prices in the United States. For example, a dramatic increase in the Dow represents a major upward movement in the overall stock prices in the stock market. You might ask the question: "how accurate has the Dow Jones Industrial Average been in reflecting the performance of the stock market?" The Dow's tracking of the stock market movements over the long run closely parallels the Standard and Poor's 500 Stock Index, commonly called the S&P 500, which consists of the prices of 500 stocks. Thus, when we are asked: "What did the stock market do today?", it would be appropriate to use the Dow Jones Industrial Average to answer the question even though it is based on only 30 stocks.

EXAMPLE 1.12   "How Many Words Did Shakespeare Know?"

In a 1976 study by Efron & Thisted, they tried to estimate the number of words that Shakespeare knew. Efron and Thisted explored the detailed structure of the word counts from all the plays of Shakespeare. Their study revealed that: *Shakespeare wrote 31,534 words, of which 14,376 appear only once, 4,343 twice, and so on. They concluded that Shakespeare knew at least 35,000 more words.*

EXAMPLE 1.13   "There is a Hurricane Watch in Effect for the Florida Coast"

Such forecasts are issued by the U.S. Weather Bureau which has the ability to gather weather data from all over the world, quickly analyze this vast amount of information, and produce relatively accurate predictions. Early warnings issued by the bureau are now responsible for the savings of thousands of lives and millions of dollars in property.

In Examples 1.14 and 1.15 the researchers analyzed the data for possible patterns or relationships that might exist. This type of analysis is called **Exploratory Data Analysis**.

EXAMPLE 1.14   "Caution: Cigarette Smoking May be Hazardous to Your Health"

In the early 1950s, Dr. Richard Doll and Professor Austin Bradford studied the relationship between cigarette smoking and lung cancer. Their conclusion that "smoking is a factor, and an important factor, in the production of carcinoma of the lung" shook the foundation of the tobacco industry.

EXAMPLE 1.15   "Rise in Rate of Breast Cancer on Long Island"

Medical researchers are trying to determine what factors have led to an abnormally high incidence of breast cancer in women on Long Island, NY. To aid in this study, the researchers will look for any patterns or relationships which may exist among the vast amounts of data. For example, the researchers will examine such factors as race, diet, age, occupation, body fat, family history, age at first child's birth, etc, and the relationship of these factors to the incidence of breast cancer.

EXAMPLE 1.16   "Morning Workout Burns More Fat"

A study conducted at Kansas State University concluded that exercise done before breakfast burns more fat than exercise done at any other time of the day. The researcher had hypothesized that the burning of fat is related to levels of insulin. Since the level of insulin is known to be low before breakfast, the researcher studied a group of runners before breakfast and after lunch.

This study illustrates an example of inferential statistics since the researcher uses a sample to draw a conclusion about the general population.

EXAMPLE 1.17   "Study States 5% of Young Adults Are Illiterate"

The Department of Education found that 5% of young adults between the ages of 21 to 25 years old read below the fourth grade level. The report is based on a survey of 3600 people.

This example illustrates another use of inferential statistics because the Department of Education is using a sample to infer about the general population of young adults aged 21 to 25 years old.

The previous examples have illustrated the many uses of statistics. Some of the examples emphasized the use of descriptive statistics and exploratory data analysis, while others illustrated the use of inferential statistics in forecasting, predicting and the testing of hypotheses. In the next section, we will discuss some of the misuses of statistics.

1.5   MISUSES OF STATISTICS

Disraeli, a British Statesman, was quoted as saying, "There are three kinds of lies: lies, damned lies, and statistics." Disraeli's statement attests to the fact that there are many instances where statistics are abused.

In this section, our objective is to briefly discuss some of the misuses of statistics. Hopefully, the illustrations presented will make you aware of the need to become statistically literate. After reading this section, we believe you will be more inclined to agree with H. G. Wells' statement that:

Statistical thinking will one day be as necessary for efficient citizenship as the ability to read and write.

We will examine four techniques to illustrate how information can be presented in a misleading fashion. These techniques are: (I) Misleading Graphs, (II) Non-Representative Samples, (III) Inappropriate Comparisons and (IV) The Omission of Variation About an Average. Let's illustrate how graphs can be misleading.

I   Misleading Graphs

> **DEFINITION 1.19**
> A **graph** is a descriptive tool used to visually describe the characteristics and relationships of collections of data quickly and attractively.

However, graphs also provide an excellent opportunity to distort the truth.

EXAMPLE 1.18

An investment analyst could use a graph to show that the rate of return on retirement annuities are falling. This is shown in Figure 1.12.

However, if the analyst wanted to make the decrease in the rate of return appear more dramatic, she could simply change the units of the vertical scale and delete its lower portion. This is illustrated in Figure 1.13.

FIGURE 1.12

FIGURE 1.13

Although Figures 1.12 and 1.13 present the same information, Figure 1.13 presents the distorted impression that the rate of return is dropping at an incredible rate.

Another graph commonly used is the **bar graph** as illustrated in Example 1.19.

EXAMPLE 1.19

In order to attract new advertisers, a magazine that wishes to depict dramatic growth in its circulation produced the bar graph shown in Figure 1.14a.

FIGURE 1.14a

FIGURE 1.14b

Notice the bars in Figure 1.14a are presented with a portion missing. If not examined carefully this gives the visual impression that the magazine's circulation for 2000 is twice the circulation for 1998. However, when the bars are completely drawn as illustrated in Figure 1.14b, one sees only a slight increase in circulation.

A *pictograph* is another popular graphing technique used to distort the truth.

> **DEFINITION 1.20**
> A **pictograph** is a graph involving pictures of objects in which the size of the object in the picture represents the relative size of the quantity being represented by the object.

EXAMPLE 1.20

During a recent contract negotiation, the owner of a baseball team decided to dramatize the fact that his players' salaries have doubled from 1996 to 2000 by placing an advertisement in a local newspaper as illustrated by Figure 1.15.

1996

2000

FIGURE 1.15

This pictograph is misleading because it creates a visual impression that the baseball players' salaries have more than doubled since 1996. This impression was created by doubling both dimensions of the 1996 picture. This doubling of both dimensions quadrupled the area of the 2000 picture. ∎

II   Non-Representative Samples

Since a sample is only a portion of a population, great care must be taken to insure that the sample is representative of the population. Drawing a conclusion from a non-representative sample (or a biased sample) is another device often used to distort the truth.

Let's take a look at an instance where a non-representative sample led to an inappropriate inference about the population. The 1936 *Literary Digest Poll* predicted that the Republican Presidential Candidate Alfred M. Landon would defeat the Democratic incumbent Franklin D. Roosevelt by an overwhelming margin. However, to the surprise of the *Literary Digest* pollsters, Roosevelt won the election by a landslide. The *Literary Digest* made a staggering error when it used an unrepresentative sample. The Digest's sampling procedure involved mailing sample ballots to ten million prospective voters of which only 2.3 million ballots were returned.

However, the 2.3 million ballots represented people who had a "relatively intense interest" in expressing their opinion on the election. Thus, this sample was non-representative (biased). In the 1936 election, it seems clear that the minority of anti-Roosevelt voters felt more intense about expressing their opinions about the election than did the pro-Roosevelt majority. In essence, the Digest's error was in basing their prediction of the outcome of the 1936 election on a *biased* voluntary response to its survey. (Incidentally, the *Literary Digest* went bankrupt soon after).

Examples 1.21, 1.22 and 1.23 contain conclusions based upon samples where the information regarding the sampling selection process is not mentioned. In particular, information such as sample size and representativeness of the population have been conveniently omitted. In such instances an informed citizen must question the procedures used to gather the sample information. For each of the examples we have suggested a possible deception that could have been used in selecting the sample that led to the conclusion.

EXAMPLE 1.21

One recent study stated that "90% of the people surveyed were in favor of nuclear power."

What if this survey was based on only 10 workers whose livelihood is dependent upon the construction of nuclear power plants, would you consider the 90% statistic startling?

Probably not, because the study was based on a small non-representative sample!

EXAMPLE 1.22

An advertisement in a digital video magazine stated that "8 out of 10 DVD owners recommend the DVD-R format over the DVD+R format."

What if the ad agency trying to market DVD-R Format Recorders polled many groups of 10 DVD owners until they obtained a result favorable to their product, never mentioning the unfavorable results, would you then consider this advertisement to be misleading?

Yes, because the ad agency's advertisement is only using the sample result that supports the use of the DVD-R Recorders.

EXAMPLE 1.23

An independent laboratory test showed that "People who use DPT toothpaste have 30% fewer cavities."

This laboratory made an impressive statement about DPT toothpaste. **But, there are some questions which need to be answered.**

First, how many people were sampled? **Second,** was this the only sample selected? **Third,** what does the statement ". . . . 30% fewer cavities" mean? Fewer than what?! Could this mean fewer than those people who did not use any toothpaste at all?

III   Inappropriate Comparisons

The statement "Do Not Compare Apples to Oranges," conveys the essence of this next deceptive technique.

EXAMPLE 1.24

During the gasoline shortage of the 70's, people started buying foreign cars because they were more fuel efficient. A television commercial for an American automobile manufacturer showed two automobiles, the American-made auto and the foreign import, side-by-side. The commercial emphasized the Environmental Protection Agency's (EPA) fuel efficiency rating of the two autos which were shown in bold print as illustrated in Figure 1.16.

FIGURE 1.16

The EPA ratings represented two different driving conditions which were inconspicuously written in small print. The fact that the EPA rating of the American-made auto was based on highway driving while the import's EPA rating was *not* based on highway driving made this an inappropriate comparison.

IV   The Omission of Variation About an Average

The omission of pertinent statistical figures concerning variation about an average can result in the public drawing inaccurate conclusions.

EXAMPLE 1.25

New mothers usually read many books about child development. However, these books can cause many unpleasant moments, especially if the reader misinterprets the author's statements concerning a child's development rate.

For instance, a new mother may interpret "A child begins to walk on average around 12 months," to mean that if her child does not walk by 12 months, her baby is abnormal or could be a late developer.

This type of misinterpretation can be avoided if the author provided a **range** of months for the developmental walking stage, such as: "a child begins to walk between 11 and 15 months." To the new mother, the range of ages for walking is much more informative than an average walking age.

1.6   OVERVIEW AND SUMMARY

In this chapter we introduced the two branches of statistics, **descriptive** and **inferential**, and showed how statistics are used and misused. We also discussed the notion of sampling, reasons for sampling and various sampling techniques. The next two chapters will first explore ways to describe and summarize collections of data. We will then consider the concepts and techniques associated with inferential statistics. These include the study of probability, the notion of a sampling distribution, and the statistical models of inference.

Throughout the text, we will present real life examples, case studies, and articles to help you develop an appreciation of the use of statistics. In addition, technology tools such as the graphing calculator and computer statistical software outputs will be illustrated at the end of each chapter. View screens from the TI-83 Plus graphing calculator will be presented to illustrate how a statistical graphing calculator can be used to analyze data sets. Computer outputs will be displayed using the statistical packages MINITAB and EXCEL.

Both MINITAB and EXCEL were used to generate computer outputs of the following 50 IQ scores. The first computer output, generated by MINITAB, was used to analyze and graph the distribution of the following 50 IQ scores.

				IQ Scores					
95	115	120	105	116	127	101	125	99	104
114	130	130	107	122	110	145	103	103	135
118	105	115	128	131	118	117	113	104	126
104	107	129	134	108	112	104	98	123	105
134	138	121	99	112	127	136	121	102	111

In MINITAB, the command DESCRIBE is used to generate the following analysis of the distribution of IQ scores. We will explain this output and analysis as we study the appropriate concepts within the following chapters.

MTB > DESCRIBE C8

	N	MEAN	MEDIAN	TRMEAN	STDEV	SEMEAN
IQ	50	116.12	115.00	115.80	12.47	1.76

	MIN	MAX	Q1	Q3		
IQ	95.00	145.00	104.75	127.00		

The command HISTOGRAM is used to generate the following graph of the distribution of IQ scores. Histograms will be discussed in Chapter 2.

In Excel, the descriptive statistics command generates the following analysis of the same distribution of IQ scores.

MTB > HISTOGRAM C8
Histogram of IQ N = 50

Midpoint	Count	
95	1	*
100	5	*****
105	11	***********
110	5	*****
115	6	******
120	6	******
125	5	*****
130	5	*****
135	4	****
140	1	*
145	1	*

Excel Descriptive Statistics

Mean	116.12
Standard Error	1.763725186
Median	115
Mode	104
Standard Deviation	12.47142039
Sample Variance	155.5363265
Kurtosis	-0.890208609
Skewness	0.307653738
Range	50
Minimum	95
Maximum	145
Sum	5806
Count	50

The TI-83 Plus graphing calculator was used to statistically describe the same 50 IQ scores. Figures 1.17 and 1.18 show the graphing calculator's numerical analysis of the IQ scores. The graph in Figure 1.19 represents a histogram of the IQ scores that was generated using the graphing calculator.

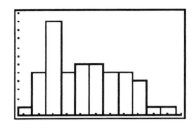

FIGURE 1.17   **FIGURE 1.18**   **FIGURE 1.19**

KEY TERMS

Raw Data   2
Statistics   2
Descriptive Statistics   2
Inferential Statistics   6
Population   5
Sample   5
Representative Sample   8, 14
Statistic   8
Parameter   8
Exploratory Data Analysis   26
Graph   27
Bar Graph   28

Pictograph   29
Non-representative Sample   14
Range   31
Sampling   10
Census   11
Destructive Testing   12
Sample Size   13
Population Size   13
Population Average   13
Probability or Random Sample   15
Random or Probability Sampling
    Techniques   14

Simple Random Sampling or Random
    Sampling   15
Systematic Sampling   19
Stratified Sampling   20
Cluster Sampling   21

SECTION EXERCISES

Sections 1.1

1. Before they are arranged or analyzed information or observations are called _____ data.

2. The collection, presentation, analysis and interpretation of data is called _____.

3. The study of statistics can be separated into two areas: _____ statistics and _____ statistics.

4. The branch of statistics that uses numerical and/or visual techniques to summarize data is called ____ _____.

5. The total collection of individuals or objects under consideration is called the _____.

6. Inferential statistics is the process of using a sample to draw inferences or conclusions about a _____.

7. A number that is used to describe a characteristic of a sample, such as a sample average, is called a _____.

For questions numbered 8 to 10 use one of the following words: Sample, Population, Statistic, Parameter, Descriptive, Inferential

8. The average IQ score of a sample of 100 college students represents a _____.

9. The population of basketball players at UCLA has an average height of 6'3". This is an example of _____ statistics.

10. During the month of December, a county hospital recorded 450 live births. Of these births, 52% were boys.
    a) The percentage value, 52%, represents a _____ of the population of December births.
    b) If the data on December births is used to estimate the percentage of boy births for the past year, then the percentage value of 52% would represent a statistic, since the December births would represent a _____ of the population.

For problems 11 to 12 use the information in each problem statement to fill in the blanks.

11. A study of all working women in San Francisco, was conducted to determine their average annual salary. A sample of 250 working women was selected, and their salaries were recorded.

a) The population is _____.

b) The sample is _____.

c) The population parameter being studied is_____
_____.

12. A sociologist used the average annual income to measure the socio-economic level of the 10,000 families living in a community. To estimate the average annual income, the sociologist randomly selects 100 families. Determine:

a) The population._____.

b) The sample._____.

c) The parameter being studied._____.

d) The statistic used to estimate the parameter. _____
_____.

13. A research medical team, using data collected from a sample of 4000 sport-related injuries, reported that the average recovery time for a broken ankle is eight weeks. This average is an example of a:

a) Parameter

b) Statistic

14. The results of a survey indicate that 23% of the election district will support the proposition. This is an example of:

a) Descriptive statistics

b) Inferential statistics

15. Statistics describe the characteristics of a _____.

a) Population

b) Sample

16. Which of the following is an example of a parameter?

a) In a sample of 10,000 children under age fifteen, 2,466 play soccer.

b) The average male SAT verbal score is 460.

c) Sixty-seven out of 100 pollsters surveyed predict Mayor DePortoro will win the election.

17. Data exploration techniques are primarily used to help discover errors in the collected information. (T/F)

(II)

Statistical Snapshot

U.S. Mail vs. E-mail

Which do you trust more to send a message: computer E-mail or the U.S. Postal Service?

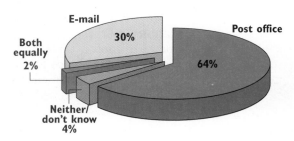

Source: ICR Survey Research Group, survey of 1,014 households.

18. Population characteristics are called parameters. (T/F)

19. A sample represents a portion of the population. (T/F)

20. For each of the statistical snapshots I and II, identify which illustrate inferential statistics.

For those examples of inferential statistics:

a) Identify the population being sampled

b) The sample size

c) State one conclusion or inference being drawn and whether or not you are in agreement. Explain.

21. Read the following article entitled "Two-years Measure Up."

Two-Years Measure Up

Community colleges take heart: That common assumption that community colleges may broaden access for students but do not provide the academic opportunities of four-year colleges ain't necessarily so. Cash-strapped students will also find welcome recent research that shows little difference in the academic outcomes of the freshman year experience at two-year and four-year institutions.

A study published in the Spring 1995 issue of *Educational Evaluation and Policy Analysis* reports on the work of four researchers working with the national Center for postsecondary Teaching, Learning and Assessment. Over the course of a year, they tested 2,685 freshman at five two-year colleges and six four-year colleges drawn from all regions of the United States. Test-

(I)

Statistical Snapshot

The typical NFL player weighs 237.7 pounds. Heaviest and lightest teams in the NFC and AFC, in average pounds:

NFL Weigh In

	AFC			NFC	
	Jaguars 245.3			Panthers 240.0	
Colts 234.1			Eagles 233.4		
Lightest	Heaviest		Lightest	Heaviest	

Source: NFL

ing the students as they began their studies in the fall of 1992 and again in the spring of 1993 and controlling for pre-college ability, they found a general parity in the impact of their first year of study on reading comprehension, mathematics, critical thinking and composite achievement.

The research team, headed up by Ernest T. Pascarella, a professor of higher education at the University of Illinois at Chicago, paid the students a $25 stipend to take a three-hour series of tests at the outset. They also collected information on their demographic characteristics and backgrounds, their aspirations and expectations and their orientations toward learning. The following spring, the students received another stipend of $35 to take three and a half hours more of tests. For comparison purposes, the researchers eliminated the most selective four-year institutions with five two-year institutions whose student bodies were most similar in terms of pre-college academic preparation.

The study found that the two-year college sample had slightly higher end-of-freshman-year gains in mathematics and composite achievement, while the four-year students had slightly higher gains in reading comprehension and critical thinking. It also showed that woman tended to do a little better at the four-year schools and men at the two-year schools. Likewise, non-white students tended to do slightly better at two-years and white students at four-years. The researchers noted that these findings require further testing.

Pascarella and his colleagues conclude that differences in institutional resources such as library size, student-faculty ratio, money spent per student and physical facilities may have little influence on the academic achievement of students. More salient, they say, may be the influences of quality of teaching, curricular experiences and general education coursework taken.

There are obvious policy implications from these findings, say the researchers. Other studies have shown that students initially attending two-year colleges compete on equal footing with their four-year counterparts in such areas as occupational status, earnings, job stability and job satisfaction. "My feeling is that 99 percent of all colleges and universities give students the same impact: They move similar

people a similar amount." Therefore, he concludes, undergraduate students concerned about cost should know that attending a low-tuition community college will "not necessarily come at the price of a less intellectually rigorous academic program."

21. a) What two populations did the researchers compare?
     b) How did the researchers select the students to try to ensure that they were representative of the populations they were comparing?
     c) How did the researchers measure the differences between the students from the two groups? How did they account for any differences in the students abilities prior to their college education?
     d) State and discuss the research results.

22. The article entitled *Slippery Statistics* appeared in Newsday on September 9, 1996.
     a) What two studies are reported in the article?
     b) Identify the two populations surveyed in the article.
     c) What was the purpose of each survey?
     d) Explain some of the reasons why the survey results differed for each of the surveys discussed.
     e) Explain what you think Joseph Gfroerer meant when he said "There are sampling errors associated with these data . . ." Give examples to support your explanation.

Slippery Statistics

by Robert Fresco

Last winter, federal researchers carried wheatyellow, 98-page surveys bursting with questions into thousands of homes across the country.

How long has it been since you last used marijuana or hashish? Have you ever, even once, used any form of cocaine? How old were you the first time you smoked a cigarette, even one or two puffs?

Although the survey is aimed at finding drug, alcohol and tobacco use at every age, the results concerning youngsters produced the most surprises. And what researchers found—that adolescent drug use increased sharply in 1995 over 1994—sparked banner headlines about a teen drug crisis as well as Republican charges that the Clinton administration is not doing enough to combat the drug menace.

But with interviews with federal officials and academic experts indicate that the survey released last month, may be presenting an inaccurate portrait—actually understating drug use by adolescents and overstating the one-year increase, especially in the use of harder drugs.

The federal study found that 11 percent of youngsters between the ages of 12 and 17 had taken illegal drugs in the previous month and that the rate had jumped by one-third from the previous year. It also showed a 167 percent increase in recent cocaine use.

But Lloyd Johnston, a University of Michigan researcher, who is one of the nation's top experts on adolescent drug use, said his latest annual study found higher numbers of students using drugs and a more gradual increase. His study, released in December, showed that 12 percent of eighth-graders, 20 percent of 10th-graders and 24 percent of high school seniors had used drugs in the previous month, higher than the federal numbers.

The federal study also showed a 33 percent increase in drug use from 1994 to 1995, while Johnston's figures showed a rise of 8 percent to 12 percent—part of a steady increase since 1991.

The reasons for the disparities could include the setting of the federal government's survey at young people's homes—with parents sometimes nearby—and the small numbers of youngsters using such drugs as cocaine and heroin. There's also the question of whether youngsters are telling the truth.

"When you're doing a survey, you don't have any gold standard. You really don't know if people are telling the truth," cautioned Robert Schilling, associate professor of social work at Columbia University.

Federal and private experts agreed that drug use among junior high and high school-age students has continued to rise since the early 1900's. And they also said studies show that teenage cigarette smokers are far more likely to abuse drugs than are nonsmokers.

Johnston and other experts said a key reason the federal numbers showed lower drug use may relate to the places where the data was gathered. While the federal report was based on questionnaires given to 4,600 youngsters in their homes, the Michigan study got its answers from forms filled in by 50,000 eighth-, 10th-, and 12th-graders at school.

Johnston believes that youngsters are more likely to tell lies at home to hide drug use from their parents: "More kids are going to be concealing. We have a self-administered questionnaire. It's confidential. It's collected by University of Michigan staff. The teachers are asked to stand in the front of the classroom, "so they can't see what students are writing.

Officials who ran the federal survey said the government's questionnaires were also confidential, and most students filled them in without parents present. But they also acknowledged that in some cases—they did not know how many—parents were on the scene. And they said home surveys have, for years, showed lower drug use rates than studies done in schools.

One of those officials, statistician Joseph Gustin, said: "The interviews are all supposed to be private. We do everything we possibly can to prevent anyone from actually standing around." But he acknowledged that interviewers cannot prevent parents from looking over their children's shoulders or wandering in and out of the room.

Federal officials said, however, that the $7-million study is much more comprehensive than the Michigan report, since it includes people of all ages from 18,000 households, not just youngsters in school.

The study showed that more than 8 percent of youngsters had smoked marijuana—by far the most popular drug with teenagers—in the 30 days before they filled out the questionnaire. Johnston's numbers showed that 9 percent of eighth-graders, 17 percent of 10th-graders and 21 percent of high school seniors used marijuana.

Far fewer adolescents reported using stronger drugs. The federal study found that eight adolescents out of 1,000 had used cocaine in the previous month, up from three in 1994— 1 167 percent increase.

But the administrator of the study, Joseph Gfroerer, acknowledged that with such small numbers, there might be substantial errors. He said: "There are sampling error associated with these data . . . As far as the size of the increase being 160 percent, we can't say that. All we can say is . . . (usage) went up."

Reprinted by permission of Tribune Media Services.

Section 1.2

23. The idea of selecting a sample to determine the characteristics of the population is the essence of _____ statistics.

24. Sampling is the process of selecting a _____, or sample, of the entire _____

25. A survey that includes every item or individual of the population is called a _____.

26. The goal of sampling is to obtain a _____ sample of the population.

27. The objective of Inferential Statistics is to draw a conclusion about the entire _____ using a _____.

28. The size of a sample is denoted by ____.

29. The size of a finite population is denoted by _____.

30. A numerical characteristic of a population such as the population average is called a _____.

31. A numerical characteristic of a sample such as the sample average is a _____.

32. A portion or part of a population is called:
    a) proportion   **b)** subset   **c)** sample   **d)** census

33. The symbol used to represent the size of a sample is
    a) N   **b)** S   **c)** X   **d)** n

Section 1.3

34. A representative sample is a sample containing similar characteristics of the _____.

35. A random or probability sample is a sample which is selected in such a manner that each data value of the population has a _____ _____ of being selected for the sample.

36. A simple random sample is a sample of data values selected from a population in such a way that every sample of size n has an equal _____ of being selected and every data value of the population has the same chance of being selected for the _____.

37. Random sampling techniques are very important because of their use in formulating valid generalizations about population parameters.
    (T/F)

38. In a systematic sampling, the data values of the population are _____ in some way.

39. In stratified sampling, the population is first divided into subgroups or subpopulations called _____.

40. Stratified random sampling should be used when the variability within the strata is large.
    (T/F)

41. In cluster sampling, the population is divided into groups called _____ where the groups are relatively similar and a representative small-scale version of the overall _____.

42. Cluster sampling can be used when each cluster represents a small scale version of the population.
    (T/F)

43. Classify each of the following sampling techniques as either random or not random.
    a) A college student is trying to determine an estimate for the mean height of the entire student body. The student interviews and measures 200 students in the math and science building.
    b) A social worker wants to study the 5000 senior citizens in a Florida retirement community. The social worker decides to select 100 senior citizens by first assigning an identification number, from 0000 to 4999, to each of the 5000 senior citizens. She then spins the number wheels pictured in Figure A to form a four digit number. This is continued until a sample of 100 unique identification numbers has been obtained. These 100 senior citizens will constitute the sample.

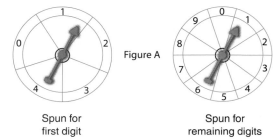

Figure A	
Spun for first digit	Spun for remaining digits

44. Determine whether each of the following sampling methods for selecting a sample from a population will result in a random sample. Explain.
    a) A city political organization wishes to obtain a random sample of its registered voters. A list of all registered city voters is obtained. The organization selects its sample by taking every 24th name on the list after a starting point was randomly selected.
    b) A civic association wants to conduct a survey of the residents living in their town. The residents responding to their survey are selected from the town's telephone directory. The association randomly selects both the pages of the telephone directory and the residents from these pages using a table of random numbers.

45. Mr. GB, the director of a summer basketball camp, is planning a telephone survey of last year's campers. GB will be using an alphabetical list of the previous year's campers to conduct his survey. Devise a sampling technique that could be used to select the campers to survey.

46. Consider the problem of drawing a simple random sample of 15 people from a list of 580 people. The 580 people are assigned a number from 001 to 580. Use the following list of random numbers to identify the 15 people selected for the random sample by using the first 3 digits of the 5 digit random numbers:
    a) If you start with the random number 63271 and move to the right of each row.

b) If you begin with the random number 63271 and move down each column.

63271	59986	71744	51102	15141
80714	58683	93108	13554	79945
88547	09896	95436	79115	08303
01041	20030	63754	08459	28364
55957	57243	83865	09911	19761
66535	40102	26646	60147	15702
46276	87453	44790	67122	45573
84358	21625	16999	13385	22782

47. Using the Random Number Table, Table VI in Appendix D: Statistical Tables, start at the top row of the first column of the table and read across the row, select 10 random numbers falling within the values 0000 to 6700.

48. The publishers of a health magazine are considering a change in the format of their magazine. They would like to survey 1,000 subscribers from their list of 350,000 subscribers about the proposed changes. Each subscriber is randomly assigned a number from 000001 to 350,000. Use the systematic sampling procedure to identify the subscriber number corresponding to each of the 350,000 subscribers which would be selected if the first subscriber selected has the number 000028.

49. A bank auditor decides to select a random sample, without replacement, of size 15 from the 9,500 five year CD accounts. The auditor decides to use the last four digits of each CD account number as a means of identification. The account numbers are in consecutive order and begin with the number 10 – 50001 and end at 10 – 59500. The bank auditor will use the following table of 5-digit random numbers to select the bank accounts. An account number will be selected from these 9,500 accounts when the last four digits of the account number match the first four digits of the random number.

Use this table to determine the 15 account numbers of the bank customers the auditor will select for the audit if the auditor begins with the number 99041 and reads down each column.

99041	04024	77919	36103	13300	40719
24878	96096	12777	00102	92259	55157
98901	34693	85963	97809	64760	64951
84673	07844	38917	99505	75470	35749
18988	62028	79656	83149	96402	58104

Section 1.4–1.5

50. When a researcher analyzes data for possible patterns or relationships that might exist, this is called _____ Data Analysis.

51. A graph involving pictures of objects in which the size of the object represents the relative size of the quantity being represented by the object is called a _____ .

52. The 1936 *Literary Digest Poll* is an instance where a _____ sample led to an inappropriate inference about the population.

53. The following data represents the unemployment rates from a large northeast city.

Month	Jan	Feb	Mar	Apr	May	Jun
Unemployment rate in %	4.5	4.6	4.6	4.7	4.8	4.9

Month	Jul	Aug	Sep	Oct	Nov	Dec
Unemployment rate in %	4.8	4.9	4.0	5.1	5.2	5.3

Using this data sketch:
a) A graph making the unemployment rate appear to be stable.
b) A graph that exaggerates the rise in the unemployment rates.

54. Discuss how the presentation of the statistics within each of the following statements could be misleading.
a) Ivory Soap is 99.44 % pure.
b) Nine out of ten dentists recommend chewing sugarless gum for their patients who chew gum.
c) One recent study claimed that 55% of all insured homes in America are underinsured, that is, insured for less than 80% of actual replacement cost.
d) The profits of a foreign owned oil company have doubled in the last two years.

e) A prominent mathematics association journal used the following graph to illustrate its increase in circulation. The ad read:

In Five Years, We'll Have 10 GREAT Years BEHIND us!

f) Rio Oro, an Arizona land developer, used the following pictographs in their advertisements to emphasize why investors should purchase undeveloped land in Arizona. The ad was stated as:

Here's why so many investors PREFER Arizona land.

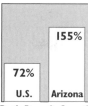

g) The book value of this automobile has increased through the years.

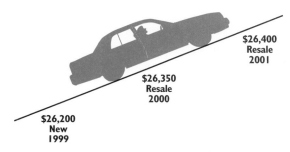

55. Read the following satiric essay entitled: **I'm Tired**, which comments on how many people work in the United States. Discuss the author's misuse of data and facts within the essay. Within your discussion, comment on:
a) The author's biases on who works and who doesn't work.
b) The author's misuse of facts. For example, are there some groups listed in the nonworking categories who do work? Is it possible to belong to two or more of these categories?
c) What the author used as the population of the labor force and why it is not as useful as the Census Bureau's definition. (Note: the Census Bureau calculates labor force statistics for persons who are 16 years and over.)
d) The percentage of people that work as stated by the author.
e) What suggestions you would give the anonymous author that would help him/her to use the data more accurately.

I'm Tired

I'm tired. For several years I've been blaming it on middle age, iron poor blood, lack of vitamins, air pollution, obesity, dieting, and a dozen other maladies that make you wonder if life is really worth living. But now I find out, tain't that. I'm tired because I'm overworked.

The population of this country is 200 million. Eighty-four million are retired. That leaves 116 million to do the work. There are 74 million in school, which leaves 42 million to do the work. Of this total, there are 23 million employed by the Federal Government. That leaves 19 million to do the work.

Four million are in the Armed Forces, which leaves 15 million to do the work. Take from that total the 14,800,000 people who work for States and Cities. That leaves 200,000 to do the work. There are 188,000 in hospitals, so that leaves 12,000 to do the work.

Now, there are 11,998 people in prisons. That leaves just two people to do the work. You and me. And you're sitting there reading this.

No wonder I'm tired!!

56. A cereal manufacturer used the following graph within its advertisement to convince prospective buyers to purchase their new cereal CRUNCH-O. The advertisement claimed that their new packaging technique called "THE SEAL" keeps the cereal fresher.

a) Examine the graph and explain why it is misleading.
b) The advertisement also states the following:

"THE SEAL" retains the perfect moisture level in an unopened box. In fact, it retains moisture 10 times better than conventional packaging. *Ten times better! And it's 1000 times better at keeping out air.*

Comment on why this statement can be misleading. Select the words or phrases that need to be further explained.

CHAPTER REVIEW

57. The portion of the population that is selected for study is called a _____.

58. The use of sample information to estimate a population characteristic is the primary objective of _____ statistics. Thus, the researcher must take care to insure that the sample is _____ of the population.

59. A number such as the population average that describes a characteristic of a population is called a _____.

For questions numbered 60 to 61 use one of the following words: Sample, Population, Statistic, Parameter, Descriptive, Inferential

60. On the basis of an independent poll, it is estimated that 57% of the voters will vote for politician DePortoro. This is an example of _____ statistics.

61. A survey of 1,000 undergraduates at a midwestern university of 40,000 undergraduates was taken to determine the percentage of undergraduates living at home. The survey indicated that 20% of the students live at home.
  a) The 1,000 undergraduates surveyed represent the _____.
  b) The 40,000 undergraduates attending the midwestern university represent the _____.
  c) The percentage value, 20%, represents a _____.

For exercise 62, use the information to fill in the blanks.

62. A survey was conducted to determine the opinion of people in a Miami suburb on a proposed law to legalize casino gambling. A sample of 400 people were questioned. It was determined that 58% favored legalizing casino gambling.
  a) The population is _____.
  b) The sample is _____.
  c) The percentage value, 58%, is a statistic because it describes a characteristic of a _____.

63. Most psychology texts report that the average IQ score for an adult male is between 90 and 110. This average is an example of a:
  a) Parameter   **b)** Statistic

64. The average age of those surveyed is 26.73 years. This is an example of
  a) Descriptive statistics   **b)** Inferential statistics

65. Parameters describe the characteristics of a _____.
  a) Population   **b)** Sample

66. Inferential statistics helps researchers make generalizations about large populations by using data from a sample of the population. (T/F)

67. Sample characteristics are called statistics. (T/F)

68. In applications of inferential statistics all the observations of the population should be obtained. (T/F)

69. Predictions made from a straw poll are an example of inferential statistics. (T/F)

70. If a sample is not representative of the population, inferences made from the sample information may not be correct. (T/F)

71. **a)** Define the following terms:
    (i) inferential statistics
    (ii) sampling
    (iii) census
    (iv) destructive testing
    (v) population
    (vi) sample
    (vii) parameter
    (viii) statistic
    (ix) sample size
    (x) population size
  b) Discuss the reasons of why it is necessary to sample.
  c) Identify the symbol for each of the following terms:
    (i) population size
    (ii) sample size

72. A random sample will always be a representative sample. (T/F)

73. If a quality control manager were to test every item produced by the manufacturer, then there would be no items left to sell. This type of testing is called destructive testing. (T/F)

74. Systematic sampling differs from simple random sampling since each sample does not have an equal chance of being selected. (T/F)

75. In stratified sampling, an attempt is made to define the strata such that the population of data values within each stratum are as much alike as possible. (T/F)

76. A United States senator mailed a questionnaire to all the constituents living in her state. She randomly selected 200 of the questionnaires which were returned to her office. Would this sample represent a random sample of all the constituents living in her state? Explain your answer.

77. A community consists of people in three distinct income brackets: low, middle and high. Depending upon the income bracket, the opinions of the people regarding the upcoming vote on the school budget may differ.

To obtain an accurate opinion of the people living in the community, the school board decides to select a stratified random sample.

a) What would be appropriate subpopulations for this stratified sample, and what are these subpopulations called?

b) What sampling procedure is used to select the people from the community for the stratified sample and how is the overall stratified sample formed?

78. A pollster wants to conduct a survey of households in the state of Arizona. To minimize the cost of selecting a sample, the pollster divides the state of Arizona into regions and uses cluster sampling to select the sample.

a) What do the regions represent within this cluster sampling?

b) What assumptions are made about the regions of the sample?

c) How is the sample selected?

79. Chris, a history instructor at Columbus University, decides to conduct an opinion poll of the students attending the university during the fall semester. Using a random number table, she selects 100 students from all the students attending the morning European History classes.

a) Does this sample represent a random sample? Explain.

b) Is this a representative sample of all the students attending the University? Explain.

c) Identify a population for which this sample could be a representative sample.

80. A college student wants to estimate the average weight of all the students at her college. Her sampling technique is designed to select the first 25 students on line when the dining hall begins to serve lunch. Do you believe this sampling procedure represents an appropriate technique in obtaining a random sample of the weights of the college students? Explain.

81. CCC, a television network, decides to poll its viewers on gun control. The network requests its viewers to call 1-900-GUNSYES if they are against gun control. All viewers who favor gun control are asked to call 1-900-GUNSSNO. Do you believe this sampling procedure represents an appropriate technique in obtaining a random sample of the all the viewers of CCC regarding their views on gun control? Explain.

82. The 7-Eleven stores in Nassau County, Long Island, conduct a weekly opinion survey of their customers. The customers who decide to answer the opinion question will select a coffee cup marked "yes" or one marked "no" when purchasing their coffee. Do you believe this sampling procedure represents an appropriate technique in obtaining a random sample of the opinion of all 7-Eleven customers? Explain.

83. A new home wares department store called Home Arsenal is planning to expand into a new market area.

One aspect of its study will be to determine the spending habits of the prospective customers for the type of goods Home Arsenal will sell. Assume the selected marketing area consists of the size of a small town, how would you go about selecting a sample of prospective customers to interview?

84. The service manager of an automobile dealership decides to sample her customers to determine if they are satisfied with the service they receive. The manager prepares a list of 630 customers from the service records of the previous 12 months. Each customer is assigned a number from 000 to 629. The service managers decides to sample 20 customers. The manager used the following list of random numbers to identify the customers. The sample is selected by using the last 3 digits of each random number. Begin with the random number 08723 and read down each column. Make a list of the 20 customers selected for the sample.

08723	67422	68479	10097	85017	13618	91494
56239	17691	26640	37542	16719	69041	80336
44915	79655	85157	08422	65842	82186	44104
41976	48274	11100	99019	84532	39187	12550
15694	60523	16505	12807	82789	41453	63606

85. The Student Government Association (SGA) at a small community college having 5,000 students is considering increasing the student activities fee. Since its decision will effect all the students, the SGA has decided to interview a random sample of twenty students regarding their opinion about the fee increase. To select this sample, the SGA assigns a number from 0001 to 5000 to each student. Using the Random Number Table, Table VI in Appendix D: Statistical Tables, and starting at the top row of the first column of the table, determine the 4 digit numbers corresponding to the 20 students who should be selected for this interview.

86. Each year Fortune magazine publishes a list of the top 500 U.S. companies based upon their annual earnings. The companies are ranked from 1 to 500. Using the random sampling procedure, identify the numbers of twenty companies from Fortune magazine's list of 500 companies. Start at the 3rd column and 26th row of the Random Number Table, Table VI in Appendix D: Statistical Tables, and read across the table to determine the 20 companies.

87. The Daily Satellite, a newspaper company, has received 15,000 entries for its Super Bowl contest. Lois Road and Clark Hent, two newspaper reporters, will randomly select the 10 winners from the entries. If each entry is numbered from 00001 to 15,000, then select the ten winners of the contest by using the Random Number Table, Table VI in Appendix D: Statistical Tables, starting at the 31st row of the first column of the table and moving across each row.

88. A bank auditor is planning to take a systematic random sample from a list of bank customer's. The auditor decides to select a sample of 300 bank customers from the bank's list of 60,000 customers. If customer has an account number ranging from 1 to 60,000 and she randomly selects 140 as her starting point, then:
   a) Determine the ratio of the population size to the sample size, and
   b) Identify the customers selected for the audit.

89. The following data represents the trend of U.S. imports of foreign automobiles from 1990 to 2000.

Year	90	91	92	93	94	95
Auto Imports per million Population	35	44	54	65	76	87

Year	96	97	98	99	00	
Auto Imports per million Population	98	109	120	131	151	

Using this data construct:
   a) A graph exaggerating the rise in U.S. imports of foreign auto's due to the gasoline shortage.
   b) An accurate graph depicting the trend of U.S. imports of foreign autos.

90. Discuss how the presentation of the statistics within each of the following statements could be misleading.
   a) Four out of five doctors prescribe the pain reliever found in aspirin for headache pain.
   b) A brand of chewing tobacco claims that it is 40% juicier.
   c) The bar graph indicates how the top five insurance companies pay off on auto accidents. Company X is using the graph to express just the *plain truth*.

The Plain Truth

   d) A New Mexico land developer, Rio Oro, used the following ad to influence people to purchase land in Arizona.

A GOOD Investment!

Land values usually go up . . .

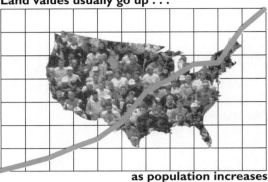

as population increases

   e) "Join The Army—It's Safer."
      An Army recruiting center in Texas coined the above slogan based on the following statistical data.
      The death rate in the Army is 5 per thousand while the death rate for civilians is 20 per thousand during the same period.
      The Army recruiting center tried to persuade individuals to join the Army by explaining it was safer in the Army than out of it.

91. For each of the following two media examples of statistics, identify which illustrate inferential statistics.

   For those examples of inferential statistics:
   a) Identify the population being sampled
   b) The sample size
   c) State one conclusion or inference being drawn and whether or not you are in agreement. Explain.

(I)

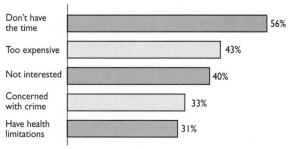

Statistical Snapshot

Why We Don't Just Do It

Major reasons we don't take part in recreational sports*:

Don't have the time	56%
Too expensive	43%
Not interested	40%
Concerned with crime	33%
Have health limitations	31%

* Respondents could choose more than one.
Source: The Recreation Roundtable poll of 2,000 persons

(II)

Statistical Snapshot

When Pets Get 'People Food'

How often pet owners say they feed their pet human food:

Source: American Animal Hospital Association survey of 1,049 pet owners

92. The article entitled *Enough polls!* appeared in *USA Today* on October 7, 1996. The author is writing about the numerous political surveys taken prior to the presidential election.

   a) What is the author's main concern about polls in general?

   b) Is the author against political polls?

   c) What are some of the concerns the author has about political polls?

   d) According to the author, what are some of the characteristics of a good poll?

   e) What do you think the author means when he writes: " And even with impeccable surveys, the nature of sampling is such that roughly one poll in 20 will be an aberration—have results outside sampling error."? What do you think he means by *sampling error*?

   f) Discuss what the author means when he states "We have surveys of all voters, of registered voters, of very likely voters—all giving very different results, but often with no distinction made."

   g) Why is the author upset about people who report the results of "focus groups with 25 people" as "full-blown surveys"? What does the author believe is a reasonable number of people to survey for a good poll?

   h) What are some of the things the author recommends that you should look for in a poll before you can have confidence in the results?

   i) What does Charles Cook do with the major political polls to obtain a good result? Do you see any problems with his technique?

Enough polls!

by Norman Ornstein

If there were a Political Environmental Protection Agency, it would be preparing a case against some of the major polluters in our political process this election season—the pollsters. It has been building for years, but this year the haze caused by overpolling, shoddy polling and poor poll reporting has blocked out any clear view of the election and our choices.

Not all polls or pollsters are culpable, of course, any more than all cars or all companies are guilty of air pollution. But this year we have been deluged with hugh numbers of political surveys, including a raft of daily national tracking polls, regular national voter surveys, frequent focus groups, and hundreds of surveys for and about particular interest groups and the range of state and local races.

Don't misunderstand me—I am not against polling. I have been around survey research for my entire professional career, rely on good surveys for my own research and writing, and follow the surveys as avidly as I do batting averages during the baseball pennant race. I love to discuss interesting survey results with my colleagues and fellow political junkies.

But there can be too much of a good thing. And this year, we have had the logical culmination of a process in which every political actor wants his or her own survey to justify actions or to hype one's standing; where every journalistic organization, including local TV stations and newspapers, networks, magazines and radio stations, not to mention networks and national papers, has to have its own regular poll; and where the single largest news feature about the campaign is the poll results.

This is bad in several ways. First, it puts even more attention on the horse-race component of the campaign and less on either the issues or the policy agenda for 1997 and beyond. Figuring out who is ahead, who is behind, and what is interesting and important, has become a venerable part of every election process. But understanding what the choices are and what they mean for governing is even more significant. That kind of news is by no means ignored during the campaign. But the flood of polls tends to crowd out other kinds of news and, just as bad, tends to frame political reporters' questions to the candidates. Instead of asking things like, "What would you do in your first 100 days in office?" reporters are inclined to ask questions like, "Why are you lagging in the polls?"

Second, it increases the spin candidates and pundits put on the campaign. Already, we are overwhelmed by spin artists—designated hitters on each side who try to put the best light on every piece of information out there about their candidates. Partisan pollsters and campaign officials now can find or create poll results that prove anything they want—leading only to more cynicism and more confusion among voters.

Third, the spate of polls has damaged our ability to distinguish between good, solid surveys that tell us something about voter preferences or public opinion, and opinion, and shock polls that aren't to be trusted. The bad has driven out the good in this case, affecting all polls.

When I was in graduate school at the Survey Research Center at the University of Michigan, I learned that a good national survey should have around 1,200 to 1,500 respondents, carefully worded questions, systematic call backs to account for people not being at home, and careful mechanisms to ensure that samples were reliable and representative. Phone surveys, the less expensive and more efficient alternative to face-to-face interviewing require special and careful methods of control. And even with impeccable surveys, the nature of sampling is such that roughly one poll in 20 will be an aberration—have results outside sampling error.

Today, we have regular surveys of 500 to 600 or even less, done by phone overnight, and sold as the equivalent of a good, systematic poll. We have surveys of all voters, of registered voters, of very likely voters—all giving very different results, but often with no distinction made. And we have focus groups, the latest media rage—25 or 30 voters brought into a room to talk with an interviewer and give us a more personalized sense of public opinion. Focus groups are a fine way to test hypotheses or to flesh out the findings of a more impersonal national survey. But

we have pollsters and journalists taking focus groups with 25 people and reporting their "results" as if they were full-blown surveys—down to relaying percentages!

The bottom line for readers who want to follow the political numbers: Don't trust a survey until you see a "brand name" you are familiar with; look at the sample size; see if the poll was done hurriedly without any opportunity for call back, and see if the sample is registered or likely voters; look at the question wording, if it is available; and ignore any survey that shows shocking results different from all the others— it is probably the one in 20 that is an aberration. One more piece of advice: If you are interested in tracking the trial heats for the White House, do as top-flight analyst Charles Cook does— take the results over a week of the top polls, including the Pew Research, CNN/Gallup, ABC/Washington Post, NBC/Wall Street Journal and CBS/New York Times surveys, and average them. And then ignore all the other polls that journalists and political operatives thrust in your face.

93. The article entitled "How Ads Can Bend Statistics" appeared in the *NY Times* on January 17, 1981.

Consumer Saturday

How Ads Can Bend Statistics

"Doctors recommend" "Four out of five people preferred. . . ." "Twice as many repairmen choose. . . ." The slogans and claims are survey advertisements, a technique of selling products that has grown in use over the last five years and one in which the Federal Trade Commission is increasingly interested.

"It is an important technique because consumers give it credibility and they use the information contained in them to make important purchasing decisions," Wallace S. Synder, assistant director for the F.T.C.'s advertising practices division, said in Washington this week. Regulation of advertising is a traditional function of the F.T.C.

Survey advertisements are an effective tool increasingly used in the 60 billion-a-year advertising trade, but such advertisements are not always as scientific or responsible as they may sound.

During the last two weeks, three manufacturers have made consent agreements with F.T.C. to discontinue the use of less-than-substantive claims for their products.

In one, Litton Industries agreed not to advertise its microwave oven as superior to others unless there is a "reasonable basis" for such claims. The company had been claiming that independent technicians preferred their product over competing products, but their survey used only authorized Litton service agencies' technicians who could possibly have a bias toward their product. In addition, there was no effort to make sure that the technicians who preferred Litton microwave ovens were experienced at repairing ovens other than Litton's.

Under F.T.C. regulation, "reasonable basis" means that competent and reliable surveys or tests are conducted by qualified persons. The results, say the regulation, must be objectively evaluated "using procedures that ensure accurate and reliable results." The Litton advertisements, the agency said, did meet such standards.

In a similar case, Standard Brands and Ted Bates & Company, formerly the advertising agency for Standard Brand's Fleischmann's Margarine, agreed not to make claims based on surveys or tests unless they were scientifically conducted and the claims accurately reflected the results.

The agreements between the companies and the F.T.C. cover all the products of Standard Brands, one of the nation's largest food and beverage companies, and every advertisement created by the advertising agency.

At issue were advertisements used between 1974 and 1977. They claimed the doctors preferred and recommended Fleischmann's Margarine. Two of the four advertisements, allegedly based on a national survey of doctors stated:

"When a doctor chooses margarine, chances are it's Fleischmann's."

The F.T.C. alleged that the claims were unproven, charging that only 15.5 percent of the doctors surveyed recommended any specific name brand.

The companies have now agreed that any surveys or tests featured in advertisements will be designed and analyzed in a reliable scientific manner and must clearly establish any superiority claims.

In another case, Teledyne Inc. and Teledyne Industries Inc. makers of Water Pik, and J. Walter Thompson, its advertising agency, agreed that their advertising claims about the effectiveness of the dental-care product in preventing gum diseases would have a "reasonable basis." The Water Pik is an "oral irrigator" that sprays water into the mouth and that, advertisements say, flushes away debris from beneath the gum line and "reduces the causes of gum disease."

The F.T.C. further alleged that Teledyne falsely claimed that the Water Pik is approved by the American Dental Association. To make such a claim, the endorsement must be made in writing, according to the F.T.C.

C. Collot Guerard, deputy assistant director of the F.T.C.'s advertising division, offered pointers for consumers when they read or see an advertisement:

"Ask yourself," she said, "how many doctors were actually surveyed when you see something like 'five out of six doctors.' Comsumers tend to think of big, nationally projected surveys, but it might not be so."

Learn to recognize the "dangling comparatives" in advertisements such as "Product X will get your teeth whiter than ever" and ask yourself just what does that mean. Whiter than the same product did a year ago? Whiter than other products.

Watch for parity claims. "If an advertisement states that 'no hair dryer will dry your hair quicker,'" she said, "it implies that it dries faster than other brands. Usually it means that it dries just as quickly as other products."

Maintain a healthy skepticism.

New York Times © 1981. Reprinted by permission.

a) This article discusses various problems that arise when claims are made within advertisements. Enumerate several of these problems and discuss some of the possible solutions.

WHAT DO YOU THINK?

94. Examine the snapshot entitled "Learned Believers."
   a) Identify the population being surveyed.

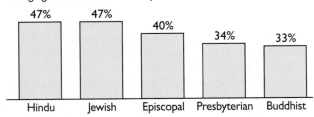

Statistical Snapshot

Learned Believers

Religious denominations in the USA with the highest percentage of college graduates in membership:

Source: ICR Survey Research Group survey of 113,000 adults for City University of New York Graduate School

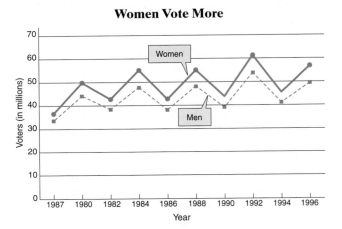

Women Vote More

   b) Since there is a greater number of Roman Catholics in the US than Hindus, why don't the Roman Catholics appear as one of the top percentages?
   c) Why are Hindus one of the top percentages?
   d) What information would you like to see that was not included?

95. Examine the graphic entitled "Women Vote More."
   a) Identify the populations presented within the graphic.
   b) What factors might contribute to the comment "Women vote more"?

   c) What reason can you give for both of these graphs rising and falling every two years? When would you expect the next peak to occur for both graphs? Why?
   d) Do you notice any pattern with respect to certain years for the men and women voters? Explain. In what future year would you expect the number of men voters to be approximately 40 million? Why? In what future year would you expect the number of women voters to be approximately 44 million? Why?
   e) In what year did the number of men and women voters reach their maximum? Can you give an explanation for this?
   f) Would you predict that the number of women and men voters will reach a maximum in the year 2000? Explain.

PROJECTS

96. While watching TV pay close attention to the commercials.
   a) Determine the type of statistics (descriptive or inferential) being presented.

   b) Comment as to what information (if any) has been left out that might lead you to a different conclusion.

97. Look in magazines or newspapers for ads using statistics. Comment on the presentation and state if you think any deceptive tricks might have been utilized.

ANALYZING THE DATABASE USING TECHNOLOGY

The following exercises refer to the file DATABASE listed in Appendix A. Using your technological tool, answer each exercise.

98. For the following variables, identify what each variable represents.
a) AGE
b) AVE
c) SEX
d) MAJ
e) STY
f) GPA
f) GFT

For the variables SEX and MAJ identify what each data value represents.
For the other variables except SEX and MAJ determine the lowest and highest data values.

99. Discuss the characteristics of the student whose ID number is:
1) 8573
2) 7679
3) 8809
4) 3529

CHAPTER TEST

100. The branch of statistics that uses sample information to draw a conclusion about the population is called _____.

101. A number that is used to describe a characteristic of a population, such as a population proportion, is called a _____.

102. Sample characteristics are called statistics. (T/F)

103. Which of the following is an example of descriptive statistics?
a) In a sample of 1,000 college students, their average I.Q. score is 115.
b) The average height of all NBA basketball players is 6'7".
c) Nine out of 10 doctors recommend non-aspirin pain reliever.

104. A survey of 1,500 college students within the U.S. was conducted to determine the proportion of students who listen to classical rock music.
a) The population is _____.
b) The sample is _____.
c) The population parameter being studied is _____.

105. A population is divided into groups where the individuals within these groups are not homogenous but the groups are essentially similar. The appropriate sampling technique for this population is:
a) Random
b) Systematic
c) Stratified
d) Cluster

106. A population is divided into groups where the individuals within these groups are relatively homogenous but the groups are not alike. The appropriate sampling technique for this population is:
a) Random
b) Systematic
c) Stratified
d) Cluster

107. Determine whether each of the following sampling methods for selecting a sample from a population will result in a random sample. Explain.
a) The charge account manager of the department store Lacy's decides to obtain a random sample of all Lacy's customers. The manager proposes to assign a number to all charge account holders. A sample would be selected from this list using a random number table.
b) To obtain a random sample of customers of the shopping mall Green Pastures, a group of interviewers are placed at all entrances to the mall for 5 consecutive mornings. Each interviewer selects a typical customer carrying packages as they leave the mall.

108. Dear Abby, a newspaper columnist, decides to poll her readers regarding the question: "Would you have children again, if you had to do it all over?". Abby requests her readers to mail in their responses to her survey. Her sample consists of all the responses she receives. Do you believe Abby's sampling procedure represents an appropriate technique in obtaining a random sample of all her readers regarding their views on having children again? Explain.

109. During Wednesday's statistics class, a college instructor requested that her students answer the following questions: Is your birthdate an even or an odd number? If it is even, please answer question (a), but if it is odd, then answer question (b).

Question (a): Is today Wednesday?

Question (b): Did you cheat on the last statistics exam?

Of the 120 responses, 72 had responded yes while 48 responded no. Assuming that even and odd birthdates are equally-likely, what is your estimate of the fraction of the class who cheated on the last exam?

110. Discuss how the presentation of the statistics within each of the following statements could be misleading.
   a) GoodMonth Radial tires stop 45% faster.
   b) Eight out of ten dentists prefer Brand X sugar free gum.

111. The primary reason for the error in prediction made by *Literary Digest* in predicting the 1936 Presidential winner is _____.
   a) Insufficient sample size
   b) The sample of 10 million was unrepresentative
   c) The 2.3 million voluntary responses was biased

112. Which of the following is the most important criteria for a sample to be considered unbiased?
   a) Representativeness   **b)** Size   **c)** Inferential

113. The incorrect prediction made by the *Literary Digest* for the 1936 presidential election was primarily due to the mailing of the ballots to a non-representative sample of 10 million prospective voters. (T/F)

114. A pictograph is a popular technique used to distort the truth because it can create a visual impression that does not accurately represent the relative size of the quantities being represented. (T/F)

115. The following advertisement appeared in a wildlife magazine:

Environmental T-Shirts
Support wildlife by wearing environmental t-shirts.
(10% of profits go to environmental groups)

   a) If each t-shirt costs $15 and the manufacturer's profit per t-shirt is $5, then how much of your $15 is being contributed to the environmental groups?
   b) Calculate the percent of the $15 that would be contributed to the environmental groups.
   c) Do you feel this advertisement can be misleading?

116. For each of the following two media examples of statistics, identify which illustrate inferential statistics. For those examples of inferential statistics:
   a) Identify the population being sampled
   b) The sample size
   c) State one conclusion or inference being drawn and whether or not you are in agreement. Explain.

(I)   Long Island Household Statistics (1997)

Number of Households consisting of:

One person	154,674	17%
Two people	261,620	29%
Three people	173,194	19%
Four people	173,792	19%
Five people	81,631	9%
Six people	47,554	5%

Total Households: 892,465

Average household size: 2.95

(II)

Statistical Snapshot

Busy Days at the Cash Machine

Two-thirds of people say they have a regular day when they're most likely to use an automatic teller machine:

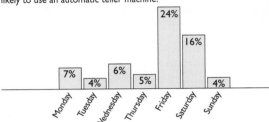

Source: AT&T Global Information Systems poll of 1,011

117. In the December, 1991 issue of The Journal of the American Medical Association, a study disclosed that walking improves health regardless of the pace.

The 24-week study was conducted on 102 women of sedentary life style who did not exercise regularly. These women were divided into a control group, and groups who walked a mile at a pace of 20 minutes a mile, 15 minutes a mile and 12 minutes a mile. Initially the three walking groups went a distance of 1.5 miles five times a week. They gradually increased the distance until they reached three miles on the seventh week, and continued for a total of 24 weeks.

The researchers found that a smaller amount of regular exercise was needed to improve health than once thought. They stated that those women who took 12 minutes to walk a mile and those who took 20 minutes each mile had the same increase of 6 percent in high-density lipoproteins, the good cholesterol. However "the amount of exercise needed to improve health and reduce risk of heart disease is considerably less than is required to improve fitness." The study also found that women walking at the fastest pace increased their cardiorespiratory fitness by an average of 16 percent, roughly the same as women who jog.

The researchers stated that the participants had normal levels of cholesterol and normal blood pressures before they began the study. The women were approximately 20 to 25 percent overweight. At the end of the study, the women did not lose weight, but decreased their percentage of body fat as fatty tissue was replaced by muscle tissue.

a) Define the population for this study.

b) Explain what is meant by a control group? Why do you believe a control group was included within this study?

c) What was the purpose of checking the cholesterol levels and the blood pressures of the women before the study?

d) Why do you believe they choose women who were overweight and lead a sedentary existence?

e) Can you conclude from these findings that men who walk regardless of pace will also improve their health?

CHAPTER 2

Organizing and Presenting Data

Contents

2.1 INTRODUCTION

Graphs are commonly used to organize, summarize, and analyze collections of data. In this chapter, we will show how to use tables and graphs to organize, to summarize and to display the important characteristics of a data set. Using a graph to visually present a data set makes it easy to comprehend and to describe the data.

Suppose the student government association of a local college is interested in exploring some characteristics of its student body. They surveyed a sample of 150 students requesting the following information:

- the student's sex
- the number of credits they are currently taking
- the number of hours per week they study
- their current cumulative grade point average (GPA)
- their area of concentration

Table 2.1 shows the raw data collected from this survey. In this form, it is very difficult to observe the characteristics of the data set.

TABLE 2.1   Student Government Survey Data of 150 Students

The column abbreviations are defined as follows:

SEX:	student sex	MAJ:	college major
	M: male	LIB:	liberal arts
	F: female	BUS:	business
		CMP:	computers or mathematics
HR:	study hours per week	SCI:	natural and applied sciences
GPA:	student grade point average	HTH:	health sciences
CR:	number of credits this semester	FPA:	fine and performing arts

SEX	MAJ	HR	GPA	CR	SEX	MAJ	HR	GPA	CR	SEX	MAJ	HR	GPA	CR	SEX	MAJ	HR	GPA	CR
M	LIB	15	2.79	14.0	M	BUS	24	3.61	18.0	F	LIB	19	3.05	17.0	F	LIB	8	2.47	15.5
M	BUS	18	2.87	12.5	M	BUS	20	3.45	19.0	M	BUS	31	3.62	15.0	M	LIB	10	2.66	13.0
F	LIB	17	2.71	15.0	F	BUS	15	2.42	15.0	F	CMP	33	3.67	18.0	M	BUS	12	3.28	15.0
M	CMP	20	3.42	17.0	F	LIB	12	2.49	14.0	F	BUS	23	2.25	10.5	F	LIB	15	3.41	17.0
M	BUS	19	2.88	6.0	M	CMP	24	3.41	13.0	M	LIB	20	2.70	15.0	M	LIB	31	3.88	18.0
F	LIB	23	2.91	12.0	F	BUS	29	3.18	12.0	F	LIB	17	2.30	7.5	F	LIB	11	2.32	10.5
M	LIB	8	1.76	18.0	M	CMP	30	3.65	7.5	M	LIB	16	2.51	8.0	F	HTH	20	2.97	16.0
M	SCI	10	2.95	15.0	F	LIB	32	3.55	10.5	M	BUS	26	3.54	18.0	F	BUS	29	3.75	15.5
F	LIB	27	2.82	4.5	F	LIB	30	3.45	12.0	M	BUS	12	1.92	4.5	F	LIB	20	2.78	12.0
M	SCI	28	2.96	12.0	M	LIB	19	2.35	16.0	F	LIB	20	3.15	13.0	F	HTH	15	2.84	16.0
M	BUS	20	2.48	17.0	M	BUS	20	2.37	15.0	F	BUS	11	2.00	3.0	F	HTH	10	3.10	17.0
F	BUS	27	2.24	15.0	F	LIB	21	2.54	17.0	F	LIB	9	1.95	15.0	F	LIB	6	2.49	10.0
F	LIB	36	3.02	14.0	F	BUS	21	2.00	10.0	M	BUS	9	2.88	13.0	F	HTH	10	3.24	15.5
F	LIB	17	2.45	15.5	M	LIB	22	2.59	17.0	F	LIB	9	2.65	15.0	M	BUS	21	2.95	7.5
F	HTH	24	3.39	15.0	F	LIB	17	1.94	14.0	F	LIB	8	1.98	12.0	M	BUS	23	2.81	8.0
F	SCI	26	2.75	17.0	F	BUS	16	2.59	15.5	F	BUS	19	3.21	16.0	F	HTH	10	2.36	17.0
M	BUS	28	2.82	16.5	M	LIB	19	3.16	16.5	M	BUS	7	1.95	12.0	M	CMP	17	3.10	15.0
F	BUS	22	2.29	15.0	F	LIB	18	2.66	7.5	F	LIB	10	2.96	15.0	F	LIB	28	3.78	16.0
F	BUS	16	3.56	12.0	M	BUS	22	3.05	13.0	M	LIB	8	2.95	16.5	M	LIB	15	3.08	17.0
M	LIB	27	3.28	8.0	M	LIB	21	3.16	15.0	M	BUS	18	2.00	10.5	M	BUS	11	3.07	15.0
F	BUS	20	3.06	14.0	M	LIB	24	3.29	12.0	F	LIB	16	2.82	16.0	F	LIB	12	3.15	13.0
M	SCI	24	3.56	7.5	F	LIB	20	2.01	12.0	F	BUS	10	1.95	11.0	F	LIB	15	3.65	12.0
M	BUS	27	3.54	4.5	M	BUS	27	3.51	7.5	F	LIB	12	3.01	13.0	M	BUS	14	3.70	17.0
F	BUS	18	3.07	12.0	F	BUS	18	2.84	15.0	F	HTH	15	2.70	14.0	F	LIB	21	2.73	15.0
M	SCI	28	3.05	12.0	F	LIB	29	3.59	16.0	F	LIB	11	2.67	17.0	M	LIB	17	3.75	17.0
M	BUS	24	2.92	14.0	M	CMP	23	3.25	17.0	M	CMP	9	2.81	16.0	F	LIB	20	3.17	14.0
F	HTH	12	2.48	15.0	M	LIB	25	3.65	7.5	M	LIB	27	3.76	15.5	M	BUS	25	3.56	12.0
M	SCI	24	3.23	13.0	M	CMP	31	3.89	12.0	F	CMP	10	2.67	14.0	F	FPA	30	3.75	17.0
F	LIB	25	3.17	7.5	F	BUS	23	2.96	15.0	F	HTH	7	2.32	14.0	F	BUS	33	3.66	18.0
M	BUS	26	3.57	10.0	F	BUS	18	2.77	15.5	F	BUS	8	2.09	16.0	M	LIB	28	3.85	7.5
F	BUS	28	3.19	11.0	F	LIB	26	3.28	12.0	F	LIB	9	2.42	17.0	M	LIB	9	2.74	17.0
F	LIB	30	3.08	12.0	M	LIB	27	3.13	10.0	F	LIB	10	1.90	6.0	F	BUS	9	2.64	15.0
M	CMP	15	2.47	6.0	F	BUS	33	2.75	7.5	M	LIB	7	1.98	12.0	F	FPA	12	2.93	12.0
F	LIB	12	1.88	7.5	M	CMP	20	2.76	17.0	F	LIB	12	3.15	16.0	M	LIB	24	2.47	16.0
M	BUS	11	2.40	15.0	M	LIB	17	3.17	6.0	F	HTH	14	3.40	17.0	M	FPA	8	2.18	14.0
F	BUS	24	2.89	17.0	M	HTH	15	1.86	16.0	F	BUS	10	2.87	15.0	M	LIB	6	2.43	13.0
F	LIB	25	3.25	14.0	F	BUS	17	2.81	13.0	F	LIB	28	3.51	17.0					
F	LIB	16	2.65	14.0	M	LIB	11	1.87	6.0	F	BUS	8	1.95	12.0					

> **DEFINITION 2.1**
> **Raw Data** is data before it has been arranged in a useful manner or analyzed using statistical techniques.

Compare the raw data table to the graph "Major by Sex" in Figure 2.1. This graph depicts a student's major area of concentration to the student's sex. Notice how this graph is a convenient way to display the number of males and females belonging to each of the five listed areas of concentration. The graph makes the data easier to comprehend. From this graph, you can instantly see that there is a greater number of females than males majoring in Liberal Arts, Business, Health Sciences and Fine and Performing Arts.

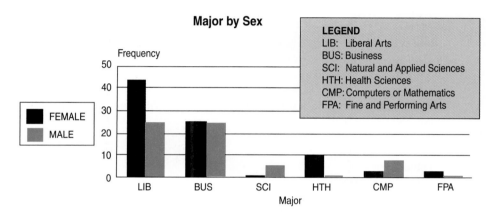

FIGURE 2.1

This chapter will present techniques that will help you organize, summarize, and explore data to determine if patterns or relationships exist. For a given data set, these techniques will help answer questions such as:

- How many credits do most students take for a semester?
- What is the most popular major?
- How many hours do students usually study per week?

or to explore meaningful comparisons such as:

- the number of hours that females study to the number of hours that males study.
- the relationship of the type of major to a student's sex.
- the number of study hours per student to the student's GPA.

This chapter presents a variety of techniques that demonstrate the use of tables and graphs to display the important characteristics of the data. The type of raw data collected will determine the technique. In Section 2.2, we will discuss the different classifications and characteristics of data.

2.2 CLASSIFICATIONS OF DATA

The type of graph you use depends on the type of information about a person or thing you have collected. For example, a person's height or sex, a student's GPA, the circumference of a redwood tree, the closing price of a stock, the pollen count for a given day, or one's preference when buying an automobile illustrate types of information that can be obtained about a person or thing. These types of information are called **variables**.

> **DEFINITION 2.2**
> A **variable** is a type of information, usually a property or characteristic of a person or thing, that is measured or observed.

A **specific measurement or observation** for a variable is called the **value** of the variable. Suppose you are interested in the variables height, sex and GPA for the students in your class. If a female student is 63 inches tall, has a GPA of 3.23, then female is the value for the variable sex, 63 inches represents the value for the variable height and 3.23 is the value for the variable GPA. A collection of several data pertaining to one or more variables is called a **data set**.

> **DEFINITION 2.3**
> A **data set** is a collection of several data pertaining to one or more variables.

Table 2.1 represents a data set. In Example 2.1, we will examine the variables of this data set.

EXAMPLE 2.1

Using Table 2.1:
a)   Identify the variables.
b)   Determine the value of each of these variables for the first student listed in the table.

Solution

a)   The variables are Sex, Major, Study Hours, GPA, and Credits.
b)   The first student is a Male with a Major in Liberal Arts, who studies 15 hours per week, has a GPA of 2.79 and is taking 14 credits.
Therefore, the variable:
  sex has a value of male;
  major has a value of Liberal Arts;
  study hours has a value of 15 hours per week;
  GPA has a value of 2.79; and
  Credits has a value of 14.

Categorical and Numerical Variables

There are basically two types of variables: **Categorical** and **Numerical**. A categorical variable yields values that denote categories. For example, the variable sex is a categorical variable since sex is classified by the categories male or female. The variable major is a categorical variable where the values are classified by the categories liberal arts, business, health sciences, computers or mathematics, natural and applied sciences, or fine and performing arts. The values of these categorical variables are referred to as categorical data.

> **DEFINITION 2.4**
> A **categorical variable** represents categories, and is non-numerical in nature. These values are known as categorical data.

A numerical variable yields numerical values that represent a measurement. For example, the variable GPA is a numerical variable because it represents a numerical measurement of a student's academic performance. The variable study hours is a numerical variable since it numerically measures the number of hours per week a student studies.

> **DEFINITION 2.5**
> A **numerical variable** is a variable where the value is a number that results from a measurement process. The specific values of numerical variables are called numerical data.

Continuous and Discrete Data

Numerical data can be further classified as either continuous or discrete depending upon the numerical values it can assume.

Numerical data such as height, weight, temperature, and distance are examples of continuous data because they represent measurements that can take on any intermediate value between two numbers. The values of continuous data are usually expressed as a rounded-off number.

> **DEFINITION 2.6**
> **Continuous data** are numerical measurements that can assume any value between two numbers.

A person's weight is an example of continuous data since it is a measurement that can assume any value between two numbers. For example, a person's true weight could be any value between two numbers such as 150.5 and 151.5 pounds. Usually, we represent this person's weight as the *rounded-off weight* of 151 pounds.

Numerical data such as the number of full-time students attending Yale Law School, the number of automobile accidents in Arizona per year, or the number of unemployed people in New York City are examples of discrete data because these data can only take on a limited number of values.

> **DEFINITION 2.7**
> **Discrete data** are numerical values that can assume only a limited number of values.

The closing price of a stock selling between $24 and $25 is considered discrete data since it can only take on a limited number of price values such as: $24, $2 ⅛, $24¼, $24⅜, $24½, $24⅝, $24¾, $24⅞, $25.

Usually discrete data values represent **count** data and are expressed as whole numbers. However, the main characteristic of discrete data is the **break** between successive discrete values.

■
EXAMPLE 2.2

For each of the following:
a) Identify each variable and classify as either categorical or numerical, and
b) If the variable is numerical, then further classify it as either continuous or discrete.
1) a person's height
2) an individual's political affiliation

3) the number of rainy days in July
4) the number of gallons of fuel used to travel from New York to Chicago
5) a person's hair color
6) an opinion to the question: "Is the President of the United States doing a good job?"
7) a shoe size
8) the number of inches of snowfall per year
9) the number of vowels in a paragraph
10) the amount of soda in a 2 liter bottle
11) a student's credit load for the semester

Solution

1) A person's height is a numerical variable. Since it is a measurement that has been rounded off, it is continuous.
2) Political affiliation is a categorical variable.
3) The number of rainy days in July is a numerical variable. Since this number represents count data, it is discrete.
4) The number of gallons of fuel used to travel from New York to Chicago is a numerical variable. It is a measurement that has been rounded off and is continuous.
5) A person's hair color is a categorical variable.
6) One's opinion is a categorical variable.
7) Shoe size is a numerical variable. Since shoe sizes can only take on a limited number of values, it is discrete.
8) The number of inches of snow is a numerical variable which represents a rounded off measurement. Thus it is continuous.
9) The number of vowels in a paragraph represents a numerical variable. Since this number is count data, it is discrete.
10) The amount of soda in a 2 liter bottle is a numerical variable. The amount represents a measurement that has been rounded off. Therefore, it is continuous.
11) The number of credits is a numerical variable. Since the number of credits can only take on a limited number of values, it is discrete.

2.3   EXPLORING DATA USING THE STEM-AND-LEAF DISPLAY

Statistical studies, marketing surveys, scientific and medical experiments all involve collections of data. Before any conclusions can be drawn from these collections, the data must be carefully explored to discover any useful aspects, information, or unanticipated patterns that may exist. This approach to the analysis of data is called **Exploratory Data Analysis**. The idea of exploratory data analysis is to learn as much as possible about the data before conducting any statistical testing of hypotheses or relationships, or drawing any conclusions about the data. The assumption of exploratory data analysis is that the more you know about the data, the more effectively the data can be used to perform any subsequent statistical analysis. The emphasis of exploratory data analysis is to use visual displays, such as tables or graphs, of the data to reveal vital information about the data. To help examine the shape or pattern of the data values, it is necessary to *organize* the data values to form a **distribution**.

DEFINITION 2.8

A **distribution** of a numerical variable represents the data values of the variable from the lowest to the highest value along with the number of times each data value occurs. The number of times each data value occurs is called its *frequency*.

When examining the data, it is important to know what to look for in the data. The important aspects of the data are called the *characteristics of a distribution*. Let's discuss how some of these characteristics are identified. More characteristics of a distribution will be discussed in Section 2.7.

Identifying Characteristics of a Distribution

Center of the Distribution
Determine the location of the middle value of all the data values.

Overall Shape of the Distribution
Look for the number of peaks within the distribution: Is there one peak or are there several peaks? How are the data values clustered? Are they symmetric about the center or skewed in one direction?

a) A distribution is *symmetric* when the distribution of the data values greater than the center of the display and the data values less than the center of the display are mirror images of each other.

b) A distribution is *skewed* when the distribution of the data values tend to be concentrated toward one end of the display or tail of the distribution, while the data values in the other tail are spread out through extreme values resulting in a longer tail.

c) A *positively skewed* or *skewed to the right distribution* is one in which the data values are concentrated in the left tail (or end of the display containing the smaller data values) with the longer tail of the display on the right.

d) A *negatively skewed* or *skewed to the left distribution* is one in which the data values are concentrated in the right tail (or end of the display containing the larger data values) with the longer tail of the display on the left.

Spread of the Data Within the Distribution
Examine the distribution of data values to determine whether the data values are clustered or spread out about the center. Look for any gap(s) within the distribution or for any individual data value that falls well outside the overall range of the data values, that is, look for any *outliers*.

Outliers can indicate significant deviations from typical data values within a distribution and can provide valuable information about a distribution. Examining the reasons for an outlier are essential to exploring data. There are possible explanations for an outlier. They are:

1. The outlier is due to a recording error.
2. The outlier is due to chance.
3. The outlier is due to an unusual occurrence which may help to provide valuable information about the data set.

In Chapter 3, we will discuss a technique to define what we mean by "a data value that lies far" from the other data values. For now, we will define an outlier as follows.

DEFINITION 2.9
An **outlier** is an individual data value which lies far (above or below) from most or all of the other data values within a distribution.

A visual display of a distribution of data values helps to highlight these important characteristics of a distribution. One such visual technique used to explore data is the **stem-and-leaf display** developed by Professor John W. Tukey of Princeton University. The stem-and-leaf display helps to provide information about the shape or pattern of the data values of the variable. To help examine the shape or pattern of the data values, it is necessary to organize the data values to form a distribution using a stem-and-leaf display.

DEFINITION 2.10

A **stem-and-leaf display** is a visual exploratory data analysis technique that shows the shape of a distribution. The display uses the actual values of the variable to present the shape of the distribution of data values.

To see how the stem-and-leaf display is constructed, let's analyze the following data values representing the cholesterol levels of 50 middle-aged men on a regular diet.

Cholesterol Levels (expressed as milligrams of cholesterol per 100 milliliters of blood)

263,	258,	240,	233,	225,	222,	199,	282,	239,	236,	232,	283,	200,
212,	225,	235,	240,	258,	263,	274,	250,	259,	241,	237,	226,	213,
269,	199,	253,	201,	265,	226,	238,	242,	259,	233,	238,	229,	215,
202,	319,	277,	229,	239,	243,	248,	245,	219,	276,	246		

To construct a stem-and-leaf display for the 50 cholesterol levels we will use the following procedure. *Each data value is rewritten into two components called a stem and a leaf.*

Step 1   Identify the stem and leaf for your data values. For each cholesterol level, the stem value will pertain to the first two digits of the data value, while the leaf value will indicate the last digit of each data value. Let's discuss how to do this. The first data value of 263 is written as: **26 | 3** within the stem-and-leaf display. The first two leading digits (**26**), appearing to the left of the vertical line, are referred to as the **stem**. The last digit of the data value (**3**), which appears to the right of the vertical line, is called the **leaf**. This is illustrated as follows: **the data value of 263 is displayed as: 26 | 3**. The second data value of 258 would be represented as: **25 | 8** within the stem-and-leaf display, where the 25 represents the stem value and 8 is the leaf value. The stem portion of the third data value of 240 is 24, while the leaf portion is 0. Thus, the cholesterol level of 240 is expressed as: **24 | 0**. To construct a stem-and-leaf display for the 50 cholesterol levels, we will use the following procedure:

Step 2   Start with the smallest stem on top, and end with the largest stem at the bottom, list all the possible stems in order and in a vertical column. Include even the stems with no corresponding leaves. Draw a vertical line to the right of the column of stems as in Figure 2.2. The vertical line separates the stem and leaf of each data value.

Since the smallest data value is **19**9 and the largest data value is **31**9, then the top stem value 19 (which corresponds to the smallest value of 199) and the bottom stem value is **31** (corresponding to the largest value of 319). Thus, the vertical column representing the stem values will include stem values starting with 19 and ending with 31 as in Figure 2.2.

Step 3   Place the leaf of each data value with the same stem in the same row corresponding to the stem of the data value. Place this leaf to the right of the vertical line that separates the stem portion (or left side) from the leaf portion (or right side).

For the first data value of 263, the leaf portion 3 will be written within the stem row 26 to the right of the vertical line. This procedure of placing the leaf of each data value within the

```
Stem |
     |_____
  19 |
  20 |
  21 |
  22 |
  23 |
  24 |
  25 |
  26 |
  27 |
  28 |
  29 |
  30 |
  31 |
```

FIGURE 2.2

```
Stem | Leaf
     |_____
  19 | 9 9
  20 | 0 1 2
  21 | 2 3 5 9
  22 | 5 2 5 6 6 9 9
  23 | 3 9 6 2 5 7 8 3 8 9
  24 | 0 0 1 2 3 8 5 6
  25 | 8 8 0 9 3 9
  26 | 3 3 9 5
  27 | 4 7 6
  28 | 2 3
  29 |
  30 |
  31 | 9
```

FIGURE 2.3

appropriate stem row is continued until all the data values are included within the stem-and-leaf display. The completed stem-and-leaf display is illustrated in Figure 2.3.

Step 4 Arrange the leaves within each stem row in increasing order from left to right. In practice, it is not necessary to name the stem and leaf portions within the display, so we've omitted them in Figure 2.4.

**Stem–and–leaf display of cholesterol levels
of 50 middle–aged men on a regular diet**

```
  19 | 9 9
  20 | 0 1 2
  21 | 2 3 5 9
  22 | 2 5 5 6 6 9 9
  23 | 2 3 3 5 6 7 8 8 9 9
  24 | 0 0 1 2 3 5 6 8
  25 | 0 3 8 8 9 9
  26 | 3 3 5 9
  27 | 4 6 7
  28 | 2 3
  29 |
  30 |
  31 | 9
```

FIGURE 2.4

Stem-and-leaf displays have several important advantages as a first step to exploratory data analysis. Notice that the number of leaves in each stem indicates the number of data values pertaining to that stem. For example, in the second row of Figure 2.4, we have: **20 | 0 1 2**. This row represents the three data values: 200, 201, and 202. In addition, turning the page sideways, shows the shape of the distribution of cholesterol levels. When viewed in this manner the stem-and-leaf display has a likeness to a bar graph. From Figure 2.4, we notice that the greatest number of cholesterol levels are concentrated between the values 222 to 248. **We can see that a major advantage of a stem-and-leaf display is that it shows the shape of the distribution by displaying the number of data values pertaining to each stem using the actual values from the distribution.**

We can also examine the leaves within each stem to determine the distance between the data values, thus providing more information on the shape of the distribution. For example, looking at the two rows for the stems 28 and 31, **28 | 2 3** and **31 | 9**, notice that the largest distance between any two data values within the distribution occurs between data values 283 and 319. In fact, you should notice that the cholesterol level of 319 stands apart from the pattern of all the other cholesterol levels. The cholesterol level of 319 is an **outlier** since it lies well above all the other cholesterol levels within the distribution.

In Figure 2.4, we have seen that the stem-and-leaf display presents the data values of a distribution in a more convenient form that will make it easier to study the shape and important characteristics of a distribution while preserving the actual data values. As we explained before, the stem-and-leaf display is an exploratory data analysis technique that assists one in looking at the data. Let's now summarize the procedure to construct a stem-and-leaf display.

Procedure To Construct a Stem-And-Leaf Display

Step 1   Identify the stem and leaf portion of your data values. Generally, the stem can have as many digits as needed to represent the beginning digit(s) of each data value. The leaf should only contain the last or terminating digit of the data values.

Step 2   List each possible stem once, in a vertical column starting with the smallest stem on top and ending with the largest stem at the bottom. List even the stems with no corresponding leaves. Draw a vertical line to the right of the column of stems.

Step 3   For each data value, record the leaf within the corresponding stem row and to the right of the vertical line.

Step 4   Arrange the leaves within each stem row in increasing order from left to right. This provides a more informative stem-and-leaf display.

Let's illustrate the use of this procedure in Example 2.3.

EXAMPLE 2.3

For the following data values representing the cholesterol levels of 50 middle-aged men on a low-fat diet and exercise program:
a)   Construct a stem-and-leaf display.
b)   Describe the characteristics of the distribution. Is it symmetric, skewed to the right, or skewed to the left?
c)   Determine the center of the distribution and then decide between which two values on a stem are the greatest concentration of data values located?

Cholesterol Levels (expressed as milligrams cholesterol per 100 milliliters of blood)

161,	172,	193,	190,	205,	214,	217,	205,	168,	176,	188,	195,	209,
219,	189,	209,	220,	211,	200,	195,	184,	175,	198,	209,	211,	228,
199,	188,	172,	165,	177,	197,	202,	211,	198,	184,	171,	200,	218,
220,	210,	189,	231,	176,	180,	193,	230,	200,	181,	190		

Solution

a)   To construct a stem-and-leaf display, we will use the previously outlined procedure:

Step 1   The first two digits of each cholesterol level are the stem value while the last digit is the leaf value.

Step 2   List all the possible stems once in a vertical column starting with the smallest stem on top and ending with the largest stem at the bottom of the column. Draw a vertical line to the right of the column of stems.

Since the smallest data value is 161 and the largest data value is 231, then the stem values will range from 16 to 23. This is illustrated in Figure 2.5.

Step 3 For each cholesterol value, record the leaf within the corresponding stem row and to the right of the vertical line as shown in Figure 2.6.

Stem
16
17
18
19
20
21
22
23

FIGURE 2.5

Stem	Leaf
16	1 8 5
17	2 6 5 2 7 1 6
18	8 9 4 8 4 9 0 1
19	3 0 5 5 8 9 7 8 3 0
20	5 5 9 9 0 9 2 0 0
21	4 7 9 1 1 1 8 0
22	0 8 0
23	1 0

FIGURE 2.6

Step 4 Arrange the leaves within each stem row in increasing order from left to right as illustrated in Figure 2.7 for a more informative stem-and-leaf display.

**Stem–and–leaf display of cholesterol levels
of 50 middle–aged men on a low–fat diet and exercise program**

16	1 5 8
17	1 2 2 5 6 6 7
18	0 1 4 4 8 8 9 9
19	0 0 3 3 5 5 7 8 8 9
20	0 0 0 2 5 5 9 9 9
21	0 1 1 1 4 7 8 9
22	0 0 8
23	0 1

FIGURE 2.7

b) Rotating the stem-and-leaf display in Figure 2.7 sideways, we see that the shape of the distribution of the men's cholesterol levels is approximately symmetrically bell-shaped.

c) Starting from the lowest data value and counting to the twenty-fifth data value (or to the middle of the data values), we determine that the center of the distribution is between 197 and 198. The greatest concentration of cholesterol levels on a stem falls between 190 and 199, with the majority (more than 50%) of cholesterol levels falling between 171 and 219. _____ ∎

Back-to-Back Stem-and-Leaf Display

At times, it might be of interest to compare two distributions using a stem-and-leaf display with a common stem. This type of display is called a **back-to-back stem-and-leaf display**.

In the next example, we will examine how to construct a back-to-back stem-and-leaf display to compare the distribution of cholesterol levels for middle-aged men who are on a regular diet to those on a low-fat diet and exercise program.

EXAMPLE 2.4

Using the stem-and-leaf display for the cholesterol levels for middle-aged men on a regular diet (shown in Figure 2.4) and the stem-and-leaf display for middle-aged men on a low-fat diet and exercise program (shown in Figure 2.7):

a)   Construct a back-to-back stem-and-leaf display.

b)   Use the back-to-back stem-and-leaf display to compare the two distributions.

Solution

a)   A back-to-back stem-and-leaf display is constructed by writing **one common** stem for both displays. This **common stem** is placed between the leaves of both displays. **This stem must contain all the possible stem values that can exist for both displays.** If you examine Figures 2.4 and 2.7, you will see that the possible stem values range from 16 to 31. Thus, the back-to-back display is constructed using the form shown in Figure 2.8.

   Figure 2.9 shows the back-to-back display comparing the cholesterol levels for middle-aged men on a regular diet to the cholesterol levels of middle-aged men on a low-fat diet and exercise program.

Leaf	Stem	Leaf
	16	
	17	
	18	
	19	
	20	
	21	
	22	
	23	
	24	
	25	
	26	
	27	
	28	
	29	
	30	
	31	

FIGURE 2.8

Back-to-Back Stem-and-Leaf Display

Leaves for regular diet	Stem	Leaves for low–fat diet
	16	1 5 8
	17	1 2 2 5 6 6 7
	18	0 1 4 4 8 8 9 9
9 9	19	0 0 3 3 5 5 7 8 8 9
2 1 0	20	0 0 0 2 5 5 9 9 9
9 5 3 2	21	0 1 1 1 4 7 8 9
9 9 6 6 5 5 2	22	0 0 8
9 9 8 8 7 6 5 3 3 2	23	0 1
8 6 5 3 2 1 0 0	24	
9 9 8 8 3 0	25	
9 5 3 3	26	
7 6 4	27	
3 2	28	
	29	
	30	
9	31	

FIGURE 2.9

b)   Comparing the two distributions shown in the back-to-back stem-and-leaf display of Figure 2.9, we can see that there is a greater number of lower cholesterol levels for the men on the low-fat diet and exercise program. Both distributions are essentially symmetric, but they have different data values representing their centers (239 for the regular diet distribution and 197 or 198 for the low-fat distribution). For the regular diet distribution, the greatest concentration of data values falls between 232 and 239, while the low fat distribution has the greatest concentration from 190 to 199. The cholesterol level of 319 in the regular diet distribution represents an outlier.

2.4   FREQUENCY DISTRIBUTION TABLES

In many statistical studies, a large quantity of data is usually collected and the statistician is interested in summarizing the large data set by placing it in a more manageable form. The stem-and-leaf display that was developed in Section 2.3 is an example of one way that data can be put into a more manageable form. In this section we will present another form of representing data called a **frequency distribution**. A frequency distribution lists the values of a variable(s) and how often each value occurs. The frequency distribution of a variable can be displayed by a table or graph. In either form we will be able to determine such things as: the highest and lowest values, apparent patterns of a variable, apparent patterns between variables, what values the data may tend to cluster or group around, or which values are the most common. We will first examine the **frequency distribution table** to help determine these characteristics of the data.

DEFINITION 2.11

A **frequency distribution table** is a table in which a data set has been divided into distinct groups, called classes, along with the number of data values that fall into each class, called the frequency.

Frequency Distribution Table for Categorical Data

The first step in constructing a frequency distribution table is to organize the data into distinctive groups called **classes** (or **class intervals**). If the data collected are categorical, then **each category** will be used to represent a **class** (or **class interval**).

For example, if a biology student is investigating the prevalence of eye color within his college and records the data as either hazel, brown, blue, or black, then each of these four categories of eye color will represent a class.

The second step is to determine the frequency of each class by counting the number of data values that fall within each category or class.

In Example 2.5, we will use this procedure to construct a **frequency distribution table for the categorical data** pertaining to a student's major presented earlier in this chapter in Table 2.1.

EXAMPLE 2.5

Using the raw data pertaining to the Student Government Survey Data of 150 Students listed in Table 2.1,
a) construct a frequency distribution table for the categorical variable **major**, and
b) determine the most popular major for the 150 students.

Solution

a)   To construct a frequency distribution table for the categorical variable **major**, we will need to organize the data into classes and then determine the frequency for each class.

Step 1   **Organize the data into distinct classes**. For a categorical variable, the categories of the variable represent the classes. For the variable **major**, these categories or classes are: **liberal arts, business, computers or mathematics, health sciences, natural and applied sciences or fine and performing arts.**

Step 2   **Determine the frequency of each class by counting the number of data values that fall within each class**. From Table 2.1, we count 54 students that are liberal arts majors; therefore, the class labeled liberal arts has a frequency of 54. Continuing this procedure for the remaining five classes, the frequency distribution table for the categorical variable **major** is constructed and shown in Table 2.2.

b)   From Table 2.2, one is able to see at a glance that Liberal Arts and Business are the most popular majors for the students within the data set.

TABLE 2.2   Frequency Distribution Table For The Variable Major

Classes (Major)	Frequency
Liberal Arts	68
Business	51
Computers or Mathematics	11
Health Sciences	11
Natural and Applied Sciences	6
Fine and Performing Arts	3

Notice that the frequency distribution table in Table 2.2 displays the data pertaining to majors in a concise and convenient form and makes it easier to interpret the data than the original data set contained in Table 2.1. ▪

Frequency Distribution Table for Numerical Data

Organizing *categorical data* into a frequency distribution table is a relatively simple task since the classes represent the categories of the variable.

On the other hand, constructing a frequency distribution table for *numerical data* is not as obvious. There are two problems that need to be addressed:

(1) How many classes should be used for the data set?
(2) How should these classes be defined?

The choice of the number of classes representing the data set is arbitrary. However, if there are **too many classes**, then it would be difficult to see any apparent pattern within the distribution of the data set. For example, in Table 2.1 the **numerical** variable **study hours** ranges from 6 hours to 36 hours. If we were to construct a frequency distribution for study hours using **each study hour as a separate group or class**, then this procedure would give us too many classes (31 classes, in fact). This is illustrated in Table 2.3. Notice that Table 2.3 would not accomplish our objective of summarizing and examining any patterns that may exist for the study hours.

TABLE 2.3   Frequency Distribution of Study Hours

Study hours	Frequency	Study hours	Frequency	Study hours	Frequency	Study hours	Frequency
6	2	14	2	22	3	30	4
7	3	15	9	23	5	31	3
8	7	16	5	24	9	32	1
9	7	17	8	25	4	33	3
10	10	18	6	26	4	34	0
11	6	19	5	27	7	35	0
12	9	20	12	28	7	36	1
13	0	21	5	29	3		

On the other hand, using **too few classes**, we would lose much of the information provided by the data. For example, if we were to use only *two* classes as shown in Table 2.4, then the data would be so clustered together that it would be difficult to discover any existing patterns.

TABLE 2.4   Frequency Distribution of Study Hours

Classes (Study Hours)	Frequency
6–21	96
22–37	54

Thus, although there are no hard and fast rules for making a choice on the number of classes to use, we will use the following guidelines to help us in our decision.

Guidelines For Constructing a Frequency Distribution Table for Numerical Data

1. The number of classes should be neither too small nor too large. Generally, the number of classes should be between 5 and 15. The number of classes will depend on the number of data values within the data set as well as how much the data values vary.
2. Define the classes so that they cover the entire range of the data values and that each data value will fall into one and only one class.
3. Whenever possible every class should have an equal range of values, called the class width. A frequency distribution with unequal class widths is more difficult to interpret than one with equal class widths.

We will now outline a procedure to construct a frequency distribution table for the variable study hours using the data set in Table 2.1.

Step 1 Decide on the number of classes into which the data are to be grouped.

Using the guideline of a number between 5 and 15, we will use 7 classes for the variable study hours in Table 2.1. This selection of 7 classes is arbitrary.

Step 2 Define the individual classes.

If we want the 7 classes to accommodate the entire data set and each class to have an equal width, then we must decide upon a class width large enough to include all the data within these 7 classes. You should realize that the number of classes and the class width are dependent upon one another. Since the fewer the number of classes, the larger the class width, and vice versa. To determine an approximate class width, we will use the rule:

$$\text{approximate class width} = \frac{\text{largest data value} - \text{smallest data value}}{\text{number of classes}}$$

Therefore, for the variable study hours in Table 2.1, the approximate width for 7 classes is:

$$\text{approximate class width} = \frac{36-6}{7} = \frac{30}{7}$$
$$\approx 4.29$$

Thus, the class width must be **at least 4.29 to accommodate all the data into 7 classes.** However, **the actual class width we will use will be dependent upon the number of significant digits used to measure the data values and will always be rounded up to the number of significant digits in the data value.** Since the data values are all expressed as *whole numbers,* we will **round up** this result of 4.29 to **5**. Thus, **our choice for the width of each class will be 5.** (If our data values were expressed with tenths we would have rounded to 4.3.)

Step 3   To construct each class using the appropriate class width we must define the limits of each class so that each data value will fall into one and only one class. Each class must have an upper and lower class limit. The **class limits** represent the **smallest and largest data values** of each class. The **lower class limit is the smallest data value of the class** while the **upper class limit is the largest data value of the class**. The class limits will depend upon the types of data that are being grouped and the way the data were recorded or rounded off.

For example, the study hour data in Table 2.1 represent continuous data that have been rounded off to the nearest hour. Thus, the data values are recorded as whole numbers so the class limits will be expressed as whole numbers. Use the smallest data value of 6 hours as the lower class limit of the first class. Add **one unit** less than the class width to obtain the upper class limit. Since the data values are whole number's, the unit value is 1. (If tenths were used one unit would be 0.1 or one tenth.) Thus, the upper class limit will be:

$$6 + (5 - 1) = 10.$$

Thus, **the first class represents the data values 6 to 10 and is written as: 6 – 10.**

We can now form the remaining classes by adding the class width to the previous lower and upper class limits. That is:

lower class limit = lower class limit of previous class plus class width

upper class limit = upper class limit of previous class plus class width

Following this procedure for each successive class until the 7 classes have been constructed for our study hour data set, we have:

Classes (Study Hours)
6 – 10
11 – 15
16 – 20
21 – 25
26 – 30
31 – 35
36 – 40

Observe that the class width of 5 is the difference between two consecutive lower class limits and *not* the difference between the upper and lower limits of a class.

DEFINITION 2.12
The **class width** is the difference between two consecutive lower class limits.

Notice all 7 classes have the same class width of five; they do not overlap so every data value will fall into only one class and the classes cover the entire range of data values for the variable study hour. The first class contains the study hours 6 to 10, where the lower class limit is 6 hours and the upper class limit is 10 hours. The second class contains the study hours 11 to 15 where 11 is the lower class limit and 15 is the upper class limit. The last class has a lower class limit of 36 hours and an upper class limit of 40 hours.

Step 4   Determine the frequency of each class.

Tally the number of data values falling within each class. This number is called the **frequency of the class** and is recorded under the frequency column of the frequency distribution table. Table 2.5 represents the **frequency distribution table** for the study hour data of Table 2.1.

TABLE 2.5   Frequency Distribution Table for the Variable Study Hour

Classes (Study Hours)	Frequency
6 – 10	29
11 – 15	26
16 – 20	36
21 – 25	26
26 – 30	25
31 – 35	7
36 – 40	1

Examining Table 2.5, we see that the data values for the distribution of study hours are now organized into a more compact and useful form that tends to highlight the important characteristics of the data. We now can notice that the majority of students study from 6 to 30 hours, with the greatest concentration of students within the class of 16 to 20 study hours. Also, rarely does any student study more than 36 hours. Although, the frequency distribution in Table 2.5 does summarize the data in a more convenient form, information about the original study hour data set is sacrificed. **Unlike a stem-and-leaf display, the actual individual values of the data in a frequency distribution table are no longer apparent**. Notice that one student who studied from 36 to 40 hours; however, from Table 2.5 we cannot determine the exact number of hours that this particular student studied. Thus, for each class of a frequency distribution table, we need to **identify a particular value to represent all the data values within that class**. The **midpoint of the class** is used for this purpose, and it is called the **class mark**. The class mark of a class is obtained by calculating the average of the class limits for the class.

DEFINITION 2.13

The **class mark** is the midpoint of a class and is used as the representative value for the class. The formula to calculate the class mark is:

$$\text{Class Mark } = \frac{\textit{upper class limit} + \textit{lower class limit}}{2}$$

For the frequency distribution in Table 2.5, the class mark of the first class, 6–10, is 8. This class mark is determined by adding the class limits of 6 and 10 and dividing by 2. That is:

$$\text{class mark of first class is: } \frac{10 + 6}{2} = 8$$

The class mark of each class is obtained using this class mark formula. In Table 2.6, the class marks of the frequency distribution of study hours have been added to the frequency distribution table under the column labeled *class mark*.

TABLE 2.6   Frequency Distribution Table for the Variable Study Hour

Classes (Study Hours)	Frequency	Class Mark
6 – 10	29	8
11 – 15	26	13
16 – 20	36	18
21 – 25	26	23
26 – 30	25	28
31 – 35	7	33
36 – 40	1	38

In examining the class mark column of Table 2.6, you should notice that the difference between each successive class mark is 5. This difference is the class width. **Within a frequency distribution table, the difference between successive class marks will always be equal to the class width.**

Although Table 2.6 represents the frequency distribution for the continuous variable study hours, it is not apparent that the data is continuous. We see that 28 students studied 6 to 10 hours, while 26 students studied 11 to 15 hours. Since study hours represents continuous data, it is possible for a student to have studied 10.7 hours. *In which class would this student be included?* Although the study hours data are continuous, they were recorded and rounded off to the nearest hour. Thus, the 10.7 study hours would be rounded-off to 11 hours, and the student would be included in the class: 11–15. You should understand the class limits shown in Table 2.6 are not the **"real class limits"** or the so-called **"class boundaries"** of the data. For example, consider the first class: 6–10. Since the study hours were originally rounded to the nearest hour, any actual study time greater than or equal to 5.5 hours but less than 10.5 hours is included in the class: 6–10. Thus, the numbers 5.5 and 10.5 are referred to as the **class boundaries** or **real class limits** of the class: 6–10. The class boundaries of the second class: 11–15 are 10.5 and 15.5. The class boundaries of the last class: 36–40 are 35.5 and 40.5.

DEFINITION 2.14

The **class boundary** of a class is the midpoint of the upper class limit of one class and the lower class limit of the next class. The formula to determine the class boundary is:

$$\text{Class Boundary} = \frac{\text{Upper Class Limit of one class} + \text{Lower Class Limit of the next class}}{2}$$

In order to present study hours as continuous data and to identify the real class limits of each class, the frequency distribution table in Table 2.7 contains the class boundaries.

TABLE 2.7 Frequency Distribution Table for the Variable Study Hour

Classes (Study Hours)	Frequency	Class Mark	Class Boundaries
6 – 10	29	8	**5.5–10.5**
11 – 15	26	13	**10.5–15.5**
16 – 20	36	18	**15.5–20.5**
21 – 25	26	23	**20.5–25.5**
26 – 30	25	28	**25.5–30.5**
31 – 35	7	33	**30.5–35.5**
36 – 40	1	38	**35.5–40.5**

Notice the classes show a gap of one unit between successive class limits. That is, the first class ends at 10 hours while the second class begins at 11 hours. However, **the class boundaries have eliminated this gap of one unit** by taking one-half of this unit gap and adding it to the upper class limit and subtracting one-half of this unit gap from the lower class limit of the following class. Thus, **class boundaries are numbers midway between consecutive upper and lower class limits that are used to eliminate the gap between the class limits to signify continuous data**. In actual practice, class boundaries are numbers created when a measurement of a continuous variable has been rounded off. Therefore, **when constructing a frequency distribution table for a continuous variable we will include class boundaries as a column within the frequency distribution table**.

On the other hand, **when constructing a frequency distribution table for discrete data, a column for the class boundaries is not required.** Let's now summarize the steps required for constructing a frequency distribution table for numerical data.

Procedure for Constructing a Frequency Distribution Table for Numerical Data

Step 1 Decide on the number of classes for the data set.

Step 2 Determine the class width. The approximate class width formula is:

$$\text{approximate class width} = \frac{\text{largest data value} - \text{smallest data value}}{\text{number of classes}}$$

Always round up the approximate class width result to the next significant digit used to measure the data. This rounded up number is used to represent the CLASS WIDTH of each class.

Step 3 Construct the class limits for the first class by:
a) Selecting the smallest data value within the data set as the lower class limit of the first class, and
b) Using the formula below to obtain the upper class limit of the first class:

upper class limit = lower class limit plus the class width minus one unit[1]

---

[1]If the data values are whole numbers, the unit is 1. On the other hand, if the data values are expressed as tenths, then the unit would be 0.1 or one tenth.

Procedure for Constructing a
Frequency Distribution Table for Numerical Data (continued)

The remaining class limits of the frequency distribution table can be constructed using the formulas:

lower class limit = lower class limit of previous class plus class width
upper class limit = upper class limit of previous class plus class width

Step 4   To determine the class marks for each class, use the formula:

$$\text{Class Mark} = \frac{\text{Upper Class Limit} + \text{Lower Class Limit}}{2}$$

Step 5   For continuous data, determine the class boundaries by finding the midpoint between two successive class limits using the formula:

$$\text{Class Boundary} = \frac{\text{Upper Class Limit of one class} + \text{Lower Class Limit of the next class}}{2}$$

• Class boundaries are not required for discrete data. •

Step 6   Determine the frequency for each class by finding the number of data values that fall into each class.

Relative Frequency Distributions

Within a frequency distribution table, the frequency of each class is the number of data values within each class. At times, however, it is useful to report the **proportion** or the **percentage** of data values that belong to each class. This is called the **relative frequency** of the class.

DEFINITION 2.15
The **relative frequency** of the class is the proportion of data values within the class. The relative frequency is computed by the formula:

$$\text{Relative Frequency of a Class} = \frac{class\ frequency}{total\ number\ of\ data\ values}$$

The sum of the relative frequencies of all the classes will always be one except for possible round-off error. If the relative frequencies are multiplied by 100, then they are expressed as percents and are referred to as the **relative percentage frequencies, or relative percentages.**

DEFINITION 2.16
The **relative percentage frequency** of a class is the percent of data values within a class. The formula to calculate the relative percentage frequency is:

Relative Percentage Frequency = (relative frequency)(100%)

The sum of the relative percentage frequencies of all the classes will always equal 100 except for possible round-off error.

A frequency distribution table that displays either the relative frequencies or the relative percentage frequencies of each class is a **relative frequency distribution table**.

Relative frequencies are needed when comparing the frequency distribution tables of two data sets with a different number of data values within each data set.

Let's construct a relative frequency distribution table for the frequency distribution table given in Example 2.6.

EXAMPLE 2.6

Use the frequency distribution table of the weekly earnings of 50 university students shown in Table 2.8,
a)   To construct a relative frequency distribution table.
b)   To determine the sum of the relative frequencies and the sum of the relative percentages.
c)   To identify the class that has the greatest relative percentage.

TABLE 2.8   Frequency Distribution Table
Weekly Earnings of the University Students

Classes (Earnings)	Frequency
52 – 85	5
86 – 119	10
120 – 153	21
154 – 187	10
188 – 221	4

Solution

a)   The **total number of students** is determined by summing the frequencies of each class: $5 + 10 + 21 + 10 + 4 = 50$. Since there are 50 students that comprise the data set, and there are 5 students that earn from 52 to 85 dollars weekly, then the relative frequency of this class is: $\frac{5}{50} = 0.10$. If we multiply this result by 100%, we get: $(0.10)(100\%) = 10\%$. We can state that 10% of the university students earn from 52 to 85 dollars.

The relative frequency of the second class, 86–119, is: $\frac{10}{50} = 0.20$. Multiplying this result by 100%, we obtain: $(0.20)(100\%) = 20\%$. Therefore, 20% of the university students earn from 86 to 119 dollars per week. The relative frequency of the third class, $120 - 153$, is: $\frac{21}{50} = 0.42$. As a percent, we have: $(0.42)(100\%) = 42\%$. Thus, 42% of the university students earn from 120 to 153 dollars per week.
The relative frequency of the class: 154–187 is:

$$\frac{10}{50} = 0.20 \text{ or } 20\%,$$

while the relative frequency of the last class, 188–221, is:

$$\frac{4}{50} = 0.08 \text{ or } 8\%.$$

The relative frequencies along with the relative percentages corresponding to each class is shown

TABLE 2.9   Relative Frequency Distribution Table Weekly Earnings of the University Students

Classes (Earnings)	Frequency	Relative Frequency	Relative Percentages
52 – 85	5	0.10	10
86 – 119	10	0.20	20
120 – 153	21	0.42	42
154 – 187	10	0.20	20
188 – 221	4	0.08	8
TOTAL = 50		**SUM = 1.00**	**SUM = 100%**

in Table 2.9. This table is referred to as a **Relative Frequency Distribution Table**.

b) **The sum of the relative frequencies is:**
   relative frequencies sum $= 0.10 + 0.20 + 0.42 + 0.20 + 0.08$
   $\qquad\qquad\qquad\qquad\quad = 1.00$

   The sum of the relative percentages is:
   relative percentages sum $= 10\% + 20\% + 42\% + 20\% + 8\%$
   $\qquad\qquad\qquad\qquad\qquad = 100\%$

c) The greatest percentage of students, which is 42%, earn from 120 to 153 dollars per week. Thus, the class 120–153 has the largest relative percentage. This type of information is very useful in making a comparison between classes or when comparing the 50 university students to another sample of students.

Cumulative Frequency Distributions

Suppose, in considering the information within Table 2.9, we were interested in knowing how many students are earning **less than** a particular weekly salary or how many students are earning **more than** a particular weekly salary. This type of information is displayed in a frequency distribution table called a **cumulative frequency distribution table,** which shows the number of data values that are **less than** or **greater than** a particular data value. There are two types of cumulative frequency distributions, a **"less than" cumulative frequency distribution** and a **"more than" cumulative frequency distribution**.

In a **"less than" cumulative frequency distribution table**, the cumulative frequency of a particular class indicates the number of data values within the class plus the sum of all the data values **less than** this particular class. Such a distribution is constructed by starting with the lowest class and successively summing up all the frequencies within each of the other classes.

In constructing a cumulative frequency distribution table, the manner in which each class is defined is changed. Each class is defined using **the lower class limit**.

Let's examine the technique to construct a "less than" cumulative frequency distribution table for the data in Table 2.10.

EXAMPLE 2.7

Construct a "Less Than" Cumulative Frequency Distribution for the data in Table 2.10.

TABLE 2.10   Frequency Distribution Table
Weekly Earnings of the University Students

Classes (Earnings)	Frequency
52 – 85	5
86 – 119	10
120 – 153	21
154 – 187	10
188 – 221	4

Solution

The classes for the "less than" cumulative frequency distribution will be constructed first. Except for the last class of a "less than" cumulative frequency distribution, **each class is constructed by taking the lower class limit within Table 2.10 and expressing the class of the cumulative frequency table in the form**:

less than the lower class limit

For example, the first class is written as: **less than $52.** An extra class must be added so that the data values greater than 188 can be accounted for. To construct the extra or last class of a "less than" cumulative frequency distribution table, **the lower class limit of the previous class**, which is 188, **is added to the class width**, which is 34, to obtain 222 (188 + 34). Using this value of 222, write the last class using the same form as in the previous classes. That is, the last class would be written as **less than $222.** This procedure is illustrated in Table 2.11.

TABLE 2.11   "Less Than" Cumulative Frequency
Distribution Table for the Weekly Earnings
of the University Students

Classes (Earnings)	Cumulative Frequency
less than $52	
less than $86	
less than $120	
less than $154	
less than $188	
less than $222	

   In comparing Table 2.10 to Table 2.11, Table 2.11 has two changes:
(1) there is one additional class.
(2) the classes have been changed to allow for the frequencies to be summed or accumulated. That is, the classes are now written as: "less than 52" dollars, "less than 86" dollars and so on.
   The frequencies of any of these classes is the sum of all the frequencies of each class below it. These summed frequencies are listed under the column labeled cumulative frequency. Thus, we simply sum the class frequencies of Table 2.11 as we move down the table. That is, the first class "less than 52" has a frequency of 0 since there are no students who earned less than 52 dollars. The second class "less than 86" has a frequency of 5 since there are 5 students who earned less than 86 dollars. These 5

students represent all the students in the class 52–85 of Table 2.11. The third class "less than 120" has a frequency of 15, which represents the sum of the 5 students of the class 52–85 and the 10 students of the class 86–119 of Table 2.11. Continuing in this manner, the "less than" cumulative frequency distribution is shown in Table 2.12.

TABLE 2.12   "Less Than" Cumulative Frequency Distribution Table for the Weekly Earnings of the University Students

Classes (Earnings)	Cumulative Frequency
less than $52	**0**
less than $86	**5** (0 + 5)
less than $120	**15** (0 + 5 + 10)
less than $154	**36** (0 + 5 + 10 + 21)
less than $188	**46** (0 + 5 + 10 + 21 + 10)
less than $222	**50** (0 + 5 + 10 + 21 + 10 + 4)

In a "Less Than" Cumulative Frequency Distribution, the cumulative frequency of the first class is always zero since there are no data values smaller than its lower class limit. **The cumulative frequency of the** last class always equals the total number of data values, since all data values are smaller than the lower class limit of the last class.

Some observations that can be made from Table 2.12 are:

• all the 50 students made at least $52 per week.
• no student made more than $222 per week.
• the 15 students of the class that earned less than $120 per week includes the 5 students who earned less than $86 per week.
• thirty-six students earned less than $154 per week.

Sometimes cumulative frequency values are expressed using relative percentages of the cumulative frequencies. To represent a cumulative frequency value as a relative percentage, divide each cumulative frequency value by the **total** number of data and **multiply by 100 percent**.

DEFINITION 2.17
Relative Percentage Cumulative Frequency $= \dfrac{(Cumulative\ Frequency)}{(Total\ Number\ of\ Data)} (100\%)$

Table 2.13 represents the relative percentages for the "less than" cumulative frequency distribution in Table 2.12.

Using the "less than" cumulative percentage distribution in Table 2.13, we can conclude that 72% of the students earned less than $154 per week.

In some instances, we are interested in knowing the number of university students that earned $154 or more per week. This type of information is contained within a distribution referred to as a **"more than" cumulative distribution**. In a **"More Than" Cumulative Distribution** the frequencies are summed from the highest class to the lowest class, and the classes are written in the form: **lower class limit or more**. This is the reverse of the "less than" cumulative frequency distribution. Thus, in a

TABLE 2.13   "Less Than" Cumulative Percentage Distribution Table Weekly Earnings of the University Students

Classes (Earnings in dollars)	Cumulative Frequency	Relative Percentage Cumulative Frequency $\dfrac{\text{Cumulative Frequency}}{\text{Total number of data}}$ (100%)
Less than 52	0	$\dfrac{0}{50}(100\%) = 0\%$
Less than 86	5	$\dfrac{5}{50}(100\%) = 10\%$
Less than 120	15	$\dfrac{15}{50}(100\%) = 30\%$
Less than 154	36	$\dfrac{36}{50}(100\%) = 72\%$
Less than 188	46	$\dfrac{46}{50}(100\%) = 92\%$
Less than 222	50	$\dfrac{50}{50}(100\%) = 100\%$

"more than" cumulative frequency distribution table, the cumulative frequency of a particular class indicates the number of data values within the class plus the sum of all the data values **greater than** this particular class.
                                                                                                    ▬

2.5   GRAPHS: BAR GRAPH, HISTOGRAM, FREQUENCY POLYGON AND OGIVE

A graph is a descriptive tool used to visualize the characteristics and the relationships of the data quickly and attractively. A well-constructed graph will reveal information that may not be apparent from a quick examination of a frequency distribution table. There are many different types of graphs, one is a **Bar Graph**.

Bar Graph

Figures 2.10a and 2.10b display examples of bar graphs commonly seen in a newspaper or magazine. What kind of summary statements can you conclude from the graph in Figure 2.10a? What kind of information can you infer from the graph in Figure 2.10b?

The bar graphs displayed in Figures 2.10a and 2.10b are **using bars** to represent discrete or categorical data. Let's examine how to construct and when to use a bar graph.

> **DEFINITION 2.18**
> A **bar graph** is generally used to depict discrete or categorical data. A bar graph is displayed using two axes. One axis represents the discrete or categorical variable while the other axis usually represents the frequency, or percentage, for each category of the variable.

FIGURE 2.10a

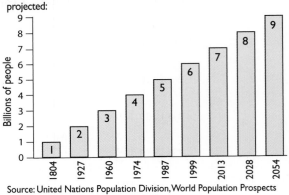

FIGURE 2.10b

Bar graphs are sometimes displayed either **horizontally** or **vertically**. A **horizontal bar graph** entitled "The Leisure Lag" is illustrated in Figure 2.10a. The bar graph shows the vacation time, in days, for employees with one year of service for the seven listed countries. The vertical axis represents the different countries, while the horizontal axis depicts the number of vacation days. Furthermore, the longer the horizontal bar, the greater the vacation time. Since this type of graph is used to represent a categorical variable, such as countries, preferences, sex, etc., the categorical values are placed along the vertical axis. The frequencies, or percentages, for each of the categories are placed along the horizontal axis, where the length of each bar represents the frequency, or percentage, of the categorical value.

A **vertical bar graph** entitled "World Population Milestones" is displayed in Figure 2.10b. In this vertical bar graph, one variable is **time**, represented in years, and is scaled along the horizontal axis displaying selected years from 1804 to 2054. The vertical axis represents the variable **world population**, in billions, which ranges from 0 to 9. Generally in a vertical bar graph, the height of each bar represents the frequency or relative percentage for the discrete data. The bar graph in Figure 2.10b is a **Time-Series Graph**, since it represents the value of a variable, world population, over selected time periods, years.

> **DEFINITION 2.19**
> A **time-series graph** contains information about two variables, where one of the variables is time.

EXAMPLE 2.8

The frequency distribution in Table 2.14 represents the categorical data resulting from a wine merchant's preference survey of 500 customers in the San Francisco Bay Area. The customers were asked

TABLE 2.14   Wine Drinker's Preference Survey

Classes (Wine Types)	Frequency
Fume Blanc	35
Chablis	65
Chardonnay	80
Chenin Blanc	45
Cabernet Sauvignon	110
Zinfandel	50
Other	115

to respond to the question: "Which type of wine do you prefer?" The survey responses are shown in Table 2.14. Construct a horizontal bar graph using the data in the frequency distribution table.

Solution

To construct a horizontal bar graph the vertical axis is labeled "wine type" and the horizontal axis is labeled frequency. The categories of the variable "wine type" are listed in Table 2.14. These wine categories are represented on the vertical axis as illustrated in Figure 2.11. The frequencies in Table 2.14 range from 35 to 115, and the horizontal axis is scaled in units of 20 to represent these frequency values.

Figure 2.11 represents a vertical bar graph for the categorical data of Table 2.14.

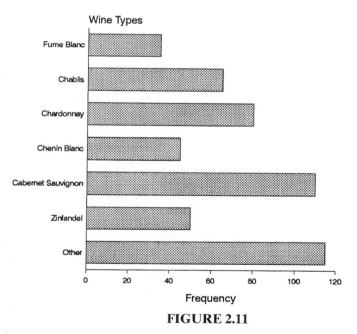

FIGURE 2.11

Notice that the wine types have been placed along the vertical axis while the number of customers preferring each wine type have been placed along the horizontal axis. The length of each horizontal bar represents the number of customers preferring that wine type. The space between the bars emphasizes that the data is discrete.

The second bar graph we will construct is the **vertical** bar graph. This type of bar graph is generally used to represent numerical data that is discrete or data that is classified by time.

EXAMPLE 2.9

The frequency distribution in Table 2.15 represents the rate of marriages per 10,000 population in the United States for selected years from 1960 to 1995. Construct a vertical bar graph.

TABLE 2.15   U.S. Marriages, 1960–1995

Year	Rate of Marriages (per 10,000 population)
1960	85
1965	93
1970	106
1975	100
1980	106
1985	102
1990	98
1995	89

Source: Department of Health & Human Services, National Center for Health Statistics

Solution

In constructing a vertical bar graph, the vertical axis represents the "frequency". This vertical axis represents the rate of marriages per 10,000. Since the largest rate of marriages is 106, the vertical axis is scaled in units of twenty. The horizontal axis depicts the selected years from 1960 to 1995.

Figure 2.12 is a vertical bar graph representing the numerical data in Table 2.15 where the length of each bar corresponds to the rate of marriages per 10,000 for each selected year. This vertical bar graph is a time-series graph since the variable on the horizontal axis represents time in years.

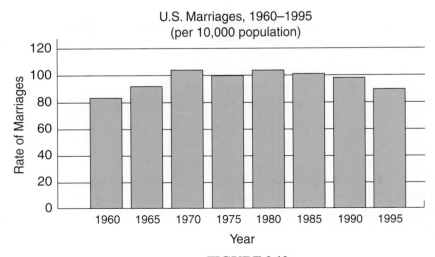

FIGURE 2.12

Histogram

The next graph we will consider is the histogram. It is the most common graphical representation of a frequency distribution.

DEFINITION 2.20

A **histogram** is a vertical bar graph that represents a **continuous** variable. To depict the continuous nature of the data, the rectangles are connected to each other **without any gaps or breaks** between two adjacent rectangles.

The width of each rectangle corresponds to the width of each class of the frequency distribution and the height of each rectangle corresponds to the frequency, or relative frequency, of the class.

The vertical sides of each rectangle of a histogram correspond to the class boundaries of each class, and so, there are no breaks or gaps between the rectangles.

Let us examine how to construct a histogram using the frequency distribution data in Table 2.16 which represents the average daily temperatures of a South Pacific Island during the month of December.

TABLE 2.16   Average Daily Temperatures of a South Pacific Island

Classes (Temperatures)	Frequency	Class Boundaries
74–77	1	73.5–77.5
78–81	7	77.5–81.5
82–85	15	81.5–85.5
86–89	6	85.5–89.5
90–93	1	89.5–93.5
94–97	1	93.5–97.5

In constructing a histogram, the horizontal axis is labeled with the class boundaries. The use of class boundaries for the histogram depicts that the variable temperature is continuous. The class boundaries of each class of daily temperatures are shown in the third column of Table 2.16.

The horizontal axis is scaled from the lowest class boundary of 73.5 to the highest class boundary of 97.5. All the other class boundaries are marked off in equal distances between 73.5 to 97.5, along the horizontal axis. The class frequencies are scaled along the vertical axis. Since the greatest frequency is 15, the vertical axis will be scaled from 0 to 16 in increments of 2.

Rectangles are constructed representing each class of the frequency distribution. The width of each rectangle equals the class width, and the height of each rectangle corresponds to the frequency of each class. In constructing each rectangle, the lower class boundary of each class is used as the beginning point of each rectangle, and the lower class boundary of the next class is the ending point. Thus, the first class, which has the class boundaries 73.5–77.5 and a class width of 4, would be represented by a rectangle with a width of 4 that begins at the lower class boundary of 73.5 and ends at the class boundary of 77.5. The second class, which has the class boundaries 77.5–81.5 and a class width of 4, would be represented by a rectangle with a width of 4 that begins at the lower class boundary of 77.5 and ends at the class boundary of 81.5. This process continues until the last class 93.5–97.5 is represented by a rectangle with a width of 4 that begins at the lower class boundary of 93.5 and ends at the class boundary of 97.5.

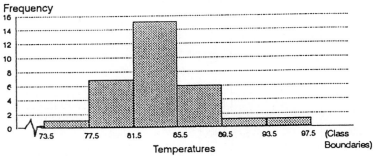

FIGURE 2.13

Figure 2.13 illustrates the histogram for the frequency distribution in Table 2.16. Notice that this histogram is basically a vertical bar graph where each rectangle or bar has equal widths and there are no breaks or gaps between the adjacent rectangles or bars. Thus, the histogram portraying the daily temperatures of the South Pacific Island is conveying the fact that the temperature data is **continuous**.

The histogram in Figure 2.13 indicates that the greatest frequency of days during the month of December had an average daily temperature from 81.5 to 85.5 degrees, and rarely does the average daily temperature drop below 77.5 degrees or greater than 89.5 degrees on this South Pacific Island.

Notice that a **squiggle** (√⁻) has been placed on the horizontal axis in Figure 2.13. This indicates that some values have been omitted. Specifically, the temperatures 0 to 73 have been omitted. This is often done for artistic balance in the presentation of the graph. **In general, a squiggle (√⁻) is used to indicate the omission of values on either the horizontal or vertical axes.**

Let's summarize the procedure to construct a histogram.

Procedure to Construct a Histogram

Step 1   Organize the data into a frequency distribution table.

Step 2   Label the horizontal axis with the name of the variable. Scale the horizontal axis starting from the lowest class boundary to the highest class boundary, while marking off all the other class boundaries in increments equal to the class width.

Step 3   Label the vertical axis as the frequency, relative frequency, or relative percentage frequency. Determine the largest frequency value and scale the vertical axis using an appropriate increment to represent the frequencies.

Step 4   Construct a rectangle for each class where the class boundaries correspond to the vertical sides of the rectangle, and the height of the rectangle corresponds to the frequency, relative frequency, or relative percentage frequency. Each rectangle should have the same width, and this width is the class width.

EXAMPLE 2.10

In Table 2.1, at the beginning of this chapter, survey data for 150 students was given. Table 2.17 is a frequency distribution representing the study hour data from Table 2.1.

a) Change the frequencies in Table 2.17 to relative percentage frequencies and construct a histogram using the relative percentage frequencies.

b) From the histogram determine the percentage of students who study from 11 to 25 hours.

TABLE 2.17 Study Hours for Students

Classes (Study Hours)	Frequency	Class Boundaries
6–10	29	5.5–10.5
11–15	26	10.5–15.5
16–20	36	15.5–20.5
21–25	26	20.5–25.5
26–30	25	25.5–30.5
31–35	7	30.5–35.5
36–40	1	35.5–40.5

Solution a

Step 1 Since the class boundaries for each class are included, we need only to determine the relative percentage frequencies for each class. We determine the relative percentage frequencies for each class, using the formula:

$$\text{relative percentage frequency} = \frac{class\ frequency}{total\ number\ of\ data}\ (100\%)$$

Since the total number of data is 150, divide each class frequency by 150 to determine the relative percentage frequency for each class. For example, the first class representing 6–10 study hours has a frequency of 29. Its relative percentage frequency is:

$$\text{relative percentage frequency for the first class} = \frac{29}{150}\ (100\%)$$
$$= 19.33\%$$

The relative percentage frequencies for the remaining classes are included in Table 2.18.

Step 2 Label the horizontal axis Study Hours. Scale the axis starting with the lowest class boundary of 5.5 to the largest class boundary of 40.5 while marking off all the other class boundaries in increments equal to the class width of 5. This is illustrated in Figure 2.14.

Step 3 Label the vertical axis Relative Percentage Frequency. To determine an appropriate scale, find the largest percentage. Since the largest percent is 24%, the vertical axis will be scaled in increments of 5%. Examine the scaling of the vertical axis in Figure 2.14.

Step 4 Construct a rectangle for each class. Make the class boundaries correspond to the vertical sides of the rectangle, and the relative percentage frequency of the class corresponds to the height of the rectangle. The class boundaries of the histogram depicts the variable study hours as continuous. This is illustrated in Figure 2.14.

TABLE 2.18   Study Hours for Students

Classes (Study Hours)	Relative Percentage	Class Boundaries
6–10	19.33%	5.5–10.5
11–15	17.33%	10.5–15.5
16–20	24.00%	15.5–20.5
21–25	17.33%	20.5–25.5
26–30	16.67%	25.5–30.5
31–35	4.67%	30.5–35.5
36–40	0.67%	35.5–40.5

Histogram
Study Hours

FIGURE 2.14

Solution b

The study hours 11 to 25 are being represented by the three rectangles starting with the class boundary of 10.5 and ending with the boundary of 25.5. To determine the percentage of students corresponding to these study hours we need to sum up the relative percentages of these rectangles. This sum is:

sum = 17.33% + 24.00% + 17.33%

sum = 58.66%

Thus, 58.66% of the students study from 11 to 25 hours.

CASE STUDY 2.1   Relative Percentage Histogram of Infertility Incidence

The snapshot entitled "Infertility Incidence" shown in Figure 2.15 displays an example of a relative percentage histogram. Using the information contained within the histogram,

a) State the classes used to construct this histogram.

b) What variable do the classes represent? Is this a continuous or discrete variable? Explain.

c) What does the height of each bar within the histogram represent? Interpret the meaning of 4% for the bar representing the ages 15–24.

d) Identify the people who were surveyed. How many people were surveyed? Identify the people who are being represented by the histogram. Does this histogram represent all the people who were surveyed? Explain.

e) Can you determine the total percentage of infertile women within the survey who never had children? If so, what is it? Now determine the total number of infertile women within the survey who never had children.

CASE STUDY 2.1   Relative Percentage Histogram of Infertility Incidence (continued)

Statistical Snapshot

Infertility Incidence

Infertility among women who have never had children:

Age

Source: National Center for Health Statistics survey of 8,500 women. Incidence represents those who know they are infertile or have had difficulty conceiving.

FIGURE 2.15

f) Construct a frequency distribution table—include the classes, frequencies, class boundaries, class marks and relative percentages.

g) Describe the shape of the histogram.

h) Does it seem reasonable that there is no class lower than the class 15–24 or greater than the class 35–44? Explain.

i) Is this an example of descriptive or inferential statistics? Explain.

j) What conclusion can you conclude about the infertility for women who have never had children as their age increases? Explain.

Frequency Polygon and Ogive

A frequency polygon is similar to a histogram. It depicts a frequency distribution by using line segments to connect the midpoints of the bars in a histogram. Frequency polygons are very useful when comparing two or more distributions on the same set of axes.

DEFINITION 2.21

A **frequency polygon** is a line graph that uses the class marks of a frequency distribution to represent continuous data.

Construct a frequency polygon by placing a dot corresponding to the frequency or percentage of each class above each class mark or midpoint. Use straight line segments to connect these dots.

Let's examine how to construct a frequency polygon using the data in Table 2.19. Table 2.19 is the frequency distribution table for the 150 student responses listed in Table 2.1 representing the variable Study Hours. A column for **class marks** has been included in the table since class marks are needed to construct a frequency polygon. Remember, the class mark represents the **midpoint** of each class.

TABLE 2.19   **Study Hours for 150 student Responses**

Classes (Study Hours)	Class Mark	Frequency
6–10	8	29
11–15	13	26
16–20	18	36
21–25	23	26
26–30	28	25
31–35	33	7
36–40	38	1

To construct a frequency polygon for these data, a horizontal axis is constructed listing the class marks from Table 2.19 and a vertical axis listing the percentages represented in the table. A dot is placed directly above each class mark of a corresponding height to the class's frequency (see Figure 2.16a). Use line segments to connect the adjacent dots. Notice that the frequency polygon is not connected to the horizontal axis. To connect the frequency polygon to the horizontal axis, add an **additional class mark to each end of the axis**. These additional class marks have **zero frequency** since no students study less than 6 or more than 40 hours.

Using the additional class marks, the graph is connected to the horizontal axis. Figure 2.16b represents the graph of the frequency polygon.

FIGURE 2.16a

FIGURE 2.16b

Let's summarize the steps to construct a frequency polygon.

Procedure to Construct a Frequency Polygon

Step 1   Organize the data into a frequency distribution table and include the class marks.

Step 2   Label the horizontal axis with the name of the variable. The horizontal axis represents the class marks. Scale this axis by marking the class marks from the lowest class mark to the highest class mark. Add two additional class marks calculated by sub-

(continues)

Procedure to Construct a Frequency Polygon (continued)

tracting the class width from the lowest class mark and adding the class width to the highest class mark.

Step 3   Place a dot representing the frequency or percentage of each class above the class mark. Remember, the two additional class marks have zero frequency or percentage, and their dots are placed on the horizontal axis.

Step 4   Connect the adjacent dots using straight line segments. The resulting line graph is called a frequency polygon.

The techniques used to construct frequency polygons can be extended to construct other types of line graphs. These line graphs are especially useful when you wish to compare two or more distributions on the same set of axes. This idea is illustrated in Case Study 2.2.

CASE STUDY 2.2   Charting Crime on Long Island

Table 2.20 entitled "Charting Crime on LI" gives the number of crimes per 100,000 residents for Nassau and Suffolk Counties of Long Island, New York. These figures, reported in the FBI's Uniform Crime Index, represent the number of burglaries, murders, assaults, rapes and car thefts per 100,000 residents.

TABLE 2.20   Charting Crime on Long Island
Number of crimes per 100,000 residents

Year	Nassau	Suffolk
1980	4,108	6,190
1985	3,465	3,810
1990	3,273	4,637
1991	3,344	5,102
1992	3,100	4,810
1993	2,978	4,405

Inspecting the information contained within Table 2.20, it is not easy to compare the crime rates of these counties. But now, let's construct two line graphs to compare the crime rates of Nassau and Suffolk Counties.

The horizontal axis will represent the years and be scaled from 1980 to 1994. The vertical axis will represent the number of crimes (per 100,000 residents) and will be scaled from 2,000 to 8,000. To construct a line graph for each county, a dot corresponding to the crime rate was placed above each respective year. Connecting these dots with line segments produced the line graphs shown in Figure 2.17. These graphs are *time-series line graphs* since the horizontal axis represents time in years. For time-series graphs it is inappropriate to extend each line graph to the horizontal axis, since this would indicate that the crime rate per county is zero for the years prior to 1980 and after 1994.

Notice how quickly these line graphs reveal information about the two counties crime rates that were not apparent from a quick examination of Table 2.20. In examining the line graph pertaining to Nassau's crime rate, we notice that the crime rate has **essentially been on the decrease from 1980 to 1994**. During the four year period from 1991 to 1994, the crime rate decreased from 3,344 to 2,645. This represents a decrease of 699 in the crime rate over this four year period, or **an approximate decrease of 175 crimes per 100,000 residents per year from 1991 to 1994**.

CASE STUDY 2.2   **Charting Crime on Long Island (continued)**

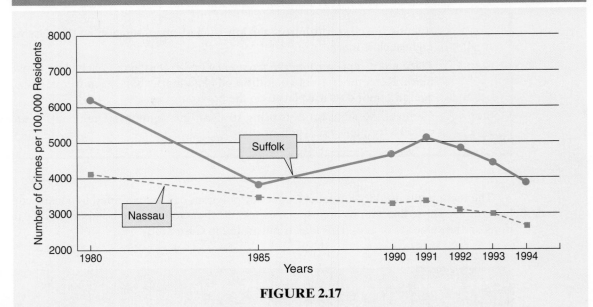

FIGURE 2.17

On the other hand, the line graph pertaining to Suffolk's crime rate **decreases very rapidly for the years 1980 to 1985** and then the **crime rate starts an upswing during the years 1985 to 1991**. However, during the four year period from 1991 to 1994, the crime rate decreases dramatically from 5102 to 3852. This decrease represents a drop in the crime rate of 1250 over this four year period or **an approximate decrease of 313 crimes per 100,000 residents per year from 1991 to 1994**.

If Nassau's crime rate continues to decrease at the rate of 175 crimes per year, while Suffolk's crime rate decreases at the rate of 313 crimes per year, then estimate the year that their crime rates will be approximately the same.

DEFINITION 2.22

A graph of a cumulative frequency distribution is called an **ogive** (pronounced "oh-jive"). It is a line graph of a cumulative frequency distribution that represents the left end of each class on the horizontal axis and the corresponding cumulative frequency on the vertical axis. The ogive of a "less than" cumulative frequency distribution is always increasing while the ogive of a "more than" cumulative distribution is always decreasing.

Table 2.21 is a cumulative frequency distribution representing the weekly earnings of 50 university students.

Let's develop a procedure to construct an ogive using the data in the cumulative frequency distribution of Table 2.21.

Step 1   Create the cumulative frequency distribution table. This is shown in Table 2.21.

Step 2   List the class values on the horizontal axis and label the axis.
    From Table 2.21, we will scale the horizontal axis from 52 to 222. The class values are labeled *earnings* (in dollars).

TABLE 2.21   "Less Than" Cumulative Frequency Distribution Representing Weekly Earnings of 50 University Students

Classes (Earnings in dollars)	Cumulative Frequency
less than 52	0
less than 86	5
less than 120	15
less than 154	36
less than 188	46
less than 222	50

Step 3   Scale the vertical axis using an appropriate increment and list the cumulative frequencies.
Examining Table 2.21, we see that the greatest frequency is 50. An appropriate way to scale the vertical axis would be in units of 10.

Step 4   Place a dot above the value representing the left end of each class at a height corresponding to the cumulative frequency of the class.
Since the first class, less than $52, has a frequency of zero, a dot is placed on the horizontal axis at 52. For the second class, less than $86, a dot is placed above 86 at a frequency height of 5. The remaining dots are placed at a height that corresponds to the frequencies listed in Table 2.21.

Step 5   To construct the ogive, the adjacent dots are connected using line segments.
Figure 2.18 represents the ogive for the "less than" cumulative frequency Table 2.21.

FIGURE 2.18

Examine the ogive in Figure 2.18. Between what two successive classes is the change in cumulative frequencies the greatest?
The procedure to construct an ogive is summarized below.

Procedure to Construct an Ogive

Step 1   Organize the data into a Cumulative Frequency Distribution Table.

Step 2   Label the horizontal axis with the name of the variable. Scale the horizontal axis starting from the lowest class value which represents the left end of each class to the highest class value, while marking off all the other class values in equal increments.

Step 3   Label the vertical axis as the cumulative frequency. Determine the largest cumulative frequency value and scale the vertical axis using an appropriate increment to represent these frequencies.

Step 4   Place a dot above the value which represents the left end of each class and that corresponds to the cumulative frequency for each class.

Step 5   Use line segments to connect the adjacent dots. The resulting graph is called an ogive.

2.6   SPECIALTY GRAPHS: PIE CHART AND PICTOGRAPH

Let's examine two specialty graphs called the **pie chart** and the **pictograph**.

DEFINITION 2.23

A **pie chart** is useful in representing categorical data in a circular format. In the pie chart, each category is represented by a sector of the circle or pie that corresponds to the percent or proportion of the data within each category.

Case Study 2.3   How Live-In Partners Fared

The pie chart in Figure 2.19 was constructed from a survey that sampled 8,450 women aged 15–44 regarding the outcomes of unmarried couples who lived together. Each sector represents a different outcome that can be categorized as: successful marriage, marriage dissolved, still living together and broke up. The area of the different sectors of the pie chart reflects the percent of the women who have indicated how their relationship fared. For example, 40% of the women indicated that their relationship resulted in a successful marriage. Thus, 40% of the area of the circle has been sectioned to represent this response.

From Figure 2.19:

a)   What percent of the unmarried couples are now not living together?

b)   Is there enough information to draw any conclusions regarding whether living together results in a successful marriage? Explain.

c)   Do we know the number of women within the survey who were unmarried but lived together as a couple? Can we assume it was all 8,450 women surveyed? Comment.

Case Study 2.3   How Live-In Partners Fared (continued)

FIGURE 2.19

DEFINITION 2.24

A **pictograph** uses pictures to represent data in a more attractive and eye catching manner.[2]

Case Studies 2.4 and 2.5 are examples of pictographs.

Case Study 2.4   Data Snapshots

The snapshots entitled "Birthday Party Months," "USA's Stand on Lemonade" and "Kids Who Smoke" use appropriate pictures of objects to present information about birth months, lemonade entrepreneurs, and children smokers. All these snapshots display the data using graphs that were discussed within this chapter but use pictures to replace traditional graph elements.

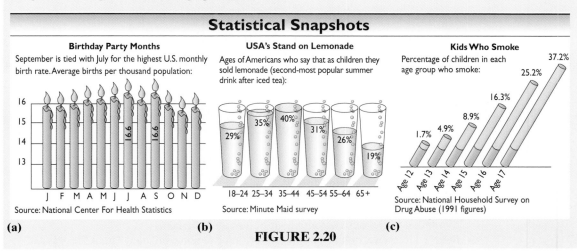

FIGURE 2.20

[2]A word of caution: Pictographs can be used to misrepresent data. See Section 1.5 for more information on the misuses of statistics.

Case Study 2.4   Data Snapshots (continued)

For each snapshot within Figures 2.20(a), 2.20(b) and 2.20(c),

a) Identify the variables being displayed. Are they continuous or discrete?
b) Identify the object being displayed and discuss how it is used to present the data, for example, how size plays a role in presenting the data.
c) State the type of graph that is used. For example, is it a histogram, a vertical bar graph or a time-series graph? If it is a histogram, identify the classes. If it is a time-series graph, identify the way time is displayed within the graphic.
d) Discuss the shape of each graphic and how its shape can be used to draw an inference or conclusion from the graphic.

CASE STUDY 2.5   Marriage, Heartburn a Couple

The snapshot entitled "Marriage, Heartburn a Couple" in Figure 2.21 uses eye-catching pictographs and pie charts to present the data.

FIGURE 2.21

For the snapshot within Figure 2.21,

a) Identify the variable being displayed and state whether the variable is continuous or discrete.
b) Identify the object being displayed and discuss how it is used to present the data.
c) What type of graph is used within the pictograph? Does the type of graph used have any relationship to whether the variable is continuous or discrete? Explain.
d) Draw an inference or conclusion from the information contained within the graphic.

2.7 IDENTIFYING SHAPES AND INTERPRETING GRAPHS

Shapes of Distributions

A frequency distribution can have an unlimited number of shapes. We will discuss and examine the standard shapes and their characteristics for a few different types of distributions. The shapes of these distributions are smooth curves which represent a frequency distribution using very small classes.

The **symmetric bell-shaped distribution**, Figure 2.22, is a familiar distribution that we often encounter in statistics.

DEFINITION 2.25

A **symmetric bell-shaped distribution** has its highest frequency, or peak, at the center with the frequencies steadily decreasing but identically distributed on both sides of the center.

If the symmetric bell-shaped distribution were folded along the center, the right and left side would be mirror images of itself as seen in Figure 2.22.

The bell-shaped distribution indicates that there are as many data values in both the low and high classes of the distribution. Data representing adult characteristics such as IQ scores, heights, or weights usually have a symmetric bell-shaped distribution since most adults have IQs, heights or weights that are bunched near the center value with few adults falling at the extreme values.

Symmetric Bell-shaped curve	Positively skewed curve or skewed right	Negatively skewed curve or skewed left
FIGURE 2.22	**FIGURE 2.23**	**FIGURE 2.24**

A distribution which is not symmetric and extends more to one side than the other side is said to be a **skewed distribution**.

DEFINITION 2.26

A **skewed distribution** is a non-symmetric distribution that has most of the data values falling into one side of the distribution with very few but extreme data values falling in the other side.

There are two types of skewed distributions. A distribution of incomes represents one type of a skewed distribution since usually most of the people have incomes on the lower end of the income scale with a relatively few people who are millionaires falling into the higher end of the income scale. This type of skewed distribution is called **a positively skewed or skewed right distribution**.

On the other hand, a person's age at death represents a second type of skewed distribution since there are a relatively few people who die at a very young age with the frequency of death increasing as a person ages. This type of skewed distribution is called **a negatively skewed or skewed left distribution.** Let's define the characteristics of these two skewed distributions.

DEFINITION 2.27

A **positively skewed, or skewed right, distribution** has a greater number of relatively low scores and a few extremely high scores. The shape of a skewed right distribution has a longer tail on the right side which represents the few extremely high scores.

A positively skewed or a skewed right distribution is illustrated in Figure 2.23. We notice that the distribution has the longer tail on the right side which represents the few extremely high scores.

DEFINITION 2.28

A **negatively skewed, or a skewed left, distribution** is a distribution that has a larger number of relatively high scores and a few extremely low scores. Its shape has a longer tail on the left side which represents the few extremely low scores.

The shape of a skewed left distribution is illustrated in Figure 2.24. We notice that the distribution has the longer tail on the left side which represents the few extremely low scores.

Notice that the skewness of a distribution results from the extreme data values falling into one of the tails of the distribution.

If the extreme values occur in the upper or right tail, the distribution has a longer right tail and is referred to as a positively skewed or skewed right distribution.

When the extreme values occur in the lower left tail, then the distribution has a longer left tail and is referred to as negatively skewed or skewed left distribution.

Let's define some other distribution shapes which are illustrated in Figure 2.25.

DEFINITION 2.29

A **Uniform** or **Rectangular Distribution** is a distribution where all the classes contain the same number of data values or frequencies.

A uniform distribution is illustrated in Figure 2.25a. A uniform distribution usually occurs when tossing a fair die say 600 times. We would expect the frequency distribution representing the outcome of the die to be the same for each number 1 to 6.

DEFINITION 2.30

A **U-shaped Distribution** is a distribution, as the name suggests, that has a U-shape. That is, it has its two greatest frequencies occurring at each extreme end of the distribution with the lower frequencies of the distribution occurring in the center.

Figure 2.25b illustrates a U-shaped distribution. Death rates by age within the United States form a distribution that is roughly U-shaped.

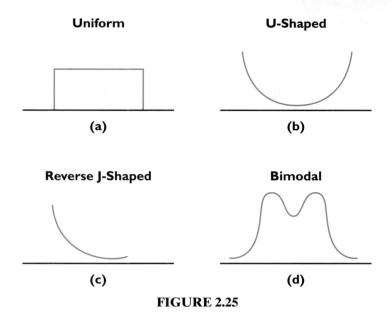

FIGURE 2.25

DEFINITION 2.31
A **Reverse J-Shaped Distribution**, similar to its name, has the greatest frequency of data values occurring at one end of the distribution and then tails off gradually in the opposite direction.

A reverse J-shaped distribution is illustrated in Figure 2.25c. If a pair of fair dice were tossed 720 times, and the outcomes were classified as no sixes, one six, or two sixes, the resulting distribution would resemble a reversed J-shape.

DEFINITION 2.32
A **Bimodal Distribution** is a distribution that has two separate, distinct, and relatively high peaks with the greatest frequencies. It usually indicates the distribution represents two different populations.

Figure 2.25d illustrates a bimodal distribution. A bimodal distribution usually represents the data values of two different groups or populations. For example, a distribution containing both the weights of males and females would be a bimodal distribution where each peak would represent the most frequent weight for each sex.

EXAMPLE 2.11

For the four distributions pictured in Figure 2.26 identify the shape of each distribution and explain what the shape indicates for the variable represented.

Solution

a) The shape of the distribution in Figure 2.26a is bell-shaped. This indicates most of the females have heights that are clustered in the center of the distribution with very few females having extreme heights, i.e. too short or too tall.

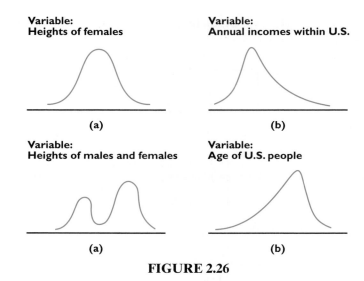

FIGURE 2.26

b)   The shape of the distribution in Figure 2.26b is skewed right. This indicates that few incomes are very high with a greater number of incomes being relatively low.

c)   The shape of the distribution in Figure 2.26c is bimodal. Each peak within the distribution represents the most frequent height for each sex.

d)   The shape of the distribution in Figure 2.26d is skewed left. This indicates that there are a greater number of older people and relatively fewer younger people.

Interpreting Graphs

Besides identifying the shape of a graph, reading and interpreting the information from a graph are essential. There are no principles taught in this section, it is really just practice. The following example illustrates how to read and interpret information within graphs.

E X A M P L E   2 . 1 2

Use the information in the histogram in Figure 2.27 to answer the following questions.

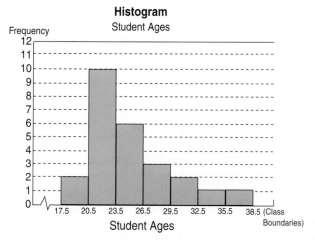

FIGURE 2.27

a) How many students are represented by this histogram?
b) How many students are older than 26?
c) What percent of the students are older than 26?
d) What percent of the students are younger than 21?
e) What percent of the students are older than 20 but younger than 30?

Solution

Table 2.22 has been constructed using the histogram in Figure 2.27.

TABLE 2.22 Frequency Distribution of Student Ages

Student Ages	Frequency
18–20	2
21–23	10
24–26	6
27–29	3
30–32	2
33–35	1
36–38	1

a) To calculate the number of students represented by the graph, add the frequencies of all the classes.
     The total number of students is 25.
b) Any student older than 26 must be in one of the classes: 27–29, 30–32, 33–35, and 36–38.
     To calculate the number of students older than 26, add the frequencies of these four classes. Therefore, 7 students are older than 26.
c) To calculate the percent of students older than 26:

Step 1 Divide the number of students older than 26 by the total number of students in the distribution. That is,

$$\frac{\text{The number of students older than 26}}{\text{Total number of students in the dist.}} = \frac{7}{25} = 0.28$$

Step 2 Multiply this decimal by 100% to convert the decimal to a percent.

$$0.28 \times 100\% = 28\%$$

Therefore, 28% of the students in the distribution are older than 26.

d) To calculate the percent of students younger than 21:
     Divide the number of students younger than 21 by the total number of students in the distribution:

$$\frac{\text{Number of students younger than 21}}{\text{Total number of students in the dist.}} = \frac{2}{25} = 0.08$$

Multiply this decimal by 100% to convert the decimal to a percent.

$$0.08 \times 100\% = 8\%$$

Therefore, 8% of the students in the distribution are younger than 21.

e) Calculate the percent of the students older than 20 but younger than 30.
     Using the same procedure illustrated in part d (above), we obtain 19/25 or 76% of the students in the distribution are older than 20 but younger than 30. ∎

CASE STUDY 2.6   Source of State Governments' Revenue

Examine the pie chart in Figure 2.28 which represents the source of state governments' revenue.

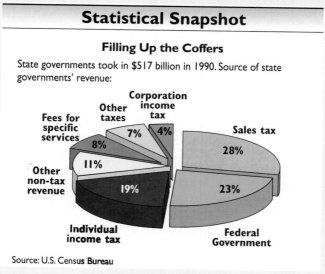

FIGURE 2.28

Using this information, answer the following questions:

a) How much state revenue was generated from the sales tax?

b) Suppose we assume that the state sales tax is 8.5%. What was the base sales amount used to generate the sales tax portion of the state revenue?

c) If the state was planning to increase the sales tax to 9.5% next year, estimate the revenue due to sales tax using the results obtained in part "b".

d) Determine the percentage due to sales tax revenue if the state increased the sales tax to 9.5%. (Assume that all other conditions remained the same.)

Solution

a) According to the graph, the state government received $517 billion. Twenty-eight percent was from sales tax. Thus,

$$28\% \text{ of } \$517 \text{ billion} = \$144.76 \text{ billion}$$

That is, the state tax revenue generated from sales tax is $144.76 billion.

b) If we assume that the state sales tax is 8.5% and this tax generated $144.76 billion then:

$$8.5\% \text{ of } (\textbf{a base amount due to sales}) = \$144.76 \text{ billion.}$$

This can be expressed as:

$$(0.085)(\text{base amount due to sales}) = \$144.76 \text{ billion,}$$

or,

$$\text{base amount due to sales} = \frac{\$144.76 \text{ billion}}{(0.085)}$$
$$= \$1{,}703.06 \text{ billion.}$$

Thus, state-wide sales of $1,703.06 billion yielded $144.76 billion of sales tax revenue.

c) If state-wide sales remained the same and the sales tax increased to 9.5%, then the state could expect to generate:

CASE STUDY 2.6   Source of State Governments' Revenue (continued)

9.5% of $1,703.06 billion = $161.79 billion

The state tax revenue from a 9.5% sales tax is $161.79 billion.

d) Since a 9.5% sales tax would have produced a revenue of $161.79 billion, this revenue represents an increase of $17.03 billion compared to an 8.5% sales tax. Adding this to the initial $517 billion state budget yields $534.03 billion.

   The projected $161.79 billion from a 9.5% sales tax represents an increase to 30.30% revenue generated from sales tax.

CASE STUDY 2.7   Living Solo in the USA

Examine the histogram in Figure 2.29 which represents the percentage of men and women by age who live alone in the USA.

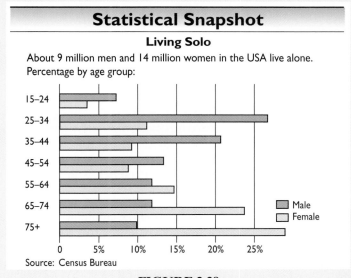

FIGURE 2.29

a) For which age class do you find the greatest number of men living alone?
b) For which age class do you find the greatest number of women living alone?
c) Are there more men or women living alone in the age class 45–54?
d) Describe the shape of the graph representing the women living alone.
e) Describe the shape of the graph representing the men living alone.
f) Why do you think the shapes of the graphs for parts "d" and "e" are different?

Solution

a) In Figure 2.29, the horizontal bar representing the 25–34 years old class for the males has the longest length. Thus, greatest number of men living alone are men 25–34 years old.
b) In Figure 2.29, the class 75+ years old has the longest length for the females. So, the greatest number of women living alone are women over the age of 75.
c) In the 45–54 age class, the horizontal bar for the males appears to represent 13% of the 9 million males. Thirteen percent of the 9 million males is 1.17 million males. While, the horizontal bar for the

CASE STUDY 2.7   Living Solo in the USA (continued)

females in the 45–54 age class appears to represent 9% of the 14 million females. Nine percent of the 14 million females is 1.26 million females. Although, the *percentage* of males is greater, the *number* of females living alone is more than the number of males living alone in the 45–54 age class.

d) The shape of the graph for the male population living alone tends to be skewed to the right.
e) The shape of the graph for the female population living alone tends to be skewed to the left.
f) Women tend to live longer than males.

2.8   USING TECHNOLOGY

Table 2.23 represents 150 responses to a student survey.

In MINITAB, the Stem-and-Leaf command for the variable hours studied per week produced the output presented in Figure 2.30.

```
MTB > Stem-and-Leaf 'hr';
SUBC>   Increment 10.

Stem-and-leaf of hr       N  = 150
Leaf Unit = 1.0


   19    0 6677788888889999999
  (60)   1 0000000000111111222222222244555555555566666777777778888889999
   71    2 0000000000001111122233333344444444455556666777777778888888999
   12    3 000011123336
```

FIGURE 2.30

The numbers in the first column represent the cumulative frequency up until the row containing the middle value of the distribution is reached. After the row containing the middle value, the row frequencies represent the number of remaining data values within the distribution. The middle value of the distribution is contained within the row identified by a set of parentheses around the row frequency.

MINITAB can be used to construct a histogram. The Frequency Distribution Table in Table 2.23 represents a summary of the 150 student responses pertaining to the variable Study Hours.

TABLE 2.23   Study Hours for 150 Student Responses

Classes (Study Hours)	Class Mark	Frequency
6–10	8	28
11–15	13	26
16–20	18	37
21–25	23	26
26–30	28	25
31–35	33	7
36–40	38	1

Figure 2.31, represents MINITAB's version of a histogram for the data represented in Table 2.23. Notice that the midpoint and frequency count is indicated on the output.

```
MTB > Histogram 'hr'.

Histogram of hr   N = 150

Midpoint   Count
     8       19   ******************
    12       25   *************************
    16       24   ************************
    20       28   ****************************
    24       21   *********************
    28       21   *********************
    32       11   ***********
    36        1   *
```

FIGURE 2.31

Using Excel, a histogram of the data set in Table 2.23 is represented in Figure 2.32. A pie chart of the same data is shown in Figure 2.33.

FIGURE 2.32   **FIGURE 2.33**

The graphing calculator is becoming a powerful tool today to help students explore important statistical concepts. It allows students to explore these concepts on their own. In this section, we will display a histogram, a frequency polygon and an ogive that was generated using a graphing calculator. The TI-83 Plus graphing calculator was used to obtain these graphs.

Graphing Calculator Display of a Histogram, Frequency Polygon and Ogive

Different graphing calculators follow different steps to generate and display a histogram. The histogram in Figure 2.34 was generated using the TI-83 Plus for the data set in Table 2.23.

Notice in Figure 2.34, the class boundaries and the frequency for the 1st class are shown as **Min=5.5, Max<10.5,** and **n=28**.

A frequency polygon using the information in Table 2.23 of the text is shown in Figure 2.35.

Notice in Figure 2.35, the class mark and the frequency for the 1st class appear as X=3 & Y=0. **The x value represents the class mark while the y value represents the class frequency.**

FIGURE 2.34	**FIGURE 2.35**

Table 2.24 is a cumulative frequency distribution representing the data set shown in Table 2.23. An ogive for the data in Table 2.24 is shown in Figure 2.36.

Table 2.24   "Less Than" Cumulative Frequency Distribution Representing Study Hours of 150 Student Responses

Classes (Study Hours)	Cumulative Frequency
less than 6	0
less than 11	28
less than 16	54
less than 21	91
less than 26	117
less than 31	142
less than 36	149
less than 41	150

FIGURE 2.36

In Figure 2.36, the X=6 represents the **class value** while the Y=0 represents the **cumulative frequency of the first class.**

KEY TERMS

Raw Data   53
Variable   54
Data Set   54

Categorical Variable   54
Numerical Variable   55
Continuous Data   55

Discrete Data   55
Exploratory Data Analysis   56
Distribution   56

SECTION EXERCISES

Section 2.2

1. A _____ is a type of information, usually a property or characteristic of a person or thing, that is measured or observed.

2. A specific measurement or observation for a variable is called the _____ of the variable.

3. There are two types of variables: _____ and _____.

4. A categorical variable is a variable where the values represent _____ .

5. A variable whose values are the result of a measurement process is called a _____ variable. Its values are referred to as numerical _____ .

6. Numerical data can be classified as either _____ or _____ .

7. Numerical data such as weight, height, and temperature are examples of _____ data.

8. The values of a variable characterized by descriptive words such as good, poor, or excellent are referred to as categorical data.
   (T/F)

9. A discrete variable can be represented using a frequency distribution table.
   (T/F)

10. Classify the following data as either categorical or numerical. If the data is numerical, then classify it as either continuous or discrete data.
    a) The life of an automobile tire.
    b) The number of children in a family.
    c) A person's educational degree.
    d) The number of registered conservatives in a county.

11. The following table represents a sample of data collected on college students. Each column abbreviation represents the following information:

sex: student's sex
status: fr = freshman, sp = sophomore, jr = junior,
        sr = senior
age: student's age
ht: student's height in inches
wt: student's weight in lbs
frat: fraternity or sorority membership: N= No or
        Y= Yes
havg: high school average
gpa: grade point average

Student #	Sex	Status	Age	Ht	Wt	Frat	Havg	GPA
5629	f	fr	19	64	110	N	89	2.99
6052	m	jr	22	73	195	N	93	3.45
7679	m	sp	20	71	145	Y	86	2.86

a) Identify each variable and type of variable within the data set.
b) For the student identified by the number 7679, specify the value of each of the variables.

Section 2.3

12. The approach to carefully examining a data set to discover any useful aspects, information, or unanticipated patterns that may exist in the data is called _____ .

13. A _____ represents the numerical data values of a variable from the lowest to the highest value along with the number of times each data value occurs.

14. A relatively simple exploratory data analysis technique that helps to visually show the shape of a distribution by using the actual values of the variable is called a _____ display.

15. If a data value within a stem-and-leaf display is written as: 34 | 6, then the stem value is _____ and the leaf value is _____ .

16. An individual data value which lies far from most or all of the other data values within a distribution is called an_____.

17. When two distributions are compared using a back-to-back stem-and-leaf display, a common _____ used to display each distribution.

Use the following information for questions 18 and 19: In constructing a Stem-and-Leaf display, a collection of anxiety scores are represented as whole numbers ranging from 15 to 40.

18. What would be the range of values used to construct the Stems?
    a) 1 to 4   **b)** 15 to 40   **c)** 10 to 100   **d)** 20 to 35

19. How many digits are used to represent a leaf?
    a) 1   **b)** 2   **c)** 5   **d)** 9

20. Express the following data values in a stem-and-leaf format using the given information.

data value	leaf portion
102	units digit
31	units digit
2.4	tenths digit

21. A health club is interested in the distribution of ages for its members that use the club on Friday evenings. The club's personnel director surveys the membership one Friday evening and collects the following data:

    Club Members' Ages in Years

    19 31 52 34 84 63 52 37 24 29
    33 46 19 32 41 49 26 32 46 44
    28 76 49 34 73 63 56 35 74 66
    59 39 61 50 37 29 30 51 54 41

    a) Construct a stem-and-leaf display for the distribution of ages.
    b) Describe the shape of the distribution.
    c) In which age decade are most people?
    d) In which fifteen year age difference are most people?

22. The following distribution represents the 1995 average American College Testing (ACT) scores for state and the district of Columbia. The ACT score is used by some colleges as an admission criteria. The average national ACT score was 20.8 out of a possible 36.

    STATE AVERAGE ACT SCORES

    20.0, 21.0, 21.0, 20.2, 20.9, 21.4, 21.4, 21.6, 18.9, 20.7, 20.2, 21.8, 21.2, 21.1, 21.2, 21.8, 21.2, 20.1, 19.4, 21.5, 20.6, 20.9, 21.1, 21.9, 18.8, 21.3, 21.8, 21.4, 21.3, 22.3, 20.4, 20.1, 21.7, 19.6, 21.2, 21.2, 20.3, 22.6, 20.6, 20.6, 19.1, 21.2, 20.3, 20.1, 21.4, 21.7, 20.6, 22.2, 20.0, 22.0, 21.3

    a) Construct a stem-and-leaf display for the ACT scores.
    b) Using the stem-and-leaf display, describe the shape of the distribution.

23. A medical study was performed to determine if a special new drug could lower a person's blood pressure. The study was conducted with two groups, an experimental group and a control group. The experimental group received the new drug, while the control group was given a dummy pill called a placebo. The systolic blood pressure for each participant was measured while the participant was at rest before the study began. Both groups had similar blood pressure distributions before the experiment began. The following data represents the blood pressures of the participants within each group after the study was conducted.

    Experimental Group

    109, 119, 128, 131, 105, 113, 108, 113, 125, 130, 120, 123, 120, 119, 126, 125, 118, 107, 114, 117, 121, 112, 105, 127, 115

    Control Group

    117, 127, 135, 142, 124, 137, 113, 109, 126, 135, 143, 138, 145, 136, 126, 136, 147, 138, 128, 138, 137, 139, 148, 149, 148

    a) Construct a back-to-back stem-and-leaf display to compare these two groups.
    b) Does it appear that the new drug had an effect on lowering the blood pressures of the participants, if both groups began with similar blood pressure distributions?
    c) Describe the shape of each distribution for the experimental and control groups.

24. The following distributions represent the ages of the New York major league baseball teams, the Mets and the Yankees, at the start of the 1995 season.

    Mets

    24,25,25,21,27,32,25,27,28,28,27,37,23,32
    26,29,29,28,31,24,25,23,27,29,26,29,31,23

    Yankees

    31,31,36,30,32,27,34,27,32,32,32,30,32,26
    28,29,31,26,23,37,31,34,29,26,29,22,28,26

    a) Construct a back-to-back stem-and-leaf display for the ages of both baseball teams.
    b) Using the stem-and-leaf display, describe the shape of each distribution.
    c) Compare the age distributions of both teams and discuss the differences.
    d) One of these teams had the one of the largest payrolls for the 1995 season. Using only the age distribution for both teams, which team would you believe had the highest payroll? Give an explanation for your answer.

Section 2.4

25. A frequency distribution table helps describe the general characteristics of a distribution. It divides the data into groups, called _____ and the number of data that fall into each class, called the _____.

26. In constructing a frequency distribution table for a categorical variable, the classes represent the _____ of the variable.

27. In constructing a frequency distribution table, the actual class width is dependent upon the number of _____ digits used to measure the data values.

28. The representative value of a class is called a class _____.

29. The class boundary of a class is the _____ of the upper class limit of one class and the lower class limit of the next class.

30. The proportion of data values within a class is called the _____ frequency of the class and is calculated by dividing the class frequency by the _____ _____ of data values.

31. The relative percentage frequency of a class is the _____ of data values within a class. To determine the relative percentage frequency of each class, multiply the relative frequency of each class by _____ %. The sum of all the relative percentage frequencies will always be _____ except for possible round-off error.

32. In a "less than" cumulative frequency distribution table, the cumulative frequency of a particular class indicates the number of data values within the class plus the _____ of all the data values _____ _____ this particular class.

33. In a "more than" cumulative frequency distribution table, the cumulative frequency of a particular class indicates the number of data values within the class plus the _____ of all the data values _____ _____ this particular class.

34. The class boundaries for the class 20–26 are:
   a. 20.5–25.5   **b.** 19.5–25.5
   c. 20.5–26.5   **d.** 19.5–26.5

35. The class width for the class 25–30 is:
   a. 7   **b.** 6   **c.** 5   **d.** 4

36. If the lower class limit is 17 and the class width is 7, then the upper class limit is:
   a. 23   **b.** 24   **c.** 22   **d.** 25

37. What is the class mark for the class 10–16?
   a. 10   **b.** 13   **c.** 12.5   **d.** 16

38. When constructing a frequency distribution table, the number of classes is always 10.
   (T/F)

39. Class boundaries are used in the construction of a histogram but not in the construction of a bar graph.
   (T/F)

40. A survey on the number of hours a college student works per week showed that the hours varied from 1 to 40. Determine the class limits, class marks, and class boundaries of a frequency distribution table if the work hours were grouped using 5 classes.

41. The following distribution represents the demand for electricity on Long Island for a sample of two months.

Demand for Electricity
(measured in KW hours)
20, 25, 27, 30, 33, 37, 40, 35, 32, 29, 26, 23, 22, 24, 28,
31, 32, 37, 35, 34, 30, 27, 24, 25, 28, 29, 33, 34, 30, 28,
26, 31, 29, 30, 33, 32, 34, 30, 31, 27, 26, 28, 29, 30, 31,
34, 32, 29, 31, 27, 28, 26, 31, 33, 34, 29, 31, 28, 26, 30

a) Construct a frequency distribution table using 7 classes. Include within the table: classes, frequencies, class boundaries, class marks, and relative percentages.

b) Using only the table, is it possible to determine the number of days the demand for electricity was:
   i) at least 26 KWH?
   ii) less than 31 KWH?
   iii) more than 33 KWH?
   iv) exactly 29 KWH?

42. According to the National Center for Health Statistics, the most popular birth months are July and September.

Birth Months
October, December, August, May, September, May, May, April, August, January, December, May, July, June, February, November, March, April, November, August, October, September, April, July, November, April, October, August, February, May, June, September, March, November, June, July, March, June, March, August, July, September, June, October, September, January, February, September, January, July, April, November, December, May, June, October, July, May December, September, June, August, July, September, July

Using the given distribution of birth months for a sample of college students:
a) Identify the variable and specify the type of variable.
b) Construct a frequency distribution table for the birth months.
c) How many classes did you use? Why?

43. According to an *CNN/Gallup Poll* conducted on April 17–19, 1995, sports fans were asked the question: "What's your favorite sport?". Football received the most votes as the leading sport. The following distribution represents the ages of some of the sport fans who selected football.

Ages
20, 31, 33, 25, 19, 34, 25, 50, 35, 49, 45, 31, 42, 23, 20
66, 53, 27, 65, 23, 19, 45, 31, 42, 23, 66, 19, 24, 27, 31

48, 34, 27, 29, 19, 20, 35, 45, 49, 36, 55, 60, 63, 65, 67
68, 66, 69, 55, 52, 59, 34, 38, 36, 22, 25, 28, 23, 29, 27
27, 28, 30, 39, 43, 44, 50, 51, 60, 66, 70, 18, 27, 26, 23
30, 40, 48, 62, 58, 54, 69, 68, 21, 29, 27, 26, 49, 30, 38
53, 55, 61, 66, 68, 18, 21, 27, 28, 33, 41, 45, 53, 59, 62
66, 69, 50, 60, 62, 36, 39, 44, 22, 28, 27, 29, 25, 21, 55

a) Identify the variable and type of variable.
b) Construct a frequency distribution table using 5 classes.
Include within the table: classes, frequencies, class boundaries, class marks, and relative percentages.
c) Construct a "Less Than" cumulative frequency distribution using the frequency distribution table in part (b).
d) Construct a "More Than" cumulative frequency distribution using the frequency distribution table in part (b).
e) What percent of the sports fans are younger than 51?
f) What percent of the sports fan are 40 or older?
g) Is it possible to determine from the distribution tables how many sports fans are 45 years old? Explain.
h) What information is lost when you group data into a frequency distribution table? Is the same information lost when constructing a stem-and-leaf display? Explain.

Section 2.5

44. Graphs are used to accurately depict distributions. (T/F)
45. A bar graph is generally used to depict _____ or _____ data.
46. A time-series graph contains information about two variables, where one of the variables is _____.
47. Generally, in a horizontal bar graph, the categories of the categorical data are placed along the _____ axis, while the frequencies are placed along the _____ axis.
48. In a vertical bar graph, the height of each bar represents the _____.
49. A squiggle is used to represent the _____ of values in either a horizontal or vertical axis.
50. A histogram is a graph of a continuous _____ . It consists of rectangles connected to each other without any _____ or _____ between two adjacent rectangles thus showing continuity.
51. A frequency polygon is a line graph that uses the class _____ of a frequency distribution to represent a _____ variable.
52. A graph of a cumulative frequency distribution is called an _____ .
53. The frequency polygon is a better graphical representation of data than a histogram. (T/F)

54. If two distributions have the same histogram, then the percent of terms greater than the center of the distribution is the same.(T/F)
55. According to an AT&T Global Information Systems poll two-thirds of the people surveyed indicated that they have a regular day they are most likely to use an ATM machine. Using the following table information,
a) Identify the variable and type of variable.
b) Construct a horizontal bar graph.
c) Calculate the percent for each day.
d) Construct another horizontal bar graph using the percentages.
e) Compare the two bar graphs.

Day of Week	Number of People Who Use ATM on a Particular Day
MONDAY	71
TUESDAY	40
WEDNESDAY	81
THURSDAY	51
FRIDAY	243
SATURDAY	162
SUNDAY	40

56. The National Survey of Families and Households, a national sample on family issues, has compiled the following table to represent the percentage of people in certain age groups who have ended a marriage or a cohabiting relationship within the last five years.

Ages	Percentage of people who ended a marriage or cohabiting relationship within 5 years
30–34	20%
35–39	17%
40–44	13%
45–49	11%
50–54	8%
55–59	8%
60–64	7%

a) Use this table to determine the number of people within each age group if the sample size was 1300.
b) What is the width of each class?
c) Construct a frequency table containing classes, frequency, class boundaries, class marks, and relative percentages.
d) Construct a histogram and frequency polygon.
e) Describe the shape of the frequency polygon. What does it seem to indicate about a person's age and ending a relationship?
f) Construct a "Less Than" cumulative frequency distribution table and an "ogive" graph using this table.
g) Construct a "More Than" cumulative frequency distribution table.

h) What percent of the people ended a marriage or a cohabiting relationship when they were less than 45?

i) What percent of the people ended a marriage or a cohabiting relationship within their 30's?

j) What percent of the people ended a marriage or a cohabiting relationship when they were at most 49?

57. According to the National Survey of Families and Households, a national sample on family issues, the following table represents the number of middle-aged people scoring in the highest quartile of distress.

	Number of people in mid-life who are in the highest quartile of frequency of distress	
Ages	Married	Unmarried
30–34	299	481
35–39	247	429
40–44	286	455
45–49	286	468
50–54	247	325
55–59	260	429
60–64	260	325

a) What is the width of each class?

b) Construct a frequency table containing classes, frequency, and class marks for both married and unmarried people.

c) Construct a frequency polygon for both married and unmarried people on the same set of axes.

d) By comparing the two polygons, what can you conclude about the distress level of married and unmarried people?

e) Which group has a more stable distress level as they age?

58. The manager of Fast Food Grocery Store is preparing a marketing report to present to his district manager. Construct a horizontal bar graph from the information in the following table.

Cereal	Number of Cases
Bran Chex	20
Raisin Bran	35
Wheat Bran	14
Corn Bran	16

59. According to the National Cable Television Association, the following data represents the basic cable subscribers. Use this table to construct a vertical bar graph.

The Cable Picture	
Year	Number of Basic Cable Subscribers
1994	60,495,090
1995	62,956,470
1996	64,654,160
1997	65,929,420
1998	67,011,180

Section 2.6

60. A graph used to represent categorical data in a circular format is called a _____ chart.

61. A graph that uses pictures to represent data in an interesting and eye catching way is called a _____.

62. Pie charts are usually constructed using percentages. (T/F)

Section 2.7

63. A symmetrically bell-shaped distribution has its highest frequency or peak at the _____ with the frequencies steadily _____ and identically distributed on both sides of the center.

64. A distribution which is not symmetric is a _____ _____ distribution.

65. A positively skewed or skewed _____ distribution has a greater number of relatively_____ _____ scores and a few extremely_____ scores.

66. A negatively skewed or skewed _____ distribution has a larger number of relatively _____ _____ scores and a few extremely _____ scores.

67. A uniform or rectangular distribution is a distribution where all the classes contain the _____ number of data values or frequencies.

68. A U-shaped distribution has its greatest frequencies occurring at each _____ of the distribution with the lower frequencies occurring in the _____.

69. A reverse J-shaped distribution has its greatest frequency of data values occurring at _____ end of the distribution and tails off gradually in the _____ direction.

70. A bimodal distribution is a distribution that has _____ greatest frequencies or peaks.

71. If the population of ages of college students is skewed right, then this indicates:

a) there are more older students within the population

b) there are just as many younger students as there are older students

c) as the age of a student increases, the frequency of the ages also increases.

d) there is a greater number of younger students within the population.

To answer questions 72–78 use the following histogram.

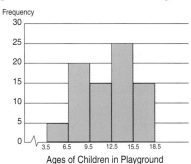

Ages of Children in Playground

72. Find the total number of children represented in the graph.
  a) 25   **b)** 80   **c)** 100   **d)** 50

73. How many children in the playground are older than 12?
  a) 40   **b)** 25   **c)** 15   **d)** 30

74. What percent of the children are in the last two classes?
  a) 40%   **b)** 50%   **c)** 25%   **d)** 15%

75. Which class has the largest frequency?
  a) 4–6   **b)** 10–12   **c)** 13–15   **d)** 16–18

76. What percent of the children are older than 9 but younger than 16 years old?
  a) 40%   **b)** 50%   **c)** 25%   **d)** 15%

77. What percent of the children are younger than 4 years old?
  a) 40%   **b)** 50%   **c)** 25%   **d)** 0%

78. How many children in the playground are older than 3?
  a) 25   **b)** 80   **c)** 100   **d)** 50

CHAPTER REVIEW

79. Classify the following data as either categorical or numerical. If the data is numerical, then classify it as either continuous or discrete data.
  a) The breaking strength of a fishing line.
  b) The amount of time needed to go to work.
  c) A person's occupation.
  d) The number of bushels of apples produced by a farmer.

80. The following table represents a sample of data collected on college students. Each column abbreviation represents the following information:

  sex: student's sex
  status: fr= freshman, sp= sophomore, jr= junior, sr=senior
  age: student's age
  ht: student's height in inches
  wt: student's weight in lbs
  frat: fraternity or sorority membership:N=No or Y=Yes
  havg: high school average
  gpa: grade point average

Student#	Sex	Status	Age	Ht	Wt	Frat	Havg	GPA
3748	m	jr	20	68	170	N	77	2.89
9857	f	fr	18	62	105	N	93	3.45
7194	f	sr	21	65	135	Y	82	2.76

  a) Identify each variable and type of variable within the data set.
  b) For the student identified by the number 9857, specify the value of each of the variables.

81. A statistics instructor has recorded the amount of time students need to complete the final examination. The times, stated to the nearest minute, are:
  50, 70, 62, 55, 38, 42, 49, 75, 80, 79, 48, 45, 53, 58, 64, 77, 48, 49, 50, 61, 72, 74, 10, 95, 120, 79, 75, 48, 72, 37, 35, 79, 72, 75, 77, 32, 30, 77, 75, 79, 45, 70, 39, 75, 72, 45, 47, 73, 72, 71

  a) Construct a stem-and-leaf display.
  b) Describe the shape of the distribution.
  c) Are there any outlier(s) in the data set? If so, give an explanation for the outlier(s)?
  d) What percentage of the class required from 40 to 75 minutes to complete the test?
  e) If the statistics instructor only allowed one hour and 20 minutes for the exam, what percentage of the class would not have had enough time to complete the exam?

82. The following stem-and-leaf display represents the fuel consumption in miles per gallon for 45 vehicles. The stem represents the tens and unit digit of the mpg data value, while the leaf represents the tenths digit of the mpg value.

```
13 | 8 9
14 | 0 3 5 7
15 | 1 1 4 4 8
16 | 1 2 9
17 | 0 2
18 | 0 1 3
19 | 0 1 4 4 5
20 | 0 5 6 6 8
21 | 1 1 5 5
22 | 0 1 2 2 3
23 | 1 4 7 8
24 | 1 3
25 |
26 |
27 |
28 | 4
```

  a) Write the data values that are being represented by this stem-and-leaf display.
  b) Is there a data value that falls outside the range of all the other data values? If so, what is that value? What is such a value called?
  c) Construct a frequency distribution table using four classes for the data values in the stem-and-leaf display.
  d) Compare the frequency distribution table to the stem-and-leaf display. In particular, what information

is contained in the stem-and-leaf display that is not contained in the frequency distribution table?

83. A medical researcher surveyed one hundred mothers who recently gave birth. The researcher determined whether the mothers smoked during pregnancy and the babies' birth weights. The birth weights were separated into two groups, smoking mothers and non-smoking mothers. The following data represents the researchers findings.

Smoking Mothers

5 lbs 7 ozs, 6 lbs 6 ozs, 7 lbs 2 ozs, 9 lbs 2 ozs, 7 lbs 3 ozs, 8 lbs 2 ozs, 7 lbs 5 ozs, 6 lbs 2 ozs, 5 lbs 3 ozs, 3 lbs 4 ozs, 5 lbs 3 ozs, 7 lbs 6 ozs, 6 lbs 1 oz, 5 lbs 4 ozs, 5 lbs 2 ozs, 6 lbs 8 ozs, 7 lbs 4 ozs, 7 lbs 2 ozs, 9 lbs 3 ozs, 6 lbs 5 ozs, 7 lbs 7 ozs, 8 lbs 2 ozs, 7 lbs 6 ozs, 3 lbs 1 oz, 5 lbs 12 ozs, 6 lbs 2 ozs, 7 lbs 5 ozs, 6 lbs 5 ozs, 8 lbs 8 ozs, 9 lbs 1 oz, 8 lbs 3 ozs, 7 lbs 8 ozs, 6 lbs 1 oz, 5 lbs 9 ozs, 6 lbs 5 ozs, 6 lbs 6 ozs, 8 lbs 3 ozs, 7 lbs 8 ozs, 6 lbs 6 ozs, 5 lbs 12 ozs, 5 lbs 9 ozs, 6 lbs 9 ozs, 6 lbs 8 ozs, 5 lbs 2 ozs, 7 lbs 4 ozs, 6 lbs 9 ozs, 7 lbs 5 ozs, 7 lbs 0 ozs, 8 lbs 0 ozs, 8 lbs 0 ozs

Non-smoking Mothers

8 lbs 2 ozs, 7 lbs 1 oz, 6 lbs 6 ozs, 5 lbs 9 ozs, 9 lbs 4 ozs, 7 lbs 0 ozs, 8 lbs 5 ozs, 6 lbs 9 ozs, 5 lbs 13 ozs, 8 lbs 4 ozs, 7 lbs 6 ozs, 6 lbs 6 ozs, 5 lbs 11 ozs, 9 lbs 0 ozs, 8 lbs 9 ozs, 7 lbs 1 oz, 6 lbs 8 ozs, 7 lbs 9 ozs, 9 lbs 3 ozs, 8 lbs 8 ozs, 6 lbs 6 ozs, 7 lbs 3 ozs, 7 lbs 14 ozs, 8 lbs 1 oz, 7 lbs 5 ozs, 6 lbs 5 ozs, 7 lbs 6 ozs, 6 lbs 12 ozs, 7 lbs 8 ozs, 7 lbs 9 ozs, 9 lbs 3 ozs, 8 lbs 4 ozs, 7 lbs 11 ozs, 6 lbs 14 ozs, 5 lbs 11 ozs, 8 lbs 6 ozs, 5 lbs 15 ozs, 6 lbs 10 ozs, 7 lbs 3 ozs, 9 lbs 8 ozs, 7 lbs 15 ozs, 7 lbs 2 ozs, 6 lbs 14 ozs, 7 lbs 12 ozs, 7 lbs 10 ozs, 6 lbs 8 ozs, 6 lbs 14 ozs, 11 lbs 2 ozs, 10 lbs 1 oz, 10 lbs 5 ozs,

a) Construct a back-to-back stem-and-leaf display for the birth weights of the babies for the smoking and non-smoking mothers using lbs for the stem portion.
b) Describe the shape of each distribution of birth weights for smoking and non-smoking mothers.
c) Does it appear from the stem-and-leaf display that smoking may have an effect on the birth weight of a newborn? Support your conclusion.

84. The test scores on a statistics exam ranged from 44 to 94. Determine the class limits, class marks, and class boundaries of a frequency distribution if these test scores were grouped using:
a) 8 classes
b) 7 classes
c) How many classes should you use if you want the class marks to be a whole number?

85. A frequency distribution table representing the number of live births to U.S. mothers for the past year was grouped according to the following classes: 15–19 years, 20–24 years, 25–29 years, 30–34 years, 35–39 years, 40–44 years, and 45–49 years. Using this information, is it possible to determine the exact number of live births to U.S. mothers having an age:
a) 25 years or older?

b) More than 25 years?
c) More than 24 years?
d) Exactly 25 years?
e) At least 24 years?

86. The following data set represents the IQ Scores of 120 high school students.

145, 126, 118, 95, 110, 150, 108, 128, 107, 123, 100, 113, 109, 130, 98, 118, 110, 121, 105, 109, 136, 123, 112, 117, 113, 92, 118, 104, 117, 97, 127, 108, 122, 105, 117, 121, 109, 138, 125, 118, 99, 97, 149, 92, 113, 100, 109, 117, 113, 116, 116, 98, 125, 123, 124, 129, 94, 148, 144, 127, 119, 101, 127, 95, 107, 112, 121, 125, 113, 99, 120, 122, 123, 127, 128, 117, 114, 129, 95, 113, 145, 112, 122, 106, 119, 93, 132, 122, 110, 117, 98, 121, 110, 97, 121, 131, 109, 145, 103, 135, 98, 142, 127, 116, 111, 104, 112, 116, 125, 109, 134, 110, 107, 97, 101, 131, 96, 113, 107, 115

a) Construct a frequency distribution table using 10 classes. Within the table include classes, class marks, class boundaries, relative frequencies and percentages.
b) Find the sum of the relative frequencies and percentages.
c) Using this table, determine the percentage of students that have an IQ Score which is:
1) less than 116
2) between 128 to 133 inclusive
3) greater than 121
4) at most 109
5) at least 134

87. Fifty people were given a blind taste test to determine their preference for the soft drink colas Sipeps and Coaks. Their responses to the taste test were classified as: S for Sipeps, C for Coaks, and N for Neither. The responses to the taste test were:

S, S, C, S, C, N, N, C, S, C, C, N, C, S, C, C, C,
C, S, S, S, S, C, C, S, N, S, C, C, S, S, S, C, C, S,
N, C, S, N, C, S, C, S, C, S, C, S, C, C, S, C

a) Construct a frequency distribution table representing the responses to the taste test.
b) Calculate the relative frequencies and relative percents for each of the responses.

88. After the holiday season, 748 people were polled about when they finished their holiday shopping. The results of the poll were as follows:

Finished Shopping By:	Number of Shoppers
November 30	45
December 15	389
December 23	127
December 25	187

a) Determine the percentage of shoppers corresponding to each date.
b) By what date are the majority of the shoppers finished shopping?

c) What percent of the shoppers finish by December 23?

d) What percent of the shoppers are NOT finished by December 23?

89. Pollution indices for a city in the northeast for 100 consecutive days are given in the following table.

59 54 63 60 69 66 42 47 48 41
43 33 48 52 41 48 44 42 40 47
62 70 54 83 69 57 46 58 52 54
58 54 67 49 61 62 54 57 30 44
33 41 52 43 47 54 59 62 68 66
60 57 57 61 58 59 54 48 39 61
60 53 50 44 58 46 57 63 69 72
42 70 54 77 81 84 33 37 44 52
41 43 37 70 72 59 54 61 50 73
61 73 74 72 67 58 49 82 79 68

Construct:
a) A frequency distribution table using seven classes; include class marks and class boundaries within the table.
b) A histogram.
c) A frequency polygon.

90. A bank executive compared the length of time required to service the customers using the auto teller to the customers using the regular banking service. To obtain information on these two distributions, two samples of fifty service times were recorded to the nearest second.

Auto Teller Service
(time measured to the nearest second)
195, 123, 126, 178, 168, 132, 180, 204, 228, 216, 276, 228, 138, 286, 150, 192, 156, 186, 268, 222, 204, 132, 198, 208, 204, 258, 228, 428, 274, 162, 156, 288, 270, 186, 144, 192, 144, 350, 378, 207, 195, 193, 170, 181, 276, 265, 306, 282, 194, 197

Regular Banking Service
(time measured to the nearest second)
173, 309, 264, 310, 174, 428, 317, 246, 204, 262, 426, 306, 234, 298, 161, 156, 175, 168, 198, 179, 210, 228, 240, 174, 312, 288, 360, 216, 210, 282, 252, 322, 246, 366, 252, 192, 186, 246, 304, 234, 216, 228, 252, 378, 198, 216, 348, 123, 310, 318

a) Construct a "less than" cumulative frequency distribution table for both samples using 8 classes.
b) Determine what percentages of the service times for the customers using the auto teller are less than or equal to 4 minutes.
c) Determine what percentages of the service times for the customers using the regular banking service have times less than or equal to 4 minutes.
d) Compare the waiting times of both services using the distribution tables.

e) Construct a "less than" ogive for the waiting times of both services.

91. A survey conducted by Court TV during the O.J. Simpson Trial determined the income of viewers who watch Court TV. The following distribution represents the income of some of the surveyed viewers to the nearest thousands of dollars.

Income
(in thousands of dollars)
19, 33, 49, 65, 43, 73, 62, 50, 37, 25, 44, 55, 70, 65, 54, 35, 40, 57, 61, 70, 56, 68, 38, 42, 55, 69, 72, 58, 36, 24, 70, 41, 64, 28, 60, 33, 63, 54, 20, 66, 32, 27, 49, 62, 42, 22, 37, 52, 67, 15

a) Identify the variable and type of variable.
b) Construct a frequency distribution table using 4 classes. Include within the table: classes, frequencies, class boundaries, class marks, and relative percentages.
c) Construct a "Less Than" cumulative frequency distribution using the frequency distribution table in part (b).
d) What percent of the viewers earned less than $60,000?
e) What percent of the viewers earned $30,000 or more?
f) Is it possible to determine from the distribution table what percent of the viewers earned less than $53,000? Explain.
g) What information is lost when you group data into a frequency distribution table? Is the same information lost when constructing a stem-and-leaf display? Explain.

92. The following data set represents the ages of 110 runners who competed in a city marathon.

44, 23, 19, 51, 22, 69, 31, 30, 41, 21, 52, 27, 20, 32, 23, 71, 37, 60, 29, 54, 27, 31, 23, 27, 44, 29, 58, 43, 49, 38, 60, 32, 34, 50, 28, 18, 29, 54, 41, 22, 37, 36, 37, 35, 33, 37, 20, 26, 22, 27, 31, 29, 41, 43, 67, 55, 35, 29, 48, 19, 25, 69, 60, 43, 26, 33, 24, 22, 35, 34, 18, 28, 65, 58, 21, 60, 59, 45, 27, 26, 42, 34, 52, 61, 56, 72, 19, 29, 19, 28, 44, 56, 29, 43, 50, 49, 19, 22, 23, 27, 30, 58, 64, 59, 24, 55, 48, 18, 40, 21

a) Construct a stem-and-leaf display.
b) Construct a frequency distribution table using 8 classes. Within the table include class marks, class boundaries, and relative percentages.
c) Construct a histogram and frequency polygon for the distribution.
d) Describe the shape of the polygon and classify the shape as either symmetric bell-shaped, skewed right, or skewed left.

93. The following table contains 150 test scores representing the results of an IQ test that was administered to the third graders at an elementary school in Merrick, New York.

Classes (IQ Scores)	Boys Frequency	Girls Frequency
60–79	8	2
80–99	27	35
100–119	23	15
120–139	10	25
140–159	2	3

a) Construct a relative frequency percentage distribution table for:
  1) the IQ scores of the third grade boys.
  2) the IQ scores of the third grade girls.
  3) all IQ scores of the third graders at the school.
Using the relative frequency percentage distribution tables of part a:

b) Construct a histogram for:
  1) the IQ scores of the third grade boys.
  2) the IQ scores of the third grade girls.
  3) all IQ scores of the third graders at the school.

c) Calculate the following:
  1) the percent of girls that have an IQ of at least 100.
  2) the percent of boys that have an IQ of at least 100.
  3) the percent of third graders that have an IQ of at least 100.
  4) the percent of third graders that have an IQ between 80 and 159 (inclusive).
  5) the percent of third graders that have an IQ of less than 80.

94. The following blood pressures are for men and women within the age group 19–25 years.

a) Construct a back-to-back stem-and-leaf display for these blood pressures.

b) Construct a "less than" cumulative frequency distribution table for both the men and women blood pressure readings using 5 classes.

c) Determine the percentage of men who have blood pressures between 104 and 136 inclusive.

d) Determine the percentage of women who have blood pressures between 104 and 136 inclusive.

e) Construct an ogive for the blood pressure readings for both men and women.

Men Blood Pressures
146, 130, 115, 120, 104, 143, 120, 146, 116, 118, 130, 130, 145, 132, 118, 136, 104, 126, 156, 145, 150, 110, 130, 126, 106, 112, 120, 130, 136, 134, 156, 120, 110, 150, 105, 130, 124, 128, 130, 122, 142, 130, 106, 110, 112, 120, 126, 126, 112, 110, 120, 120, 120, 120, 130, 110, 106, 112, 134, 110, 120, 120, 128, 120, 140, 118, 120, 130, 114, 118, 120, 116, 120, 106, 118

Women Blood Pressures
134, 124, 108, 112, 126, 114, 118, 114, 110, 112, 122, 128, 135, 118, 110, 110, 105, 106, 122, 129, 105, 110, 110, 134, 130, 140, 116, 110, 112, 110, 110, 116, 114, 110, 107, 130, 139, 126, 138, 120, 118, 116, 118, 112, 104, 116, 104, 114, 124, 156, 120, 118, 120, 128, 116, 126, 128, 112, 128, 108, 108, 130, 116, 118, 122, 126, 128, 120, 119, 130, 125, 120, 126, 112, 138

95. The following table gives the number of deaths per 100,000 contributed to coronaries and cardiovascular diseases by age group for men and women.

At High Risk
(percentage of adults with serum cholesterol of 240 mg/dl or more)

Age	Men	Women
20-24	6.2%	6.6%
25-34	15.3	11.8
35-44	27.9	20.7
45-54	36.9	40.5
55-64	36.8	52.9
65-74	31.7	51.6

Source: National Center for Health Studies

a) Determine the class width for each class.
b) Find the class mark and class boundaries for each class. Determine the relative percentages for the males and females for each class.
c) Find the sum of the relative percents for the males and females.
d) Construct two frequency polygons one representing the males and one representing the females. Compare the two polygons and comment about the differences between the two groups.

96. A national park foundation allocates funds to individual parks according to park size. In preparing a report, an official must summarize the information regarding park size. He prepares the frequency table that follows:

Park Size in Acres	Number of Parks
1–9	17
10–49	34
50–99	52
100–199	47
200–499	32
500–749	25
750–999	68

Using the frequency table:
a) Construct a "less than" cumulative frequency distribution table.
b) Use this distribution table to construct an ogive.
c) Represent the cumulative frequency values as relative frequency percentages.
d) What percentage of parks are:
  1) less than 10 acres?
  2) less than 100 acres?
  3) less than 750 acres?

e) Within what range of acres does the middle 50% of the distribution fall?

97. A business magazine randomly surveyed 210 business owners to determine the age at which they first began their own business. The following distribution represents the survey results:

Age	Frequency
18–22	27
23–27	54
28–32	55
33–37	31
38–42	21
43–47	10
48–52	7
53–57	3
58–62	2

a) Find the class mark, class boundaries, and relative frequencies for each class.
b) Construct a frequency polygon and describe the shape of the distribution.
c) Construct a "less than" cumulative frequency distribution.
d) Construct a "more than" cumulative frequency distribution.
e) Construct an ogive for the "less than" cumulative frequency distribution.
f) What percentage of the business owners started their first business when they were younger than 33 years old?
g) What percentage of the owners started their first business when they were 43 years or older?
h) What percentage of the business owners started their first business when they were 23 to 32 years old?

98. Using the data given in the following table, construct a horizontal bar graph.

Where the Millionaires Live

State	Number of Millionaires
New York	56,096
California	38,691
Illinois	35,545
Ohio	31,202
Florida	29,523
New Jersey	28,613
Indiana	24,880
Idaho	24,738
Minnesota	23,381
Texas	23,002

99. The following data was compiled by an Education Commission regarding the question:

In different countries, how long do kids go to school each year?

The average number of days per year for the listed countries were as follows:

Country	Average Number of School Days
England	192
France	185
Netherlands	200
Israel	216
Japan	243
Germany	210
Thailand	200
USA	180
Sweden	180

Arrange the data from highest to lowest and construct a horizontal bar graph.

100. At the High Roller High School in Kings Park, California, all seniors are required to take the Scholastic Aptitude Test (SAT). The following table summarizes last year's test scores.

Classes (SAT Scores)	Verbal		Mathematics	
	# of Males	# of Females	# of Males	# of Females
200–299	15	10	10	25
300–399	45	30	30	55
400–499	35	30	30	35
500–599	45	60	55	45
600–699	10	15	15	10
700–799	25	50	35	25

a) Construct a relative frequency percentage distribution table representing the:
  1) males
  2) females
Using the classes within the table:
b) Construct a histogram for the verbal SAT scores representing the:
  1) males
  2) females
c) Construct a histogram for the mathematics SAT scores representing the:
  1) males
  2) females
d) Construct frequency polygons comparing the:
  1) verbal SAT scores representing the males to the verbal SAT scores representing the females.
  2) mathematics SAT scores representing the males to the mathematics SAT scores representing the females.
e) Calculate the percent of:
  1) females that have a verbal SAT score of at least 400.
  2) males that have a verbal SAT score of at least 400.
  3) females that have a mathematics SAT score of at least 600.
  4) males that have a mathematics SAT score of at least 600.

101. Central General Hospital in Phoenix has the following data representing weight in pounds at birth for 500 premature babies:

Class	Frequency
0.5–0.9	26
1.0–1.4	48
1.5–1.9	60
2.0–2.4	66
2.5–2.9	73
3.0–3.4	85
3.5–3.9	100
4.0–4.4	42

a) Construct a "less than" cumulative frequency table.

b) Use the "less than" cumulative frequency table constructed in part (a) to construct an ogive.

c) If babies that weigh less than 3.0 pounds need incubators, then what percentage of the premature babies will need incubators?

102. Construct two horizontal bar graphs to represent the results of a poll conducted by the American Communications Group of 1,000 households to determine **how often people watch movies**. The following frequency distribution table represents the results of the poll.

How Often People Watch Movies	Percentage of People Who Watch Movies	
	At Home	**At Theater**
Less Than Once a Month	13%	46%
Once a Month	12%	24%
Twice or More a Month	75%	30%

103. The Department of Education surveyed seventeen year-old students pertaining to the amount of time the students spend doing homework. The results of their survey are given in the following table.

Number of Hours Spent Doing Homework	Number of students
Less than 1 hour	196
1 to 2 hours	182
More than 2 hours	84
None assigned	147
Didn't do it	91

a) Using the table information, convert the number of students to a percentage and construct a horizontal bar graph.

b) What percentage of the students spend at least one hour doing homework?

c) What percentage of the students spend at most two hours doing homework?

104. The following bar graph shows the percentage of injuries for different levels of football. Using this information, construct a frequency distribution table to display the number of injuries per level of football for the sample of 400.

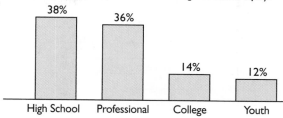

Statistical Snapshot

Sports Injuries

Level of football considered to have the highest risk of injury:

Total number of injuries reported is 400.

105. A writing sample (composition) was submitted by each of 50 students applying for admission to Wrighter's College. Each composition was rated by 3 readers and a composite grade was assigned. The following graph represents the 50 grades.

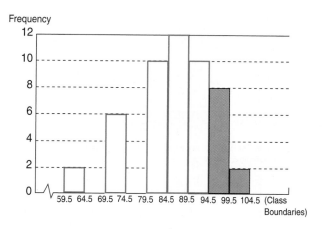

a) How many compositions were rated between 90 and 100?

b) What percent of students scored between 80 and 85?

c) What percent of the total area is in the shaded section?

d) What percent of the students scored between 90 and 100?

e) What percent of the total area is contained under the graph in the 7th and 8th intervals combined?

f) Did anyone receive a perfect grade of 100?

g) What percent of the total area is contained under the graph in the last interval?

106. Each of the following tables or graphs has a newspaper heading. Using this heading as your main theme, write a paragraph that supports this theme using the information contained in the table or graph.

Statistical Snapshot

(a)

Who Cheats More at College

INTENDED CAREER	CHEATED ONCE	REGULARS
Business	76%	19%
Engineering	71%	12%
Medicine	68%	11%
Public Service/Government	66%	10%
Arts	64%	14%
Law	63%	12%
Education	57%	8%

Source: Donald McCabe, Rutgers University
Reprinted by permission of *Fortune*.

Statistical Snapshot

(d)

Education Pays Dividends

Estimated lifetime earnings for those who have:

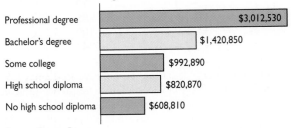

Source: Census Bureau

107. Examine each of the following snapshots.

Statistical Snapshot

(b)

Red-light Runners

A national survey found that 56% of all drivers admitted they run red lights. Percentage admitting to running red lights, by age groups:

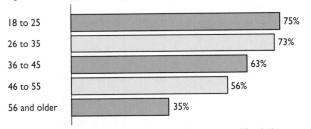

Source: The Social Science Research Center, Department of Psychology, Old Dominion University

Statistical Snapshot

(a)

Middle Age at the Top

Percentages of top executives (CEOs, partners, owners, presidents, chairmen, principals) in these age groups:

Source: Dun & Bradstreet

Statistical Snapshot

(c)

Surviving Bad Days at Work

Most common ways men and women say they cope with bad workdays:

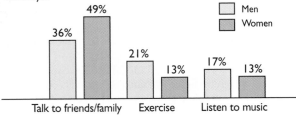

Source: CJ Olson Market Research for Windsor Canadian Supreme

Statistical Snapshot

(b)

Cable Calling

Estimated percentage of homes that will get phone service via cable:

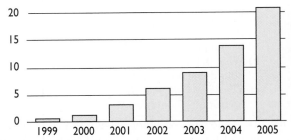

Source: Forrester Research
Reprinted by permission of Tribune Media Services.

For each snapshot:
a) Identify the variables being displayed. Are they continuous or discrete?
b) State the type of graph that is used. For example, is it a histogram, a vertical bar graph or a time-series graph? If it is a histogram, identify the classes. If it is a time-series graph, identify the way time is displayed within the graphic.

c) Discuss the shape of each graphic and how its shape can be used to draw an inference or conclusion from the graphic.
d) If an outlier were to exist within the distribution, then where would you expect the outlier to fall? Explain.

WHAT DO YOU THINK?

108. During the first month of the 1995 baseball season after the strike of the 1994 season, attendance and TV ratings were down compared to the first month of the previous seasons. According to a CNN/Gallup poll, sport fans were asked the question: "What's your favorite sport?". The results were presented within the graphic entitled "Fan Favorites" shown in the following figure.

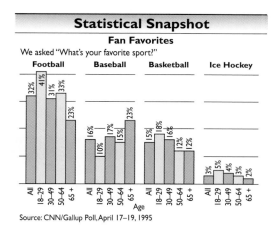

Source: CNN/Gallup Poll, April 17–19, 1995

a) Baseball has been referred to as "America's Pastime." According to this poll, do you agree with this statement? Explain.
b) How could you defend the statement that baseball used to be America's pastime using the results of this poll? Explain.
c) Which sport do you believe has been losing popularity over the years? How could you defend your answer using the results of this poll?
d) Which sport do you believe has been gaining the most popularity over the years? How could you defend your answer using the results of this poll?
e) Examine the football graph and explain how you can have a greater percentage of sport fans aged 18–29 than the sport fans pertaining to the All category.
f) Describe the shape of each graph for the respective sport.

If 1500 fans were surveyed, then:
g) How many sport fans overall selected hockey as their favorite sport? baseball? football? basketball? Why doesn't this account for all the fans surveyed? Explain.
h) Can you determine whether there were **more, less or the same number of fans** aged 65 or older who selected football over baseball as their favorite sport? Explain.
i) Can you determine whether there were **more, less or the same number of fans** aged 18–29 who selected basketball over the fans aged 30–49 who selected baseball as their favorite sport? Explain.

109. The following two graphs represent average number of cars hourly traveling on the Long Island Expressway (LIE) from the Queens County line and Lakeville Road in Lake Success, LI during March, 1975 and June, 1994.

Source: New York State Department of Transportation
Reprinted by permission of Tribune Media Services.

a) During what 1 hour period in March, 1975, did the LIE have the greatest number of cars traveling westbound? eastbound? In June, 1994 when did the LIE have the greatest number of cars traveling westbound? eastbound?

b) During what 1 hour period in March, 1975, did the LIE have the greatest total number of cars traveling in both directions? During what 1 hour period in June, 1994 did this occur?

c) Generally, people try to avoid traveling on the LIE during rush hour while preferring the off peak hours. In March, 1975 what 2 hour period would you identify as "rush hours" for westbound traffic? eastbound traffic?

d) In March, 1975 what hours would you consider to be off-peak hours? Would you consider these same hours in June, 1994 to also be off-peak hours? Explain.

e) In March, 1975 would you consider the greatest number of cars on the LIE to be traveling eastbound or westbound?

f) In March, 1975 the traditional traffic model was that people would drive westbound in the morning and drive eastbound in the afternoon. Does this model still hold for June, 1994? Explain.

g) Determine the percent of increase in traffic during 1 to 2 PM from March, 1975 to June, 1994. during 10 AM to 8 PM from March, 1975 to June, 1994.

h) During what 1 hour period did the greatest percentage increase in traffic occur from March, 1975 to June, 1994?

i) During what 1 hour period was the greatest number of cars traveling on the LIE in March, 1975? Compare this number to the same time period in June,

1994. Was there an increase or a decrease? Determine the percentage change.

j) During what 1 hour period was the greatest number of cars traveling on the LIE in June, 1994? Compare this number to the same time period in March, 1975? Was there an increase or a decrease? Determine the percentage change.

k) Over the past years, there has been a change in lifestyles and employment patterns such as people are dropping off and picking up their children from child care centers before and after work, people working different shifts, and service people working different hours. Explain how these changes and other possible changes have had an effect on the traffic on the LIE. Use the two graphics to support your views.

l) A commuter who travels on the LIE has the following philosophy: "If I have an 8 am meeting and traveling eastbound, then I leave at 6 am. If I have to travel eastbound from the city before 2:30 pm, then I will leave by 12:30 pm. However, if I can't leave by 12:30 pm, then I have dinner in the city and leave at 8 pm." Does this commuter's philosophy make any sense? Use the June, 1994 graph to support your answer.

m) If you had to travel at least fifty minutes westbound on the LIE to work and your job started at 9 am, what would be your philosophy? Support your answer using the June, 1994 graph.

PROJECTS

110. Inspect recent issues of your local tabloids and/or business magazines.

Find *one* of each of the following:
a) A frequency distribution table
b) A bar graph
c) A histogram
d) A frequency polygon
e) A pie chart
f) A pictograph
For each example determine:
a) The variables and the variable values
b) The type of data (categorical, discrete or continuous)
c) Comment as to whether or not you believe the example has been depicted appropriately.

111. Survey one hundred students and record for each student the responses to the following questions:

Ques #1: How many hours of television do you watch each week?

Ques #2: Is a Cable TV service installed in your home?

a) Construct a stem-and-leaf display for the student responses to Ques #1.
 1) Describe the shape of the display.
 2) Are there outlier's present? If so, try to explain why the outlier(s) occurred.
b) Construct a back-to-back stem-and-leaf display for the responses to Ques #1 comparing those students that have Cable TV service to those students that do not have Cable TV service.
c) Describe the differences (if any) of each category represented in the back-to-back stem-and-leaf display.
d) Construct a "less than" cumulative frequency table for the responses to Ques #1.
e) Construct an ogive for the information in part d.
f) Formulate three observations using the ogive.

ANALYZING THE DATABASE USING TECHNOLOGY.

The following exercises refer to the file DATABASE listed in Appendix A. Using a technological tool, answer each exercise.

112. Construct a Stem-and-Leaf display for the variables:
  a) AGE   **b)** AVE
  c) WRK   **d)** STY
  Describe the general shape of each of the distributions using the terms developed in Section 2.7.

113. Construct a Histogram for the variables:
  a) GPA using increments of 0.5 by MAJ.
  b) Which majors have the highest GPAs?
  c) Which majors have the lowest GPAs?

114. Construct a Frequency Polygon for the variables:
  a) AGE
  b) AGE using increments of 5
  c) AGE by SEX using increments of 5 on the same set of axes.
  How do the shapes of the graphs differ? Compare the shapes of the graphs for males verses females.

115. Construct a Pie Chart using the variables:
  a) LK   **b)** HND
  c) AST   **d)** MAJ
  For each of these variables, construct a Pie Chart by the variable SEX.

CHAPTER TEST

116. Explain what variable and the value of a variable mean.

117. State the difference between a continuous and discrete data value. Give an example of each.

118. State the difference between a categorical and numerical variable. Give an example of each.

119. Classify the following data as either categorical or numerical. If the data is numerical, then classify it as either continuous or discrete data.
  a) A person's weight.
  b) A person's eye color.
  c) The annual income of a family.
  d) The volume of water in a reservoir.
  e) An individual's IQ.
  f) A person's opinion on the type of job Congress is doing.

120. The following table represents a sample of data collected on college students. Each column abbreviation represents the following information:
  sex: student's sex
  status: fr = freshman, sp = sophomore, jr = junior, sr = senior
  age: student's age
  ht: student's height in inches
  wt: student's weight in lbs
  frat: fraternity or sorority membership: N = No or Y = Yes
  havg: high school average
  gpa: grade point average

Student #	Sex	Status	Age	Ht	Wt	Frat	Havg	GPA
4233	f	jr	19	61	135	Y	81	2.79
7679	m	sr	24	70	165	Y	95	3.37
6203	m	sp	19	75	195	Y	91	2.94
5924	f	jr	21	60	124	Y	87	3.12

  a) Identify each variable and type of variable within the data set.

  b) For the student identified by the number 6203, specify the value of each of the variables.

121. Exploratory Data Analysis is used to learn as much as possible about data before conducting statistical tests.
  (T/F)

122. The difference between two successive class marks is equal to the class _____.

123. The sum of all the relative frequencies of all the classes will always be _____, except for possible round-off error.

124. A survey on the number of hours a college student works per week showed that the hours varied from 1 to 40. Determine the class limits, class marks, and class boundaries of a frequency distribution table if the work hours were grouped using 6 classes.

125. Bar graphs are usually used to represent categorical variables.
  (T/F)

126. Histograms are usually used to represent continuous variables.
  (T/F)

127. According to an Opinion Research Corporation survey, the average U.S. shower is 12.2 minutes with men staying in the shower 11.4 minutes on average and women having a longer average time of 13 minutes. Using the following information, construct:
  a) A stem-and-leaf display for the all times.
  b) Describe the shape of the distribution.
  c) A back-to-back stem-and-leaf display for the male and female times.
  d) Describe the shape of each distribution.
  e) Compare these distributions.
  f) Are there any outliers? If so, can you give a possible explanation for the outlier.

Shower times in minutes
(with the sex given in parentheses)

8(F), 14(F), 1(M), 5(M), 4(M), 12(F), 13(F), 12(F),
17(F), 12(F), 6(M), 5(M), 3(M), 11(F), 4(M), 16(F),
5(M), 8(F), 15(F), 12(F), 7(M), 9(M), 9(M), 9(M),
11(F), 17(F), 11(F), 10(M), 15(M), 10(F), 15(M), 13(F),
13(F), 10(F), 12(M), 15(M), 10(F), 18(M), 9(M), 16(M),
17(M), 20(M), 23(M), 18(M), 30(M), 21(F), 23(F)

128. The following distribution represents the IQ scores of 120 high school students.

Classes (IQ Score)	Frequency
81–90	2
91–100	13
101–110	44
111–120	40
121–130	17
131–140	4

Determine, if possible, the number and percent of the students who have IQ scores that are:
a) Less than 101.
b) At most 110.
c) 111 or less.
d) Exactly 121.
e) Between 101 to 120 inclusive.
f) At least 121.

129. According to the latest Census Bureau figures, the following table has been compiled for the given ages of women who have never been married.

Ages	Number of Never Married Women
20–24	5,940,000
25–29	3,356,000
30–34	2,122,000
35–39	1,334,000
40–44	795,000
45–54	744,000
55–64	445,000

Using the table information,
a) Identify the variable and type of variable.
b) Determine the class width.
c) Construct another table containing class boundaries, class marks and relative percentages.
d) Construct a histogram.
e) Construct a frequency polygon.
f) Describe the shape of the frequency polygon.

130. According to the latest Census Bureau figures, the following table represents the estimated lifetime earnings for those people with the stated amount of education. Using this information, construct a horizontal bar graph.

Estimated Lifetime Earnings For Those Who Have:	
Education Level	**Lifetime Earnings**
PROFESSIONAL DEGREE	$3,012,530
BACHELOR'S DEGREE	$1,420,850
SOME COLLEGE	$992,890
HIGH SCHOOL DIPLOMA	$820,870
NO HIGH SCHOOL DIPLOMA	$608,810

131. The test scores on a statistics exam ranged from 44 to 94. Determine the class limits, class marks, and class boundaries of a frequency distribution if these test scores were grouped using:
a) 9 classes
b) 10 classes
c) How many classes should you use if you want the class marks to be a whole number?

132. Given the following distribution of statistics test grades: 73, 92, 57, 89, 70, 95, 75, 80, 47, 88, 47, 48, 64, 86, 79, 72, 71, 77, 93, 55, 75, 50, 53, 75, 85, 50, 82, 45, 40, 82, 60, 55, 60, 89, 79, 65, 54, 93, 60, 83, 59
a) Construct a stem-and-leaf display.
b) Describe the shape of the distribution.
c) Construct a frequency distribution table and a histogram using six classes.
Using the histogram, answer the following questions:
d) How many test grades are greater than 89?
e) What percent of the test grades are greater than 79?
f) What percent of the test grades are lower than 70?
g) What percent of the test grades are between 70 and 79 (inclusive)?

133. The following frequency distribution table represents information collected by a local service station owner on the number of gallons of gasoline, recorded to the nearest gallon, purchased per customer.

Gallons of Gasoline	Frequency
5–7	17
8–10	33
11–13	42
14–16	88
17–19	61
20–22	38
23–25	21

a) What is the class width of each class?
b) Determine the class mark, class boundaries, and relative percents for each class.
c) Construct a "less than" cumulative frequency distribution table and an ogive for this "less than" cumulative frequency distribution table.
d) How many customers purchased less than 11 gallons of gasoline? What percent of the customers does this represent?
e) What percent of the customers purchased less than 17 gallons of gasoline?

f) How many customers purchased from 11 to 19 gallons? What percent of the customers does this represent?

134. The student government recently surveyed 300 students over a period of five consecutive registration days as to how long it takes students to register for next semester's classes. The following table represents the registration time for the surveyed students:

Number of Minutes to Register for Class	Number of Students
1–15	20
16–30	45
31–45	90
46–60	110
61–75	30
76–90	5

a) For the given frequency table, add the class boundaries and construct a histogram.
b) Construct a "less than" cumulative frequency table and an ogive.
c) From the ogive, determine how long 75% of the students would take to register?

135. A national survey found that the distribution of all drivers that admit to running a red light is skewed right. If the survey results grouped the driver's ages as: 18–25, 26–33, 34–41, 42–49, 50–57 and 58 and older, then:

a) There were a greater percentage of drivers aged 50–57 who ran a red light than those aged 26–33.
b) The age group 18–25 contained the smallest percentage of drivers that ran a red light.
c) As the age of a driver increased, the percentage of the drivers who ran a red light also increased.
d) Younger drivers ran a red light more frequently.

136. Examine each of the following snapshots.

Statistical Snapshot

Cellular Phones Hot With Teens

The USA's 28.5 million teens—consumers who spend about $100 billion a year—are a prime cellular phone market. Age of buyers of cellular phones in the past year:

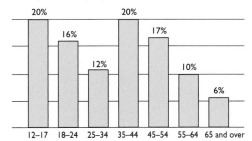

Note: Adds up to 101% due to rounding
Source: Interep Radio Store

Statistical Snapshot

Population Age 85 Plus (in millions)

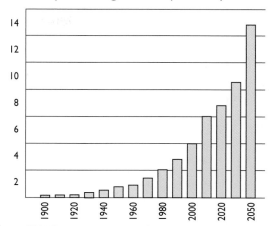

Source: 1995 "65+ in the United States," U.S. Bureau of the Census. Special Studies, p23–190. April, 1996.

For each snapshot:

a) Identify the variables being displayed. Are they continuous or discrete?
b) State the type of graph that is used. For example, is it a histogram, a vertical bar graph or a time-series graph? If it is a histogram, identify the classes. If it is a time-series graph, identify the way time is displayed within the graphic.
c) Discuss the shape of each graphic and how its shape can be used to draw an inference or conclusion from the graphic.
d) If an outlier were to exist within the distribution, then where would you expect the outlier to fall? Explain.

Numerical Techniques for Describing Data

Contents

3.6 Using Technology
MINITAB Descriptive Statistics: SALARIES
EXCEL Descriptive Statistics
MINITAB Box Plot of 1999 MLB SALARIES
EXCEL Box Plot of 1999 MLB SALARIES
Graphing Calculator Display

In Chapter 2 we discussed descriptive methods for organizing and summarizing data into tables and presenting data graphically. This chapter examines *numerical descriptive methods* and techniques to compute a number that describes the main characteristics of a data set. These numerical techniques will allow us to describe the center and the spread of a data set, and the relative position of a specific data value within the data set.

3.1 MEASURES OF CENTRAL TENDENCY

Are you an *average* American?"
    If you are, you . . .

> . . . would be a 29-year old hermaphrodite (slightly more female than male) who stands about 5'4', weighs about 150 pounds, earns close to $17,000 a year, and eats a hamburger three times a week. He (she? it?) has 1.4 children and watches television about 2.5 hours a day.[1]

The previous statement supposedly describes an "average" or a "typical" person for the population of American people. In this section, we will be discussing statistical methods used to depict a **typical or representative value** for all the data values within a distribution. The methods used in determining the average or typical value are trying to give some idea about where the **center** of all of the data values lie. Let's examine this concept using the following quote from a recent baseball negotiation.

> After five years as a professional, a player would become a free agent if earning less than the "average" salary. (Owners estimate this at $1,121,000; the players at $1,118,000).

This proposal was one of the principal issues in the negotiations between the baseball club owners and the Major League Players Association. In the previous quote, both groups are trying to describe the "typical" or "representative" salary. However, one might ask why there is a discrepancy of $3,000 between the owners' and players' estimate of the **average** or typical salary if both groups are using the same data. To most people the word "average" has just one meaning. However, in statistics, there are different ways of computing the *average or typical data value* of a distribution. We will examine three such ways. They are the **mean**, the **median**, and the **mode**. These measures are referred to as **Measures of Central Tendency**.

Measures of central tendency are important tools of descriptive statistics because each measure, in its own way, enables a statistician to describe with a single number, the center or typical value of all the data values. However, using a single number to represent an **average** or a **typical data value** may not adequately describe **all the data values** within the distribution. The intent of an average is only to depict where the central or typical data value lies. "How is a typical data value determined?" Should we use the *average value, the middle value* or *the common value* to represent the typical data value? This section presents techniques to compute each of these different measures of central tendencies, examines what each of these measures really describes, and discusses their advantages and disadvantages.

The Mean

The first measure of central tendency that we will discuss is the **mean**. The mean is the most common and useful measure of central tendency and is usually referred to as the **"average."**

---

[1] This appeared in *The Average American*, by Barry Tarshis.

DEFINITION 3.1

The **mean** is the number obtained by summing up all the data values and dividing this sum by the total number of data values.

$$\text{Mean} = \frac{\text{sum of all the data values}}{\text{total number of data values}}$$

The notation used for the mean depends upon whether the data values represent a sample or a population. As mentioned in Section 1.1, it is often impractical or impossible to obtain all the data values of a population. In such instances, a sample is selected from the population and the mean of the sample is calculated. The sample mean is used to estimate the mean of the population. We will now discuss the definition and notation for the mean of a sample.

Sample Mean

In general, the data are represented by $x_1, x_2, x_3, x_4, \ldots , x_n$ where x_1 represents the first data value, x_2 represents the second data value, and x_n represents the last [or nth] data value of the sample. The total number of data values within a sample is called the *sample size* and is represented by the lower case letter n. Using this notation, the sample mean, symbolized by $\bar{x}$ and *read x bar*, can be written as:

Sample Mean Formula

$$\text{sample mean} = \frac{\text{sum of all the sample data values}}{\text{total number of sample data values}}$$

or

$$\bar{x} = \frac{x_1 + x_2 + x_3 + x_4 + \ldots + x_n}{n}$$

In statistics a more concise representation of $x_1 + x_2 + x_3 + x_4 + \ldots + x_n$ is written using the *capital Greek letter Σ (pronounced "sigma") which represents the operation SUM.* Thus, **$x_1 + x_2 + x_3 + x_4 + \ldots + x_n$ can be represented by Σx or "sum of all the data values."** Thus, the formula for the sample mean can now be written as:

$$\bar{x} = \frac{\Sigma x}{n}$$

DEFINITION 3.2

The **mean of a sample** is determined by summing up all the data values of the sample and dividing this sum by the total number of data values.

The symbol for the sample mean is $\bar{x}$ and the formula to calculate the sample mean is:

$$\bar{x} = \frac{\Sigma x}{n}$$

The **sample mean** can be used as an estimate of the mean of a population.

EXAMPLE 3.1

Let $x_1 = 12, x_2 = 25, x_3 = 21$ and $x_4 = 8$. Calculate the sample mean, $\bar{x}$.

Solution

1. Calculate Σx, the sum of all the data values.
    $\Sigma x = x_1 + x_2 + x_3 + x_4 = 12 + 25 + 21 + 8$
    $\Sigma x = 66$
2. Determine n, the number of data values.
    $n = 4$

The sample mean is:

$$\bar{x} = \frac{\Sigma x}{n} = \frac{66}{4} = 16.5$$

EXAMPLE 3.2

A quality control inspector of a battery manufacturer would like to estimate the life expectancy of the manufacturer's 9 volt batteries manufactured during the day shift. In order to estimate the life expectancy of all the batteries manufactured during the day shift, a sample of 20 batteries was randomly obtained. The following data represents the battery life in months of the 20 batteries.

$$20, 11, 15, 18, 24, 17, 19, 12, 19, 22$$
$$18, 15, 19, 21, 20, 15, 17, 24, 16, 18$$

a) Calculate the sample mean, $\bar{x}$.
b) What value can the inspector use as an estimate of the average of **all** the 9 volt batteries manufactured?

Solution

a) The sample mean is calculated by using the formula:

$$\bar{x} = \frac{\Sigma x}{n}$$

Since

$$\Sigma x = 20+11+15+18+24+17+19+12+19+22+18+15+19+21+20+15+17+24+16+18$$
$$= 360$$

and $n = 20$, then the sample mean is:

$$\bar{x} = \frac{\Sigma x}{n} = \frac{360}{20}$$
$$\bar{x} = 18 \text{ months}$$

b) The quality control inspector can use the sample mean of 18 months as an estimate of the average life of all the batteries.

Population Mean

The formula to compute the mean of a finite population is essentially the same as the sample mean formula. Only the notation is different to indicate we have **all** the data values of the population.

When **all** the data values of a population are obtained, the *Greek letter mu, written μ,* (pronounced "mew") denotes the population mean. The number of data values within the population is symbolized by the upper-case letter N. Using this notation, we can write the formula for the mean of a finite population mean.

Population Mean Formula

The symbol for the population mean is μ. The formula to calculate the mean of a finite population of size N is:

$$\mu = \frac{\Sigma x}{N}$$

As mentioned in Chapter 1, the purpose of inferential statistics is to use sample information to describe the characteristics of a population since it is usually impractical or impossible to obtain all the data values of a population.

Table 3.1 summarizes the notations for the mean of a sample and a population. It is important that you use the proper notation when symbolizing the mean.

TABLE 3.1 **Notation**

	Sample	Population
Mean	$\bar{x}$, read x bar	μ, read mu
Size	n	N

In Example 3.3, we consider a small population of data values to illustrate the use of notation and formula for the mean of a population.

EXAMPLE 3.3

According to the U.S. Department of Energy, the following data represent the estimated miles per gallon (mpg) for the 1999 minicompact cars under city driving conditions.

$$9, 20, 20, 20, 23, 20, 22, 21, 22, 17, 17, 16, 13, 21, 22, 28, 30, 18, 18$$

Assuming these estimated mpg represent the population of all minicompact cars, find the mean of this population.

Solution

To determine the population mean: $\mu = \dfrac{\Sigma x}{N}$, we need to first compute Σx.

Σx = 9+20+20+20+23+20+22+21+22+17+17+16+13+21+22+28+30+18+18
    = 377

Since N = 19, then the population mean equals:

$$\mu = \frac{\Sigma x}{N} = \frac{377}{19}$$

$$\mu \approx 19.84 \text{ MPG}$$

Thus, the population mean mpg is approximately 19.84 for the minicompact cars under city driving conditions.

Other Calculations Using Σ

There are many formulas in statistics involving the use of Σ, and it is important to know how to interpret and evaluate expressions containing Σ. We will consider some of these expressions and discuss how to evaluate them. We will first consider the expression: $(\Sigma x)^2$, the square of the sum of the data values.

Procedure to Calculate $(\Sigma x)^2$
(The Square of the Summed Data Values)

$(\Sigma x)^2$ represents $(x_1 + x_2 + x_3 + x_4 + \ldots + x_n)^2$
   1. Sum the data values, (Σx)
   2. Square the sum, $(\Sigma x)^2$

The next example will illustrate the procedure used to calculate $(\Sigma x)^2$.

EXAMPLE 3.4

Let $x_1 = 3, x_2 = 4, x_3 = 1$ and $x_4 = 6$.
   Determine $(\Sigma x)^2$.

Solution

Notice the sum of the data values, Σx, is being squared. This means we must first find the sum of all the data values, and then **square** this sum.
   That is,
1. sum all the data values: (Σx)
   $\Sigma x = x_1 + x_2 + x_3 + x_4 = 3 + 4 + 1 + 6$
   $\Sigma x = 14$
2. square this sum: $(\Sigma x)^2$
   $(\Sigma x)^2 = (14)^2 = 196$

Now, we will consider the meaning of the expression Σx^2, the sum of the squared data values.

Procedure to Calculate Σx^2
(The Sum of the Squared Data Values)

Σx^2 represents $(x_1)^2 + (x_2)^2 + (x_3)^2 + \ldots + (x_n)^2$
1. Square each data value.
2. Sum these squared data values.

The next example illustrates the calculation of Σx^2.

EXAMPLE 3.5

Let $x_1 = 2, x_2 = 4, x_3 = 1$ and $x_4 = 3$. Find Σx^2.

Solution:

1. square each data value

$(x_1)^2 = (2)^2 = 4 \qquad (x_2)^2 = (4)^2 = 16$
$(x_3)^2 = (1)^2 = 1 \qquad (x_4)^2 = (3)^2 = 9$

2. sum these squared data values

$\Sigma x^2 = (x_1)^2 + (x_2)^2 + (x_3)^2 + (x_4)^2 = 4 + 16 + 1 + 9$
$\Sigma x^2 = 30$

Summary for Calculating $(\Sigma x)^2$ and Σx^2

When calculating $(\Sigma x)^2$ you first **add** all the data values and then **square** this sum. When calculating Σx^2 you first **square** each individual data value and then **add** these squared data values.

Statistical calculators have built-in programs to calculate the expressions Σx and Σx^2. You should become familiar with the operation of your calculator and review the examples in this section that refer to these expressions.

An important concept involving the mean is the *deviation from the mean*. The deviation from the sample mean for a particular data value, x, is the amount by which the data value deviates from the mean. This deviation is the difference between the data value and the mean. It is represented as: $x - \bar{x}$. We will now examine the expression $\Sigma(x - \bar{x})$ and how to evaluate it. The expression $\Sigma(x - \bar{x})$ represents the sum of the deviations from the sample mean. To evaluate this expression, we use the following steps.

Procedure to Compute the Sum of the Deviations from the Sample Mean, $\Sigma(x - \bar{x})$

$\Sigma(x - \bar{x})$ represents $(x_1 - \bar{x}) + (x_2 - \bar{x}) + (x_3 - \bar{x}) + \ldots + (x_n - \bar{x})$
1. Compute the sample mean.
2. Subtract the mean from each data value.
3. Sum these differences.

EXAMPLE 3.6

Let $x_1 = 5, x_2 = 3, x_3 = 7$. Find $\Sigma(x - \bar{x})$, that is, the sum of the deviations from the mean.

Solution

1. Compute the mean: $\bar{x}$.

$$\bar{x} = \frac{\Sigma x}{n} = \frac{15}{3} = 5$$

2. Subtract the mean, $\bar{x}$, from each data value. These differences, $(x - \bar{x})$, are referred to as **deviations from the mean**.

$(x_1 - \bar{x}) = (5 - 5) = 0$
$(x_2 - \bar{x}) = (3 - 5) = -2$
$(x_3 - \bar{x}) = (7 - 5) = +2$

3. Find the sum of the deviations from the mean, $\Sigma(x - \bar{x})$.

$\Sigma(x - \bar{x}) = 0 + (-2) + 2$
$= 0$

The deviations from the mean is equal to zero, that is:
$\Sigma(x - \bar{x}) = 0.$

EXAMPLE 3.7

Given the following ages of seven children at a playground: 5, 4, 4, 8, 4, 9, 8
a) Compute the mean age, $\bar{x}$.
b) Evaluate $\Sigma(x - \bar{x})$, the sum of the deviations from the mean.

Solution

a) Calculate the mean, $\bar{x}$.

$$\bar{x} = \frac{\Sigma x}{n} = \frac{42}{7} = 6$$

b) To evaluate $\Sigma(x - \bar{x})$:
1. Subtract the mean, $\bar{x} = 6$, from each data value.

$(5 - 6) = -1$ $(4 - 6) = -2$ $(4 - 6) = -2$ $(8 - 6) = 2$
$(4 - 6) = -2$ $(9 - 6) = 3$ $(8 - 6) = 2$

2. Find the sum of the deviations from the mean, $\Sigma(x - \bar{x})$.

$\Sigma(x - \bar{x}) = -1 + -2 + -2 + 2 + -2 + 3 + 2$
$= 0$

From the previous two examples we might guess that the **sum of the deviations from the mean is always zero**. That is, $\Sigma(x - \bar{x}) = 0$. In fact, this is true, and it is **a property of the mean**. **This property indicates that the mean is the balance point within a set of data values**. The mean is like the fulcrum on a seesaw. We will examine this idea using the ages of the seven children from Example 3.7. If the ages of the seven children were marked along a number line on a board, and a one-pound weight is placed on the board corresponding to each child's age, then this board would have its balance point at the mean value of 6. That is, if a fulcrum is placed underneath the board at the position corresponding to the mean value of 6, then the board containing the 7 one-pound weights would be perfectly balanced at the mean! This illustrates the fact that the mean represents the balance point of a distribution. This property is illustrated in Figure 3.1.

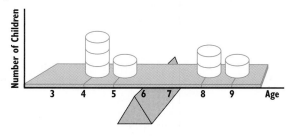

FIGURE 3.1

From Figure 3.1, since the fulcrum of the board is at the mean value of 6, this serves to illustrate that the mean is the point that balances all the values on either side of it. In other words, the sums of the distances from the mean is the same on each side of the mean. This is symbolized as: $\sum(x - \bar{x}) = 0$.

Property of the Mean

The sum of the deviations from the mean is always zero.
This is expressed symbolically as:

$$\sum(x - \bar{x}) = 0 \text{ for sample data, or}$$
$$\sum(x - \mu) = 0 \text{ for population data.}$$

This property states that the mean is the balance point within a distribution. That is, the mean balances the data values on either side of it since the sums of the distances from the mean is the same on each side of the mean.

The Median

Another measure of central tendency is the **median**. The median is the middle value of a data set after the data values have been arranged in numerical order. The procedure to determine the median is dependent upon the number of data values, and not on the actual value of the data.

DEFINITION 3.3
The **median** is the *middle value* of a set of data values after they have been arranged in *numerical order*. The number of data values below and above the position of the median are equal.

The procedure to determine the median is dependent upon whether the number of data values within the data set is odd or even.

Procedure to Determine the Median

1. First arrange the data values in numerical order.
2. a. For an **odd number** of data values, the median is the middle data value.
   b. For an **even number** of data values, the median is the mean of the two middle data values.

EXAMPLE 3.8

For the quiz grades: 8, 7, 9, 9, 9, 6, 10, 7, 5 find the median quiz grade.

Solution

1. Arrange the data values in numerical order.

   5, 6, 7, 7, 8, 9, 9, 9, 10

2. Since there is an odd number of data values (9 data values), the median is the middle grade. Thus, the median quiz grade is 8.   ■

Median's Location within a Distribution

In general, the median's location within a set of n data values that have been arranged in numerical order is determined by the formula:

$$\text{Location of median} = \frac{n+1}{2} \text{th data value}$$

For Example 3.8, the location of the median can be determined using the formula:

$$\text{Location of median} = \frac{n+1}{2} \text{ th data value}$$

For n = 9 data values, then the location of the median is:

$$\text{Location of median} = \frac{9+1}{2} = 5\text{th data value}$$

In Example 3.8, the **median's location**, as illustrated in Figure 3.2, **is the 5th data value** within the ordered data set.

```
                          MEDIAN
                            |
          5, 6, 7, 7, 8, 9, 9, 9, 10

                    5  th  data value
```

FIGURE 3.2

EXAMPLE 3.9

Table 3.2 represents the attendance figures of the 10 American League opening day games in 1995.

TABLE 3.2   American League Opening Day Attendance

Home Team	1995 Attendance
Boston	32,980
California	51,145
Chicago	31,073
Kansas City	24,170
Milwaukee	31,426
Minnesota	26,425
Yankees	50,245
Seattle	34,656
Texas	32,161
Toronto	50,426

a) Find the median attendance.
b) Determine the percentage of games that are below the median attendance.
c) Determine the percentage of games that are below the mean attendance.
d) Compare the percentage of games below the mean and the median attendances. Explain the differences if any.

Solution

a) 1. Arranging the attendances in numerical order, we have:

24,170   26,425   31,073   31,426   32,161   32,980   34,656   50,245   50,426   51,145

2. For a data set of 10 attendances, the location of the median is determined by the formula:

$$\text{Location of median} = \frac{n+1}{2} \text{ th data value}$$

For n = 10, the median's position is:

$$\text{Location of median} = \frac{10+1}{2} = \frac{11}{2} = 5.5$$

This value tells us that the median is equal to the mean of the 5th and 6th attendances which are: 32,161 and 32,980. Thus, we have:

$$\text{median} = \frac{32,161 + 32,980}{2} = \frac{65,141}{2} = 32,570.5$$

Thus, the median attendance is approximately 32,571.

b) Five of the 10 opening day games had an attendance below the median attendance of 32,571. Therefore, 50% of the games had an attendance below the median attendance.

c) The mean attendance is found by summing up the 10 attendances and dividing by 10. Thus the mean attendance is:

$$\frac{24,170 + 26,425 + 31,073 + 31,426 + 32,161 + 32,980 + 34,656 + 50,245 + 50,426 + 51,145}{10}$$

mean attendance = 36,4707/10 = 36,470.7

Hence, the mean attendance is approximately 36,471.

Seven of the 10 opening day games had an attendance that was below the mean attendance. Therefore, 70% of the games had attendances that were below the mean attendance.

d) Since the median, by definition, is equal to the middle number, we would expect approximately 50% of the games to be below the median attendance. On the other hand, the mean is the balance point so we would **not** expect to have 50% of the games below the mean attendance. In fact, 70% of the games were below the mean attendance. The reason more than 50% of the games had an attendance below the mean attendance is that the mean is being influenced by the 3 extreme attendances: 51,145, 50,245 and 50,426. ■

The Mode

The last measure of central tendency we will examine is the mode. The mode is the easiest measure to compute and the simplest to interpret.

> **DEFINITION 3.4**
> The **mode** of a data set is the data value which occurs most frequently. A data set may **not** have a mode or may have **more** than one mode.

E X A M P L E   3 . 1 0

Find the modal test score for the following eight test scores: 65, 75, 45, 90, 75, 68, 85, 60.

Solution

Since 75 appears most frequently, it is the modal test score.

E X A M P L E   3 . 1 1

Find the mode for the following screw lengths.

screw lengths
(measured in inches)
0.25, 0.33, 0.5, 0.33, 0.5, 0.33, 0.25, 0.16, 0.5, 0.5, 0.33

Solution

Notice there are two data values which appear most frequently. Therefore, this data set has *two* modes. The modes are 0.33 and 0.5.

In the previous example, there were two modes. This type of data set is called *bimodal.*

> **DEFINITION 3.5**
> A distribution is a called a **bimodal** distribution if it has two data values which appear with the greatest frequency.

E X A M P L E   3 . 1 2

Find the mode for the following distribution:

5, 4, 6, 10, 6, 4, 10, 3, 8, 7

Solution

Since there are more than two data values which appear most frequently, (i.e. 4, 6 and 10 appear twice), we will refer to such a distribution as having *no mode.*

A distribution having *no mode,* as illustrated in the previous example, will be referred to as a *non-modal distribution.*

> **DEFINITION 3.6**
> If a distribution has more than two modes, then the distribution is **nonmodal.**

E X A M P L E   3 . 1 3

A college professor randomly selects 36 students from her classes to try to estimate the typical eye color for college students attending the university. The following data set represents her survey results:

brown, blue, hazel, brown, black, blue, blue, brown, hazel, brown, hazel, black, brown, blue, brown, brown, blue, blue, black, brown, brown, blue, hazel, blue, blue, brown, hazel, brown, brown, black, brown, blue, brown, black, blue, brown.

Which measure of central tendency should the professor use to estimate the typical college student eye color and what is the typical student eye color for the university?

Solution

Since the mean and median would not be appropriate [WHY?], the professor would need to use the mode. The most frequent eye color is brown. Therefore, the typical college student at the university has brown eyes.

EXAMPLE 3.14

The small community of Poorich is applying for federal aid. One question on the application requests the *average* family income for the community.

    The following data are the family incomes for the five community residents:

$$\$25,000; \$20,000; \$200,000; \$30,000; \$15,000.$$

    If the town uses the mean income of \$58,000 to represent the average family income, do you believe this number accurately represents the income level of the community?

    If not, which measure of central tendency would you use to represent the income level of this community?

Solution

Since the mean income of \$58,000 is greater than four of the five family incomes, it does not represent the typical income level of the community. The median income of \$25,000 more accurately depicts the typical income level of the residents since it is not sensitive to the extreme values within the community.

CASE STUDY 3.1   Average Costs

Examine the three snapshots shown in Figure 3.3. In each snapshot a measure of central tendency is being used to describe an aspect of a person's life. For each snapshot, state the measure of central tendency being applied and explain why you believe this is or isn't an appropriate measure to use in each instance.

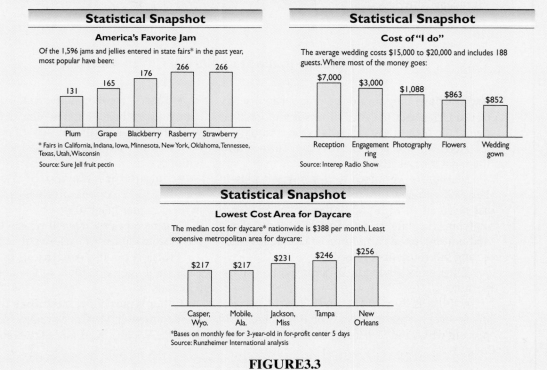

FIGURE3.3

CASE STUDY 3.2 Average vs. Typical

Read the two articles "The Average Man" and "Welcome to the Most Normal City in America" displayed in Figure 3.4. Discuss how the word *average* and *typical* are being used in each of the articles. For each article review each statement that contains a statistic and state which measure of central tendency you believe was used or could have been used to determine that statistic. Also, explain why you chose that particular measure of central tendency.

The Average Man

From *Men's Health*

- Is 5 feet 9 inches tall and 173 pounds.
- Is married. 1.8 years older than his wife and would marry her again.
- Has not completed college.
- Earns $28,605 per year.
- Prefers showering to taking a bath.
- Spends about 7.2 hours a week eating.
- Does not know his cholesterol count, but it's 211.
- Watches 26 hours and 44 minutes of TV a week.
- Takes out the garbage in his household.
- Prefers white underwear to colored.
- Cries about once a month—one-fourth as much as Jane Doe.
- Falls in love an average of six times during his life.
- Eats his corn on the cob in circles, not straight across, and prefers his steak medium.
- Can't whistle by inserting his fingers in his mouth.
- Prefers that his toilet tissue unwind over, rather than under, the spool.
- Has sex 2.55 times a week.
- Daydreams mostly about sex.
- Thinks he looks okay in the nude.
- Will not stop to ask for directions when he's in the car.

Welcome to the Most Normal City in America

Experts have pinpointed the most ordinary city in the U.S.—and because of this it will become one of the biggest test markets in the country.

According to 1990 census data, Tulsa is now the most typical city in the nation.

Marketers who used to ask, "Will it play in Peoria?" can now turn to Tulsa, which came closest of all cities with populations over 50,000 to matching the national average for ages, racial mix and housing prices, according to Donnelley Marketing Information Services.

What makes living in Tulsa such a typical experience?

- Tulsa is 79 percent white and 14 percent black—very close to the national average of 80 percent white and 12 percent black.

- Tulsa's median home value is $60,500—compared to the national median of $79,100.
- Tulsa's age distribution—of children, baby boomers and seniors—is almost identical to the nation's.
- Tulsans, like the rest of Americans, are spending more conservatively now than they did in the designer-label 80's.

Businesses look to such typical towns to test out new products or measure public opinion.

"Tulsa is middle America to the max," says Rick Bahlinger, President of Golden Eagle Distributing.

Other typical cities, according to Donnelley. are Charleston, W. Va.; Midland, Texas; Springfield, Ill., Wichita, Kan. and Oklahoma City.

FIGURE 3.4

CASE STUDY 3.3

For each snapshot in Figure 3.5, identify which measure of central tendency is used. For each measure, state whether it is a statistic or a parameter. Explain.

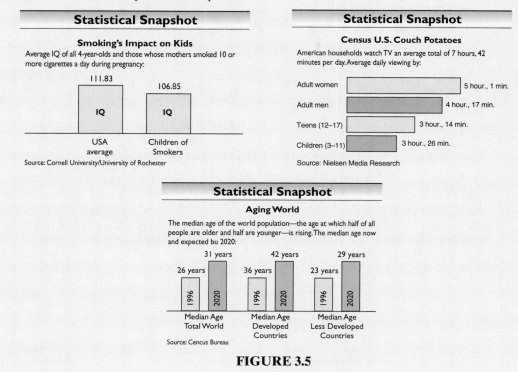

Statistical Snapshot

Smoking's Impact on Kids

Average IQ of all 4-year-olds and those whose mothers smoked 10 or more cigarettes a day during pregnancy:

111.83 — IQ — USA average
106.85 — IQ — Children of Smokers

Source: Cornell University/University of Rochester

Statistical Snapshot

Census U.S. Couch Potatoes

American households watch TV an average total of 7 hours, 42 minutes per day. Average daily viewing by:

Adult women — 5 hour., 1 min.
Adult men — 4 hour., 17 min.
Teens (12–17) — 3 hour., 14 min.
Children (3–11) — 3 hour., 26 min.

Source: Nielsen Media Research

Statistical Snapshot

Aging World

The median age of the world population—the age at which half of all people are older and half are younger—is rising. The median age now and expected bu 2020:

Median Age Total World: 26 years (1996), 31 years (2020)
Median Age Developed Countries: 36 years (1996), 42 years (2020)
Median Age Less Developed Countries: 23 years (1996), 29 years (2020)

Source: Cencus Bureau

FIGURE 3.5

The Relationship of the Mean, Median and Mode

In this chapter, we've discussed three ways to describe the center or the "typical" or "representative" value of a distribution. To help decide which measure of central tendency would be appropriate in describing the center of a specific distribution type, we will examine the relationship of the mean, median, and mode within three common distribution shapes: *symmetric bell-shaped*, *skewed left*, and *skewed right*. We will first discuss how to determine where each measure of central tendency will be positioned within each of these distribution shapes.

The Mode and Its Location within the Distribution Shapes

Within each of the distribution shapes illustrated in Figure 3.6, you will notice that the mode, the most frequent value, is located at the point on the curve corresponding to the highest value.

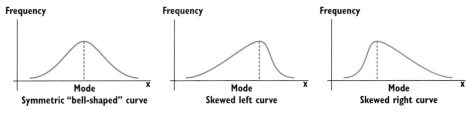

Symmetric "bell-shaped" curve   Skewed left curve   Skewed right curve

FIGURE 3.6

The Median and Its Location within the Distribution Shapes

The median is located at the point on the curve which divides the area under the curve exactly in half. That is, half or 50% of the area lies to the left of the median value while half or 50% of the area lies to the right of the median value. This is illustrated in Figure 3.7.

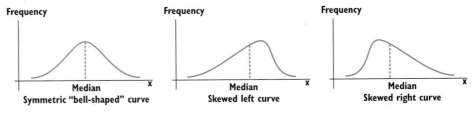

FIGURE 3.7

The Mean and Its Location within the Distribution Shapes

The mean of a distribution is the value which represents the "balance point" of the curve. To understand the idea of a balance point, try to think of the curve as a solid object. The point beneath the curve which will balance the solid curve is the mean. Thus, at the balance point half the weight of the solid curve is to the left of this point and half the weight is to the right of this point. The idea of the balance point for each distribution shape is illustrated in Figure 3.8

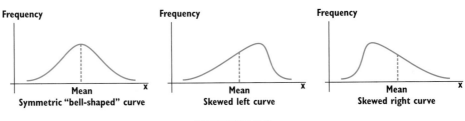

FIGURE 3.8

Now let's examine the position of each measure of central tendency with respect to each other within these three distribution shapes.

Symmetric Bell-Shaped Distribution

The mean, median, and mode are all at the center of the distribution represented by the symmetric bell-shaped curves in Figures 3.6 to 3.8. The mean or balance point is at the center since every data value to the left of the center is balanced by a corresponding data value to the right of the center. The median is located at the center since it divides the area under the curve into two equal halves (50% of the area to the left and 50% of the area to the right). The mode is located at the center since this is the point at which the curve attains its highest value.

Skewed to the Left Distribution

Within a skewed left distribution, the mode is the highest point. Its value is greater than both the median and the mean as illustrated in Figure 3.9.

In a skewed left distribution, the mean has the smallest value of all the measures of central tendency because the mean is influenced the most by the extreme data values that occur in the left tail of the distribution and is *pulled in the direction of the extreme values in the left tail*. The median has a smaller value than the mode since the median is *pulled to the left by the extreme values in the left tail* of the distribution. However, the median will be greater than the mean since the median is not as sensitive or as greatly influenced as the mean to the extreme data values in the left tail.

FIGURE 3.9

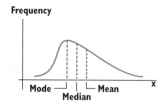

FIGURE 3.10

Skewed to the Right Distribution

Within a skewed right distribution, the mode occurs at the highest point and has a value smaller than the median or the mean as illustrated in Figure 3.10.

   The mean has the largest value of all the measures of central tendency because the mean is greatly influenced by the extreme data values that occur in the right tail of the distribution. The median has a value greater than the mode since the median is affected by the extreme values within the distribution and *pulled in the direction of the right tail.* However, the median has a value smaller than the mean since the median is not as sensitive or as greatly influenced as is the mean to the extreme data values in the right tail.

EXAMPLE 3.15

Using Figure 3.11, determine the value for:
a)   the mode
b)   the mean
c)   the median

FIGURE 3.11

Solution

a)   Within a distribution, the mode occurs at the highest point. Therefore, the mode is 25.
b)   Since the distribution in Figure 3.11 is skewed right, then the mean is greater than both the median and the mode. Thus, the mean is 35.
c)   In a skewed right distribution, the median is greater than the mode but less than the mean. Therefore, the median is 30.

Comparing the Mean, the Median and the Mode

From the examples and discussions within this section, you should have noticed that there are advantages and disadvantages for each measure of central tendency.

   As illustrated in Example 3.14, the mean is a measure of central tendency that is affected by the extreme data values or outliers within a distribution.

DEFINITION 3.7
A measure is a **resistant measure** if its value is not affected by an outlier or an extreme data value.

Thus we say that **the mean is not a resistant measure of central tendency**, because it is not resistant to the influence of the extreme values or outliers. On the other hand, **the median is a resistant measure of central tendency**. Since the median is resistant to the influence of extreme data values or outliers, its value does not respond strongly to the changes of a few extreme data values regardless of how large the change may be.

Thus, if a distribution has an outlier or is skewed, then the mean and median may differ greatly in value. The mean is sensitive to the extreme data values and will move toward the direction of the long tail in a skewed distribution. On the other hand, the median is resistant to, or unaffected by, outliers or extreme data values. (Figures 3.9–3.10) However, in a symmetric bell-shaped curve (Figures 3.7–3.8), the mean and median will have the same value.

Since only the mean is sensitive to outliers or extreme data values, **a difference between the mean and the median can inform us that an outlier may exist within a distribution**. Once an outlier is detected, the statistician can investigate the reason for such an extreme data value. The statistician can then decide whether to use a measure of central tendency that is resistant to these outliers or to give individual attention to the outliers. Notice in Example 3.14, the existence of the outlier $200,000 was detected by the fact that the mean ($58,000) was much larger than the median ($25,000). In this particular instance, the Poorich Community decided to use the median to represent the "average" or center value to ignore the presence of the outlier, since the median value of $25,000 is resistant to the outlier $200,000.

The mode has an advantage over both the mean and median when the data is categorical, since it is not possible to calculate a mean or median for this type of data. This is illustrated in Example 3.13. In addition, the mode usually indicates the location within a large distribution where the data values are concentrated. A shoe retailer would be interested in modal shoe sizes when placing an order for new shoes since the shoe sales will be concentrated around the modal size; while a discount consumers club is interested in the brands of items that most people are purchasing, since these items represent the modal brands.

However, the mode has some disadvantages too. One disadvantage is that the mode cannot always be calculated. For example, if a distribution has all different data values, then the distribution is nonmodal.

Let's now summarize some advantages and disadvantages of the measures of central tendency.

Summarizing the Measures of Central Tendency

Measure of Central Tendency	Definition	Resistant to Outliers	Advantages and Disadvantages
Mean	Sample: $\bar{x} = \dfrac{\Sigma x}{n}$ Population: $\mu = \dfrac{\Sigma x}{N}$	No	Appropriate for use in other statistical methods and for making inferences; affected by outliers; its value takes all data values into account
Median	Middle Data Value	Yes	Excellent choice when outliers exist; its value does not take all data values into account
Mode	Most Frequent Data Value	Yes	Appropriate for categorical data; may not exist or may have more than one mode; its value does not take all data values into account

CASE STUDY 3.4   Baseball Salaries

The graphic in Figure 3.12 entitled "The Baseball Salary Breakdown" presents a summary of the salaries of all 920 Major League Baseball Players on opening day of the 1999 baseball season.

THE BASEBALL SALARY BREAKDOWN
Who makes what in major league baseball, based on opening day 1999 rosters of 920 players. Although the average salary was $1,570,786, the median salary is $470,833. The modal salary was only $200,000, which was also the minimum salary. The maximum salary was $11,949,794; earned by Albert Belle of the Orioles.

= 10 players

$6 million and above: 52 players

$6 million

$5 million to $6 million: 39 players

$5 million

$4 million to $5 million: 36 players

$4 million

$3 million to $4 million: 51 players

$3 million

$2 million to $3 million: 76 players

$2 million

MEAN: $1,570,786 — $1 million to $2 million: 88 players

$1 million

$475,000 to $1 million: 118 players

MEDIAN: $470,833 — $205,000 to $466,666: 315 players

MODE: $200,000 — $200,000: 145 players

$0

SOURCE: MAJOR LEAGUE BASEBALL

FIGURE 3.12

Using the graphic in Figure 3.12,
    a) Which measure of central tendency was used to compute the average? Explain.
    b) Which symbol would you use to symbolize this average? Explain.
    c) Identify the shape of the distribution of baseball salaries.

CASE STUDY 3.4   Baseball Salaries (continued)

  d) Why would you expect the average and the median to be different?
  e) Determine the **position** of the median within this salary distribution.
  f) Determine the percent of players who made less than the value located at the position of the median. Determine the percent of players who made more than the value located at the position of the median.
  g) Determine the percent of players who made less than the average salary. Determine the percent of players who made more than the average salary.
  h) Explain why you would expect the percentages of parts (f) and (g) to be different.
  i) Do you believe any outliers exist? If so, can you indicate the value of an outlier? Explain how the value of the mean and median might indicate that an outlier may exist.

3.2   MEASURES OF VARIABILITY

A favorite folktale told by the statistics faculty to their students is how a 10 foot fisherman and non-swimmer known as "Big John" drowned while fishing in a lake whose **average depth was only 2 feet!** The purpose of this anecdote is to realize that just knowing a measure of central tendency may not be enough information to adequately describe a data set.

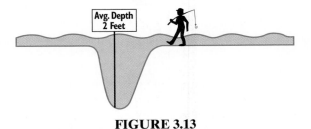

Avg. Depth 2 Feet

FIGURE 3.13

If the fisherman had been aware of the tremendous variations in depth as illustrated in Figure 3.13, he would have realized that knowing *only* the lake's average depth does not adequately describe its depth everywhere.

As this fable illustrates, the measures of central tendency sometimes fail to adequately describe a distribution. Additional descriptive measures, such as the measures of variability, enhance our ability to describe the main characteristics of a distribution.

Before we discuss the measures of variability, let's discuss the notion of variability by examining the two distributions shown in Table 3.3.

TABLE 3.3

Distribution 1	Distribution 2
4	1
4	22
4	24
4	31
4	100

Notice in Distribution 1, there is **no variability** since all the data values have the same value. While in Distribution 2, there is **variability** because the data values *vary* from 1 to 100.

Let us now examine techniques for measuring variability. The three measures of variability we will discuss are: the range, the variance, and the standard deviation.

The Range

The range provides a quick method of describing the variability of a distribution since it relies only on the extreme values of a distribution.

DEFINITION 3.8

The **range** of a distribution is the number representing the difference between the largest and smallest data values.

Range = largest data value – smallest data value

EXAMPLE 3.16

The math test grades for two students are:
 student A: 50, 70, 70, 70, 70, 70, 90
 student B: 50, 55, 62, 70, 78, 85, 90
a) Compute the range for each student.
b) Examine the variability of the test grades for both students. Do you believe that the grades for both of these students have the same variability? Explain.

Solution

a) For both students, the range is: 90 – 50 = 40.
b) Although the range for both students is the same, the grades for student B vary more than the grades for student A. The variability of student B becomes noticeable when examining all the test grades of each student rather than just their two extreme grades.

CASE STUDY 3.5   Price Performance of Fonix

The graphic in Figure 3.14 represents the price performance of the stock Fonix Corporation for the period from March 20th to April 18th.

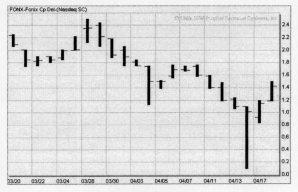

FIGURE 3.14

CASE STUDY 3.5   Price Performance of Fonix (continued)

Each bar represents the price of Fonix for each day displayed within Figure 3.14. The small horizontal lines on each side of the bar indicates the price of Fonix for that day. The line on the left side of each bar indicates the opening price while the line on the right side indicates the closing price.

a) In Figure 3.14, examine the bar representing April 4th. What does the distance between the left and right line for that bar indicate to you about the price of Fonix? Does this distance represent a measure of central tendency or variability? Explain.

b) From Figure 3.14, which day had the shortest bar? the longest bar? What does the length of the bar in Figure 3.14 indicate about the variability of Fonix's price?

c) What does the distances between the daily closing prices measure about the Fonix?

d) Observe the **closing** prices of Fonix for March 25th and March 28th. How much did the closing price of Fonix vary from 3/25 to 3/28? What was the percentage change for this period?

e) On which day could you have bought this stock and sold it the next trading day for the greatest profit? for the greatest loss? for a zero loss?

f) During what 3 day trading period did the closing price of Fonix remain relatively stable?

g) What measure of variability is being presented by the statement *FONIX SURGES 60 CENTS TO CLOSE AT $1.42*? Explain.

In Example 3.16, the range for both students is the same, since the calculation of the range involves only the two extreme data values (the largest and the smallest). Overall, the test grades of student B appear to **vary** more than the test grades of student A. Table 3.4 highlights the two distributions with the box separating the extreme test grade values.

TABLE 3.4

student A:	50	70	70	70	70	70	90
student B:	50	55	62	70	78	85	90

Examining the test grades within the box, you should notice that the variability of the two distributions is different. In this instance, the range may not be a completely adequate way of distinguishing between the variability of these two test grade distributions. Thus, **one disadvantage of the range is that it does not take into consideration the value of all the data values when measuring the variability of a distribution.**

Let's examine two additional measures of variability, where *every* data value within the distribution is taken into consideration when computing variability.

The Variance and Standard Deviation of a Sample

The variance and standard deviation are two measures of variability that are determined using all the data values of a distribution. Before we define these measures, let's examine the development of the variance and standard deviation so we can get a better understanding of their definitions and how to compute their formulas.

To develop these new measures of variability, we will first use the mean, as the measure of central tendency, to depict the **typical value** of a distribution, and then determine how far each data value varies from the **mean**.

For the following sample data, find the mean:

$$1, \quad 2, \quad 3, \quad 4, \quad 5, \quad 6, \quad 7$$

$$\bar{x} = \frac{\Sigma x}{n} = \frac{28}{7} = 4$$

Now *determine how far each data value varies from the mean.* We begin by subtracting the mean from each data value. These differences are called **deviations from the mean** and are illustrated in Table 3.5.

TABLE 3.5

Data Value x	Deviation from the Mean $x - \bar{x}$	Explanation
1	$1 - 4 = -3$	-3 indicates that the value 1 is 3 units *below* the mean
2	$2 - 4 = -2$	-2 indicates that the value 2 is 2 units *below* the mean
3	$3 - 4 = -1$	-1 indicates that the value 3 is 1 unit *below* the mean
4	$4 - 4 = 0$	0 indicates that the value 4 *is* the mean
5	$5 - 4 = 1$	1 indicates that the value 5 is one unit *above* the mean
6	$6 - 4 = 2$	2 indicates that the value 6 is two units *above* the mean
7	$7 - 4 = 3$	3 indicates that the value 7 is three units *above* the mean

Each of these deviations measure the variability of a single data value. Since we would like these new measures to reflect the variability of *all* the data values, we add together all the deviations from the mean that were obtained in Table 3.5.

Notice that the sum of these deviations is:

$$(-3) + (-2) + (-1) + (0) + (1) + (2) + (3) = 0$$

Did we expect this sum to be zero? Indeed we did! WHY? Remember back in Section 3.1, we explained that **the sum of the deviations from the mean**, expressed as $\Sigma(x - \bar{x})$, **is always zero**. Therefore, just finding the sum of the deviations from the mean is not a good way to define a measure of variability since the result will always equal zero!

To remedy this problem we need to consider a technique which will change each deviation to a nonnegative number before calculating the sum. One method of making the deviations nonnegative is to square each deviation. This is illustrated in Table 3.6.

TABLE 3.6

Data Value x	Deviation from the Mean $x - \bar{x}$	Squared Deviation from the Mean $(x - \bar{x})^2$
1	-3	$(-3)^2 = 9$
2	-2	$(-2)^2 = 4$
3	-1	$(-1)^2 = 1$
4	0	$(0)^2 = 0$
5	1	$(1)^2 = 1$
6	2	$(2)^2 = 4$
7	3	$(3)^2 = 9$

We will now use the squared deviations, symbolized as $\Sigma(x - \bar{x})^2$, to define these new measures of variability. Let's now calculate the sum of these squared deviations. This result is:

$$\Sigma(x - \bar{x})^2 = 9 + 4 + 1 + 0 + 1 + 4 + 9 = 28$$

Therefore, the sum of the squared deviations is 28.

Dividing the sum of the squared deviations, $\Sigma(x - \bar{x})^2$, by the number of sample data values minus 1, we obtain the *sample variance.*

DEFINITION 3.9

The **variance for a sample** of n data values is equal to the sum of the squared deviations from the mean divided by (n – 1). The sample variance is symbolized by the square of the lower-case letter s, written s^2.

The formula for the sample variance is:

$$\text{sample variance} = \frac{\Sigma\,(data\ value - sample\ mean)^2}{number\ of\ data\ values - 1}$$

OR

$$s^2 = \frac{\Sigma(x - \bar{x})^2}{n - 1}$$

The sample variance uses all the data values to measure the variability of the sample. Although the variance is an important measure of variability, there are instances when the variance is extremely difficult to interpret as a measure of variability. We will explore this disadvantage in Example 3.17.

EXAMPLE 3.17

The following sample data represents the hourly wages of five employees of a small cannoli bakery in Boston.

$$\$6, \quad \$10, \quad \$9, \quad \$12, \quad \$8$$

Compute the sample variance of the hourly wages.

Solution

Step 1   Compute the mean, $\bar{x}$.

$$\bar{x} = \$45/5 = \$9$$

Step 2   Subtract the mean of $9 from each wage and then square the deviations from the mean. These results are shown in Table 3.7.

TABLE 3.7

Data Value x	Deviation from the Mean $x - \bar{x}$	Squared Deviation from the Mean $(x - \bar{x})^2$
$ 6	$6 – $9 = –$3	$(-\$3)^2 = $ 9 squared dollars
$10	$10 – $9 = $1	$(\$1)^2 = $ 1 squared dollar
$ 9	$9 – $9 = $0	$(\$0)^2 = $ 0 squared dollars
$12	$12 – $9 = $3	$(\$3)^2 = $ 9 squared dollars
$ 8	$8 – $9 = –$1	$(-\$1)^2 = $ 1 squared dollar

Step 3 To calculate the sample variance, divide the sum of the squared deviations from the mean by the number of data values minus 1.

The sum of the squared deviations is:

$$\Sigma(x - \bar{x})^2 = (9 + 1 + 0 + 9 + 1) \text{ sq. dollars} = 20 \text{ sq. dollars}$$

and n–1 = 4, thus the sample variance is:

$$\text{sample variance} = \frac{\Sigma(x - \bar{x})^2}{n - 1}$$

$$= \frac{20 \text{ squared dollars}}{4}$$

$$\text{sample variance} = 5 \text{ squared dollars}$$

The sample variance is symbolized as:

$$s^2 = \textbf{5 squared dollars}$$

One disadvantage of the variance is that the variance is measured in squared units, while the data values within the distribution are not measured in squared units.

Since the unit measurements for the variance and the data will always be different, it may be difficult to interpret and relate the variance as a measure of variability to the data values within the distribution.

Examining Example 3.17, we see that the variance is expressed in squared dollar units while the data values were given in dollars. We would like to define a new measure of variability, which is expressed in the same unit as the original data values. This can be accomplished by taking the positive square root of the sample variance. This new measure of variability is called the sample standard deviation, and is symbolized by the lower-case letter s.

Let's now define this new measure of variability called the sample standard deviation.

DEFINITION 3.10
The **sample standard deviation**, s, is the positive square root of the sample variance.

$$\text{sample standard deviation} = \sqrt{sample\ variance}$$

Therefore, the formula for the sample standard deviation is symbolized as:

$$s = \sqrt{\frac{\Sigma(x - \bar{x})^2}{n - 1}}$$

We will refer to this formula for the standard deviation as the ***definition formula for the sample standard deviation***.

To calculate the sample standard deviation for Example 3.17, take the positive square root of the sample variance. Since the sample variance is 5 squared dollars, then the sample standard deviation is:

$$\text{sample standard deviation} = \sqrt{5\ squared\ dollars}$$

$$\text{sample standard deviation} \approx 2.24 \text{ dollars}$$

This is symbolized as:

$$s \approx \$2.24$$

Notice that the standard deviation expresses the variability in the *same* unit of measure as the original data values. That is, the hourly wages and the standard deviation are both expressed in dollars.

Intuitively, we can interpret the standard deviation to be the "average" or "typical" deviation from the mean. Thus, in Example 3.17 we can interpret a standard deviation of $2.24 as indicating that the hourly wages of $6, $10, $9, $12, and $8 vary by an "average" of 2 dollars and 24 cents from the mean hourly wage of $9.

Interpretation of the Standard Deviation

The standard deviation of a set of data values measures the average or typical deviation from the mean. The more the data values are dispersed or spread out, the larger the value of the standard deviation. However, the more the data values are clustered together, the smaller the value of the standard deviation. Thus if there is no variation in the data values, then the standard deviation will equal zero!

Although the variance provides the same information as the standard deviation regarding the variability of a set of data values, we will primarily use the standard deviation because it's expressed in the original units of the data values.

EXAMPLE 3.18

Calculate the standard deviation for the following sample of ages (represented in years) using the definition formula for the sample standard deviation.

$$1, \quad 3, \quad 5, \quad 18, \quad 8$$

Solution

Step 1 Calculate the mean, $\bar{x}$.

$$\bar{x} = \frac{\Sigma x}{n} = \frac{35}{5} = 7 \text{ years}$$

Step 2 Subtract the mean of 7 years from each age and then square these deviations. These results are shown in Table 3.8.

TABLE 3.8

Data Value x	Deviation from the Mean $x - \bar{x}$	Squared Deviation from the Mean $(x - \bar{x})^2$
1	−6	$(-6)^2 = 36$
3	−4	$(-4)^2 = 16$
5	−2	$(-2)^2 = 4$
18	11	$(11)^2 = 121$
8	1	$(1)^2 = 1$

Step 3 Divide the squared deviations by the number of data values minus 1. This result is the sample variance.

The sum of the squared deviations is: $\Sigma(x - \bar{x})^2 = 178$

and $n - 1 = 4$, thus the sample variance is:

$$\text{sample variance} = \frac{\Sigma(x - \bar{x})^2}{n - 1} = \frac{178}{4} = 44.5 \text{ squared years}$$

In symbols, the sample variance is written:

s^2 = 44.5 squared years

Step 4 Take the square root of the sample variance. This is the sample standard deviation.

$$s = \sqrt{sample\ variance}$$

$$s = \sqrt{44.5\ squared\ years}$$

$s \approx 6.67$ years

A sample standard deviation of 6.67 years indicates that the ages within this sample vary by an "average" of 6.67 years from the mean age of 7 years. ■

There is a shortcut formula for computing the standard deviation. This formula is called the ***computational formula for the sample standard deviation.***

The Computational Formula for the Sample Standard Deviation

$$s = \sqrt{\dfrac{\Sigma x^2 - \dfrac{(\Sigma x)^2}{n}}{n-1}}$$

The computational formula is typically a quicker and faster way to compute the standard deviation since it reduces the number of calculations and round-off errors.

The Variance and Standard Deviation of a Population

In the beginning of this section, we developed and discussed the formulas for the variance and standard deviation of a **sample** since, in practice, we usually work with sample data. But remember, as discussed in Chapter 1, the objective of inferential statistics is to use sample data to describe the characteristics of the **population**. Although we rarely ever work with all the data values of a population, we now present the formulas and notations for the population variance and the population standard deviation of a finite population, to help explain how the sample variance and sample standard deviation are used to estimate these population parameters.

Recall the formula to compute the sample variance, s^2, for a sample of n data values is:

$$s^2 = \dfrac{\Sigma(x - \bar{x})^2}{n-1}$$

The formula to compute the variance of a finite population of N data values is essentially similar to the sample variance formula except the sample mean, $\bar{x}$, is replaced by the Greek symbol for the population mean, μ, and the denominator, n – 1, is replaced by the upper-case letter N, the number of population data values.

DEFINITION 3.11

The **variance for a finite population** of N data values is equal to the sum of the squared deviations from the mean divided by N. The population variance is symbolized by the square of the lower-case Greek letter sigma: σ, written σ^2 and pronounced sigma squared. The formula for the population variance is:

$$\text{population variance} = \frac{\Sigma(data\ value - population\ mean)^2}{number\ of\ population\ data\ values}$$

OR

$$\sigma^2 = \frac{\Sigma(x - \mu)^2}{N}$$

In the formula for the population variance, when we divide the sum of the squared deviations from the mean by the total number of data values, N, we are finding the mean average of the squared deviations from the mean. Thus, the *population variance is the mean of the squared deviations from the mean.*

The formula to compute the population standard deviation is found by taking the positive square root of the population variance. The population standard deviation is denoted by the lower-case Greek letter sigma, written σ. The following formula for the population standard deviation will be referred to as the definition formula for the population standard deviation.

DEFINITION 3.12

The **standard deviation for a finite population** of N data values is the positive square root of the population variance. The population standard deviation is symbolized by the lower-case Greek letter sigma, written σ. The formula for the population standard deviation is:

$$\text{population standard deviation} = \sqrt{\frac{\Sigma(data\ value - population\ mean)^2}{number\ of\ population\ data\ values}}$$

OR

$$\sigma = \sqrt{\frac{\Sigma(x - \mu)^2}{N}}$$

As mentioned in Chapter 1, the purpose of inferential statistics is to use sample information to describe the characteristics of a population since it is usually impractical or impossible to obtain all the data values of a population. In such instances, it is important that you understand that the sample standard deviation is used to estimate the value of the population standard deviation. It is also important to know and understand the appropriate notation used for the variance and standard deviation of a sample and of a population. Table 3.9 summarizes these notations.

In Example 3.19, we will treat all the data values of this example as a population to demonstrate the formula and notation for the population standard deviation.

TABLE 3.9   Sample and Population Notation for the Variance and the Standard Deviation

	Sample	Population
Variance	s^2	σ^2, read sigma squared
Standard Deviation	s	σ, read sigma

◼
EXAMPLE 3.19

Two high school women basketball players are being considered for an award to be given to the most consistent player with the highest scoring average for the season. The number of points scored per game for **all the games played during the season** is given in Table 3.10.

TABLE 3.10

Points per game for player A	Points per game for player B
5	18
32	20
45	22
25	15
8	35
10	24
35	29
12	19
37	25
21	23

a. Calculate the population mean and population standard deviation of the number of points scored per game for each player.
b. Using the results of part (a) determine which player should receive the award.

Solution

a. Find the mean number of points scored for each player.
    For player A, the population mean number of points per game is:

$$\mu = \Sigma x / N = 230/10 = 23$$

For player B, the population mean number of points per game is:

$$\mu = \Sigma x / N = 230/10 = 23$$

The population standard deviation of the number of points scored for each player is determined using the formula:

$$\sigma = \sqrt{\frac{\Sigma(x - \mu)^2}{N}}$$

For player A, the population standard deviation of the number of points scored is determined by the following steps:

Step 1   Subtract the mean of 23 from each points per game value and then square the deviations from the mean. These results are shown in Table 3.11.

TABLE 3.11

Data Value x	Deviation from the Mean x − μ	Squared Deviation from the Mean (x − μ)²
5	5 − 23 = −18	(−18)² = 324
32	32 − 23 = 9	(9)² = 81
45	45 − 23 = 22	(22)² = 484
25	25 − 23 = 2	(2)² = 4
8	8 − 23 = −15	(−15)² = 225
10	10 − 23 = −13	(−13)² = 169
35	35 − 23 = 12	(12)² = 144
12	12 − 23 = −11	(−11)² = 121
37	37 − 23 = 14	(14)² = 196
21	21 − 23 = −2	(−2)² = 4

Step 2   Add the squared deviations from the mean: $\Sigma(x - \mu)^2$

$\Sigma(x - \mu)^2 = 324 + 81 + 484 + 4 + 225 + 169 + 144 + 121 + 196 + 4$

$\Sigma(x - \mu)^2 = 1752$

Step 3   To obtain the population variance, σ^2, divide the sum of the squared deviations from the mean, $\Sigma(x - \mu)^2$, by the number of data values, N.

population variance = $\Sigma(x - \mu)^2/N = 1752/10$

$\sigma^2 = 175.2$

Step 4   To obtain the population standard deviation, σ, take the square root of the variance

population standard deviation = $\sqrt{population\ variance}$

$$\sigma = \sqrt{\frac{\Sigma(x - \mu)^2}{N}} = \sqrt{175.2}$$

$$\sigma \approx 13.24 \text{ points}$$

The standard deviation for player A is approximately 13.24 points which indicates that player A's points per game varied, on the average, by 13.24 points from her mean of 23 points per game.

For player B, the population standard deviation of the number of points scored is determined by the following steps:

Step 1   Subtract the mean of 23 from each points per game and then square the deviations from the mean. These results are shown in Table 3.12.

Step 2   Add the squared deviations from the mean: $\Sigma(x - \mu)^2$

$\Sigma(x - \mu)^2 = 25 + 9 + 1 + 64 + 144 + 1 + 36 + 16 + 4 + 0$

$\Sigma(x - \mu)^2 = 300$

Step 3   To obtain the population variance, σ^2, divide the sum of the squared deviations from the mean, $\Sigma(x - \mu)^2$, by the number of data values, N.

population variance = $\Sigma(x - \mu)^2/N = 300/10$

$$\sigma^2 = 30$$

TABLE 3.12

Data Value x	Deviation from the Mean $x - \mu$	Squared Deviation from the Mean $(x - \mu)^2$
18	$18 - 23 \;=\; -5$	$(-5)^2 \;=\; 25$
20	$20 - 23 \;=\; 3$	$(3)^2 \;=\; 9$
22	$22 - 23 \;=\; -1$	$(-1)^2 \;=\; 1$
15	$15 - 23 \;=\; -8$	$(-8)^2 \;=\; 64$
35	$35 - 23 \;=\; 12$	$(12)^2 \;=\; 144$
24	$24 - 23 \;=\; 1$	$(1)^2 \;=\; 1$
29	$29 - 23 \;=\; 6$	$(6)^2 \;=\; 36$
19	$19 - 23 \;=\; -4$	$(-4)^2 \;=\; 16$
25	$25 - 23 \;=\; 2$	$(2)^2 \;=\; 4$
23	$23 - 23 \;=\; 0$	$(0)^2 \;=\; 0$

Step 4 To obtain the population standard deviation, σ, take the square root of the variance.

population standard deviation $= \sqrt{population\ variance}$

$$\sigma = \sqrt{\frac{\Sigma(x - \mu)^2}{N}} = \sqrt{30}$$

$$\sigma \approx 5.48 \text{ points}$$

The standard deviation for player B is approximately 5.48 points which indicates that player B's points per game varied, on the average, by 5.48 points from her mean of 23 points per game. The mean and standard deviation for each player is shown in Table 3.13.

TABLE 3.13

Player	Mean, μ	Standard Deviation, σ
A	23	13.24
B	23	5.48

b. Although both players had the same average number of points per game as shown in Table 3.13, player B should receive the award for the most consistently outstanding woman's scorer for the season. Player B had the smaller standard deviation. The smaller standard deviation indicates that player B was more consistent because her points per game were closer to the mean than player A.

An equivalent formula to calculate the population standard deviation, σ, is called the computational formula for the population standard deviation. This formula is a quicker and faster way to compute the standard deviation since it reduces the number of calculations and round-off errors.

The Computational Formula for the Population Standard Deviation, σ

$$\sigma = \sqrt{\frac{\Sigma x^2 - \frac{(\Sigma x)^2}{N}}{N}}$$

Using the Sample Standard Deviation to Estimate the Population Standard Deviation

In inferential statistics, a *representative sample* is selected from the population and is used to *estimate* the main characteristics of the population, such as the population variance or the population standard deviation. Usually when a sample variance is computed, we are interested in using this sample variance, s^2, as an estimate of the population variance, σ^2.

Statisticians prefer to use a denominator of n – 1 rather than n in the formula for the sample variance. The resulting sample variance provides an unbiased estimate of the population variance, σ^2, and, on the average, the resulting sample standard deviation, s, is a **better estimate** for the population standard deviation, σ.

One reason we use a denominator of n – 1 in the sample standard deviation formula is that a sample generally has less variability than a population. Thus using n rather than n – 1 in the denominator of the formula for the sample standard deviation, we obtain a smaller result for the sample standard deviation and the estimate of the population standard deviation would tend to be too small. To obtain a better estimate for the population standard deviation, a denominator of n – 1 is used for the sample standard deviation.

In Example 3.20, we illustrate the use of the sample standard deviation to estimate a population standard deviation.

E X A M P L E   3 . 2 0

Professor Candida Hart, a college nursing instructor, randomly selects 30 students from the college to estimate the mean and standard deviation of the pulse rate of all the students at the university. She collected the following 30 pulse rates.

pulse rates (measured in heart beats per minute while resting)
52, 74, 76, 70, 75, 45, 70, 50, 76, 65, 73, 78, 74, 73, 66, 59, 70, 62, 65, 72, 55, 70, 60, 72, 76, 66, 73, 76, 68, 79

a. Compute the sample mean, $\bar{x}$
b. Compute the sample standard deviation, s.
c. Determine an estimate of the population mean, μ, and an estimate of the population standard deviation, σ.

Solution

a. Using the sample mean formula,

$$\bar{x} = \frac{\Sigma x}{n}$$

we have:

$$\bar{x} = \frac{2040}{30} = 68 \text{ heart beats per minute}$$

Therefore, 68 heart beats per minute is the sample mean pulse rate for the 30 students.

b. Computing the sample standard deviation, we obtain:

$$s \approx 8.72 \text{ heart beats/minute}$$

The sample standard deviation is approximately 8.72 heart beats per minute.

c. The sample mean of 68 heart beats per minute serves as an estimate of the population mean, μ. That is, 68 heart beats per minute is an estimate of the average heart beat for all the college students. The sample standard deviation (s = 8.72) serves as an estimate of the population standard deviation, σ. Thus, an estimate of the standard deviation of the pulse rates for all the college students is 8.72 heart beats per minute.

CASE STUDY 3.6   **Highest and Lowest Percentages**

Examine the two snapshots in Figure 3.15. The snapshot entitled "Teens at Loose Ends" in Figure 3.15a presents the highest and lowest percentages of teenagers who are neither attending school nor working. In Figure 3.15b, the snapshot entitled "What's Spent on Car Insurance" shows the highest and lowest average car insurance premiums for some states.

(a)   (b)

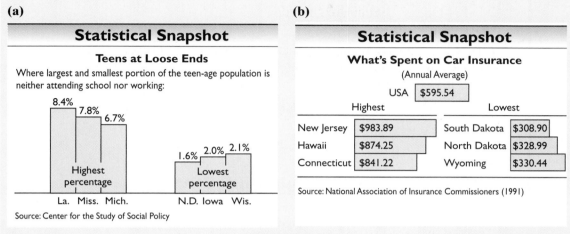

FIGURE 3.15

1. Explain how the information contained in each snapshot is useful in describing the variability of all states.
2. What additional descriptive measure is contained in the snapshot pertaining to the car insurance premiums in Figure 3.15b? What does this additional measure describe and how is it helpful in describing the data on car insurance premiums within the USA?
3. Which measure of variability can be calculated using the information contained within each snapshot of Figure 3.15? What disadvantage(s) is/are there in using this measure to indicate the variability of all the data values?

CASE STUDY 3.7   **SAT Score Averages**

Examine the sample of verbal and mathematical SAT score averages for college-bound high school seniors shown in Figure 3.16. In your observation, which data set of SAT scores seems to have the **more consistent** SAT scores? Would you expect this data set to have a smaller or a larger standard deviation?

SAT SCORE AVERAGES FOR COLLEGE-BOUND HIGH-SCHOOL SENIORS

School Year	Verbal	Mathematical	School Year	Verbal	Mathematical
1983–84	426	471	1988–89	427	476
1984–85	431	475	1989–90	424	476
1985–86	431	475	1990–91	422	474
1986–87	430	476	1991–92	423	476
1987–88	428	476			

Source: College Entrance Examination Board. Copyright 1993. Newsweek. Reprinted with permission.

FIGURE 3.16

Calculating the mean and standard deviation for the verbal and mathematical SAT averages, we obtain:

SAT	Verbal	Mathematical
Mean	426.89	475
Standard Deviation	3.41	1.56

Using this information, we can see that the more consistent mathematical SAT scores had the smaller standard deviation than the verbal scores.

Compare the SAT score for the 1983–84 school year to the other scores within each data set. Do you think the standard deviation of the verbal and mathematical SAT scores would decrease, increase or stay the same, if the score for the 1983-84 school year is omitted?

3.3   APPLICATIONS OF THE STANDARD DEVIATION

In this section, we will look at some rules that illustrate the relationship between the value of the standard deviation and the percentage of data values within a distribution that fall within a certain distance from the mean.

Two measures that help to describe a distribution of data values are the mean and the standard deviation. Remember that the mean is a measure that is used to describe the center of the distribution, while the standard deviation measures the spread of the data values within the distribution. But how can one use the mean and standard deviation to interpret the spread of data values within a distribution? There are two general rules that establish a relationship between the standard deviation and the distribution of data values. These rules are **Chebyshev's Theorem** and the **Empirical Rule**.

Chebyshev's Theorem

For a distribution of data values, regardless of shape, Chebyshev's Theorem states the percentage of data values that **may** lie within various standard deviations from the mean.

Chebyshev's Theorem

Chebyshev's Theorem states for any distribution, regardless of its shape:

at least $1 - \frac{1}{k^2}$ of the data values will lie within k standard deviations of the mean, where k is greater than one.

For example, the percent of data values in a distribution which lie within **two standard deviations of the mean** (k=2) must be at least: $\mathbf{1 - 1/k^2 = 1 - 1/2^2 = 1 - 1/4 = 3/4}$ **or 75%**

This is interpreted to mean that at least 75% of the data values within a distribution will lie within plus and minus 2 standard deviations from the mean.

The percent of data values in a distribution which lie within three standard deviations of the mean (k=3) must be at least: $1 - 1/k^2 = 1 - 1/3^2 = 1 - 1/9 = 8/9$ or 89%.

This is interpreted to mean that at least 89% of the data values within a distribution will lie within plus and minus 3 standard deviations from the mean.

Keep in mind that Chebyshev's Theorem only indicates the minimum percentage of data values that will lie within a specific number of standard deviations of the mean. In many distributions, this percentage will be greater than the minimum guaranteed by Chebyshev's Theorem.

In Figure 3.17, the results of Chebyshev's Theorem are shown for the shapes of the following distributions:
a) symmetric bell-shaped shown in Figure 3.17a.
b) skewed left shown in Figure 3.17b.
c) skewed right shown in Figure 3.17c.

FIGURE 3.17

EXAMPLE 3.21

A statistics instructor has recorded the amount of time students need to complete the final examination. The times, stated to the nearest minute, are:

50, 70, 62, 55, 38, 42, 49, 75, 80, 79, 48, 45, 53, 58, 64, 77, 48, 49, 50, 61, 72, 74, 10, 95, 120, 79, 75, 48, 72, 37, 71, 35, 79, 72, 75, 76, 32, 30, 77, 75, 79, 45, 70, 39, 75, 72, 45, 47, 73, 72

Using this data, determine:
a) $\bar{x}$ and s to the nearest minute.
b) The percent of data values that are within 2 standard deviations of the mean.
c) The percent of data values that are within 3 standard deviations of the mean.
d) Compare the results of parts (b) and (c) to the results of Chebyshev's Theorem.
e) Is there any data value within the distribution that falls outside 3 standard deviations from the mean? If there is such a data value, then can this data value be considered an outlier? Explain.

Solution

a) The mean and standard deviation, to the nearest minute, are $\bar{x} = 61$ minutes and s = 19 minutes.
b) The time which represents the value that is 2 standard deviations below the mean is:

$$\bar{x} - 2s = 61 - 2(19) = 23 \text{ minutes}$$

While the time which represents the value that is 2 standard deviations above the mean is:

$$\bar{x} + 2s = 61 + 2(19) = 99 \text{ minutes}$$

The number of times that are within 2 standard deviations of the mean, that is from 23 to 99 minutes, is 48. Therefore, the percent of times that are within 2 standard deviations of the mean is:

$$\frac{48}{50}(100\%) = 96\%$$

c)   The time which represents the value that is 3 standard deviations below the mean is:

$$\bar{x} - 3s = 61 - 3(19) = 4 \text{ minutes}$$

While the time which represents the value that is 3 standard deviations above the mean is:

$$\bar{x} + 3s = 61 + 3(19) = 118 \text{ minutes}$$

The number of times that are from 4 to 118 minutes, that is within 3 standard deviations of the mean, is 49. Therefore, the percent of times that are within 3 standard deviations of the mean is:

$$\frac{49}{50}(100\%) = 98\%$$

d)   Chebyshev's Theorem asserts that the percent of data values that are within 2 standard deviations from the mean is **at least 75% or a minimum of 75%**. From part b, we determined that the percent of actual times that are within 2 standard deviations of the mean is 96%. This is consistent with Chebyshev's Theorem since 96% is **more than the minimum of 75%**.

According to Chebyshev's Theorem, the percent of data values that are within 3 standard deviations from the mean is **at least 89% or a minimum of 89%**. From part c, we determined that the percent of actual times that are within 3 standard deviations of the mean is 98%. This is consistent with Chebyshev's Theorem since 98% is **more than the minimum of 89%**.

e)   The data value 120 minutes is outside the range of values representing 3 standard deviations from the mean, 4 to 118 minutes. The data value 120 minutes can be considered to be an outlier since it is considered to lie far from most of the other data values within the distribution.

————————————————————■

Another rule that measures with more precision the percentage of data values that fall within a certain distance from the mean for a symmetric bell-shaped distribution is described by the Empirical Rule.

Empirical Rule

Although Chebyshev's Theorem applies to any distribution regardless of shape, the Empirical Rule provides an explanation of how the standard deviation measures the spread of the data values from the mean only for a distribution that is mound or approximately bell-shaped.

Empirical Rule

———————

Empirical Rule states that for a mound or bell-shaped distribution:
1. Approximately 68% of the data values will lie within 1 standard deviation of the mean. $(\bar{x} - s \text{ to } \bar{x} + s)$
2. Approximately 95% of the data values will lie within 2 standard deviations of the mean. $(\bar{x} - 2s \text{ to } \bar{x} + 2s)$
3. Approximately all (99% to 100%) of the data values will lie within 3 standard deviations of the mean. $(\bar{x} - 3s \text{ to } \bar{x} + 3s)$

Figure 3.18 illustrates the Empirical Rule for a symmetric bell-shaped distribution.

The Empirical Rule is a widely used rule in real life applications and provides a reasonable estimate for distributions that are approximately bell-shaped. However, you may find that the percentage of data values may not be exactly equal to the stated percentages for the intervals within the Empirical Rule. The Empirical Rule is especially useful when the mean and standard deviation of a

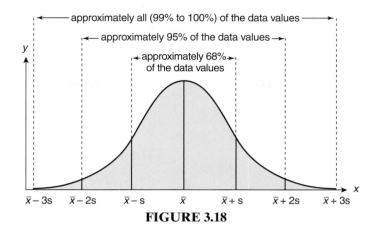

FIGURE 3.18

bell-shaped distribution are known but all the data values of the distribution are not known. This type of application of the Empirical Rule is illustrated in Example 3.22.

EXAMPLE 3.22

The results of a standardized achievement test are approximately bell-shaped with $\bar{x} = 350$ and $s = 85$. According to the Empirical Rule, approximately what percentage of test scores would you expect to fall between:
a)   265 to 435?
b)   180 to 520?
c)   95 to 605?
d)   If there were a test score equal to 625, could you consider such a score an outlier? Explain.

Solution

a)   Since the values 265 and 435 are one standard deviation from the mean, that is, $\bar{x} - 1s = 350 - 85 = 265$ and $\bar{x} + 1s = 350 + 85 = 435$, then according to the Empirical Rule the percentage of test scores between 265 to 435 is approximately 68%.

b)   The interval 180 to 520 represents test scores that are two standard deviations from the mean, that is, $\bar{x} - 2s = 180$ and $\bar{x} + 2s = 520$. Therefore, approximately 95% of the scores should lie within this interval.

c)   Almost all the test scores, or 99% to 100%, are expected to lie in the interval 95 to 605 because these test scores are three standard deviations from the mean. That is, $\bar{x} - 3s = 95$ and $\bar{x} + 3s = 605$.

d)   The test score 625 is considered an outlier, since an outlier is a test score that lies far from the other test scores. According to the Empirical Rule, the test scores that lie more than three standard deviations from the mean occur less than 1% of the time. This makes the test score 625 a very rare score, therefore, it should be considered an outlier.

Using the Range to Obtain an Estimate of the Standard Deviation

According to the Empirical Rule, a bell-shaped distribution would have most of the data values within 2 standard deviations of the mean. This means that the range for the data values will be about 4 standard deviations apart (that is: 2 standard deviations below the mean to 2 standard deviations above the mean). Meanwhile, Chebyshev's Theorem states that for any distribution regardless of shape, approximately all the data values lie within 3 standard deviations of the mean. This results in a range of values that are 6 standard deviations apart (that is: 3 standard deviations below the mean to 3 standard deviations above the mean). This is shown in Figure 3.19.

The Range Rule

FIGURE 3.19

From Figure 3.19, we obtain the following relationships:

$$\text{range} \approx 4s \quad \text{or} \quad \text{range} \approx 6s$$

Solving for s in each relationship, we obtain the following estimates for the standard deviation:

$$s \approx \text{range}/4 \quad \text{OR} \quad s \approx \text{range}/6$$

From these rules, *the standard deviation should lie within a distance of range/6 (the smaller estimate of s) to the range/4 (the larger estimate of s).*

In Example 3.21, the standard deviation of the 50 data values was $s \approx 19$ minutes (to the nearest minute). For this distribution of data values, the range = 120 − 10 = 110. Using the rules range/6 and range/4 to obtain an estimate of the standard deviation we get an:

over-estimate: $s \approx \text{range}/4 = 110/4 = 27.5$

OR

under-estimate: $s \approx \text{range}/6 = 110/6 \approx 18.33$

According to these estimates, we would expect the standard deviation to lie between the lower estimate of 18.33 and the upper estimate of 27.5. Notice that the standard deviation $s \approx 19$ does lie between these estimates. However, please note that these rules will only provide rough estimates of the standard deviation. **If a distribution has outliers, then the standard deviation may not lie within these two estimates.** In fact, large data sets will usually be more varied since they have a greater chance of containing an outlier. When there are outliers, the range may exceed more than 6 standard deviations from the mean. Therefore, to obtain a better estimate of s using the range, it is necessary to consider the size of the sample. Table 3.14 provides an approximate rule for estimating s based on the sample size.

TABLE 3.14   Rule For Estimating s Using the Range

Sample Size	Rule for Estimating the Standard Deviation, s
5	$s \approx \text{range}/2.5$
10	$s \approx \text{range}/3$
25	$s \approx \text{range}/4$
100	$s \approx \text{range}/6$

Please keep in mind that whenever possible you should always calculate the exact value of the standard deviation of data values. These estimates of the standard deviation are only intended to provide you with a rough estimate of the standard deviation if needed.

EXAMPLE 3.23

For a sample containing 30 data values, the range is 47. Using Table 3.14, determine an estimate of the standard deviation, s.

Solution

Notice from Table 3.14, a sample of size n = 30 falls between sample sizes of 25 and 100. We will select the rule: **s ≈ range/4** to estimate the standard deviation, s, since n = 30 is closer to 25. Therefore, an estimate for the sample standard deviation is:

$$s \approx range/4 = 47/4 = 11.75$$

Thus an estimate of the sample standard deviation is approximately 11.75.   ∎

CASE STUDY 3.8   Home Prices by Region

The newspaper clipping in Figure 3.20 presents the "Home Prices By Region" for typical homes within the United States.

HOME PRICES BY REGION

Area	Median Price	%chg. From Year Ago	Area	Median Price	%chg. From Year Ago	Area	Median Price	%chg. From Year Ago
Akron	$77,400	2.5	Honolulu	347,000	1.5	Orange Co., Calif.	222,200	-5.6
Albany	109,900	0.5	Houston	78,000	-0.3	Orlando, Fla.	86,900	0.8
Albuquerque	94,400	8.9	Indianapolis	83,800	4.6	Philadelphia	108,900	9.0
Atlanta	87,500.	N.A.	Jacksonville, Fla.	74,100	-1.3	Phoenix	86,300	1.9
Baltimore	113,200	1.4	Kansas City, Mo.	79,100	3.9	Pittsburgh	75,900	1.5
Birmingham, Ala.	89,000	-0.6	Knoxville, Tenn.	82,400	5.2	Portland, Ore.	99,600	5.0
Boston	165,200	-1.8	Las Vegas	105,200	3.7	Providence	112,500	-5.0
Buffalo	84,200	5.6	Lexington, Ky.	76,900	-1.8	Riverside/San		
Charleston, W.Va.	75,400	10.2	Little Rock, Ark.	N.A.	N.A.	Bernardino, Calif.	135,400	-1.5
Charlotte, N.C.	102,800	-4.1	Los Angeles	199,700	-8.0	Rochester	83,300	-0.6
Chattanooga, Tenn.	69,800	-4.0	Louisville, Ky.	69,900	0.3	Sacramento, Calif.	130,400	-3.4
Chicago	131,300	-1.1	Madison, Wis.	97,700	9.3	St. Louis	80,900	-2.5
Cincinnati	85,600	-2.2	Memphis, Tenn.	84,200	0.7	Salt Lake City	79,000	7.9
Cleveland	89,200	1.2	Miami	98,000	1.4	San Antonio, Tx.	72,600	6.8
Columbia, S.C.	82,300	-3.3	Milwaukee	98,400	2.4	San Diego	175,500	-3.8
Columbus, Ohio	89,300	-1.1	Minneapolis/			San Francisco	249,300	0.8
Dallas	89,600	-1.3	St. Paul	96,400	1.8	Seattle	145,000	2.6
Dayton, Ohio	78,400	-0.5	Mobile, Ala.	66,200	4.6	Spokane, Wash.	79,100	10.9
Daytona Beach, Fla.	67,600	3.8	Montgomery, Ala.	79,100	-0.6	Springfield, Mass.	106,300	-9.1
Denver	96,200	1.9	Nashville, Tenn.	87,000	-2.2	Syracuse	86,100	11.2
Des Moines, Iowa	71,600	0.6	**Nassau/Suffolk, NY**	**158,000**	**0.4**	Tampa/		
Detroit	92,200	19.0	New Haven, Conn.	142,600	0.1	St. Petersburg, Fla.	69,900	-0.3
El Paso, Tx.	67,900	3.0	New Orleans	73,000	4.0	Tulsa, Okla.	68,200	-0.4
Fort Lauderdale, Fla.	99,500	5.7	**NY/Long Island**			Washington	153,500	0.7
Fort Worth, Tx.	79,700	-1.2	**/N. New Jersey**	**168,000**	**-0.5**	West Palm		
Greenville, S.C.	82,800	4.0	Oklahoma City	61,100	2.2	Beach, Fla.	108,600	-1.9
Hartford	135,500	-4.2	Omaha	64,300	-4.6	**United States**	**104,200**	**5.1**

Source: National Association of Realtors

FIGURE 3.20

a) What measure of central tendency is being used to represent the typical home price? What advantage is there to use this measure of central tendency over the mean?

b) Compare and interpret the median price for a home in Nashville, Tenn., to a home in Orange Co., Calif.

c) Determine the $\bar{x}$ and s of the median home prices.

d) Find the percentage of prices that fall within two standard deviations of the mean, three standard deviations of the mean, and four standard deviations from the mean.

e) Calculate the minimum percent of data values that are expected to fall within two, three and four standard deviations from the mean according to Chebyshev's Theorem.

f) Compare the results of parts (b) and (c). Do the results differ or are they equal? If the results differ, explain why they are different.

g) Is there any home price that falls outside the range of four standard deviations from the mean? If such a value exists, identify this value, and would this value be an outlier? Explain.

CASE STUDY 3.9   Security and Exchange Commission

The time-series vertical bar graphs in Figure 3.21 displays the Securities and Exchange Commission's (SEC) staff (Figure 3.21a) and budget (Figure 3.21b) for the five selected years from 1976 to 1992. Based on these bar graphs, which one has more variability over the selected years?

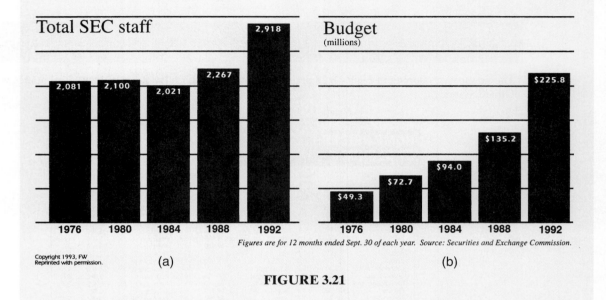

FIGURE 3.21

From the figure, you should observe that the budget bar graph indicates more variability than the SEC staff graph. Using the information in the bar graphs, the mean and standard deviation for the SEC staff and budget are given in Table 3.15.

TABLE 3.15

Statistic	Staff	Budget
Sample Mean	2277.4	115.4
Sample Standard Deviation	369.55	69.34

Notice that in Table 3.15 the standard deviation for the SEC staff data is greater than the standard deviation for the SEC budget. Why is there a discrepancy between the variability indicated by the graphs in Figure 3.21 verses the variability shown in Table 3.15?

Let's compare this information about the mean and standard deviation to the heights of the bars within the graphs.

For each graph, draw a line on the bar graph that represents the mean. Within which bar graph does there appear to be a greater fluctuation among the heights of the bars with respect to the mean? Explain why the standard deviation reflects the variability among the heights of the bars.

In Case Study 3.9 we observed that when comparing the variability of distributions where the size or magnitude of the data values are very different, the standard deviation **doesn't** take into consideration the magnitude of the data values. That is, the standard deviation is an absolute measure of variability. In such situations we need a **relative measure** of dispersion, that is, a measure that takes into consideration the magnitude and the variability of the data values. This objective can be accomplished by comparing the standard deviation relative to the mean of the distribution. Such a relative measure of variability is called the **coefficient of variation.**

DEFINITION 3.13

The **Coefficient of Variation** is the ratio of the standard deviation to the mean, expressed as a percent.

$$Coefficient\ of\ Variation = \frac{standard\ deviation}{mean}(100\%)$$

When to Use the Coefficient of Variation

The coefficient of variation is a very effective measure to use when one needs to make a meaningful comparison of the dispersion of two distributions under the following two situations.
1. The data values of the two distributions are in different units.
2. The data values of the two distributions are in the same unit, but the distance between their means is large.

Let's reinterpret the information in Table 3.15 by calculating the coefficient of variation for the staff and budget data.

For SEC staff data, the coefficient of variation is:

$$Coefficient\ of\ Variation = \frac{standard\ deviation}{mean}(100\%)$$

$$= \frac{369.55}{2277.4}(100\%)$$

$$\approx 16\%$$

For SEC budget data, the coefficient of variation is

$$= \frac{69.34}{115.4}(100\%)$$

$$\approx 60\%$$

We find that the SEC staff, which has the greater **absolute** variation (i.e., standard deviation = 369.55), has the less **relative** variation as measured by the coefficient of variation. In this particular situation, the coefficient of variation was an appropriate measure to use because the data values were expressed in different units. The SEC staff data values represent the number of staff members, while the data values of the SEC budget is dollars.

EXAMPLE 3.24

An investor has studied the performance of two stocks for one year. The following data summarizes their performance:

Stock A: mean = $98.38   standard deviation = $9.78
Stock B: mean = $23.50   standard deviation = $6.95

a. Which stock has the greater absolute variation?
b. Which stock has the greater relative variation?
c. If the investor decides to use the standard deviation as a measure of the **risk** of the investment, explain why the coefficient of variation is a more useful measure of risk in comparing these two stocks.

Solution

a. Since the standard deviation is an absolute measure of dispersion, then the larger standard deviation of $9.78 has the greater absolute standard deviation.
b. Using the coefficient of variation as a relative measure of dispersion, we need to calculate the coefficient of variation for each stock. For stock A we have:

$$Coefficient\ of\ Variation = \frac{standard\ deviation}{mean}(100\%)$$

$$= \frac{9.78}{98.30}(100\%) \approx 10\%$$

For stock B we have:

$$Coefficient\ of\ Variation = \frac{standard\ deviation}{mean}(100\%)$$

$$= \frac{6.95}{23.50}(100\%) \approx 30\%$$

Therefore, stock B has the greater relative measure of variability.

c. Notice the standard deviation of the two stocks are relatively close in value. Yet the mean for stock A is about four times larger than the mean of stock B. Since the distance between the means of each stock is large, then the coefficient of variation is a very useful measure to make a meaningful comparison of the dispersion between the two stocks. In particular, a change of one standard deviation from the mean price of either stock will have a more profound effect on the total investment in stock B than in stock A because the standard deviation of stock B represents 30% of mean as compared to 10% of the mean for stock A. Therefore stock B represents a riskier investment.   ■

3.4   MEASURES OF RELATIVE STANDING

John Gulliver, the famous British traveler, in his fantastic journeys to faraway lands encountered many strange situations. Two of these situations are pictured in Figures 3.22 and 3.23.

As can be seen from the pictures, Gulliver's size is extreme relative to the inhabitants of the kingdoms he visits. In the land of Lilliput, where the inhabitants are only as large as Gulliver's thumb, he is considered a giant (see Figure 3.22). On the other hand, in the land of Brobdingnag, where Gulliver is only as large as an acorn, he is a dwarf among giants (see Figure 3.23).

Although Gulliver's height remains constant, throughout his travels, his height is interpreted or ranked differently relative to the heights of the people within each kingdom. For example, in the kingdom of Lilliput, Gulliver is considered a giant, while in the kingdom of Brobdingnag, he is regarded as a dwarf.

In statistics, one encounters numerous situations where it will be necessary to describe the position of a particular data value relative to the other data values of a distribution. In the previous two sections we discussed how the statistical measures of central tendency and variability can be used to

John Gulliver

(I) Lilliput: the land of the Little People

FIGURE 3.22

(II) Brobdingnag: the land of Giants

FIGURE 3.23

describe the center and variability of an entire collection of data values. Now we will examine descriptive techniques which will describe *the position of an individual data value* within a data set. A statistical measure that describes the position of a particular data value relative to the other values of the data set is called a *Measure of Relative Standing.*

z Score

In Example 3.25 we will examine a Measure of Relative Standing which uses the mean and the standard deviation to describe the relative location of a particular data value. This Measure of Relative Standing is called the **z score**.

EXAMPLE 3.25

Debbie earned a grade of 87 on her History exam, and a grade of 39 on her English exam. She would like to determine on which exam she did better, relative to the students in each class. How can this be accomplished using the information in Table 3.16?

TABLE 3.16

Exam	Mean	Standard Deviation	Debbie's Grade
History	75	6	87
English	27	4	39

Solution

Using the mean as a typical grade, we can calculate the deviation from the mean for each of Debbie's exams. A deviation from the mean is called a deviation score, and is calculated by the formula:

deviation score = data value – mean.

On the History exam, Debbie's deviation score is:

Test Grade – Mean = Deviation Score
87   –   75   =   12

On the English exam, Debbie's deviation score is:

$$\textbf{Test Grade} - \textbf{Mean} = \textbf{Deviation Score}$$
$$39 \quad - \quad 27 \quad = \quad 12$$

In both of Debbie's classes, her test grades are twelve units greater than the mean, thereby producing no meaningful comparison. To obtain a meaningful comparison consider the different variations in the test grades for each of her classes. Since the standard deviation reflects the typical deviation from the mean, let's reevaluate her test grades using the standard deviation. Table 3.17 shows the necessary information to reevaluate Debbie's test grades.

TABLE 3.17

	Deviation Score = test grade – mean	Standard Deviation	Number of Standard Deviations from the Mean
History Exam	$87 - 75 = 12$	6	2
English Exam	$39 - 27 = 12$	4	3

We can interpret Debbie's History grade of 87 to be **two standard deviations** greater than the mean of 75. That is,

$$\textbf{mean} + \textbf{2(standard deviation)} = \textbf{Debbie's History grade}$$
$$75 \quad + \quad 2(6) \quad = \quad 87$$

While Debbie's English grade of 39 is **three standard deviations** greater than the mean of 27. That is,

$$\textbf{mean} + \textbf{3(standard deviation)} = \textbf{Debbie's English grade}$$
$$27 \quad + \quad 3(4) \quad = \quad 39$$

We can conclude that Debbie's English test grade of 39 showed a better achievement relative to her English class since it is three standard deviations greater than the mean English grade, whereas her History exam grade of 87 is only two standard deviations greater than the mean History grade.

The statistical Measure of Relative Standing used in Example 3.25 to describe the position of each of Debbie's test grades relative to the test grades of the other students is called a z score. The z score of each of Debbie's grades expresses the relative position of Debbie's grade from the mean grade in terms of *standard deviation units*.

DEFINITION 3.14

The **z score** of a data value indicates the number of standard deviations that the data value deviates from the mean. The formula for the z score of a data value is:

$$\text{z score of a data value} = \frac{\text{data value} - \text{mean}}{\text{standard deviation}}$$

$$\text{z score of a data value} = \frac{\text{deviation score}}{\text{standard deviation}}$$

In symbols, the z score formula for sample data is:

$$z = \frac{x - \bar{x}}{s}$$

The z score formula for population data is:

$$z = \frac{x - \mu}{\sigma}$$

Let's use the z score formula to determine the z score for each of Debbie's exam grades from Example 3.25, and interpret these results. The pertinent data of Example 3.25 is summarized in Table 3.18.

TABLE 3.18

Exam	Mean (μ)	Standard Deviation (σ)	Debbie's Grade (x)
History	75	6	87
English	27	4	39

The z score for the history test grade of 87 is computed using the formula: $z = \dfrac{x - \mu}{\sigma}$ and the information contained in Table 3.18. Thus, the z score for the data value 87 is:

$$z = \frac{87 - 75}{6} = 2$$

Thus, the test grade of 87 has a z score of 2. This indicates that **87 is two standard deviations greater than the mean of 75**.

The z score for the English test grade of 39 is:

$$z = \frac{39 - 27}{4} = 3$$

Thus, the test grade of 39 has a z score of 3. This indicates that **39 is three standard deviations greater than the mean of 27**. In comparing the two z scores as illustrated in Figure 3.24, we see that Debbie's English grade, because it has a larger z score, has a better relative standing in the English class than her History grade's relative standing within her History class.

FIGURE 3.24

Since Debbie's relative standing in the English class is higher than the relative standing in her History class, then we can conclude that her English test grade is better relative to the students in the English class than the History grade is with respect to the students in her History class.

E X A M P L E   3 . 2 6

Calculate the z scores for each of the following three test grades that were selected from all the college students who took the final exam in Freshman Psychology 101 class, if the population mean is 75 and the population standard deviation is 10.

Psychology test grades:

65, 80, 75

Solution

To calculate the z score of 65, use $z = \dfrac{x - \mu}{\sigma}$.

Since x = 65, μ = 75 and σ = 10, then z of 65 is:

$$z = \frac{65 - 75}{10} = \frac{-10}{10} = -1$$

To compute the z score of 80, we have:

$$z = \frac{80 - 75}{10} = 0.5$$

Using the z score formula, the test score x = 75 has a z score of:

$$z = \frac{75 - 75}{10} = 0$$

Notice, in Example 3.26 the test grade of 65 is less than the mean and has a negative z score. The test grade of 75 is equal to the mean and has a z score of 0, while the test grade of 80 is greater than the mean and has a positive z score. Notice from the previous results, the sign of the z score indicates the location of the test score relative to the mean. These results are summarized in Table 3.19.

Interpreting the Sign of a z Score

The sign of the z score of a data value indicates the location of the data value relative to the mean as is displayed in Table 3.19.

TABLE 3.19

z Score	Location of Data Value
z score is positive	Data Value is greater than the mean
z score is zero	Data Value is equal to the mean
z score is negative	Data Value is less than the mean

EXAMPLE 3.27

At the end of each Major League Baseball season, an award is given to the hitter with the highest batting average (BA) and an award is given to the pitcher with the lowest earned run average (ERA). During the 1980 season, George Brett of the Kansas City Royals had the best batting average with a batting average of .390. During the 1985 season, Doc Gooden of the New York Mets had the best earned run average with an ERA of 1.53. Use the following information to answer the questions. During the 1980 season, the American League hitters had a mean BA of .270 with a standard deviation of 0.031. During the 1985 season, the National League Pitchers had a mean ERA of 4.16 with a standard deviation of 1.43.

a) Compute the z score of each player's outstanding season

b) Interpret the z scores and determine which player during their respective best season had the more outstanding performance relative to the other players in the category.

Solution

a) Compute the z score for each player.
   For George Brett, the z score of his batting average of .390 is:

$$z = \frac{.390 - .270}{.031} = 3.87$$

   For Doc Gooden, the z score of his earned run average of .153 is:

$$z = \frac{1.53 - 4.16}{1.43} = -1.84$$

b) George Brett's BA of .390 with a z score of 3.87 means that his batting average was 3.87 standard deviations above the mean batting average of .270. Doc Gooden's ERA of 1.53 was 1.84 standard deviations below the mean ERA of 4.16. Although both player's performances were better than the mean performance, George Brett's performance was more outstanding relative to the other American League hitters since he had a better z score. ∎

Detecting Outliers Using z Scores

As discussed in Chapter 2, an outlier is an extreme data value that falls far from most of the other data values. A z score can be used to identify an outlier since the farther the data value is from a z score of z = 0 the more likely the data value is an outlier. According to the Empirical Rule, any data value within an approximately bell-shaped distribution having a z score less than –3 or greater than +3 can be considered as an outlier since such a data value is considered an extreme data value.

In Example 3.27, Brett's batting average of .390 is almost 4 standard deviations above the mean. According to the Empirical Rule, we would expect almost all of the batting averages to fall within 3 standard deviations of the mean. Since Brett's batting average is almost 4 standard deviations from the mean we can interpret his batting average to be an outlier. That is, it is an extreme batting average that lies well outside the range of all the other batting averages.

Converting z Scores to Raw Scores

We will now develop a formula to convert a z score to a raw score or data value. In Example 3.28, we begin the development of this formula.

EXAMPLE 3.28

A recent medical report claimed that if a male weighs more than one standard deviation from his mean weight, then he is either overweight or underweight. Compute the weights that determine overweight and underweight for a male who stands 5 feet 8 inches, if the mean weight for his height is 155 lbs. and the standard deviation is 10 lbs.

Solution

Step 1 Determine the Overweight.
   To determine the overweight we must determine the weight which is one standard deviation greater than the mean. That is, we need to determine the weight corresponding to:

mean + 1 standard deviation

Since the mean is 155 lbs and the standard deviation is 10 lbs then we have:

mean + 1 standard deviation = 155 + 1(10) = 165 lbs.

Therefore, a male who stands 5'8" is considered overweight if he weighs more than 165 lbs.

Step 2   Determine the Underweight.

To determine the underweight we must determine the weight which is one standard deviation less than the mean. That is, we need to find the weight corresponding to:

mean − 1 standard deviation

Using a mean of 155 lbs and a standard deviation of 10 lbs then we have:

mean − 1 standard deviation = 155 − 1(10) = 145 lbs.

Thus, a 5'8" male is considered underweight if he weighs less than 145 lbs.

Consequently, if a 5'8" male has a weight outside the range of 145 to 165 lbs., then the male is either underweight or overweight. ∎

In the previous example, we examined the approach to convert a z score to a raw score, x. Now we present a formula called the **raw score formula** to change a z score to a raw score or data value.

Raw Score Formula

To convert a z Score to a Raw Score

Raw Score = Mean + (z Score)(Standard Deviation)

The raw score formula for a sample is: $x = \bar{x} + zs$

The raw score formula for a population is: $x = \mu + z\sigma$

EXAMPLE 3.29

On each of her student's test papers, a statistics instructor writes the z score rather than the actual test score. The statistics for the test are: $\bar{x} = 72$ and $s = 9.6$. Determine the student's test score (to the nearest whole number) if the test grade:

a)   Has a z score of 1.65.
b)   Is 2 standard deviations below the mean test grade.
c)   Has a z score of 0.

Solution

a)   To determine a student's test grade for a z score of 1.65, we will use the raw score formula for a sample: $x = \bar{x} + zs$. Substituting the statistics: $\bar{x} = 72, s = 9.6$ and $z = 1.65$ into the raw score formula, we have:

$$x = \bar{x} + zs.$$
$$x = 72 + (1.65)(9.6)$$
$$x = 87.84$$
$$x \approx 88$$

Thus, a student with a z score of 1.65 has a test score approximately equal to 88.

b)   A student's test grade which is 2 standard deviations below the mean has a z score of: $z = -2$. To obtain the test grade, substitute the statistics: $\bar{x} = 72, s = 9.6$ and $z = -2$.

$$x = \bar{x} + zs.$$
$$x = 72 + (-2)(9.6)$$
$$x = 52.8$$
$$x \approx 53$$

Therefore, a student with a test score of approximately 53 is 2 standard deviations below the mean.

c)   A student with a z score of 0 has a test score equal to the mean score of 72. ────── ∎

Percentile Rank and Percentiles

A common Measure of Relative Standing used to describe the position of a particular data value relative to the other data values is its **percentile rank**. The percentile rank of the data value X indicates the percent of data values within the distribution less than the data value X.

For example, Steven scored 687 on a national aptitude exam. How should we interpret Steven's score? Is 687 an exceptional score, an average score or below average score? In order to interpret this score more information is needed. Further investigation of the national results shows that Steven's aptitude score has a percentile rank of 90. We interpret this to mean that 90% of all the students who took the aptitude exam scored below Steven's score of 687 while 10% of the students scored higher than Steven's score. We can thus interpret Steven's score as an exceptional score!

Let's define this percentile rank concept and examine the formula to calculate the percentile rank.

DEFINITION 3.15

The **percentile rank** of a data value, X, is equal to the percentage of data values less than the data value, X, plus one-half the percentage of data values equal to the data value, X, within the distribution.

Formula to Compute the Percentile Rank of a Data Value

After arranging the data values in numerical order, the formula to compute the percentile rank is:

$$\text{PR of the data value X} = \frac{[B + (\frac{1}{2})E]}{N}(100)$$

where: PR = percentile rank
   B   = the number of data values less than X
   E   = the number of data values equal to X
   N   = the total number of data values

Percentile ranks are always expressed as whole numbers.

Percentile ranks are meaningful for large data sets. Scores from college boards, I.Q. tests and family incomes in the U.S. represent examples of large data sets where it is practical to report the data values both as a score and as a percentile.

EXAMPLE 3.30

On an exam, 25 college students receive scores of:

102, 85, 109, 83, 112, 105, 98, 115, 91, 117, 88, 95, 116, 105, 130, 80, 115, 84, 95, 121, 85, 89, 94, 111, 106.

Compute the percentile ranks of the following scores:
a)   102
b)   84
c)   115

Solution

Step 1   First *arrange* the data in numerical order. We get:

80, 83, 84, 85, 85, 88, 89, 91, 94, 95, 95, 98, 102, 105, 105, 106, 109, 111, 112, 115, 115, 116, 117, 121, 130

Step 2   a)   To find the percentile rank of the score 102, use the formula:

$$\text{PR of the data value X} = \frac{[B+(\frac{1}{2})E]}{N}(100)$$

Arrange the scores in numerical order, and determine the values of B, E, and N. Examining the ordered scores, we observe that there are twelve scores less than 102, so B = 12. Since there is only one 102, then E = 1. Finally, N = 25 since there are 25 scores.

Substituting the values of B, E and N into the percentile rank formula, we have:

$$\text{PR of the score 102} = \frac{[12+(\frac{1}{2})1]}{25}(100)$$

$$\text{PR of the score 102} = \frac{12.5}{25}(100) = 50$$

Thus, the PR of the score 102 is 50. This indicates that approximately 50% of the scores are below the score of 102.

b)   To compute the percentile rank of 84, determine the values of B, and E for 84. For the score 84, B = 2 and E = 1. Therefore,

$$\text{PR of the score 84} = \frac{[2+(\frac{1}{2})1]}{25}(100)$$

$$= \frac{2.5}{25}(100) = 10$$

The PR of the score 84 is 10. This means that approximately 10% of the scores are below the score of 84.

c)   To use the formula to compute the percentile rank of 115, the values for B and E are: B = 19 and E = 2. Thus,

$$\text{PR of the score 115} = \frac{[19+(\frac{1}{2})2]}{25}(100)$$

$$= \frac{20}{25}(100) = 80$$

Thus, the PR of the score 115 is 80. This indicates that approximately 80% of the scores are below the score of 115. ∎

Another concept closely related to percentile rank is that of **percentile**. Let's examine this concept.

> **DEFINITION 3.16**
> The **pth percentile** is the data value within the distribution which has p percent of the data values less than its value and the rest of the data values greater than its data value. 99 percentiles divide the data set into 100 groups.

In Example 3.30 part a, the score 102 has a percentile rank of 50. This indicates that 102 is the median because 50% of the scores are less than 102 and 50% of the scores are greater than 102. Using percentiles, we state that 102 is the 50th percentile. This is written as:

$$P_{50} = 102$$

In Example 3.30 part b, the score 84 has a percentile rank of 10. Therefore, we can state that 84 is the tenth percentile, written as:

$$P_{10} = 84.$$

In Example 3.30 part c, the score 115 has a percentile rank of 80. 115 is the 80th percentile, expressed:

$$P_{80} = 115.$$

Meaning of Percentile and Percentile Rank

There is a difference in the use of the words **percentile** and **percentile rank**. In general, the **percentile** is a **data value** of the distribution while a **percentile rank** is a **percentage** value ranging from 0 to 100.

EXAMPLE 3.31

Identify the percentile and the percentile rank in each statement.
a) Exactly 62 percent of the students in a given school system received IQ scores less than 112.
b) In Christopher's third grade class, 70% of the students have heights less than 54 inches.

Solution

a) 112 is the 62nd percentile and 62 is the percentile rank of 112.
b) 54 is the 70th percentile of the student's heights in the third grade class and 70 is the percentile rank of the height of 54 inches.

Deciles and Quartiles

Some important percentiles have individual names. Two such names are ***deciles*** and ***quartiles***. There are nine deciles, and three quartiles. We will first examine the relationship between percentiles and deciles.

Deciles

The nine deciles which divide the data set into tenths or ten equal parts are:
- The **10th percentile** is called the **1st decile**
- The **20th percentile** is called the **2nd decile**
- The **30th percentile** is called the **3rd decile**
- The **40th percentile** is called the **4th decile**
- The **50th percentile** is called the **5th decile**
- The **60th percentile** is called the **6th decile**
- The **70th percentile** is called the **7th decile**
- The **80th percentile** is called the **8th decile**
- The **90th percentile** is called the **9th decile**

The relationship between the nine deciles and the corresponding percentiles are shown in Figure 3.25.

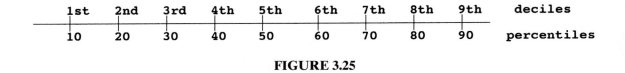

FIGURE 3.25

Notice in Figure 3.25, the 1st decile is the value at the tenth percentile.

Let's now examine the relationship between the three quartiles and the corresponding percentiles.

Quartiles

The three quartiles which divide the data set into quarters or four equal parts are:
- The **25th percentile** is called the **1st quartile, Q_1.**
- The **50th percentile** is called the **2nd quartile, Q_2.**
- The **75th percentile** is called the **3rd quartile, Q_3.**

The relationship between the three quartiles and the corresponding percentiles are shown in Figure 3.26.

FIGURE 3.26

EXAMPLE 3.32

Some results from the mathematics reasoning part of the Scholastic Aptitude Test (SAT) are given in Table 3.20.

TABLE 3.20

Score	Percentile
320	10
365	20
380	25
400	30
410	35
474	50
510	60
570	75
595	80
650	90
750	99

Using Table 3.20 determine:
a) The score which is the 1st decile.
b) The median.
c) The score which has a percentile rank of 90.
d) The percentile rank of the score 380, and state what quartile it represents.
e) The 3rd quartile.
f) The score which is the 6th decile.

Solution

a) The first decile is another name for the 10th percentile. Thus, since 320 is the 10th percentile, it is also the 1st decile.
b) The median is the 50th percentile. Thus, the median score is 474.
c) A score that has a percentile rank of 90 is the 90th percentile. Thus, the 90th percentile is the score 650.
d) The score 380 is the 25th percentile and has a percentile rank of 25. Thus, 380 represents the 1st quartile, since it has a percentile rank of 25.
e) The 3rd quartile is another name for the 75th percentile. The 75th percentile is 570 and thus, 570 is the 3rd quartile.
f) The sixth decile is the 60th percentile. Since 510 is the 60th percentile and thus the sixth decile is 510.

CASE STUDY 3.10   SAT Scores

Examine the statistical tables shown in Figure 3.27. The table in Figure 3.27a presents the percentile ranks of SAT-verbal and SAT-mathematical scores while the table in Figure 3.27b shows the standard error of measurement (SEM) for the different educational tests given the Admissions Testing Program(ATP) for the years 1992–93.

CASE STUDY 3.10 SAT Scores (continued)

Statistical Tables

Percentile ranks of SAT scores
(for national college-bound seniors)

Score	Verbal	Mathematical
800	99+	99+
750	99+	99
700	99	95
650	97	90
600	93	82
550	86	71
500	75	57
450	60	43
400	42	29
350	26	17
300	13	6
250	5	1
200		
Average score	422	474

(a)

Standard errors of measurement
of ATP scores*

Test	SEM
SAT	
Verbal	31
Reading Comprehension	4.0
Vocabulary	4.3
Mathematical	36
Test of Standard Written English	3.7
Achievement Tests	
American History &	
Social Studies	28
Biology	27
Chemistry	29
English Composition	29
English Comp. with Essay	35**
European History &	
World Cultures	27
French	28
French with Listening†	
German	27
Modern Hebrew	30
Italian	28
Japanese with Listening†	
Latin	34
Literature	37
Mathematics Level I	33
Mathematics Level II	31
Mathematics Level IIC	31
Physics	29
Spanish	27

(b)

FIGURE 3.27

a) Interpret the percent of students that scored below a score of 600 on the SAT-verbal.

b) Interpret the percent of students that scored below a score of 650 on the SAT-mathematical.

c) What percent of students scored above a score of 400 on the SAT-verbal? above the score of 500 on the SAT-mathematical?

d) What SAT-verbal score represents the 6th decile? the 3rd quartile?

e) What SAT-mathematical score represents the 9th decile?

f) What is the average score for the SAT-verbal? Examining the table, what do you think is the percentile rank of this score?

g) What is the average score for the SAT-mathematical? Examining the table, what do you think is the percentile rank of this score?

h) Using the standard errors of measurement of the ATP scores as an estimate of the standard deviations of the different tests, what is the standard deviation of the SAT-verbal and the SAT-mathematical?

i) Using the results of parts f, g and h, determine the z score of the SAT-verbal scores: 500, 400, and 450? What is the percentile rank for each of these scores? Interpret these results.

j) Using the results of parts f, g and h, determine the z score of the SAT-mathematical scores: 500, 400, and 450? What is the percentile rank for each of these scores? Interpret these results.

k) On which SAT test would a score of 500 be considered to be a better test score? Explain your answer using the information in part (j).

3.5 BOX-AND-WHISKER PLOT:
AN EXPLORATORY DATA ANALYSIS TECHNIQUE

The Box-and-Whisker Plot is an Exploratory Data Analysis technique developed by Professor John Tukey of Princeton University to visually display several summary statistics in order to describe the location of the center of the data, the spread and shape of a distribution, and to identify any outliers that may exist within the data. It is also helpful in comparing **two** or **more** distributions.

Before we discuss the construction of a Box-and-Whisker Plot, we will discuss a 5-number summary to describe the characteristics of a data set.

> **DEFINITION 3.17**
> A **5-number summary** uses the following five numbers to describe a data set:
> 1. The smallest data value
> 2. The first quartile (Q_1)
> 3. The median
> 4. The third quartile (Q_3)
> 5. The largest data value

To provide a **5-number summary** of data set, we must determine the smallest data value, Q_1, the median, Q_3, and the largest data value of the data set. In Section 3.1, we developed a procedure to determine the median of a data set. Remember, the median is the middle value of a data set **after** the data values have been arranged in numerical order.

In a similar manner, the first and third quartiles can be determined. The first quartile, Q_1, is essentially the *median* of the data values below the **position** of the median, while the third quartile, Q_3, is the *median* of the data values above the **position** of the median.

In Example 3.33, we examine how to determine the numbers of a 5-number summary.

EXAMPLE 3.33

Determine the 5-number summary for the following distribution of annual salaries.

Annual Salaries (in Thousands of Dollars)

55 57 60 62 63 64 65 66 67 67 67 70 72 75 78 83 86 87 90

Solution

The 5-number summary of a distribution consists of the smallest data value, Q_1 : the first quartile, the median, Q_3: the third quartile, and the largest data value.

Step 1 **Find the smallest and largest data values.**
The smallest data value is 55 while the largest data value is 90.

Step 2 **Determine the median by determining its position in the data set.**

Since the data are arranged in numerical order the median is the $\frac{n+1}{2}$ th data value. For this distribution of 19 data values, the median is the $\frac{19+1}{2}$ or 10th data value which is 67.

Step 3 **Determine the 1st quartile, Q_1.**
The 1st quartile, Q_1, is the median of the data values which are below the position of the median. In Figure 3.28, the median's position is enclosed within a box, and the values below are shown in bold print.

67 at the 10th data value
represents the median's position

55 57 60 62 63 64 65 66 67 | 67 | 67 70 72 75 78 83 86 87 90

FIGURE 3.28

To determine Q_1, we need to find the median of the data values which are below the position of the median. The values below the median are:

55   57   60   62   63   64   65   66   67

The median of these data values is 63, since it is the middle value of these nine numbers. Thus, 63 represents the first quartile, that is $Q_1 = 63$.

Step 4   **Determine the 3rd quartile, Q_3.**
The third quartile, Q_3, is the median of the data values which are above the position of the median. In Figure 3.29, the median's position is enclosed within a box. The values above the median's position are shown in bold print.

```
            67 at the 10th data value
          represents the median's position
```

55 57 60 62 63 64 65 66 67 | 67 | **67 70 72 75 78 83 86 87 90**

FIGURE 3.29

To determine Q_3, we need to find the median of the data values which are above the position of the median. The values above the median are:

67   70   72   75   78   83   86   87   90

The median of these data values is 78, since it is the middle value of these numbers. Thus 78 represents the third quartile, that is $Q_3 = 78$.

Therefore, the 5-number summary for the distribution of annual salaries is:

smallest data value = 55
1st quartile: $Q_1 = 63$
median = 67
3rd quartile: $Q_3 = 78$
largest data value = 90

Let's summarize the procedure used to determine the 5-number summary.

Procedure to Determine the 5-Number Summary

Step 1   Find the smallest and largest data values.
Step 2   Find the median.
Step 3   Find the 1st quartile, Q_1.
Step 4   Find the 3rd quartile, Q_3.

We will now examine a visual exploratory data analysis technique called a Box-and-Whisker Plot that displays the 5-number summary of a data set.

DEFINITION 3.18
A **Box-and-Whisker Plot** or **Box plot** is a visual device that uses a 5-number summary to reveal the characteristics of a data set.

A Box-and-Whisker Plot is a graphical display that can be used when there is a small number of data values in a distribution and therefore the construction of either a stem-and-leaf display, a bar chart, or a histogram may not be appropriate.

The graph in Figure 3.30 consisting of horizontal lines, called the whiskers, and extending outward from a rectangular box is an example of a Box-and-Whisker Plot.

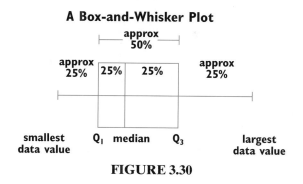

A Box-and-Whisker Plot

FIGURE 3.30

Notice, in Figure 3.30, the values of a 5-number summary, smallest data value, the 1st quartile, the median, the 3rd quartile and the largest data value, are used to construct the rectangular Box and the Whiskers of the box plot. Specifically, the sides of the rectangular box are constructed by using Q_1, the 1st quartile, and Q_3, the 3rd quartile, with a vertical line drawn within the rectangle to represent the median's position. The length of the whiskers (or the horizontal lines) of the box plot are determined by the distance between the quartiles to the smallest and largest data values.

EXAMPLE 3.34

For the following 5-number summary:

smallest data value = 55
the 1st quartile, Q_1 = 63
median = 67
the 3rd quartile, Q_3 = 78
largest data value = 90

construct a Box-and-Whisker plot.

Solution

To construct a Box-and-Whisker plot, the five numerical values from the 5-number summary are graphed and labeled on a horizontal axis.

Step 1   Draw a horizontal axis and scale it appropriately from the smallest to the largest values of the 5-number summary. This is illustrated in Figure 3.31(a).

Step 2   Draw a rectangle above the horizontal scale by drawing vertical lines at the 1st quartile, Q_1, and the 3rd quartile, Q_3, to represent the sides of the rectangle. Thus, the left side of the rectangle is placed at the value of Q_1 which is 63, while the right side of the rectangle is placed at the value of Q_3 which is 78. The height of the rectangle is unimportant. This is illustrated in Figure 3.31(b).

Step 3   Draw a vertical line within the rectangle to represent the position of the median. Thus, the vertical line representing the median is drawn at 67. This is illustrated in Figure 3.31(c).

Step 4   Draw two horizontal lines. One line connects the smallest data value to the left side of the box. The second horizontal line is drawn connecting the largest data value to the right side of

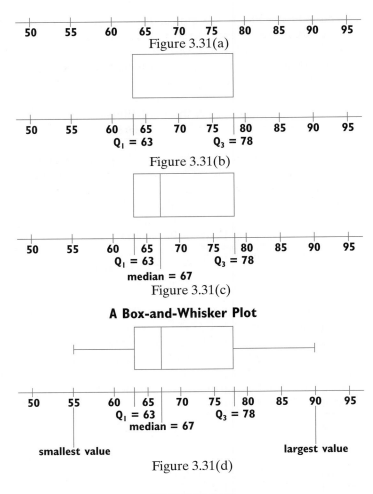

FIGURE 3.31

the box. These horizontal lines connecting the 1st quartile, Q_1, to the smallest data value and the 3rd quartile, Q_3, to the largest data value are called the Whiskers. The completed Box-and Whisker Plot is illustrated in Figure 3.31(d).

Let's summarize the procedure to construct a Box-and-Whisker Plot.

Procedure to Construct a Box-and-Whisker plot

Step 1   Draw a horizontal line and scale it from the smallest to the largest data values.

Step 2   Draw a rectangular box above the horizontal line with the sides at the 1st quartile, Q_1, and the 3rd quartile, Q_3.

Step 3   Draw a vertical line within the box to represent the position of the median.

Step 4   Draw horizontal lines from the box to the smallest and largest data values. These are called the Whiskers of the box plot.

A Box-and-Whisker Plot is useful in identifying whether a distribution's shape is symmetric or skewed. Notice that in Figure 3.31(c), the median is not centered within the box. It is positioned closer to Q_1 than to Q_3. Furthermore, notice that the whisker to the right of the third quartile is longer than the whisker to the left of the first quartile. This is an indication that the distribution is not symmetric. In fact it is **skewed** to the right. This suggests that there may be outliers present that are greater than Q_3.

In Figure 3.32 three box plots have been constructed. In Figure 3.32(a) notice that the whisker to the left of Q_1 is longer than the whisker to the right of Q_3. Perhaps there are outliers less than Q_1. Also notice that the median line is positioned closer to Q_3 than to Q_1. This suggests that the distribution is skewed to the left.

In Figure 3.32(b) notice that the whisker to the left of Q_1 is the same length as the whisker to the right of Q_3 and that the median line is positioned in the middle of the box. Although this distribution may contain outliers we can certainly conclude that the distribution is symmetric.

In Figure 3.32(c), as was the case in Figure 3.31, the whisker to the left of Q_1 is shorter than the whisker to the right of Q_3 and the median line is closer to Q_1 than to Q_3. This distribution is skewed right.

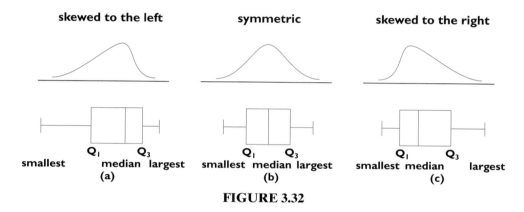

FIGURE 3.32

In summary, a box plot is particularly useful in conveying the location of the center, the variability and the shape of a distribution of data. Let's discuss some observations that can be made by examining a Box-and-Whisker Plot.

Box-and-Whisker Plot Interpretations

1. The median represents a measure of the center and is denoted by a vertical line within a rectangular box.
2. Approximately 50% of the data values are contained within the box.
3. Within each component of the box, separated by the median, are approximately 25% of the data values.
4. Approximately the lower 25% of the data values is represented by the whisker connecting the first quartile to the smallest data value.
5. Approximately the upper 25% of the data values is represented by the whisker connecting the third quartile to the largest data value.
6. The length of the box is a measure of the variability of the data set. A longer box indicates more variability, while a shorter box will indicate less variability.
7. The length of the whiskers will provide an idea about the shape of the data set. If one whisker is noticeably longer, then the shape of the data set is probably skewed in the direction of the longer whisker.

EXAMPLE 3.35

The 5-number summaries of the distributions of the calories per serving of several brands of ice cream verses frozen yogurt are given in Table 3.21.

TABLE 3.21   Calories Per Serving

Dessert	smallest value	Q_1	median	Q_3	largest value
Ice Cream	155	165	175	195	210
Yogurt	125	145	165	185	205

a) Construct a box plot for each of the 5-number summaries.
b) Examine the shape of each distribution, and determine what can you conclude about the calories per serving of ice cream compared to yogurt?

Solution

a) Using the 5-number summary per each frozen dessert the box plots are shown in Figure 3.33:

FIGURE 3.33

b) In examining the box plots of Figure 3.33, it appears that ice cream tends to have more calories per serving than frozen yogurt. Notice that the median calories per serving for ice cream is 175 while the median calories per serving for frozen yogurt is 165. The box plot for ice cream indicates the shape of the distribution is skewed to the right, since the upper whisker is longer. Whereas the box plot for yogurt has a symmetric shaped distribution since the median is in the middle of the box and both whiskers have approximately the same length.

Box plots are also useful in detecting the presence of an outlier. Data values that are outside the first and third quartiles, Q_1 and Q_3, may be considered somewhat extreme. In fact, the difference between Q_1 and Q_3, is often used as a guide for determining **outliers**. The difference between Q_1 and Q_3 is called *The Interquartile Range (IQR)*.

DEFINITION 3.19
The **Interquartile Range** (IQR) is the difference between the first quartile, Q_1, and the third quartile, Q_3. It is symbolized as IQR.

$$IQR = Q_3 - Q_1$$

The **Interquartile Range**, IQR, is a measure of the spread within a distribution. Usually, data values that are **at least a distance of 1.5 times the IQR above the third quartile or at least a distance of 1.5 times the IQR below the first quartile** are considered to be potential outliers for a distribution. In fact, Tukey's terminology of **inner and outer fences** to identify potential and definite outliers uses the IQR. Inner fences are located a distance of 1.5*IQR below Q_1 and above Q_3, while outer fences are located a distance of 3*IQR below Q_1 and above Q_3. Using this idea of inner and outer fences, we can now state a rule for detecting an outlier.

Rule for Detecting Outliers

An **outlier** is identified as any data value that falls outside of the outer fences.
   A **potential outlier** is identified as any data value that falls between the inner fences and the outer fences.

Using the box portion of the box plot to represent the IQR, the relationship between the IQR and the inner and outer fences are illustrated in Figure 3.34.

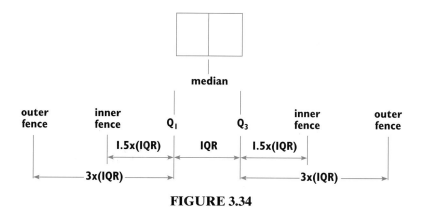

FIGURE 3.34

An outlier is an extreme data value that may be a valid data value or it can be a data value due to an error such as a measurement error or a recording error. Therefore, when an outlier or a potential outlier has been detected it is necessary to determine whether the outlier is due to error or is an unusual data value. If the outlier is due to error, then it should be removed. If the outlier represents an unusual but valid data value, then it should be investigated further since it may reveal useful information about the distribution of data values and may play an important role in subsequent statistical data analysis.

CASE STUDY 3.11   Salary Survey

Examine the graphic in Figure 3.35 which represents a Salary Survey of Biostatistics and Other Biomedical Statistics Departments and Units. The Table in Figure 3.35 shows the academic year (9 month equivalent) salary and time in rank information from approximately 275 departments of U.S. colleges and universities that list programs in statistics during the fall 1996.

CASE STUDY 3.11   Salary Survey (continued)

Research Institutions

Assistant Professors

		Number	First Quartile	Median	Third Quartile
Years	1 or fewer	28	40,000	42,450	47,250
In	2	13	44,400	45,700	49,100
Rank	3	12	41,485	44,450	52,500
	4	15	43,050	46,500	48,400
	5 or more	32	40,275	46,700	49,700

Associate Professors

Years	2 or fewer	25	45,800	51,360	58,710
In	3 to 4	29	47,000	49,700	56,000
Rank	5 to 7	28	47,143	52,950	59,750
	8 to 10	20	47,150	50,900	58,700
	11 or more	35	49,531	53,300	58,000

Professors

Years	3 or fewer	28	55,200	58,000	62,250
In	4 to 6	39	59,800	64,500	73,600
Rank	7 to 9	29	62,000	67,600	77,500
	10 to 12	28	63,500	72,500	85,869
	13 to 16	36	62,753	71,408	90,900
	17 to 20	34	64,000	80,000	89,900
	21 to 24	18	66,000	82,900	97,900
	25 or more	24	67,032	82,450	105,650

Liberal Arts, Other Institutions

Assistant Professors

Years In Rank	0 to 8	14	42,000	44,500	49,700

Associate Professors

Years In Rank	0 to 23	22	44,230	47,500	53,500

Professors

Years	1 to 9	29	59,500	62,000	65,000
In Rank	10 or more	33	59,300	65,000	82,700

FIGURE 3.35

a) What salary represents the 25th percentile for assistant professors at Research Institutions with 3 years in rank?

b) What percent of the associate professors at Research Institutions with 3 to 4 years in rank have a salary which is:
   1) at most $56,000?
   2) at least $47,000?
   3) between $47,000 and $56,000 inclusive?
   4) Approximately how many associate professors with 3 to 4 years in rank have a salary between $47,000 and $56,000 inclusive?

c) For full professors at Research Institutions with 25 or more years in rank
   1) what salary represents the 75th percentile?
   2) the 25th percentile?
   3) the 50th percentile?
   4) What is the interquartile range? What percent of the salaries fall within the interquartile range? Approximately how many professors have salaries within the interquartile range?
   5) Approximately how many of these professors have salaries between the first quartile and the median? between the median and the 3rd quartile?
   6) Calculate the range in salaries between the first quartile and the median? between the median and the 3rd quartile? Which has the smaller range?
   7) Associate with each range of part 5, the number and percent of professors that fall within that range. Comment on these results. What does the smaller range indicate regarding the variability of the salaries?

CASE STUDY 3.11 **Salary Survey (continued)**

d) For full professors at Research Institutions with 4 to 6 years in rank, and full professors at Liberal Arts with 1 to 9 years in rank: draw a box diagram representing the 1st quartile, median and 3rd quartile salary on the same scale. Compare these boxes and draw a conclusion regarding this comparison. What can you say about the shape of each of these salary distributions?

3.6 USING TECHNOLOGY

The software packages MINITAB and EXCEL were used to summarize the 920 salaries of the 1999 Major League Baseball players.

Examine the output for both MINITAB and EXCEL. Can you identify the 5-number summary for each output? Notice that the EXCEL Descriptive Statistics output contains different statistical measures than MINITAB.

MINITAB Descriptive Statistics: SALARIES

Variable	N	Mean	Median	TrMean	StDev	SE Mean
SALARIES	920	1570786	470833	1289359	2115414	69743

Variable	Minimum	Maximum	Q1	Q3
SALARIES	200000	11949794	215000	2200000

EXCEL Descriptive Statistics

1999 MLB Salaries	
Mean	1570786.34
Standard Error	69743.13806
Median	470833
Mode	200000
Standard Deviation	2115414.116
Sample Variance	4.47498E+12
Kurtosis	3.687404885
Skewness	1.963515035
Range	11749794
Minimum	200000
Maximum	11949794
Sum	1445123433
Count	920

Examine the MINITAB (Figure 3.36) and EXCEL (Figure 3.37) box plots of the 1999 MLB Salaries. The EXCEL box plot doesn't display outliers while the MINITAB box plot displays each outlier by the symbol "*". Notice since there are so many outliers in the MINITAB box plot that they run into each other. Why do you think the lower whisker is not noticeable in each of the box plots?

MINITAB Box Plot of 1999 MLB SALARIES

FIGURE 3.36

EXCEL Box Plot of 1999 MLB SALARIES

1999 MLB Salaries

0th %ile	200000
25th %ile	215000
50th %ile	470833
75th %ile	2200000
100th %ile	11949794

FIGURE 3.37

Graphing Calculator Display

We present view screens from the TI-83 Plus graphing calculator to show how technology tools like a statistical graphing calculator can be used to compute the mean, median, standard deviation, quartiles, and to evaluate the expressions Σx and Σx^2 for a data set. In addition, view screens showing the 5-number summary of a data set and box-and-whisker plots will be displayed.

We will use the TI-83 Plus graphing calculator to compute a numerical descriptive statistics summary of the 920 salaries of the 1999 Major League Baseball players.

On the TI-83 Plus, you can use 1-variable statistics, displayed as 1-VAR STATS under CALC column within the STAT function, to generate the view screens shown in Figures 3.38a and 3.38b. These view screens show the essential numerical descriptive statistics of the 920 salaries of the 1999 Major League Baseball players. Notice in Figure 3.38a, the descriptive statistics shown are the mean, $\bar{x}$; sum of the data values: Σx; the sum of the squared data values, Σx^2; the standard deviation of a sample, Sx; the standard deviation of a population, σx; and the number of data values, n. In Figure 3.38b, the descriptive statistics: minX, Q1, Med, Q3 and MaxX represent the 5-number summary for the salaries.

FIGURE 3.38a

FIGURE 3.38b

The TI-83 Plus graphing calculator can also be used to generate box plots. Figure 3.39a shows a box-and-whisker plot for the salaries. Once the box plot is graphed on the TI-83 Plus, you can press the trace key to identify each number of the 5-number summary for the salaries. In Figure 3.39b, the trace key was used to display the third quartile: Q3 = 2200000 on the box plot for the salaries.

FIGURE 3.39a

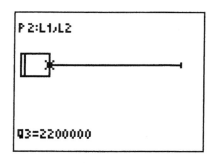

FIGURE 3.39b

The TI-83 Plus graphing calculator has the ability to plot potential outliers on a box plot. A box plot that displays the potential outliers is called a modified box plot. Any data value that is either **SMALLER THAN THE VALUE: Q1 − 1.5*IQR or GREATER THAN THE VALUE: Q3 + 1.5*IQR** is plotted individually using the box symbol: "□" and is either a potential or a definite outlier. On the TI-83 Plus, these outliers can be identified using the TRACE key. Figure 3.40a shows a modified box plot for the salaries. Notice that in Figure 3.40a there are so MANY salary outliers marked by the box (□) symbol that they run into each other. In the TI-83 Plus view screens of Figures 3.40b and 3.40c, the trace key was used to identify ONLY two of these outliers. The minimum outlier is identified as X=5150000 while the maximum outlier is identified as maxX=11949794. These outliers are displayed at the bottom of the view screens of Figures 3.40b and 3.40c.

FIGURE 3.40a

FIGURE 3.40b

FIGURE 3.40c

 KEY TERMS

Measures of Central Tendency   120
Sample Mean, $\bar{x}$ 121
Population mean, μ 122
Median   127
Mode   129
Bimodal   130
Nonmodal   130
Resistant Measure   136
Measures of variability   138
Range   139
Sample variance, s^2 142

Sample standard deviation, s   143
Variance of the population, σ^2 146
Population standard deviation, σ 146
Chebyshev's Theorem   152
Empirical Rule   154
Range Rule to Estimates   156
Coefficient of Variation   159
z Score, z   162
Percentile Rank, PR   167
Percentile   169
Decile   170

Quartile   170
Five-number Summary   173
Box-and-Whisker Plot   174
Interquartile Range (IQR)   178
Outlier   179
Potential Outlier   179
Inner Fence   179
Outer Fence   179

EXERCISES

Section 3.1

1. Three measures of central tendency are _____ , _____ and _____ .

2. The measures of central tendency usually describe the _____ of a distribution.

3. Since the mean is sensitive to outliers, then it isn't a _____ measure of central tendency.

4. If $\bar{x} = 5$, and n=2, then $\Sigma x = $ _____.

5. A distribution $x_1, x_2, \ldots, x_n$ has a mean of 15. Then for the distribution:
   a) $3x_1, 3x_2, \ldots, 3x_n$, the mean is _____.
   b) each data value is divided by 5, the mean is _____.
   c) $x_1 - 10, x_2 - 10, \ldots, x_n - 10$, the mean is _____.
   d) formed by adding 5 to each data value, the mean is _____.

6. If the data values $x_1, x_2, \ldots, x_n$ have a mean of 13, then $\Sigma(x - 13) = $ _____.

7. If a distribution of 5 data values has $\bar{x} = 11$, and if four of the data values are 5, 10, 20, 25 then the fifth data value is _____.

8. When a distribution with an even number of data values is arranged in numerical order, the median is the _____ of the two middle data values of the distribution.

9. In a distribution, the data value that appears most frequently is called the _____.

10. The sample mean is used as an estimate of the _____ mean.

11. If the data values are categorical, the _____ is the best measure of central tendency to use.

12. In a symmetric bell-shaped distribution, the measures of central tendency are located at the _____ of the distribution.

13. Which of the following is commonly referred to as the "average"?
   a) Mean   b) Median   c) Mode

For questions 14–17 consider the following distribution:
   25, 20, 8, 7, 9, 6, 8, 4, 5, 8

14. The mean of this distribution is:
   a) 12   b) 16   c) 10   d) 7

15. The median is:
   a) 7.5   b) 8   c) 9   d) 10

16. The mode is:
   a) 10   b) 8   c) 20   d) 4

17. If we removed the extreme data values (25 and 20) from the distribution, which measure of central tendency would not change?
    a) Mean b) Median c) Mode

18. In a skewed to the left distribution, the mean is located to the _____ of the median.
    a) Left b) Right

19. Since the median is unaffected by an outlier, it is said to be _____ to outliers.

20. The mean, median, and mode are never the same value. (T/F)

21. If the mean of a distribution is equal to 5 and the mode equals 3, then the median must equal 4. (T/F)

22. Both the population mean and the sample mean represent parameters of a distribution. (T/F)

23. For the distribution: 6, 2, 4, 4, 5, 3, 5, 3, 1, 7, find:
    a) the mean
    b) the median
    c) the mode
    d) $\Sigma(x-4)$
    e) Σx^2
    f) $(\Sigma x)^2$
    g) $\Sigma(x-4)^2$
    h) $[\Sigma(x-\bar{x})]^2$
    i) $\Sigma x^2 - (\bar{x})^2$

24. Given:

x	y
1	3
2	5
2	4
3	4
4	5

    Compute the following:
    a) Σx b) Σy c) $\Sigma x \Sigma y$ d) $(\Sigma x)^2$
    e) $(\Sigma y)^2$ f) Σx^2 g) Σy^2 h) Σxy
    i) $\dfrac{5(\Sigma xy) - \Sigma x \Sigma y}{\sqrt{5\Sigma x^2 - (\Sigma x)^2}\sqrt{5\Sigma y^2 - (\Sigma y)^2}}$

25. In order to determine a fair market price for a particular DVD player, a consumer obtained the following selling prices: $210, $215, $240, $195, $220, $215, $245
    a) Calculate the mean, median and mode.
    b) Which measure(s) of central tendency, if any, do you think best illustrates a fair price?

26. A statistics instructor gave the following final semester grades to his students:
    86, 82, 100, 96, 91, 94, 85, 95, 78, 80, 87, 92, 85, 81, 97, 98, 89, 90, 84, 92, 91, 87, 98, 90
    a) Compute the mean grade.
    b) Comment on the remark of one of the instructor's statistics students: " On the average, this instructor does not give grades above 90."

27. Given the distribution: 10, 20, 30, 40, 50, 60, 70, 80, 900.
    a) Calculate the mean and the median.
    b) Which measure seems to be a better indicator of the central tendency of this distribution?
    c) For this distribution, change the last data value (900) to 90 and recalculate the mean and the median.
    d) Now which measure seems to be a better indicator of central tendency? Explain.
    From your observation, which measure of central tendency was:
    e) more resistant to the extreme data values?
    f) less resistant to the extreme data values?

28. The student government association is in the process of planning a special awards dinner. To try to determine the menu for the awards dinner the association surveyed the number and types of meals purchased at the campus cafeteria. The following meal table was recorded during the past week.

Meals	Monday	Tuesday	Wednesday	Thursday	Friday
Fried Chicken	125	45	80	100	80
Meat Loaf	40	60	95	70	75
Veal Cutlets	50	35	55	75	45
Spag. & Meatball	100	135	90	125	135
Beef Stew	120	90	80	135	90
Pizza	30	80	70	45	160

    a) What are the most popular daily meals?
    b) What is the most popular weekly meal?
    c) Based on the survey, which meal do you believe the association should choose for the awards dinner?

29. A mutual fund company bases its quarterly management and investment service charge on the fund's average market value per share.

    If the following stocks represent the fund's portfolio for the first quarter, determine the mean market value per share.

Number of Shares	Company	Market Value
200,000	CNET, Inc.	11,350,000
590,800	Gaylord Entertainment Co.	17,687,075
745,200	Comcast Corporation	37,446,300
845,000	INTEL	37,496,875
800,000	Apache Corporation	29,550,000
1,109,000	Parametric Technology Corp.	30,012,313
510,000	Sun Microsystems, Inc.	39,493,125
600,000	Omnipoint Corporation	72,375,000
835,400	Global Telesystems Group	28,925,725
465,000	Corning, Inc.	59,955,938
1,020,000	Albertson's Inc.	32,895,000
1,450,000	ProLogis Trust	27,912,500
1,481,300	Baker Hughes, Inc.	31,199,881
850,000	The Mead Corporation	34,967,188
1,063,000	Seagate Technology, Inc.	49,495,937
940,000	Unocal Corporation	31,548,750

30. A leading manufacturer of radial tires claims that their X-60 radial tire will last an average of 60,000 miles. To test this claim, a consumer protection group purchases and tests 32 of these tires.

The number of miles each tire lasted before needing replacement is recorded below:

60,900 59,500 58,900 59,700 60,350 60,100 60,500 58,500
58,800 58,200 60,000 60,400 60,500 58,000 59,000 58,900
59,500 60,000 61,000 61,000 59,700 59,800 59,600 60,100
60,500 61,500 59,950 59,700 59,750 60,150 60,200 62,000

  a) Using the sample information, determine the mean tire life of the X-60 radial tire. Comment on the manufacturer's claim.
  b) Assume you are a statistician working for the tire manufacturer. Using the same information, determine which measure of central tendency you would use to support the manufacturer's claim.

31. If a distribution of study hours is skewed left, then the:
  a) Most frequent study hour equals the median study hour
  b) Most frequent study hour is greater than the median study hour
  c) Most frequent study hour is less than the median study hour
  d) Not enough information

32. Using the following figure which represents a skewed distribution, determine the value for:
  a) the mode
  b) the mean
  c) the median
  d) Identify the shape of the distribution.
  e) In which tail would you expect to find an outlier? Explain.
  f) Which Measure of Central Tendency would be closest to a possible outlier? Explain.

Frequency

18 19 20   X

33. For each of the following distribution of data values,
  a) identify the general shape that you believe best describes each distribution, and
  b) identify whether the mean or median would have the largest value within this type of distribution.
  1) The age of people living in the United States.
  2) The amount of soda dispensed into 2 liter bottles.
  3) The amount of soda dispensed by an under-filling malfunctioning machine into 2 liter bottles.
  4) The amount of time to complete an easy exam, if the class is 75 minutes long.

5) The weights of all the female students at a University.

Section 3.2

34. Three measures of variability are: _____, _____, and _____.

35. Measures of variability describe the _____ of the data values.

36. The range is calculated by subtracting the _____ value of the distribution from the _____ value of the distribution.

37. If the range is 5 and a constant of 6 is added to each data value, then the range of the new data values is _____.

38. If a distribution of five data values has a variance of 100, then the sum of the squared deviations from the mean, $\Sigma(x-\bar{x})^2$, is _____.

39. The symbol used to represent the sample standard deviation is _____. The Greek symbol used to represent the population standard deviation is _____.

40. In a sample, if the variance is 144, then s = _____.

41. For a distribution, if $x-\bar{x}$ has a negative value, then x is positioned _____ the mean. If $x-\bar{x}$ has a positive value, then x is positioned _____ the mean. If $x-\bar{x}=0$ then x = _____.

42. For a distribution where $\bar{x}=50$ and s = 5, calculate:
  $\bar{x}+s$ _____
  $\bar{x}+2s$ _____
  $\bar{x}+3s$ _____
  $\bar{x}-s$ _____
  $\bar{x}-2s$ _____
  $\bar{x}-3s$ _____

43. Which measure of variability is always expressed in squared units?
  a) Range   **b)** Variance   **c)** Standard deviation

44. Which measure of variability is the square root of another measure of variability?
  a) Range   **b)** Variance   **c)** Standard deviation

45. The standard deviation of a distribution is _____.
  a) Never negative
  b) Always a whole number
  c) Always positive

46. The range of a distribution is _____.
  a) Never negative
  b) Always a whole number
  c) Always positive

47. For the same set of data, which formula will yield a larger value:
  a) σ **b)** s

48. The standard deviation is sensitive to the extreme data values.
  (T/F)

49. If a distribution consists of all negative data values then the range is negative.
(T/F)

50. In a distribution whose data values all have the same numerical value, the standard deviation is always zero.
(T/F)

51. A distribution that has a range of one must also have a standard deviation of one.
(T/F)

52. For the data values: $2, 3, 7, 8, 15$ compute:
a) The range
b) The sample variance, s^2
c) The sample standard deviation, s
d) An estimate of the population standard deviation
e) The population standard deviation, assuming the data values represent a population.

53. The following data represents annual salaries (expressed in thousands of dollars) of real estate agents from two different offices located in Palmetto Beach, Florida.

Real Estate Office	One	Two	Three	Four	Five	Six
Sarabell	400	42	100	300	75	37
20th Century	200	50	410	47	150	250

(Agent)

In which real estate office are the salaries more varied?

54. Consider the data values: $2, 9, 16, 23, 30, 37, 44$.

Calculate the range and sample standard deviation for:
a) The original data values.
b) The data values formed by subtracting 10 from each original data value. Compare this result to the answer for part a.
c) The data values formed by multiplying each original data value by (–4). Compare this result to answer for part a.

55. Three candidates applied for a legal secretarial opening in the office of I. M. Guilty. A four hour standardized test was administered to each candidate to determine their typing skills, writing skills, word processing skills, stenographic skills and knowledge of the law. The scores for each candidate are:

Candidate	Typing	Writing	Steno	Word proc.	Law
Ms. Libel	7.9	7.9	7.8	7.7	8.8
Ms. Sue	8.6	8.1	7.9	7.5	8.0
Mr. Will	7.8	8.4	8.0	7.4	8.5

The candidates are told that the sole selection criterion will be based on the highest total of the five skill scores. If this criterion is unable to separate the candidates, then the candidate who has the highest total with the most consistent scores will be hired.

Based on this criteria, which candidate should be hired for the job? (Hint: The measures of variability should be used to measure consistency among the scores.)

56. For the distribution: $42, 30, 24, 48, 60, 36, 54$
a) Find the $\bar{x}$ and s.
b) Compute $\bar{x} + s$.
c) Find the data value that is one standard deviation above the mean. Compare this result to part b.
d) Compute $\bar{x} - 2s$.
e) Find the data value that is 2 standard deviations below the mean. Compare this result to part d.
f) Compute $\bar{x} - 2s$ and $\bar{x} + 2s$.
g) Find the data values that are within two standard deviations of the mean. Compare this result to part f.
h) What percent of the data values are at least 3 standard deviations above the mean?
i) What percent of the data values are between $\bar{x} - 2s$ and $\bar{x} + 2s$?

57. The closing prices of three common stocks traded on the New York Stock Exchange for two weeks during the past month are given in the following table:

	Stock X	Stock Y	Stock Z
First Week	66	70	74
	68	64	78
	67	70	69
	66	68	64
	66	69	60
Second Week	68	67	65
	68	66	70
	70	70	66
	71	72	70
	70	64	64

a) Compare the three stocks using the sample mean.
b) Compute the sample standard deviation for each of the three stocks.
c) Based upon this information which stock is speculative (more varied) and which one is more conservative (less varied)? Explain.

58. A study was conducted by a consumer protection group to determine the effectiveness of two leading pain relievers, Afferin and Banacin. The pain relievers were administered to a sample of 30 subjects suffering from headache pain. Fifteen subjects were administered Afferin while 15 were administered Banacin. The amount of time it took the drug to become effective in relieving the pain was recorded and the results are listed in the following table:

Number of minutes for relief of headache pain	
Afferin Group	**Banacin Group**
45	48
63	54
54	42
37	38
42	42
58	53

Number of minutes for relief of headache pain (cont.)

Afferin Group	Banacin Group
47	64
36	44
41	44
39	50
48	52
54	42
55	51
49	52
52	44

a) Compute the sample mean and sample standard deviation for each group.

b) Determine which drug has the more consistent time for relieving headache pain. Explain.

59. The following table shows the amount spent for research, development and marketing for the past year by eight drug and eight cosmetic firms. (note: expenditures are measured in millions of dollars.)

Expenditures for Research and Development	Expenditures for Marketing	Type of Company
2.64	1.74	Drug
3.79	2.59	Drug
1.84	1.97	Drug
2.36	3.64	Drug
3.59	2.18	Drug
4.61	2.64	Drug
3.17	2.55	Drug
2.89	1.90	Drug
1.17	3.75	Cosmetic
2.38	4.69	Cosmetic
0.87	2.75	Cosmetic
1.24	3.15	Cosmetic
1.75	3.56	Cosmetic
0.75	2.94	Cosmetic
1.29	4.75	Cosmetic
1.67	3.87	Cosmetic

a) Compute the sample mean and standard deviation for each type of company and for each type of expenditure.

b) Based on the given data, what conclusions can you draw concerning these expenditures?

60. Steven, a college professor, computed the mean and the standard deviation of the final exam which he administered to his day and evening statistics classes.

Class	Mean Grade	Standard Deviation
day	66	16
evening	66	2

a) In which class would you expect to find the lowest grade on this test? the highest grade? Explain.

b) If Steven randomly selects a student from each one of these classes, then from which class would Steven have a better chance of selecting a student with a grade closer to the mean grade? Explain.

Section 3.3

61. Two general rules that establish a relationship between the standard deviation and the distribution of data values are _____ Theorem and the _____ Rule.

62. Chebyshev's Theorem states for any distribution, regardless of its shape, at least $1 - \frac{1}{k^2}$ of the data values will lie within k _____ of the mean, where k is greater than one.

63. Empirical Rule states for a bell-shaped distribution that:
    a) Approximately _____ % of the data values will lie within 1 standard deviation of the mean.
    b) Approximately _____ % of the data values will lie within 2 standard deviations of the mean.
    c) Approximately _____ or _____ % to _____ % of the data values will lie within 3 standard deviations of the mean.

64. If a sample contains 25 data values, then the rule for estimating s using the range is: _____. However, if the sample contains 100 data values, then the rule for estimating s using the range is: _____.

65. Which of the following can be applied to a skewed shaped distribution?
    a) Chebyshev's Theorem
    b) Empirical Rule
    c) Schwartz' Rule

66. According to the Empirical Rule, the approximate percentage of data values that are within 2 standard deviations is:
    a) 68%   b) 95%   c) 99%   d) 100%

67. For a bell-shaped distribution, which of the following gives a conservative estimate for the percentage of data values that are within two standard deviations of the mean?
    a) Chebyshev's Theorem
    b) Empirical Rule
    c) Schwartz' Rule

68. For a skewed distribution, the approximate percentage of data values that are within 2 standard deviations is:
    a) At least 68%
    b) At least 75%
    c) At least 89%
    d) At least 100%

69. The coefficient of variation represents the ratio of the standard deviation to the _____.
    a) Median
    b) Mean
    c) Range
    d) Variance

70. Which of the following is a measure of absolute variability?
    a) Standard deviation
    b) Mean
    c) Coefficient of variation

71. If the range for a sample of 10 values is 60, then an approximate value for s is:
a) 10   **b)** 15   **c)** 20   **d)** 24

72. Chebyshev's Theorem states that at least 89% of the data values within a distribution will lie within 3 standard deviations from the mean.
(T/F)

73. The Empirical Rule can be applied to either a bell-shaped or a skewed distribution.
(T/F)

74. When comparing two distributions, the distribution with the larger standard deviation will have the greater value for the coefficient of variability.
(T/F)

75. If the coefficient of variation is 20% then this indicates that the standard deviation is 20% of the mean.
(T/F)

76. In a bell-shaped distribution, if a data value lies more than 3 standard deviations from the mean then the data value is considered a definite outlier.
(T/F)

77. The standard deviation is a relative measure of dispersion.
(T/F)

78. Use Chebyshev's Theorem to answer the following questions: A machine is set to produce screws with a mean size of 0.42 mm and a standard deviation of 0.003 mm.
a) If screws smaller than 0.411mm or greater than 0.429mm are unusable, at most what percentage of the screws would one expect to be unusable?
b) Would a screw of size 0.435 mm be considered an unusual size? Explain.

79. Assuming the IQ scores of a distribution of 8,000 college-aged students is bell-shaped with a mean of 120 and a standard deviation of 8. Using the Empirical Rule, determine the approximate percentage and number of students who are expected to have IQ scores from:
a) 104 to 136.
b) 112 to 128.
c) 112 to 136.
d) 104 to 144.
e) Would you interpret an IQ score of 150 to be an unusual IQ or a typical IQ? Explain.
f) Would you interpret an IQ score of 90 to be a potential outlier? Explain.

80. The following figures represent the salaries of the chief executives of the given Environmental Groups.

Environmental Group	Salary
National Wildlife Federation	$242,060
Environmental Defense Fund	$213,504
Ducks Unlimited	$194,884
National Parks & Conservation Assoc.	$185,531
The Nature Conservancy	$185,000
World Wildlife Fund	$185,000
National Audubon Society	$171,154
The Wilderness Society	$ 90,896
Sierra Club	$ 77,142
Greenpeace Inc.	$ 65,000

a) Calculate the sample standard deviation of the salaries.
b) Use the appropriate range rule to estimate the standard deviation, s. Compare this estimate to the value computed in part (a).

81. Each day, employment officer A reviews 40 resumes with a standard deviation of 5. Employment officer B completes 150 resumes with a standard deviation of 15. Compare the absolute variability and relative variability of each employment officer to determine which officer shows less variability in output?

82. Ellen, a stock broker, is studying the performance of two stocks over a three month period. Stock D had a mean selling price of $13.38 with a variance of 5.62, while Stock E had a mean selling price of $98.13 with a variance of 61.62.
a) Which stock has a greater relative variation in the selling price per share?
b) Why should you consider using a measure of relative dispersion to compare these two stocks?

83. A machine is set to produce a bolt with a mean size of 4.50 inches with a standard deviation of 0.35 inches. If any bolt smaller than 3.45 inches or greater than 5.55 inches are defective, then according to Chebyshev's Theorem at most what percentage of the bolts would one expect to be defective?

Section 3.4

84. The statistic that measures the relative position of an individual data value from the mean using standard deviation units is called a _____ .

85. The z score of a sample data value is calculated by the formula: $z =$ ___.

The z score of a population data value is calculated by the formula: $z =$ ___.

86. A data value that is one standard deviation greater than the mean has a z score of _____.

87. The z score of a data value indicates how many standard deviations the data value is above or below the _____.
a) Mean   **b)** Mode   **c)** Median

88. A data value that has a z score of zero is the _____.

89. For a distribution, $\bar{x} = 100$ and s = 4.
a) If $x = \bar{x}$, then $z =$ _____.
b) If x = 90, then $z =$ _____.
c) If z = 2, then $x =$ _____.
d) If z = 1.5, then $x =$ _____.

90. If a raw score has a z score of 3, then the raw score is _____ standard deviations _____ than the mean.

91. The percentile rank formula for a data value, X, is calculated by:

PR of the data value X = $\dfrac{[B + (\frac{1}{2})E]}{N}$ (100)

where: B = the number of data values _____ than X.
E = the number of data values _____ to X.
N = the _____ number of data values

92. The percentile rank of X indicates the percent of values within the distribution that are _____ than X.

93. A percentile rank is rounded off to a _____ number.

94. The pth percentile is the data value in the distribution which has _____ percent of the data values less than this data value and the rest of the data values greater than it.

95. Lorenzo's IQ score of 120 has a percentile rank of 90. This means that _____ percent of the individuals have IQ scores less than 120 and _____ percent have IQ scores greater than 120.

96. If P_{20} = 75, then we state that 75 is the 20th _____.

97. If the median IQ score is 100, then we can write: $P_{\_\_}$ = 100.

98. The percentile is a _____ of the distribution, while the percentile rank of a data value is a percentage value ranging from _____ to _____.

99. A z score is used to summarize a distribution's variability. (T/F)

100. If a standard deviation is equal to 10 units then the z score of a data value one standard deviation greater than the mean is equal to 10 units. (T/F)

101. A z score is always a whole number. (T/F)

102. Negative raw scores can never have positive z scores. (T/F)

103. A percentile is a data value of the distribution. (T/F)

104. The data value that represents the 1st quartile is greater than the data value that represents the 3rd quartile. (T/F)

105. a) Using the z score formula, calculate and interpret the z scores for each raw score given in the table below.
b) Using the results of part a, which raw score would you consider to be a potential outlier? Explain.

Raw Score	Mean	Standard deviation
i) 45	60	9
ii) 165	120	10
iii) 590	400	150
iv) 830	750	100
v) 1470	1470	210

106. a) Using the raw score formula, calculate the raw score for each z score given in the table below.
b) Using the information in the table and the results of part a, state which raw score might be considered a potential outlier? Explain.

Mean	Standard deviation	z Score
i) 120	50	+2.33
ii) 500	160	−1.96
iii) 75	25	+0.56
iv) 450	90	−3.58
v) 290	75	+1.65

107. Given the sample of temperatures:
90, 100, 79, 70, 95, 85
a) Find the mean temperature.
b) Find the standard deviation.
c) Convert each temperature to a z score.
d) Interpret each z score.

108. Assume you have recently taken a Biology exam and you earned a grade of 85. Your friend, who is in a different biology class, receives a grade of 77. Although you have a higher test score, based upon the information contained in the following table, you feel your friend's test score is more outstanding relative to her class. Using the table information, show that your claim is justified.

Student	Mean Bio Grade	Standard Deviation	Test Score
You	76	4	85
Friend	69	3	77

109. The following chart contains the percentiles of three SAT II subject tests for Steven, a college bound student.

Subject	Test Score	Percentile Rank
English Writing	700	85
Math: Level I	700	90
World History	675	75

a) Interpret Steven's relative standing on each of the tests.
b) Determine the percent of students who scored higher than Steven on each of the tests.
c) Which test score represents the 3rd quartile? the 9th decile?

110. Two amateur athletes, a bowler and golfer, are being considered for the Amateur Athlete of the Year Award in their country club. The award will be given to the athlete who has had the most outstanding season relative to their sport. The bowler's summer league average was 201, while the golfer averaged 74 for her summer league play. Based on these facts and the additional data given in the following table, determine which athlete should win the Amateur Athlete Award.

	Mean Score	Standard Deviation
Bowling League	170	21
Golf League	85	7

111. Some of the I.Q. scores of 250 college students are given in the following table.

I.Q. Score	102	104	110	112	114	120	122
z Score	–2.5	–2.0	–0.5	0	0.5	2	2.5
Percentile Rank	10	15	25	40	50	75	99

By inspection of the table, determine:
a) The mean I.Q. score of all 250 students.
b) The median I.Q. score of all 250 students.
c) The percent of students who have an I.Q. score below 112.
d) The standard deviation of all 250 students.
e) The I.Q. score representing the 1st decile.
f) The I.Q. score representing the 1st quartile.
g) The I.Q. score representing the 3rd quartile.

112. What percentage of a population of statistics test scores are:
a) Above the first quartile?
b) Below the third quartile?
c) Greater than the 43rd percentile?
d) Above the 7th decile?
e) Between the first and third quartiles?
f) Between the 3rd and 8th decile?

Section 3.5

113. A 5-number summary consists of the following values: _____, _____, _____, _____, and _____.

114. The Box-and-Whisker Plot is an _____ Data Analysis technique used to visually display several summary statistics to describe the location of the _____ of the data, the _____ and _____ of a distribution.

115. On a box-and-whisker plot, the middle 50% of the data values fall between the _____ and _____ quartiles.

116. The line connecting the 3rd quartile to the largest value of a box-and-whisker plot is called the _____ of the box plot.

117. The Interquartile Range (IQR) is the difference between the _____ and the _____ quartile. On a box plot, the IQR is represented by the length of the _____. The percent of data values that are represented by the IQR is _____.

118. If the length of the lower and upper whiskers are approximately equal and the median is positioned in the middle of the 1st and 3rd quartiles, then we would expect the shape of the distribution to be _____.

119. The left vertical line of the box of the box plot represents the _____.
a) Q_1
b) Q_3
c) Median
d) Lowest data value

120. An outlier is identified as any data value that falls outside of the _____ fences.
a) Extreme   b) Inner   c) Outer

121. An _____ is an extreme data value that may be a valid data value or it can be a data value due to an error.
a) Largest data value
b) Median
c) Mean
d) Quartile
e) Outlier

122. If $Q_1 = 45$ and $Q_3 = 68$, then the IQR is _____ .

123. Tukey defines an inner fence to be a distance of ___*IQR from the 1st and 3rd quartiles. An outer fence is defined to be a distance of ____*IQR from the 1st and 3rd quartiles.

124. The Whiskers in a Box-and-Whisker Plot can be used to indicate the presence of data values that are outliers. (T/F)

125. The 5-number summary uses the mean as a measure of the center of the data set. (T/F)

126. When comparing the box plots of two distributions, then the distribution represented by the larger box has the greater variability within the middle 50% of the data values. (T/F)

127. When comparing two distributions, the distribution that has an outlier will have the larger IQR. (T/F)

128. A class of psychology students were given a standardized test and their scores were:

119, 118, 115, 114, 114, 113, 112, 107, 117, 116,
122, 119, 119, 119, 118, 118, 118, 118, 117, 117,
116, 115, 115, 115, 114, 112, 107, 107, 111, 109,
107, 107, 107, 106, 105, 104, 103, 83, 109, 108

a) Determine the 5-number summary for the test scores.
b) Construct a Box-and-Whisker Plot.
c) Describe the shape of the Box-and-Whisker Plot.
d) Calculate the interquartile range (IQR).
e) Determine if there are any outliers within the data set. If there is an outlier, state its value(s).
f) Find the z score of each outlier if any exists and interpret their relative position in terms of standard deviations.
g Explain what effect an outlier, if any exists, has on the mean and median test score.

129. For the following distribution of statistics test grades:

19, 29, 40, 42, 53, 55, 58, 60, 61, 61, 62, 64, 65, 75, 76, 76, 77,
77, 78, 78, 79, 80, 80, 81, 82, 83, 83, 84, 85, 86, 86, 87, 88, 88,
89, 89, 90, 90, 91, 92, 93, 93, 94, 94, 95, 98, 98

a) Determine the 5-number summary for the statistics grades.
b) Construct a Box-and-Whisker Plot.
c) Describe the shape of the Box-and-Whisker Plot.
d) Calculate the interquartile range (IQR).

e) Determine if there are any outliers within the data set. If there is an outlier, state its value(s).

f) Find the z score of each if any exists and interpret their relative position in terms of standard deviations.

g) Explain what effect an outlier, if any exists, has on the mean and median grade.

130. The following distributions represent the number of homeruns that Mark McGuire and Sammy Sosa hit during the designated years. The homeruns identified by an asterisk indicate the years that the player had less than 100 at bats.

The number of homeruns hit by Mark McGuire during each baseball season for the years 1986-1999
3*, 49, 32, 33, 39, 22, 42, 9*, 9, 39, 52, 58, 70, 65

The number of homeruns hit by Sammy Sosa during each baseball season for the years 1989–1999
1*, 3*, 15, 10, 8, 33, 25, 36, 40, 36, 66, 63

For each homerun distribution, determine:

a) The 5-number summary.

b) Construct a Box-and-Whisker Plot for each distribution on the same scale.

c) Compare the box plots, and discuss the differences between the two distributions.

d) Which distribution has the smaller variability? the larger variability?

e) Calculate the Interquartile Range.

f) Identify any outliers, if any exist, for each distribution. Give an explanation for any outlier that may exist.

g) Describe the shape of each distribution.

131. The following **samples** of raw scores represent the number of work hours for male and female students per week.

Male Students
45, 23, 27, 23, 30, 27, 0, 30, 18, 36, 15, 60, 30, 38, 26, 30, 36, 8, 55, 50

Female Students
29, 15, 18, 20, 15, 28, 19, 17, 29, 14, 20, 28, 34, 69, 14, 20, 27, 29, 12, 16

For each sample:

a) Construct a box-and-whisker plot.

b) State the shape.

c) Determine the first quartile, the median and the third quartile.

d) Determine if there are any outliers. If there is an outlier, state its value.

e) Find the z score of each outlier if any exists and interpret its relative position in terms of standard deviations.

f) Explain what effect, if any, these outliers have on the mean and median number of work hours.

CHAPTER REVIEW

132. The mean, median, and mode are known as measures of relative position. (T/F)

133. The mode of a distribution is the data value which appears:
a) Least   **b)** Most   **c)** In the middle

134. The symbol used to represent the mean of a sample is:
a) n   **b)** x   **c)** μ **d)** $\bar{x}$

135. A distribution containing more than two modes is called a _____ distribution.

136. When a distribution with an odd number of data values is arranged in numerical order, the median is the _____ data value of the distribution.

137. The formula for the sample mean is: _____ while the formula for the population mean is _____.

138. $\bar{x}$ is often used to estimate the _____ of a population.
a) Mean   **b)** Median   **c)** Mode

139. If a mean is computed using only a portion of the population data, then this statistic is called the _____ mean.

140. The mean is always one of the data values of a distribution. (T/F)

141. In a distribution with an odd number of data values, the mean is 100, and the median is 75. Fifty percent of the data are less than the data value _____ .

142. If $\Sigma(x-3)=0$, then 3 is _____.

143. The mean is a more resistant measure of central tendency than the median. (T/F)

144. In a skewed to the right distribution, the median is located to the left of the mean. (T/F)

145. For the following distribution:
25, 20, 8, 7, 9, 6, 8, 4, 5, 8
Which of the three measures of central tendency will change if we remove one of the data values from the above distribution?
a) Mean
b) Median
c) Mode

146. For the sample: 12, 9, 7, 13, 9, 8, 10, 9, 11, 12, find:
1. the mean and state the appropriate symbol to represent this mean.
2. the median

3. the mode

4. $\Sigma(x - 10)$

5. Σx^2

6. $(\Sigma x)^2$

7. $\Sigma(x - \bar{x})^2$

8. $[\Sigma(x - \bar{x})]^2$

9. $\Sigma x^2 - (\bar{x})^2$

147. Given:

x	y
1	7
2	8
3	9
4	10

Compute the following:

a) Σx **b)** Σy **c)** $\Sigma x \Sigma y$ **d)** $(\Sigma x)^2$

e) $(\Sigma y)^2$ **f)** Σx^2 **g)** Σy^2 **h)** Σxy

i) $\dfrac{4(\Sigma xy) - \Sigma x \Sigma y}{\sqrt{4\Sigma x^2 - (\Sigma x)^2}\sqrt{4\Sigma y^2 - (\Sigma y)^2}}$

148. In a population, if all the data values have the same numerical value of 14, then:

Mean = _____

Mode = _____

Median = _____

Range = _____

Variance = _____

Standard deviation = _____

149. A travel agent, trying to promote travel to a particular Caribbean island, began an intensive ad campaign. The campaign stressed the good weather of the island. For this island, the number of sunny days per month for the last year were:

27, 24, 28, 22, 26, 28, 25, 28, 23, 29, 24, 28.

a) Calculate the mean, median, and mode.

b) Which one of the three measures would you use for the ad campaign? Why?

150. The following data values represent a sample of real estate listings for homes in southern California:

$375,000, $525,000, $425,000, $1,486,000, $510,000, $655,000, $425,000, $490,000, $575,000 and $505,000.

a) Determine the mean, median, and mode for these prices.

b) Why are the mode and mean not good measures of central tendency for this distribution?

c) What symbol would you use to represent the mean?

151. The following table represents a summary of the final exam scores for all the students at a small community college.

Final Exam	Number of Students
90	2
87	1
86	2
85	5
84	2
83	6
82	8
79	1
76	3
66	7
60	5
20	4
10	5
0	1

a) Determine the mean, median, and modal test grade.

b) What symbol would you use to represent the mean?

c) Which measure of central tendency is less resistant to the extreme data values? Explain.

152. At a recent golf tournament the following data were reported for the 10th hole.

10th Hole Data

Strokes to Hole	Number of Golfers
3	30
4	220
5	120
6	5
7	5

a) Find the mean, median, and modal number of strokes for the 10th hole.

b) Which measure of central tendency is least appropriate in describing the typical number of strokes for the 10th hole? Explain.

153. Twenty-four baseball players earn the following annual salaries: 2 players at $14.6 million; 4 at $7.45 million; 4 at $3.93 million; 5 at $450,000; 2 at $390,000; and 7 at $200,000.

a) Determine the mean, median, and modal salary.

b) Which measure is a poor measure of central tendency? Explain.

154. The following data represents a psychiatrist's rating of fifty severely depressed mental patients' responses to drug therapy.

Response to Drug Therapy	Number of Patients
Excellent	12
Very Good	17
Good	16
No Response	5

The psychiatrist claimed that "very good" was the typical response to this drug. Explain which measure of central tendency she used, and why it is appropriate in this situation.

155. The following data represents the shoe sizes of a popular brand of women's shoes sold at Sole City during the past week:

5, 5½, 6½, 7, 5½, 6½, 7, 8, 9, 5½, 6, 7, 7½, 8, 5, 6, 6½, 9, 5½, 5, 5½, 6, 6½, 8, 5½, 6½, 5½, 5, 5½, 7½

Use the data to compute the:
a) Mean shoe size sold.
b) Median shoe size sold.
c) Modal shoe size sold.
d) Which measure(s) of central tendency would be most beneficial to the store manager when she places her order for purchasing more of these shoes? Explain.

156. A manufacturer needs to maintain a close check over the performance of their production process. For example, a sugar refinery needs to control the weight of their 5 lb bag of sugar to determine if the weights fluctuate due to gradual changes in the production process. This controlling process is referred to as *quality control*. Suppose the sugar refinery decides to use the mean weight of 20 bags of sugar that were randomly selected from the production line to monitor their production process.

Actual Weight in Lbs for the Five-Pound Bag of Sugar
4.8750 5.2500 4.8750 4.8750 4.8750 4.8750 5.2500
4.8750 4.8750 4.9375 5.1875 4.9375 5.1875 4.9375
5.2500 4.9375 5.2500 4.9375 4.8750 4.9375

a) Using the sample data, calculate the mean weight.
b) Examine the 20 weights used for part a and comment as to whether you believe the estimate is sufficient to check the quality control of the production process.

157. A sociology professor wants to get an estimate of the "average" age of the students in his large lecture. The professor randomly selects 10 students from his class and records their ages. The ages are as follows:

19, 18, 18, 22, 19, 58, 20, 23, 21, 22

a) Compute the mean age for this sample.
b) At the next class meeting the professor states the average age to the class. One of the students is startled at the response to the professor's question: "Who is 24 or older?" Almost no one responded. Can you explain this?

158. Two baseball veterans are going to compute their respective lifetime batting averages by adding all their season averages and dividing by the number of seasons. The following table contains the data for the two players.

Season	Player A			Player B		
	AB	Hits	Ave	AB	Hits	Ave
1	203	54	.266	310	90	.290
2	392	120	.306	204	64	.314
3	151	37	.245	426	106	.246
4	435	148	.340	126	46	.365
5	215	59	.274	515	145	.281
6	574	181	.315	224	74	.330
7	263	75	.285	374	110	.294
8	271	71	.261	335	93	.278
9	380	116	.305	180	56	.311

Is the procedure the veterans are using to compute their lifetime batting averages correct? If not, how should they compute their lifetime batting averages? Justify your answer.

159. A student states that his cumulative grade point average for the past three semesters is 3.0. The student's reasoning is as follows: "I earned a 3.5 average for 4 credits during the summer semester, a 3.0 average for 12 credits in the fall and a 2.5 average for 16 credits in the spring." Is the student correct in his reasoning? Justify your answer.

160. Fourteen psychology exam scores and their respective deviations from the mean of a class of 15 students are listed in the following table. The exam score for student number 7 is missing. Using the information in the table, find the missing psychology score. (Hint: Use the property $\Sigma(x - \bar{x}) = 0$).

Student #	Psychology Score	Deviation from Mean
1	125	2
2	130	7
3	115	−8
4	126	3
5	132	9
6	127	4
7		
8	118	−5
9	128	5
10	134	11
11	126	3
12	119	−4
13	118	−5
14	115	−8
15	125	2

161. The sex and hair and eye color of twenty babies born at a county hospital during the previous week are listed in the following table.

Sex	Hair Color	Eye Color
M	BROWN	BROWN
M	BROWN	BROWN
F	BLONDE	BLUE
F	RED	BROWN
M	BROWN	BROWN
M	BLONDE	BLUE
F	BROWN	BROWN
F	BROWN	BLUE
F	BROWN	BROWN
M	BLACK	BROWN
F	BLONDE	BLUE
M	BLACK	BROWN
M	BROWN	BLUE
M	BROWN	BROWN
F	BROWN	BLUE
F	BROWN	BLUE
F	BLACK	BROWN
F	RED	BLUE
M	BLACK	BROWN
M	BROWN	BLUE

a) Estimate the typical:
   1) hair color.
   2) eye color.
   3) characteristics for a male baby.
   4) characteristics for a female baby.
b) Which measure of central tendency did you use to calculate the answers to the part (a), and explain why you chose this measure?

162. An investor decides to diversify his $450,000 investment by opening a $150,000 one-year CD with an effective yield of 9.25% and purchasing 2000 shares at $50 per share of a blue chip stock paying a 7.5% yearly dividend and two hundred triple A bonds at $1000 per bond yielding 9.75% per year. Determine:
   a) The total interest earned on the CD for the year.
   b) The total stock dividend earned for the year.
   c) The total bond interest earned for the year.
   d) The mean monthly return on the total investment.

163. An exercise equipment manufacturer states that their new electronic treadmill will burn an *average of 900 calories for a thirty minute workout.* The following sample data represents the number of calories burned per individual for twenty men aged 18–24 years.

   930, 890, 920, 910, 850, 870, 895, 880, 940, 830
   825, 890, 925, 855, 960, 860, 915, 830, 920, 875

   a) Calculate the sample mean number of calories burned per individual.
   b) Does the sample mean calculated in part (a) equal the average claimed by the equipment manufacturer? If there is a difference, what might be an explanation for this difference?
   c) If an individual loses one pound for every 3500 calories burned, based on the sample mean calculated in part (a), determine the mean number of pounds lost per individual for a thirty minute workout.
   d) If an individual works out 30 minutes a day for 30 days on this treadmill, determine the expected number of pounds lost.

164. Eastinghouse, an electric company, advertises that their new improved energy-saving light bulb has a mean life of 2500 hours. A consumer group decides to sample 30 of these bulbs to determine if the company's advertisement is correct. The following data represents the consumer group's sample.

   2540, 2340, 2325, 2300, 2510, 2380, 2520, 2370, 2390, 2540, 2400, 2430, 2500, 2520, 2320, 2550, 2410, 2535, 2510, 2405, 2315, 2515, 2415, 2540, 2305, 2570, 2580, 2415, 2445, 2305

   a) Calculate the sample mean life of these bulbs.
   b) Calculate the difference between the sample mean life and the company's advertised population mean life.
   c) The consumer group decides to dispute the company's claim if the difference between the sample and the population mean life is greater than 50

hours. Does the consumer group have reason to dispute the company's claim?

165. Comment on how the word **"average"** is being used in the following statements:
   • The **average** physician earned $164,300 in 1990 while working 59.9 hours.
   • The starting salary for the **average** graduate of N.Y.U. Law School is $76,424.
   • Pediatricians **averaged** $106,500—and that's 170 % of what an **average** newspaper reporter earns for a 35-hour week.
   • An **average** American eats 50 bananas a year, drinks 374 beers, goofs off 45 minutes a day at work, swallows 215 aspirins a year, and owes more than $5,000.

166. Using the following figure which represents a skewed distribution, identify the letter which represents the position of:
   a) The mode
   b) The mean
   c) The median
   d) Identify the shape of the distribution.
   e) In which tail would you expect to find an outlier? Explain.
   f) Which Measure of Central Tendency would be closest to a possible outlier? Explain.

167. For each of the following distribution of data values,
   a) Identify the general shape that you believe best describes each distribution, and
   b) Identify whether the mean or median would have the largest value within this type of distribution.
      (i) The annual income of people living in the United States.
      (ii) The number of calories consumed weekly by twenty-five-year-old Las Vegas women weighing 125 pounds.
      (iii) The heights of all the male college students playing basketball within the state of North Carolina.
      (iv) The number of words typed per minute by executive secretaries working in the Empire State Building.

168. Which measure of variability is determined only by the extreme values of a distribution?
   a) Range   b) Variance   c) Standard deviation

169. An estimate of a population standard deviation is denoted by the symbol _____.

170. If the variance of a distribution is 25, and n = 8 then $\sum(x - \bar{x})^2 =$ _____.

171. For the data 3, 5, 8, 13, 21 compute:
  a) The range
  b) The sample variance, s^2
  c) The sample standard deviation, s
  d) An estimate of the population standard deviation
  e) The population standard deviation, assuming the data represents a population.

172. If a distribution consists of all negative data values, the standard deviation is also negative. (T/F)

173. Two distributions that have the same range are not necessarily the same. (T/F)

174. If the range of distribution x is denoted by R_x and every data value in this distribution is increased by adding seven to form a new distribution y with a range denoted as R_y, then _____.
  a) R_x is larger than R_y.
  b) R_x equals R_y.
  c) R_y is larger than R_x.

175. A distribution that has a range equal to zero must also have a standard deviation equal to zero. (T/F)

176. Matthew, an employee of the utility company ILLCO, enrolls in the company's reinvestment plan to purchase 10 shares of ILLCO stock per month. The following dollar figures represent Matthew's purchase price per share for the ILLCO stock during the previous year:

ILLCO Stock
(price per share in dollars)
15.25, 16.00, 17.50, 16.50, 15.00, 15.75
16.25, 16.75, 16.00, 15.25, 15.50 15.50

  a) Compute the mean price per share that Matthew paid for the stock.
  b) Compute the sample standard deviation of the stock prices per share.

177. The points allowed by two Los Angeles pro football teams in games against their common opponents are given in the following table.

team x:	35	29	17	30	20
team y:	27	31	29	25	19

  a) Calculate the population standard deviation for each team.
  b) Using the population standard deviation as a measure of consistency, determine which team has the *more* consistent defense? (Hint: Defense can be measured by the points allowed in a game.)

178. A travel agency, trying to promote travel to two ski resorts, base their ad campaign on the following sample temperature data: (data measured in degrees Fahrenheit)

Temperature Data
(in degrees Fahrenheit)

Resort 1	34	37	15	38	42	−16
Resort 2	25	32	16	20	27	30

The ad emphasizes the mean temperature. Observe that the two temperature distributions are not identical.
  a) Calculate the standard deviation for each resort.
  b) Using the results from part (a), explain which resort has the more consistent weather.

179. Consider the following distribution:

22, 7, 26, 32, 13, 47, 34

Calculate the range and sample standard deviation for each of the following:
  a) The original distribution.
  b) The distribution formed by subtracting 10 from each data value in the original distribution.
  c) The distribution formed by multiplying each data value in the original distribution by (−4).

180. Craig has recorded prices for a statistical calculator at three discount electronic stores during the last three months. Based on this data, Craig calculated the mean and standard deviation of the calculator prices for each store.

Discount Store	Mean Price	Standard Deviation
store 1	$105.00	$26.25
store 2	$105.00	$12.50
store 3	$105.00	$0

During the past 3 months, in which store did Craig have a better chance to purchase the calculator at a cheaper price?

181. For the distribution: 14, 10, 8, 16, 20, 12, 18
  a) Find the $\bar{x}$ and s.
  b) Compute $\bar{x} + s$.
  c) Find the value that is one standard deviation above the mean. Compare this result to part (b).
  d) Compute $\bar{x} - s$.
  e) Find the value that is 1 standard deviation below the mean. Compare this result to part (d).
  f) Find the data values within $\bar{x} - s$ and $\bar{x} + s$.
  g) Find the data values that are within one standard deviation of the mean. Compare this result to part (f).
  h) Compute the percent of data values that are at least $\bar{x} + 2s$.
  i) What percent of the data values are at least two standard deviations above the mean? Compare this result to part (h).
  j) What percent of the data values are between $\bar{x} - s$ and $\bar{x} + 2s$?

182. An award is going to be given to the player on a women's college basketball team who has shown the most consistent performance over the entire season. The coach feels that consistent play is a very important factor in team performance. To measure consistency, she decides to use the standard deviation for those players that have scored an mean average of 10 points or more per game. What follows are the scoring distributions for all the players on the team:

Games

Player	1	2	3	4	5	6	7	8	9	10
Lucy	7	5	0	16	X	7	4	0	7	8
Allison	12	17	X	10	5	12	0	20	X	7
Lilia	16	18	19	X	15	20	20	14	17	14
Kathleen	9	12	7	14	8	5	4	16	18	7
Debbie	28	18	24	19	22	17	24	12	20	16
Ellen	15	3	9	8	9	13	7	18	9	19
Grace	11	8	20	25	17	16	8	5	10	10

X denotes the player did not play in that game.
a) Calculate the population mean and standard deviation of each player.
b) Which player gets the award for the most consistent performance? Explain.

183. A group of fifteen economists were asked to estimate the discount rate that will be in effect at the start of the new year. The following figures represent their estimates:

0.065 0.080 0.060 0.090 0.105 0.080 0.075 0.095
0.080 0.095 0.100 0.090 0.085 0.075 0.070

Compute (to three decimal places):
a) The sample mean, $\bar{x}$
b) The sample standard deviation, s.
c) Determine how many of the estimated discount rates fall within the range: $\bar{x} - s$ and $\bar{x} + s$.
d) Determine the percent of estimated rates that are within one standard deviation of the mean.
e) Determine the percent of estimated rates that are within two standard deviations of the mean.

184. A beverage company samples 10 soda bottles from two dispensing machines to check the output quality of the production process. The dispensing machines are set to fill the bottles with two liters of soda (67.6 oz). The actual amounts of soda which was dispensed into the bottles per machine are recorded in the following table.

Output (in ounces) for Machine One	Output (in ounces) for Machine Two
67.8	67.9
67.5	67.4
67.7	67.8
67.6	67.3
67.9	67.2
67.5	67.9
67.4	67.3
67.7	67.8
67.4	67.6
67.5	67.8

a) Using these results, compare the output quality of the two dispensing machines by computing the sample mean amount of soda dispensed per bottle by each machine as your standard.
b) Compute the sample standard deviation, s, for each machine's output.

c) Using this additional information, compare the output quality of the two dispensing machines.

185. During twenty randomly selected days, a measurement of the pollutant level of a toxic chemical is made in a stream running adjacent to a steel mill that has complied with the established Environmental Protection Agency's (EPA) water pollution standards. The results are listed in the following table:

Pollutant Level of the Toxic Chemical (in parts per million)

17.1	18.1
16.8	15.8
17.3	17.5
16.4	16.6
16.8	15.2
18.1	18.3
15.7	17.5
16.3	16.9
17.4	17.1
15.2	16.2

a) Using this information, compute $\bar{x}$, and s.
b) If the EPA's safety level standard is $\bar{x} + 2s$, determine the percentage of days sampled that exceeded this standard.

186. The Student Government Association (SGA) at a community college conducted a survey of faculty and students to determine their opinions about instituting a preferred parking area for faculty members only. The responses to the poll were ranked from one to ten, where 1 meant strongly against the preferred parking for faculty and 10 meant strongly in favor of the preferred parking for faculty. A random sample of 15 student and faculty responses were: 1, 10, 1, 10, 1, 2, 9, 8, 1, 10, 2, 1, 9, 10, 10
a) Compute the sample mean and standard deviation of the responses to the opinion poll.

A second opinion poll conducted by the SGA asked for students and faculty to express their views about whether the college should conduct a seminar on Literacy. The following responses reflect the opinions of 15 student and faculty members, where 1 meant strongly against the seminar and 10 meant strongly in favor of the seminar.

5, 6, 5, 5, 4, 5, 5, 6, 5, 5, 5, 6, 5, 5, 6

b) Compute the sample mean and standard deviation of the responses to the opinion poll.
c) Compare the results of parts a and b. Does the mean of the opinion polls distinguish a difference between the two issues? Does the standard deviation reflect a difference between the two issues? Explain your answer.

187. If the data values of two distributions have different units, then you should use the standard deviation rather than the coefficient of variation as a measure of variability. (T/F)

188. In a bell-shaped distribution, if a data value falls beyond 3 standard deviations from the mean, then we might consider this data value to be a:
a) Typical data value
b) Data value smaller than the mean
c) Greater than the mean
d) An outlier

189. Chebyshev's Theorem can only be applied to a bell-shaped distribution.
(T/F)

190. When comparing the variability of two distributions the coefficient of variation is a meaningful measure of variability when the data values are measured in _____ units or when the _____ of the distributions are far apart.

191. During last December in Boston, 40 degrees was the high temperature for the month while 28 degrees was the low temperature for the month. Using this information, an approximation of the variability for the month of December is:
a) 4.8 degrees
b) 4 degrees
c) 3 degrees
d) 2 degrees

192. Use Chebyshev's Theorem to answer the question: A bus company's records indicate that its buses complete their routes 9.3 minutes late on the average with a standard deviation of 2.1 minutes. At least what percentage of its buses complete their routes anywhere between:
1. 5.1 minutes and 13.5 minutes late?
2. 3.0 minutes and 15.6 minutes late?
3. 0.9 minutes and 17.7 minutes late?

193. The nation's 15 largest bank holding companies have the following assets in billions of dollars:

$194.4, $98.9, $96.9, $78.4, $74.7, $73.8, $64.7, $54.7, $51.8, $44.7, $41.9, $41.7, $34.4, $33.4, $33.2

Using this data, calculate:
a) $\bar{x}$ and s.
b) The percent of assets within 2 standard deviations of the mean.
c) The percent of assets within 3 standard deviations of the mean.
d) Compare the results of parts (b) and (c) to the results of Chebyshev's Theorem.

194. A radial tire manufacturer claims that their new radial Z-80 tire has an average life of 80,000 miles with a standard deviation of 2,500 miles. Assuming that the tire life is approximately bell-shaped, then use the Empirical Rule to determine the percentage of tires that will last:
a) From 75,000 to 85,000 miles.
b) More than 77,500 miles.
c) Less than 72,500 miles.
d) If you purchased one of these radial tires and it lasts 71,250 miles, what would you infer about the manufacturer's claim?

195. During last year's Marathon on Long Island, the average time to run the marathon was 225 minutes with a standard deviation of 25 minutes.
a) What can be said about the percentage of runners that took more than 275 minutes to finish the Marathon, if you have no information about the shape of this distribution?
b) What is the approximate percentage of runners that took more than 275 minutes to finish the Marathon, if the distribution has an approximate bell-shaped distribution?
c) If the distribution is approximately bell-shaped, then which which of the following times might be considered a potential outlier: 230, 275 or 375 minutes? Explain.

196. The president of Debbie's Daytime Secretarial school is trying to determine which computer processing training program to use. Two groups were trained for the same task each using a unique training program. Group 1 used training program A; group 2 used training program B. It took the first group an average of 25 hours with a standard deviation of 6 hours to train each student. Whereas, the second group took an average of 16 hours with a standard deviation of 5 hours to train each student. Which training program has less relative variability in its performance?

197. An investor is examining the past performance of three growth mutual funds which invest primarily in small-sized companies. During the past 5 years, the average return on investment and standard deviation of the investment return for each mutual fund are given in the following table.

Mutual Fund	Average Five Year Return	Standard Deviation
Fund A	27.6%	6.47%
Fund B	25.7%	5.91%
Fund C	31.8%	6.92%

a) Which fund had a greater absolute variability in return over this 5 year period?
b) If this investor considers risk to be associated with a greater relative dispersion, then which of these three mutual funds has pursued a riskier strategy?
c) If this investor decides to narrow the selection down to mutual fund B and C because they both belong to excellent mutual fund families, then which fund should the investor choose if he is interested in a less riskier investment strategy?

198. Scientists have been studying data dealing with the earth's weather to determine whether there is a **Global Warming Effect** going on. However, there are conflicting conclusions drawn from the data. Some scientists are proclaiming that there is a dangerous warming in progress due to a **greenhouse effect**. But, there are other scientists who believe that there is little evidence within the data to conclude that there is a greenhouse effect in progress. Examine the following statements made by scientists regarding the earth's climate and *write your interpretation* of this global warming phenomena in response to the question: "Do you believe that the 1980's is the start of a global warming trend or is this just the start of a natural variability of the weather pattern?"

- Every annual high (temperature) since 1950 falls below the trend of the natural increase.

- About 1950, emissions of greenhouse gases rose very rapidly. Yet, the warming rate, which should have escalated, promptly slowed.

- A net advance of about one third of 1 degree is what made the 1980's the hottest decade "on record." Some researchers believe that this amount is within the **standard deviation**, or natural variability, of the weather.

- Through the 1980's one warm year followed another. Some scientists attributed this increase in temperatures to a greenhouse effect. They speculate that an increase of carbon dioxide in the atmosphere is the culprit and the future can only get hotter.

- The greenhouse effect has been concluded based upon the fact that there has been a slight increase in temperature from past data records. However, scientists state that the data records are fuzzy by a few shades of a degree, plus or minus. And, this increase in temperature is at best only slightly larger than the margin of error for the data.

199. A psychologist has recorded the amount of time students need to complete a battery of tests. The times, stated to the nearest minute, are:

60, 80, 72, 65, 48, 52, 59, 85, 90, 89, 58, 55, 63, 68, 74, 87, 58, 59, 60, 71, 82, 84, 10, 105, 120, 89, 85, 58, 82, 47, 81, 45, 89, 82, 85, 86, 42, 40, 87, 85, 89, 55, 80, 49, 85, 82, 55, 57, 83, 82

Using this data, determine:
a) $\bar{x}$ and s to the nearest minute.
b) The percent of data values that are within 2 standard deviations of the mean.
c) The percent of data values that are within 3 standard deviations of the mean.
d) Compare the results of parts (b) and (c) to the results of Chebyshev's Theorem.
e) Is there any data value within the distribution that falls outside 3 standard deviations from the mean? If there is such a data value, then can this data value be considered an outlier? Explain.

200. The heights of women ages 18 to 24 are approximately bell-shaped with $\bar{x} = 64.5$ inches and s = 2.5 inches. According to the Empirical Rule, approximately what percentage of the women heights would you expect to fall between:
a) 62 to 67 inches?
b) 59.5 to 69.5 inches?
c) 57 to 72 inches?

d) If there was a height equal to 77 inches, could you consider such a height as an outlier? Explain.

201. For a sample containing 90 data values, the range is 55. Using Table 3.14, determine an estimate of the standard deviation, s.

202. According to the Census Bureau, the following 39 data values represent the average commuting times in metropolitan areas with more than 1 million people.

30.6, 29.5, 28.1, 26.4, 26.1, 26.0, 26.0, 25.6, 24.4, 24.3, 24.2, 24.1, 24.1, 24.1, 23.4, 23.1, 23.0, 22.9, 22.6, 22.4, 22.2, 22.1, 22.0, 21.9, 21.9, 21.8, 21.8, 21.7, 21.6, 21.6, 21.4, 21.2, 21.1, 20.6, 20.0, 19.8, 19.7, 19.7, 19.4

a) Calculate the sample standard deviation, s, of the commuting times.
b) Use the range rule in Table 3.14 to determine an over-estimate and an under-estimate of the standard deviation, s. Compare these estimates to the value computed in part (a).
c) Determine the percent of data values that are within 2 standard deviations of the mean.
d) The percent of data values that are within 3 standard deviations of the mean.
e) Compare the results of parts (c) and (d) to the results of Chebyshev's Theorem.

For questions 203 through 206, use the following information:

At Jefferson High, the final average with a percentile rank of 50 was 82. Mike's average has a percentile rank of 74. Pete's average is equal to the 9th decile. Maria's average has a percentile rank of 94. Joe's average is between the first and second quartile. Susan's average was less than 82. Jeff's average has a percentile rank which is lower than Maria's but greater than Mike's.

203. Of those students mentioned above, who had the highest average?
a) Joe   **b)** Maria   **c)** Mike   **d)** Susan

204. What is the median average?
a) 74   **b)** 94   **c)** 82   **d)** 50

205. Of those students mentioned above, how many had an average less than 82?
a) 0   **b)** 3   **c)** 1   **d)** 2

206. Whose average was equal to the 90th percentile?
a) Maria   **b)** Mike   **c)** Pete   **d)** Susan

207. If a data value is two standard deviations less than the mean, it has a z score of 2.
(T/F)

208. The 7th decile is the data value, X, within a distribution that has the property that 70 percent of the data values are less than X and 30 percent of the data values are greater than X.
(T/F)

209. Which measure of variability is used in calculating the z score of a data value?
   a) Range
   b) Variance
   c) Standard deviation

210. Which of the following indicates the relative position of a data value within its distribution?
   a) Mean
   b) Raw score
   c) z score
   d) Standard deviation

211. The _____ indicates the number of standard deviations a data value is greater than or less than the mean.

212. In a population, if x = 545, μ = 525 and z = 5, then σ = _____.

213. In a distribution, $\bar{x}$ = 75, and s = 5. If z = 3 is the maximum z score value of a data value in the distribution, and z = –2 is the minimum z score value of a data value in the distribution, then, the range of the distribution is equal to _____.

214. If P_{50} = 100, then we state that 100 is the 2nd _____.

215. If a data value has a z score of zero, this indicates that the data value is the _____.
   a) Standard deviation
   b) Median
   c) Mean
   d) None of these

216. If two distributions have equal means, then the data values that have z scores equal to 1 will always be the same.
   (T/F)

217. The 40th percentile is the data value, X, in a distribution that equals 40.
   (T/F)

218. **a)** Using the z score formula, calculate and interpret the z scores for each raw score given in the table below.
   b) Using the results of part a, identify which raw score might be considered a potential outlier. Explain your reasoning.

Raw Score	Mean	Standard Deviation
i) 24	16	8
ii) 65	100	10
iii) 440	460	15
iv) 875	450	100
v) 1150	1150	120

219. **a)** Using the raw score formula, calculate the raw score for each z score given in the following table.
   b) Using the table information and the results of part a, state the raw score that might be considered a potential outlier. Explain.

	Mean	Standard Deviation	z Score
i)	20	5	+4.51
ii)	50	6	–1.65
iii)	110	15	+0.95
iv)	500	100	–2.33
v)	90	20	+1.96

220. An instructor assigns letter grades in the following manner:

To achieve a letter grade of:	z score of test grade must be:
A	Greater than 1.5
B	From 0.5 to 1.5
C	Between –0.5 and 0.5
D	From –1.5 to –0.5
F	Less than –1.5

   a) If the mean is 83 and the standard deviation is 8, find the test scores that determine the letter grades.
   b) If the mean is 70 and the standard deviation is 18, find the test scores that determine the letter grades.

221. DEB Homes, Inc., a Long Beach real estate agency, sold three condominiums during the past week. Condo M, a waterfront condo, sold for $305,000 while Condo A, on the canal side of town, sold for $275,000 and Condo T, in the heart of town, sold for $215,000.

   In Long Beach, the purchase price of a condo is dependent upon its location. City Hall calculates the mean price of a waterfront condo to be $245,000 (with s = $50,000), while the mean price of a canal side condo is $230,000 (with s = $23,000) and a town condo to have a mean price of $190,000 (with s = $15,000). Based upon its geographic location, which of the three condos was sold for the relatively:
   a) Higher purchase price?
   b) Lower purchase price?

222. Watergate Price Inc., a consumer group, surveys a Washington, D.C. urban area to compare the basic service charges of the three most frequently called service people to determine the highest repair charge relative to their respective occupation. According to the survey, the 3 most frequently called service people were: a plumber, an auto mechanic and an electrician. In this area the survey indicates that the basic service charge per occupation is:

plumber—$35/hour,

auto mechanic—$40/hour,

electrician—$47.50/hour.

The following table represents the union mean and standard deviation service charges per occupation.

Occupation	Mean(μ)	Standard Deviation(σ)
plumber	$26.50/hour	$3.50/hour
auto mechanic	$23.75/hour	$5.75/hour
electrician	$35.90/hour	$4.25/hour

Determine which of the three service people charge the highest repair charge relative to their respective occupation.

223. Michael and Lorenzo both took the same calculus test. Michael scored an 87 on the test. Lorenzo's test paper only had the z score of his grade which was +1.2. The instructor gave Lorenzo the following information about the distribution of test grades: the mean test grade is 76 and the standard deviation is 15. Who had the higher grade, Michael or Lorenzo?

224. Two track athletes, a sprinter and a long jumper, break their school's record in their respective events. To determine which feat is more outstanding relative to his respective event, the school's statistician collects the best performances for each event within the United States and lists the necessary data below:

Athlete	Event	Record	Mean	Standard Deviation
sprinter	100m run	10.3 sec	10.6 sec	0.15 sec
long jumper	long jump	7.82 m	7.62 m	0.13 m

Which of the two athletic records is more outstanding?

225. In certain manufacturing processes, parts must be machined to within specified tolerances. The parts must have a mean length of six inches plus or minus 0.26 inches. A sampling procedure has been established to determine whether the parts are within the specified tolerances. If for a sample of ten parts selected at random, the mean plus 1.5 standard deviations and the mean minus 1.5 standard deviations are within the specified limits of 5.74 inches to 6.26 inches, then the parts are meeting the specified tolerances. This means that a z score of 1.5 and a z score of -1.5 must be within the limits of 5.74 inches and 6.26 inches. The lengths (in inches) representing the ten parts are as follows:

5.94, 6.20, 5.86, 6.08, 6.14, 6.12, 6.01, 5.92, 5.90, 6.23

Procedure:
a) Calculate the mean, $\bar{x}$, and standard deviation, s.
b) Convert $z = -1.5$ and $z = 1.5$ into inches (data values).
c) Compare these values with the specified limits of 5.74 inches to 6.26 inches and determine if this sample meets the stated conditions.

226. Using the following collection of 50 IQ scores, compute the percentile rank of the IQ scores and interpret each result:
a) 87   **b)** 91   **c)** 105   **d)** 115   **e)** 119   **f)** 121

IQ Scores

81, 85, 85, 86, 87, 87, 88, 89, 89, 90, 90, 90, 91, 93, 93, 94, 95, 97, 98, 99, 100, 101, 102, 104, 105, 105, 107, 107, 110, 112, 112, 113, 114, 115, 115, 115, 115, 119, 120, 121, 121, 121, 122, 123, 125, 125, 126, 126, 127, 135

227. Using the results of problem #226, determine the IQ score representing the :
a) 7th decile
b) 3rd quartile
c) 2nd quartile
d) 1st decile
e) median
f) 1st quartile

228. Some results of the Graduate Record Examination (GRE) Mathematics part are recorded in the following table:

GRE Score	372	433	475	500	525	567	604	628	733
Percentile Rank	10	25	40	50	60	75	85	90	99

Using the table, determine:
a) The 1st decile score.
b) The 1st quartile score.
c) The median score.
d) The 6th decile score.
e) The 3rd quartile score.
f) Percentage of students who scored below 604.
g) Percentage of students who scored higher than 525.
h) Percentage of students who scored between 433 and 567.
i) The difference between the 3rd quartile score and the 1st quartile score.

229. The reaction time of 250 people is measured after a new drug is administered. Some results of this test are given in the following table.

Reaction Time (sec)	8	12	16	20	28	36	40
z score	-1.5	-1	-0.5	0	1	2	2.5
Percentile Rank	17	25	30	42	50	75	85

By inspection of the table, determine:
a) The mean reaction time for all 250 people.
b) The median reaction time for all 250 people.
c) The standard deviation time for all 250 people.
d) The percent of people who had reaction times 40 secs or below.
e) The reaction time representing the 3rd decile.
f) The reaction time representing the 1st quartile.
g) The reaction time representing the 3rd quartile.

230. The following table indicates the performance of six students on the law boards. Using this information, compute the percentile rank of each student if 10,000 students took the law boards.

Student I.D.	Number of students who scored less than this student	Number of students who scored the same as this student (including student)
L	2,250	500
A	2,900	200
W	4,800	400
Y	7,475	50
E	8,000	100
R	9,000	25

231. To qualify for a scholarship at Richman's College, a student must score at least 1.5 standard deviations above the mean on the entrance exam. Which of the following students qualify if the mean and standard deviation for the entrance examination is 60 and 12 respectively?

Student	Score on Exam
George	75
Alice	78
Barbara	81
Mauro	77
Mike	79

232. If the mean cholesterol count of two hundred nutritionists is 176 with a standard deviation of 12, determine the cholesterol limits that cut off all the cholesterol counts that are within:
a) One standard deviation of the mean
b) 1.96 standard deviations of the mean
c) Two standard deviations of the mean
d) 2.58 standard deviations of the mean
e) Three standard deviations of the mean.

233. A male is considered to be hypertensive for his age group if he has a systolic blood pressure of more than two standard deviations greater than the mean.

The following table contains the mean and standard deviation for systolic blood pressures for some male age groups.

Male systolic blood pressure parameters

Age	Mean	Standard Deviation
18	121	8
25	125	8
35	127	9
45	130	13
60	142	14

The following readings of systolic blood pressure were taken for a sample of males.

Male	Age	Systolic Blood Pressure
Craig	18	134
Jim	25	142
Mike	35	142
Lou	60	150

Determine which (if any) of the males are classified as hypertensive.

234. A 5-number summary is used to describe the shape, center and _____ of a data set.
a) Mean
b) Spread
c) Variance
d) Percentile

235. The percent of data values represented by the IQR is:
a) 25%   **b)** 50%   **c)** 75%   **d)** 100%

236. If the whiskers of a box plot are approximately equal and the median falls within the middle of the box, then the shape of the distribution is skewed. (T/F)

237. The length of the upper whisker represents approximately the top _____ percent of the data values.

238. According to Tukey, a potential outlier is a data value that is less than the ____ fence but greater than the ____ fence.

239. Outer fences are located at (____)*IQR below Q_1 and above Q_3.
a) 1.5   **b)** 2   **c)** 3   **d)** 4

240. If the IQR = 40 then the outer fences are located a distance of _____ below Q_1 and above Q_3.
a) 60   **b)** 80   **c)** 100   **d)** 120

241. If the length of the lower whisker is longer than the upper whisker and the position of the median is closer to the 3rd quartile, then we would expect the shape of the distribution to be _____.

242. If the largest data value within a distribution is an outlier, then the percent of data values between Q_3 and the largest data value is greater than the percent of data values between Q_1 and the smallest data value. (T/F)

243. An instructor from the school of business samples the students in his introduction to business class to learn about the amount of dollars students spend per semester on textbooks. The distribution that follows indicates the results of his sample.

Textbook Costs per Student per semester (in dollars)

65 147 171 142 153 187 195 106 127 178 178 205
175 178 133 186

a) Determine the 5-number summary for the textbook spending data.
b) Construct a Box-and-Whisker Plot.
c) Describe the shape of the Box-and-Whisker Plot.
d) Calculate the interquartile range(IQR).
e) Determine if there are any outliers within the data set. If there is an outlier, state their value(s).
f) Find the z score of each if any exists and interpret their relative position in terms of standard deviations.
g) Explain what effect an outlier, if any exists, has on the mean and median textbook cost.

244. The following distributions represent the number of homeruns that Roger Maris and Babe Ruth hit during the designated years.

> The number of homeruns hit by Roger Maris during each baseball season for the years 1957-1968
>
> 14, 28, 16, 39, 61, 33, 23, 26, 8, 13, 9, 5
>
> The number of homeruns hit by Babe Ruth during each baseball season for the years 1919–1934
>
> 29, 54, 59, 35, 41, 46, 25, 47, 60, 54, 46, 49, 46, 41, 34, 22

For each homerun distribution, determine:

a) The 1st quartile, median, and 3rd quartile.

b) Construct a Box-and-Whisker Plot for each distribution on the same scale.

c) Compare the box plots, and discuss the differences between the two distributions.

d) Use the box plots to compare the variability of each distribution. Which distribution has the smaller variability? the larger variability? Now, calculate the Interquartile Range and the standard deviation of each distribution. Compare the IQR and the standard deviation of each distribution. Are these results similar? With respect to variability, what is the relationship between the value of the IQR and the standard deviation of each distribution?

e) Identify any potential outliers for each distribution, and give an explanation for the outlier. Find the z score of any outlier and interpret the meaning of the z score.

f) Describe the shape of each distribution.

245. The following two Box-and-Whisker Plots represent the test results of a statistics final for two different instructors.

Test results for Instructor A

Test results for Instructor B

From each of the previous two box plots representing the test results of instructors A and B, approximate the:

a) 1st quartile test score.

b) 3rd quartile test score.

c) Median test score.

d) Smallest and largest test score.

e) Interquartile range(IQR).

f) Shape of the distribution.

g) Percent of test results to the left of the 3rd quartile.

h) Percent of test results to the right of the median.

i) Percent of test results between the 1st and 3rd quartile.

j) Compare the two test distributions and explain the differences about the test results.

k) Each instructor had a different objective in mind when constructing the final exam. One instructor was trying to determine the top students in the class, while the other instructor was trying to determine the minimum knowledge of the poorest students. Based on the box plots, explain which instructor you believe was trying to determine the top students in her class? Which test do you believe was the easiest test? Explain.

246. The rate in which red blood cells settle in a tall narrow tube (known as the erythrocyte sedimentation rate) is an indication of a person's health. A sample of blood from 20 randomly selected elderly males was measured for this rate. The data values are as follows:

Red Blood Cell Sedimentation Rate (millimeters per 1 hour)

13 9 9 105 8 4 5 10 8 120 8 5 12 5 7 10 9 8 5 10

a) Determine the 5-number summary for the blood sedimentation rate data.

b) Use the 5-number summary to construct a Box-and-Whisker Plot.

c) Describe the shape of the Box-and-Whisker Plot.

d) Calculate the interquartile range and determine the data values that are greater than
  1) 1.5*IQR.
  2) 3*IQR.

e) Are any of the data values considered to be outliers? Why? If there are any possible outliers, discuss reasons that might contribute to these data values being an outlier.

247. An instructor from the school of business surveys the students in his introduction to business class to learn about the amount of dollars students spend per semester on textbooks. The distribution that follows indicates the results of his survey.

Textbook Costs per Student per semester (in dollars)

147 160 142 153 187 195 106 127 178 178 272 175 178 133 186

a) Determine the 5-number summary for the textbook spending data.

b) Use the 5-number summary to construct a Box-and-Whisker Plot.

c) Describe the shape of the Box-and-Whisker Plot.

d) Calculate the interquartile range and determine the data values that are greater than
  1) 1.5*IQR.
  2) 3*IQR.

e) Are any of the data values considered to be outliers? Why? If there are any possible outliers discuss reasons that might contribute to these data values being an outlier.

248. A statistics instructor at a community college administers the same exam to two groups of students. The first group represents full-time day students, while the second group is composed of part-time evening students.

The results of the exam for each group are:

Full-Time Day Students

22, 32, 41, 50, 62, 74, 80, 90, 95, 86, 86, 74, 75, 62, 62, 53, 53, 43, 43, 35, 35, 27, 29, 29, 38, 39, 39, 87, 87, 75, 79, 69, 69, 59, 58, 49, 48, 53, 59, 59, 64, 62, 62, 68, 76, 79, 87, 96, 76, 97, 79, 76, 98, 62, 65, 54, 59, 44, 49

Part-Time Evening Students

32, 47, 58, 17, 64, 77, 89, 86, 99, 92, 80, 71, 63, 55, 46, 49, 57, 65, 74, 86, 94, 92, 86, 89, 96, 74, 61, 70, 84, 85, 92, 97, 78, 65, 56, 64, 84, 86, 95, 98, 86, 72, 52, 94, 96, 84, 94

For each distribution:

a) Construct a stem-and-leaf display.

b) Discuss the shape of the distribution.

c) Determine the mean, median, mode, and the trim-mean for the distribution, and interpret these measures.

d) Locate the value of the mean, median, and mode on each stem-and-leaf display.

e) What does the relationship between the location of the measures of central tendency indicate about the skewness or symmetry of the two distributions.

f) Determine if there is a measure of central tendency that is very sensitive to the extreme data values? If there is such a measure, then identify the measure, the shape of the distribution, and the direction in which this measure is shifted. Explain why the measure has shifted in that direction.

g) Compare the value of the mean to the trimmean. In which distribution is the difference larger? Can you explain what might attribute to this larger difference?

h) Determine, overall, which group you believe did better on the exam? Explain your answer.

249. The following MINITAB output represents a stem-and-leaf display for 42 freshman enrolled at a small community college. The display represents the number of hours worked per week for both male and female students.

```
MTB  >  Stem-and-Leaf 'hrswrk';
SUBC >  Increment 10.

Stem-and-leaf of hrswrk      N = 42
Leaf Unit = 1.0

   4    0   0000
  12    1   00005555
  21    2   000555555
  21    3   0005555
  14    4   0000005555
   4    5   005
   1    6   5
```

a) Draw the shape of the display using a smooth curve.

b) Indicate, by drawing a line, where the mean, median and mode fall.

c) Discuss the shape of the distribution in terms of the relationship between the location of the mean, median and mode within the distribution.

250. The following MINITAB outputs indicate two stem-and-leaf displays representing 42 freshman enrolled at a small community college.

The first display indicates the number of hours worked per week for the female students, while the second display indicates the number of hours worked per week for the male students.

OUTPUT for Female Students

```
MTB  >  Stem-and-Leaf 'hrswrk';
SUBC >  By sex;
SUBC >  Increment 10.

Stem-and-leaf of hrswrk    sex = 1      N = 20
Leaf Unit = 1.0

   2    0   00
   8    1   000555
  (7)   2   0005555
   5    3   005
   2    4   05
```

OUTPUT for Male Students

```
Stem-and-leaf of hrswrk       sex = 2      N = 22
Leaf Unit = 1.0

   2    0   00
   4    1   05
   6    2   55
  10    3   0555
  (8)   4   00000555
   4    5   005
   1    6   5
```

For each display:

a) Draw the shape using a smooth curve.

b) Indicate, by drawing a line, where the mean, median, and mode fall.

c) Discuss the shape of the distribution in terms of the relationship between the location of the mean, median, and mode within the distribution.

d) Compare the shapes of each of the distributions. What are the differences between the work habits of the male and female students?

251. The test results for the Midterm Exam Scores for two statistics classes are given as follows:

Class 1	Class 2
33	9
34	33
24	28
32	15
19	28
21	13
20	16
17	25
21	25
9	23
23	19
27	17
25	16
28	28
25	31
17	17
24	15
26	34
24	22
34	19
22	24
25	22
32	23
34	20
26	14
20	18
22	22
22	20
19	19
33	20

a) Use a technological tool to construct a histogram for each class' Midterm Exam Scores.
b) Using the graphs, estimate which class's exam scores are more varied.
c) Using a technological tool, compute the standard deviation for each class's exam scores.
d) Which class's scores indicate the greater variability?
e) Is your estimate for part b and the calculation for part d consistent?

252. The systolic blood pressures for a sample of twenty 45 year old females and twenty 45 year old males are represented as follows:

Females	Males
105	105
120	95
110	140
95	130
100	125
125	120
95	150
100	120
105	125
110	140
105	130
95	125
120	110
125	120
110	120
115	115
115	125
120	140
105	120
95	110

a) Using a technological tool construct a histogram for each group of data values.
b) Using the graphs, estimate which group's blood pressures are more varied.
c) Using a technological tool compute the standard deviation for each group of data values.
d) Which group's blood pressures indicate the greater variability?
e) Is your estimate for part b and the calculation for part d consistent?

253. The data values in the table compare the amount of dietary fiber for three different cereal types.

**Amount of Dietary Fiber for Cereal Type
(measured in grams)**

Cereal	Whole-Grain Cereal with Bran	All-Bran Cereal
3.0	5.0	13
2.1	4.0	12
2.0	4.0	10
2.0	4.0	9
2.0	3.1	8
1.6	2.9	5

For each cereal type:
a) Construct a Box and Whisker Plot and identify its shape.
b) Numerically describe the data.
c) Find the 5-number summary.
d) Identify potential outliers.
e) Write a description comparing the similarities and/or differences for the cereal data.

254. The following letter appeared in the *New York Times* on October 3, 1996.

Misusing Statistics

To the Editor:

In his Sept. 29 letter defending Bob Dole's tax plan, Senator William V. Roth Jr. says that "the average American family pays more in taxes than it spends on food, shelter and clothing." This exemplifies a common misuse of statistics. While it is probably an accurate statement if you add up the taxes paid and divide it by the number of taxpayers, it is not true for typical taxpayers. The more meaningful average is the median, that is, the taxes paid by the taxpayer at the midpoint. That middle taxpayer's taxes do not come close to equaling the cost of food, shelter, and clothing.

The fallacy of Senator Roth's approach reminds me of of the excellent opportunities that were available since "the average employee in our firm makes $100,000 a year." What he didn't tell them was that he made $910,000 and his nine employees made $10,000 each.

Jerome Trupin
Scarborough, N.Y., Sept. 29, 1996

a) What does the author mean by the "average American family"?

b) What average does the author believe Senator William V. Roth Jr. used in his article? Why do you think this average is not true for the typical taxpayer in this particular example?

c) What does the author believe is the relationship between the median taxpayer's taxes and the average taxpayer's taxes? Based on the author's opinion, what do you think would be the shape of the distribution of taxes? Explain.

d) If the distribution of taxes has an outlier, then which measure of central tendency do you think is affected the most by the outlier? Would it increase or decrease this measure of central tendency? Explain.

e) Explain the fallacy in the example the author refers to when he states that "the average employee in our firm makes $100,000 a year." Explain which measure of central tendency would have been more appropriate in the example the author gives.

f) Do you think that the standard deviation of this distribution of taxes is a large or a small value? Explain.

255. Mutual fund companies recommend a diversified investment portfolio. One diversification strategy is to include foreign stocks to balance the overall volatility of a portfolio while increasing the opportunity for long-term growth. The question becomes "What percentage of the portfolio should include foreign stocks?" A mutual fund company provided their clients with the following chart entitled "How Foreign Stocks Benefit a Domestic Portfolio" to help them decide. This chart provides information on average annual returns with respect to the portfolio's level of risk.

Examine the curve shown within the chart. The percentages shown along the curve indicate the amount of international stocks added to a domestic portfolio (U.S. stocks). Notice that the level of risk is measured by the standard deviation.

a) For this example, the standard deviation is defined as a risk statistic that measures the range of performances within which investment returns have varied over a period of time. Explain how the standard deviation changes as the percentage of foreign stocks within the portfolio changes from:
0% to 30%?
30% to 60%?
60% to 100%?

b) As the percentage of foreign stocks within the portfolio increases from 0% to 30%, describe how the level of risk changes along with the average annual return? What do you think this might mean to you as a conservative investor? as a speculative investor?

c) As the percentage of foreign stocks within the portfolio increases from 30% to 60%, describe how the level of risk changes along with the average annual return? What do you think this means to you as a conservative investor? as a speculative investor?

d) As the percentage of foreign stocks within the portfolio increases from 60% to 100%, describe how the level of risk changes along with the average annual return? What do you think this means to you as a conservative investor? as a speculative investor?

e) If you are an investor with a portfolio containing 100% U.S. stocks, how would changing your portfolio to include 30% foreign stocks affect your annual return? how would this change affect your risk? Would you consider this change to be reasonable if you are a conservative investor? Explain.

f) If you are an investor with a portfolio containing 100% U.S. stocks, how would changing your portfolio to include 60% foreign stocks affect your annual return? how would this change affect your risk? Would you consider this change to be reasonable if you are a conservative investor? Explain.

g) If you are an investor with a portfolio containing 70% U.S. stocks and 30% foreign stocks, how would changing your portfolio to 70% foreign stocks affect your annual return? how would this change affect your risk? Would you consider this change to be reasonable if you are a conservative investor? Explain.

256. For each of the following graphics,

a) Define the population and identify the variable being presented.

b) Discuss which measure of central tendency might have been used or was used to describe the variable within the graphic.

c) Explain why you believe this measure of central tendency is or is not the appropriate measure to use to describe the data.

d) State whether the number stated within the graphic represents a statistic or a parameter. Explain.

e) If possible, draw a conclusion using the information within the graphic.

(a)

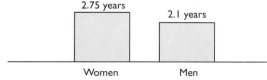

Statistical Snapshot

Are You STILL in there?
How long we spend in the bathroom during our lifetime:

Source: KRC Research and Consulting for Northern Bathroom Tissue (projected based on average life expectancy)

(b)

Statistical Snapshot

Eye Appeal
About 80% of women say they'd change the color of their eyes to make them sexier. Color they would prefer:

Source: Advantage Business Research Inc. for Wesley-Jessen

(c)

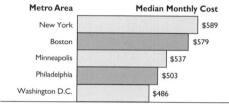

Statistical Snapshot

Where Daycare is No Bargain
The median cost for daycare* nationwide is $388 per month. Most expensive metropolitan areas for daycare:

*Based on monthly fee

257. Examine the vertical bar graph in the following figure. The graph represents the number of passengers expected to travel by air each day of the Christmas holidays, in millions.

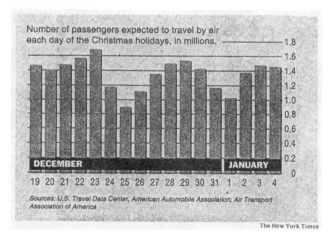

a) For which of the following three day period: Dec. 19—21st, Dec. 23—25th, or Dec. 28—30th, do you believe the variability of the number of passengers is the largest? the smallest variability? Explain.

b) From the bar graph, estimate the variability of the all the data values using the range. What is a disadvantage in using the range as a measure of variability?

c) For which any three consecutive day period, is the variability the greatest? the smallest? Explain.

258. The following bar graph represents the time the winning goal was scored in overtime for the 251 National Hockey League playoff overtime games from 1970 to 1993.

a) State the shape of the graph.
b) Using this graph, when can you expect the winning goal to be scored in a playoff overtime game? What measure of central tendency did you use to answer this question?
c) Place a mark on the graph where you would think the median time would fall? the mean time? Explain your answer.
d) Calculate the median time and mean time from the information given in the bar graph. Compare these results to your answer to part c. Explain any discrepancies.
e) Calculate the standard deviation of the times shown in the bar graph. Explain what this statistical measure tells you about the time to score the winning goal in overtime?
f) Calculate the percentage of goals scored within 1 standard deviation of the mean, 2 standard deviations of the mean and 3 standard deviations of the mean. Compare these results to the expected results using Chebyshev's Theorem.

259. The following information represents the listing of stock quotations for six stocks. Examine the information contained within this listing. Notice that the listing includes the high and low price for each stock during the past 52 weeks, as well as the high, low and closing price for each stock for the previous trade day. The last column represents the net change in the stock price from the previous day's quotation. The stock's name and symbol are also included within the listing.

a) Which measure of variability is being used to reflect the variability in the stock prices for the year? for the day?
b) Over the year, which stock has been less volatile? more volatile?
c) From the previous trading day, which stock has been less volatile? more volatile?
d) Which stock had the greatest percentage gain in its price for the previous day's trading price? the smallest percentage gain?
e) Which stock had the greatest percentage loss in its price for the previous day's trading price? the smallest percentage loss?
f) The following graph represents the daily prices for the stock First National Film Corp (Symbol: FNAT) for the period from January to April.

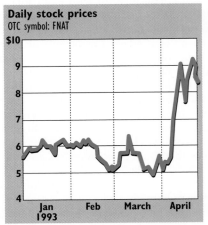

First National Film Corp.

(i) Within which month, was the variability in First National Film Corp. stock's price the smallest? the greatest?
(ii) What information is contained within the graph for First National Film Corp. that is not represented by the stock quotation listed below? Explain how this shows a disadvantage of the range as a measure of variability as compared to the graphic information for First National Film Corp.

260. The following distribution list represents the ages of the 400 USA's wealthiest people, according to *Forbes Magazine*, for the year 1992.

52 weeks							net
Hi	Lo	Stock	Sym	Hi	Lo	Close	chg
13 1/2	4	Aileen	AEE	5 1/2	5 1/8	5 1/8	−1/2
43 3/4	25 1/8	AutoZone	AZO	40 7/8	39 5/8	40 5/8	−1/2
15 1/2	12 5/8	WestcstEngy	WE	15 1/4	15	15 1/8	. . .
28 1/4	11 1/8	Marvel Entn	MRV	28 1/8	24 7/8	27 5/8	+2 5/8
15	9 5/8	Homestake	HM	16 1/4	14 7/8	16	+1 5/8
3 3/4	9 5/8	Ft Nt Film	FNAT	8 9/16	8 7/16	8 7/16	−1/16

Data for exercise 259

260. (continued)

The Ages of the 400 Wealthiest

71, 46, 81, 43, 73, 44, 48, 70, 43, 62, 43, 69, 65, 47, 80, 67, 67, 58,
60, 79, 75, 64, 73, 69, 72, 49, 61, 40, 63, 69, 64, 61, 48, 64, 59, 75,
62, 75, 68, 49, 70, 68, 58, 52, 65, 47, 64, 71, 52, 63, 69, 40, 35, 38,
77, 60, 79, 79, 70, 54, 46, 52, 93, 67, 91, 72, 45, 64, 66, 55, 50, 85,
50, 76, 75, 57, 83, 82, 66, 90, 69, 68, 78, 75, 43, 69, 50, 52, 68, 71,
76, 86, 56, 75, 58, 46, 79, 72, 77, 91, 81, 86, 80, 62, 74, 49, 56, 68,
50, 54, 64, 85, 73, 52, 67, 86, 65, 82, 73, 53, 92, 74, 56, 51, 87, 75,
72, 54, 63, 50, 85, 69, 60, 74, 69, 86, 83, 70, 66, 67, 67, 70, 81, 51,
55, 64, 55, 86, 54, 61, 51, 66, 64, 64, 61, 66, 75, 56, 64, 76, 92, 75,
77, 72, 60, 69, 62, 80, 48, 67, 54, 55, 66, 68, 69, 67, 55, 63, 69, 86,
67, 56, 84, 68, 78, 77, 64, 63, 76, 59, 58, 69, 70, 72, 70, 63, 58, 62,
83, 86, 67, 69, 34, 38, 55, 50, 52, 55, 79, 74, 74, 54, 47, 64, 63, 64,
49, 61, 63, 69, 66, 74, 52, 53, 77, 79, 83, 84, 59, 48, 90, 82, 76, 84,
54, 62, 84, 53, 83, 56, 78, 67, 82, 52, 58, 67, 48, 79, 84, 77, 66, 76,
83, 82, 81, 49, 71, 89, 84, 51, 50, 44, 88, 76, 64, 78, 57, 31, 60, 47,
49, 53, 36, 82, 60, 77, 51, 60, 55, 55, 86, 79, 70, 59, 72, 80, 78, 71,
78, 57, 51, 67, 73, 50, 54, 50, 80, 73, 84, 42, 60, 64, 64, 59, 77, 74,
54, 64, 73, 61, 69, 54, 53, 50, 52, 76, 58, 76, 74, 63, 60, 59, 66, 54,
52, 49, 58, 62, 36, 49, 49, 44, 47, 76, 61, 66, 63, 87, 73, 57, 65, 64,
64, 75, 69, 48, 54, 87, 74, 66, 53, 48, 56, 67, 67, 58, 27, 72, 67, 48,
50, 44, 68, 71, 55, 69, 97, 78, 61, 57, 85, 79, 65, 88, 79, 70, 59, 35,
36, 36, 39, 36, 60, 43, 46, 41, 39, 56, 64, 59, 72, 48, 59, 76, 61, 60,
45, 68, 57, 57

a) Construct a histogram for these ages using the classes: 20–29, 30–39, 40–49, 50–59, 60–69, 70–79, 80–89, and 90–99.

b) Describe the shape of the histogram.

c) Using Chebyshev's Theorem, determine the minimum percentage of ages that fall within two standard deviations of the mean? within three standard deviations of the mean?

d) Using the Empirical Rule, determine the approximate percentage of ages that fall within one standard deviation of the mean? within two standard deviations of the mean? within three standard deviations of the mean?

e) Calculate the actual percentage of ages that fall within one, two or three standard deviations of the mean.

f) Compare the actual results of part (e) to the results found by using Chebyshev's Theorem and the Empirical Rule. Which rule provides a better approximation? Which rule gives a more conservative estimate?

g) For this type of shaped distribution, which rule would be more appropriate to use to approximate the percentage of ages that fall within k standard deviations of the mean? Explain.

261. Examine the graphic entitled "It was a very wet year in the USA."

Statistical Snapshot

It Was a Very Wet Year in the USA

1996 was USA's seventh wettest year since comprehensive record-keeping began in 1895. The precipitation was driven up by record rainfall in the Northwest and Northeast. The West had its second warmest year, but that was offset by cold in the East and North. The nation's average temperature matched the 102-year average:

Precipitation (in inches): 32.10 (1996), 29.46 (Normal), 24.17 (Driest 1910), 33.99 (Wettest 1973)

Temperatures: 52.4° (1996), 52.4° (Normal), 50.7° (Coldest 1917), 54.7° (Warmest 1934)

Source: William Brown, National Climate Data Center

a) Define the population and identify the variables being presented.

b) What measure do you think is being used to describe the Normal Precipitation and Temperature? Explain how this is useful to interpret the precipitation and temperature for 1996.

c) What is the purpose of including the information about the driest and wettest? How is this useful when interpreting the precipitation for 1996?

d) What is the purpose of including the information about the coldest and warmest? How is this useful when interpreting the temperature for 1996?

e) Explain why it would be difficult to interpret the precipitation and temperature for 1996 without the information on the driest and wettest precipitation and the coldest and warmest temperature for 1996.

262. According to the U.S. Bureau of the Census, International Data Base, the following data set represents the life expectancy at birth for both males and females for a selected sample of world countries (1996).

Life Expectancy at Birth by Sex for Selected Countries, 1996

Country	Males	Females
NORTH AMERICA		
Canada	75.7	82.7
United States	72.7	79.4
Mexico	70.1	77.5
CENTRAL & SOUTH AMERICA		
Brazil	56.7	66.8
Chile	71.3	77.7
Costa Rica	73.3	78.2
Ecuador	68.5	73.8
Guatemala	62.6	68.0
Panama	71.2	76.8
Peru	67.0	71.4
Trindad & Tobago	67.9	72.8
Uruguay	71.8	78.3
Venezuela	69.1	75.3

Life Expectancy at Birth by Sex
for Selected Countries, 1996 (cont.)

Country	Males	Females
EUROPE		
Austria	73.4	79.8
Belguim	73.9	80.5
Cyprus	74.1	78.5
Czech Republic	70.1	77.7
Denmark	73.8	81.0
Finland	73.8	77.2
France	74.5	82.5
Germany	72.8	79.3
Greece	75.6	80.8
Hungary	64.2	74.0
Ireland	72.9	78.5
Italy	74.9	81.5
Netherlands	74.9	80.7
Norway	74.6	80.6
Poland	68.0	76.4
Portugal	71.5	79.3
Russia	56.5	70.3
Slovakia	69.0	77.2
Spain	74.9	81.8
Sweden	75.6	80.6
Switzerland	74.6	80.8
United Kingdom	73.8	79.2
ASIA		
Bangladesh	56.0	55.7
China	68.3	71.1
India	59.1	60.3
Iran	66.1	68.7
Israel	76.2	80.0
Japan	76.6	82.7
Pakistan	57.7	59.3
South Korea	69.7	77.4
Sri Lanka	69.8	75.1
Syria	65.9	68.4
AFRICA		
Egypt	59.5	63.5
Kenya	55.5	55.7
South Africa	57.2	61.8
OCEANIA		
Australia	76.4	82.5
New Zealand	74.0	80.2

a) Define the population and identify the variable being presented for each distribution.

b) For each distribution, calculate the mean, median, mode and sample standard deviation.

c) Using the information in part b, describe the shape of the distribution for each data set.

d) For the males, compare the value of the mean and median. If they are not the same, explain why you think this to be the case.

e) For the females, compare the value of the mean and median. If they are not the same, explain why you think this to be the case.

f) Calculate the 5-number summary for both the males and the females.

g) Construct a box plot for both the males and females.

h) From the box plot, identify the shape of the distribution for both males and females. Compare this result to the result of part c.

i) Determine if there exists an outlier for the male and female distributions. If an outlier exists, then calculate the z score of each outlier. Interpret each z score.

j) If an outlier exists, state what effect it had on the mean and the median of the distribution.

263. Examine the graphic entitled Average Teacher Salaries By State which represents a state-by-state estimate of the average salaries of classroom teachers in 1999–2000.

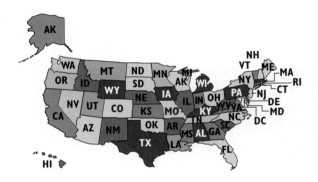

Reprinted by permission of Edulink, Inc.

Alabama: $33000	Louisiana: $30000	Ohio: $39000
Alaska: $52000	Maine: $34000	Oklahoma: $31000
Arizona: $34000	Maryland: $42000	Oregon: $42000
Arkansas: $31000	Massachusetts: $43000	Pennsylvania: $48000
California: $44000	Michigan: $49000	Rhode Island: $44000
Colorado: $37000	Minnesota: $39000	South Carolina: $33000
Connecticut: $51000	Mississippi: $28000	South Dakota: $27000
Delaware: $42000	Missouri: $34000	Tennessee: $35000
Florida: $34000	Montana: $30000	Texas: $34000
Georgia: $36000	Nebraska: $32000	Utah: $32000
Hawaii: $36000	Nevada: $38000	Vermont: $37000
Idaho: $32000	New Hampshire: $37000	Virginia: $36000
Illinois: $43000	New Jersey: $51000	Washington: $38000
Indiana: $40000	New Mexico: $31000	West Virginia: $34000
Iowa: $34000	New York: $49000	Wisconsin: $40000
Kansas: $36000	North Carolina: $32000	Wyoming: $32000
Kentucky: $34000	North Dakota: $28000	

a) Using this information, find the mean and the standard deviation of the 50 salaries.

b) For each of the following salaries, compute the z score and percentile rank:
  1) $27,000
  2) $32,000
  3) $36,000
  4) $42,000
  5) $52,000

c) Interpret the z score and percentile rank for each salary of part (b).

d) What is the median salary? What is the z score of the median salary?

e) What is the lowest salary? Is the percentile rank of the lowest salary zero? Why not?

f) What is the highest salary? Is the percentile rank of the highest salary 100? Why not?

g) Find the interquartile range(IQR), and determine the number of salaries that fall within this range. What percent of the salaries lie within the IQR? Did you expect this result? Explain.

h) Would you consider any of these salaries to be outliers? Explain. If there are any outliers, compute the z score and interpret it.

i) Construct a box plot and state its shape. Did you expect a salary distribution to have this shape? Explain.

264. Examine the graphic entitled Bank Money Accounts which represents annual effective yields, in percents, on money market account, three-month CDs, and six-month CDs.

a) Find the z scores of all the money market rates for the commercial banks in the New York Area.

b) Without rounding off the results of part a, determine the mean and standard deviation of all the z scores.

c) Repeat steps a and b for the three-month CD rates. Do you get approximately the same results? What conclusions can you draw from these results?

d) Identify the mean rate and median rate for the money market rate and six-month CD rates for the commercial and savings banks in the New York Area, and the Major Banks outside N.Y. Interpret these results.

e) Compare the money market rate of 2.53 for the New York commercial and savings banks, and the major

Bank Money Accounts

Annual effective yields, in percent, on money market accounts, three-month certificates of deposit and six-month C.D.'s expected at selected institutions on Wednesday, April 21, 1993. Some C.D. yields assume reinvestment after maturity. Yields are based on the method of compounding and the rate stated for the lowest minimum to open an account, but minimum vary. Higher yields may be offered for larger deposits. C.D. figures are for fixed rates only.

New York Area

	Money Mkt.	3-mo. C.D.	6-mo. C.D.
COMMERCIAL BANKS			
Banco Popular	2.63	2.78	2.99
Bank of N.Y.	2.37	2.58	2.69
Bank of Tokyo Trust	2.17	2.19	2.25
Chase Manhattan	2.12	2.28	2.33
Chemical	2.07	2.65	2.70
Citibank	1.91	2.35	2.40
EAB	2.28	2.58	2.69
First Fidelity (N.J.)	2.50	2.60	2.85
Fleet Bank (Conn)	2.35	2.73	2.94
Key Bank of N.Y.	2.13	2.32	2.58
Marine Midland	2.15	2.42	2.53
Midlantic Bank (N.J.)	2.50	2.60	2.80
NatWest	2.53 ·	2.43	2.48
Republic Nat'l	2.48	2.63	2.79
Shawmut Bank (Conn)	2.38	2.74	2.94
SAVINGS BANKS			
Anchor Savings	2.65	2.80	3.05
Apple Bank Savings	2.61	2.66	2.95
Astoria Fed Savings	2.94	2.79	2.89
Carteret Savings (N.J.)	2.53 ˅	2.80	3.00
Crossland Savings	2.65	2.75	3.08
Dime Savings Bank	2.64	2.64	3.00
Emigrant Savings	2.60	2.75	3.00
First Fed (Rochester)	3.05	2.95	3.05
First Nationwide	2.20	2.65	2.75
Greater NY Savings	2.60	2.80	3.00
Green Point Savings	3.00	N.O.	3.20
Home Savings Amer	2.63	2.69	3.05
Hudson City SB (N.J.)	3.00	3.30	3.40
People's Bank (Conn.)	2.53	2.74	3.05
River Bank America	2.80	2.85	3.10

Major Banks Outside N.Y.

	Money Mkt.	Wkly. Chg.	6 Mo. C.D.	Wkly. Chg.
Bank One Texas (Dallas)	2.43	0.00	2.95 ˙	0.00
Bank of Boston	2.63	0.00	2.78	0.00
Citibank, S.D.	2.76	0.00	3.51	0.00
Comerica (Detroit)	2.78	0.00	2.78	U.00
Fidelity Bank (Philadelphia)	2.50	0.00	2.85	0.00
First Bank (Minnesota)	2.22	–0.05	2.80	0.00
First Interstate (L.A.)	2.34	0.00	2.48	0.00
First National (Chicago)	2.53 ·	0.00	2.73	0.00
First Union (Charlotte, N.C.)	2.55	–0.10	2.80	0.00
Fleet Bank (Boston)	2.68	0.00	2.94	0.00
Maryland Natl	2.75	0.00	3.10	–0.10
Mellon (Pittsburgh)	2.53	0.00	2.55	0.00
Meridian Bank (Reading Pa)	2.19	0.00	2.90	–0.05
National Bank (Detroit)	2.78	0.00	2.75	–0.05
NationsBank (Tampa)	2.35	0.00	3.10	0.00
Seafirst (Seattle)	2.50	0.00	3.00	0.00
Shawmut Bank (Boston)	2.48	0.00	2.80	0.00
Texas Commerce (Houston)	2.27	0.00	2.75	–0.03
Union Bank (S.F.)	2.43	0.00	2.53	0.00
Wachovia (Winston Salem, N.C.)	2.55	0.00	2.80 ˙	0.00

Reprinted by permission of The New York Times Company.

banks outside the N.Y. area to determine in which category 2.53 is a better rate relative to the rates within each category. Explain.

f) Compare the six-month rate of 2.80 for the commercial, and the major banks outside the N.Y. area to determine in which category 2.80 is a better rate relative to the rates within each category. Explain.

g) Compare the six-month rate of 2.95 for the savings banks, and the six-month rate of 2.94 for the major banks outside the N.Y. area to determine which rate is considered better relative to the rates within the respective categories. Explain.

265. Examine the graphic entitled 1999–2000 Salary Survey of Academic Statisticians on page 213 which presents the results of a Fall 1999 survey of chairs of statistics departments and professors not associated with a statistics department at U.S. colleges and universities to provide salary, rank, and length of service information for instructors, assistant professors, associate professors, and full professors. The survey results divide the academic institutions into two categories, (1) research institutions and (2) liberal arts colleges. Salaries reflect academic year(nine month equivalent) compensation.

Using the survey results, determine:

a) For assistant professors at Research Institutions with 1 or fewer years in rank
  1) the salary that represents P_{25}
  2) the salary that represents the 5th decile
  3) the salary that represents the 75th percentile
  4) the percent of salaries that are at least $53,200
  5) the number of salaries between $45,800 and $50,500 inclusive

b) For assistant professors at Liberal Arts Colleges with 2–3 years in rank
  1) the salary that represents P_{75}
  2) the salary that represents the 2nd quartile
  3) the salary that represents the 25th percentile
  4) the percent of salaries that are at most $53,225
  5) the number of salaries between $46,750 and $53,225 inclusive

c) The Interquartile range for the assistant professors at Research Institutions with 6 or more years in rank.

d) The Interquartile Range of associate professors at Liberal Arts Colleges with 8 or more years in rank.

e) Compare the Interquartile Ranges of parts c and d. Which one has the larger IQR? What does this indicate about the variability of the salaries?

f) The number of salaries that fall within the IQR for each of parts c and d.

g) On the same scale, construct a box diagram representing the 1st quartile, median and the 3rd quartile for the full professors at Research Institutions with 10-11 years in rank and the full professors at Liberal Arts Colleges with 11-15 years in rank. Compare each box diagram. What do you conclude about the salaries

about these two full professors? What can you conclude about the shape of each salary distribution?

h) Construct a box diagram representing the 1st quartile, median and the 3rd quartile for full professors at Research Institutions with 33 or more years in rank and full professors at Liberal Arts Colleges with 21 or more years in rank on the same scale. Compare these two box diagrams, and comment on the differences in these salary distributions. What is the Interquartile Range for each distribution, and why do you believe there is such a discrepancy? What do you think is the shape of each these salary distributions?

i) For full professors at Research Institutions with 22 to 24 years in rank, what salary represents:
  1) The 75th percentile?
  2) P_{25}?
  3) The 5th decile?
  4) What percent of the salaries fall within the interquartile range? How many professors have salaries within this interquartile range?
  5) Approximately how many of these professors have salaries between P_{25} and the 5th decile? between the 2nd quartile and P_{75}?
  6) Calculate the range of salaries between the first quartile and the median. between the median and the 3rd quartile. Are the ranges the same? What does the range value indicate about the variability of the salaries?

266. A researcher randomly places ten students into two statistics groups. Group I was taught statistics using a calculator while group II was taught without the use of a calculator. At the end of the semester a final exam was given to each group. The results are as follows.

Group I	Group II
76	73
75	75
77	71
78	74
74	72

a) Determine the mean and variance of each group.

b) Combine the survey data for the two groups. Compute the mean and variance of the combined data. This variance is called the "total" group variance.

c) Using the mean for each group, find the variance of the two means. This variance is called the "between" group variance.

d) Find the mean of the variances of each group. This result is referred to as the "within" group variance.

e) Does the relationship: Total group variance = between group + within group variance hold true?

f) Construct a box plot for each group. Examine the box plots with respect to variability. That is, look at the length of each box plot as an estimate of the "within" variability. Compare this visual representation of the

1999–2000 Salary Survey of Academic Statisticians

Research Institutions

Rank	Years in Rank	Number	First Quartile	Median	Third Quartile
Instructors					
	0 to 10	12	31325	35050	39750
Assistant Professors					
	1 or Fewer	63	45800	50500	53200
	2	34	50025	53400	57175
	3	23	47500	50400	53400
	4 to 5	27	46700	52500	55100
	6 or more	15	49900	55000	67700
Associate Professors					
	1 or Fewer	31	49900	56600	65600
	2 to 3	39	53000	61400	68500
	4 to 5	31	53700	61400	71800
	6 to 8	31	52800	57100	64300
	9 to 12	31	55700	61700	75000
	13 or more	29	55300	59900	67400
Full Professors					
	1 or Fewer	23	55100	65000	70000
	2 to 3	32	61675	68150	82825
	4 to 5	38	62875	68100	75225
	6 to 7	37	70300	78700	92000
	8 to 9	29	71800	89800	95800
	10 to 11	31	69700	79100	94700
	12 to 13	34	67225	82500	98650
	14 to 15	30	68725	81800	96875
	16 to 17	22	66150	90450	108400
	18 to 19	28	79950	94850	111925
	20 to 21	27	68500	83300	106100
	22 to 24	20	72775	95950	109650
	25 to 27	23	78500	94400	112900
	28 to 32	10	78625	94150	126125
	33 or more	10	66000	78850	118375

Liberal Arts

Rank	Years in Rank	Number	First Quartile	Median	Third Quartile
Assistant Professors					
	1 or Fewer	9	37000	41000	42500
	2 to 3	10	41525	46750	53225
	4 or more	11	47000	52200	54800
Associate Professors					
	0 to 3	11	42500	58000	60100
	4 to 7	12	44850	54200	65875
	8 or more	13	50400	63200	68700
Full Professors					
	0 to 4	12	61675	71900	80975
	5 to 10	10	61600	66650	73625
	11 to 15	10	65325	69200	88675
	16 to 20	9	70000	79400	89000
	21 to more	13	71000	76200	98700

within variability to the numerical computation of variability computed in part a. Comment.

g) Using the box plots of part f, compare the differences between the "average" grade of each group. What variability is indicated by differences in the position of the "average" grade of each group? Comment.

h) The researcher would like to determine if using the calculator results in a higher level of achievement for group I. Examine the value of the means computed in part (a). Do you think it is reasonable for the researcher to conclude that using the calculator to teach statistics results in higher achievement? Explain.

i) Should the researcher take into consideration the variability in the achievement scores for each group? Explain.

267. A health insurance company has conducted a survey that determines the length of hospital stay (in days) for three hospitals in Cincinnati for the same medical procedure. The following data represent the survey results.

Length of Hospital Stay for Patients (in days)

Hospital I	Hospital II	Hospital III
12	20	23
6	14	8
3	5	11
21	17	5
18	2	17
9	11	20
15	8	14

a) Determine the mean and variance length of hospital stay for each hospital.

b) Combine the survey data for all three hospitals. Compute the mean and variance of the combined data. This variance is called the "total" group variance.

c) Using the mean length of stay for each hospital, find the variance of the three means. This variance is called the "between" group variance.

d) Find the mean of the variances of each hospital. This result is referred to as the "within" group variance.

e) Does the relationship: Total group variance = between group + within group variance hold true?

f) Construct a box plot for each hospital. Examine the box plots with respect to variability. That is, look at the length of each box plot as an estimate of the "within" variability. Compare this visual representation of the within variability to the numerical computation of variability computed in part a. Comment.

g) Using the box plots of part f, compare the differences between the "average" length of hospital stay. What variability is indicated by differences in the position of the "average" length of hospital stay? Comment.

h) The insurance company would like to estimate a reasonable length of stay for this medical procedure. Examine the value of the means computed in parts (a) and (b). What do you think is the insurance company's best estimate for the average length of hospital stay for a patient having this medical procedure? Explain.

i) Should the insurance company take into consideration the variability of the length of stay for each hospital? Explain.

PROJECTS

268. Choose 10 stocks arbitrarily form the New York Stock Exchange and compute the mean stock price for these stocks per day for one week. Compare your results per day with the Dow Jones Industrial Stock Average per day by using the chart below:

Day	10 Stock Average	Dollar Change per Day	Dow Jones	Dollar Change per Day
Monday				
Tuesday				
Wednesday				
Thursday				
Friday				

269. Consider the table below:

	Ages			
	16–25	26–35	36–45	46–55
1.				
2.				
3.				
4.				
5.				
6.				
7.				
8.				
9.				
10.				

For each age group, survey ten people and record their answer to the question, "How many years should a married couple wait before having children?"

a) According to your survey, what is the mean number of years a couple should wait before having children as answered by each group?

b) What is the modal number of years a couple should wait before having children as answered by each group?

c) Consider all the responses as one group. What are the mean and mode of this distribution?

d) Do you think people in different age groups responded with a significantly differently waiting period?

270. The following data represents personal information for fifty students.

Student ID	Hair Color	Eye Color	Ht Inchs	Wt Lbs	# Hours Worked Weekly	Sex	IQ Score	# of Sib	Age
8476	BR	HAZEL	66	118	22	M	95	2	19
3834	BK	BROWN	67	107	32	F	115	2	18
3165	BL	BROWN	69	154	35	M	120	5	18
1207	BL	BROWN	72	176	23	M	105	3	23
6784	BR	BROWN	60	103	20	F	116	1	19
6780	BR	HAZEL	67	132	18	M	127	5	20
5380	BK	BLUE	66	123	13	M	101	1	18
4227	BR	BROWN	66	121	40	M	125	1	18
8625	BR	HAZEL	64	105	0	F	99	0	19
0817	BR	BLUE	71	170	35	M	104	3	32
0882	BR	HAZEL	71	175	24	M	114	4	18
0638	BR	HAZEL	67	135	30	M	121	2	19
4390	BK	BROWN	74	206	35	M	130	2	20
5345	BK	BROWN	63	98	0	F	107	2	19
6819	BK	BLUE	74	198	0	M	122	0	20
4002	RD	HAZEL	59	99	10	F	110	2	18
1252	BR	BROWN	68	143	28	F	145	5	18
1031	BL	BROWN	61	115	35	F	109	0	43
7873	BR	HAZEL	60	93	19	F	103	3	19
0194	BR	BROWN	70	160	15	M	135	5	20
9189	BR	BLUE	56	144	23	F	118	5	18
3695	BR	BROWN	64	115	22	F	105	3	18
2444	BK	BROWN	71	172	16	M	115	2	17
2467	BK	BROWN	61	113	19	F	128	2	19
7286	BR	HAZEL	67	98	25	F	131	1	20
7896	BR	BROWN	61	105	24	F	118	2	18
8905	BR	HAZEL	65	135	25	F	117	0	19
7299	BR	BROWN	65	122	0	F	113	3	18
9638	BK	BROWN	67	129	26	M	104	1	29
6798	BR	BROWN	66	118	20	F	126	4	21
4442	BL	BROWN	69	143	44	F	104	1	26
0132	BL	BROWN	73	194	16	M	107	3	18
1884	RD	BROWN	70	157	31	M	129	2	19
7345	BK	BROWN	63	126	9	F	134	1	20
0655	BK	HAZEL	69	149	7	M	108	2	18
4982	BR	HAZEL	73	193	36	M	112	1	24
8825	BL	HAZEL	73	188	17	M	104	3	37
6696	BR	HAZEL	61	122	44	F	98	1	18
9498	BR	BROWN	70	164	10	M	123	3	19
6217	RD	HAZEL	66	133	37	F	105	0	20
6014	BK	BLUE	66	123	24	M	134	1	18
1394	RD	BROWN	69	184	9	M	138	2	17
3199	BR	BROWN	69	190	21	M	121	0	19
2426	BR	HAZEL	66	122	15	M	99	2	19
2033	BR	BROWN	74	207	0	M	112	2	22
2435	BK	HAZEL	68	157	33	M	127	5	20
3173	RD	HAZEL	69	176	28	M	136	2	19
3361	BR	BROWN	70	192	14	M	121	2	36
8886	BR	BROWN	70	125	31	F	102	3	21
3593	BR	BROWN	74	197	41	M	111	2	24

Compute the suitable measure of central tendency for each characteristic and construct a composite description of the typical student at this school. Use the composite of the average American given in the introduction to this chapter as a guide.

271. Select 25 male students and 25 female students and administer the following arithmetic test. Allow 10 minutes for the examination.

The correct answers are (1) b (2) c (3) d (4) d (5) a.

Grade each of the tests and determine which sex had more consistent grades (Calculate the range and standard deviation for the grades for each sex).

The directions: Answer all questions by choosing the letter of the answer of your choice.

1) $\dfrac{4}{3} \div \dfrac{1}{2} = ?$

   a) $\dfrac{2}{3}$ **b)** $\dfrac{8}{3}$ **c)** $\dfrac{4}{5}$ **d)** $\dfrac{3}{8}$

2) $18 + 24 + ? = 60$

   a) 28   **b)** 8   **c)** 18   **d)** 38

3) $(0.03\%) = \dfrac{3}{?}$

   a) 10   **b)** 100   **c)** 1000   **d)** 10,000

4) $\dfrac{2}{5} + \dfrac{3}{4} = ?$

   a) $\dfrac{9}{5}$ **b)** $\dfrac{5}{9}$ **c)** $\dfrac{6}{20}$ **d)** $\dfrac{23}{20}$

5) $7 - 2/5 + 0.12 = ?$

   a) 6.72   **b)** 5.22   **c)** 6.52   **d)** 6.12

272. Select a well-known brand name food product for which there is a comparable store brand. For example, a brand name peanut butter and a store brand peanut butter (same size jar). Get the prices for the brand name product and the store brand product from as many different food stores as you can (at least five). Form two distributions, one from the name brand prices and the other from the store brand prices. Use the standard deviation to determine which price distribution is more variable.

273. Look up the home run records of Babe Ruth, Mickey Mantle, Roger Maris, Mel Ott, Hank Greenberg, Hank Aaron, Mark McGuire, Sammy Sosa, Barry Bonds and Ken Griffey, Jr.

   a) Calculate μ and σ for the number of home runs each player hit during his career.

   b) For each player, take the maximum number of home runs he hit during any one season of his career and determine which player's maximum one year production is most outstanding relative to his career.

274. a) Calculate the mean and standard deviation of the number of electoral votes each Democratic and Republican presidential candidate received in each presidential election since 1900 inclusive.

   b) From your data, choose the Democratic and Republican candidates who received the maximum number of electoral votes and calculate the z score of their electoral votes.

   c) Compare the two z scores and decide which presidential candidate was the higher electoral vote getter relative to his party.

ANALYZING THE DATABASE USING TECHNOLOGY

The following exercises refer to the file DATABASE listed in Appendix A. Using a technological tool, answer each exercise.

275. Determine the measures of central tendency for the variables:

   a) AGE
   b) AVE
   c) STY
   d) GPA
   e) GFT

276. Display a table representing the effect of subtracting the mean of each variable from the data for the variables:

   a) AGE
   b) GPA
   c) GFT

The table should include columns representing:

   1) the variable name along with the data values

   2) the data value minus the mean, as well as the *mean* of the variable and the *mean* of the column for the data value minus the mean.

Examine the results within each column. Did you expect these results? Comment.

277. Determine the range and sample standard deviation for the variables:

   a) AGE
   b) AVE
   c) STY
   d) GPA
   e) GFT

278. Determine the mean and standard deviation of the variables:

   a) AVE
   b) STY
   c) GPA
   for

1) the male students (Males are coded 0)
2) the female students (Females are coded 1)

279. Determine the measures of central tendency and variability, and the first and third quartiles for the variables:
  a) AGE
  b) AVE
  c) STY
  d) GPA
  e) GFT

280. Numerically describe each of the given variables and answer the question using the statistical results:
  a) AGE
    What percent of the student ages are between 17 and 20?
  b) AVE
    What percent of the students have high school averages greater than 80?

  c) STY
    What percent of the students study more than 20 hours per week?
  d) GPA
    What percent of the students have grade point averages less than 3.0?
  e) GFT
    Determine the data value representing P_{90}.

281. Compute and display a table representing the data value, the z score for the data value, and the percentile rank for the data value for each of the variables:
  a) AGE
  b) AVE
  c) STY
  d) GPA
  e) GFT

CHAPTER TEST

282. The symbol used for the sample mean is ____ while the Greek symbol used for the population mean is _____.

283. Which measure of central tendency is more resistant to extreme data values or outliers?
  a) Mean
  b) Median

284. The symbol used for the sample standard deviation is _____ and the symbol used to denote the population variance is ____.

285. The formula used to compute the sample standard deviation, s, is the same as the formula that is used to compute the population standard deviation, σ.
  (T/F)

286. If the range is 10, and the largest data value is 12, then the smallest data value is _____.

287. The Interquartile Range (IQR) is a measurement that indicates the middle 50% of the distribution.
  (T/F)

288. If $Q_1 = 420$ and $Q_3 = 510$, then which one of the following data values is considered an outlier.
  a) 140   **b)** 190   **c)** 500   **d)** 700

289. If the population of ages of college students is skewed right, then this indicates:
  a) There are more older students within the population.
  b) The median age is greater than the mean age.
  c) As the age of a student increases, the frequency of the ages also increases.
  d) There is a greater number of younger students within the population.

290. For each of the following distribution of data values,
  a) identify the general shape that you believe best describes each distribution, and

  b) identify whether the mean or median would have the largest value within this type of distribution.
    (i)   The test results of an easy exam.
    (ii) The test results of a difficult exam.
    (iii) The heights of all the female students at a University.

291. For the following sample of IQ scores:
  106, 102, 104, 104, 105, 103, 105, 103, 101, 107, 114, 119, 116, 118, 128, 109, 103, 112, 111, 110, 112, 106, 108, 110, 111, 107
  find:
  a) The mean
  b) The median
  c) The mode
  d) The standard deviation
  e) $\Sigma(x - 109)$
  f) $(\Sigma x)^2$
  g) The sum of the squared IQ values
  h) $\Sigma(x - 109)^2$
  i) $[\Sigma(x - \bar{x})]^2$
  j) The percentile rank of 112 and interpret it.
  k) The z score of 128 and interpret it.
  l) The 5-number summary.
  m) The IQR.
  n) What data value represents the 1st quartile? 3rd quartile?
  o) Is there a data value that you consider to be outlier? If an outlier exists, then explain why you believe it is an outlier? Do you believe the outlier is an unusual value or is due to an error? Give an explanation for your answer.
  p) Construct a box plot for the IQ scores.
  q) State the shape of the box plot.

292. Linda, a sports guru, is interested in comparing the careers of the New York Yankee players Mickey Mantle and Whitey Ford to determine which player had a more consistent career. Mickey Mantle's career batting average was .298 with a standard deviation of 0.033, while Whitey Ford had a career ERA of 3.14 with a standard deviation of 0.46.

a) If you use the coefficient of variation to compare the consistency of both players' career, which player had the more consistent career?

b) Why is the coefficient of variation an appropriate measure to use in making this comparison?

293. If the tire life of a certain brand of an all-season radial tire approximates a symmetric bell-shaped distribution with mean = 65,000 miles and standard deviation = 5,000 miles, then use the Empirical Rule to:

a) Determine the percentage of tires you would expect to last between 60,000 to 70,000 miles?

b) Determine the percentage of tires you would expect to last between 55,000 to 75,000 miles?

c) Determine the percentage of tires you would expect to last between 50,000 to 80,000 miles?

d) Determine the percentage of tires you would expect to last between 60,000 to 75,000 miles?

e) Can Chebyshev's Theorem be applied to answer part (b) of this question? If it is possible, use Chebyshev's Theorem to answer part (b) and compare the two results.

f) If a tire lasts 85,000 miles, would you consider this tire wear to be typical or unusual? Explain.

294. A New York Realty Association surveys local banks and mortgage lenders to determine the trends in 30 year fixed and adjustable mortgage rates. Based on their survey, the mean rate for a 30 year fixed mortgage is 10.97% (with s = 0.14%) and the mean rate for a one year adjustable mortgage is 7.79% (with s = 0.17%).

If Matcraig, a mortgage lender, is offering a 30 year fixed mortgage rate of 10.75%(& no points) and a one year adjustable mortgage rate of 7.5%(& no points), which rate would be considered the best deal relative to its type of mortgage?

295. A sample of the number of study hours per week of college students is collected. Some of the sample results of this survey are given in the following table.

Study Hours	4	10	20	24	34	36	42
z Score	-2.5	-1.75	-0.5	0	1.25	1.5	2.25
Percentile Rank	10	25	35	40	50	75	95

By inspection of the table, determine:

a) The mean study time for all the students.

b) The median study time for all the students.

c) The percent of college students who study between 20 and 36 hours per week.

d) The study time representing the 4th decile.

e) The study time representing the 1st quartile.

f) The study time representing the 3rd quartile.

g) The interquartile range

h) The standard deviation study time for all the students.

i) The study time corresponding to a z score of 1.75.

j) The study time that is 2.5 standard deviations above the mean.

296. Corinne, an Investment analyst, has been plotting the cyclic pattern of the stock of a fast food company. Based upon her analysis, she decides to purchase the stock when it is selling at least one and a half standard deviations below its mean cyclic price. Her plan is to sell the stock when its price is at least 1.65 standard deviations above the mean price. Determine her maximum buying price and her minimum selling price for this stock if its mean cyclic price is $27.65 with a standard deviation of $9.95.

297. What percentage of a population of psychology test scores are:

a) Above the third quartile?

b) Below the first quartile?

c) Greater than the 23rd percentile?

d) Above the 6th decile?

e) Between the first and third quartiles?

f) Between the 2nd and 6th decile?

298. The following data values represent a sample of the heights of female college basketball players.

Heights in Inches

63 71 69 66 73 85 70 69 67 74 75 68 65 63
67 69 68 72 73 75 72 75 73 68 69 75 65 65

a) Determine (to 2 decimal places) the mean height and standard deviation of the heights.

b) Determine the z score & percentile rank of the following heights. Interpret these results.
i) 67   ii) 69   iii) 66   iv) 73   v) 85   vi) 74

c) Determine the height that represents the:
i)   1st quartile
ii) 2nd decile
iii) 5th decile
iv) 3rd quartile
v)   8th decile

d) Determine the height which represents the 2nd quartile.

e) Find P_{25} and P_{75}.

f) Determine the 5-number summary.

g) Construct a box plot for this 5-number summary.

h) Using the box plot, identify the shape of the distribution of the female basketball player's heights.

i) Calculate the Interquartile Range (IQR). Determine the percentage of heights represented by the IQR? Did you expect this result? Explain.

j) Identify any outliers. If any data value is identified as an outlier, then indicate whether you believe this data value is an exceptional data value or a data value due to error. Explain. Determine the z score of any possible outlier? Interpret this z score. Explain how the value of a z score may indicate the presence of an outlier.

k) Determine the percentile rank of the maximum data value. Explain why it isn't 100%.

299. Use this graph to answer the questions a to h.

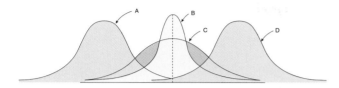

a) Which distributions have the same measures of central tendency but a different standard deviation? Explain.

b) Which one of the distributions identified in part (a) has the smaller standard deviation? Explain.

c) Which distribution has the smallest value for the mode?

d) Which distribution has the largest value for the median?

e) If distribution B had the data value X as an outlier, then in what other distribution would X also be considered an outlier? Explain your answer.

f) For which of these distributions could you use the Empirical Rule? Chebyshev's Theorem? Explain.

g) Would distribution B or C have a larger value for the 1st quartile? 3rd quartile? Explain.

h) Sketch a box plot for each of these distributions using the same horizontal axis.

Probability

Contents

4.1   INTRODUCTION

The Birthday Problem

A long long time ago B.C.

FIGURE 4.1 (continues)

By permission of Johnny Hart and Creators Syndicate, Inc.

FIGURE 4.1 (continued)

200,000 years later A.D.

Is Charlie Brown a loser? Lucy thinks so. In every wager Lucy makes with Charlie Brown, Charlie Brown loses. At tomorrow's Christmas party Lucy plans to wager Charlie Brown a brand-new bicycle that "at least two kids have the same birthday". (i.e., born on the same month and day).

Charlie Brown reasons that since there are going to be 50 kids at the Christmas Party and there are 365 possible birthdays, he believes that he is going to win his first bet ever with Lucy.

Do you think Charlie Brown's **chances** are good for winning this bet with Lucy?

Chance! Chance! Chance!

People have always been intrigued with **chance**. In fact an individual's own life involves chance. For example a person's sex is determined by the chromosomes of the parents. Also the purchase of a "lucky" lottery ticket could make one an instant millionaire.

As early as medieval times, man has been concerned with games of chance. In the 16th century, an Italian mathematician, Jerome Cordan (1501–1576), wrote the first book on this subject entitled: *The Book on Games of Chance.*

During the mid-17th century the French mathematician Pierre de Fermat (1601–1660) and Blaise Pascal (1623–1662) were inspired by a gambling friend to study the problem of how one should split the stakes in an interrupted dice game. Their study of this game of chance led to the development of the modern theory of probability.

In today's world probability plays an important role. The French mathematician Pierre Simon de Laplace (1749–1827) in his work, *Theorie Analytique des Probabilities* did a good job defining this role when he stated:

. . . it is remarkable that a science which began with the consideration of games of chance should have become the most important object of human knowledge . . . the most important questions of life are, for the most part, really only problems of probability.

Before we investigate problems of probability, let's develop some elementary probability concepts. By the way, Charlie Brown lost the bet! We will examine this problem in detail in Example 4.53.

4.2   SOME TERMS USED IN PROBABILITY

To begin the study of probability, several important terms used in probability need to be defined. The first term we will discuss is what is meant by an *experiment.*

> **DEFINITION 4.1**
> An **experiment** is the process by which an observation is made or obtained. An **outcome** of an experiment is any result that is obtained when performing the experiment.

For example rolling a fair die[1], tossing a fair coin, selecting a card from a deck of cards or selecting the winning numbers of a lottery ticket are all examples of an experiment. For the experiment: selecting a card from a regular deck of 52 playing cards, one possible outcome for this experiment is selecting the three of diamonds.

When performing an experiment, we may be interested in a *particular collection of outcomes.* Such a collection of interested outcomes is called an *event.*

DEFINITION 4.2

An **event** is a particular collection of outcomes of an experiment.

The following illustrations should be helpful in clarifying the terms: an *experiment,* an *outcome* and an *event.*

Experiment: Rolling a fair die

Possible Outcomes	Rolling a one
	Rolling a two
	Rolling a three
	Rolling a four
	Rolling a five
	Rolling a six
Possible events	Rolling an odd number
	Rolling a number smaller than 3

Experiment: Selecting a card from a deck of playing cards

Possible Outcomes	Selecting a two of clubs
	Selecting a three of clubs
	.
	.
	.
	Selecting a jack of clubs
	Selecting a queen of clubs
	Selecting a king of clubs
	Selecting an ace of clubs
	Selecting a two of diamonds
	Selecting a three of diamonds
	.
	.
	.
	Selecting a jack of diamonds
	Selecting a queen of diamonds
	Selecting a king of diamonds
	Selecting an ace of diamonds
	Selecting a two of hearts
	Selecting a three of hearts

---

[1]A fair die is a die that has the same chance of landing with a 1, 2, 3, 4, 5 or a 6 face up. Similarly, a fair coin is a coin that has the same chance of landing with heads face up as it does with tails face up.

.
.
.

Selecting a jack of hearts
Selecting a queen of hearts
Selecting a king of hearts
Selecting an ace of hearts
Selecting a two of spades
Selecting a three of spades

.
.
.

Selecting a jack of spades
Selecting a queen of spades
Selecting a king of spades
Selecting an ace of spades

Possible events   Selecting a red card
Selecting a picture card
Selecting a diamond

.
.
.

Once an experiment is defined, it is necessary to determine *how many* **outcomes** and *what* outcomes are possible when performing the experiment. The collection of all possible outcomes of an experiment is referred to as a **sample space.**

DEFINITION 4.3
A **sample space** is a representation of all the possible outcomes of an experiment.

In the next few examples, we will illustrate the idea of a sample space and examine different ways to construct a sample space.

EXAMPLE 4.1

A single toss of a coin is an experiment having **two** possible outcomes. Construct a sample space for this experiment.

Solution

The sample space consists of the two possible outcomes: heads and tails. These outcomes are represented in Figure 4.2a.

Outcomes

Head	Tail

FIGURE 4.2a

The sample space in Example 4.1 can also be represented using a *tree diagram.*

Using a Tree Diagram to Construct a Sample Space

A tree diagram can be very helpful in listing the different possible outcomes of an experiment. A tree diagram for the experiment of a single toss of a coin is illustrated in Figure 4.2b.

FIGURE 4.2b

Notice that in Figure 4.2b the tree diagram is constructed by first drawing a point or a dot and then drawing lines leading out from the dot ,which correspond to the different possible outcomes for the experiment. *These lines represent the branches of the tree.* For this experiment, the two possible outcomes, head and tail, are represented by the two branches.

Since a sample space is a representation of all possible outcomes either Figure 4.2a or Figure 4.2b are ways to display the sample space for the experiment of a single toss of a coin.

EXAMPLE 4.2

Use a tree diagram to construct a sample space for the experiment of tossing a fair coin twice.

Solution

To construct a tree diagram for this experiment, you start by drawing two lines which correspond to the possible outcomes of a head and a tail for the first toss. This is illustrated in the tree diagram of Figure 4.3a. Since the second toss can result in either a head or a tail, start from the tip of each first branch and draw two lines corresponding to the possible outcomes of the second toss. Thus we have two lines branching out from the first possible outcome of a head and two lines from the first possible outcome of a tail. The four possible outcomes of this experiment are illustrated by the tree diagram in Figure 4.3b. Starting from the initial point, one possible outcome of this experiment is determined by moving along one of the initial two branches following by selecting one of the branches of the second toss. This results in the four possible outcomes of tossing a fair coin two times which are a:

head on the first toss and a head on the second toss: HH
head on the first toss and a tail on the second toss: HT
tail on the first toss and a head on the second toss: TH
tail on the first toss and a tail on the second toss: TT

These outcomes are shown to the right of the tree diagram.

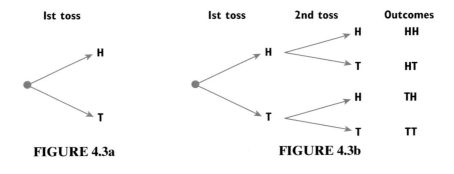

FIGURE 4.3a　　　　　　　　　　**FIGURE 4.3b**

The sample space for two tosses of a coin can also be represented as shown in Figure 4.3c.

1st toss	2nd toss	Outcomes of both tosses
H	H	- - - - ➤ HH
H	T	- - - - ➤ HT
T	H	- - - - ➤ TH
T	T	- - - - ➤ TT

FIGURE 4.3c ■

In Example 4.2, the sample space consisted of four possible outcomes. For this experiment, the *number of possible outcomes can be determined by* **multiplying** *the number of outcomes for the first toss of the coin by the number of outcomes for the second toss.* That is,

$$\begin{aligned}\text{total number of}\atop\text{possible outcomes} &= \left(\text{number of outcomes}\atop\text{for first toss}\right) * \left(\text{number of outcomes}\atop\text{for second toss}\right) \\ &= \quad (2)(2) \\ &= \quad 4\end{aligned}$$

Thus, there are four possible outcomes for tossing a coin two times. Furthermore, Example 4.2 is considered a **compound or multi-stage experiment** since the *coin* **is tossed** *more than once.* In fact, this is considered a *two-stage experiment* since the coin is tossed *twice.*

The rule to determine the number of possible outcomes for *a compound or multi-stage experiment* will be referred to as the *Fundamental Counting Principle: Multiplication Rule.*

Fundamental Counting Principle: Multiplication Rule

The total number of possible outcomes for a compound or multi-stage experiment is the product of the number of possible outcomes for each stage of the experiment.

Fundamental Counting Principle
For a Two-Stage and Three-Stage Experiment

Two-Stage Experiment

The total number of possible outcomes for a compound experiment having **two stages**, where there are m ways of doing the first stage and there are n ways of doing the second stage is determined by multiplying the n ways of the first stage by the m ways of the second stage.

The formula for a two-stage experiment is:

total number of possible outcomes = (m)(n).

Three-Stage Experiment

For a compound experiment with **three stages** where there are m ways for the first stage, n ways for the second stage and p ways for the third stage, the total number of possible outcomes is determined by multiplying these possibilities.

The formula for a three-stage experiment is:

total number of possible outcomes = (m)(n)(p).

EXAMPLE 4.3

An experiment consists of a single roll of a die and a single toss of a coin.
a)   Use the *Fundamental Counting Principle: Multiplication Rule* to determine the total number of possible outcomes for this experiment.
b)   Construct a sample space.

Solution

a)   This compound experiment is a two-stage experiment where the single roll of the die is the first stage and the single toss of the coin is the second stage. A single roll of a die has **6 possible outcomes** and a single toss of a coin has **2 possible outcomes**. To determine the total number of possible outcomes for this compound experiment using the fundamental counting principle, multiply the number of outcomes for rolling a single die by the number of outcomes for tossing a coin. This can be expressed using the multiplication rule formula:

$$\left(\begin{array}{c}\text{number of outcomes}\\ \text{for rolling a die}\end{array}\right) \quad * \quad \left(\begin{array}{c}\text{number of outcomes}\\ \text{for tossing a coin}\end{array}\right) \quad = \quad \begin{array}{c}\text{total number}\\ \text{of possible}\\ \text{outcomes}\end{array}$$

Therefore, there are **6 x 2 = 12 possible outcomes** for this compound experiment.

b)   The 12 outcomes can be determined by listing the two outcomes of the coin (head and tail) and the possible six outcomes of the die (1 to 6) along the sides a table. The 12 outcomes of the sample space are displayed within the body of Table 4.1.

TABLE 4.1   Sample Space for Tossing a Coin and Rolling a Die

Outcomes of the coin	Outcomes of the die					
	1	**2**	**3**	**4**	**5**	**6**
Head	H1	H2	H3	H4	H5	H6
Tail	T1	T2	T3	T4	T5	T6

In Example 4.3, a table rather than a tree diagram was used to illustrate another method to construct a sample space. For this experiment, it is appropriate to use a table to construct the sample space since the two objects are each being thrown only once.

EXAMPLE 4.4

Suppose your cat has a litter of three kittens, but you are unaware of the gender of these kittens.
a)   Use the Fundamental Counting Principle to determine the number of possible outcomes for the gender of the litter.
b)   Construct a sample space for this experiment.
Using the sample space, determine which outcomes satisfy the following events:
c)   the first kitten of the litter is male.
d)   only one kitten is female.
e)   *at least one* kitten is female.
f)   *at most one* kitten is male.

Solution

a)   Each kitten represents a stage of this three-stage compound experiment, where the kitten's gender represents the outcome for each stage. Using the **Fundamental Counting Principle** to determine the number of possible outcomes in the sample space, we multiply the number of possible outcomes for each stage.

That is,

$$\begin{array}{c}\text{Total number of}\\\text{possible outcomes}\end{array} = \left(\begin{array}{c}\text{gender}\\\text{possibilities}\\\text{of first kitten}\end{array}\right) * \left(\begin{array}{c}\text{gender}\\\text{possibilities of}\\\text{second kitten}\end{array}\right) * \left(\begin{array}{c}\text{gender}\\\text{possibilities of}\\\text{third kitten}\end{array}\right)$$

$$= [\,2\,] * [\,2\,] * [\,2\,]$$

$$= 8$$

Thus, there are eight possible outcomes for the litter.

b) The eight outcomes in the sample space are displayed by the tree diagram in Figure 4.4.

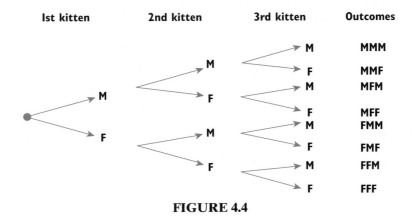

FIGURE 4.4

c) In examining the sample space of Figure 4.4, notice that there are **four outcomes** that satisfy **the event that the first kitten of the litter is male**. These outcomes are: **MMM, MMF, MFM and MFF**.

d) From Figure 4.4, there are **three outcomes** that satisfy **the event that only one kitten is female**. The outcomes are: **FMM, MFM and MMF**.

e) **At least one kitten is female** *means* **one or more kittens are female**. Therefore, we are looking for all the outcomes in the litter that contain one or more female kittens. There are seven outcomes satisfying **the event of at least one kitten is female**. As illustrated in Figure 4.4, these outcomes are: **MMF, MFM, MFF, FMM, FMF, FFM, FFF.**

f) **At most one kitten is male** *means* **one male kitten or less than one male kitten**. Therefore, we are looking for all the outcomes that contain *one or less male kittens*. There are four outcomes satisfying **the event at most one male kitten**. These four outcomes are: **FFF, FFM, FMF, MFF.** *Notice the outcome of all female kittens (FFF) satisfies the statement "at most one male kitten" since this outcome (FFF) has no male kittens which is less than one male kitten.*

Example 4.5 contains the phrase *without replacement*. This means when an object is selected it is **not** replaced for the next selection. A detailed explanation is presented in the next section under the heading: Methods of Selection.

E X A M P L E 4 . 5

Suppose an urn contains 4 balls numbered 1, 2, 3 and 4. Consider the experiment of selecting two balls from the urn *without replacement* and constructing a two-digit number.

a) Use the Fundamental Counting Principle to determine the number of possible outcomes in the sample space for this experiment.

b) Construct a sample space for this experiment.

Using the sample space, determine which outcomes satisfy the following events:
c)   both digits of the number are even.
d)   only one digit of the number is even.
e)   *at least one* digit of the number is even.
f)   *at most one* digit of the number is even.

Solution

a)   Using the **Fundamental Counting Principle** to calculate the number of possible outcomes in the sample space, we need to multiply the number of possible choices for each selection from the urn. For the first selection, we can choose from any one of the 4 balls in the urn. In a *"without replacement"* experiment, the first selected ball is **not** placed back into the urn. Therefore, for our second selection, we are choosing one ball from the remaining 3 balls left in the urn. Using the **Fundamental Counting Principle**, we have:

$$\text{total number of possible outcomes} = \begin{pmatrix}\text{number of possible}\\\text{outcomes for the}\\\text{1st selection}\end{pmatrix} * \begin{pmatrix}\text{number of possible}\\\text{outcomes for the}\\\text{2nd selection}\end{pmatrix}$$
$$= (4) \quad * \quad (3)$$
$$= 12$$

Thus, there are 12 possible outcomes for the experiment of selecting two balls from the urn *without replacement.*

b)   The 12 outcomes representing the sample space of this experiment are illustrated in Table 4.2. Notice there are cells in Table 4.2 containing an X. This represents the possibilities that are impossible. That is, in a *without replacement experiment,* it is impossible to select the same numbered ball twice such as 1 and 1, 2 and 2, etc.

Table 4.2

First Ball Selected	Second Ball Selected			
	1	2	3	4
1	X	12	13	14
2	21	X	23	24
3	31	32	X	34
4	41	42	43	X

c)   In examining the sample space of Table 4.2, notice there are **two outcomes** that satisfy the event **both digits of the number are even**. The outcomes are: **24 and 42**.
d)   In the sample space of Table 4.2, there are **eight outcomes** that satisfy **the event that only one digit of the number is even**. The outcomes are: **12, 14, 21, 23, 32, 34, 41, and 43**.
e)   **At least one digit of the number is even** *means* **one or more digits must be even**. Therefore, we are looking for all the numbers that contain **one or two even digits**. There are 10 outcomes satisfying **the event of at least one digit of the number is even**. As illustrated in Table 4.2, these numbers are: **12, 14, 21, 22, 23, 32, 34, 41, 42, and 43.**
f)   **At most one digit of the number is even** *means* **one or less digits are even**. Therefore, we are looking for all the numbers that contain **one or no even digits**. There are 10 numbers satisfying **the event of at most one digit of the number is even**. These numbers are: **12, 13, 14, 21, 23, 31, 32, 34, 41, and 43** as shown in Table 4.2.

The phrases **"at least"** and **"at most"** used to define events in Examples 4.4 and 4.5 are frequently used in probability. It is important that you become familiar with the meaning of these expressions. Let's consider the general interpretation of these phrases.

Interpretation of the Expressions "At Least" and "At Most"

"At least N outcomes" is interpreted as N or more outcomes
"At most N outcomes" means N or less outcomes
(remember to include N = 0 as a possible outcome).

4.3   PERMUTATIONS AND COMBINATIONS

Permutation

When the total number of possible outcomes in a sample space is extremely large, there are techniques that can be used to count the outcomes without having to list every possible outcome. The counting techniques are called **permutations** and **combinations**[2]. **We will first examine the idea of a permutation.**

> **DEFINITION 4.4**
> A **permutation** is an arrangement of objects in a *definite* order.

For example, let's examine the number of ways the three symbols: **@, #, *** can be arranged in order. These three objects can be arranged in order six ways as illustrated in Figure 4.5a.

Carefully examining Figure 4.5a, we should notice that within *each* arrangement of the three symbols the **order is different** and there are six different possible arrangements. Each arrangement is referred to as a **permutation**. If we want to determine *how many* arrangements there are without listing them, we could use the following counting technique. Each position in the arrangement is represented by a box as shown in Figure 4.5b.

@ * #
@ # *
# @ *
# * @
* @ #
* # @

FIGURE 4.5a

1st Position	2nd Position	3rd Position
3	2	1

FIGURE 4.5b

---

[2]Most calculators have the formulas for permutations and combinations built-in. We encourage you to use a calculator when evaluating these formulas.

Since *any one of the three objects* (@,#,*) could have been chosen to be placed in the *first position,* a *three (3)* is written in the box representing position #1 as shown in Figure 4.5b. Once an object has been selected for the first position, there are only two objects left to choose from for the remaining positions. The two (2) written in position #2 within Figure 4.5b represents the two objects that can be chosen for the second position. Finally, once the first two objects are chosen there is only *one* object left to place in the third position. The one (1) written in the 3rd position in Figure 4.5b represents the last object that is chosen.

To determine the number of different arrangements we *multiply* these three numbers obtaining the result:

$$(3)(2)(1) = 6.$$

Thus, the six represents the number of different arrangements that are possible for the three objects: @,#,*.

These were illustrated in Figure 4.5a. In mathematics, we have a shorthand notation for the product $(3)(2)(1)$. The product: $(3)(2)(1)$ is written as *3!* and it is read as *3 factorial.* Let's define this new notation.

---

n factorial: n!

In general, *n!* is read as *n "factorial"* and is defined to be:
$$n! = n(n-1)(n-2)(n-3) \cdots 2 \cdot 1$$
where $0! = 1$.

Using this factorial notation, we can define the counting technique that is used to determine the number of ways of arranging n objects in order. We will call this rule as: ***counting rule 1 or the permutation rule***.

DEFINITION 4.5
Counting Rule 1: Permutation Rule. The number of permutations (arrangements) of *n **different** objects taken *altogether,* denoted $_nP_n$, is:

$$_nP_n = n!$$

Let's apply this rule to Example 4.6.

EXAMPLE 4.6

How many different arrangements can be found for the following five symbols (objects)?

$$@, \#, \%, \&, *$$

Solution

Using the permutation rule: $_nP_n = n!$ for n = 5 objects, we get:

$$
\begin{aligned}
_5P_5 &= 5! \\
&= (5)(4)(3)(2)(1) \\
&= 120
\end{aligned}
$$

Therefore, there are 120 different arrangements for these five different objects.

EXAMPLE 4.7

In how many different ways can the manager of a baseball team arrange the batting order of the nine players in his starting line-up?

Solution

Using the permutation rule: $_nP_n = n!$ for $n = 9$ players, we have:

$$
\begin{aligned}
_9P_9 &= 9! \\
&= (9)(8)(7)(6)(5)(4)(3)(2)(1) \\
&= 362{,}880 \text{ different batting orders}
\end{aligned}
$$

In the next example we will consider a slight variation of Counting Rule 1. We will consider arranging *only **some*** of the *n* objects, ***not*** *all of the n objects.*

EXAMPLE 4.8

In a *six* horse race how *many different ways of win, place and show* positions (first, second and third position) are possible, assuming no dead heats?

Solution

Although six horses are racing we are only interested in the order of finish for the first three horses as illustrated in Figure 4.6a.

Since any one of the six horses could win the race, there are six possibilities for the first position as displayed in Figure 4.6b.

Once the winner has been determined, any one of the remaining five horses could finish second as shown in Figure 4.6c.

Now that first and second positions have been determined, any one of the remaining four horses could finish third. This is illustrated in Figure 4.6d.

Therefore, the total number of different ways for win, place and show is $(6)(5)(4) = 120$.

We will now generalize this counting technique and call it counting rule 2 or permutation rule for n objects taken s at a time.

1st Place	2nd Place	3rd Place

FIGURE 4.6a

1st Place	2nd Place	3rd Place
6	5	

FIGURE 4.6c

1st Place	2nd Place	3rd Place
6		

FIGURE 4.6b

1st Place	2nd Place	3rd Place
6	5	4

FIGURE 4.6d

DEFINITION 4.6

Counting Rule 2: Permutation Rule for n objects taken s at a time. The number of permutations of *n different* **objects taken** *s* at a time, denoted $_nP_s$, is:

$$_nP_s = n(n-1)(n-2) \cdots (n-s+1)$$

The value of s equals the number of factors for $n(n-1)(n-2) \ldots (n-s+1)$.

The solution to Example 4.8 is determined using the formula for Counting Rule 2:

$$_nP_s = n(n-1)(n-2) \cdots (n-s+1)$$

The number of arrangements of six horses taken three at a time is expressed as $_6P_3$. The value of n is 6 because there are six horses in the race and the value of s is 3 since we are only interested in the first three finishers. To apply the formula, we need to determine the number of factors required in the expression: $n(n-1)(n-2) \cdots (n-s+1)$. Since the value of s is 3, the expression $_6P_3$ contains 3 factors.

Thus,
$$\begin{aligned} _6P_3 &= n(n-1)(n-s+1) \\ &= (6)(6-1)(6-3+1) \\ &= 120 \end{aligned}$$

EXAMPLE 4.9

Using counting rule 2, find the number of permutations (arrangements) there are of seven different objects taken:
a) 3 at a time
b) 4 at a time
c) 7 at a time

Solution

a) The number of permutations of seven different objects taken three at a time is written as:

$$_7P_3 \text{, where: } n = 7 \text{ and } s = 3.$$

Thus, we have:
$$\begin{aligned} _7P_3 &= (7)(6)(5) \\ &= 210 \end{aligned}$$

b) The number of permutations of seven different objects taken four at a time is written as: $_7P_4$.
Thus, we have:
$$\begin{aligned} _7P_4 &= (7)(6)(5)(4) \\ &= 840 \end{aligned}$$

c) The number of permutations of seven different objects taken seven at a time is written as: $_7P_7$.
Thus, we have:
$$\begin{aligned} _7P_7 &= 7! \\ &= (7)(6)(5)(4)(3)(2)(1) \\ &= 5040 \end{aligned}$$

EXAMPLE 4.10

In how many different ways can a club that has twelve members select a running slate of four officers: *President, Vice President, Treasurer and Secretary?*

Solution

Since a club member can only run for only one office, we are interested in a definite arrangement of the four officers. Therefore, we use Counting Rule 2, where n = 12 and s = 4. Thus, the number of possible permutations of twelve club members taken four at a time is $_{12}P_4$.
Thus, we have:
$$\begin{aligned} _{12}P_4 &= (12)(11)(10)(9) \\ &= 11{,}880 \end{aligned}$$

EXAMPLE 4.11

List all different arrangements for the letters in the word:
a) *TEA*
b) *TEE*

Solution

a) Since there are three distinct letters to be taken 3 at a time, the number of different arrangements is determined by $_3P_3$.

$$_3P_3 = (3)(2)(1)$$
$$= 6$$

Listing these six arrangements we get:

TEA
TAE
EAT
ETA
ATE
AET

b) The three letters in the word TEE are *not* all distinct. If we take the six arrangements from part a) and change the letter A to E we get:

	TEA		TEE	
	TAE		TEE	[repeated]
arrangements	EAT	**changing the A to E**	EET	
from part a)	ETA		ETE	
	ATE		ETE	[repeated]
	AET		EET	[repeated]

Notice there are only **three *different* arrangements** for the letters *T, E, and E*. These three arrangements are: *TEE, EET and ETE. There are only three different arrangements since the arrangements containing EE are not distinguishable and thus* **reduces the number of distinct arrangements by a factor of 2!**. (This is because the letters E and E can be arranged in 2! ways.) Consequently, the number of different arrangements of three letters *when two are the same* can be determined by the formula:

$$\frac{3!}{2!} = \frac{(3)(2)(1)}{(2)(1)} = 3$$

Now, we will use Examples 4.12 and 4.13 to help generalize a counting rule for all possible different arrangements that can be made from a group of objects in which **some** objects are **alike**.

EXAMPLE 4.12

a) List all the different arrangements of the letters in the word ***FOOT***.
b) Determine the number of different arrangements.

Solution

a) Listing the different arrangements we get:

FTOO	*TFOO*
OFTO	*OTFO*
OOFT	*OOTF*
FOTO	*TOFO*
OFOT	*OTOF*
FOOT	*TOOF*

b) The number of different arrangements of the word FOOT is twelve. The twelve arrangements of the letters in the word FOOT can be determined by the formula:

$$\frac{4!}{2!} = \frac{(4)(3)(2)(1)}{(2)(1)} = 12$$

EXAMPLE 4.13

    a)   List the different arrangements of the letters in the word *NOON*.

    b)   Determine the number of different arrangements.

Solution

    a)   Listing the arrangements we get:

NNOO	*NONO*
ONNO	*ONON*
OONN	*NOON*

    b)   The number of different arrangements of the letters in the word NOON is six. The six different arrangements of the letters in the word NOON can be determined by the formula:

$$\frac{4!}{(2!)(2!)} = \frac{(4)(3)(2)(1)}{(2)(1)(2)(1)} = 6$$

       Examine carefully Examples 4.12 and 4.13. In Example 4.12 the word FOOT contained four letters *two of which were the same.* We determined that twelve different arrangements of the letters were possible. In the word NOON, there were also four letters but *both* the letters N and O were the same. That is, in the word NOON there were *two sets of letters that were the same.* It was determined that six arrangements of the letters were possible.

       We can now generalize the formula used to calculate the number of permutations of n objects where some objects were the same as illustrated in Examples 4.12 and 4.13. We will call this technique counting rule 3 or the number of permutations of N objects with alike objects.

DEFINITION 4.7

Counting Rule 3: Permutation Rule of N objects with k alike objects. Given N objects where n_1 are alike, n_2 are alike, . . . , n_k are alike, then the number permutations of these N objects is:

$$\frac{N!}{(n_1!)(n_2!) \; . \; . \; . \; (n_k!)}$$

EXAMPLE 4.14

Use counting rule 3 to determine the number of different arrangements for the letters in each of the following words:

a)   BANANA

b)   MISSISSIPPI

Solution

    a)   The word BANANA has six letters with the letter A repeated three times and the letter N repeated twice, therefore the number of different arrangements is:

$$\frac{6!}{3!2!} = \frac{(6)(5)(4)(3)(2)(1)}{(3)(2)(1)(2)(1)} = 60$$

b)   The word MISSISSIPPI has eleven letters with the letter I repeated four times, the letter S repeated four times and the letter P repeated twice, therefore the number of different arrangements is:

$$\frac{11!}{4!4!2!} = \frac{(11)(10)(9)(8)(7)(6)(5)(4)(3)(2)(1)}{(4)(3)(2)(1)(4)(3)(2)(1)(2)(1)} = 34,650$$ ∎

Combination

In our discussion of permutations we were concerned with the number of ways of arranging s objects selected from n objects in a *particular order.* Now we will consider a selection process where the *order is not important.* This selection process is called a *combination.*

> **DEFINITION 4.8**
> A **combination** is a selection of objects *without* regard to order.

Let's examine this idea of a combination in Example 4.15.

EXAMPLE 4.15

The chief Systems Analyst at H.A.L. Computer Systems, Inc. has to choose two programmers to work overtime on Sunday. If the company employs four programmers, then how many different ways can the Systems Analyst make her selection?

Solution

We will use the letters A, B, C and D to represent the four programmers. The analyst would like all possible arrangements of the four programmers where the ordering of the programmers within each arrangement is *not important.* For example, the selection of programmers A and C where programmer A is chosen first and C second *is the same* as the selection of C and A where programmer C is chosen first and A second. Thus, the **order** *of selecting the programmers is* **not** important.

If **order were important**, then we could use Counting Rule 2 which determines the number of ways to make a selection of n different objects taken s at a time. For n = 4 and s = 2, Counting Rule 2 would yield:

$$_4P_2 = (4)(3) = 12.$$

However, the twelve different ways determined by Counting Rule 2, counts the number of permutations or arrangements of the four programmers if order were important. Within these 12 different arrangements, an arrangement such as AC would be counted as different from arrangement CA. However, the analyst would still end up with the *same* combination of programmers. Therefore to determine the number of different combinations of two programmers, we need to adjust these 12 arrangements since each pair of programmers is *counted twice.* Thus, we must divide the formula $_4P_2$ by 2 to determine the actual number of **different combinations** of 2 programmers.

Thus, there are:

$$\frac{_4P_2}{2} = \frac{(4)(3)}{2} = 6 \text{ different ways}$$

that the systems analyst can make her selection.   ∎

We can now generalize the counting technique developed in Example 4.15 to determine the number of ways that s objects can be selected from n objects where ***order is not important***. We will call this technique counting rule 4.

DEFINITION 4.9

Counting Rule 4: Number of Combinations of n objects taken s at a time. The number of combinations of n objects taken s at a time, symbolized as $_nC_s$, is:

$$_nC_s = \frac{_nP_s}{s!}$$

The formula for $_nC_s$ in factorial notation is written as:

$$_nC_s = \frac{n!}{s!(n-s)!}$$

EXAMPLE 4.16

Use counting rule 4 to determine the number of combinations of n objects taken s at a time if:
a)   n = 5 and s = 3.
b)   n = 6 and s = 2.

For part a, use formula: $_nC_s = \frac{_nP_s}{s!}$

For part b, use formula: $_nC_s = \frac{n!}{s!(n-s)!}$

Solution

To determine the number of combinations of n objects taken s at a time, we will use counting rule 4.

a)   If n = 5 and s = 3 then $_5C_3 = \frac{_5P_3}{3!} = \frac{(5)(4)(3)}{(3)(2)(1)} = 10$

b)   If n = 6 and s = 2 then $_6C_2 = \frac{6!}{2!4!} = \frac{(6)(5)(4)(3)(2)(1)}{(2)(1)(4)(3)(2)(1)} = 15$

EXAMPLE 4.17

Use counting rule 4 to determine the number of combinations for each of the following parts. For parts a and c, use the formula:

$$_nC_s = \frac{_nP_s}{s!}$$

For parts b and d, use the formula: $_nC_s = \frac{n!}{s!(n-s)!}$

a)   the number of combinations of 6 objects taken 4 at a time.
b)   the number of ways two books can be chosen from a group of five.
c)   the number of ways a college student can choose 3 college courses out of 10 possible choices.
d)   the number of ways a student can choose to answer 8 of the 10 questions on an examination.

Solution

a) To determine the number of combinations of 6 objects taken 4 at a time, use the formula:

$$_nC_s = \frac{_nP_s}{s!}$$

For n = 6 and s = 4, we have: $_6C_4 = \frac{_6P_4}{4!} = 15$

Thus, the number of combinations of 6 objects taken 4 at a time is 15.

b) The number of ways to choose 2 books from a group of five is determined by using formula:

$$_5C_2 = \frac{5!}{2!(5-2)!} = 10$$

Therefore, there are 10 ways to choose 2 books from five books.

c) The number of ways a student can select 3 college courses from 10 choices is:

$$_{10}C_3 = \frac{_{10}P_3}{3!} = 120$$

Thus, there are 120 ways to select 3 courses from 10 choices.

d) The number of ways a student can choose to answer 8 out of 10 questions is:

$$_{10}C_8 = \frac{10!}{8!(10-8)!} = 45$$

Therefore, there are 45 ways to answer 8 out of 10 questions.

EXAMPLE 4.18

An offer from the Record of the Month Club to any new member is a choice of 5 records for 99 cents from a list of 25 records. How many combinations of 5 records can be chosen from this list?

Solution

Since we are choosing from 25 records, then n = 25. The fact that we are selecting 5 records makes s = 5. Therefore the number of combinations of 25 records taken 5 at a time is:

$$_{25}C_5 = \frac{25!}{5!(25-5)!} = 53,130$$

EXAMPLE 4.19

The Holiday Basketball Festival selection committee is considering 20 teams for their 12-team tournament. In how many ways can the 12 teams be selected?

Solution

The fact that the committee is selecting from 20 teams, n = 20. Since they are selecting 12-teams, s = 12. Therefore, the number of combinations of 20 teams taken 12 at a time is:

$$_{20}C_{12} = \frac{20!}{12!(20-12)!} = 125,970$$

Remark: The values of $_nC_s$ can be obtained using **Table I: The Success Occurrence in Appendix D: Statistical Tables** for values of n as large as 20. However, we recommend that you use your calculator to evaluate $_nC_s$.

Methods of Selection

When performing experiments which involve the selection of objects and/or people from a group, it is important that you understand the manner in which the object or person is to be selected from the group. Consequently, it is necessary to briefly discuss some different methods of selection and the wording used in the design of the experiment.

Suppose that you have an urn that contains 5 numbered objects, and the experiment requires you to select 2 objects from this urn. The manner in which the objects are selected depends upon the wording stated within the problem. We will consider two ways the objects can be drawn from the urn.

Methods of Selecting Two Objects From a Group of Objects

Selection Without Replacement
If the two objects are selected one at a time from the urn, where the first object *is not* placed *back* into the urn before the second object is selected, then this type of selection process is called *selection without replacement*.

Selection With Replacement
If the two objects are selected one at a time from the urn, where the first object *is placed back* into the urn before the second object is selected, then this type of selection process is called *selection with replacement*.

Suppose, for example, two balls are selected *without replacement* from an urn containing 5 numbered balls .

a) If order is important, then the selected arrangement of the two balls is considered a permutation with a total of:

$_5P_2$ or $(5)(4) = 20$ **permutations or ordered arrangements of the two numbered balls.**

b) If order is not important, then the selected balls are considered a combination with a total of:

$$_5C_2 = \frac{5!}{2!(5-2)!} = 10 \text{ combinations of the two numbered balls.}$$

On the other hand, if the two balls are selected *with replacement* from the urn containing the 5 numbered balls, then the order in which the balls are selected is usually considered to be of importance. Under these conditions, the number of ways the two balls can be selected is determined by the fundamental counting principle. Since each time a ball is drawn from an urn it contains 5 balls, then there are:

$(5)(5) = 25$ **ways** to select the two numbered balls.

From the previous discussion of the different selection methods used in an experiment, you should realize that *the counting technique employed to determine the number of ways k objects can be selected from a group of n objects is dependent upon the selection method used to choose the k objects, and whether order is an important factor of the experiment.*

■
EXAMPLE 4.20

An urn has 7 wooden blocks with each block containing only one of the letters: A, C, E, I, M, N, R inscribed on it.

If three blocks are selected, then determine:

a) the number of different *arrangements* of the three letters, if the blocks were selected *without* replacement.
b) the number of *combinations* of the three letters, if the blocks were selected *without* replacement.
c) the number of ways to select the three letters, if the blocks are selected *with* replacement.

Solution

a) Since the blocks are being selected **without** replacement, and order **is** important, then this is a permutation problem employing Counting Rule 2 for *n **different*** objects taken *s* at a time, denoted $_nP_s$. Because we are selecting from 7 objects, we have n = 7, and since we are choosing 3 objects then s = 3. Substituting this information into the formula for $_nP_s$, we have:

$$_7P_3 = (7)(6)(5) = 210 \text{ different arrangements of the three letters.}$$

b) Since the blocks are being selected **without** replacement, and order **is not** important, then this is a combination problem using Counting Rule 4 for the number of combinations of n objects taken s at a time, symbolized as $_nC_s$. Substituting n = 7 and s = 3 into the formula, we have:

$$_7C_3 = \frac{7!}{3!\,4!} = 35 \text{ combinations of the three letters.}$$

c) Since the blocks are being selected with replacement, and order is usually important, then the number of ways to select the letters is determined by the Fundamental Counting Principle. Since each time a block is drawn from an urn it contains 7 blocks, there are:

$$(7)(7)(7) = 343 \text{ ways to select three lettered blocks.}$$
■

Explaining the Difference Between the Idea of a Permutation and a Combination

If the *order of the objects must be different* for each possible outcome then the total number of possible outcomes is determined using a *permutation* formula. For example, the number of different ways that three people Abe, Bill and Carl can be elected for the three different positions: President, Vice President and Secretary of an organization are:

Abe as President, Bill as VP and Carl as Secretary,
or   Bill as President, Carl as VP and Abe as Secretary,
or   Carl as President, Abe as VP and Bill as Secretary,
or   etc.

Thus, the total number of possible arrangements of these three people into these three positions are determined by the permutation formula:

$$_nP_n = n!$$
$$= 3! = (3)(2)(1)$$
$$= 6 \text{ different arrangements}$$

On the other hand, if *the order of the objects is NOT important,* then the total number of possible outcomes is determined using the *combination* formula. For example, the number of different ways that the three people Abe, Bill and Carl can be selected to form a committee is only one way, since a committee of:

Abe, Bill and Carl is the same as Bill, Carl and Abe.

Thus the total number of ways to form a committee for these three people is determined by the combination formula:

$$_nC_s = \frac{n!}{s!(n-s)!}$$

$$_3C_3 = \frac{3!}{3!(3-3)!}$$

$$= \frac{(3)(2)(1)}{(3)(2)(1)(1)}$$

$$= 1 \text{ way to form a committee for these three people}$$

4.4 PROBABILITY

Each day people make probability statements for such things as the weather, the price of a stock, a baseball team winning the World Series, or a student passing a particular course. For example, a weather forecaster may announce that there is a 50% chance of snow for tomorrow. A stock broker speculates that a particular stock has a 75% chance that its price will double within 6 months. A sportscaster may predict that the likelihood of the National League Baseball Champion beating the American League Baseball Champs in the World Series is 10%. An instructor may indicate that the probability of a student passing his/her course is 90% if the student attends classes every day.

Although you are familiar with such probability statements, how does one go about interpreting these statements? Each of these statements is using a percentage to indicate the likelihood that an event will occur. For example, the statement pertaining to the chance of it snowing tomorrow has the percentage 50% attached to this statement. The weather forecaster is using a percentage (50%) TO REPRESENT THE CHANCE IT WILL SNOW TOMORROW. The percentage 50% or the number 0.50 provide a measure of how likely it is that it will snow tomorrow, and is referred to as the probability of the event that it will snow tomorrow.

> **DEFINITION 4.10**
> **Probability** is a numerical measure of the likelihood that a particular event will occur in the future. The probability of an event can only be a number from zero to one inclusive, or in terms of percent, from zero to 100% inclusive.

The probability or chance of the outcome occurring is expressed as a number ranging from 0 to 1, or as a percentage ranging from 0 to 100%. Probability values can be expressed in the form of a fraction, decimal or percent. For example, one could express the chance of getting a head on a single toss of a fair[3] coin either as: $\frac{1}{2}$ (fraction form) or 0.5 (decimal form) or 50% (percentage form).

---

[3]A fair coin is a coin that has the same chance of landing with heads face up as it does with tails face up.

A probability value of zero for an outcome is interpreted to mean that the outcome will never happen; while a probability value of one (or 100%) indicates that the outcome will definitely happen. Figure 4.7 shows a scale representing the probability of an outcome and some interpretations of these probabilities.

Probability of an Outcome

form of probability value: interpretation of probability:

fraction or decimal   percent

0 ————————————— 0%: outcome will never occur

any probability value between 0–50% is unlikely to occur

½ or 0.50 ———————— 50%: outcome is just as likely to occur as not occur

any probability value between 50–100% is likely to occur

1 ————————————— 100%: outcome will definitely occur

FIGURE 4.7

Alternate Approaches to Assigning a Probability

There are three main approaches to assigning a probability value to the likelihood that a particular outcome or event will occur. These commonly used approaches to assigning a probability are:

Approaches to Assigning a Probability

(I)   *Classical or a priori probability,*
(II)   *Relative frequency concept of probability or posteriori concept*
and   (III) *Subjective or personal probability.*

We will first define the **classical** or **a priori approach** to assigning a probability.

DEFINITION 4.11
Classical or *A Priori Probability*: The classical approach to probability is based upon the assumption that each outcome of the experiment is EQUALLY LIKELY.

Consider the experiment of rolling a fair die once. The six outcomes: 1, 2, 3, 4, 5, 6 are equally likely, since the die is fair and each outcome is assumed to have an equal chance of happening.

DEFINITION 4.12
All the possible outcomes of an experiment are **equally likely** if each outcome has the **same chance** of happening or occurring.

If each possible outcome is equally likely, then the probability of an event E can be defined using the Classical Approach.

Classical Probability Definition for Equally Likely Outcomes

Definition: The **probability of an Event E**, written P(Event E), is equal to the number of outcomes satisfying the event E divided by the total number of outcomes in the sample space, provided each outcome within the sample space is equally likely. This formula can be written as:

$$P(\text{Event E}) = \frac{\text{number of outcomes satisfying event E}}{\text{total number of outcomes in the sample space}}$$

In this text, we will primarily use the **Classical Approach of Defining Probability** to assign to an outcome a probability value. Remember, this classical approach can only be used if each outcome of the sample space is equally likely. We will illustrate the classical approach to defining probability in the next few examples.

EXAMPLE 4.21

Consider once again the experiment of tossing a fair coin twice. The sample space for this experiment consists of the four outcomes illustrated in Figure 4.8.

| HH | HT | TH | TT |

FIGURE 4.8

Since the coin is *fair,* each outcome has the *same chance of occurring.* If a fair coin is tossed two times, find the probability of the event that it will land:
a)   heads on both tosses, denoted P(HH).
b)   heads at most once, denoted P(at most one head).
c)   tails at least once, denoted P(at least one tail).

Solution

a)   The number of outcomes satisfying the event that the coin will land heads on both tosses is 1. It is HH. Since the total number of outcomes in the sample space is 4 as illustrated in Figure 4.8, the probability of getting two heads is:

$$P(HH) = \frac{\text{number of outcomes satisfying two heads}}{\text{total number of outcomes}} = \frac{1}{4}$$

The probability of two heads is 1/4. This means that if the experiment of tossing a fair coin twice is repeated a large number of times, we would *expect* one-fourth of the outcomes to be two heads.

b)   At most one head *means one or less heads.* From Figure 4.8, there are three outcomes which satisfy the event of at most one head. These outcomes are: HT, TH and TT. Since the total number of outcomes in the sample space is 4, the probability of getting at most one head is:

$$P(\text{at most 1 head}) = \frac{\text{number of outcomes satisfying at most one head}}{\text{total number of outcomes}} = \frac{3}{4}$$

The probability of at most one head is 3/4. Therefore, if this experiment were repeated a large number of times, we would *expect* 3/4 of the outcomes to be at most one head.

c)   At least one tail *means one or more tails*. The number of outcomes satisfying the event of at least one tail is 3. They are HT, TH and TT. The total number of outcomes in the sample space is 4. Thus, the probability of at least one tail is:

$$P(\text{at least 1 tail}) \ = \ \frac{\text{number of outcomes satisfying at least 1 tail}}{\text{total number of outcomes}} = \frac{3}{4}$$

E X A M P L E   4 . 2 2

Debbie, the chairperson of the Office Technology Department at a community college, decides to observe the time that two newly hired instructors get to class. Before she performs her experiment, she decides to make a list of all the different possibilities. If she decides to use the notation: E for early to class, O for on time, and L for late to class, then:

a)   construct a sample space for this experiment. If each outcome in the sample space is equally likely, then what is the probability that:
b)   both instructors will arrive to class late?
c)   neither instructor is late for class?
d)   at least one instructor is late?
e)   both instructors arrive to class at the same time?

Solution

a)   Using the Fundamental Counting Principle for this two-stage experiment, the total number of possible outcomes for this sample space can be determined by:

number of possible $=$ $\left(\begin{array}{c}\textbf{Number of outcomes} \\ \textbf{for instructor \#1}\end{array}\right) * \left(\begin{array}{c}\textbf{Number of outcomes} \\ \textbf{for instructor \#2}\end{array}\right)$
outcomes in sample space

Since there are 3 possible outcomes for both instructors, that is: early, on time and late, then:

number of possible $=$ **(3)(3) or 9 possibilities**
outcomes in sample space

The sample space containing these 9 possibilities are illustrated in Table 4.3, using E for early to class, O for on time, and L for late to class.

Table 4.3   Sample Space for Two Instructors

Instructor #1	Instructor #2		
	E	**O**	**L**
E	EE	EO	EL
O	OE	OO	OL
L	LE	LO	LL

b)   There is only one outcome satisfying the event that *both instructors arrive to class late,* which is LL. Since there are 9 outcomes in the sample space and assuming each outcome in the sample space is equally likely, then:

$$P(\text{both instructors arrive to class late}) = \frac{1}{9}.$$

c)   The number of outcomes satisfying the event *neither instructor is late for class* is 4. These four outcomes are: EE, EO, OE and OO. Since there are four outcomes out of the 9 possible outcomes satisfying the event, and assuming each outcome in the sample space is equally likely, then:

$$P(\text{neither instructor is late for class}) = \frac{4}{9}.$$

d) The event *at least one instructor is late for class* is satisfied when one or both of the instructors are late. Thus, the outcomes that satisfy this event are: EL, OL, LE, LO, and LL. Since 5 outcomes satisfy this event out of 9 equally likely outcomes, then:

$$P(\text{at least one instructor is late for class}) = \frac{5}{9}.$$

e) There are 3 outcomes satisfying the event *both instructors arrive to class at the same time,* since the event is satisfied by the outcomes: EE, OO and LL. Since 3 outcomes satisfy this event out of 9 equally likely outcomes, then:

$$P(\text{both instructors arrive to class at the same time}) = \frac{3}{9} \, or \, \frac{1}{3}.$$

EXAMPLE 4.23

An experiment consists of tossing one fair die twice. Find the probability of the following events:
a) the sum of the two tosses is seven, denoted as P(sum is 7).
b) the sum of the two tosses is an odd number, denoted as P(sum is an odd number).
c) the sum of the two tosses is greater than six, denoted as P(sum > 6).

Solution

To enable us to calculate these probabilities, we will use a sample space. But before we construct the sample space we should determine the *total number* of possible outcomes in the sample space by using the Fundamental Counting Principle. Thus, we have:

$$\begin{pmatrix} \text{total number} \\ \text{of} \\ \text{possible outcomes} \end{pmatrix} = \begin{pmatrix} \text{number of} \\ \text{possible outcomes} \\ \text{for first toss} \end{pmatrix} * \begin{pmatrix} \text{number of} \\ \text{possible outcomes} \\ \text{for second toss} \end{pmatrix}$$

$$= (6) * (6)$$
$$= 36$$

The 36 outcomes for this experiment are shown in Table 4.4.

Table 4.4

Outcome of First Toss	Outcome of Second Toss					
	1	2	3	4	5	6
1	1,1	1,2	1,3	1,4	1,5	1,6
2	2,1	2,2	2,3	2,4	2,5	2,6
3	3,1	3,2	3,3	3,4	3,5	3,6
4	4,1	4,2	4,3	4,4	4,5	4,6
5	5,1	5,2	5,3	5,4	5,5	5,6
6	6,1	6,2	6,3	6,4	6,5	6,6

a) There are six outcomes that satisfy the event that the sum of the tosses is seven. They are (6,1), (5,2), (4,3), (3,4), (2,5) and (1,6). The number of outcomes in the sample space is 36. Therefore,

$$P(\text{sum is 7}) = \frac{6}{36} \, or \, \frac{1}{6}.$$

b) The number of outcomes satisfying the event that the sum of the two tosses is odd is 18. Therefore,

$$P(\text{sum is an odd number}) = \frac{18}{36} \text{ or } \frac{1}{2}.$$

c) The number of outcomes satisfying the event that the sum of the two tosses is greater than six is 21. Therefore,

$$P(\text{sum} > 6) = \frac{21}{36} \text{ or } \frac{7}{12}.$$

EXAMPLE 4.24

A four cylinder automobile engine has 2 defective spark plugs. Two plugs are randomly removed from the engine **without replacement**. After each plug is removed, it is tested.
a) Construct a sample space for this experiment.
 Assuming each outcome is equally likely, what is the probability that:
b) only the first plug removed will be defective?
c) at most one plug will be defective?
d) both plugs will be good?

Solution

a) To help compute these probabilities, we will construct the sample space for this experiment. To determine the total number of possible outcomes within the sample space, use the Fundamental Counting Principle.

$$\begin{matrix} \text{total number} \\ \text{of} \\ \text{possible} \\ \text{outcomes} \end{matrix} = \begin{pmatrix} \text{number of possible} \\ \text{plugs to choose} \\ \text{from for 1st} \\ \text{selection} \end{pmatrix} * \begin{pmatrix} \text{number of possible} \\ \text{plugs to choose} \\ \text{from for 2nd} \\ \text{selection} \end{pmatrix}$$

Since the two plugs are being selected **without replacement**, the first selection will be made from an engine having 4 plugs. However, since *the first plug selected is **not** replaced,* then the second plug selected will be made from an engine containing only 3 plugs. Thus, the total number of possible outcomes is equal to:

$$\text{total number of possible outcomes} = (4) \times (3)$$
$$= 12$$

To help to distinguish between the 2 good plugs, the good plugs will be labelled as: G_1, and G_2, while the two defective plugs will be labelled as: D_1, and D_2. The 12 equally likely outcomes of the sample space for this experiment are listed in Table 4.5.

b) There are four outcomes where *only the first plug removed will be defective.* These outcomes are:

TABLE 4.5   The Sample Space For Selecting 2 Plugs Without Replacement From a 4-Cylinder Engine

1st PLUG SELECTED	2nd PLUG SELECTED			
	G_1	G_2	D_1	D_2
G_1	X	G_1G_2	G_1D_1	G_1D_2
G_2	G_2G_1	X	G_2D_1	G_2D_2
D_1	D_1G_1	D_1G_2	X	D_1D_2
D2	D_2G_1	D_2G_2	D_2D_1	X

D_1G_1, D_1G_2, D_2G_1 and D_2G_2. Since there are 4 outcomes out of 12 equally likely outcomes of the sample space that satisfy this event, then:

P(only the first plug removed will be defective) $= \dfrac{4}{12}$ or $\dfrac{1}{3}$.

c)   The event *at most one plug will be defective* is the same as **one or less plugs** will be defective. For this particular event, it is easier to count the number of outcomes that **do not** satisfy this event. That is, the number of outcomes having two defective plugs. There are only two outcomes where both plugs are defective, thus there are 10 outcomes satisfying the event at most one plug will be defective out of the 12 equally likely outcomes. Therefore,

P(at most one plug will be defective) $= \dfrac{10}{12}$ or $\dfrac{5}{6}$.

d)   The event *both plugs will be good* has only two outcomes satisfying two good plugs. These outcomes are: G_1G_2 and G_2G_1. Since there are 2 outcomes out of 12 equally likely outcomes of the sample space that satisfy this event, then:

P(both plugs will be good) $= \dfrac{2}{12}$ or $\dfrac{1}{6}$.

EXAMPLE 4.25

Five billiard balls numbered from 1 to 5 are placed in an urn. Two balls are selected in succession from the urn *with replacement,* that is, the first ball selected is returned to the urn before the second ball is selected. Find the probability of selecting:
a)   two even-numbered balls
b)   two odd-numbered balls
c)   one even- and one odd-numbered ball

Solution

To help compute these probabilities, construct the sample space. To determine the total number of possible outcomes within the sample space, use the Fundamental Counting Principle.

$$\begin{array}{ccc} \text{total number of possible outcomes} & = & \left(\begin{array}{c}\text{number of possible}\\ \text{outcomes for the}\\ \text{first selection}\end{array}\right) \quad * \quad \left(\begin{array}{c}\text{number of possible}\\ \text{outcomes for the}\\ \text{second selection}\end{array}\right) \\ & = & (\,5\,) \quad\quad * \quad\quad (\,5\,) \\ & = & 25 \end{array}$$

The sample space for this experiment is listed in Table 4.6.

TABLE 4.6

Outcome of First Ball	Outcome of Second Ball				
	1	2	3	4	5
1	1,1	1,2	1,3	1,4	1,5
2	2,1	2,2	2,3	2,4	2,5
3	3,1	3,2	3,3	3,4	3,5
4	4,1	4,2	4,3	4,4	4,5
5	5,1	5,2	5,3	5,4	5,5

a) The number of outcomes satisfying the event of selecting two even-numbered balls is 4. They are: (4,2),(2,4),(2,2) and (4,4). The number of outcomes in the sample space is 25. Therefore,

$$P(\text{two even-numbered balls}) = \frac{4}{25}$$

b) The number of outcomes satisfying the event of selecting two odd-numbered balls is 9. Therefore,

$$P(\text{two odd-numbered balls}) = \frac{9}{25}$$

c) The number of outcomes satisfying the event of selecting one even and one odd numbered ball is 12. Therefore,

$$P(\text{one odd and one even numbered ball}) = \frac{12}{25}$$

Another Approach to Defining Probability

Relative Frequency Concept of Probability or Posteriori Probability

The **relative frequency concept or posteriori probability** is based on observing the number of times an event has occurred over a *long run* in the past and using this information to assign a probability value to the event for the future.

For example, suppose you were interested in assigning a probability value to the following events:

1. the chance that a particular basketball player makes a foul shot.
2. the chance that your favorite coin falls with heads facing up on the next toss.
3. the chance that the next child born at a particular hospital is a boy.
4. the chance that it will rain tomorrow.

The probability for each one of these events **cannot** be calculated using the **classical approach to probability** since the outcomes of these experiments are **not equally likely**. For example, the chance that it will rain tomorrow is not equally likely for each day of the week.

In such cases, **the probability of an event is determined by examining past information on this event or by generating information on this event by performing the experiment a large number of times**. Using this information about the event, the relative frequency of the event can be determined. The formula to compute the relative frequency is:

Relative Frequency Approach to Calculating Probability

For an experiment that is repeated many times, the probability of an event A occurring is:

$$P(\text{Event A}) = \frac{\text{number of times event A occurred}}{\text{total number of times the experiment was repeated}}$$

This relative frequency formula *may not be the exact* probability but it represents an *approximate* probability.

EXAMPLE 4.26

A graduate student at the University of California at Berkeley conducted an experiment to observe the frequency of occurrences for the numerical outcomes of a particular roulette wheel in a Las Vegas

Casino. In 1,900 spins of this roulette wheel, the student observed that the number 7 occurred 200 times. Using this information and the relative frequency approach to probability, determine the probability that a 7 will occur on the next spin of this wheel.

Solution

Since the outcome 7 occurred 200 times within a total of 1,900 spins of the roulette wheel, then using the relative frequency approach, the probability of obtaining a 7 on the next spin is equal to:

$$P(\text{obtaining a 7}) = \frac{\text{number of times a 7 occurred}}{\text{total number of times the roulette was spun}}$$

$$P(\text{obtaining a 7}) = \frac{200}{1,900} \approx 0.1053$$

◼

You should realize that the relative frequency approach will most likely not yield an exact probability value. Consider the following case study which illustrates this idea.

CASE STUDY 4.1   Chasing the Perfect Game in Bowling

The snapshot entitled "Elusive Perfect Game" in Figure 4.9 displays the chances an amateur bowler will roll a 300 game for men, women and all bowlers. These probabilities are based upon information available from the American Bowling Congress.

Statistical Snapshot

Elusive Perfect Game

Chances of an amateur bowler rolling a 300 game:

Men	1 in 12,500 games
Women	1 in 644,000 games
All bowlers	1 in 24,000 games

Source: American Bowling Congress

FIGURE 4.9

The probabilities of rolling a 300 game displayed in Figure 4.9 were calculated using the relative frequency approach of defining probability. For example, using the available information, the probability of an amateur male bowler rolling a 300 game was calculated by dividing the *number of times a 300 game was rolled by an amateur male bowler* by the *total number of games an amateur male bowled*.

a) If no male amateur bowler rolls a 300 game during the bowling season following those which produced the information contained in the snapshot, would the relative frequency probability value change for a male bowler rolling a 300 game? Would this relative frequency probability value increase or decrease? Explain.

b) Using the answers to part (a), explain why you would consider the relative frequency probability values in the snapshot to be estimates and not the actual probability values for rolling a 300 game by males, females or all amateur bowlers.

From Case Study 4.1, you should realize that since a relative frequency probability is calculated either from past information or information generated by performing an experiment a large number of times, it provides only an estimate of the actual probability. This is because the relative frequency probability will most likely change as the experiment is repeated more and more times.

Let's examine how a relative frequency probability may change almost each time the experiment is performed. Consider the experiment of tossing your favorite coin 100 times. When you perform this experiment you observe heads 53 out of the 100 tosses; while your friend tosses the coin 100 times and observes 48 heads. You would estimate the probability of getting a head to be 53/100, while your friend would estimate the probability of getting a head as 48/100. Although both you and your friend used the relative frequency approach to calculate the probability of getting a head for this coin, both of you arrived at two different probability values. Consequently, if you were interested in finding the probability of getting a head on the next toss of this coin, which of these two different probability values is the correct one? The idea of the relative frequency approach is not to select one of these probability values, but to realize that both of these serve as estimates of the actual probability value while a better estimate of the actual probability can be determined by tossing this coin a greater number of times. That is, if the coin tossing experiment were repeated a large number of times, say like 1,000 or 10,000 or 100,000 times, the relative frequency probability will begin to stabilize and the relative frequency will begin to approach the actual probability of the event. The law that guarantees this result is called the *Law of Large Numbers*.

Law of Large Numbers

The Law of Large Numbers states that if an experiment is repeated a large number of times, then the probability of an event obtained using the relative frequency formula will approach the actual or theoretical probability of the event.

Let's demonstrate the law of large numbers for this coin tossing experiment. Suppose your favorite coin is a fair coin and is tossed 1520 times. The number of heads is recorded at each of the following tosses: 10, 20, 120, 320, 520, 720, 920, 1120, 1320, and 1520. These results are shown in Table 4.7.

Examine the last column in Table 4.7. This column shows the value of the relative frequency as the number of tosses of the coin is increased. Although the coin landed heads 13 times out of the first 20 tosses, which yields a relative frequency of 0.65, notice as the coin was tossed more and more times, the relative frequency is getting closer to 0.5 or ½, which represents the actual probability of getting a head for a fair coin.

Figure 4.10 represents the relative frequency of the coin landing heads for this experiment. The horizontal line within the figure indicates the actual probability of 0.5. The irregular pattern of * shows the relative frequency approaching the actual probability of 0.5 as the number of tosses of the fair coin gets larger and larger. Notice, however, even after 120 tosses of the fair coin, the relative frequency (0.475) and the actual probability (0.5) are still not equal.

The Law of Averages: A Common Fallacy

Many people have a misconception about the *law of large numbers*. These people believe, for example, that:

• if a coin lands heads in ten consecutive tosses, then the *next toss* is almost guaranteed to be a tail.
or
• if a roulette wheel has a run of 15 straight red numbers, then you should place your money on a black number because the odds have increased immensely that the *next number* will be black.

TABLE 4.7

Number of Tosses	Number of Heads	Relative Frequency of number of heads to total number of tosses
10	6	$\dfrac{6}{10} = 0.60$
20	13	$\dfrac{13}{20} = 0.65$
120	57	$\dfrac{57}{120} = 0.475$
320	167	$\dfrac{167}{320} = 0.5219$
520	268	$\dfrac{265}{520} = 0.5154$
720	359	$\dfrac{359}{720} = 0.4986$
920	464	$\dfrac{464}{920} = 0.5043$
1,120	565	$\dfrac{565}{1120} = 0.5045$
1,320	658	$\dfrac{659}{1320} = 0.4992$
1,520	761	$\dfrac{761}{1520} = 0.5007$

FIGURE 4.10

or
- if a family, who has 7 girls, is interested in having a boy, then the family shouldn't hesitate one moment to experience the joys of having their eighth child, since their chances that the *next or eighth child* will be a boy are almost certain to happen.

The *incorrect reasoning* used in each of the previous illustrations is what some individuals frequently call the *Law of Averages!* In reality, there is no such law of averages which can **guarantee** the behavior of a random occurrence such as the **next toss** of a fair coin, or the **next spin** of the roulette wheel or the sex of the **next child**. People who believe in this mythical law of averages are actually misinterpreting the law of large numbers.

Let's try to explain this misinterpretation by using a coin tossing experiment. For 100,000 tosses of a fair coin, some people are under the misconception that a fair coin must land heads EXACTLY 50,000 times or half the number of tosses! Continuing with this incorrect reasoning, if the coin were to land tails for the first 10 tosses, they then believe that the next flip or even the next few flips have a greater chance of landing heads since this will begin to AVERAGE OUT to half heads and half tails. However, this logic is false, because the coin is an inanimate object and *doesn't* have a memory to remember that the first ten tosses were all tails. In fact, each toss of the fair coin has no effect on any other toss. Thus, the coin is no more—and no less—likely to land heads on the next toss than any other. Therefore, why should a fair coin have a greater chance of landing heads on the eleventh toss? **It doesn't!!** Suppose out of the next 99,990 tosses, the coin lands heads 49,900 times, then those first 10 consecutive tails will not have any effect on the relative frequency of a head *in the long run. In essence, there is no averaging out effect for a short run.* The law of large numbers guarantees that for **a large number of tosses of a fair coin, the relative frequency of the number of heads will approach 0.5, which is the probability of getting a head**. Table 4.8 illustrates the law of large numbers concept.

TABLE 4.8

number of tosses: N	number of tails: T	Difference between the number of heads: H	Relative frequency number of tails and heads: T − H	of a head: $\dfrac{H}{N}$
10	10	0	10	$\dfrac{0}{10} = 0$
100	57	43	14	$\dfrac{43}{100} = 0.43$
1,000	510	490	20	$\dfrac{490}{1000} = 0.49$
5,000	2,525	2,475	50	$\dfrac{2,475}{5,000} = 0.495$
10,000	5,030	4,970	60	$\dfrac{4,970}{10,000} = 0.497$
100,000	50,100	49,900	100	$\dfrac{49,900}{100,000} = 0.499$

From Table 4.8, as the number of tosses of the fair coin increases from 10 to 100,000, *the relative frequency of a head is approaching 0.5 even though the difference between the number of tails and heads is getting larger.* The underlying fallacy of the law of averages lies with the fact that people believe the number of heads must be balanced by an equal number of tails in order for the relative frequency to approach 0.5. This is not true! As shown in Table 4.8, there are 14 more tails than heads after 100 tosses of the fair coin, however, these extra 14 tails do not have to be balanced out by 14 heads to average things out to half heads and half tails. In fact, these 14 tails will eventually be diluted by the thousands of heads and tails obtained in the next 99,990 tosses. Consequently, these 14 tails will have no effect on the relative frequency of a head in the long run of 100,000 tosses. Thus, the law of large numbers, as illustrated in Table 4.8, shows that the coin can still continue to land more tails than heads even while the relative frequency of a head approaches 0.5.

In essence, there is no "law of averages" which maintains that the chances of getting a head on the eleventh toss has increased, after a run of 10 straight tails. Instead, the law of large numbers guarantees that after an extensive number of tosses, it is very likely that the proportion of heads and tails will each turn up approximately half the time. The law does not say anything about a small number of tosses, much less about the outcome of one particular toss. The law of large numbers does not work by offsetting what has happened on the previous tosses, instead, any unusual run of many tails will simply be overcome in the long run. Consequently, you shouldn't expect some heads to balance out the first 10 tails because there is no averaging out effect for a short run. Rather, it is true that in the long run, according to the law of large numbers, the relative frequency of a head will approach the probability of getting a head, which is 0.5, even though the first ten tosses were tails.

Another Approach to Defining Probability

Subjective or Personal Probability

There are times when the probability of the outcomes of an experiment cannot be assigned using either the classical definition of probability since the outcomes are not equally likely or approximated by the relative frequency approach because there is no past information generated from repeating the experiment a large number of times. In such instances, the probability may be arrived at *subjectively.* Essentially, this means that the probability is based on a person's judgement, belief, experience or available information. Such a probability is called *Subjective or Personal Probability.*

> **DEFINITION 4.13**
>
> **Subjective or Personal probability** is the probability assigned to an event based upon an individual's judgement, or available information.

Since, most of the time, there is either little or no information concerning the experiment, the only choice is to use an educated guess at assessing the probability of an event of the experiment. However, even though subjective probability is assigned arbitrarily, this does not imply that the individual assigning the probability randomly selects a number out of the air for this probability assignment. The subjective probability assignment made by the individual reflects the measure of the degree of the individual's personal belief that is based on the knowledge of the situation and the assessment of any other relevant information.

We will now consider some examples which illustrate events of an experiment where the probability assignments rely on the subjective or personal approach to probability. In the following instances, subjective probability is used to estimate the chance that:

1. Steven, a college student, will pass his statistics course this semester.
2. The New York Yankees will win the next World Series.
3. The Centers for Disease Control accurately predicts the percentage of children that will contract chicken pox during the present school year.
4. Tony, a bond-market watcher, will successfully predict when the long-term interest rates will begin to rise this year.
5. Vince, a football coach, will select a first round draft choice that will successfully live up to expectations in the upcoming season.
6. Glenn, an astronaut, estimates the chance that the space shuttle will have a successful launch.

In each of the previous examples, the classical or relative frequency approach to assigning probability are not appropriate since the outcomes of the experiment are not equally likely nor can the experiment be repeated. For example, Vince will select **only one first round draft choice this year**, and the ability of this football player will determine whether he lives up to the coaches expectations in the upcoming season. Therefore, *the relative frequency approach cannot be used* since we cannot repeat this experiment. The *classical approach to probability cannot be used* because **the chance that this player lives up to expectations is not equally likely to the chance that the player does not live up to expectations**. Consequently, in this situation, subjective probability was the approach used to determine the probability of the event that the first round draft choice will successfully live up to expectations since the coaches' personal belief, judgment, information and experience was used in this assignment. Although Vince may assign this event a high probability, it is very likely that Don, another football coach, might assign to this same event a completely different probability value.

CASE STUDY4.2   Probability Statements

Examine the probability statements contained in each of the three news items of Figure 4.11 and answer the following questions.

(a)

Statistical Snapshot

I in 131: The Chance of Catastrophe

The odds of another shuttle being lost are I in 131. Figures in parentheses denote the probability that each component will fail and cause the shuttle to be destroyed. For each component, percentages denote portion of total risk of flying the shuttle.

Shuttle craft (I in 330) 39%
Solid-rocket booster (I in 755) 17%
Main Engine (I in 348) 37%
External tank (I in 5,208) 2%
Landing (I in 2,433) 5%

Source:
Newsday/Linda
McKenney

(b) ## Where to go for a holiday snow show

If you're dreaming of a white Christmas, you might want to be in International Falls, Minn., or Sault Ste. Marie, Mich. Although there's no way to accurately predict Christmas weather this far in advance, climatologists say that based on 30 years of records there is a 100% probability that those cities will be white on Christmas morning. "It wouldn't be Christmas without snow," says Jason Thrope, 28, a firefighter in Sault Ste. Marie. "Family is what it's all about, but snow makes it better."
— *Diane Harris*

(c)

Statistical Snapshot

Prizes/Chance of Winning Lotto

Match	Prize	Chance of Winning on a $1 Bet
Match 6 ○○○○○○	JACKPOT**	1: 18,009,460
Match 5 + Bonus Ball ○○○○ + ○	PARI-MUTUAL**	1: 3,001,577
Match 5 ○○○○○	PARI-MUTUAL**	1: 68,218
Match 4 + Bonus Ball ○○○○ + ○	PARI-MUTUAL**	1: 27,287
Match 4 ○○○○	PARI-MUTUAL**	1: 1,269
Match 3 + Bonus Ball ○○○ + ○	PARI-MUTUAL	1: 952
Match 3 ○○○	FREE PLAY	1: 68

Overall odds of winning a prize are approximately 1 : 60
** Pari-mutual prize is divided equally among multiple winners.

Statistical Snapshot

Expecting a White Christmas

The historical probability there will be at least an inch of snow on the ground on Christmas in these cities:

City	Chance of Snow	City	Chance of Snow
Albuquerque	9%	Eugene, Ore.	5%
Baltimore	13%	Flagstaff, Ariz.	51%
Billings Mont.	63%	Hartford, Conn.	57%
Boise, Idaho	26%	Indianapolis	30%
Boston	23%	Louisville	13%
Buffalo	67%	Milwaukee	60%
Burlington, VT	77%	Minneapolis	73%
Cheyenne Wyo.	35%	New York	13%
Chicago	40%	Omaha	41%
Cincinnati	17%	Philadelphia	10%
Cleveland	50%	Salt Lake City	52%
Columbus Ohio	23%	Seattle	5%
Denver	42%	St Louis	23%
Des Moines	50%	Tahoe City, Calif.	85%
Detroit	50%	Washington	13%

Source: Northeast Regional Climate Center at Cornell University

FIGURE 4.11

a) For each of the probability statements contained within the news items, explain which probability approach was used to define these probability statements.

b) Select a probability statement about an event contained within each news item and interpret the meaning of each probability. Explain whether you believe the probability of the event is likely to happen or not likely to happen.

c) In the news item entitled "Expecting a White Christmas," what do you think historical probability means? Explain.

d) In "Expecting a White Christmas," interpret the statement: " . . . there is a 100% probability that those cities will be white on Christmas morning." To which cities does this statement pertain? How do you think they arrived at this statement for these cities? Explain.

e) In the news item regarding the space shuttle, how do you think they arrived at the overall probability statement: "1 in 131: The Chance of Catastrophe"? That is, do you think they used the other probability information contained within the news item? Explain.

f) In the lotto graphic, what do you think the overall odds: 1:60 mean? How do you think they arrived at this overall odds? Do you think they used any of the probability information contained within the Lotto graphic? Explain.

g) Could the classical approach to assigning probability have been used to define the probabilities for "1 in 131: The Chance of Catastrophe" or "Expecting a White Christmas"? Explain.

h) Could the relative frequency approach to assigning probability have been used to determine the probabilities for "1 in 131: The Chance of Catastrophe"? Explain.

i) Using the lotto graphic, do you think that if you played one game that you would have an excellent chance of matching all the 6 selected numbers? Explain.

j) If 18.1 million people played one lotto game each and one of these people were randomly selected, do you think that this individual would have an excellent chance of matching all the 6 selected numbers? Explain.

k) If 18.1 million people played one lotto game each, do you think that there would be an excellent chance that one of these individuals would match all the 6 selected numbers? Explain.

Reprinted by permission of Tribune Media Services.

4.5   FUNDAMENTAL RULES AND RELATIONSHIPS OF PROBABILITY

Now that we have discussed the concept of probability, we are going to study some of the rules which probabilities must obey. The first basic rule states that the probability of an event must range from zero to one.

Probability Rule I

The **probability of an event E ranges from 0 to 1 inclusive.** Symbolically, this is expressed as:

$$0 \leq P(\text{Event E}) \leq 1$$

This rule is a consequence of the classic definition of the probability of an event. The classic definition states:

$$P(\text{Event E}) = \frac{\text{number of outcomes satisfying event E}}{\text{total number of outcomes in the sample space}}$$

Since the number of outcomes satisfying event E and the total number of outcomes cannot be negative numbers, the number P(E) must be greater than or equal to zero. Furthermore since the number of outcomes satisfying event E would always be less than or equal to the total number of outcomes, the number P(E) would have to be less than or equal to one.

Probability Rule 1 indicates that the smallest probability of an event E is zero. Thus, if an event E cannot occur, then the probability of Event E is zero. That is,

$$P(\text{Event E}) = 0.$$

E X A M P L E   4 . 2 7

An experiment consists of rolling a fair die once. Determine the probability of rolling a nine.

Solution

Of the six possible outcomes there are **no outcomes** corresponding to a nine. Therefore:

$$P(\text{rolling a 9}) = \frac{0}{6} = 0$$

Probability Rule 1 also indicates that the largest probability of an event E is one. An event with a probability of one is an event which is certain to occur.

E X A M P L E   4 . 2 8

An experiment consists of rolling a fair die once. Determine the probability of rolling a number less than seven.

Solution

All six possible outcomes for this experiment are less than seven. Therefore:

$$P(\text{rolling a number less than seven}) = \frac{6}{6} = 1$$

The second probability rule explains the relationship about the sum of the probabilities of all the outcomes within a sample space.

Probability Rule 2

The **sum of the probabilities of all the outcomes in the sample space of an experiment always equals 1.**

E X A M P L E   4 . 2 9

For the experiment of rolling a fair die, the sample space consists of the six outcomes illustrated in Figure 4.12.

FIGURE 4.12

Determine the sum of the probabilities of all the outcomes of this experiment.

Solution

The sample space consists of six equally likely outcomes. The probability for *each* of these six equally likely outcomes is $\frac{1}{6}$. That is,

$$P(\text{rolling a 1}) \;=\; P(1) \;=\; \frac{1}{6}; \qquad P(\text{rolling a 2}) \;=\; P(2) \;=\; \frac{1}{6}$$

$$P(\text{rolling a 3}) \;=\; P(3) \;=\; \frac{1}{6}; \qquad P(\text{rolling a 4}) \;=\; P(4) \;=\; \frac{1}{6}$$

$$P(\text{rolling a 5}) \;=\; P(5) \;=\; \frac{1}{6}; \qquad P(\text{rolling a 6}) \;=\; P(6) \;=\; \frac{1}{6}$$

Observe that the sum of all the probabilities of the outcomes of this experiment is one. That is,

$$P(1) \;+\; P(2) \;+\; P(3) \;+\; P(4) \;+\; P(5) \;+\; P(6) \;=\; 1.$$

This illustrates probability rule 2.

CASE STUDY4.3

The American Cancer Society announced in January, 1991 that a woman's odds of getting breast cancer had risen to 1 in 9. The Cancer Society has been heavily publicizing this 1 in 9 statistic to persuade woman to have more regular mammograms and to examine their own breasts. However, this probability figure has terrified many women and made them feel doomed. In fact, many young woman have interpreted this 1 in 9 statistic to mean that one of their nine girl friends will get cancer this year. Yet, this is not a correct conclusion based upon the calculated risk of getting breast cancer. Examine the chart shown in Figure 4.13, which indicates a woman's risk of getting breast cancer according to the American Cancer Society.

Statistical Snapshot

Odds of Developing Breast Cancer

By age:		By age:	
25	I in 19,608	60	I in 24
30	I in 2,525	65	I in 17
35	I in 622	70	I in 14
40	I in 217	75	I in 11
45	I in 93	80	I in 10
50	I in 50	85	I in 9
55	I in 33	Ever	I in 8

Source: National Cancer Institute

FIGURE 4.13

CASE STUDY 4.3 (continued)

Using the information in Figure 4.13, what is the probability of a woman getting breast cancer:

  a) by age 30?
  b) by age 40?
  c) by age 50?
  d) by age 60?
  e) by age 70?
  f) by age 80?
  g) by age 85?
  h) By what age does a woman's risk rise to the 1 in 9 chance of getting breast cancer?
  i) Would you interpret this 1 in 9 chance as a woman's risk of getting breast cancer for any particular age or the cumulative chance of a woman's risk of getting breast cancer during her lifetime? Explain.
  j) Explain what you believe the American Cancer Society means when they say the 1 in 9 chance is meant to be "more of a metaphor than a hard figure."

The third probability rule explains how to calculate the probability of the **compound event (A or B)**. This probability rule is called the **addition rule**.

Probability Rule 3: The Addition Rule

The probability of satisfying the event A or the event B is equal to the probability of event A plus the probability of event B minus the probability that both A and B occur at the same time. The addition rule is written as:

$$P(A \text{ or } B) = P(A) + P(B) - P(A \text{ and } B)$$

The key word in knowing when to use the addition rule is **or**. The *word or* within the probability statement P(A **or** B) indicates *addition.* Let's explain and apply the addition rule using the probability problem in Example 4.30.

EXAMPLE 4.30

In the experiment of tossing a fair die twice, what is the probability that the sum of the two tosses is greater than 4 **or** an odd sum?

Solution

The sample space for tossing a fair die twice is shown in Table 4.9. To determine the probability that the sum of the two tosses is greater than 4 **or** an odd sum, the addition rule is used since the probability statement is an **or** statement. If *event A represents the sum is greater than 4* while *event B represents the sum is odd,* then the probability that the sum is greater than 4 (sum > 4) or an odd sum can be written as:

$$P(A \text{ or } B) = P(\text{sum} > 4 \text{ or odd sum}).$$

To determine this probability, we need to calculate the following three probabilities: **P(sum > 4)**, **P(odd sum)** and **P(sum > 4 and odd)**.

TABLE 4.9 Sample Space For Tossing a Fair Die Twice

Outcome of First Toss	Outcome of Second Toss					
	1	**2**	**3**	**4**	**5**	**6**
1	1,1	1,2	1,3	1,4	1,5	1,6
2	2,1	2,2	2,3	2,4	2,5	2,6
3	3,1	3,2	3,3	3,4	3,5	3,6
4	4,1	4,2	4,3	4,4	4,5	4,6
5	5,1	5,2	5,3	5,4	5,5	5,6
6	6,1	6,2	6,3	6,4	6,5	6,6

The probability that the sum is greater than 4 is $\frac{30}{36}$ since there are 30 outcomes out of the 36 equally likely outcomes of the sample space which satisfy the sum is greater than 4. Thus,

$$P(\text{sum} > 4) = \frac{30}{36}$$

The probability that the sum is odd is $\frac{18}{36}$ since there are 18 outcomes out of the 36 equally likely outcomes of the sample space which satisfy the sum is odd. Thus,

$$P(\text{odd sum}) = \frac{18}{36}$$

Notice if you simply tried to add these two probabilities together to determine the probability that the sum > 4 or an odd sum, you would obtain a probability of $\frac{30}{36} + \frac{18}{36} = \frac{48}{36}$ which is INCORRECT because this would give us a probability that is greater than one which violates probability rule 1. The reason for this error is that the outcomes satisfying **both a sum > 4 and an odd sum have been counted twice** when the probabilities were added together. Consequently, the probability of a sum > 4 **and** an odd sum must be **subtracted** from this probability of $\frac{48}{36}$. Thus, it is necessary to determine the probability of a sum > 4 and an odd sum. That is, P(sum > 4 and odd).

The probability that the sum > 4 and an odd sum is 16/36. That is,

$$P(\text{sum} > 4 \text{ and odd}) = \frac{16}{36}$$

Now, the **P(sum > 4 and odd) can be subtracted from the sum of the probabilities: P(sum > 4) and P(odd sum)** as verified by the addition rule. Thus, using the addition rule to determine the probability that the sum is greater than 4 (sum > 4) or an odd sum, we have:

P(sum > 4 or odd sum) = P(sum > 4) + P(odd sum) – P(sum > 4 and odd).

$$= \frac{30}{36} + \frac{18}{36} - \frac{16}{36}$$

$$\textbf{P(sum > 4 or odd)} = \frac{32}{36} \; or \; \frac{8}{9}$$

■

E X A M P L E   4 . 3 1

Consider the experiment of selecting one card from an ordinary deck of 52 playing cards. The sample space for this experiment is shown in Figure 4.14.

The first row shows spades and clubs, while the second row shows hearts and diamonds. The club and spade suits are black and the diamond and heart suits are red. Each suit has 13 cards and contains the ranks: Ace, 2, 3, 4, 5, 6, 7, 8, 9, 10, jack, queen and king. Find the probability of selecting:

a)   A spade or a diamond
b)   A king or a club
c)   A picture card or a heart

FIGURE 4.14

Solution

a) The probability of selecting a spade **or** a diamond requires the use of the addition rule because we are dealing with an **or** statement. Using the addition rule, we can express the probability of a spade of a diamond as:

$$P(\text{spade or diamond}) = P(\text{spade}) + P(\text{diamond}) - P(\text{spade and diamond})$$

Since the selection of any card from a deck of 52 playing cards is equally likely and there are 13 cards which are spades and 13 card that are diamonds, then:

$$P(\text{spade}) = \frac{13}{52}, \text{and } P(\text{diamond}) = \frac{13}{52}$$

Since it is impossible for one card to be both a spade *and* a diamond, then:

$$P(\text{spade and diamond}) = 0.$$

Substituting these probabilities into the addition rule, we have:

$$P(\text{spade or diamond}) = P(\text{spade}) + P(\text{diamond}) - P(\text{spade and diamond})$$

$$P(\text{spade or diamond}) = \frac{13}{52} + \frac{13}{52} - 0 = \frac{26}{52} \text{ or } \frac{1}{2}.$$

b) Using the addition rule for the probability of selecting a king or a club, we can write:

$$P(\text{king or club}) = P(\text{king}) + P(\text{club}) - P(\text{king and club}).$$

Since there are 4 kings within the deck and 13 cards are clubs where one card is the king of clubs, then we have the following probabilities assuming each card has an equal chance of being selected:

$$P(\text{king}) = \frac{4}{52}, P(\text{club}) = \frac{13}{52}, \text{and } P(\text{king and club}) = \frac{1}{52}$$

Substituting these probabilities into the addition rule, we get:

$$P(\text{king or club}) = P(\text{king}) + P(\text{club}) - P(\text{king and club}).$$

$$P(\text{king or club}) = \frac{4}{52} + \frac{13}{52} - \frac{1}{52} = \frac{16}{52} \text{ or } \frac{4}{13}$$

c) The probability of selecting a picture card **or** a heart requires the use of the addition rule because we are working with an **or** statement. Using the addition rule, we can express the probability of a picture card or a heart as:

$$P(\text{picture card or heart}) = P(\text{picture card}) + P(\text{heart}) - P(\text{picture card and heart})$$

Since a picture card is either a king, a queen or a jack, then there are 12 chances out of 52 to select a picture card. Thus,

$$P(\text{picture card}) = \frac{12}{52}.$$

There are 13 hearts in the deck, so the chance of selecting a heart is:

$$P(\text{a heart}) = \frac{13}{52}.$$

Since there are only 3 picture cards that are hearts (jack, queen and king of hearts), then the chance of selecting a picture card and a heart is:

$$P(\text{picture card and a heart}) = \frac{3}{52}$$

Substituting these probabilities into the addition rule, we have:

$$P(\text{picture card or heart}) = P(\text{picture card}) + P(\text{heart}) - P(\text{picture card and heart})$$

$$P(\text{picture card or heart}) = \frac{12}{52} + \frac{13}{52} - \frac{3}{52} = \frac{22}{52} \text{ or } \frac{11}{26}$$

If **two events A and B cannot occur at the same time**, then the addition rule can be simplified. These events are said to be **mutually exclusive**. This leads us to the following definition.

> **DEFINITION 4.14**
> Two events A and B are **mutually exclusive events** if both events A and B cannot occur at the same time.

For mutually exclusive events, the probability of event A and event B occurring at the same time is zero, that is: $P(A \text{ and } B) = 0$. In such instances, the addition rule for two mutually exclusive events A and B is simply the probability of event A plus the probability of event B. This leads us to the following addition rule for mutually exclusive events.

Probability Rule 3A: The Addition Rule for Mutually Exclusive Events

If two events A and B are mutually exclusive, then the probability that event A or event B will occur is equal to the sum of their probabilities. This rule is written as:

$$P(A \text{ or } B) = P(A) + P(B)$$

The next example illustrates the concept of mutually exclusive events.

EXAMPLE 4.32

Which of the following events are mutually exclusive?
a) Rolling a single die once and getting a 2 or an even number.
b) Rolling a single die once and getting a 2 or an odd number.
c) Rolling a single die once and getting a 3 or a 4.
d) Tossing a coin twice and getting two heads or at least one head.
e) Tossing a coin twice and getting at least two heads or at most one head.

Solution

a) The sample space for rolling a single die once is given in Figure 4.15.

In Figure 4.16, we circled the outcomes that satisfy the event of getting a 2 and placed an X through the outcomes that satisfied the event of getting an even number.

Notice in Figure 4.16 the outcome 2 has a circle around it and an "X" through it. The events of getting a 2 and an even number can occur at the same time. Therefore, these two events are *not* mutually exclusive.

b) The sample space for rolling a single die once is given in Figure 4.17.

In Figure 4.18, we circled the outcome(s) that satisfy the event of getting a 2 and placing an "X" through the outcome(s) that satisfy the event of getting an odd number.

In Figure 4.18 we notice that there are no outcomes that satisfy both events at the same time. Therefore, the two events *are* mutually exclusive.

c) It is impossible to roll a single die once and get the two outcomes 3 and 4 at the same time. Therefore, the two events *are* mutually exclusive.

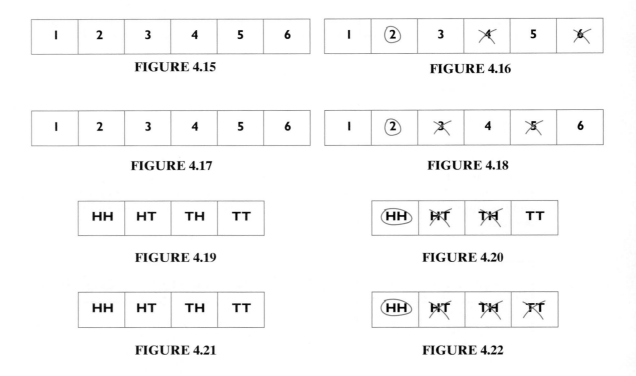

FIGURE 4.15

FIGURE 4.16

FIGURE 4.17

FIGURE 4.18

FIGURE 4.19

FIGURE 4.20

FIGURE 4.21

FIGURE 4.22

d) The sample for tossing a coin twice is given in Figure 4.19.

Circling the outcome(s) that satisfy the event of getting two heads and placing an "X" through the outcome(s) that satisfy the event of getting at least one head, we obtain the results shown in Figure 4.20.

In Figure 4.20, we notice that there is one outcome that satisfies both events at the same time. Therefore, the two events are *not* mutually exclusive.

e) The sample space for tossing a coin twice is given in Figure 4.21.

Circling the outcome(s) that satisfy the event of getting at least two heads and placing an "X" through the outcome(s) that satisfy the event of getting at most one head are shown in Figure 4.22.

In Figure 4.22 we notice that there is no outcome that satisfies both events at the same time. Therefore, the two events *are* mutually exclusive.

The fourth probability rule explains the relationship between the probability of an event E and the probability of the complement of Event E. Let's first define the complement of event E.

DEFINITION 4.15

Given an event E, the **complement of event E**, symbolized as E' and pronounced as E-complement, represents all the outcomes of an experiment that are not in event E.

If event E represents *it will rain tomorrow,* then event E' (the complement of event E) represents *it will **not** rain tomorrow*. Therefore, if event E **occurs** (that is, it rains tomorrow), then the complement of event E (it doesn't rain tomorrow) **cannot occur** and vice versa. Thus, if the chance that it will rain tomorrow is 30%, then the chance that it will not rain tomorrow is 70% since the chance it will rain tomorrow (event E) plus the chance it will not rain tomorrow (the complement of event E) must add up to 100% or be equal to a probability of one. This leads us to the Complement Rule.

Probability Rule 4: The Complement Rule

The sum of the probabilities of event E and the complement of event E always equals one. That is,

$$P(\text{Event E}) + P(\text{complement of Event E}) = 1$$

The complement rule can be symbolized as:

$$P(E) + P(E') = 1$$

The next few examples illustrate the application of the complement rule.

EXAMPLE 4.33

Consider the experiment of rolling a fair die once. If event E is rolling a 3, then:
a) identify event E',
    and identify and compute the following probabilities:
b) P(E)
c) P(E')
d) P(E) + P(E')

Solution

a) Since event E represents rolling a 3, the **event E' is *not* rolling a 3**.
b) P(E) is the probability of rolling a 3. Of the six possible outcomes for a single roll of a fair die, only one is a 3. Therefore,

$$P(E) = P(\text{rolling a 3}) = \frac{1}{6}$$

c) P(E') is the probability of not rolling a 3. Since there are five outcomes that are *not* a 3 on the die, then

$$P(E') = P(\text{not rolling a 3}) = \frac{5}{6}$$

d) $P(E) + P(E')$ is the sum of the probabilities of rolling a 3 or not rolling a 3 for a single roll of a fair die. Using parts (b) and (c), we have:

$$P(E) + P(E') = P(\text{rolling a 3}) + P(\text{not rolling a 3})$$

$$= \frac{1}{6} + \frac{5}{6} = 1$$

Thus, the *probability of rolling a 3* **plus** the *probability of not rolling a 3* **must equal one**, because no matter what outcome appears on the die it must satisfy one of the events E or E'. That is,

$$P(E) + P(E') = 1.$$

EXAMPLE 4.34

A young couple planning to have 3 children has eight family possibilities, which are illustrated in Table 4.10.

TABLE 4.10   Sample space for a 3 child family

First Child	Second Child	Third Child
boy	boy	boy
boy	boy	girl
boy	girl	boy
boy	girl	girl
girl	boy	boy
girl	boy	girl
girl	girl	boy
girl	girl	girl

Assuming each outcome is equally likely, compute the following probabilities.
a) P(couple will have 3 boys)
b) P(couple will not have 3 boys)
c) 1 – P(couple will have 3 boys)

Solution

a) Of the eight possible outcomes listed in Table 4.10, only one outcome corresponds to the event the couple will have 3 boys. Therefore,

$$P(\text{couple will have 3 boys}) = \frac{1}{8}$$

b) Of the eight possible outcomes listed in Table 4.10, seven outcomes correspond to the event the couple will not have 3 boys. Therefore,

$$P(\text{couple will not have 3 boys}) = \frac{7}{8}$$

c) From part a, the P(couple will have 3 boys) $= \frac{1}{8}$

Therefore,

$$1 - P(\text{couple will have 3 boys}) = 1 - \frac{1}{8}$$

$$= \frac{7}{8}$$

From Example 4.34, you should notice that the results of part b and part c are equal. That is,

P(couple will not have 3 boys) = 1 – P(couple will have 3 boys).

This is a direct result from the complement rule since it uses the probability of event E to compute the probability of the complement of event E. In general, this can be written as follows.

Computing the probability of the complement of event E using event E

P(complement of event E) = 1 – P(event E)

This can be further symbolized as:

P(E') = 1 – P(E)

Furthermore, we can also compute the probability of event E using the complement of event E. This is expressed as follows:

P(event E) = 1 – P(complement of event E)

That is,

P(E) = 1 – P(E')

The next example illustrates the use of these rules.

EXAMPLE 4.35

If a young couple is planning on having three children, then the $P(\text{couple will have 3 girls}) = \frac{1}{8}$. Using this information, compute the:

P(couple will not have 3 girls).

Solution

Using: $P(E') = 1 - P(E)$, we have:

P(couple will not have 3 girls) = 1 – P(couple will have 3 girls)

$$= 1 - \frac{1}{8}$$

$$= \frac{7}{8}$$

EXAMPLE 4.36

If a young couple is planning on having three children, then the P(couple will not have any girls) = $\frac{1}{8}$.

Using this information, compute the:

P(couple will have at least one girl).

Solution

Using: $P(E) = 1 - P(E')$, we have:

P(couple will have at least one girl) $= 1 - $ P(couple will not have any girls)

$$= 1 - \frac{1}{8}$$

$$= \frac{7}{8}$$

The next probability concept we will examine is the idea of independent events.

DEFINITION 4.16
Independent Events. Two events A and B are independent if the occurrence or nonoccurrence of event A has no influence on the occurrence or nonoccurrence of event B.

The following example illustrates the concept of independent events.

EXAMPLE 4.37

For each of the following experiments determine which events are independent events.
a) Consider the experiment of rolling a single die twice. Let event A be the outcome that the 1st roll is a 5, while event B represents the outcome that the 2nd roll is a 2.
b) Consider the experiment of tossing a coin twice. Let event A be the outcome that the 1st toss is a head. Let event B be the outcome that the 2nd toss is a head.
c) Consider the experiment of selecting two marbles **without** replacement from an urn containing 5 blue marbles and 1 red marble. Let event A be the outcome that the first marble chosen is red while event B is the outcome that the 2nd marble chosen is red.

Solution

a) When rolling a die twice, does the outcome of the first roll influence the outcome of the second roll? No. Thus, getting a 5 on the first roll has no influence on the second event B, getting a 2 on the second roll. Therefore, events A and B are independent.
b) When tossing a coin twice, does the outcome of the first toss influence the outcome of the second toss? No. Thus, getting a head on the first toss has no influence on getting a head on the second toss. Therefore, events A and B are independent.
c) If the red marble is selected on the first pick, then it cannot be selected on the second pick. There-fore, the two events are **not** independent.

Whenever two events A and B are independent, then the probability of A and B is very simple to calculate. This is illustrated in the next probability rule.

Probability Rule 5: Multiplication Rule for Independent Events

---

If two events A and B are **independent**, then the probability of A and B equals the probability of A multiplied by the probability of B.
This rule can be symbolized as:

$$P(A \text{ and } B) = P(A) \cdot P(B)$$

The next few examples illustrate the use of the multiplication rule for independent events.

EXAMPLE 4.38

Consider the experiment of tossing a fair coin twice. Find the probability of the following events:
a) both outcomes are heads
b) both outcomes are tails

Solution

a) Since the successive tosses of a coin are independent, use the multiplication rule for independent events.

$$P(\text{head and head}) = P(\text{head}) \cdot P(\text{head}) = (\tfrac{1}{2})(\tfrac{1}{2}) = \frac{1}{4}$$

Therefore, the probability of getting two heads in two tosses is 1/4.

b) Using the multiplication rule for independent events, we have:

$$P(\text{tail and tail}) = P(\text{tail}) \cdot P(\text{tail})$$

$$= \frac{1}{2} \cdot \frac{1}{2} = \frac{1}{4}$$

Therefore, the probability of getting two tails in two tosses is 1/4.

EXAMPLE 4.39

Two cards are selected **with replacement** from an ordinary deck of 52 playing cards. Find the probability of the following events:
a) both cards are clubs.
b) both cards are aces.
c) the first card is a picture card and the second card is an ace.

Solution

a) First notice that in a deck of cards, two successive selections, with replacement of the card after each selection, are independent events. Therefore, we can apply the multiplication rule for independent events. Therefore,

$$P(\text{club and club}) = P(\text{club}) \bullet P(\text{club}) = \frac{13}{52} \cdot \frac{13}{52}$$

$$= \frac{1}{4} \cdot \frac{1}{4}$$

$$= \frac{1}{16}$$

b) Similarly, for the event ace followed by ace with replacement, we can apply the multiplication rule for independent events. Thus,

$$P(\text{ace and ace}) = \frac{4}{52} \cdot \frac{4}{52}$$

$$= \frac{1}{13} \cdot \frac{1}{13}$$

$$= \frac{1}{169}$$

c) Using the multiplication rule for independent events, we have:

$$P(\text{picture card and ace}) = \frac{12}{52} \cdot \frac{4}{52}$$

$$= \frac{3}{13} \cdot \frac{1}{13}$$

$$= \frac{3}{169}$$

EXAMPLE 4.40

Two balls are selected **with replacement** from an urn containing 4 red, 6 green and 2 yellow balls. Find the probability of:
a) selecting 2 yellow balls.
b) selecting first a red ball and then a yellow ball.
c) selecting first a green ball and then a blue ball.

Solution

a) Using the multiplication rule for independent events, we can write:

$$P(\text{yellow and yellow}) = P(\text{yellow}) \cdot P(\text{yellow})$$

$$= \frac{2}{12} \cdot \frac{2}{12}$$

$$= \frac{1}{6} \cdot \frac{1}{6} = \frac{1}{36}$$

b) Using the multiplication rule for independent events, we have:

$$P(\text{red and then yellow}) = P(\text{red}) \cdot P(\text{yellow})$$

$$= \frac{4}{12} \cdot \frac{2}{12}$$

$$= \frac{1}{3} \cdot \frac{1}{6} = \frac{1}{18}$$

c) Using the multiplication for independent events, we can write:

$$P(\text{green and then blue}) = P(\text{green}) \cdot P(\text{blue})$$

$$= \frac{6}{12} \cdot \frac{0}{12} = 0$$

Probability Problems Using Permutations and Combinations

In many instances when the outcomes of a sample space are too large to list, it becomes necessary to use the counting rules to calculate the probability. The next few examples illustrate the use of the counting rules of permutations and combinations in computing probability.

EXAMPLE 4.41

If the four letters A, B, C, K are randomly arranged, what is the probability that the resulting arrangement is the word BACK?

Solution

Since the order of the letters is important this is a permutation problem. First determine the number of ways the letters can be arranged using $_nP_n$, where n=4. Thus,

$$
\begin{aligned}
_4P_4 &= 4! \\
&= (4)(3)(2)(1) \\
&= 24
\end{aligned}
$$

Since only one of these arrangements is the word BACK, the probability that the resulting arrangement is the word BACK is:

$$P(\text{the arrangement spells BACK}) = \frac{1}{24}$$

EXAMPLE 4.42

a) If the five letters A, I, C, R, G are randomly arranged what is the probability that the resulting arrangement is CRAIG?
b) If three of the previous five letters are selected and randomly arranged what is the probability that the result is CAR?

Solution

a) Since the order of the letters is important, this is a permutation problem. There are $_5P_5$ ways to arrange all 5 letters. CRAIG is 1 of these arrangements, therefore:

$$P(\text{the arrangement spells CRAIG}) = \frac{1}{_5P_5} = \frac{1}{120}$$

b) Since we are concerned with the order of selecting and arranging only 3 of the 5 letters, there are $_5P_3$ or 60 arrangements. Therefore:

$$P(\text{the arrangement is CAR}) = \frac{1}{_5P_3} = \frac{1}{60}$$

EXAMPLE 4.43

At a conference 9 executives consisting of 5 men and 4 women are required to sit along one side of a long table as illustrated in Figure 4.23. If they randomly take a seat what is the probability that the women occupy the even places?

Solution

If we consider the seats to be numbered from 1 to 9, this arrangement requires that the four women occupy seats 2, 4, 6 and 8. There are $_4P_4$ ways that the women can be arranged in these even numbered

FIGURE 4.23

seats. The 5 men must then occupy seats 1, 3, 5, 7 and 9. There are $_5P_5$ ways to arrange them in the odd numbered seats.

Hence using the **fundamental counting principle** we get: $(_4P_4)(_5P_5)$ ways that the women can end up in the even numbered seats.

The total number of possible seating arrangements for all nine people is $_9P_9$. Thus, the probability that the women occupy the even places is:

$$\frac{(_4P_4)(_5P_5)}{_9P_9} = \frac{(24)(120)}{362,880}$$

$$= \frac{2880}{362,880}$$

EXAMPLE 4.44

Joe and Laura are part of a group of 5 people waiting for a bus. If as it pulls up they get in line, what is the probability that Joe and Laura are *not* next to each other on line?

Solution

There are $_5P_5$ or 120 different ways for the five people to get in line. How many of these *don't* have Joe and Laura next to each other? It's easier to determine the number of ways the people can get in line with Joe and Laura *next* to each and then subtract from 120 (the total number of ways) to get the number we need. For Joe and Laura to be next to each other they can be arranged in two ways either as Joe and Laura or Laura and Joe. If we treat Joe and Laura as **one item**, then there are now $_4P_4$ ways to arrange the other three people with the duo of Joe and Laura. Remembering that Joe and Laura can be arranged in 2 ways we get: $2(_4P_4) = 2(4!) = 48$ ways to form a line with Joe and Laura next to each other. Hence, the number of ways of Joe and Laura *not* being next to each other is:

$$_5P_5 - 2(_4P_4) = 120 - 48 = 72$$

Therefore, the probability of Joe and Laura *not* being next to each other on the bus line is:

$$P(\text{Joe and Laura are not next to each other}) = \frac{(_5P_5) - 2(_4P_4)}{_5P_5} = \frac{72}{120}$$

EXAMPLE 4.45

Using a regular deck of 52 playing cards:
a) how many different five card poker hands are possible?
b) what is the probability of being dealt five hearts in a five card poker hand?
c) what is the probability of being dealt a flush (all five cards of the same suit) in a five card poker hand?

d)   what is the probability of being dealt 4 kings in a 5 card poker hand?
e)   what is the probability of being dealt 4 of a kind in a 5 card poker hand?

Solution

a)   Since there are 52 cards in a deck, n=52. A poker hand contains 5 cards, therefore: s=5. Using the formula,

$$_nC_s = \frac{n!}{(n-s)!s!}$$

we have:

$$_{52}C_5 = \frac{52!}{47!5!} = 2{,}598{,}960 \text{ different five card poker hands}$$

b)   Since a deck contains thirteen hearts and any five would make a five heart hand, there are $_{13}C_5$ five card heart hands. Therefore,

$$P(\text{five heart poker hand}) = \frac{_{13}C_5}{_{52}C_5} = \frac{1287}{2{,}598{,}960} = 0.0005$$

c)   Since there are four suits (diamonds, hearts, clubs and spades) and a flush is possible in any suit, then the probability of being dealt a flush is *four* times the probability of being dealt a flush in any one particular suit. From part (b) we know the probability of a flush in hearts is 0.0005. Thus the probability of a flush in any one suit is also 0.0005. Therefore,

$$P(\text{being dealt a flush}) = 4(\text{probability of a flush in any one particular suit})$$
$$= 4(0.0005)$$
$$= 0.002$$

d)   Since there are only 4 kings, you must be dealt all of them. This can only happen in one way. The fifth card can be any one of the remaining 48 cards. Therefore, there are 48 ways to get a fifth card or 48 five card hands which contain 4 kings. Thus,

$$P(\text{4 kings in a 5 card poker hand}) = \frac{48}{2{,}598{,}960} = 0.0000185$$

Remark: The probability of 4 of any one kind (4 aces, 4 sevens, etc) is the same as P(4 kings in a 5 card poker hand).

e)   Since there are thirteen ranks within any suit, ace through king, and 4 of a kind is possible for any rank (i.e. 4 aces, 4 two, etc.) thus the

$$P(\text{being dealt 4 of a kind for any rank}) = 13(\text{probability of four of a kind for any particular rank})$$
$$= 13\,(0.0000185)$$
$$= 0.0002405$$

EXAMPLE 4.46

If you're a member of an office staff of 25 clerks, what is the probability that you'll be selected as a member of a three person committee which is randomly chosen from the 25 clerks?

Solution

Since there are 25 clerks in the office and 3 clerks are to be chosen where order is not important, then there are $_{25}C_3$ ways to select the committee of 3 clerks. If you're to be included on this committee then only two other clerks from the remaining 24 clerks can be chosen. This is done in $_{24}C_2$ ways. Therefore,

$$P(\text{you are selected to a committee of 3 clerks}) = \frac{_{24}C_2}{_{25}C_2} = \frac{276}{2300} = 0.12$$

CASE STUDY 4.4   Playing to Win

The snapshot in Figure 4.24 indicates the number of $1 tickets necessary to cover every 6-number combination in selected lotto games.

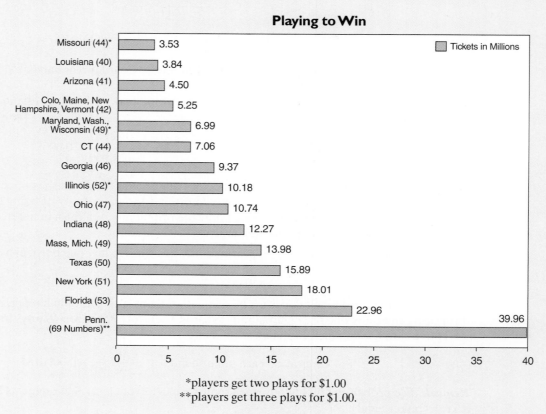

Playing to Win

State	Tickets in Millions
Missouri (44)*	3.53
Louisiana (40)	3.84
Arizona (41)	4.50
Colo, Maine, New Hampshire, Vermont (42)	5.25
Maryland, Wash., Wisconsin (49)*	6.99
CT (44)	7.06
Georgia (46)	9.37
Illinois (52)*	10.18
Ohio (47)	10.74
Indiana (48)	12.27
Mass, Mich. (49)	13.98
Texas (50)	15.89
New York (51)	18.01
Florida (53)	22.96
Penn. (69 Numbers)**	39.96

*players get two plays for $1.00
**players get three plays for $1.00.

FIGURE 4.24

a)   What counting technique is used to determine the total number of possible 6-number choices?

b)   What is the total number of ways to choose every possible 6-number combination out of 51 numbers? How does this result compare to the value listed in Figure 4.24 for the state of New York?

c)   What is the total number of ways to choose every possible 6-number combination out of 49 numbers? How does this result compare to the value listed in Figure 4.24 for the states of Massachusetts and Michigan?

d)   For the state of Florida, what is the probability that a person who buys a $1 lotto ticket will win the lottery? For the state of Texas, what is the probability that a person who buys a $1 lotto ticket will win the lottery?

e)   For the states Maryland, Washington and Wisconsin, what is the number of ways to choose every possible 6-number combination out of 54 numbers? What is the probability that a person who buys a $1 lotto ticket in Maryland will win the lottery?

f)   In which state Texas or Illinois does a person have the maximum number of possible ways to select every possible 6-number combination? Explain.

g)   For a $1 ticket, is the probability of winning the lotto greater for Texas or Illinois? Does this result agree with the result of part (f)? Explain.

CASE STUDY4.5

The article entitled "1-in-a-Trillion Coincidence, You Say? Not Really, Experts Find" appeared in the *New York Times* on February 27, 1990. The article explains why seemingly unlikely events are almost certain to happen.

Science Times

1-in-a-Trillion Coincidence, You Say? Not Really, Experts Find

Statisticians show that events that look unlikely are almost to be expected.

by Gina Kolata

Coincidences, those surprising and often eerie events that add spice to everyday life, may not be so unusual after all, researchers say.

After spending 10 years collecting thousands of stories of coincidences and analyzing them, two Harvard statisticians report that virtually all coincidences can be explained by some simple rules.

Some of the analyses performed by them or other statisticians showed that events that looked extremely unlikely were almost to be expected. When a woman won the New Jersey Lottery twice in four months, the event was widely reported as an amazing coincidence that beat odds of one in 17 trillion. But when carefully analyzed, it turned out that the chance that such an event could happen to someone somewhere in the United States was more like one in 30.

It was an example of what the authors, Dr. Persi Diaconis, a professor of mathematics at Harvard University, and Dr. Frederick Mosteller, an emeritus mathematics professor at Harvard, call "the law of very large numbers." That long-understood law of statistics states, in their formulation: "With a large enough sample, any outrageous thing is apt to happen."

Some of the findings are published in the December issue of The Journal of the American Statistic Association; others are now appearing in other professional journals. Dr. Diaconis, whose work also led to the recent discovery that seven shuffles are needed to mix a 52-card deck randomly, said the findings on coincidence were meeting with mixed reactions. "Some people are enormously relieved, but others are furious," he said. Not everyone who supplied an amazing coincidence to the researchers wanted to hear that a cherished dramatic story was really nothing special.

"I think the whole subject is fascinating," said Dr. Erich Lehmann, a statistician at the University of California at Berkeley. Although it can be a difficult statistical problem to decide just how unlikely an event is, Dr. Lehmann said, there is no dispute about the validity of the findings of Dr. Diaconis and Dr. Mosteller, some of which have been discussed at statistical meetings in recent years.

The two Harvard statisticians reviewed a large body of calculations and analyses of coincidences performed by other researchers, and they devised new techniques and approaches for studying the phenomenon in a wide range of circumstances. The research results, Dr. Diaconis said, "are aimed at very basic problems of inference that arise in messy, real statistical problems."

Dr. Bradley Efron, a statistician at Stanford University, said coincidences arise "all the time" in statistical work. When researchers find odd clusters of cancers or birth defects or other diseases, statisticians are asked "to decide which events are the luck of the draw" and which may reflect some underlying cause, Dr. Efron said. "That's what Persi and Fred are trying to unravel," he added. "I think it's a very interesting enterprise."

Dr. Diaconis said one application of the new analyses is in scrutinizing data from clinical trials of new drugs. "As you are looking around in that mass of data," he said, "you find that in a certain subgroup, there are twice as many deaths in people taking drug A as there are in people taking drug B." Is it a coincidence or an indication that drug A is so dangerous to some patients that the trial must be stopped?

Dr. Diaconis and Dr. Mosteller said they decided to study coincidences because they were fascinated by the role these odd events play in everyone's lives. "All of us feel that our lives are driven by coincidences," Dr. Diaconis said. "Who we live with and where we work, why we do the things we do often rest on slim coincidences." These chance events "touch us very deeply," he said.

The two statisticians defined a coincidence as "a surprising concurrence of events, perceived as meaningfully related, with no apparent causal connection."

Dr. Diaconis and Dr. Mosteller began with the presumption that there are no extraordinary forces outside the realm of science that are acting to produce coincidences. But they also recognized that seeming coincidences are an important source of insight in science and so should not be dismissed out of hand. What looks like a coincidence may in fact have hidden cause, which can lead to a new understanding of a phenomenon. A sequence of odd blips on a chart, a clustering of cases of a rare disease can tell researchers that a new event is occurring.

Anthologies of Happenstance

A decade ago, Dr. Diaconis and Dr. Mosteller started asking their colleagues, friends and friends of friends to send them examples of surprising coincidences. The collection quickly mushroomed. Dr. Mosteller said he had 13 notebooks, each three and a half inches thick, full of coincidences. "These notebooks are eating up the shelves in my den," he said. Dr. Diaconis said he had 200 file folders full of coincidences.

When they began to study these coincidences, they learned that they fell into several distinct groups. Some coincidences have hidden causes and are thus not really coincidences at all. Others arise from psychological factors, like selective memory or sensitivities, that make people think particular events are unusual whether they are or not. But many coincidences are simply chance events that turn out to be far more likely statistically than most people imagine. The analysis often required the researchers to develop new statistical methods, but in the end almost all coincidences could be analyzed.

The law of truly large numbers, which explains the double winner of the New Jersey Lottery, says that even if there is only a one-in-a-trillion chance that something will happen, it will happen eventually given enough time or enough people. "It's the blade-of-grass paradox," Dr. Diaconis said. "Suppose I'm standing in a large field and I put my finger on a blade of grass. The chance that I would choose that particular blade may be one in a million. But it is certain that I will choose a blade." So if something happens to only one in a million people per day and the population of the United States is 250 million, "you expect 250 amazing coincidences every day."

"If a one-in-a-million thing happens to you, you start telling people about it," Dr. Diaconis went on. "You might say to me, 'so what do you think of that, wise guy?' And I say, 'It's an example of the law of truly large numbers.'"

Right Answer, Wrong Question

When a New Jersey woman won the lottery twice in a four-month period, it was reported as a one-in-17-trillion long shot. Narrowly speaking, that is correct. But as Dr. Diaconis and Dr. Mosteller reported, one in 17 trillion is the odds that a given person who buys a single ticket for exactly two New Jersey lotteries will win both times. The true question, they say, is, "What is the chance that some person, out of all the millions and millions of people who buy lottery tickets in the United States, hits a lottery twice in a lifetime?"

That event was called "practically a sure thing" by Dr. Stephen Samuels and Dr. George McCabe, two statisticains at Purdue University. Over a seven-year period, they concluded, the odds are better than even that there will be a double lottery winner somewhere in the United States. Even over a four-month period, the odds of a double winner somewhere in the country are better than one in 30.

Another principle that demystifies many coincidences is what the researchers call "multiple end points"—occasions when what might qualify as a coincidence is not spelled out ahead of time, and when many chance events would qualify. This could apply, for example, at a party, where two people might discover that they come from the same town. This may seem a surprising coincidence. But the truth is that almost anything two strangers have in common would count as a coincidence—same first or last name, the same birthday, same item of clothing.

"Clearly, the chances of getting a match in any of several things is bigger than if you look at just one thing," Dr. Diaconis said. He and Dr. Mosteller have developed a formula that can evaluate such problems.

Multiple end-point coincidences often sound amazing on the surface. For example, Dr. Diaconis said, "I had a friend who said, 'Gee, I was watching a James Bond movie and there was a four-digit code on a bomb that was exactly the same as the code on my Israeli bank account.'" It sounded extraordinary, since there are 10,000 possible four-digit numbers. But Dr. Diaconis went on: "If you know 120 numbers—Social Security numbers, bank codes, telephone numbers of friends—there are even odds that four digits of two of them will match," he said.

Researchers say a two-time lottery winner is 'practically a sure thing.'

A third category of coincidences is those that are close but not exact. The odds of a coincidence then go up enormously. Once again, the two Harvard statisticians have developed a formula to analyze these problems.

Birthdays and Near-Birthdays

For example, with 23 people in a room, the chances are even that two of them will have the same birthday. But with only 14, there is an even chance of finding two people born within a day of each other, and if you ask instead that the birthdays match within a week, you need only seven people. "I have a friend who said, 'My daughter, myself, and my husband all have a birthday on the 11th of a month,'" Dr. Diaconis recalled. "O.K., there are 30 categories, 30 days of the month. How many birthdays do we have to know so that three are on the same day of the month?" The answer, he calculated, is 18. "So if you know 18 people, it's even odds that three will be born on the same day of the month," he explained. So the friend's birthday coincidence, he said, "is not so unusual."

CASE STUDY 4.5 (continued)

By analyzing coincidences with these three principles in mind, Dr. Diaconis and Dr. Mosteller find that what looks unexpected usually turns out to be expected. No strange forces outside the realm of science are needed to explain coincidences.

"Why does an educated person think there might really be something in coincidences?" Dr. Diaconis asked, and answered his own question: "No one story holds up on its own. But taken together, they mean something." If you put all these near-coincidences together, doesn't it indicate that something strange is going on?

It does not, Dr. Diaconis replied, and quoted another fundamental law of logic: "A lot of flawed arguments don't produce a sound conclusion."

a) Read the article and explain what is meant by the law of very large numbers.
b) To win the Pennsylvania lottery, an individual must select the six correct numbers out of 69 possible numbers. How many possible ways can a person select six such numbers?
c) If an individual gets 3 games for each $1 lottery ticket in the Pennsylvania lottery, then what is the probability that the individual will win when he/she buys a $1 lottery ticket?
d) As the lottery prize money increases, the number of people that play the lottery also increases. Keeping this in mind, explain why when the lottery pot hits $20 million you might expect to have multiple winners even though the probability is extremely small as shown in part (c).
e) Explain what is meant by a coincidence?
f) Explain the different distinct groups that the coincidences fall into as categorized according to the article.
g) What is meant by the blade-of-grass paradox? How does this relate to an individual winning the lottery?

4.6   CONDITIONAL PROBABILITY

Consider an experiment of selecting two balls in succession from an urn. The selection of the 2 balls can be done in one of two different ways: **with** replacement or **without** replacement.

Selection *with replacement* requires that the first selected ball is returned back to the urn *before* the second ball is selected.

Selection *without replacement* requires that the first ball selected is *not* returned to the urn before the second ball is selected. Let's examine these concepts in the next example.

EXAMPLE 4.47

Let's consider the experiment of selecting two balls in succession from an urn containing 3 balls numbered 1, 2 and 3. First we will examine the experiment where the selection is done *with replacement* and then we will reconsider the experiment *without replacement*.

Find the probability of selecting two odd-numbered balls from this urn and we are:

a)   selecting with replacement.
b)   selecting without replacement.

Solution

a)   The sample space for the experiment in which the selection is done *with replacement* is given in Table 4.11.

TABLE 4.11 Selection of Two Balls with Replacement

Outcome for First Ball	Outcome for Second Ball		
	1	2	3
1	1,1	1,2	1,3
2	2,1	2,2	2,3
3	3,1	3,2	3,3

Using the sample space in Table 4.11, then the:

$$P(\text{selecting two odd numbered balls with replacement}) = \frac{4}{9}$$

Since the first selected ball was returned back to the urn before the second ball was selected, these two selections have no affect on each other. Therefore, they are independent events. Another method of solution is to use the *multiplication rule for independent events* to calculate this probability. Thus,

P(selecting two odd balls with replacement) = P(1st ball selected is odd) · P(2nd ball selected is odd)

$$= \frac{2}{3} \cdot \frac{2}{3}$$
$$= \frac{4}{9}$$

b) The sample space for the experiment in which the selection is done *without replacement* is illustrated in Table 4.12.

TABLE 4.12 Selection of Two Balls Without Replacement

Outcome for First Ball	Outcome for Second Ball		
	1	2	3
1	X	1,2	1,3
2	2,1	X	2,3
3	3,1	3,2	X

Notice that the sample space does not have the outcomes 1,1; 2,2; and 3,3 since it is impossible to select the same numbered ball twice. Using the sample space in Table 4.12, the

P(selecting two odd numbered balls without replacement) = 2/6 or 1/3

Comparing the answers to parts a and b of Example 4.47, notice that the results are different. This is because in part a, the two selections were **independent**. However in part b, the selection of the second ball **was affected by the outcome of the first selection**. Therefore, we refer to this type of selection process as being **dependent**. Let's now formulate a multiplication rule for **dependent events**.

> ## Probability Rule 6: Multiplication Rule for Dependent Events: Conditional Probability
>
> **If two events A and B are dependent, then the probability of A *and* B equals the probability of A multiplied by the probability of B given that A has occurred.**
>   This can be symbolized as:
>
> $$P(A \text{ and } B) = P(A) \cdot P(B, \text{given A has occurred})$$
>
>   This can be further symbolized as:
>
> $$P(A \text{ and } B) = P(A) \cdot P(B|A)$$
>
>   where: $P(B|A)$ means $P(B, \text{given A has occurred})$.

   We will use the multiplication rule for dependent events to recalculate the P(selecting two odd numbered balls without replacement) as described in Example 4.47 part b. Using Probability Rule 6, the P(selecting two odd numbered balls without replacement) can be written:

P(selecting 2 odd balls without replacement) = P(1st ball is odd) · P(2nd ball is odd | 1st ball was odd)

   To compute the P(1st ball is odd), examine the urn pictured in Figure 4.25, where the three numbered balls have now been described as either odd or even. Using Figure 4.25,

$$P(\text{1st ball selected is odd}) = \frac{2}{3}$$

   To calculate:

the P(2nd ball selected is odd | 1st ball selected was odd),

the urn in Figure 4.25 must be **modified** to reflect the condition that the 1st ball selected was odd. This modified urn is illustrated in Figure 4.26. Using Figure 4.26, the:

$$P(\text{2nd ball selected is odd} \mid \text{1st ball selected was odd}) = \frac{1}{2}$$

Therefore,

P(selecting 2 odd balls without replacement) = P(1st ball is odd) · P(2nd ball is odd | 1st ball was odd)

$$= \frac{2}{3} \cdot \frac{1}{2}$$

$$= \frac{2}{6} \text{ or } \frac{1}{3}$$

FIGURE 4.25

FIGURE 4.26

Notice the previous result obtained using probability rule 6 is the same as the result computed in Example 4.47 part b.

EXAMPLE 4.48

If two balls are selected *without* replacement from an urn containing two red balls and three white balls, then what is the probability of choosing:
a) 2 white balls?
b) 2 red balls?
c) a red ball and a white ball?

Solution

a) To compute the P(of selecting 2 white balls) without replacement we must use the multiplication rule for **dependent events** since the selection of the 2nd white ball is dependent upon the selection of the 1st white ball.

Using Probability Rule 6, we have:

P(of selecting 2 white balls) =P(1st ball is white) · P(2nd ball is white | 1st ball was white)

To compute these probabilities, examine the urns shown in Figures 4.27a and 4.27b.

Urn prior to first selection   Urn prior to second selection

FIGURE 4.27a   **FIGURE 4.27b**

To determine the P(1st ball selected is white), examine the urn pictured in Figure 4.27a. Therefore,

$$P(\text{1st ball selected is white}) = \frac{3}{5}$$

Examine Figure 4.27b to help calculate the:

P(2nd ball selected is white | 1st ball was white) .

Using Figure 4.27b, we have:

$$P(\text{2nd ball selected is white | 1st ball was white}) = \frac{2}{4}$$

Now substitute these two results into Probability Rule 6, we get the following result:

P(of selecting 2 white balls) = P(1st ball is white) · P(2nd ball is white | 1st ball was white)

$$= \frac{3}{5} \cdot \frac{2}{4}$$

$$= \frac{6}{20} \text{ or } \frac{3}{10}$$

b) To compute the P(of selecting 2 red balls) without replacement, use the multiplication rule for dependent events. Thus,

$$P(\text{of selecting 2 red balls}) = P(\text{1st ball is red}) \cdot P(\text{2nd ball is red} \mid \text{1st ball was red})$$

$$= \frac{2}{5} \cdot \frac{1}{4}$$

$$= \frac{2}{20} \text{ or } \frac{1}{10}$$

c) In order to compute the P(of selecting a red ball and a white ball), we must consider the fact that there are two distinct ways of selecting a red and a white ball from the urn. They are:

1st way	or	*2nd way*
selecting a red ball first		selecting a white ball
then a white ball		first then a red ball

That is,

a red ball then white	or	a white ball then red

Therefore, we can express this probability as:

P(of selecting a red ball and a white ball) as

P(a red ball first then a white ball)   or   a white ball first then a red ball).

Using the addition rule for mutually exclusive events, Probability Rule 3A, we have:

P(a red and a white ball) = P(first a red ball then a white ball or first a white ball then a red ball)
= P(first a red ball then a white ball) + P(first a white ball then a red ball)

First, we will compute the P(of selecting a red ball first and then a white ball), using Probability Rule 6. Thus, we have:

P(1st a red ball then a white ball) = P(1st ball is red) · P(a white ball is selected | 1st ball was red)

$$= \frac{2}{5} \cdot \frac{3}{4}$$

$$= \frac{6}{20} \text{ or } \frac{3}{10}$$

Second, we will compute the:

P(of selecting a white ball first and then a red ball)

using Probability Rule 6. Thus,

P(1st a white ball then a red ball) = P(1st ball is white) · P(a red ball | the 1st ball was white)

$$= \frac{3}{5} \cdot \frac{2}{4}$$

$$= \frac{6}{20} \text{ or } \frac{3}{10}$$

Adding the last two results together, we have:

P(red and a white ball) = P(red ball first then a white ball) + P(white ball first then a red ball)

$$= \frac{3}{10} + \frac{3}{10}$$

$$= \frac{6}{10} \text{ or } \frac{3}{5}$$

In the previous example, you might have noticed that the P(of selecting a red ball first and then a white ball) and P(of selecting a white first and then a red ball) were equal. This is always true, and is referred to as the commutative probability rule. In general, we can state the commutative probability rule as:

Commutative Probability Rule

For two events A and B, the following probabilities are equal:

P(A and B) = P(B and A).

Using Probability Rule 6, we can write:

$$P(A \text{ and } B) = P(A) \cdot P(B \mid A)$$

and also

$$P(B \text{ and } A) = P(B) \cdot P(A \mid B).$$

These two results can be combined to form a new probability rule. This probability rule is called the **general multiplication rule**.

Probability Rule 7: General Multiplication Rule

For any two events A and B, the probability of A and B can be determined by either one of the following formulas:

P(A and B) = P(A) · P(B|A)

In words, the probability of A and B is equal to the probability of A multiplied by the probability of B, given that event A has occurred.

OR

P(A and B) = P(B) · P(A|B)

In words, the probability of A and B is equal to the probability of B multiplied by the probability of A, given that event B has occurred.

EXAMPLE 4.49

Consider the hopper in Figure 4.28 containing 6 balls where two balls are numbered 1, two balls are numbered 2 and two balls are numbered 3.

FIGURE 4.28

If this hopper is used to create a two-digit numeral for a lottery game by selecting two balls in succession without replacement, find the probability that:

a)   The lottery number 32 is selected
b)   The lottery number 33 is selected

Solution

a)   To compute the P(the number 32 is selected) use Probability Rule 6 for dependent events since the second numbered ball selected is dependent upon the first selected ball.

$$P(\text{the number 32 is selected}) = P(\text{first ball selected is a 3 and the second ball is a 2})$$
$$= P(\text{first ball is a 3}) \cdot P(\text{second ball is a 2} \mid \text{first ball is a 3})$$

$$= \frac{2}{6} \cdot \frac{2}{5}$$

$$= \frac{4}{30} \text{ or } \frac{2}{15}$$

b)   To compute P(the number 33 is selected), we will use the Probability Rule 6 for dependent events.

$$P(\text{the number 33 is selected}) = P(\text{first ball selected is a 3 and the second ball is a 3})$$
$$= P(\text{first ball is a 3}) \cdot P(\text{second ball is a 3} \mid \text{first ball is a 3})$$

$$= \frac{2}{6} \cdot \frac{1}{5}$$

$$= \frac{2}{30} \text{ or } \frac{1}{15}$$

EXAMPLE 4.50

Five keys, of which only one works, are tried one after another to unlock a door. What is the probability that:

a)   the door does not open on either of the first two tries?
b)   the door does open within the first two tries? (HINT: use Probability Rule 4: the complement rule and the result from part a).

Solution

a)   The statement that the door does not open on either of the first two tries means that the door did not open on the first try and the door did not open on the second try. Therefore,

P(door doesn't open on either of the first two tries) = P(door doesn't open on 1st try) · P(door doesn't open on 2nd try | door didn't open on 1st try)

Since these two events are dependent, we will use Probability Rule 6 to calculate this probability. Thus,

P(door doesn't open on either of the first two tries) = P(door doesn't open on 1st try) · P(door doesn't open on 2nd try | door didn't open on 1st try)

$$= \frac{4}{5} \cdot \frac{3}{4}$$

$$= \frac{12}{20} \text{ or } \frac{3}{5}$$

b) Use the complement rule: P(E) = 1 - P(E') to compute the P(door opens within the first two tries). Thus,

P(door opens within the first two tries) = 1 – P(door doesn't open on either of the first two tries)

From part a, we have:

$$P(\text{door doesn't open on either of the first two tries}) = \frac{3}{5}$$

Therefore,

$$P(\text{door opens within the first two tries}) = 1 - \frac{3}{5}$$

$$= \frac{2}{5}$$

Using Probability Rule 6: the multiplication rule for dependent events, we can algebraically obtain a formula for the conditional probability of event A, given that event B has occurred.

This result is called **Probability Rule 8: Conditional Probability Formula, denoted P(A | B)**, and is stated as follows:

Probability Rule 8: Conditional Probability Formula

For two events A and B, the probability of A given B has occurred is equal to the probability of A and B divided by the probability of B. This is rule symbolized as:

$$P(A \mid B) = \frac{P(A \text{ and } B)}{P(B)}$$

where P(B) > 0

EXAMPLE 4.51

In a single toss of a fair die, what is the probability of getting a 1, given the occurrence of an odd number?

Solution

Let's define event A to be the outcome is a 1 and event B to be the outcome is an odd number. Symbolically we want to determine P(A | B), i.e. the probability of getting a one, given that the outcome is odd. To compute this probability, we must first determine P(B) and P(A and B).

Since there are only six possible outcomes of a fair die and three are odd, then:

$$P(B) = P(\text{outcome is odd})$$

$$= \frac{3}{6}$$

Since there is only one outcome satisfying both events A and B, then:

$$P(A \text{ and } B) = P(\text{outcome is a 1 and the outcome is odd})$$

$$= \frac{1}{6}$$

Therefore,

$$P(A \mid B) = \frac{P(A \text{ and } B)}{P(B)}$$

$$= \frac{\frac{1}{6}}{\frac{3}{6}} = \frac{1}{3}$$

E X A M P L E   4 . 5 2

Two boxes identical in appearance are on a table. Box 1 contains a nickel and a penny while box 2 contains two nickels. A person randomly picks a box and then randomly selects a coin from the box. If the coin selected is a nickel, what is the probability that the other coin in the box is also a nickel?

Solution

Let's define event A to be the coin remaining in the selected box is a nickel and event B is the selected coin is a nickel. Symbolically we want to determine $P(A \mid B)$, i.e. the probability the coin remaining in the selected box is a nickel given the selected coin is a nickel. To compute this probability we must first determine $P(A \text{ and } B)$ and $P(B)$. Thus,

$$P(A \text{ and } B) = P(\text{coin remaining in box is a nickel and selected coin is a nickel})$$

This is equivalent to writing:

$$= P(\text{both coins in the selected box are nickels}).$$

Since there are two boxes and only one box has two nickels, then:

$$P(A \text{ and } B) = \frac{1}{2}$$

Since a nickel can be chosen from either of the two boxes, we have to consider both these possibilities in computing $P(B)$. That is,

$$P(B) = P(\text{coin selected is a nickel})$$
$$= P(\text{box 1 is chosen}) \cdot P(\text{select a nickel} \mid \text{box 1 is chosen})$$
$$+ P(\text{box 2 is chosen}) \cdot P(\text{select a nickel} \mid \text{box 2 is chosen})$$

$$= \frac{1}{2} \cdot \frac{1}{2} + \frac{1}{2} \cdot 1$$

$$= \frac{3}{4}$$

Therefore, the probability the coin remaining in the box is a nickel given that the coin selected was a nickel can be computed using Probability Rule 8:

$$P(A \mid B) = \frac{P(A \text{ and } B)}{P(B)}$$

$$= \frac{\frac{1}{2}}{\frac{3}{4}}$$

$$= \frac{2}{3}$$

EXAMPLE 4.53 **The Birthday Problem**

In Section 4.1, Lucy wagered Charlie Brown that at least 2 children at their Christmas Party would have the same birthday (month and day).

Let's compute this probability assuming there are 365 days in a year and there were:

a) 3 children at the Christmas Party.

b) 4 children at the Christmas Party.

c) 10 children at the Christmas Party.

Solution

The easiest way to calculate the: P(at least 2 children have the same birthday) is to compute the P(no two children have the same birthday) and use the complement rule: $P(E) = 1 - P(E')$.

Using the complement rule, we can write:

P(at least 2 children have the same birthday) = 1 – P(no two children have the same birthday)

We will use this probability rule to solve the birthday problem.

a) For 3 children at the Christmas Party, we have:

P(no 2 children have the same birthday) = P(all 3 children have different birthdays)
= P(1st child has a birthday)

multiplied by

P(2nd child has a birthday | 2nd child's birthday is different from first child's birthday)

multiplied by

P(3rd child has a birthday | 3rd child's birthday is different from first 2 children's birthdays)

$$= \frac{365}{365} \cdot \frac{364}{365} \cdot \frac{363}{365}$$

= 0.992 (expressed to the nearest thousandths)

Thus,

P(at least 2 children have the same birthday) = 1 – 0.992
= 0.008

This probability is rather small for a group of three children.

b) For 4 children at the Christmas Party, we have:

P(no two children have the same birthday) = P(all 4 children have different birthdays)

$$= \frac{365}{365} \cdot \frac{364}{365} \cdot \frac{363}{365} \cdot \frac{362}{365}$$

= 0.984

Thus,

$$P(\text{at least 2 children have the same birthday}) = 1 - 0.984$$
$$= 0.016$$

c) For 10 children at the Christmas Party, we have:

P(no two children have same birthday) = P(all 10 children will have different birthdays)

$$= \frac{365}{365} \cdot \frac{364}{365} \cdot \frac{363}{365} \cdot \frac{362}{365} \cdot \frac{361}{365} \cdot \frac{360}{365} \cdot \frac{359}{365} \cdot \frac{358}{365} \cdot \frac{357}{365} \cdot \frac{356}{365}$$
$$= 0.883$$

Thus,

$$P(\text{at least 2 children have the same birthday}) = 1 - 0.883$$
$$= 0.117$$

Table 4.13 contains the probability that at least 2 children will have the same birthday for various sized groups. Notice the probability that at least 2 children will have the same birthday for a group of 50 children is 0.970 or 97%. Consequently, Lucy's chances of winning her wager with Charlie Brown (as mentioned in the introduction to this chapter) are extremely good.

TABLE 4.13

Number of People in the Group	Probability of at least two people having the same birthday
3	0.008 OR 0.8%
10	0.117 OR 11.7%
20	0.411 OR 41.1%
23	0.507 OR 50.7%
30	0.706 OR 70.6%
40	0.898 OR 89.8%
50	0.970 OR 97%
60	0.994 OR 99.4%
70	0.999 OR 99.9%

EXAMPLE 4.54

Five people are each asked to select a number from 1 to 10 inclusive. What's the probability that at least two of them will select the same number?

Solution

Using the complement rule we get:

P(at least 2 people select the same number) = 1 – P(no two people select the same number)

$$= 1 - \frac{10}{10} \cdot \frac{9}{10} \cdot \frac{8}{10} \cdot \frac{7}{10} \cdot \frac{6}{10}$$
$$= 1 - 0.302$$
$$= 0.698$$

CASE STUDY 4.6

The following article entitled "The Laws of Probability" appeared in *Time* magazine on January 8, 1965.

The Law
Trials

The Laws of Probability

Around noon one day last June, an elderly woman was mugged in an alley in San Pedro, Calif. Shortly afterward, a witness saw a blonde girl, her ponytail flying, run out of the alley, get into a yellow car driven by a bearded Negro, and speed away. Police eventually arrested Janet and Malcolm Collins, a married couple who not only fitted the description of the fugitive man and woman but also owned a yellow Lincoln. The evidence, though strong, was circumstantial. Was it enough to prove the Collinses guilty beyond a reasonable doubt?

Confidently answering yes, a jury has convicted the couple of second-degree robbery because Prosecutor Ray Sinetar, 30, cannily invoked a totally new test of circumstantial evidence—the laws of statistical probability.

In presenting his case, Prosecutor Sinetar stressed what he felt sure was already in the juror's minds: the improbability that at any one time there could be two couples as distinctive as the Collinses in San Pedro in a yellow car. To "refine the jurors' thinking," Sinetar then explained how mathematicians calculate the probability that a whole set of possibilities will occur at once. Take three abstract possibilities (A, B, C) and assign to each a hypothetical probability factor. A, for example, may have a probability of 1 out of 3: B, 1 out of 10: C, 1 out of 100. The odds against A, B, and C occurring together are the product of their total probabilities (1 out of 3 X 10 X 100), or 3,000 to 1.

After an expert witness approved Sinetar's technique, the young prosecutor asked the jury to consider the six known factors in the Collins case: a blonde white woman, a ponytail hairdo, a bearded man, a Negro man, a yellow car, an interracial couple.

Then he suggested probability factors ranging from 1-to-4 odds that a girl in San Pedro would be blonde to 1-to-1,000 odds that the couple would be Negro-white. Multiplied together, the factors produced odds of 1 to 12 million that the Collinses could have been duplicated in San Pedro on the morning of the crime.

Public Defender Donald Ellertson strenuously objected on the grounds that the mathematics of probability were irrelevant, and that Sinetar's probability factors were inadmissible as assumptions rather than facts. Sinetar, however, merely estimated the factors before inviting the jurors to substitute their own. And the public defender will not appeal because he found no trial errors strong enough to outweigh the strong circumstantial evidence. Convicted by math, Malcolm Collins received a sentence of one year to life. Janet Collins got "not less than one year."

a) Identify each of the six factors that the prosecutor used as evidence to convince the jury that the defendants committed the robbery.

b) What was the probability that the prosecutor assigned to the chance of a girl in San Pedro would have blonde hair? How do you think the prosecutor came up with this probability value? Are you absolutely convinced that this is the correct probability value?

c) What was the probability that the prosecutor assigned to the chance that an interracial couple be black-white? How do you think the prosecutor came up with this probability value? solutely convinced that this is the correct probability value?

CASE STUDY4.6 (continued)

d) To what event did the prosecutor assign the very convincing probability value of 1 in 12 million?
e) How did the prosecutor arrive at this 1 in 12 million probability value? What assumption did the prosecutor make about the relationship between the six factors before he could multiply each of the respective probability values?
f) Do you agree with the prosecutor's assumption about the relationship among the six factors? Explain.
g) If you were a lawyer who had to defend this couple, what would you say to dispute the prosecutor's mathematical argument?

4.7 USING TECHNOLOGY

The relative frequency interpretation of probability can be illustrated using a computer *simulation* of a probability experiment.

DEFINITION 4.17
Computer Simulation. The use of a computer to model or imitate an experiment by randomly generating the data of the experiment for the purpose of studying this random phenomena.

For example, we have studied the probability experiment of the tossing of a fair die one time. The classical interpretation of the probability experiment indicates that the sample space is:

$$1 \quad 2 \quad 3 \quad 4 \quad 5 \quad 6$$

with each outcome being equally likely. Thus, the probability of each outcome is 1/6 or approximately 0.17. MINITAB can simulate this experiment for various sample sizes. The first simulation represents a random sample of size 36.

```
MTB > NOTE:DICE SIMULATION
Output
C1
    1   6   3   4   4   2   3   6   5   4   3   1   5   4   1
    2   4   5   4   4   4   3   3   2   5   4   4   6   3   2
    2   1   4   5   5   4
```

A summary of this output is:

```
Output
    C1          COUNT
    1             4
    2             5
    3             6
    4            12
    5             6
    6             3
   N =           36
```

The relative frequency of each numerical value for the sample size of 36 is given in Table 4.15.

TABLE 4.15

Dice Value	Frequency in Sample Size 36	Relative Frequency (approx)
1	4	0.11
2	5	0.14
3	6	0.17
4	12	0.50
5	6	0.17
6	3	0.08
	sum=36	

With MINITAB the simulation can be repeated many times and for various sample sizes. We have repeated the simulation for samples of size 144, 216 and 1296.

C1	COUNT
1	28
2	22
3	26
4	23
5	19
6	26
N =	144

C2	COUNT
1	24
2	36
3	40
4	37
5	39
6	40
N =	216

C3	COUNT
1	215
2	208
3	210
4	220
5	210
6	233
N =	1296

Table 4.16 lists the frequency and relative frequency for each outcome as the sample size increases.

If you examine Table 4.16 you should notice that as the sample size increases the relative frequencies do not vary as much. Why do you think this happens?

Graphing and statistical calculators have the capability of computing permutations and combinations. On the TI-83 Plus graphing calculator, the probability expressions $_nP_r$ and $_nC_r$ are used to compute a permutation and a combination respectively.

TABLE 4.16

| | n = 144 | | n = 216 | | n = 1296 | |
Dice Value	Freq	Relative Frequency	Freq	Relative Frequency	Freq	Relative Frequency
1	28	0.19	24	0.11	215	0.17
2	22	0.15	36	0.17	208	0.16
3	26	0.18	40	0.19	210	0.16
4	23	0.16	37	0.17	220	0.17
5	19	0.13	39	0.18	210	0.16
6	26	0.18	40	0.19	233	0.18

Let's display how a permutation and a combination is computed using the TI-83 Plus graphing calculator by re-examining two questions which were computed earlier in Chapter 4.

We computed the number of different ways a club with twelve members can select a running slate of four officers for:

President, Vice President, Treasurer and Secretary to be $_{12}P_4$ or 11,880 different ways. Figure 4.29 shows the value of $_{12}P_4$ as computed by the TI-83 Plus graphing calculator.

Earlier the number of different ways a person could select 5 records from a list of 25 records was determined to be $_{25}C_5$ or 53,130 different ways. Figure 4.30 shows the value of $_{25}C_5$ as calculated using the TI-83 Plus graphing calculator.

FIGURE 4.29

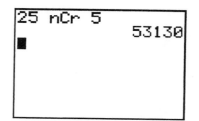

FIGURE 4.30

Using Minitab, we examined the idea of using a computer simulation to illustrate the relative frequency definition of probability. With the TI-83 Plus we can also simulate the tossing of a fair coin by using the *randBin* function to randomly generate the two outcomes: *0 and 1*. If we treat these outcomes as *0 for heads* and *1 for tails* then we can simulate the probability experiment of tossing a fair coin. Table 4.17 contains the outcome of the TI-83 Plus simulation of the experiment of tossing a fair coin "n" times. The first column of Table 4.17 contains the number of tosses, the second column contains the number of heads and the last column contains the relative frequency of heads for the n tosses. For example, the first entry of Table 4.17 shows, in 5 tosses of a fair coin, there was only 1 head, resulting in a relative frequency of ⅕ or 0.20 for a head. While the last entry shows in 200 tosses of a fair coin, there were 94 heads resulting in a relative frequency of 94/200 or 0.47 for a head.

According to the Law of Large Numbers, we would expect the relative frequency of a head to approach the classical probability value of 0.50 or ½ as the number of tosses increased. Observe that the relative frequency values of Table 4.17 changes from 0.20 to 0.47 as the number of tosses increases from n = 5 to n = 200.

Using the TI-83 Plus' graphing capabilities, we can illustrate the Law of Large Numbers for this fair coin tossing experiment by graphing the relative frequency values of a head along the y axis and

TABLE 4.17 The Results of a Calculator Simulation of Tossing a Fair Coin Using the TI-83 Plus

Number of tosses n	Number of heads h	Relative frequency of a head h/n
5	1	.2
10	3	.3
15	4	.27
20	7	.35
25	9	.36
30	10	.33
35	12	.34
40	14	.35
45	16	.36
50	19	.38
55	21	.38
60	23	.38
65	26	.40
70	27	.39
75	30	.40
80	32	.40
85	34	.40
90	37	.41
95	38	.40
100	41	.41
105	42	.40
110	45	.41
115	49	.43
120	51	.43
125	52	.42
130	54	.42
135	56	.41
140	60	.43
145	63	.43
150	64	.43
155	67	.43
160	70	.44
165	72	.44
170	76	.45
175	79	.45
180	83	.46
185	86	.46
190	88	.46
195	91	.47
200	94	.47

the number of tosses along the x axis. In Figure 4.31, the "jagged" graph represents the values of the relative frequency of a head.

The horizontal line across the middle of Figure 4.31 represents the probability value of 0.50. Notice as you move from left to right, the "jagged" graph begins to approach the horizontal line. This

FIGURE 4.31

illustrates the Law of Large Numbers. That is, as the number of tosses of the fair coin increases, the value of the relative frequency of a head begins to approach the probability value of 0.50.

Using EXCEL, another computer simulation of the fair coin tossing experiment was conducted. Examine the EXCEL printout in Figure 4.32. How many heads were observed for the first 5 tosses of the fair coin? What was the relative frequency for the first 5 tosses?

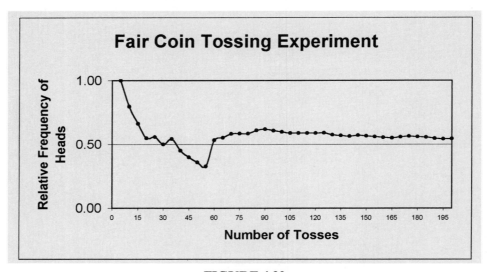

FIGURE 4.32

Why is the EXCEL computer simulation of the fair coin tossing experiment different from the TI-83 Plus' simulation of the same experiment? Does this seem to contradict the Law of Large Numbers? Explain.

KEY TERMS

Chance 222
Experiment 222
Sample Space 224
Fundamental Counting Principle: Multiplication Rule 226
Event 223
Outcome 222

Tree Diagram 225
Compound or Multi-Stage Experiment 226
Two-Stage Experiment 226
Three-Stage Experiment 226
At Least/At Most 230
Permutation 230

n factorial, n! 231
Counting Rule 1: Permutation Rule, $_nP_n$ 231
Counting Rule 2: Permutation Rule for n objects taken s at a time, $_nP_s$ 232

SECTION EXERCISES

Section 4.2

1. An _____ is the process by which an observation is made or obtained.

2. An _____ is a representation of all possible outcomes of an experiment.

3. The Fundamental Counting Principle is used to determine the number of outcomes in a sample space. T/F

4. Using the Fundamental Counting Principle, the total number of possible outcomes for the experiment of tossing a fair die three times is _____.

5. An _____ is a particular collection of outcomes in the sample space of an experiment.

6. For the experiment of tossing a fair coin four times the event of obtaining at least 3 heads is interpreted as meaning the event of obtaining 3 or _____ heads. The outcomes satisfying this event are _____, _____, _____, _____, and _____.

7. If three dice are tossed, how many different outcomes are in the sample space?
   a) 72   b) 42   c) 216   d) 18

8. If a spinner with four different outcomes is spun and a die is tossed, how many different outcomes are in the sample space?
   a) 40   b) 10   c) 24   d) 1296

9. If two cards are selected from a deck of 52 cards without replacement, how many different outcomes are in the sample space?
   a) 2704   b) 103   c) 1326   d) 2652

10. A *byte* is a computer "word" which consists of a sequence of 0's and 1's. If a particular manufacturer uses a byte of length 8, how many different bytes can be formed?

11. Construct the sample space for the following probability experiments:

a) Selecting one ball from an urn containing 4 red, 3 yellow and 3 blue balls.

b) Spinning the following spinner 2 times.

c) Tossing a fair coin three times.
d) Tossing a biased coin three times.
e) Arranging the letters in the word BYE.
f) Arranging the letters in the word GOOD.

12. Construct the sample space for the following probability experiments.

a) Selecting two balls without replacement from an urn containing 1 red, 1 yellow and 2 blue balls.

b) Selecting two balls with replacement of the first ball before the second is selected from an urn containing 1 red, 1 yellow and 2 blue balls.

c) Selecting two cards without replacement from the four cards: jack, queen, king and ace.

d) Selecting two cards with replacement from the four cards: jack, queen, king and ace.

13. Read the following famous nursery rhyme and answer the counting questions pertaining to this rhyme.

As I was going to St. Ives,
I met a man with seven wives,
Every wife had seven sacks,
Every sack has seven cats,

Every cat has seven kits,
Kits, cats, sacks and wives,
How many are going to St. Ives?
Determine the number of:

a) sacks
b) cats
c) kits

Section 4.3

14. Permutations are used as a counting technique when the objects are represented in a definite order. (T/F)

15. 4! is read as four 4 _____ and is a shorthand notation for _____ x _____ x _____ x _____ which has a value of _____.

16. The Permutation Rule or Counting Rule #1 is used to determine the number of *permutations* (or arrangements) of n different objects taken altogether, denoted _____. The formula used to calculate this number of permutations is: $_nP_n =$ _____.

17. $_6P_6$ is equal to _____.

18. How many different ways can the letters in the word MOM be arranged?
a) 6   b) 3   c) 27   d) 9

19. How many different teams containing five members each can be formed from a group of 9 players?
a) 126   b) 15,120   c) 45   d) 180

20. You've just arrived in Las Vegas for a vacation. You plan to see four dinner shows during your visit. If there are eight shows to select from, then how many ways can you select the four shows you'll see?
a) 32   b) 8   c) 1680   d) 70

21. The number of different ways four photos can be matched with a list of four names is _____.

22. a) Write the letters of the word DOG in all possible three letter arrangements.
b) Use the formula $_nP_n=n!$ to compute the number of arrangements.

23. Five textbooks are to be arranged on a shelf. In how many ways can they be arranged?

24. Counting Rule 2 is used to determine the number of permutations of n objects taken s at a time. This is denoted by: _____. The formula used to calculate this number of permutations is $_nP_s =$ _____.

25. Calculate each of the following
a) $_2P_2$ e) $_7P_3$
b) $_4P_4$ f) $_{11}P_7$
c) $_4P_2$ g) $_{12}P_5$
d) $_4P_3$

26. a) Find the number of permutations that are possible if 5 distinct objects are taken:
   1. one at a time
   2. two at a time
   3. three at a time
   4. four at a time
   5. five at a time
b) Find the number of combinations that are possible if 5 distinct objects are taken:
   1. one at a time
   2. two at a time
   3. three at a time
   4. four at a time
   5. five at a time
c) Why are the answers to part (a) larger than the answers to part (b)?

27. The number of different ways to select two numbered balls from an urn containing 5 numbered balls is _____.

28. The coach of the basketball team would like to determine how many different five man teams he can put on the court if each team must have a center, two forwards and two guards. His team has two centers, five forwards and four guards.
a) 120   b) 64   c) 462   d) 40

29. The chairperson of the scholarship committee wants to select a subcommittee of 2 men and 2 women to evaluate applications. If there are 7 women and 4 men on the committee, then how many different subcommittees can be selected?
a) 28   b) 333   c) 126   d) 27

30. Counting Rule 3 is used to determine the number of permutations of N objects, where: n_1 are alike, n_2 are alike, . . . , n_k are alike. The formula to calculate this number of permutations is : _____.

31. The number of different arrangements for the letters in the word **success** are _____.

32. a) Write the letters in the word MISS into all possible four-letter arrangements.
b) Use Counting Rule 3 to determine the number of arrangements.

33. In how many different ways can the letters in the following words be arranged?
a) Calculator
b) Tennessee
c) Scissors
d) Infinity

34. A combination is a selection of objects in which _____ is not important.

35. Counting Rule 4 is used to determine the number of combinations of n objects taken s at a time, which is symbolized as _____. The formulas used to calculate this number of combinations are _____ or _____.

36. To determine the number of ways six CDs can be chosen from a selection of 140 one must use the combination formula $_{140}C_6$. (T/F)

37. $_7C_4$ is equal to _____.

38. Calculate:
a) $_6C_3$ b) $_5C_2$ c) $_{10}C_4$ d) $_{25}C_{13}$ e) $_{52}C_7$

39. The number of ways to select 3 DVD movies from a group of 8 DVDs is _____.

40. In a given semester, a computer science major must select one of five science courses, one of three English courses and one of four psychology courses. How many different programs are available if there are no time conflicts?

41. Maria recently was sent an advertisement to join a record club. As an introductory offer she could choose *any* five selections from the one hundred listed. In how many different ways can Maria make her selections?

42. As an incentive to join a book of the month club, Grace can purchase any six selections from a list of 40 for only 99 cents. In how many different ways can Grace make her selections?

43. Twelve college graduates, of which four are female, have applied for seven vacancies in a computer company. If the company has decided to hire three females, how many ways could the company make the seven job offers?

44. On a history test part I has five questions of which three must be answered, and part II has six questions of which four must be answered. In how many ways can a student choose the questions they must answer on this test?

45. When ordering a new car the buyer has the choice of four body styles, five different engines and twelve colors.
 a) In how many different ways can a buyer order one of these cars?
 b) If the buyer also has the option of ordering the car with or without air conditioning, with one of three transmissions, with one of four radio options and with or without a sun roof, in how many ways can the buyer order one of these cars?

46. How many different license plates can be made:
 a) If all six characters are letters?
 b) If all six characters are numerals?
 c) If the first 3 characters are letters and the last 3 characters are numerals?
 d) If all six characters are letters with none repeated?
 e) If all six characters are numerals with none repeated?

47. Four married couples have purchased eight seats in a row for a Broadway show.
 a) In how many different ways can these eight people be seated?
 b) In how many different ways can they be seated if the husband must be seated immediately to the right of his wife?
 c) In how many different ways can they be seated if each couple must sit together?
 d) In how many different ways can they be seated if all the men sit together and all the women sit together?

48. Two attorneys must select nine members for a jury from a group of 15 individuals.
 a) How many different ways can the nine members be selected?

 b) Of the 15 individuals, if 9 are women and 6 are men and the attorneys would like a jury of 5 women and 4 men, how many different ways can the jury be selected?

49. Using the seven points pictured in the following diagram, how many straight lines can be constructed using only two points for each line?

Section 4.4

50. The Classical or a priori probability is based upon the assumption that each outcome of the experiment is _____ _____.

51. The Relative Frequency Concept or Posteriori Probability is based on observing the fraction of the time that an event has occurred over a ____ ____ in the past and using this information to assign a probability value to the event.

52. The probability assigned to an event based upon an individual's personal judgment, or available information is called _____ probability.

53. If an experiment is repeated a large number of times, then the probability of an event obtained using the relative frequency formula will approach the actual or theoretical probability of the event. The law that guarantees this result is called the ____ ____ _____ _____.

54. The probability that a Las Vegas odds maker assigns to the Miami Dolphins winning the Super Bowl is an example of:
 a) Classical probability
 b) Relative frequency probability
 c) Subjective probability

55. Assuming a die is fair, and assigning a probability value of ⅙ to a possible outcome is an example of:
 a) Classical probability
 b) Relative frequency probability
 c) Subjective probability

56. A quality control manager of a computer manufacturer, after testing 1,000 computer chips, estimates the probability of a defective chip is 0.01%. This probability assignment is an example of:
 a) Classical probability
 b) Relative frequency probability
 c) Subjective probability

57. If an experiment is repeated a large number of times then the relative frequency of an event will approach the actual theoretical probability.
 (T/F)

58. The law of large numbers guarantees that the probability of an event will equal the theoretical probability for all simulations of an experiment.
 (T/F)

59. Determine whether the scenario is an example of classical, relative frequency, or subjective probability.
a) Allison does not know the probability of an unbalanced coin landing heads up. She determines that for 100 tosses of the coin the frequency of heads is 65. Thus, she claims the probability that the unbalanced coin lands heads is $^{65}/_{100}$.
b) Pollsters from *The Arizona Cactus* claim that the probability of getting bitten by a rattlesnake is 1/100,000 for those hiking in the foothills of Tucson.
c) The probability that a homeless person survives for three years in a major city is $^2/_5$.
d) Based on a sample of 150,000 high school seniors the probability that a high school senior basketball player makes a professional team is $^1/_{2344}$.

60. A fair coin is tossed twenty times and lands with a tail face up on each of these twenty tosses. People who believe that the chance of getting a head on the next toss is not greater than the chance of getting a tail are using the fallacy known as the _____ ___ _____.

61. For equally likely events, the probability of an event E, denoted as P(E), is: P(E) = _____.

62. If we toss a fair coin and roll a fair die at the same time, then:
a) The probability of getting a 6 on the die and a head on the coin is _____.
b) The probability of getting an even number on the die and a head on the coin is _____.
c) The probability of getting a 7 on the die and a tail on the coin is _____.

63. Find the probability of each of the following events:
a) Selecting the ace of spades by randomly choosing one card from a well shuffled deck containing 52 cards.
b) Randomly selecting the lottery ticket numbered 0007 from a bin containing lottery tickets numbered 0001 to 9999.
c) Guessing the month in which your teacher was born.
d) Randomly selecting an incorrect response to a five item multiple choice question.
e) Randomly selecting a loser in an eight horse race.

64. Two actors are to be chosen to read the lines of a new play. If there are 17 actors applying, what is the probability that Nick and Jack are randomly chosen?
a) $^1/_{68}$ b) $^1/_{136}$ c) $^1/_{17}$ d) $^1/_{272}$

65. A wine tasting contest is being conducted at the Bowery Hotel. There are 4 varieties of wine labeled: B,M,S, and U to be rated. If one of the contestants has a hangover and has no ability to distinguish a difference in taste between the wines, then what is the probability that he will:
a) Rank wine B as the least desirable tasting wine?
b) Rank wine S as the best tasting wine and M as the least desirable tasting wine?
c) Rank the four wines in the following order: B,U,M,S?

66. a) Construct a sample space for a four child family. Assuming each outcome is equally likely, what is the probability of:
b) Exactly one boy?
c) At least one boy?
d) At least two girls?
e) At most one boy?
f) No boy?

67. A young couple plans to have three children. Assuming that the probability of having a boy is 1/2 determine:
a) The probability of having 1 boy and 2 girls.
b) The probability of having only 1 girl.
c) The probability of having at least 2 boys.

68. Derek has the following four coins: A penny, a nickel, a dime and a quarter. Construct a sample space listing all the possible sums of money Derek can form with one or more of these coins. Determine the probability that the sum of money:
a) Is greater than 10 cents?
b) Is less than 35 cents?
c) Is an even amount of money?
d) Contains a penny?
e) Contains at least one silver colored coin (nickel, dime, or quarter)?

Section 4.5

69. Probability Rule 1 states that the probability of an event E as a number between _____ and _____ inclusive.

70. Probability Rule 2 states that the sum of the probabilities of all the outcomes in the sample space of an experiment equals _____.

71. It is impossible for P(E) to equal zero (i.e. P(E) = 0). (T/F)

72. It is impossible for P(E) to equal one (i.e. P(E) = 1). (T/F)

73. It is impossible for P(E) to be greater than one (i.e. P(E) > 1). (T/F)

74. Probability Rule 3 is the Addition Rule which states that the probability of satisfying the event A or the event B is equal to the probability of event _____ plus the probability of event B _____ the probability that both events A and B occur at the _____ time. This is symbolized as:
P(A or B) = _____ + _____ − _____

75. One card is selected at random from an ordinary deck of 52 playing cards. The probability of selecting a queen or a red card is equal to the probability of selecting a _____ plus the probability of selecting a _____ minus the probability of selecting a _____ . In symbols, we have:
P(queen or red card) = P(___) + P(___) − P(___).
Thus, P(queen or red card) = ___ + ___ − ___ = ___ .

76. If the probability a person owns a Chevy is 0.60, the probability a person owns a BMW is 0.40, and the probability a person owns both a Chevy and a BMW is 0.30, then the probability a person owns a Chevy or a BMW is equal to: ____ + ____ – ____ = _____.

77. Two events A and B are _____ if both events A and B cannot occur at the same time.

78. The Addition Rule for mutually exclusive events A and B is:
P(A or B) = _____ + _____ .

79. If two events A and B are mutually exclusive then P(A and B) does not equal zero.
(T/F)

80. Two events that are mutually exclusive must also be independent.
(T/F)

81. Two events that are independent must also be mutually exclusive.
(T/F)

82. If two events C and D are mutually exclusive, then:
a) P(C and D) = _____.
b) P(C or D) = _____.

83. Consider the experiment of selecting one card at random from an ordinary deck of 52 playing cards. Let event A represent the event of selecting an ace and event B represent the event of selecting a king. Then, events A and B are _____ since a card cannot be both an ace and a king at the _____ time.
Therefore, P(ace or king) = P(____) + P(____)
= ___ + _____ = ____.

84. In a single roll of a fair die, the event of getting a 4 and the event of getting a 5 are _____ events, because a die cannot show a ____ and a ____ at the same time.

85. In a single roll of a fair die, the event of getting a 4 and the event of getting an even number are _____ events, because a die can show a ____ and an ____ at the same time. An outcome that satisfies both events is the outcome ____.

86. Probability Rule 4: The Complement Rule states that an event E can either occur or not occur. Thus, the sum of these events always equals _____ . This rule is symbolized as: P(____) + P(_____) = _____.

87. For the experiment of tossing a fair coin four times, the probability of not getting 4 heads can be rewritten using the complement rule as:
P(not getting 4 heads) = 1 – P(____).

88. Two events A and B are _____ if the occurrence or nonoccurrence of event A has no influence on the occurrence or nonoccurrence of event B.

89. Probability Rule 5 is the Multiplication Rule for _____ events. This rule states that if two events A and B are independent, then the probability if event A ____ B equals the probability of A ____ the probability of B. This is symbolized as:
P(____) = P(____) – P(_____).

90. An urn contains 4 white marbles and 3 red marbles. If two marbles are selected with replacement from this urn, then the probability of selecting two white marbles equals the probability of selecting _____ on the first selection _____ the probability of selecting _____ on the second selection since both events are _____. Therefore, P(two white marbles) = P(white marble) · P(white marble) = _____ · _____ = _____.

91. Construct a sample space for the sum of two die.
a) What is the probability of each outcome? (Hint: look at the sample space for Example 4.23.)
b) What is the probability that one rolls a sum of 7 or 11?
c) What is the probability that one doesn't roll a sum of 7 or 11?
d) What is the probability that the sum is less than 9?
e) What is the probability that the sum is odd?

92. Four balls numbered 1 to 4 inclusive are placed in an urn. Randomly choose the four balls from the urn without replacement. Record the number appearing on each ball as it is selected so as to form a four digit number. What is the probability that:
a) The number 1234 is obtained?
b) The number obtained ends in a 4?
c) The number obtained is greater than 3200?
d) The number obtained is not greater than 4000?
e) The number obtained is either even or less than 3500?
f) The number obtained is odd and greater than 5000?

93. Given five *Scrabble* blocks, each having one of the letters *a, c, e, p, l*:
a) How many 5 letter arrangements are possible?
b) How many 3 letter arrangements are possible?
c) If the 5 blocks are randomly arranged on a table, what is the probability that the word *place* is spelled?

94. A set of ten cards contains two jokers. There are two players, Bob and Audrey. Bob chooses six cards at random and Audrey gets the remaining four cards. What is the probability that Bob has at least one joker?

95. Find the probability that a poker hand will contain:
a) Full house (1 pair and 1 triple)
b) 4 of one kind
c) One pair (hint: more complicated than you may think)
d) Two pair
e) A flush (all cards of the same suit)

96. In the game of bridge four hands of 13 cards each are dealt from a regular deck of 52 cards.
a) How many different bridge hands are possible?
b) How many different ways can one be dealt a bridge hand of all hearts?
c) What is the probability of being dealt a bridge hand of ten clubs?

Section 4.6

97. If Toni, a craps player, rolls a five on her first roll, what is the probability that she makes her point? (In this case, making the point means rolling a five, before rolling a seven).

98. Consider the experiment of selecting two balls without replacement from an urn containing 6 numbered balls. If event A is the first ball selected and event B is the second ball selected, then these two events are said to be _____ . This type of probability problem is classified as _____ probability.

99. Probability Rule 6 is the multiplication rule for _____ events. This rule states that if two events A and B are dependent, then the probability of A and B is equal to the probability of A times the probability of _____ given that event A has _____ . This is symbolized as: P(_____) = P(A) · P(_____).

100. An urn contains 4 coins: a penny, two nickels and a dime. If two coins are selected without replacement, and event A is first coin selected is a nickel, while event B is second coin selected is a nickel, then events A and B are _____ events. To calculate P(A and B), one can use Probability Rule 6. This is written as: P(A and B) = P(A) · P(___). Calculating these probabilities, we have:

P(A) = P(first coin is a nickel) = _____.
P(B ∣ A) = P(second coin is nickel ∣ first coin is nickel) = _____ .

Thus, P(first coin is a nickel and second coin is a nickel)
= P(A and B)
= P(A) · P(B ∣ A)
= _____ .

101. Probability Rule 7: General Multiplication Rule states that for any two events A and B, the probability of A and B can be determined by either one of the following formulas: P(A and B) = P(A) · _____. This formula is read as: the probability of A and B is equal to the probability of A multiplied by the _____. Or the formula: P(A and B) = P(B) · _____.This formula is read as: the probability of A and B is equal to the probability of B multiplied by the _____.

102. Probability Rule 8: The Conditional Probability Formula states the probability of event A, given that event B has occurred equals the probability of event A ___ B divided by the probability of event _____. This is symbolized as:

$$P(\_\_\_) = \frac{P(A \text{ and } B)}{P(\_\_\_)}$$

103. The six chambers of a handgun randomly were filled with 4 blanks and 2 bullets. If the chambers are spun once, and the gun is fired twice in succession, then to calculate the probability a bullet is fired on the second shot given that the first shot was a blank is determined by using Probability Rule 8: The _____ Probability Formula. Thus,

P(second shot is a bullet ∣ first shot is a blank)

$$= \frac{P(\text{first shot is a blank and second shot is a bullet})}{P(_____)} = \frac{8/30}{\_\_\_\_}$$

= _____ .

104. For the Birthday Problem of Example 4.53, the complement rule is used to write: P(at least 2 people have the same birthday) = 1 − P(_____). If there are 35 people in a class, then the probability that at least 2 people have the same birthday is _____.

105. If two balls are selected one at a time from an urn, where the first ball is not placed back into the urn before the next ball is selected, then this selection process is called selection _____ _____. If the first ball is placed back into the urn before the selection of the next ball, then this selection process is called selection _____ _____.

106. The following table gives a breakdown of the students that attended the graduation picnic.

	BOYS	GIRLS	
5th Grade	24	29	53
6th Grade	18	29	47
	42	58	100

If a student is selected at random to be in charge of coordinating the games, what's the probability of:
a) The student selected being a girl?
b) The student selected is a girl if the student is a 5th grader?
c) The student selected is a 6th grader if the student selected is a boy?

107. From a regular deck of 52 cards, what's the probability of *blackjack* when selecting two cards without replacement? A blackjack has one ace and either a jack, queen, king or ten.

108. If a random drawing is performed and five letters are selected without replacement from the alphabet, determine the probability that:
a) The first three letters in order spell YES.
b) The first five letters in order spell GREAT.

109. A jar contains 5 red, 3 green, 4 blue and 2 yellow marbles. Four marbles are selected without replacement. Determine the probability of the following:
a) One marble of each color is selected.
b) Exactly three red marbles are selected.
c) Exactly two blue marbles are selected.

110. A five card poker hand is dealt to you. Determine the probability of the following:
a) The hand contains exactly 1 club?
b) The hand contains at least 1 diamond?

111. a) If two people are randomly selected and it is known that they are both born in October, what is the probability that they have the same birthday (day only)?
b) If three people are randomly selected and it is known that they are all born in April, what is the probability that their birthdays are all different?

c) What is the probability that at least two of these three people have the same April birthday?

112. Suppose a two child family is moving onto the block where you live.
   a) If you learn that not both children are girls, what is the probability that both children are boys?
   b) If you know that one child is a boy, what is the probability that the oldest child is a boy?
   c) If you learn that both children are of the same sex, what is the probability that both children are girls?

113. Craig, an investment advisor, has a portfolio of 90 stocks: 60 blue-chip and 30 growth stocks. Of the 60 blue-chip stocks, 40 have increased in price during the past month, and 25 of the 30 growth stocks have increased in price. If a stock is selected at random from the portfolio, what is the probability:
   a) It will be a growth stock that has not increased in price?
   b) If the stock has not increased in price, then it is a blue-chip stock?

114. The DPT Petroleum Enterprise exploring for oil decides to drill two wells, one after the other. Based upon their research of the area, the probability of striking oil with the first well is 0.31. Given the first attempt is successful, the probability of striking oil with the second well is 0.85. What is the probability of striking oil with both wells?

115. Vinny, the manager of a Baltimore baseball team, uses probability to help make crucial decisions during the game. In one such instance he estimated that the present pitcher had a 70% chance of getting the next batter out. However, his relief pitcher has a 95% chance of getting the batter out if he is at his best that day, but only a 45% chance if he is not. His pitching coach states that the relief pitcher has a 60% chance of being at his best.
   a) What is the probability of the relief pitcher getting the batter out?
   b) What should the manager's decision be if he uses probability to make his decisions?

CHAPTER REVIEW

116. The law that guarantees that the relative frequency of an event will begin to approach the actual probability of the event as the experiment is repeated many times is the:
   a) Law of averages
   b) Law of probability
   c) Law of large numbers
   d) Law of frequency

117. Find the probability of each of the following events:
   a) Selecting an eight by randomly choosing one card from a well shuffled deck containing 52 cards.
   b) Randomly selecting a lottery ticket beginning with the digit 5 from a bin containing lottery tickets numbered 00001 to 99999.
   c) Selecting the ace of hearts when randomly selecting one card from a deck of 52 cards.
   d) Randomly selecting your best friend's birthday from a bin containing all 365 days.
   e) Randomly selecting the correct answer to a five choice multiple choice question.
   f) Randomly selecting the winner of an eight horse race.

118. In the game of chuck-a-luck a participant wagers on the sum of two die to be above or below seven.
   a) What's the probability of the sum being below seven?
   b) What's the probability of the sum not being below seven?

119. From a regular deck of 52 cards, what's the probability of
   a) Selecting two picture cards with replacement.
   b) Selecting two picture cards without replacement.
   c) Selecting two cards with replacement whose face values are even numbers.

d) Selecting two cards without replacement whose face values are even numbers?

120. Lorenzo and Luigi play a game where they simultaneously exhibit their right hands with one, two, three or four fingers extended.
   a) List all the possible outcomes in the sample space. Determine the probability that:
   b) Both players extend the same number of fingers.
   c) Both players together extend an even number of fingers.
   d) Lorenzo shows an odd number of fingers.

121. A letter of the English alphabet is selected at random. Determine the probability that the letter selected:
   a) Is a consonant.
   b) Is a vowel (ie. a,e,i,o,u).
   c) Follows the letter k.
   d) Follows the letter k *and* is a vowel.
   e) Follows the letter k *or* is a vowel.
   f) Is one of the letters in the word "bushes".
   g) Is not in the word "bushes".
   h) Is one of the letters in the word "bushes" or the word "tushes".
   i) Is one of the letters in both the words "tushes" and "bushes."
   j) Is one of the letters in the word "bushes" but not in the word "tushes."

122. Four defective flashlight batteries are mistakenly mixed with two non-defective flashlight batteries which all look identical. If you randomly choose 2 batteries without replacement, what is the probability that:
   a) Exactly one is defective?

b) Both are defective?

c) Both are non-defective?

d) At most one is non-defective?

123. Determine whether the scenario is an example of classical, relative frequency, or subjective probability.

   a) If three cards: an ace, a deuce and a three are randomly placed face down then the probability that you correctly guess the ace is $1/3$.

   b) Madeline, a department manager, believes that if you speak quickly to a customer then the probability that you will make a sale is 90%.

   c) Debbie, a Bide-A-Wee volunteer, believes that the probability someone will adopt a lovable cat like her cat MEOW is $1/100$.

   d) Based on hospital records, women aged 35–44 have the highest percentage of Caesarean section births in the nation at 29.6%.

   e) According to Airline Quality Rating Survey, the chance that Southwest Airlines will depart on-time is 89.5%.

124. a) Write the letters of the word PIG in all possible three letter arrangements.

   b) Use the formula: $_nP_n = n!$ to compute the number of arrangements.

125. In how many ways can eight teachers be assigned to eight classrooms?

126. On the way to work Allison must pass through five traffic lights. How many different sequences of green, red could Allison observe as she drives to work?

127. If seven cars are entered in an auto race and only four cars can be placed in the front row, in how many ways can four cars be arranged in the front row?

128. Joe, the manager of an American League baseball team, decides to change the batting order of his present starting lineup to help his team get out of their slump. If he places the names of his present starting team in a hat and randomly selects the lineup, how many different batting orders can he select? If he decides to place the names of all sixteen non-pitching players in the hat and randomly draw a group of 9 players, how many different teams of 9 players can he choose?

129. Use Counting Rule 3 to determine the number of 5 letter arrangements for the letters in the word FUNNY.

130. In how many different ways can the letters in the word TOOTH be arranged?

131. A company wishes to issue ID plates to its employees.

   a) If they use a two letter code for each plate, how many different plates can be made?

   b) If no letter can be repeated in the same code, how many different plates can be made?

   c) If the code consists of two letters and one digit in the last position, now many different plates can be made?

   d) If the code consists of two letters and one digit in any order, how many different plates can be made?

132. How many different signals (hanging on a vertical line) can be made with 4 identical green flags, 3 identical blue flags and 3 identical red flags?

133. In a new version of *Master Blaster Brain* one of the players must construct a sequence of 15 colored pegs. There are 2 red, 4 green, 1 blue, 3 white, 2 yellow and 3 black pegs. How many different sequences can be made?

134. Amy has four cassettes to be played at a party.
   Cassette 1 contains songs from the early 60's
   Cassette 2 contains songs from the late 60's
   Cassette 3 contains songs from the 70's
   Cassette 4 contains songs from present day rock.

   a) How many ways can Amy play the cassettes? (Assuming once started a cassette is played to its completion).

   b) What is the probability that if the cassettes were randomly selected from a bag, the order would be cassette 1, cassette 2, cassette 3 and cassette 4?

   c) How many ways can Amy play the cassettes if cassette 1 must be played first?

   d) What is the probability that after playing cassette 1, cassette 2, 3 and 4 are played in that order?

   e) In how many ways can Amy pick two of the four cassettes?

   f) What is the probability that she chooses cassette 1 and 2 in that order?

135. If you remember the first five digits of a telephone number but you cannot recall the last two digits, what is the probability that you select the correct missing digits on your first guess?

136. Using six different *Scrabble* blocks with the letters *a, e, o, n, r, s* on them:

   a) How many six letter arrangements are possible?

   b) How many three letter arrangements are possible?

   c) If the 6 blocks are randomly arranged on a table, what is the probability that the word *reason* is spelled?

137. Of seven trees in a line, two are diseased. If any of the seven are equally likely to be affected, what is the probability that the diseased trees are side by side?

138. Calculate:

   a) $_4C_3$ **b)** $_7C_5$ **c)** $_{12}C_4$ **d)** $_{52}C_2$ **e)** $_{52}C_{13}$

139. In how many different ways can the I.R.S. select 7 tax returns to audit out of 50 tax returns?

140. Ten people meet at a pub. Find the number of handshakes that take place if each person shakes hands with everyone else in the group.

141. An urn contains 10 marbles. If there are 6 red marbles and 4 blue marbles, in how many ways can one choose 3 of these balls (one at a time) without replacement so that:

   a) None of the red marbles are selected?

   b) Exactly one of the blue marbles is selected?

   c) 1 red and 2 blue marbles are selected?

d) 3 marbles, regardless of color, are selected?

142. Mary, an intoxicated individual, has five keys on her key ring, one of which opens the front door to her house. If she randomly selected one key at a time and is unable to remember which keys she has already tried, what is the probability that:

    a) She selects the correct key for the front door on the first try?

    b) She selects the correct key for the front door on the second try?

    c) She selects the correct key for the front door on the third try?

    d) She selects the correct key for the front door within the first four tries?

143. In the casino game of CRAPS various wagers are made regarding the sum of the dice. A typical game begins when the "stickman" pushes two dice to a gambler and announces "new 'shooter' coming out." Then the shooter will start rolling the dice. On the first roll of the dice, three possible things can happen:

    a) A natural (a sum of 7 or 11) may be thrown. This is an outright win. Determine the probability of getting a natural.

    b) A craps (a sum of 2, 3, or 12) may be thrown. This is an outright loss. Determine the probability of getting a craps.

    c) A sum of 4, 5, 6 , 8, 9 or 10 may be thrown. In this case, the number you have rolled is your "point", and you then continue to roll the dice until either one of two things occur:

        1) your point is thrown again, in which case you win;

        2) a 7 is thrown, in which case you lose.

    If your point is a 4, what is the probability of making your point (i.e. rolling a 4 before rolling a 7)?

    d) If your point is a 5, what is the probability of making your point?

    e) If your point is an 8, what is the probability of making your point?

    f) One possible wager in the game of CRAPS is called the "pass line bet". This wager is won by either rolling a natural on the first roll or rolling a 4, 5, 6, 8, 9 or 10 and making the point on the subsequent rolls of the dice. Determine the possibility of winning the pass line bet. (Calculate your answer to 5 decimal places)

WHAT DO YOU THINK?

144. An article entitled "Behind Monty Hall's Doors: Puzzle, Debate and Answer?" appeared in the Sunday *New York Times* on July 21, 1991. The article discussed the debate that was raging among mathematicians, readers of the "Ask Marilyn" column of *Parade Magazine* and the fans of the TV game show "Let's Make a Deal." The argument began in September, 1990 when Ms. Vos Savant, who is listed in the Guinness Book of World Records Hall of Fame for the highest IQ, posed the following question in her "Ask Marilyn" column of *Parade Magazine*:

Suppose you're on a game show, and you're given the choice of three doors: Behind one door is a car; behind the others, goats. You pick a door, say No. 1, and the host, who knows what's behind the other doors, opens another door, say No. 3, which has a goat. He then says to you, 'Do you want to pick door No. 2?' Is it to your advantage to take the switch?

Since Ms. Vos Savant gave her answer, she has received approximately 10,000 letters with the great majority disagreeing with her answer. The most vehement from mathematicians and scientists who have called her the "goat." Her answer has been debated from the halls of the CIA to the mathematicians of MIT. Even Monty Hall conducted a simulation of the problem in his din-

ing room. After which Monty came to the conclusion that Ms. Vos Savant's critics were dead wrong when the host is required to open a door all the time and offer you a switch. However, Monty suggested since he has a choice on the show as to whether he allows the contestant the choice to switch or not, then the question cannot be answered without knowing the motivation of the host. As Monty Hall said: "If he (the host) has the choice whether to allow the switch or not, beware. Caveat emptor. It all depends on his mood. My only advice is, if you can get me to offer you $5,000 not to open the door, take the money and go home."

a) Monty Hall states in the article that the odds on the car being behind door No. 1 are still only 1 in 3 even after he opened another door to reveal a goat. Explain why this is true.

b) Some people argued with Ms. Vos Savant that if one door is shown to be a loser, that information changes the probability of either remaining choice—neither of which has any reason to be more likely—to 1/2. Explain why this is not correct reasoning.

c) Perform a simulation of this game with one of your friends by turning over three playing cards instead of opening doors and using the ace of diamonds as the prize. After doing this simulation 90 times, determine the chance of winning the car when the strategy is to switch doors. What did you get as the chance of winning the car when the strategy was not to switch doors? Are these results close to the actual probabilities?

145. "Tests for AIDS and Drugs: How Accurate Are They?" appeared in the "Ask Marilyn" column of *Parade Magazine* in the March 28, 1993 issue. The question posed was:

Suppose we assume 5% of the people are drug users. A test is 95% accurate, which we'll say means if a person is a user, the result is positive 95% of the time; and if she or he isn't, it's negative 95% of the time. A randomly chosen person tests positive. What is the probability the individual is a drug-user?

To help answer this question, let's assume the population consists of 10,000 people.
a) How many people are drug-users?
b) How many people are non-users?
c) How many of the non-users will test negative?
d) How many of the non-users will test positive?
e) How many of the drug-users will test negative?
f) How many of the drug-users will test positive?
g) How many are positive results?
h) How many are negative results?
i) How many of the positive results are drug-users?
j) How many of the positive results are non-users?
k) What is the probability that given a randomly chosen person tested positive, then the person is a drug-user?
l) What is the probability that given a randomly chosen person tested positive, then the person is a non-user?
m) What would happen to the results of parts (k) and (l) if the percent of drug users in the population was 2%, 1%, 0.5% or 0.25%? What happens as the percentage of drug-users gets closer to 0%?
n) What would happen to the results of parts (k) and (l) if the percent of accuracy for the test is increased from 95% to 98% or 99%? What effect does this have on the results?

146. The following question appeared in the "Ask Marilyn" column of *Parade Magazine* in the July 27, 1997 issue. The question posed was:

A woman and a man (unrelated) each have two children. At least one of the woman's children is a boy, and the man's older child is a boy. Do the chances that the woman has two boys equal the chances that the man has two boys?"

a) What do you think is the probability that the woman has two boys? Explain your answer.
b) What do you think is the probability that the man has two boys? Explain your answer.
c) What approach to defining probability did you use to arrive at the probabilities of part a and b? Explain.

d) This probability question caused much controversy when Marilyn Vos Savant printed her answer to the previous question. Some comments from her readers who felt that the woman and man had the same probability of having two boys were:

"I have lost nearly all my faith in you."

"This is not going to go away until you admit that you are wrong, wrong, wrong!!!"

"You are not the only genius to base your logic on a faulty major premise. Einstein did more than once."

Finally one reader even went as far as to challenge Marilyn to prove her case when the reader wrote:

"I will send $1000 to your favorite charity if you can prove me wrong. The chances of both the woman and the man having two boys are equal."

Marilyn asked her readers to help show why the woman and man have different probabilities of having two boys. She asked her woman readers to write or e-mail her if they have exactly two children (no more), and at least one of them is a boy (either child or both of them) to tell her the sex of both of the children. Marilyn said she would publish the results. What approach to defining probability is Marilyn using to argue her case? Explain.

e) How is this approach different to the one that you used to compute the probabilities in parts a and b?
f) Do you expect the probability results Marilyn will get from her survey to be exactly equal to the probabilities of parts a and b? Explain.
g) Explain how the *law of large numbers* could play an important role in Marilyn's approach to proving her case?

147. In a letter to the editor of the *New York Times* dated September 19, 1997 by Professors Charles Hailey and David Helfand of Columbia University concerning "TWA Flight 800 crash, don't discount meteor." Within their letter, the professors refer to an earlier article on TWA Flight 800 crash which reported that "more than once, senior crash investigators have tried to end the speculation by ranking the possibility of friendly fire at about the same level as that a meteorite destroyed the jet." However, the professors believe this comparison is based on a miscalculation of the probability that a meteorite could have caused the crash of Flight 800. On the other hand, the authors believe:

The odds of a meteor striking TWA Flight 800 or any other single airline flight are indeed small. However, the relevant calculation is not the likelihood of any particular aircraft being hit, but the probability that one commercial airliner over the last 30 years of high-volume air travel would be struck by an incoming meteor with sufficient energy to cripple the plane or cause an explosion.

They state:

Approximately 3,000 meteors a day with the requisite mass strike Earth. There are 50,000 commercial airline takeoffs a day worldwide. Adopting an average flight time of two hours, this translates to more than 3,500 planes in the air; these cover approximately two-billionths of Earth's surface. Multiplying this by the number of meteors per day and the length of the era of modern air travel leads to a 1-in-10 chance that a commercial flight would have been knocked from the sky by meteoric impact.

a) Do you think that the professors' numerical assumptions are reasonable? Explain.
b) What assumptions were made in the professors conclusion that there is a "1 in 10 chance that a commercial flight would have been knocked from the sky by meteoric impact"?
c) Using the same assumptions the professors did to obtain their "1 in 10 chance" do you come up with the same probability? Explain.
d) Based on the previous information, could you venture a guess at the chance that the Flight 800 was destroyed by friendly fire? That any commercial plane in the last 30 years was destroyed by friendly fire?

In a following letter to the *New York Times* dated September 24, 1996, by Guy Maxtone-Graham, he writes:

As any statistician can tell you, the outcome of past, random events has no bearing on future, unrelated random events. Toss a coin 10 times and the odds of getting heads or tails on the 11th toss are still 50–50. Likewise, calculations based on the number of flights worldwide, the number of takeoffs per day and the number of years that commercial flights have thrived have no bearing on the question of whether a rock from outer space happened to enter the atmosphere to hit one particular airliner on July 17. The odds of such a freak accident downing a specific flight remain small, and the professors' conclusion that "the meteor impact theory deserves more considered attention" is difficult to support.

e) Do you agree with the argument expressed in this letter?
f) In what has been called the "streak of streaks", Joe Dimaggio in 1941 got a hit in 56 successive games. Should you compute the probability that a typical player would achieve such a streak or that sometime in the history of baseball such a streak should occur? How would you estimate these probabilities?

In another letter to editor of the *New York Times* dated September 28, 1996 from Bill Grassman, he states:

Attempts to prove or disprove the probability that TWA Flight 800 was the victim of a meteor recall the tale of the business executive who, concerned that he might be on a plane with a bomb, commissioned a study to determine the odds of that happening. When the calculations of flights per day, when and where the bombings had occurred and the normal flying patterns of the executive disclosed that the odds of his being on a plane with a bomb were 1 in 13 million, he asked for the probability of his being on a plane with two bombs. On learning that this increased the odds to 1 in 42 billion, he always carried a bomb with him. Statistics!

g) Do you think the writer is criticizing statistics for saying this is true or criticizing those who misunderstand statistics?
h) How would you explain to your Uncle Carmine what is wrong with the executive's reasoning that he should carry a bomb?

148. A classic probability and logic problem: A missionary is captured by a tribe of cannibals who decide to have her for dinner. However, this tribe, being a more sporting group, decide to give the missionary a chance to save her life. They place before her two empty coconuts and twenty berries, ten red berries and ten blue berries. She must distribute *all* the berries as she pleases between the two coconuts, putting at least one berry in each coconut. The head cannibal will randomly choose one berry from the selected coconut. If the berry is blue, the missionary will be set free. However, if it is red, the missionary will be eaten for dinner.
a) How should the missionary distribute the berries to maximize her chances for freedom?
b) Using this distribution, what is the probability that she will be set free?

149. The following legendary problem from India prophesies the end of the world. In a great temple located at the center of the world, rests a brass plate in which are fixed three ivory rods. At the creation of the world, God placed sixty-four discs of pure gold on one of these rods with the largest disc resting on the brass plate and the remaining discs getting smaller and smaller up to the smallest disc at the top. This is referred to as the *Tower of Brahma.* Day and night, the priest on duty transfers the disc from one ivory rod to another adhering to the ancient laws of Brahma. These laws stipulate that the priest must move only one disc at a time, and he must place these discs on the rods so that there never is a smaller disc beneath a larger disc. When all the sixty-four discs have been transferred from the initial ivory rod, on which God placed them, to one of the other rods, the tower and temple will crumble into dust and with a thunderclap the world will vanish.

a) If there were only two discs on the initial rod, what is the *least* number of moves needed to transfer the discs from the initial rod to one of the other rods?

b) Determine the *least* number of moves using:
   1) three discs
   2) four discs
   3) five discs

c) Complete the following table and deduce a general rule to fit the pattern established in the table.

number of discs	least number of moves
1	1
2	
3	
4	
5	
.	
.	
.	
N	

d) Determine the least number of moves using 64 discs.

e) If the priests worked day and night, without stopping, making one move every second, how much time would it take for the priests to accomplish their task?

150. The following dialogue took place between the TV personality Monte Hall of *Let's Make a Deal* and a contestant.[4]

Monte Hall: One of the three boxes labeled A, B, and C contains the keys to that new 1975 Lincoln Continental. The other two are empty. If you choose the box containing the keys, you win the car.

Contestant: Gasp!

Monte Hall: Select one of the boxes.

Contestant: I'll take box B.

Monte Hall: Now box A and box C are on the table

[4]This problem was reprinted from *The American Statistician*, vol. 29. no. 1. February, 1975.

and here is box B (contestant grips box B tightly). Is it possible the car keys are in that box! I'll give you $100 for the box.

Contestant: No, thank you.

Monte Hall: How about $200?

Contestant: NO!

Audience: NO!

Monte Hall: Remember that the probability of your box containing the keys to the car is one-third and the probability of your box being empty is two-thirds. I'll give you $500.

Audience: NO!

Contestant: NO, I think I'll keep this box.

Monte Hall: I'll do you a favor and open one of the remaining boxes on the table (he opens box A).

Monte Hall: It's empty! (Audience: applause).

Now either box C or your box B contains the car keys. Since there are two boxes left, the probability of your box containing the keys is now one-half. I'll give you $1,000 cash for your box.

WAIT!!!!

Is Monte right? The contestant knows that at least one of the boxes on the table is empty. He now knows it was box A. Does this knowledge change his probability of having the box containing the keys from 1/3 to 1/2? One of the boxes on the table has to be empty. Has Monte done the contestant a favor by showing him which of the two boxes was empty?

a) Is the probability of winning the car 1/2 or 1/3?

Contestant: I'll trade you my box B for the box C on the table.

Monte Hall: That's weird!!

Do you agree with Monte that the contestant's proposal is "weird," or is the contestant making a logical choice?

b) What is the probability that box C contains the keys?

![PROJECTS]

151. Reread Example 4.53 *The Birthday Problem*. Ask 20 people to write a whole number between 1 and 100 inclusive onto a piece of paper. Fold the paper in half and put the folded paper into a large envelope. Before examining the results calculate the probability that at least two of the people have the same number.

152. Randomly survey (a) 10, (b) 40, (c) 70, and (d) 100 people within the election district that you live and ask them:

(1) Whether they are eligible voters within your election district?

(2a) If they answer yes to question number one, ask them to select the appropriate following statement.

I am registered in the following political party:
Democratic
Republican
Conservative

Liberal
Other

or

I am not registered for a political party.

(2b) If they answer no to question number one, exclude them from your survey. Use the probability formula:

$$P(\text{Event E}) = \frac{\text{number of outcomes satisfying Event E}}{\text{total number of outcomes}}$$

and your survey results to calculate the probability that a person chosen at random from your election district is a:

(a) Democrat, (b) Republican, (c) Conservative, (d) Liberal, (e) Not registered for a political party.

Contact the Board of Elections to determine the number of eligible voters in your election district and the actual number of democrats, republicans, conservatives, liberals and voters which are not registered for a political party within your election district. Using the Board of Election information, recalculate the above probabilities. Compare the survey probability results to the Board of Election probability results. Is there any relationship between the two as the survey size increases? Explain this relationship, if any exists.

ANALYZING THE DATABASE USING TECHNOLOGY

The following exercises refer to the file DATABASE listed in Appendix A. Using a technological tool answer each exercise.

153. Count the number of *each type* of categorical value for the variables:
   a) SEX
   b) MAJ
   c) EYE
   d) HR
   e) MOB

What is the probability of selecting each type of categorical value?

154. Construct a histogram for the variables:
   a) AGE
   b) GPA
   c) GFT
Use the histogram to determine the probability that a student selected at random:
   1) will be at least 19 years of age.
   2) will have a grade point average of 2.5.
   3) will spend at most $100 for a gift.

CHAPTER TEST

155. In New York State's numbers game, an individual chooses a 3 digit number to play the game. This 3 digit number can range from 000 to 999. What is the probability that Tony will win the game, if he selects:
   a) The number 123?
   b) The digits 4,2,7 in all possible arrangements?
   c) All numbers beginning with a 7?
   d) All numbers beginning with 46?
   e) All possible numbers using the digits 1,2,6?

156. A sociology class consists of 12 boys (5 tall, 6 average height, 1 short) and 18 girls (3 tall, 10 average height, 5 short). Suppose the name of each student is written on a slip of paper and placed in a box. After the slips are mixed vigorously, one slip is selected at random. What is the probability that the name on the slip is:
   a) A girl?
   b) A boy?
   c) A tall boy?
   d) A student of average height?
   e) A short girl or a tall boy?
   f) Not a student of average height?

157. An eight cylinder automobile engine has two defective spark plugs. If two plugs are removed from the engine, determine the probability of selecting:
   a) No defective plug.
   b) One defective plug.
   c) Two defective plugs.

158. Millie, a hat check girl, mistakenly mixes up the tickets on three hats. If she randomly places the mixed up tickets on the three hats, what is the probability that:
   a) Exactly one guest will receive the correct hat?
   b) Exactly all 3 guests will receive the correct hats?
   c) Exactly two guests will receive the correct hats?
   d) No one will receive the correct hat?

159. Classify whether each of the following events can be assigned a probability value using either classical, relative frequency or subjective approach to probability.
   a) Getting 2 heads in 3 tosses of a fair coin.
   b) A pregnant women will give birth to triplets.
   c) The Dow Jones Industrial Stock Index will increase at the close of the next trading day.
   d) The San Francisco 49ers winning the next Super Bowl.

e) A student will get a passing grade on her first exam in her freshman college introductory psychology course.

f) Getting 2 tails in 3 tosses of a biased coin.

g) A heart patient will successfully survive his bypass surgery.

h) Selecting a red card from an ordinary deck of 52 playing cards.

160. In how many ways can the officers for President, Treasurer and Secretary be filled from the 12 members of the ski club?

161. How many four letter arrangements can be made from ten different letters if:

a) Repetitions are allowed?

b) Repetitions are *not* allowed?

c) A letter can be used at most twice?

162. Matthew, a playboy, is returning to his penthouse on the thirteenth floor late one night. He is concerned that his expected date is already waiting for him in his penthouse. If seven other people get on the elevator with him and no two are together, and he knows that no one in the elevator besides himself is going to the penthouse, what is the probability that:

a) They all get off at different floors, thus delaying Matthew as long as possible?

b) All the other passengers get off at the same floor, thus delaying Matthew the least?

163. On the planet Krypton the calendar was almost identical to ours with the exception that every one of the twelve months had 30 days. What's the probability that the day the planet exploded was:

a) The thirteenth of the month?

b) A Friday?

c) A Friday given that it was the thirteenth?

d) The thirteenth given that it was a Friday?

164. Matt "The Magician" in his "three card Monte" act uses three colored cards. One is red on both sides, one is blue on both sides and the third is red on one side and blue on the other side. If one card is selected at random and the top side is red, what is the probability that the other side is also red?

165. The past weather records of a New England Airport indicate that the probability it will snow is 0.2. Given that it snows, the probability is 0.5 that the airplane will depart on time, and given it does not snow, the probability is 0.85 that the airplane will depart on time. Find the probability that:

a) It will snow and the plane will depart on time.

b) It will not snow and the plane will depart on time.

c) The plane will not depart on time.

CHAPTER 5

Random Variables and Discrete Probability Distributions

Contents

In Chapter 2, we discussed how a frequency distribution table was used to organize raw data into a more meaningful form to help describe the important characteristics of a distribution. A frequency distribution represents information pertaining to a situation that has already occurred. In Chapter 4, the concepts of probability allowed us to work with situations that have not yet occurred and where the outcomes are uncertain. In this chapter, we continue our study of probability by introducing the concept of a random variable and a probability distribution which examines all the possible values of an experiment and their associated probabilities. The emphasis of this chapter will be on a discrete random variable and its probability distribution. In particular, the binomial distribution will be presented as an example of an extremely useful discrete probability distribution.

5.1   INTRODUCTION

According to the Bureau of the Census, the latest family data pertaining to family size for a small midwestern town, Nomore, is shown in Table 5.1.

Table 5.1 shows that 43.19% of all the families within this town have a family containing 2 people, 22.76% of all family sizes have 3 people, while only 1.51% of the families have a total of 7 people within their family. The listing of all the possible family sizes with the respective proportion of families represents the probability distribution of family size. This probability distribution is useful in answering such questions as:

If a family from this town is selected **at random**, then what is the probability of selecting a 6-person family?

TABLE 5.1

Size of Family	Proportion (or percentage) of Families to the Total Number of Families
2 persons	0.4319 (or 43.19%)
3 persons	0.2276 (or 22.76%)
4 persons	0.2104 (or 21.04%)
5 persons	0.0868 (or 8.68%)
6 persons	0.0283 (or 2.83%)
7 persons	0.0151 (or 1.51%)

Using the probability distribution in Table 5.1, you can see that there is a 2.83% chance of randomly selecting a 6-person family. Because the family is being selected *at random,* and the size of the family can vary from 2 to 7, then family size is said to be a *random variable.* The proportion or percentage which is associated with each family size is interpreted as the *probability* of each value of family size. The concept of a random variable and a probability distribution will be examined in detail within the next two sections.

5.2   RANDOM VARIABLES

In Chapter 4, we developed techniques that allowed us to calculate the probability of rolling 4 consecutive sevens in four tosses of a pair of dice, or the probability of winning at least once in ten plays of the roulette wheel. In this chapter, we will discuss the numerical values associated with the outcomes of an experiment such as the **number** of heads when tossing a fair coin twice, or the **number** of sixes in five rolls of a die. Other experiments of this type are:

- the number of defective computer chips in a batch of 100 chips,
- the number of correct answers on a 35 question multiple choice test, or
- the life expectancy of a 21 year old female.

In each one of these situations, we can associate different numbers with the *uncertain outcomes* of the experiment. For instance, the number of defective computer chips within a batch of 100 chips can be represented by a whole number from 0 to 100, while the number of correct answers on a 35 question multiple choice test can vary from 0 to 35.

The experiment of determining the number of defective chips in a batch of 100 is considered a **random experiment** since *the outcome of this experiment cannot be predicted with any certainty.* Thus, the number of defective chips is determined by chance, and can be any of the following 101 possible values:

$$0, 1, 2, 3, \ldots, 99, 100.$$

If we let *X represent the number of defective computer chips within the batch,* then X can assume any one of these possible 101 values. Until each batch is tested, we are **uncertain** of the actual number of defective chips that will be found so that the number of defective chips may vary from batch to batch. For example, testing one batch of 100 computer chips could result in detecting three defective chips within the batch. This is denoted as X = 3. If the next batch were to produce only one defective chip, then the value of X would change to X = 1. As each batch of 100 chips is tested, the value of X will assume one of the possible 101 values, and probably represent a different value. Consequently, we say that the number of defective chips within the batch, denoted by X, is a *random variable* since **the**

value of X can vary from batch to batch and is not known until the batch is tested. The numbers associated with this experiment:

$$0, 1, 2, 3, \ldots, 99, 100$$

represent the values of the random variable.

DEFINITION 5.1

A **random variable** is a variable that takes on different numerical values which are determined by chance.

The random variables are usually denoted by capital letters such as X, Y, and Z. Example 5.1 illustrates this idea of a random variable.

EXAMPLE 5.1

For each random experiment, define a random variable and identify the possible values of the variable.
a) If it is assumed that the largest number of children is 6, count the number of children within a family for a small town.
b) Select a radial tire from the production line and determine the life of the tire, assuming no tire has ever lasted less than 20,000 miles or more than 85,000 miles.
c) Count the number of heads in two tosses of a fair coin.

Solution

a) For the random experiment of counting the number of children within a family in this small town, the random variable is the number of children. If we let X denote the number of children, then the seven possible values of X are:

$$X = 0, 1, 2, 3, 4, 5, \text{ or } 6 \text{ children.}$$

b) For the random experiment of selecting a radial tire from the production line, the random variable is the life of the tire. The possible values are infinite, since the tire selected can last any mileage from 20,000 to 85,000 miles including tenths, hundredths etc. of a mile. Letting Y equal the life of the tire, the value of Y can be any number greater than or equal to 20,000 but less than or equal to 85,000. The values of Y can be expressed as:

$$20{,}000 \leq Y \leq 85{,}000.$$

c) For the random experiment of tossing a fair coin twice, the number of heads is the random variable. There are three possible outcomes when counting the number of heads in two tosses, they are:

> both tosses land heads (or 2 heads),
> only one toss lands heads (1 head), or
> neither toss lands heads (0 heads).

Thus, if we let X denote the number of heads, then the possible values of X are: $X = 0, 1, \text{ or } 2$ heads.

A random variable can be classified as either a *discrete* or *continuous* random variable depending upon the numerical values that it can assume. In Example 5.1, the number of children in a family is an example of a *discrete random variable* because the values of this variable: 0, 1, 2, 3, 4, 5, and 6 are *finite or can be counted.*

> **DEFINITION 5.2**
> A **discrete random variable** is a random variable that can take on a finite or countable number of values.

Some examples of a *discrete* random variable are:

- the number of correct answers on a 35 question multiple choice test
- the number of people attending the performance of a Broadway play
- the number of earrings a person wears
- the number of students who come to class late
- the number of cars involved in an accident at an intersection
- the daily closing price of a stock on the New York Stock Exchange

To determine a value for most of these random variables, you would have to count the number of items or people or things that would satisfy the random variable. For example, to determine the number of correct answers on a 35 question test, you would **count the number correct**, or to determine the number of people attending the performance of a Broadway play, you would **count the number of people** attending the performance. Consequently, we say that the possible numerical values of a discrete random variable usually represent a **count.** Therefore, these possible values of a discrete random variable can only represent **a limited number of values** which have a **break between successive values**. Recall that the number of correct answers a student gets on a 35 question multiple choice test represents a **count** which could result, say, in 20 correct, or possibly 21 correct. However, it is ***impossible** for the student to get a number **between** 20 and 21 correct*. The fact that there is *a **break between** successive values* of this *random variable* (between 20 and 21) is the **characteristic** that distinguishes it as a **discrete random variable**. Not all discrete random variables have values that represent a count. The values of the daily closing price of a stock *are limited and have a break between successive values.* For example, if the closing price of the stock ranged from $42 to $43 for the day, then it could only assume these limited values: $42, $42⅛, $42¼, $42⅜, $42½, $42⅝, $42¾, $42⅞, or $43. Notice the values of this discrete random variable have breaks between successive values such as $42¼ and $42⅜.

On the other hand, a random variable that *measures* the life of a radial tire is an example of a *continuous random variable.* It represents *an uncountable number of values* since it can take on ***all values** between any two possible values* of the variable.

> **DEFINITION 5.3**
> A **continuous random variable** is continuous if the value of the random variable can assume any value or an uncountable number of values between any two possible values of the variable.

The values of continuous random variables represent measurements. In measuring the life of a radial tire or the amount of time a person watches MTV, the number of different values that the variable can assume between any two possible values of the variable are uncountable. For example, the number of hours a person watches MTV could possibly be **measured to be any value** between 2 hours and 2.5 hours. Some such possible values are:

2.41 hrs, or 2.401 hrs, or 2.4001 hrs, or 2.40001 hrs, etc.

Since it is impossible to list all these values, we use the inequality symbol < to express the values of a continuous variable. Thus, if we let X = the number of hours a person watches MTV, then to represent all the values between 2.0 and 2.5, we would write: $2.0 < X < 2.5$.

Although we may record the number of hours a person watches MTV as a whole number, the random variable is treated as a continuous variable since **it can assume an uncountable number of values**. Thus, any random variable that can be measured such as height, weight, time, temperature or speed are considered continuous even though they might be recorded as a whole number or to a particular decimal place.

Some examples of a *continuous* random variable are:

- the amount of time needed to travel to college
- the height of a person
- the amount of iced tea in a 16 oz bottle
- the temperature in Central Park at noon
- the amount of rainfall during the year in San Francisco

EXAMPLE 5.2

For each random variable, state whether it is discrete or continuous.
a)   The life of a 32 inch color picture tube.
b)   The number of telephone calls arriving at a college switchboard during the day.
c)   The number of employees that are absent from work at a steel manufacturing plant during a summer day.
d)   The thickness of a multivitamin tablet.

Solution

a)   Since the life of a 32 inch color picture tube can last say 5.1 years or 5.01 or even 5.001 years, it is a continuous variable. The values represent an amount of time which can assume an uncountable number of values.
b)   The number of telephone calls is discrete because there can only be a finite or countable number of calls arriving at the switchboard during the day.
c)   If there are 300 people that work at this plant, then the possible number of employees that can be absent is: 0, 1, 2, . . . , 300. Since these represent a finite or countable number of values, the number of employees that are absent from work is a discrete random variable.
d)   The thickness of a multivitamin tablet is a continuous random variable since it represents a measurement of its width which can assume an uncountable number of values.

CASE STUDY 5.1   Random Variables

Examine each graphic or table shown in Figure 5.1. Each graphic or table presents a random variable.
  For each graphic or table,
  a) Describe each random variable being illustrated.
  b) State whether the random variable is discrete or continuous.
  c) Indicate two non-consecutive possible values of the random variable. Identify these values on a number line.
  To identify all the possible values of the random variable between these two values on the number line, could you highlight these values using separate dots or would you need a darken line to represent all the values? What does this indicate about the type of random variable? Explain your answer.

CASE STUDY 5.1   Random Variables (continued)

Statistical Snapshots

(a)   The Facts of Long Island Life

How many scoops of ice cream do you typically eat in a week?

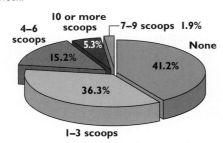

- 10 or more scoops
- 4–6 scoops
- 7–9 scoops 1.9%
- 5.3%
- 15.2%
- None 41.2%
- 36.3%
- 1–3 scoops

Source: Responses are from a Newsday-Hofstra poll that was conducted March 6–28 by telephone with 802 Long Island residents. The margin of error is plus or minus 3.5 percentage points.
Reprinted by permission of Tribune Media Services.

(b)   How Many Telephones We Have

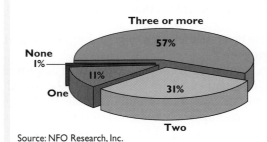

- Three or more 57%
- None 1%
- One 11%
- Two 31%

Source: NFO Research, Inc.

(c)   Age of Foreign-car Shopper

Half of U.S. adults say they would consider buying a foreign-made car. Percentage by age group:

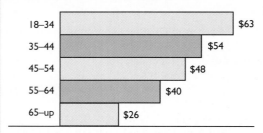

Age	Value
18–34	$63
35–44	$54
45–54	$48
55–64	$40
65–up	$26

*ICR for Japan Automobile Manufacturers Association

(d)   Beer Consumption

More than half the adults over the age of 21 had at least one serving of beer during the past month. Beer drinkers average 18.7 servings per month. Servings per month by age:

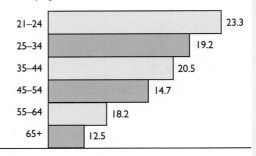

Age	Servings
21–24	23.3
25–34	19.2
35–44	20.5
45–54	14.7
55–64	18.2
65+	12.5

Note: A serving equals 12 ounces
*Source: Maritz AmeriPoll

(e)   Who's Got Mail?

Average number of e-mail received daily:

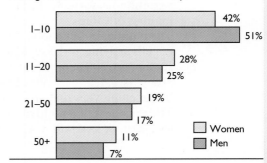

	Women	Men
1–10	42%	51%
11–20	28%	25%
21–50	19%	17%
50+	11%	7%

(f)   Who's Losing Sleep

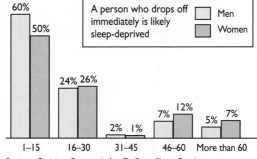

A person who drops off immediately is likely sleep-deprived

	Men	Women
1–15	60%	50%
16–30	24%	26%
31–45	2%	1%
46–60	7%	12%
More than 60	5%	7%

Source: Opinion Research for DuPont Sleep Products

In most experiments, we are interested in determining all the possible values of a random variable and the probability associated with each value. Such a listing is called a *probability distribution*. In this chapter, we will examine the concepts of a discrete probability distribution. In the next chapter, we will examine the idea of a continuous probability distribution.

5.3 PROBABILITY DISTRIBUTION OF A DISCRETE RANDOM VARIABLE

We will now examine how to assign probabilities to the values of a discrete random variable. A distribution that displays all the possible values of a random variable and the probability associated with each value of the random variable is called a probability distribution.

DEFINITION 5.4

A **probability distribution** is a distribution which displays the probabilities associated with all the possible values of a random variable.

Let's examine this idea of a probability distribution and determine how to generate a probability distribution for a discrete random variable.

To begin let's consider the experiment of tossing a fair coin twice. There are four possible outcomes for this experiment. If we are interested in counting the number of heads obtained on the two tosses of the fair coin, then each of these four outcomes can be classified within one of the 3 possible values: 0 heads, 1 head or 2 heads as illustrated in Table 5.2.

TABLE 5.2   Possible Outcomes of Two Tosses of a Fair Coin Where H Represents a Head and T is a Tail

First Toss	Second Toss	Number of Heads	Probability
H	H	2	$\frac{1}{4}$
H	T	1	$\frac{1}{4}$
T	H	1	$\frac{1}{4}$
T	T	0	$\frac{1}{4}$

Notice there is only one way to obtain 2 heads (HH), two ways to get 1 head (HT and TH), and one way to obtain no heads (TT). For a fair coin, the probability of each outcome is ¼, since each outcome is equally-likely. This is shown in the last column of Table 5.2.

Since we are interested in the number of heads obtained when a fair coin is tossed twice, we can construct another table which just lists *the possible number of heads along with their associated probabilities*. For this experiment, the number of heads can be categorized into the following three possible values: **2 heads, 1 head and no heads**. Table 5.3, which displays these possible number of heads along with their associated probabilities, is the **probability distribution of the number of heads in two tosses of a fair coin**. Notice the two column headings of the probability distribution of Table 5.3, the possible values of the number of heads is symbolized by X while the associated probabilities are denoted by P(X).

TABLE 5.3   Probability Distribution of Number of Heads in Two Tosses of a Fair Coin

Number of Heads X	Probability P(X)
0	$\frac{1}{4}$ or 0.25
1	$\frac{2}{4}$ or 0.50
2	$\frac{1}{4}$ or 0.25

You should realize that Table 5.3 *doesn't represent the actual outcomes* of tossing a fair coin twice, rather it is a **theoretical model of the possible number of heads** which indicates what we would **expect to happen in the long-run** in two tosses of a fair coin. This is the idea of a probability distribution.

It is helpful to graph a probability distribution of a random variable since this helps to visualize the probability distribution. The graph of a probability distribution is accomplished by scaling the possible values of the random variable on the horizontal axis and the corresponding probability values along the vertical axis. For example, the information contained in Table 5.3 can also be displayed graphically using a histogram as shown in Figure 5.2. This histogram is called a *probability histogram.*

DEFINITION 5.5

A **probability histogram** is a histogram representing a probability distribution. The values of the discrete random variable are scaled along the horizontal axis, while the corresponding probability values are scaled along the vertical axis.

Notice, in Figure 5.2, that the values on the horizontal axis represent the number of heads, denoted as X, and are placed at the center of the base of each bar. While the height of each bar equals the probability for the value of X. For example, the height of the bar pertaining to the value X = 0 is 0.25 because the probability of 0 heads is 0.25 (that is P(0 heads) = 0.25).

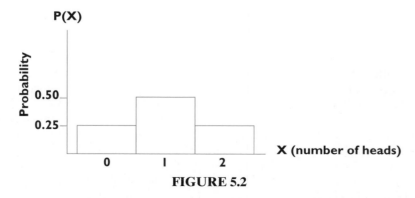

FIGURE 5.2

The probability histogram in Figure 5.2 is a graph of a probability distribution of the number of heads for two tosses of a fair coin. Notice that the probability distribution of the number of heads in two tosses of a fair coin can be displayed by a table as illustrated by Table 5.3 as well as a graph as shown in Figure 5.2. *In general, the probability distribution of a discrete random variable can be defined using a table, a graph or a formula.* We will consider the formula approach when we examine a **discrete probability distribution** called the binomial distribution in a subsequent section of this chapter.

EXAMPLE 5.3

Consider the experiment of tossing a fair coin until a head appears, or until the coin has been tossed three times, whichever occurs first.
a) Construct a probability distribution for the number of tails.
b) Construct a probability histogram for this probability distribution.
c) Using the probability histogram, what is the probability of getting no tails?

Solution

a) There are four possible outcomes for this experiment. They are:

Head on 1st toss, represented as H,
Tail on 1st toss and a Head on 2nd toss, written TH
Tail on 1st two tosses and a Head on 3rd toss, denoted TTH,
Tail on all three tosses, symbolized as TTT.

If X represents the number of tails, then the possible values of X are: 0, 1, 2, or 3 tails.
    Since the probability of getting a head is ½, and the probability of getting a tail is also ½, then the probabilities for each of these values of X are shown in Table 5.4.

TABLE 5.4

Number of Tails X	Possible outcomes	Probability P(X)
0	H	$\dfrac{1}{2}$
1	TH	$\dfrac{1}{2}\cdot\dfrac{1}{2}=\dfrac{1}{4}$
2	TTH	$\dfrac{1}{2}\cdot\dfrac{1}{2}\cdot\dfrac{1}{2}=\dfrac{1}{8}$
3	TTT	$\dfrac{1}{2}\cdot\dfrac{1}{2}\cdot\dfrac{1}{2}=\dfrac{1}{8}$

The probability assigned to the probability of 1 tail, written P(X = 1), is ¼ which was determined by multiplying the probability of a tail by the probability of a head. This is shown in the third row of Table 5.4. The probability assigned to the probability of 2 tails, written P(X = 2), is ⅛ which was determined by multiplying the probability of a tail by the probability of a tail by the probability of a head. This is shown in the fourth row of Table 5.4. Finally, the probability assigned to the probability of 3 tails, written P(X = 3), is ⅛ which was determined by multiplying the probability of a tail by the probability of a tail by the probability of a tail. This is shown in the last or fifth row of Table 5.4. Thus, the probability distribution for the number of tails is given in Table 5.5.
b) For this probability distribution, the discrete random variable is the number of tails which is scaled along the horizontal axis from 0 to 3. The probability values corresponding to the number of tails are scaled along the vertical axis from 0 to ⅛. The value of the discrete random variable,

TABLE 5.5   Probability Distribution of Number of Tails

Number of Tails X	Probability P(X)
0	$\dfrac{1}{2}$
1	$\dfrac{1}{4}$
2	$\dfrac{1}{8}$
3	$\dfrac{1}{8}$

the number of tails, is placed at the center of each bar of the histogram while the bar's height is equal to the probability of the variable. The probability histogram for this probability distribution is shown in Figure 5.3.

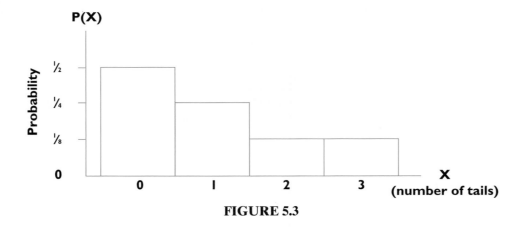

FIGURE 5.3

c)   From the probability histogram in Figure 5.3, the probability of getting no tails is equal to the height of the bar pertaining to 0 tails which is ½. Thus, the probability of getting no tails is ½.

In Figure 5.3, notice *the probability assigned to each value of the discrete random variable, number of tails, is a number between 0 and 1.* The probability values of this probability distribution are: ⅛, ¼, and ½. In addition, *notice that the sum of all the probabilities of this discrete probability distribution is equal to one.* From Figure 5.3, the sum of the probabilities of the probability distribution is:

$$\frac{1}{2}+\frac{1}{4}+\frac{1}{8}+\frac{1}{8}=1.$$

These observations represent two important characteristics of a probability distribution of a discrete random variable. Let's summarize these characteristics of a probability distribution.

Characteristics of a Probability Distribution of a Discrete Random Variable

1. The probability associated with a particular value of a discrete random variable of a probability distribution is always a number between 0 and 1 inclusive.
2. The sum of all the probabilities of a probability distribution must always be equal to one.

EXAMPLE 5.4

The graph below illustrates the lifestyle of a popular newspaper's business travelers while on the road. Their study entitled "What it's like to be a Road Warrior" appeared in the January 19, 1993 issue. One pie chart which appeared in the article is shown in Figure 5.4. The pie chart describes the number of times that the business traveler calls home per day.

Statistical Snapshot

...and Call Home
Number of calls per day

Four or more 1%
Three calls 4%
Two calls 16%
None 10%
One Call 69%

FIGURE 5.4

Using this information,
a) Identify the discrete random variable being presented in the pie chart,
b) Construct a probability distribution for this variable,
c) Construct a probability histogram for this probability distribution,
d) Find the sum of the probabilities for this probability distribution. Did you expect this result? Explain.

Solution

a) The number of times a business traveler calls home per day is the discrete random variable.
b) To construct a probability distribution for the number of times a business traveler calls home per day, we need to list all the possible values of the variable along with the respective probabilities. According to the pie chart in Figure 5.4, the possible values of the variable are: 0, 1, 2, 3, or 4. To determine the probabilities associated to each of these values of the random variable, we can use the percentages which accompany the values since they represent a reasonable estimate of the likelihood that each value will occur in the future. For example, since 69% of the business travelers called home once, then we will use 69% or 0.69 to represent the probability that a business

TABLE 5.6   Probability Distribution for the number of times a business traveler calls home per day

Number of Calls to Home per Day X	Probability P(X)
0	0.10
1	0.69
2	0.16
3	0.04
4	0.01

traveler will call home once per day while on a business trip. Thus, the probability distribution for the number of times a business traveler calls home per day is shown in Table 5.6.

c)   For this probability distribution, the discrete random variable, which is the number of calls per day, is scaled along the horizontal axis from 0 to 4. The probability corresponding to the number of calls are scaled along the vertical axis from 0 to 0.69. The value of the variable, the number of calls, is placed at the center of each bar of the histogram while the bar's height is equal to the probability associated to each value of the variable. The probability histogram for this probability distribution is shown in Figure 5.5.

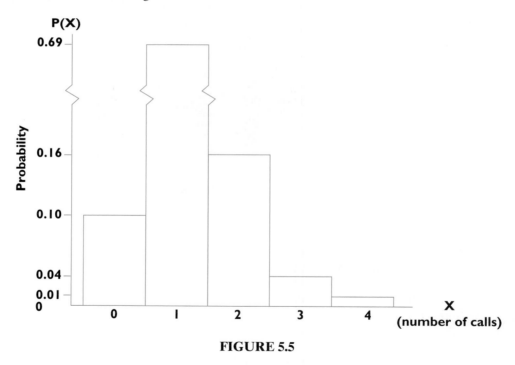

FIGURE 5.5

d)   The sum of all the probabilities for the probability distribution are:

sum of the probabilities = 0.10 + 0.69 + 0.16 + 0.04 + 0.01
= 1.00.

This result is expected since one of the properties of a discrete probability distribution is the sum of all the probabilities is equal to one.

Before we discuss other aspects of a probability distribution, you should observe that a probability distribution can be constructed in different ways. One is on the basis of theoretical considerations like the tossing of a fair coin as illustrated in both Table 5.3 and Example 5.3. Another probability distribution is established on the basis of experience and observation as discussed in Example 5.4. In addition, a probability distribution can also be based on subjective judgments of the likelihood of the possible values of the discrete random variable. At this point, we should explain the difference between a frequency distribution and a probability distribution. A frequency distribution is a listing of all the observed values and frequencies of an experiment that was already conducted; whereas, a probability distribution represents a list of all the possible outcomes of an experiment that could result when the experiment is eventually conducted. Probability distributions will serve as models of experiments. If we can find a probability distribution model that accurately fits the experiment then we can use the probability values of the model to draw conclusions or make inferences from the probability distribution.

EXAMPLE 5.5

According to the latest Census Bureau, 40% of all families have only one child. Consider the experiment of randomly selecting two families from the population of all U.S. families. Let X represent the number of families having only one child in this sample.
a) Construct a sample space for this experiment.
b) Determine the probability for each outcome in the sample space.
c) Construct a probability distribution for the discrete random variable X.
d) Construct a probability histogram for the discrete random variable X.
e) What is the probability that both families selected at random will have only one child?

Solution

a) Since X represents the number of families having only one child, then there are four possible outcomes for this sample of two families. These four outcomes are illustrated in Figure 5.6 where H represents a family having only one child while D represents that the family doesn't have only one child.

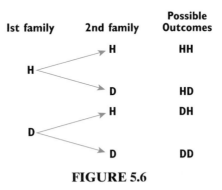

FIGURE 5.6

From Figure 5.6, the four possible outcomes are:

   HH: both families have only one child
   HD: first family selected has only one child, but second family selected doesn't have only one child.
   DH: second family selected has only one child, but first family selected doesn't have only one child.
   DD: both families have only one child.

b) To compute the probability for each of these outcomes, we need to use the Census Bureau information that 40% of all families have only one child. Thus, the probability that a family has only one child is 0.40, while the probability that a family doesn't have only one child is 0.60 (or 1 – 0.40). For a sample of two randomly selected families, the number of possible families that have only one child, denoted by X, can be classified into the three values:

$$X = 0, X = 1, \text{ or } X = 2.$$

The probability for each of these possible values of X are calculated as follows.

$$P(X = 0) \; = \; P(DD) = (0.60)(0.60)$$
$$\mathbf{P(X = 0) \; = \; 0.36}$$
$$P(X = 1) \; = \; P(HD \text{ or } DH)$$
$$= \; P(HD) + P(DH)$$
$$= \; (0.40)(0.60) + (0.60)(0.40)$$
$$= \; 0.24 + 0.24$$
$$\mathbf{P(X = 1) \; = \; 0.48}$$
$$P(X = 2) \; = \; P(HH) = (0.40)(0.40)$$
$$\mathbf{P(X = 2) \; = \; 0.16}$$

c) Assigning these probabilities to the respective possible values of X, the probability distribution of the number of families having only one child for a sample of two families is shown in Table 5.7.

TABLE 5.7   Probability Distribution For the Number of Families Having only one child

Number of Families Having Only One Child X	Probability P(X)
0	0.36
1	0.48
2	0.16

d) A probability histogram representing the number of families having only one child is constructed where the values of the number of families are scaled along the horizontal axis from 0 to 2. While the corresponding probability values are scaled along the vertical axis from 0 to 0.48. The value of the variable, the number of families having only one child, is placed at the center of each bar of the histogram while the bar's height is equal to the probability of the variable. The probability histogram for this probability distribution is shown in Figure 5.7.

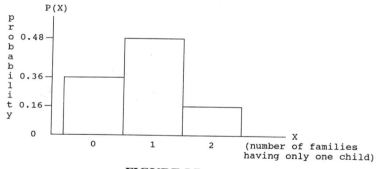

FIGURE 5.7

e)   The probability that both families selected at random will have only one child is 0.16 is equal to the height of the bar representing X = 0 as shown in Figure 5.7. Thus, the P(X = 0) = 0.16.

5.4   MEAN AND STANDARD DEVIATION OF A DISCRETE RANDOM VARIABLE

In the previous section, we examined the probability distribution for a discrete random variable. For example, we examined the number of times a business traveler calls home per day or the number of families having only one child in a sample of two families. In each of these probability distributions, a model of all the possible values of the discrete random variable along with their associated probabilities was used. Furthermore, a probability histogram was used to graphically describe the probability distribution. Now, we would like to examine the numerical measures such as the mean and the standard deviation that will help us describe the main characteristics of the distribution. Remember that the mean and the standard deviation are used to describe the center value and the variability or spread of a distribution. In this section, we will learn how to find and interpret the mean and the standard deviation of a discrete probability distribution.

The Mean Value of a Discrete Random Variable

Table 5.8 presents the probability distribution for the number of televisions per family in Poorrich, Kansas.

TABLE 5.8

Number of TV's Per Family X	Probability of the Number of TV's Per Family P(X)
0	0.05
1	0.35
2	0.40
3	0.13
4	0.07

From the information in Table 5.8, can you estimate the number of televisions a typical family in Poorrich, Kansas owns? Such an estimate can be considered to be a measure of a central tendency of the probability distribution. As discussed in Chapter 3, the *mean* represents a measure of the center of a distribution and serves as the balance point of the distribution. Thus, we can estimate the mean or typical number of televisions by trying to identify the center or balance point of the probability distribution. Examine the histogram of the probability distribution for the number of TV's per family in Poorrich, Kansas in Figure 5.8a and try to estimate the position of the balance point of the probability distribution.

At what value of the random variable, X, do you think the balance point lies? That is, at what value of the random variable, X, could we place a fulcrum which would balance the probability histogram of Figure 5.8a? Figure 5.8b shows the effect of trying to balance the distribution by placing the fulcrum under the value of X = 1 along the x axis. However, this is not the balance point since the distribution tilts down to the right. Figure 5.8c indicates the effect of placing the fulcrum under the value of X = 3. In this case the probability distribution tilts down to the left. Using the histogram, can you estimate a placement for the fulcrum so that the distribution would be balanced? The value of the mean for the probability distribution is the value of X along the horizontal axis that corresponds to the fulcrum's position that balances the histogram.

FIGURE 5.8a

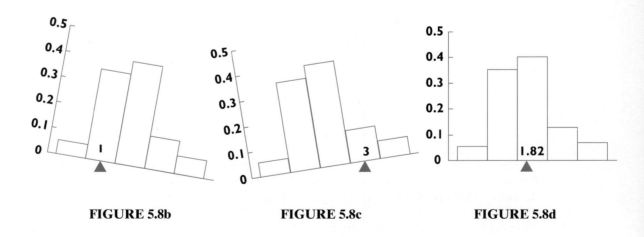

FIGURE 5.8b   **FIGURE 5.8c**   **FIGURE 5.8d**

In trying to determine this balance point for the histogram of Figure 5.8a, the height of each bar which represents the **probability weight** for each value of the random variable has to be taken into consideration. The mean value of a probability distribution is the balance point which takes into account the **weights** or **the probability for each value of the random variable**. Thus, we will refer to the mean value for a discrete random variable as a *weighted mean.*

From the probability histogram of Figure 5.8a, an estimate of the mean value or the balance point of the distribution happens to fall between 1.5 and 2. To compute the actual mean or balance point of a probability distribution, use the following formula.

The Mean of a Discrete Random Variable X

The mean of a discrete random variable X denoted by μ, is computed by *multiplying* each possible X value of the discrete random variable by its probability, P(X), and then *adding* all the resulting products: *XP(X)*. In symbols, the formula for the mean is:

$$\mu = \sum_{\substack{\text{all possible} \\ X \text{ values}}} (X \text{ value}) \cdot (\text{probability of } X)$$

$$\mu = \sum_{\substack{\text{all possible} \\ X \text{ values}}} X \cdot P(X)$$

Using this formula to determine the mean number of TV's per family for the probability distribution in Table 5.8, we can use the following procedure.

First, substitute each possible value of the random variable X into the formula for the mean:

$$\mu = \sum_{\substack{\text{all possible} \\ X \text{ values}}} X \cdot P(X).$$

Since the possible X values are: 0, 1, 2, 3, and 4, then we have:

$$\mu = 0P(0) + 1P(1) + 2P(2) + 3P(3) + 4P(4)$$

Second, substitute the probability value, P(X), corresponding to each X value into the formula.

$$\mu = 0(0.05) + 1(0.35) + 2(0.40) + 3(0.13) + 4(0.07)$$

Third, calculate the value of each product.

$$\mu = 0 + 0.35 + 0.80 + 0.39 + 0.28$$

Fourth, add up these products to obtain the mean.

$$\mu = 1.82.$$

Thus, **the mean number of TV's per family is 1.82.**

Examining the probability histogram in Figure 5.8d, we now know that the balance point is 1.82, since this is the mean value of the number of televisions. This mean value signifies that the typical family in Poorrich, Kansas has 1.82 televisions. This doesn't suggest that each family has *exactly* 1.82 televisions. Instead, the mean value of 1.82 televisions is the average number of televisions that can be **expected** per family in the long-run. For this reason this value is also referred to as the expected value. That is, if we repeatedly selected families at random living in Poorrich, Kansas and counted the number of televisions they have within their household, then, as the number of families selected gets larger and larger, the average number of televisions will approach 1.82. Therefore, in the long-run, we would expect an average value of 1.82 televisions to occur. The mean value is not necessarily a possible value of the random variable, it is an expected value that measures the typical number of televisions per family. Thus, in this case, some families will have less than 1.82 televisions, while some families will have more than 1.82 televisions, but no families will have exactly 1.82 televisions.

EXAMPLE 5.6

Consider the experiment of tossing a fair coin until a head appears, or until the coin has been tossed three times, whichever occurs first. Table 5.9 lists the outcomes and the probability distribution for this experiment. What is the expected or mean number of tosses of the coin for this experiment?

TABLE 5.9

Number of Tosses X	Possible Outcomes	Probability P(X)
1	H	$\frac{1}{2}$
2	TH	$\frac{1}{4}$
3	TTH or TTT	$\frac{1}{8}+\frac{1}{8}=\frac{1}{4}$

Solution

To find the expected or mean number of tosses of the probability distribution in Table 5.9, use the formula for the mean of a discrete variable.

To determine the mean value using the formula:

$$\mu = \sum_{\substack{all\ possible \\ X\ values}} X \cdot P(X)$$, we will use the following procedure.

First, substitute each value of the random variable X into the formula for the mean:

$$\mu = \sum_{\substack{all\ possible \\ X\ values}} X \cdot P(X).$$

Since the possible X values are: X = 1, X = 2, and X = 3, then we obtain:

$$\mu = 1P(1) + 2P(2) + 3P(3)$$

Second, substitute the probability value, P(X), corresponding to each X value into the formula.

$$\mu = 1(\frac{1}{2}) + 2(\frac{1}{4}) + 3(\frac{1}{4})$$

Third, calculate the value of each product, and sum up these products.

$$\mu = \frac{1}{2} + \frac{2}{4} + \frac{3}{4}$$

Fourth, add up these products to obtain the mean.

$$\mu = \frac{7}{4} \text{ or } 1.75 \text{ tosses}$$

Thus, the expected or mean number of tosses for this coin tossing experiment is 1.75. That is, if we were to repeat this coin tossing experiment many, many times then we would expect the long-run average number of tosses to be 1.75.

Let's now summarize the procedure used to calculate the mean of a discrete random variable.

Procedure to Calculate the Mean (or expected value) of a Discrete Random Variable Using the Formula:

$$\mu = \sum_{\substack{all\ possible \\ X\ values}} X \cdot P(X)$$

Step 1 Substitute each value of the random variable X into the formula for the mean.
Step 2 Substitute the probability value, P(X), corresponding to each X value into the formula for the mean.
Step 3 Calculate the value of each product.
Step 4 Sum up these products to obtain the mean (or expected value).

The Variance and Standard Deviation of a Discrete Random Variable

Although the mean is the balance point which helps to describe the center or the typical value of a probability distribution, it doesn't provide a measure of the spread or variability of the distribution.

Recall in Chapter 3, we used the variance and the standard deviation to measure the variability of a distribution. Remember that both of these measures of variability took into consideration how far each of the data values within a distribution deviated from the mean. Examine the probability distribution of the number of TV's per family shown in Figure 5.8a. We found that the mean number of televisions per family was 1.82. By examining the histogram in Figure 5.8a, you see that there is a greater weight or probability for families having values near the mean of 1.82 televisions such as $X = 1, X = 2$ and $X = 3$. In contrast, there is less weight or probability for families having values far from the mean such as $X = 0$ televisions or $X = 4$ televisions. Since the values closer to the mean, such as $X = 1, X = 2$ or $X = 3$, have a greater chance of occurring than the values far from the mean, $X = 0$ or $X = 4$, we should expect the variance and the standard deviation to be relatively small because the standard deviation and variance measure the concentration of the values about the mean. On the other hand, if the values of the random variable which are far from the mean had greater probabilities then we would expect the variance and the standard deviation to be relatively larger since the values further from the mean carry a greater weight or probability.

Thus, the formulas for the *variance and the standard deviation* of a probability distribution must take into consideration the probability associated with each value of the random variable. Let's examine the formulas to compute the variance and standard deviation of a discrete random variable.

Procedure to Calculate the Variance of a Discrete Random Variable Using the Formula:

$$\sigma^2 = \sum_{\substack{all\ possible \\ X\ values}} (X - \mu)^2 \cdot P(X)$$

Step 1   Subtract the mean from each possible value of the random variable X to obtain the deviation from the mean, written: $(X - \mu)$;

Step 2   Squaring each deviation and multiplying the result by the probability associated with the corresponding X value, symbolized as

$$(X - \mu)^2 \cdot P(X)$$;

Step 3   Adding these results to obtain the variance, written:

$$\sigma^2 = \sum_{\substack{all\ possible \\ X\ values}} (X - \mu)^2 \cdot P(X)$$

DEFINITION 5.6

Standard Deviation of a Discrete Random Variable, denoted by σ, is the positive square root of the variance. Thus, the formula for the standard deviation is symbolized as:

$$\sigma = \sqrt{\sum_{\substack{all\ possible \\ X\ values}} (X - \mu)^2 \cdot P(X)}$$

Let's calculate the variance, σ^2, and the standard deviation, σ, for the probability distribution in Table 5.10.

TABLE 5.10

Number of TV's per Family X	Probability of the Number of TV's per Family P(X)
0	0.05
1	0.35
2	0.40
3	0.13
4	0.07

To calculate the variance and the standard deviation for the discrete random variable X, we must first find the mean, μ. In the previous discussion on the mean, the mean for the probability distribution given in Table 5.10 was: $\mu = 1.82$ televisions.

Table 5.11 contains the necessary computations to calculate the variance and the standard deviation.

TABLE 5.11

X	P(X)	X − μ	(X − μ)²	(X − μ)²P(X)
0	0.05	0 − 1.82 = −1.82	(−1.82)² = 3.3124	(3.3124) (0.05) = 0.16562
1	0.35	1 − 1.82 = −0.82	(−0.82)² = 0.6724	(0.6724) (0.35) = 0.23534
2	0.40	2 − 1.82 = 0.18	(0.18)² = 0.0324	(0.0324) (0.40) = 0.01296
3	0.13	3 − 1.82 = 1.18	(1.18)² = 1.3924	(1.3924) (0.13) = 0.181012
4	0.07	4 − 1.82 = 2.18	(2.18)² = 4.7524	(4.7524) (0.07) = 0.332668

To construct Table 5.11, you need the following five columns:

X: *the values of the random variable,*
P(X): *the probability values associated with each X value*
(X − μ): *the deviations from the mean*
(X − μ)²: *the squared deviations from the mean*
(X − μ)²P(X): *the products of the squared deviation by the probability associated with the corresponding X value*

Using the information in Table 5.11, the variance and the standard deviation are calculated using the following steps.

Step 1   Find the sum of the quantities: $(X–μ)^2\,P(X)$, symbolized as $\Sigma(X–μ)^2{\cdot}P(X)$. This result is the variance, $σ^2$.

$$\Sigma(X–μ)^2{\cdot}P(X) = 0.16562 + 0.23534 + 0.01296 + 0.181012 + 0.332668$$

$$\Sigma(X–μ)^2{\cdot}P(X) = 0.9276$$

Thus, the variance is:

$$σ^2 = 0.9276$$

Step 2   Take the square root of the variance to obtain the standard deviation, $σ$.

That is, $σ = \sqrt{\displaystyle\sum_{\substack{all\ possible \\ x\ values}} (X - μ)^2 \cdot P(X)}$.

Thus, $σ = \sqrt{0.9276}$

or

$$σ \approx 0.96.$$

Therefore, the standard deviation for the probability distribution is approximately 0.96 televisions per family. Thus, the standard deviation of 0.96 televisions per family represents a measure of the spread of the possible values of the number of televisions from the mean of 1.82 televisions. Or intuitively, we can say that a standard deviation of 0.96 is approximately the average deviation the values of the random variable are from the mean of 1.82 televisions. Since the standard deviation measures the variability or dispersion in the random variable values from the mean, it describes how spread out a probability distribution is. Thus, a probability distribution with a small standard deviation will have a probability histogram where the bars are clustered together, while a probability distribution having a large standard deviation will have a probability histogram where the bars are more dispersed.

At this point, let's summarize the procedure used to calculate the standard deviation of a discrete random variable.

Procedure to Calculate the Standard Deviation of a Discrete Random Variable Using the Formula:

$$\sigma = \sqrt{\sum_{\substack{all\ possible \\ X\ values}} (X - \mu)^2 \cdot P(X)}$$

Step 1   Construct a table containing the following five columns:

X: the values of the random variable,

P(X): the probability values associated with each X value

$(X - \mu)$: the deviation from the mean obtained by subtracting the mean from each possible value of the random variable

$(X - \mu)^2$: square each deviation from the mean

$(X - \mu)^2 P(X)$: multiply each square deviation by the probability associated with the corresponding X value

Step 2   Find the sum of the quantities: $(X - \mu)^2 P(X)$, symbolized as $\sum (X-\mu)^2 \cdot P(X)$. This result is the variance, σ^2.

Step 3   Take the square root of the variance to obtain the standard deviation, σ.

EXAMPLE 5.7

The probability distribution given in Table 5.12 represents the number of computer systems a salesman named Hal expects to sell during a particular month.

TABLE 5.12

Number of Computer Systems Sold X	Probability P(X)
0	0.10
1	0.25
2	0.30
3	0.20
4	0.10
5	0.05

Find:

a)   The most likely number of computer systems that Hal will sell during the month.

b)   The average monthly number of computer systems that Hal expects to sell. How would you interpret this result?

c)   The standard deviation of this probability distribution.

d) The probability that the number of computer systems that Hal sells will be within one standard deviation from the mean.

Solution

a) The most likely number of computer systems that Hal will expect to sell during the month is 2, since it has the largest probability.

b) To find the average monthly number of computers that Hal expects to sell, we need to compute the mean of this probability distribution. The mean is calculated using the formula:

$$\mu = \sum_{\substack{all\ possible \\ X\ values}} X \cdot P(X) \ .$$

That is, each value of the discrete random variable, denoted by X, is multiplied by its probability, denoted by P(X).

To determine the average number of computer systems that Hal expects to sell, use the procedure to calculate the mean from the information in Table 5.12.

Step 1 Substitute each possible value of the random variable X into the formula for the mean:

$$\mu = \sum_{\substack{all\ possible \\ X\ values}} X \cdot P(X) \ .$$

We have:

$$\mu = 0P(0) + 1P(1) + 2P(2) + 3P(3) + 4P(4) + 5P(5)$$

Step 2 Substitute the probability value, P(X), corresponding to each X value into the formula.

$$\mu = 0(0.10) + 1(0.25) + 2(0.30) + 3(0.20) + 4(0.10) + 5(0.05)$$

Step 3 Calculate the value of each product.

$$\mu = 0 + 0.25 + 0.60 + 0.40 + 0.40 + 0.25$$

Step 4 Sum up these products to obtain the mean.

$$\mu = 2.1$$

Thus, **the average number of computer systems Hal expects to sell is 2.1.** We would interpret this result to mean that over a large number of months, Hal expects to sell 2.1 computer systems.

c) To calculate the standard deviation for the probability distribution we must calculate the mean, μ, and utilize the procedure to compute the standard deviation.

From part (b), the mean is: $\mu = 2.1$.

Using the procedure, we have:

Step 1 Table 5.13 contains the five columns needed to compute the standard deviation.

TABLE 5.13

X	P(X)	X–μ	(X–μ)^2	(X–μ)^{2}P(X)
0	0.10	0–2.1 = –2.1	$(-2.1)^2 = 4.41$	$(4.41)(0.10) = 0.414$
1	0.25	1–2.1 = –1.1	$(-1.1)^2 = 1.21$	$(1.21)(0.25) = 0.3025$
2	0.30	2–2.1 = 0.1	$(0.1)^2 = 0.01$	$(0.01)(0.30) = 0.003$
3	0.20	3–2.1 = 0.9	$(0.9)^2 = 0.81$	$(0.81)(0.20) = 0.162$
4	0.10	4–2.1 = 1.9	$(1.9)^2 = 3.61$	$(3.61)(0.10) = 0.361$
5	0.05	5–2.1 = 2.9	$(2.9)^2 = 8.41$	$(8.41)(0.05) = 0.4205$

Step 2   Find the sum of the quantities: $(X-\mu)^2 P(X)$, symbolized as $\Sigma(X-\mu)^2 \cdot P(X)$. This result is the variance, σ^2.

$$\Sigma(X-\mu)^2 \cdot P(X) = 0.414 + 0.3025 + 0.003 + 0.162 + 0.361 + 0.4205$$

$$\Sigma(X-\mu)^2 \cdot P(X) = 1.662$$

Thus, the variance is:

$$\sigma^2 = 1.662$$

Step 3   Take the square root of the variance to obtain the standard deviation, σ.

That is, $\sigma = \sqrt{\sum_{\substack{all\ possible \\ x\ values}} (X-\mu)^2 \cdot P(X)}$.

Thus, $\sigma = \sqrt{1.662}$

or

$$\sigma \approx 1.30$$

Therefore the standard deviation for the probability distribution is approximately 1.30 computer systems.

d) The number of computer systems that are within one standard deviation of the mean are from $\mu - \sigma$ to $\mu + \sigma$. Since the mean is: $\mu = 2.1$, and the standard deviation is: $\sigma \approx 1.30$, then:

$$\mu - \sigma = 2.1 - 1.30 = 0.8$$

and

$$\mu + \sigma = 2.1 + 1.30 = 3.4.$$

Thus, we are interested in the probability that the number of computer systems sold will range from 0.8 to 3.4. The possible values of the random variable X that fall within this range are: X = 1, X = 2, and X = 3. To determine the probability that the number of computer systems will fall within this range of 0.84 to 3.4, we must add the corresponding probability for each of these X values. That is:

probability of the number falling from X = 1 to X = 3 is: $P(X = 1) + P(X = 2) + P(X = 3)$
$$= 0.25 + 0.30 + 0.20$$
$$= 0.75.$$

Thus, the probability that the number of computer systems that Hal sells will be within one standard deviation from the mean is 0.75.

CASE STUDY 5.2

Examine the graphic entitled "How Long World Series Run" which is shown in Figure 5.9. This graphic represents World Series play from 1905 to 1999 excluding the series played during the years from 1919 to 1921 where they played more than 7 games.

a) Identify the random variable being illustrated in Figure 5.9.
b) Is this a discrete or continuous random variable? Explain your answer.
c) State the possible values of the random variable.
d) State the probability for each possible value. Interpret what each probability indicates about each possible random variable value.
e) Determine the average number of games a world series will last. Interpret this result.

CASE STUDY 5.2

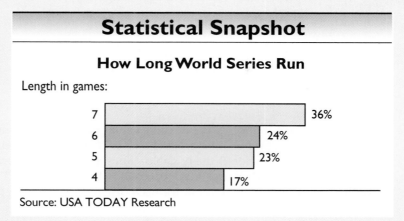

FIGURE 5.9

f) Which value of the random variable had the greatest impact on this average? Which value of the random variable has the greatest probability? Compare these answers. Did you expect these results? Using these results, explain what is meant by the statement that "*the mean is a weighted average?*" What quantities represent the "weights"? Explain.

g) Determine the standard deviation of this random variable. Interpret this result.

h) Construct a probability histogram for the probability distribution of this random variable.

i) Examine the probability histogram's spread and compare this to the value of the standard deviation. What can you indicate about the relationship between the histogram's spread and the standard deviation? Explain your answer.

EXAMPLE 5.8

Examine the two probability histograms pictured within Figures 5.10a and 5.10b.

FIGURE 5.10

a) Indicate the possible values of the random variable X for each probability distribution and the corresponding probability.
b) By examining the histograms in Figure 5.10, what is your estimate of the mean of each probability distribution?
c) Within which distribution are the values of the random variable more dispersed or scattered from the mean?
d) One of the probability distributions has a standard deviation of 0.77, while the other probability distribution has a standard deviation of 1.34. Which of the probability distributions shown in Figure 5.10 has a standard deviation of 1.34? Explain your answer.

Solution

a) For Probability Distribution A, the possible values of the random variable are: X = 1, 2, 3, 4, or 5. Their corresponding probabilities are: P(1) = 0.1, P(2) = 0.2, P(3) = 0.4, P(4) = 0.2, and P(5) = 0.1. For Probability Distribution B, the possible values of the random variable are: X = 2, 3, or 4. Their corresponding probabilities are: P(2) = 0.3, P(3) = 0.4, and P(4) = 0.3.
b) Since the mean is the balance point for each distribution, and the distributions are symmetric, then the mean for each probability distribution is 3.
c) Probability Distribution A has values which are more dispersed from the mean of 3.
d) Since Probability Distribution A has values which are more dispersed from the mean of 3, this distribution will have the greater variability. Therefore, Probability Distribution A has the larger standard deviation, which is 1.34. Thus, Probability Distribution B has the smaller standard deviation, which is 0.77.

CASE STUDY 5.3

According to the registrar records of Nassau Community College on Long Island, Table 5.14 represents the number of semesters in which 21,541 students have attended the college during the Fall semester of 1990.

TABLE 5.14   Student Duration of Attendance

Number of Semesters X	Number		
	Day	Evening	Total
1	5,704	2,059	7,763
2	1,201	843	2,044
3	3,661	969	4,630
4	900	582	1,482
5	1,741	720	2,461
6	438	437	875
7	416	439	855
8	157	269	426
9	114	232	346
10 or more	177	482	659
Total	14,509	7,032	21,541

Replace the last row of the table labelled 10 or more semesters with just 10 semesters, and let X be the number of semesters attending the college. If we imagine selecting one day student at random, then:
  a) construct a probability distribution for X for day students, for evening students and for all students.
  b) What is the probability of selecting a day student who has been in attendance for more than 4 semesters?

c) What is the probability of selecting an evening student who has been in attendance for less than 5 semesters?

d) What is the probability of selecting a student at random, day or evening, who has been in attendance for more than 4 semesters?

e) Construct a probability histogram for X for day, evening and all students.

f) Find the mean number of semesters attended for day, evening and all students.

g) Find the standard deviation of the number of semesters attended for day, evening and all students.

5.5   BINOMIAL PROBABILITY DISTRIBUTION

In this section, we will examine a discrete probability distribution called the **Binomial Probability Distribution** or **Binomial Distribution.** One of the characteristics of a binomial distribution is that it involves probability experiments where each outcome can be classified in *one of two possibilities.* For example:

- the toss of a coin results in either *a head or a tail.*
- the selection of a possible answer for a question on a multiple choice test is either *correct or incorrect.*
- the toss of a die results in an outcome which is either *a 5 or not a 5.*
- the selection of a single card from a deck of cards results in either *an ace or not an ace.*
- a new drug will either be *effective or not effective* when administered to a single patient.
- in an ESP experiment using five objects, the subject will either *guess the object or not guess the object correctly.*
- in a quality control procedure, an item tested will either be *defective or non-defective.*

An outcome, in each of these experiments, can be classified in only one of the two defined possibilities. Thus, each outcome is mutually exclusive, that is, both outcomes cannot happen at the same time. For example, when a coin is tossed it will land either heads or tails, but it cannot land both heads and tails at the same time. Also, a tested item can be either defective or not defective, but not both.

Since the outcomes of a binomial distribution can only take on one of two possible outcomes, we usually refer to these two outcomes as either a success or a failure. For example, in the coin tossing experiment, we might classify the *outcome heads as a success.* Thus, the *outcome tails will then be considered a failure.* In the quality control experiment, *a defective item might be classified as a success, while a non-defective item would be considered a failure.* Keep in mind that the use of the words **success** and **failure** are probability terms and should not be confused with your everyday meaning of these words. Consequently, our decision on what outcomes to define a success will be dependent on the probability question. That is, the selection of which one of the two possibilities to identify as a success or a failure is usually dependent upon the question being asked. The term *success is usually defined to be the outcome which is being referred to within the question,* while the word *failure refers to the outcome that is not referred to within the question.* For example, if a binomial probability question were stated as: "What is the probability of guessing 4 *wrong answers* on a 10 question multiple choice test?", then *success would be defined as a wrong answer,* while *a failure is defined to be a correct answer.* Notice, we are identifying the outcome **wrong answer** as a **success** since this is the outcome to which the question refers, while the outcome of a *correct answer* which is not referred within the question is identified as a failure. Thus, the word success is simply a term used to refer to one of the two possibilities of a binomial experiment, and should not be confused with the outcome(s) that you may find to be desirable.

A second characteristic of a binomial distribution is that it is the result of a probability experiment where *the experiment has been repeated a predetermined number of times and each repetition of the experiment is identical.* That is, it is a probability experiment having n **identical trials**, where each repetition of the experiment is referred to as a **trial**. For example, if an experiment is defined as rolling a fair die 20 times, then this experiment consists of repeatedly rolling the same die 20 times. Since the same identical die is being rolled each time, then each repetition of the experiment is said to be identical. The number of times the die will be rolled was predetermined or known prior to performing the actual experiment. Therefore, an experiment consisting of rolling a fair die 20 times is said to consist of 20 trials, since each roll is considered a trial. In addition, since the outcomes of a binomial distribution are values which were arrived at by **counting**, the *binomial probability distribution is a discrete probability distribution.* For example, the number of times a coin lands heads in 10 tosses, or the number of defective items within a batch of 50 items represent *counts,* since the results are determined by *counting* the number of heads in 10 tosses or *counting* the number of defective items within a batch of 50 items.

A third characteristic of a binomial distribution is that *the n identical trials are* **independent.** For example, in the experiment of tossing a coin 10 times, each toss is independent of all the other tosses, since regardless of what happens on any one toss, this result does not affect the outcome of any other toss.

Finally, a fourth characteristic of a binomial distribution is that *the probability of a success must remain the same for each trial.* For example, in the coin tossing experiment, the chance of a fair coin landing heads will be the same for each toss or trial. Thus, the probability of the coin landing heads on the first toss (or first trial) is ½, while the probability of the coin landing heads on the second toss (or second trial) is also ½, and this is true for the third toss (or third trial) and so on.

An experiment that has these four characteristics is classified as a binomial experiment.

> **DEFINITION 5.7**
> A **binomial experiment** satisfies the following four conditions.
> 1) There are *n identical trials.*
> 2) The n identical trials are *independent.*
> 3) The outcome for each trial can be classified as either a *success* or a *failure.*
> 4) The *probability of a success* is the *same* for *each trial.*

Let's now consider an example to explain how to identify whether a probability experiment is binomial.

EXAMPLE 5.9

Consider the experiment of tossing a fair coin five times, where we are interested in getting a head. Can this experiment be classified as a binomial experiment?

Solution

Let's determine if the four conditions for a binomial experiment are satisfied.

1) Are there n identical trials? Yes, since the same coin is being tossed 5 times and each toss is considered a trial, thus there are 5 identical trials.
2) Are the 5 identical trials independent? Yes, since the outcome for the first toss (or trial) does not influence the outcome for the second toss (or trial), or any other toss. In fact, the outcome of any toss has no influence on the outcome of any other toss. Thus, the trials are independent.
3) Can the outcome of each trial be classified as either a success or a failure? Yes, since there are only two possible outcomes heads and tails, we can define the outcome of a head as a success, and the outcome of a tail as a failure.

4) Is the probability of a success the same for each trial? Yes, for each toss (or trial) of the fair coin the probability of a success equals the probability of a head which is always ½.

Therefore, the experiment of tossing a fair coin five times is a binomial experiment.   ∎

EXAMPLE 5.10

Consider spinning the spinner shown in Figure 5.11 four times and recording the four outcomes.

FIGURE 5.11

Can this experiment be considered a binomial, if we are interested in the outcome red?

Solution

Let's check the four conditions of a binomial experiment.

1) Are there n identical trials? Yes, since the same spinner is being spun 4 times and each spin is considered a trial, then the number of identical trials is 4.
2) Are the 4 identical trials independent? Since the outcome of any spin has no influence on the outcome of the any other spin, then the 4 spins are independent of each other.
3) Can the outcome of each trial be classified as either a success or a failure? Since we are interested in the outcome red, then we can define a success to be obtaining a red, while all other outcomes: green, blue and yellow are considered to be a failure.
4) Is the probability of a success the same for each trial? The probability of a success (or a red) for each spin is ¼ since there are four equally-likely outcomes for each spin.   ∎

EXAMPLE 5.11

Medical records indicate that 40% of the people living in New York have type O+ blood. Seven people donating blood at a New York hospital are randomly selected to determine their blood type. Is this experiment a binomial experiment?

Solution

We need to determine if this experiment satisfies the four conditions of a binomial experiment. These conditions are:

1) Are there n identical trials? This experiment consists of randomly selecting 7 people and identifying the blood type of each person. Since each person selected is considered a trial, then there are 7 identical trials.
2) Are the 7 identical trials independent? Each trial or selected person is independent since whether or not one person has a O+ type blood has no affect on any other person having O+ blood. We can make this assumption since our population is very large compared to a sample of 7 people.

3) Can the outcome of each trial be classified as either a success or a failure? Since each person selected either will have O+ blood or not have O+ blood, then we can separate each of these possibilities into a success or a failure. That is, we can define a success to be a person with O+ blood and a failure to be a person not having O+ blood.
4) Is the probability of a success the same for each trial? If we define a success to be a person with O+ blood and knowing that 40% of the people have O+ blood type, then the probability of selecting a person with O+ blood type is 0.40. Thus, the probability of a success (or a person with O+ blood) is the same for each person selected.

Binomial Probability Formula

Now that we've illustrated the four conditions of a binomial experiment, let's examine how to calculate the probabilities associated with each outcome of a binomial experiment. For example, the binomial experiment of selecting a person with O+ blood type from a sample of 7 people has 8 possible values of the random variable, X, representing the number of people with O+ blood type. They are:

$$X = 0 \text{ people, } X = 1 \text{ person, } X = 2 \text{ people, } X = 3 \text{ people,}$$
$$X = 4 \text{ people, } X = 5 \text{ people, } X = 6 \text{ people and } X = 7 \text{ people.}$$

This random variable which represents the number of people with O+ blood type of a binomial experiment is called a *binomial random variable,* and the probability distribution of the binomial random variable is called the **binomial probability distribution** or simply the **binomial distribution.** To construct a binomial distribution for the number of people having O+ blood type, it becomes necessary to determine the probability for each possible value of this binomial random variable. To determine each of these probabilities, we can use a formula referred to as the **Binomial Probability Formula.**

Binomial Probability Formula

For a binomial experiment, the probability of getting **s** successes in **n** trials is computed using the binomial probability formula. This formula is written:

$$P(s \text{ successes in n trials}) = {}_nC_s\, p^s \cdot q^{(n-s)}$$

where:
- n = number of independent trials
- s = number of successes
- (n–s) = number of failures
- $_nC_s$ = the number of ways "s" successes can occur in "n" trials
- p = probability of a success for one trial
- q = probability of a failure for one trial = 1–p

A discussion of $_nC_s$ can be found in Chapter 4 section 3.[1] Most statistical calculators have the ability to evaluate $_nC_s$. Determine the procedure to evaluate $_nC_s$ on your calculator. Using your calculator, answer the following two examples.

To evaluate $_nC_s$, we must determine the number of ways **s** successes can occur in **n** trials. The following two examples illustrate this calculation.

---

[1] Any student who does not have access to a statistical calculator can evaluate $_nC_s$ for n as large as 20 using Table I: The Success Occurrence Table in the appendix.

EXAMPLE 5.12

For the binomial experiment of tossing a fair coin three times, where a success is getting a head on a single toss of the coin, determine the number of ways to get:
a) Three successes (or heads) in three tosses of the coin, written as $_3C_3$
b) Two successes (or heads) in three tosses of the coin, written as $_3C_2$
c) One success (or head) in three tosses of the coin written as $_3C_1$
d) No successes (or heads) in three tosses of the coin, written as $_3C_0$

Solution

a) There is only one way to get three successes (or 3 heads) in three tosses of a coin. To obtain 3 successes, you need to get a success (or a head) on the first toss, a success (or a head) on the second toss and a success (or a head) on the third toss. This occurrence of three successes (or 3 heads) is symbolized as: *sss*.

   Therefore, $_3C_3$, which represents the number of ways of getting 3 successes (or 3 heads) in 3 tosses of a fair coin, is 1.

b) There are three ways to get two successes (or 2 heads) in three tosses of a coin. They are: ssf, sfs, and fss.

   Therefore, $_3C_2$, which represents the number of ways of getting 2 successes (or 2 heads) in 3 tosses of a fair coin, is equal to 3.

c) There are three ways to get one success (or 1 head) in three tosses of a coin. They are: sff, fsf, and ffs.

   Therefore, $_3C_1$, which represents the number of ways of getting 1 success (or 1 head) in 3 tosses of a fair coin, is 3.

d) There is only one way to get no successes (or 0 heads) in three tosses of a coin. It is: fff.

   Therefore, $_3C_0$, which represents the number of ways of getting no successes (or 0 heads) in 3 tosses of a fair coin, is 1.

EXAMPLE 5.13

Consider the binomial experiment of rolling a fair die four times where a success is rolling a 1. Determine:
a) The number of ways to get 4 successes in four rolls of the die.
b) $_4C_2$
c) $_4C_0$

Solution

a) There is only one way to get 4 successes in four rolls or trials of the die. It is: ssss. Therefore $_4C_4 = 1$.
b) $_4C_2$ means the number of ways to get 2 successes in 4 rolls or trials which is 6, since we can get 2 successes in 4 trials six different ways. They are: ssff, sfsf, sffs, fsfs, ffss, and fssf.
c) $_4C_0$ means the number of ways to get no successes in 4 rolls or trials which is 1. Since there is only one way to get no successes in 4 trials. It is: ffff.

   In general the number of ways **s** successes can occur in **n** independent trials, written as $_nC_s$, can be determined by using Table I: The Success Occurrence Table found in Appendix D: Statistical Tables.

Evaluating $_nC_s$ Using Table I: The Success Occurrence Table

The expression: $_nC_s$ can be evaluated using Table I. To use Table I, you first find the row that corresponds to the value of n under the column labelled n. Second, you move across this row until you come to the column that corresponds to the value of s under the portion of the table labelled s. The number that you find in Table I is the value of $_nC_s$.

Let's consider evaluating the expression: $_5C_3$. For this expression, the value of n is 5 and the value of s is 3. To evaluate this expression using Table I, first, locate the row corresponding to the number 5 under the column labelled n. Second, move across this row until you come to the column corresponding to the value of s, which is 3. You should be at the table value: 10. This is illustrated in Table 5.15, which displays a portion of Table I.

TABLE 5.15   Table I: The Success Occurrence Table, $_nC_s$

n	0	1	2	3	4	5	6	7	8	9	10	11	12	13	14	15
				s												
0	1			*												
1	1	1		*												
2	1	2	1	*												
3	1	3	3	*												
4	1	4	6	*												
5	*	*	*	**10**	*	*	*									
6	1	6	15													

Thus, from Table I, the expression: $_5C_3 = 10$.

EXAMPLE 5.14

Using Table I, determine the number of ways **s** successes can occur in **n** trials if:
a) n = 10, s = 7
b) n = 3, s = 2
c) n = 7, s = 0

Solution

a) Since n = 10, and s = 7, then $_nC_s = {}_{10}C_7$
     To evaluate this expression using Table I, first, locate the row corresponding to the number 10 under the column labelled n. Second, move across this row until you come to the column corresponding to the value of s, which is 7.
     From Table I, $_{10}C_7 = 120$
b) For n = 3, and s = 2, then $_nC_s = {}_3C_2$
     To evaluate this expression using Table I, first, locate the row corresponding to the number 3 under the column labelled n. Second, move across this row until you come to the column corresponding to the value of s, which is 2.
     From Table I, $_3C_2 = 3$
c) Since n = 7, and s = 0, then $_nC_s = {}_7C_0$
     To evaluate this expression using Table I, first, locate the row corresponding to the number 7 under the column labelled n. Second, move across this row until you come to the column corresponding to the value of s, which is 0.
     From Table I, $_7C_0 = 1$.

Before we begin using the binomial probability formula, it is important to review some rules dealing with exponents.

Rules For a Fraction Raised to a Power

If a and b (b ≠ 0) are real numbers, and n is a positive whole number, then:

I) $\left(\frac{a}{b}\right)^n = \frac{a^n}{b^n}$

II) $\left(\frac{a}{b}\right)^0 = 1, a \neq 0$

Rule II states that any non-zero number raised to a power of zero is one.

Let's consider an example using these rules for a fraction raised to a power.

EXAMPLE 5.15

Evaluate the expressions:

a) $\left(\frac{3}{5}\right)^4$

b) $\left(\frac{4}{7}\right)^0$

Solution

a) The expression: $\left(\frac{3}{5}\right)^4 = \frac{3^4}{5^4}$

$$= \frac{3}{5} \cdot \frac{3}{5} \cdot \frac{3}{5} \cdot \frac{3}{5}$$

$$= \frac{81}{625} \approx 0.1296$$

b) The expression: $\left(\frac{4}{7}\right)^0 = 1$, since any non-zero number raised to a power of zero is one.

EXAMPLE 5.16

Use the binomial probability formula:

$$P(\text{s successes in n trials}) = {}_nC_s\, p^s\, q^{(n-s)}$$

to determine the probability of getting 3 successes in 4 trials if p = ⅔.

Solution

1) n = 4 (number of trials)
2) s = 3 (number of successes)
3) n − s = 4 − 3 = 1
4) ${}_nC_s = {}_4C_3 = 4$ (from Table I)
5) p = ⅔
6) q = 1 − p = 1 − ⅔ = ⅓

Substituting this information into the binomial probability formula, we get:

$$P(\textbf{3 successes in 4 trials}) = {}_4C_3(\frac{2}{3})^3(\frac{1}{3})^1$$

$$= 4\left(\frac{8}{27}\right)\left(\frac{1}{3}\right)$$

$$= \frac{32}{81} \approx 0.3951$$

EXAMPLE 5.17

Each year the FBI reports the probability of a car being stolen. In a recent report, the FBI states that the probability a new car will be stolen during the year is 1 out of 75. If you and your three friends own new cars, what is the probability that **none** of these cars will be stolen this year?

Solution

We will use the binomial probability formula since the four conditions of a binomial experiment are true. Thus, we assuming that:

1. the number of cars represent the number of identical trials.
2. whether your car is stolen or any one of your friend's car is stolen are independent of each other.
3. the possible outcomes can be classified in one of two possibilities: either the car is stolen or the car is not stolen.
4. the probability of a new car being stolen is the same for each automobile.

Since the probability question pertains to the chance that a car will be stolen, then we will define a **success to be a car is stolen**. To use the binomial probability formula to compute the probability that none of these cars are stolen, we need to determine the quantities *n, s, p and q*. Thus,

$\quad$ n $\quad$ = 4, since the total number of cars is four;

$\quad$ s $\quad$ = 0, because we are interested in zero cars being stolen;

$\quad$ ${}_nC_s = {}_4C_0 = 1$ (from Table I)

$\quad$ p $\quad$ = $\frac{1}{75}$, since this is the probability of a car being stolen;

$\quad$ q $\quad$ = $1 - p = 1 - \frac{1}{75} = \frac{74}{75}$

Substituting this information into the binomial probability formula, we have:

$$P(\text{no cars being stolen}) = {}_4C_0(\frac{1}{75})^0(\frac{74}{75})^4$$

$$\approx 0.9477$$

Therefore, the probability that none of the cars will be car stolen is approximately 0.95.

EXAMPLE 5.18

A student is going to guess at the answers to all the questions on a five question multiple choice test where there are four choices for each question. Calculate the probability of:

a) Guessing three correct answers.
b) Guessing five correct answers.
c) Guessing at most two correct answers.
d) Guessing at least four correct answers.

Solution

a) Since the question pertains to a correct answer, we will define **success to be guessing the correct answer** to a question. Using this definition of success, and considering a **trial to be a question**, then we use the following values to determine the probability of 3 correct:

1. n = 5 (since there are 5 questions)
2. s = 3 (we are interested in 3 correct answers)
3. n − s = 5 − 3 = 2
4. $_nC_s = {_5C_3} = 10$ (from Table I)
5. p = ¼ (since the probability of a correct answer is one chance out of four possible choices)
6. q = 1 − p = 1 − ¼ = ¾

Substituting these values into the binomial probability formula, we have:

$$P(3 \text{ correct answers}) = {_5C_3}\left(\frac{1}{4}\right)^3\left(\frac{3}{4}\right)^2$$

$$= 10 \cdot \left(\frac{1}{64}\right) \cdot \left(\frac{9}{16}\right)$$

$$= \frac{90}{1024} \approx 0.0879$$

b) To find the probability of guessing five correct answers, we will define success to be guessing the correct answer to a question, and use the following values in the binomial probability formula:
   1. n = 5 (because there are five questions)
   2. s = 5 (since we are interested in 5 correct answers)
   3. n − s = 5 − 5 = 0
   4. $_nC_s = {_5C_5} = 1$ (from Table I)
   5. p = ¼ (since the probability of getting a correct answer for one question is one chance out of four choices)
   6. q = 1 − ¼ = ¾ (using 1 − p)
   7. Substituting these values into the binomial probability formula, and remembering that **any non-zero number raised to a power of zero is one**, we get:

$$P(5 \text{ correct answers}) = {_5C_5}\left(\frac{1}{4}\right)^5\left(\frac{3}{4}\right)^0$$

$$= \frac{1}{1024} \approx 0.010$$

c) Again success is defined to be guessing the correct answer to a question. To determine the probability of guessing **at most one correct answer**, you must interpret this compound statement: **at most two correct answers**. **At most two correct means guessing two or less correct answers**. Thus, to calculate this probability, we need to determine and add the probabilities: *the probability of getting two correct answers, the probability of getting one correct answer* and *the probability of zero correct answers*. That is:

$$P(\textbf{at most 2 correct answers}) = P(\textbf{2 correct}) + P(\textbf{1 correct}) + P(\textbf{0 correct})$$

To determine the probability of two correct, we use the following values:
1. n = 5 (number of questions)
2. s = 2 (success is two correct answers)
3. n − s = 5 − 2 = 3
4. $_nC_s = {_5C_2} = 10$ (from Table I)
5. p = ¼ (probability of a correct answer)
6. q = 1 − ¼ = ¾ (using 1 − p)

Substituting these values into the binomial probability formula, we have:

$$P(2 \text{ correct answers}) = {_5C_2}\left(\frac{1}{4}\right)^2\left(\frac{3}{4}\right)^3$$

$$= \frac{270}{1024}$$

To determine the probability of one correct, use n, p and q from the previous part. However,

$$s = 1 \text{ (success is one correct answer)}$$

$$n - s = 5 - 1 = 4$$

and

$$_nC_s = {}_5C_1 = 5 \text{ (from Table I)}$$

Substituting these values into the binomial probability formula, we have:

$$P(1 \text{ correct}) = {}_5C_1(\frac{1}{4})^1(\frac{3}{4})^4$$

$$= \frac{405}{1024}$$

To calculate the probability of zero correct,

$$s = 0 \text{ (zero correct answers)}$$

$$n - s = 5 - 0 = 5$$

and

$$_nC_s = {}_5C_0 = 1 \text{ (from Table I)}$$

Substituting these values into the binomial probability formula, and using the fact that **any non-zero number raised to a power of zero is one**, we have:

$$P(\text{zero correct}) = {}_5C_0(\frac{1}{4})^0(\frac{3}{4})^5$$

$$= \frac{243}{1024}$$

Therefore, to calculate the probability of at most two correct, we add these three probabilities together. Thus, we have:

$$P(\textbf{at most 2 correct answers}) = P(\textbf{2 correct}) + P(\textbf{1 correct}) + P(\textbf{0 correct})$$

$$= \frac{270}{1024} + \frac{405}{1024} + \frac{243}{1024}$$

$$= \frac{918}{1024} \approx 0.8965$$

d)   Again success is defined to be guessing the correct answer to a question, since this is the outcome to which the question refers.

To determine the probability of guessing **at least four correct answers**, you must interpret this compound statement: **at least four correct answers. At least four correct means guessing four or more correct answers**.

Since there are only five questions, the most correct answers that one can guess is five. Thus, to calculate this probability, we need to add the two probabilities: the *probability of getting four correct answers* and the *probability of five correct answers*. That is,

$$P(\textbf{at least 4 correct answers}) = P(\textbf{4 correct}) + P(\textbf{5 correct})$$

To determine the probability of four correct,

$$s = 4 \text{ (four correct answers)}$$

$$n - s = 5 - 4 = 1$$

and

$$_nC_s = {}_5C_4 = 5 \text{ (from Table I)}$$

Substituting these values into the binomial probability formula, we have:

$$P(4 \text{ correct}) = {}_5C_4(\frac{1}{4})^4(\frac{3}{4})^1$$

$$= \frac{15}{1024}$$

To calculate the probability of five correct,

$$s = 5 \text{ (five correct answers)}$$

$$n - s = 5 - 5 = 0$$

and

$$_nC_s = {}_5C_5 = 1 \text{ (from Table I)}$$

Substituting these values into the binomial probability formula, and using the fact that **any non-zero number raised to a power of zero is one**, we have:

$$P(5 \text{ correct}) \quad = {}_5C_5(\frac{1}{4})^5(\frac{3}{4})^0$$

$$= \frac{1}{1024}$$

Therefore, to calculate the probability of at least four correct, we add these two probabilities together. Thus, we have:

$$P(\textbf{at least 4 correct}) = P(\textbf{4 correct}) + P(\textbf{5 correct})$$

$$= \frac{15}{1024} + \frac{1}{1024}$$

$$= \frac{16}{1024} \approx 0.0156$$

EXAMPLE 5.19

A slot machine has three windows. The wheel behind each window has the same four identical objects. They are: cherry, lemon, orange and jackpot. After the handle is pulled, the three wheels revolve independently several times before coming to a stop. If the slot machine is played once, what is the probability:
a)   Of getting 2 lemons.
b)   Of getting no cherries.
c)   Of getting only fruits.

Solution

a)   Since the question refers to getting 2 lemons, success is defined to be getting a lemon. To determine the probability of 2 lemons, we use the following values:
   1. $n = 3$ (since the slot machine has 3 windows)
   2. $s = 2$ (because the question refers to getting two lemons)
   3. $n - s = 3 - 2 = 1$
   4. $_nC_s = {}_3C_2 = 3$ (from Table I)

5. p = ¼ (since there is one lemon out of four objects on each wheel)
6. q = 1 − ¼ = ¾ (using 1 − p)

Using the binomial probability formula, and the previous information we get:

$$P(\text{exactly 2 lemons}) = {_3}C_2 \left(\frac{1}{4}\right)^2 \left(\frac{3}{4}\right)^1$$

$$= \frac{9}{64} \approx 0.1406$$

b) Now the question refers to getting a cherry, so success is now defined to be getting a cherry. To determine the probability of no cherries, we use the following values:

n = 3 (since the slot machine has 3 windows)
s = 0 (since the question refers to getting no cherries)
n − s = 3 − 0 = 3
$_nC_s = {_3}C_0 = 1$ (from Table I)
p = ¼ (because there is only one cherry out of four objects on each wheel)
q = 1 − ¼ = ¾ (using 1 − p)

Using the binomial probability formula, and the previous information we have:

$$P(\text{exactly no cherries}) = {_3}C_0 \left(\frac{1}{4}\right)^0 \left(\frac{3}{4}\right)^3$$

$$= \frac{27}{64} \approx 0.4219$$

c) Success is defined to be getting a fruit, since the question refers to getting only fruits. To determine the probability of only fruits, we use the following values:

n = 3 (since the slot machine has 3 windows)
s = 3 (because the question refers to getting all fruits)
n − s = 3 − 3 = 0
$_nC_s = {_3}C_3 = 1$ (from Table I)
p = ¾ (since there are three fruits out of four objects on each wheel)
q = 1 − ¾ = ¼ (using 1 − p)

Using the binomial probability formula, and the previous information we get:

$$P(\text{only fruits}) = {_3}C_3 \left(\frac{3}{4}\right)^3 \left(\frac{1}{4}\right)^0$$

$$= \frac{27}{64} \approx 0.4219$$

Notice that in the previous example success was defined differently for each part of the example. Our definition of success was determined by the outcome referred to within each part of the question. For part a, success was defined as getting a lemon, while in part b, we defined getting a cherry as a success. In part c, getting a fruit was defined as a success. It is very important before using the binomial probability formula, that you clearly define what you mean by a success.

EXAMPLE 5.20

After examining her college attendance records for the past few years, Professor Bea Earlee has determined that there is a 30% chance of any one student coming late to her class. Six students are randomly selected from her class rosters. Assuming her students arrive to class independently of one another, what is the probability that:

a) None of the six students arrive to class late?
b) Exactly four students arrive to class late?
c) At most one student doesn't arrive to class late?

Solution

a) To determine the probability that none of the six students arrive to class late, we need to define success and determine the appropriate values for the binomial probability formula. Success is de-fined as a student is late to class, since the question refers to coming to class late. The appropriate values for the binomial probability formula are:
   1. $n = 6$ (since there are 6 students)
   2. $s = 0$ (the number of students the question refers to as arriving late to class)
   3. $n - s = 6 - 0 = 6$
   4. $_nC_s = {_6}C_0 = 1$ (from Table I)
   5. $p = 0.30$ (since there is a 30% or 0.30 chance that a student arrives to class late)
   6. $q = 1 - 0.30 = 0.70$ (using $1 - p$)
      Using the binomial probability formula, and the previous information we get:

$$P(\text{none of the 6 students arrive to class late}) = {_6}C_0 \, (0.30)^0 \, (0.70)^6$$
$$\approx 0.12$$

b) To determine the probability that exactly four of the students arrive to class late, we need to de-fine success and determine the appropriate values for the binomial probability formula. Success is still defined as a student arriving late to class, since the question still refers to coming to class late. The appropriate values for the binomial probability formula are:

$$n = 6$$
$$s = 4$$
$$n - s = 6 - 4 = 2$$
$$_nC_s = {_6}C_4 = 15 \text{ (from Table I)}$$
$$p = 0.30$$
$$q = 1 - 0.30 = 0.70$$

   Using the binomial probability formula, and the previous information we get:

$$P(\text{four of the 6 students arrive to class late}) = {_6}C_4 \, (0.30)^4 \, (0.70)^2$$
$$\approx 0.06$$

c) To determine the probability that at most one of the six students *doesn't arrive to class late,* we need to define success and determine the appropriate values for the binomial probability formula. Success is defined as no student arrives late to class, since the question refers to **not** *arriving to class late.* To determine the number of successes you must interpret the compound statement: **at most one student isn't late to class. At most one student isn't late means one or no students aren't late to class.** Thus, to calculate this probability, we need to add the two probabilities: the *probability of no student isn't late to class* and the *probability of one student isn't late to class.* That is,

$$\textbf{P(at most 1 student isn't late)} = \text{P}(\textit{no student isn't late}) + \text{P}(\textbf{1 student isn't late})$$

   To determine the probability of no student is late to class, we use the following values in the binomial probability:
   1. $n = 6$ (since there are 6 students)
   2. $s = 0$ (the number of students the question refers to **not** arriving late to class)
   3. $n - s = 6 - 0 = 6$
   4. $_nC_s = {_6}C_0 = 1$ (from Table I)
   5. $p = 0.70$ (since there is a 30% or 0.30 chance that a student *arrives to class late,* then there is a 70% or 0.70 chance that a student *doesn't arrive late to class*)
   6. $q = 1 - 0.70 = 0.30$ (using $1 - p$)

Using the binomial probability formula, and the previous information we get:

$$P(\text{no student isn't late}) = {}_6C_0\,(0.70)^0\,(0.30)^6$$
$$\approx 0$$

To determine the probability of one student isn't late to class, we use the following values in the binomial probability:

$$n = 6$$
$$s = 1$$
$$n - s = 6 - 1 = 5$$
$${}_nC_s = {}_6C_1 = 6 \text{ (from Table I)}$$
$$p = 0.70$$
$$q = 1 - 0.70 = 0.30$$

Using the binomial probability formula, and the previous information we get:

$$P(\text{one student isn't late}) = {}_6C_1\,(0.70)^1\,(0.30)^5$$
$$\approx 0.01$$

Therefore, to calculate the probability of at most one student isn't late to class, we add these two probabilities together. Thus, we have:

$$P(\textbf{at most 1 student isn't late}) = P(\textit{no student isn't late}) + P(\textbf{1 student isn't late})$$
$$\approx 0 + 0.01$$
$$\approx 0.01$$

In Example 5.18, we examined the binomial experiment of guessing the answers to five multiple choice questions where each question has four choices. For this experiment, if we define the number of correct answers as the discrete random variable X, then there are six possible values. They are:

$$X = 0 \; correct, \; X = 1 \; correct, \; X = 2 \; correct,$$
$$X = 3 \; correct, \; X = 4 \; correct, \; X = 5 \; correct.$$

The probability associated for each of these possible values can be computed using the binomial probability formula. These probabilities were computed in Example 5.18 and are listed in Table 5.16 along with the associated values of the random variable X.

TABLE 5.16   Binomial Probability Distribution For The Number of Correct Answers For a 5 Question Test

Number of Correct Answers	Probability of the Number of Correct Answers
X	P(X)
0	243/1024
1	405/1024
2	270/1024
3	90/1024
4	15/1024
5	1/1024

Table 5.16 represents a **binomial probability distribution** for the number of correct answers on a five question multiple choice test. Recall that *a binomial probability distribution is a discrete probabil-*

ity distribution. Remember, one of the characteristics of a discrete probability distribution is that the *sum of all the probabilities is equal to one.* Let's verify that this is true for the binomial distribution in Table 5.16. The sum of all the probabilities for the binomial probability distribution for the number of correct answers is:

$$sum = 243/1024 + 405/1024 + 270/1024 + 90/1024 + 15/1024 + 1/1024$$
$$sum = 1.$$

The binomial probability distribution can also be displayed using a probability histogram as illustrated in Figure 5.12.

FIGURE 5.12

Notice that you can answer any questions pertaining to this binomial probability distribution using the probability histogram in Figure 5.12. In Example 5.18 we asked the following questions:
calculate the probability of:
a) Guessing three correct answers.
b) Guessing five correct answers.
c) Guessing at most two correct answers.
d) Guessing at least four correct answers.

The answers to these questions can be easily determined using this probability histogram. For example, *the probability of guessing three correct answers is equal to the height of the bar pertaining to the value of X = 3 which is 90/1024. While the probability of guessing at most two correct answers is equal to the sum of the height of the bars pertaining to the values of X = 0, X = 1 and X = 2. That is, the probability of at most two correct answers equals* $^{243}/_{1024} + {}^{405}/_{1024} + {}^{270}/_{1024} = {}^{918}/_{1024}.$ By examining the probability histogram of Figure 5.12 and using the idea of the mean as the balance point, what would be your estimate of the mean number of correct answers? To determine the actual value of the mean, we can use the formula for the mean of a discrete random variable. This formula is:

$$\mu = \sum_{\substack{all\ possible \\ X\ values}} X \cdot P(X).$$

Using the procedure to calculate the mean as outlined in Section 5.3 and the information in Table 5.16, we have:

First, substitute each possible value of the random variable X into the formula for the mean:

$$\mu = \sum_{\substack{all\ possible \\ X\ values}} X \cdot P(X)$$

Since the possible X values are: 0, 1, 2, 3, 4, and 5 then we have:

$$\mu = 0P(0) + 1P(1) + 2P(2) + 3P(3) + 4P(4) + 5P(5)$$

Second, substitute the probability value, P(X), corresponding to each X value into the formula.

$$\mu = 0(\frac{243}{1024}) + 1(\frac{405}{1024}) + 2(\frac{270}{1024}) + 3(\frac{90}{1024}) + 4(\frac{15}{1024}) + 5(\frac{1}{1024})$$

Third, calculate the value of each product.

$$\mu = 0 + \frac{405}{1024} + \frac{540}{1024} + \frac{270}{1024} + \frac{60}{1024} + \frac{5}{1024}$$

Fourth, add up these products to obtain the mean.

$$\mu = 1280/1024$$
or
$$\mu = 1.25 \text{ correct answers.}$$

Similarly, the standard deviation can be computed using the formula for the standard deviation of a discrete random variable as outlined in Section 5.3. Using the standard deviation formula

$$\sigma = \sqrt{\sum_{\substack{all\ possble \\ X\ values}} (X - \mu)^2 \cdot P(X)}$$

we get: $\sigma \approx 0.97$ correct answers. (Verify this result using the standard deviation formula of a discrete random variable.)

For a binomial distribution, the **mean** and **standard deviation** can be determined using the following simplified formulas.

The Formulas for The Mean and Standard Deviation of a Binomial Distribution

Mean of a Binomial Distribution, denoted by μ_s, is given by the formula:

$$\mu_s = np$$

Standard Deviation of a Binomial Distribution, denoted by σ_s, is given by the formula:

$$\sigma_s = \sqrt{np(1-p)}$$

where: n = number of identical trials
                p = probability of getting a success in one trial

Notice the use of the subscript **s** in the symbols for the mean and standard deviation. The subscript **s** pertains to the idea of a success for a binomial distribution. Thus, the symbol μ_s, read *mu sub s*, denotes the *mean number of successes* for a binomial distribution, while the symbol σ_s, read *sigma sub s*, denotes the *standard deviation of the number of successes* for a binomial distribution.

Using the formulas for the mean and the standard deviation of a binomial distribution, let's verify that the mean is 1.25 and the standard deviation is approximately 0.97 for the binomial experiment of guessing the correct answer on a five question multiple choice test.

To calculate the mean and standard deviation, we need to determine the values of n and p. For this binomial experiment, the value of n is equal to the number of questions which is 5, and the value of p is equal to the probability of guessing a correct answer which is ¼ or 0.25. Thus, substituting the values n = 5 and p = 0.25 into the formula for the mean and standard deviation, we get:

$$\mu_s = np$$
$$= (5)(0.25)$$
$$\mu_s = 1.25 \text{ correct answers}$$

and

$$\sigma_s = \sqrt{np(1-p)}$$
$$= \sqrt{(5)\cdot(0.25)\cdot(0.75)}$$
$$\sigma_s \approx 0.97.$$

Thus, assuming students guess on all 5 questions, the expected number of correct answers is 1.25 with a standard deviation of 0.97.

EXAMPLE 5.21

The following table represents a binomial probability distribution where n = 4 and p = 0.5.

Number of Successes s	Probability of Success P(s) = p
0	0.0625
1	0.2500
2	0.3750
3	0.2500
4	0.0625

a) Construct a probability histogram and describe its shape.
b) Find the binomial mean, μ_s, and the binomial standard deviation, σ_s.
c) What is the probability that the number of successes is within two standard deviations of the mean?

Solution

a) Using the number of successes, s, as discrete values along the horizontal axis and the corresponding P(s) values for the vertical axis, the probability histogram for the binomial experiment is shown in Figure 5.13.

The shape of the probability histogram is symmetric bell-shaped. Can you estimate the balance point along the s axis?

FIGURE 5.13

b) To calculate the binomial mean, μ_s, and the binomial standard deviation, σ_s where n = 4 and p = 0.5 we use the formulas:

$$\mu_s = np$$

and

$$\sigma_s = \sqrt{np(1-p)}$$

Thus, $\mu_s = (4)(0.5)$

$\mu_s = 2$

and $\sigma_s = \sqrt{(4)\cdot(0.5)\cdot(0.5)}$

$\sigma_s = 1$

c) Since to be within two standard deviations of the mean translates as $\mu_s - 2\sigma_s$ and $\mu_s + 2\sigma_s$ then

$$\mu_s - 2\sigma_s = 2 - 2(1) = 0$$

and

$$\mu_s + 2\sigma_s = 2 + 2(1) = 4$$

By examining the probability histogram in Figure 5.13 you should notice that 100% of the distribution is within two standard deviations of the mean. Therefore, the probability that the number of successes is within two standard deviations of the mean is 100%.

An Application of the Binomial Distribution: Acceptance Sampling

Everyday, both manufacturers and purchases of certain products need to determine if these products meet certain specifications before the products are sold or purchased. For example, a light bulb manufacturer is interested in knowing whether the thousand bulbs they produce meet their specifications or whether a large percentage are defective before selling these bulbs to the consumer. An automotive manufacturer who orders ten thousand computer chips for their new automobiles is interested in knowing whether all these chips meet their specifications and are not defective before accepting this entire order from the computer chip manufacturer.

In each one of these situations it is either extremely difficult or impossible to inspect each item before shipping the product or accepting the shipment. If the light bulb manufacturer were to test all the bulbs before shipment, there would be no bulbs to sell. For the automotive manufacturer, testing each computer chip prior to purchasing the chip would be extremely time consuming and expensive.

Consequently, in each of these situations, a small sample of these products, relative to the shipment size, are randomly selected and tested. From this sample result, they infer that they would probably obtain similar results if they were to test all the items within the shipment. This procedure is called **acceptance sampling**. The main objective of acceptance sampling is to use a small inexpensive sample of items which will serve as a measuring stick of the quality of the entire shipment. In many instances, the binomial distribution is used to help draw these inferences about the entire population of items from the small sample selected. To use the binomial distribution when doing acceptance sampling, it is assumed that the experiment of selecting the sample items satisfies the four conditions of a binomial experiment. That is, the random selection of the n items for the sample represents n identical and independent trials where the probability of selecting a defective item is the same for each trial.

Example 5.22 examines how the binomial probability distribution can be used to do acceptance sampling.

EXAMPLE 5.22

Suppose an automobile company decides to reject a shipment of 10,000 computer chips based upon the results of a sample of 20 chips. The company's criteria is to reject the entire shipment *if 10% or more of the chips tested are defective.*

a) What is the probability that the company will not reject (i.e. accept) this shipment of 10,000 computer chips if 25% of the chips in this shipment are actually defective?

b) What is the probability that the company will reject this shipment of 10,000 computer chips if 25% of the chips in this shipment are actually defective?

Solution

a) Since we can assume that this is a binomial experiment, we can use the binomial distribution to determine the probability of not rejecting the shipment. The shipment will not be rejected if less than 10% of the chips in the sample of 20 chips are defective. Since 10% of 20 chips is 2, then the shipment will not be rejected if less than 2 chips is determined to be defective. Thus, we need to calculate the probability that less than 2 chips, 1 chip or no chips, will be defective in a sample of 20 chips.

To calculate the probability of less than 2 defective chips, we need to add the probability of 1 defective chip to the probability of no defective chips. That is,

$$P(\text{less than 2 defective chips}) = P(1 \text{ defective chip}) + P(\text{no defective chips})$$

To determine each of these probabilities, use the binomial probability formula:

$$P(s \text{ successes in n trials}) = {}_nC_s\, p^s\, q^{(n-s)}$$

and determine:

the number of trials, n,
the definition of a success,
the number of successes, s,
the probability of a success, p,
and   the probability of a failure, $q = 1 - p$.

The size of the sample represents the number of trials, thus $n = 20$.

Since the question pertains to selecting a defective chip, then we will *define success to be selecting a defective chip,* and the number of successes will be:

$s = 1$ (for the possibility of 1 defective chip) or
$s = 0$ (for the possibility of no defective chips).

The probability of selecting a defective chip or a success has been given to be 25% or 0.25, thus p = 0.25. Therefore, the probability of not selecting a defective chip or a failure, q, is found by: q = 1 − p = 1 − 0.25 = 0.75.

Substituting these values into the binomial probability formula, we obtain:

$$
\begin{aligned}
P(\text{less than 2 defective chips}) &= P(\text{1 defective chip}) + P(\text{no defective chips}) \\
&= {}_{20}C_1\,(0.25)^1\,(0.75)^{19} + {}_{20}C_0\,(0.25)^0\,(0.75)^{20} \\
&\approx 0.0211 + 0.0032 \\
&\approx 0.0243 \text{ or } 2.43\%
\end{aligned}
$$

Thus, the probability that less than 2 chips will be defective in a sample of 20 chips, if 25% of the chips in this shipment are actually defective, is approximately 0.0243 or 2.43%. Therefore, the probability that the company will not reject (or accept) this shipment of 10,000 computer chips is approximately 0.0243 or 2.43%.

b) Since we know from part (a) that the probability that the company **will not reject this shipment** is approximately 0.0243, then the probability that the company **will reject this shipment** can be determined using the complement statement:

$$
\begin{aligned}
P(\text{company \textbf{will reject this shipment}}) &= 1 - P(\text{company \textbf{will not reject this shipment}}) \\
&= 1 - 0.0243 \\
&= 0.9757
\end{aligned}
$$

Thus, the probability that the company will reject this shipment of 10,000 chips, if 25% of the chips in this shipment are actually defective, is 0.9757 or 97.57%.   ▪

CASE STUDY 5.4   Trial by Mathematics

The following article entitled "Trial By Mathematics" appeared in *Time* magazine on April 26, 1968.

Decisions: Trial by Mathematics

After an elderly woman was mugged in an alley in San Pedro, Calif., a witness saw a blonde girl with a ponytail run from the alley and jump into a yellow car driven by a bearded Negro. Eventually tried for the crime, Janet and Malcolm Collins were faced with the circumstantial evidence that she was white, blonde and wore a ponytail while her Negro husband owned a yellow car and wore a beard. The prosecution, impressed by the unusual nature and number of matching details, sought to persuade the jury by invoking a law rarely used in a courtroom—the mathematical law of statistical probability.

The jury was indeed persuaded, and ultimately convicted the Collinses (TIME, Jan. 8, 1965). Small wonder. With the help of an expert witness from the mathematics department of a nearby college, the prosecutor explained the probability of a set of events actually occurring is determined by multiplying together the probabilities of each of the events. Using what he considered "conservative" estimates (for example, that the chances of a car's being yellow were 1 in 10, the chances of a couple in a car being interracial 1 in 1,000), the prosecutor multiplied all the factors together and concluded that the odds were 1 in 12 million that any other couple shared the characteristics of the defendants.

Only One Couple. the logic of it all seemed overwhelming, and few disciplines pay as much homage to logic as do the law and math. But neither works right with the wrong premises. Hearing an appeal of Malcolm Collins' conviction, the California Supreme Court recently turned up some serious defects, including the fact that not even the odds were all they seemed.

To begin with, the prosecution failed to supply evidence that "any of the individual probability factors listed were even roughly accurate." Moreover, the factors were not shown to be fully independent of one another as they must be to satisfy the mathematical law: the factor of a Negro with a beard, for instance, overlaps the possibility that the bearded Negro may be part of an interracial couple. The 12 million to 1 figure, therefore, was just "wild conjecture." In addition, there was not complete agreement among the witnesses about the characteristics in question. "No mathematical equation," added the court, "can prove beyond a reasonable doubt (1) that the guilty couple *in fact* possessed the characteristics described by the witnesses or even (2) that only *one* couple possessing those distinctive characteristics could be found in the entire Los Angeles area."

Improbable Probability. To explain why, Judge Raymond Sullivan attached a four-page appendix to his opinion that carried the necessary math far beyond the relatively simple formula of probability. Judge Sullivan was willing to assume it was unlikely that such a couple as the one described existed. But since such a couple did exist—and the Collineses demonstrably did exist—there was a perfectly acceptable mathematical formula for determining the probability that another such couple existed. Using the formula and the prosecution's figure of 12 million, the judge demonstrated to his own satisfaction and that of five concurring justices that there was a 41% chance that at least one other couple in the area might satisfy the requirements.

"Undoubtedly," said Sullivan, "the jurors were unduly impressed by the mystique of the mathematical demonstration but were unable to assess its relevancy or value." Neither could the defense attorney have been expected to know of the sophisticated rebuttal available to them. Janet Collins is already out of jail, has broken parole and lit out for parts unknown. But Judge Sullivan concluded that Malcolm Collins, who is still in prison at the California Conservation Center, had been subjected to "trial by mathematics" and was entitled to a reversal of his conviction. He could be tried again, but the odds are against it.

This robbery was discussed in a Case Study in Chapter 4. Recall, that the interracial couple was convicted of the crime, because they fit the characteristics of the robbers which had been established as a 1-in-12 million chance. The couple however appealed and were exonerated because the Judge used a mathematical argument of his own. The judge's argument assumed that the probability p that a couple has all the characteristics of the robbers was $\frac{1}{12,000,000}$ and that there does exist one such couple in a population of 12,000,000 (the prosecutor's figure) couples. The judge proceeded to calculate the chance that another such couple could exist. The judge's mathematical reasoning used binomial probability and conditional probability. He was trying to arrive at a value for the following probability:

P(2 or more such couples exist | at least one such couple exists).

This is equal to:

$$\frac{P(2\ or\ more\ such\ couples)}{P\ (at\ least\ one\ such\ couple)}$$

a) What probability rule was used to write the above statement?
This in turn equals:

$$\frac{1 - P(one\ or\ less\ such\ couples)}{1 - P(no\ such\ couple)}$$

b) What probability rule allowed us to write the above probability statement?
If we use p to represent the probability that a couple has all the characteristics of the robbers, and let N be the number of couples in the population, then this probability results in the following formula:

$$\frac{1 - (1-p)^n - Np(1-p)^{n-2}}{1 - (1-p)^n}$$

CASE STUDY 5.4   Trial by Mathematics (continued)

c) What probability formula did we use to arrive at the above formula?

If $\frac{1}{12,000,000}$ is substituted in for the value of p, and N equals 12,000,000 (the prosecutor's figure) couples, then the:

P(2 or more such couples exist | at least one such couple exists) is equal to approximately 41%.

d) Is the judge's argument based upon an unlikely or a likely chance that such a couple has the stated characteristics? What is this probability value that the judge is using in his argument?

Table 5.17 contains the probabilities for several values of N couples where p is equal to $\frac{1}{12,000,000}$.

TABLE 5.17

Number of Couples N (in millions)	Probability
1	4.02%
2	7.86%
3	11.60%
4	15.22%
5	18.75%
6	22.16%
7	25.47%
8	28.68%
9	31.79%
10	34.79%
15	48.35%
20	59.59%
25	68.75%
30	76.10%
40	86.44%
50	92.56%
75	98.52%
100	99.73%

e) Examining this probability table, what conclusion can you draw about the existence of another such couple as the population of N couples increases?

f) Was it to the judge's advantage or disadvantage to use the prosecutor's 12,000,000 population figure for N couples, if the judge was trying to demonstrate that there was a reasonable chance that another such couple could exist with the same characteristics?

CASE STUDY 5.5   Interactive Video and Data Services Probability Chart

The IVDS Probability Chart in Figure 5.14 was included within an advertising package to entice people to invest within a group that was going to file applications within many different cities across the USA hoping to win the operating license to Interactive Video and Data Services for that particular city.

Certain assumptions were made in constructing this probability chart:

1. Two winners will be selected from each market or city by a random selection process.

2. The number of applicants for each market or city is assumed to be the same as indicated in column one of the chart.

a) What happens to the probability of winning a license for a market or city as the number of applicants increases?

CASE STUDY 5.5 **Interactive Video and Data Services Probability Chart (continued)**

IVDS Probability Chart

PROBABILITY OF WINNING 1 OR MORE, 2 OR MORE OR
3 OR MORE MARKETS FOR VARIOUS COMBINATIONS OF
NUMBERS OF APPLICANTS AND MARKETS ENTERED WHEN
TWO WINNERS ARE SELECTED FROM EACH MARKET

NUMBER OF APPLICANTS	NUMBER OF MARKETS FILED	PROBABILITY OF WINNING 1 OR MORE	WINNING 2 OR MORE	WINNING 3 OR MORE
250	100	55%	19%	5%
250	200	80%	48%	22%
250	300	91%	69%	43%
300	100	49%	14%	0%
300	200	74%	39%	1%
300	300	87%	59%	3%
400	100	39%	9%	0%
400	200	63%	26%	1%
400	300	78%	44%	2%
500	100	33%	6%	0%
500	200	55%	19%	0%
500	300	70%	34%	1%

FIGURE 5.14

b) What happens to the probability of winning a license for a market or city as the number of applicants stays the same and the number of markets filed increases?

c) Can the binomial probability formula be used to calculate the probabilities shown within the last three columns of the chart? Explain.

d) If the binomial probability formula can be used, then what would p, the probability of a success, represent? What is the value of p for the third row where the number of applicants is 250 and the number of markets filed is 300? What are the values of n and q for this row? What is the simplest approach to calculating the probability of winning one or more markets? That is, how could you rewrite the probability statement of winning one or more markets using the complement rule to make the calculations easier? Calculate the probability of winning one or more markets using the complement rule and the values of n, p and q for the information pertaining to the third row of the chart in Figure 5.14?

e) How could you rewrite the probability statement of winning two or more markets using the complement rule to make the calculations easier? Calculate the probability of winning two or more markets using the complement rule and the values of n, p and q for the information pertaining to the third row of the chart in Figure 5.14.

5.6 USING TECHNOLOGY

To determine evaluations of binomial probabilities using the binomial probability formula:

$$P(\mathbf{s} \text{ successes in } \mathbf{n} \text{ trials}) = {}_nC_s\, p^s\, q^{(n-s)},$$

MINITAB uses the PDF command along with the BINOMIAL subcommand. In Example 5.16, we determined by using the binomial probability formula that for a binomial experiment where p = ⅔ the probability of 3 successes in 4 trials to be ³²⁄₈₁ which is approximately 0.3951.

Using the MINITAB commands we get:

```
MTB >    PDF 3;
SUBC>    BINOMIAL 4 .6667.

          K              P( X = K)
         3.00              0.3951
```

Along with the PDF command is the CDF command. The CDF gives the cumulative probability calculation for a binomial experiment. For example, in a binomial experiment where p = 0.25, the probability of at most 2 successes in 5 trials is determined by the MINITAB commands:

```
MTB >    CDF 2;
SUBC>    BINOMIAL 5 .25.

          K          P( X LESS OR = K)
         2.00              0.8965
```

To change the experiment from at most 2 successes in 5 trials to at most 20 successes in 50 trials the MINITAB commands become

```
MTB >    CDF 20;
SUBC>    BINOMIAL 50 .25.

          K          P( X LESS OR = K)
        20.00              0.9937
```

Notice that the change in the MINITAB commands are not much different! Consider the calculations you would have had to do to determine the probability in a binomial experiment for each of previous examples.

EXCEL will produce similar results for the binomial probability calculations. For example, the *binomial experiment to find at most 20 successes in 50 trials where p = 0.25* is determined using the EXCEL function BINOMDIST with the attributes of the experiment. Thus,

$$= BINOMDIST(20,50,0.25,TRUE)$$

yields the EXCEL output: 0.993737.

MINITAB and EXCEL are able to generate a list of the probabilities for a binomial experiment. In MINITAB the MACRO to generate the binomial probabilities for s ranging from 0 to 5 where n = 5, and p = 0.25 is:

```
MTB   > NAME C1 = 'K'
MTB   > SET 'K'
DATA >  1(0:5/1)1
DATA >  END.
MTB   > NAME C2 = 'P(X = K)'
MTB   > PDF 'K'      'P(X = K)'
MTB   > PDF 'K'      'P(X = K)';
SUBC > BINOMIAL 5    .25.
MTB   > PRINTC1    C2
```

This produces the binomial distribution output:

ROW	K	P(X = K)
1	0	0.237305
2	1	0.395508
3	2	0.263672
4	3	0.087891
5	4	0.014648
6	5	0.000977

Using the graph command PLOT and the subcommand SYMBOL 'x'
a graph of the binomial distribution can be constructed.

FIGURE 5.15

Describe the shape of this graph. What would you think would happen to the shape of the graph if the experiment were repeated 50 times where the probability of success remains 0.25? Let's use MINITAB to help explore this question.

```
MTB  > NAME C1 = 'K'
MTB  > SET 'K'
DATA > 1(0:50/1)1
DATA > END.
MTB  > NAME C2 =  'P(X = K)'
MTB  > PDF 'K'        'P(X = K)';
MTB  > BINOMIAL 50  .25.
MTB  > PRINT C1    C2
```

ROW	K	P(X = K)
1	0	0.000001
2	1	0.000009

3	2	0.000077
4	3	0.000411
5	4	0.001610
6	5	0.004938
7	6	0.012345
8	7	0.025865
9	8	0.046341
10	9	0.072087
11	10	0.098518
12	11	0.119416
13	12	0.129368
14	13	0.126050
15	14	0.111044
16	15	0.088836
17	16	0.064776
18	17	0.043184
19	18	0.026390
20	19	0.014816
21	20	0.007655
22	21	0.003645
23	22	0.001602
24	23	0.000650
25	24	0.000244
26	25	0.000084
27	26	0.000027
28	27	0.000008
29	28	0.000002
30	29	0.000001
31	30	0.000000
32	31	0.000000
33	32	0.000000
34	33	0.000000
35	34	0.000000
36	35	0.000000
37	36	0.000000
38	37	0.000000
39	38	0.000000
40	39	0.000000
41	40	0.000000
42	41	0.000000
43	42	0.000000
44	43	0.000000
45	44	0.000000
46	45	0.000000
47	46	0.000000
48	47	0.000000
49	48	0.000000
50	49	0.000000
51	50	0.000000

```
MTB  >   Plot C2 C1;
SUB  >   Symbol 'x'.
```

```
MTB > Plot C2 C1;
SUBC>    Symbol 'x'.


        0.150+
             -
P(X=K)       -             XX
             -            x
             -               x
        0.100+          x
             -                x
             -
             -         x
             -                 x
        0.050+       x
             -                  x
             -       x        x
             -     x           x
             -   x          XX
        0.000+ XXXXXX        XXXXXXXXXXXXXXXXXXXXXXXXXXXXXXXXXXX
             -

        +---------+---------+---------+---------+---------+------K
              0        10        20        30        40        50
```

FIGURE 5.16

Is the shape of the graph in Figure 5.15 much different from the shape of the graph in Figure 5.16? If yes, explain why you think this has occurred.

By examining the graph in Figure 5.16, estimate the probability of having more than 25 successes for a binomial experiment where the number of trials is 50 and the probability of a success for each trial is 0.25.

In EXCEL, the output for the same binomial experiment where n = 50 and p = 0.25 is shown in Figure 5.17.

Binomial Probability Distribution

FIGURE 5.17

(continues)

Success	Prob(s)		
0	5.66322E-07	25	8.44919E-05
1	9.43869E-06	26	2.70808E-05
2	7.70827E-05	27	8.02393E-06
3	0.000411108	28	2.19703E-06
4	0.001610171	29	5.5557E-07
5	0.004937859	30	1.29633E-07
6	0.012344647	31	2.78781E-08
7	0.025864974	32	5.51754E-09
8	0.046341412	33	1.00319E-09
9	0.072086641	34	1.67198E-10
10	0.09851841	35	2.54778E-11
11	0.119416254	36	3.53858E-12
12	0.129367609	37	4.46308E-13
13	0.126050491	38	5.08947E-14
14	0.11104448	39	5.21997E-15
15	0.088835584	40	4.78498E-16
16	0.064775947	41	3.89022E-17
17	0.043183964	42	2.77873E-18
18	0.0263902	43	1.72324E-19
19	0.014815551	44	9.13842E-21
20	0.007654701	45	4.06152E-22
21	0.003645096	46	1.47156E-23
22	0.001601633	47	4.17465E-25
23	0.000649938	48	8.69719E-27
24	0.000243727	49	1.18329E-28
		50	7.88861E-31

FIGURE 5.17 (continued)

The TI–83 Plus graphing calculator has the capability of computing binomial probability. On the TI–83 Plus, there is a binomial probability distribution function written *binompdf* and a binomial cumulative probability distribution function written *binomcdf*.

To illustrate how we can use these binomial distribution functions to compute binomial probability by re-examining parts a and c of Example 5.18.

To answer question part a of Example 5.18, we will use the binomial probability distribution function, *binompdf*, and key in the values of n, p and s.

Figure 5.18 shows the binomial probability of guessing three correct answers. Notice in Figure 5.18, it is necessary to key in the values of n = 5, p = ¼ and s = 3 into the binomial probability function *binompdf* to obtain the probability value 0.0879 (given to four decimal places).

For Example 5.18 part c, it is necessary to use the binomial **cumulative** probability distribution. To answer a question regarding **at most two correct**, we can use the binomial cumulative probability distribution function, *binomcdf*, and key in the values of n, p and s. For this particular problem, these values are:

$$n \; = \; 5 \; questions$$
$$p \; = \; \tfrac{1}{4}$$
$$s \; = \; at \; most \; 2 \; correct \; answers.$$

Figure 5.19 shows the binomial probability of guessing at most two correct answers as computed by the TI–83 Plus graphing calculator using *binomcdf* to be 0.8965 (given to four decimal places).

FIGURE 5.18   **FIGURE 5.19**

In the Section 5.3, we examined the idea of a probability histogram. Using the TI–83's graphing capabilities, we can construct a probability histogram. Let's consider the binomial experiment of tossing a fair coin 4 times. The following table contains the possible number of tails along with the respective probabilities.

Number of Tails s	Probability of s Tails P(s tails)
0	0.0625
1	0.2500
2	0.3750
3	0.2500
4	0.0625

Figure 5.20 shows the probability histogram for this binomial experiment as constructed using the TI–83 Plus.

FIGURE 5.20

>>>>   **SECTION EXERCISES**

Section 5.2

1. A random variable is a variable that takes on different numerical values which are determined by _____.

2. A discrete random variable is a random variable that can take on a _____ or _____ number of values.

3. A random variable is continuous if the value of the random variable can assume _____ or _____ of values between any two possible values of the variable.

4. Which is **not** an example of a discrete random variable?
   a) The number of containers of milk sold at a grocery store during a given month.
   b) The number of customers using a credit card at a restaurant during lunch time.
   c) The height of police rookies for a given entering class.
   d) The amount of vitamins taken each morning for a family of four.

5. Which is **not** an example of a continuous random variable?
   a) The time it takes for an aspirin to take effect.
   b) The amount of cavities found for a visit to the dentist.
   c) The net weight of a box of oat-bran cereal.
   d) The systolic blood pressure level for a 25 year old female.

6. State whether the following random variables are discrete or continuous.
   a) The strength of a 2X4 in pounds per square inch.
   b) The height of a person.
   c) The number of conservatives within a family in the state of Virginia.
   d) The arrival time of an Amtrak train.
   e) The number of accidents at a particular stretch of a parkway.
   f) The amount of time it takes a computer to run a program.
   g) The batting average of a baseball player.
   h) The number of people attending a rock concert on a certain day.
   i) The weight of a UPS package.
   j) A person's age.
   k) The number of flight delays per hour at an international airport.
   l) The number of students absent per class each day.
   m) The time to finish the Boston Marathon.
   n) The lifetime of an alkaline size C battery.
   o) The pulse rate of a person after an aerobic class.

7. For each of the following situations, discuss the possible values of the indicated random variable and classify the random variable as discrete or continuous.

Situation	Random Variable
a) Taking a test	The time taken to complete the test
b) CD's sold	The number of CD's sold at Skyway records.
c) Tennis player	The number of volleys per point
d) Movie theater	The number of bags of pop-corn sold

Section 5.3

8. A probability distribution is a distribution which displays the _____ associated with all the possible _____ of a random variable.

9. A histogram representing a probability distribution is called a _____ _____. The values of the discrete random variable are scaled along the _____ axis, while the corresponding probability values are scaled along the _____ axis.

10. The probability assigned to a particular value of a discrete random variable of a probability distribution is always a number between _____ and _____.

11. Which is **not** a possible probability associated with a value of a discrete random variable?
    a) 0   b) 0.34   c) $\frac{1}{9}$ d) 1.25

12. In a discrete probability experiment with four distinct outcomes, the sum of the first three probabilities is 0.80. What is the probability value of the remaining outcome?
    a) 0.2   b) 0.8   c) 1.8   d) cannot be determined

13. The probability distribution of a discrete random variable can be displayed using a graph. (T/F)

14. The sum of all the probabilities of a probability distribution can be less than one but never less than 0. (T/F)

15. Examine the probability assignments for the tossing of a biased die shown in the following table.

Possible Values of Die	Probability Assignment A	Probability Assignment B	Probability Assignment C	Probability Assignment D
1	$\frac{2}{6}$	$\frac{1}{9}$	$\frac{1}{6}$	$\frac{1}{2}$
2	$\frac{1}{6}$	$\frac{1}{9}$	$\frac{2}{6}$	$\frac{1}{12}$
3	0	$\frac{1}{9}$	$\frac{1}{6}$	$\frac{1}{12}$
4	$\frac{1}{6}$	$\frac{1}{9}$	$\frac{2}{6}$	$\frac{1}{6}$
5	$\frac{1}{6}$	$\frac{1}{9}$	$-\frac{1}{6}$	$\frac{1}{12}$
6	$\frac{1}{6}$	$\frac{1}{9}$	$\frac{1}{6}$	$\frac{1}{12}$

   a) State which assignments satisfy the probability characteristics for a probability distribution.
   b) State which assignments do not satisfy the probability characteristics for a probability distribution. Explain which probability rules are being violated.

16. Construct a probability distribution table which lists the possible values of the random variable shown within the following probability histogram along with the assigned probabilities.

17. For each of the discrete probability distributions labelled I, II, III and IV given below.
  a) Identify the values of the random variable.
  b) Construct a probability histogram and determine its shape.
  c) Determine the sum of all the probabilities. What is the value of this sum? Did you expect this value? Explain.
  d) Find the mean.
  e) Calculate the standard deviation.
  f) Estimate the probability that a random variable is within 1 standard deviation of the mean.
  g) Estimate the probability that a random variable is within 2 standard deviations of the mean.

Probability Distribution I	
x	P(x)
0	1/4
1	1/4
2	1/4
3	1/4

Probability Distribution II	
x	P(x)
1	1/2
2	1/4
3	1/8
4	1/8

Probability Distribution III	
x	P(x)
−1	1/6
0	2/3
1	1/6

Probability Distribution IV	
x	P(x)
2	1/8
4	1/3
6	13/24

18. Professor Kwizz used her previous years attendance records from her statistics classes of 32 students to construct the following probability distribution. The table lists the number of students who are absent on an exam day and its assigned probability.

Number of Students Absent per Exam	1	2	3	4	5	6	7	8
Percent of Students	15%	25%	20%	15%	5%	10%	5%	5%

  a) Construct a probability distribution for this distribution.
  b) Determine the probability that the number of students absent for Professor's Kwizz class on a given exam day is:
    1) exactly 7.
    2) more than 5.
    3) between 1 and 6.
    4) less than 4.
    5) at most 3.
    6) at least 4.

19. Nomoron, an airline company, has a policy to overbook certain domestic flights because past records indicate that not all people show up for these flights. Suppose one such flight uses a plane with a 250 seating capacity, and the airline takes 260 reservations. Let X represent the number of people who show up for a sold-out flight. From past airline records, the probability distribution of X is given in the following table.

Number of People Who Show Up for a Sold-out Flight X	Probability P(X)	Number of People Who Show Up for a Sold-out Flight X	Probability P(X)
245	0.07	253	0.02
246	0.13	254	0.01
247	0.17	255	0.0075
248	0.26	256	0.0065
249	0.19	257	0.0055
250	0.05	258	0.0045
251	0.04	259	0.0035
252	0.03	260	0.0025

  a) If all the passengers show up for the flight, what is the probability that Nomoron can accommodate everyone?
  b) What is the probability that not all passengers will be accommodated by Nomoron?
  c) If Tom is the first person on the standby list and would like a seat on such a flight, what is the probability that Tom will get on the flight?
  d) What if Tom is the fourth person on the standby list?

20. According to the latest figures, the Census Bureau states that 10% of the families have exactly 3 earners within the family. Consider the experiment of randomly selecting 3 families from the population of all U.S. families. If we let X represent the number of families having exactly 3 earners in this sample, then:

a) Construct a sample space of all the possible outcomes for this experiment.

b) Determine the probability of each one of the possible outcomes of the sample space, assuming each family has a 10% chance of having 3 earners.

c) Construct a probability distribution for the number of possible families who have 3 earners in a sample of 3 families.

d) Determine the most likely value of X.

e) Determine the probability that at least one family of the 3 families randomly selected has 3 earners.

f) Determine the probability that more than one family of the 3 families randomly selected has 3 earners.

g) Determine the probability that none of the 3 families randomly selected has 3 earners.

h) Determine the probability that at most one family of the 3 families randomly selected has 3 earners.

Section 5.4

21. The mean of a discrete random variable X, denoted by _____, is calculated by the formula: _____, or _____.

22. The standard deviation of a discrete random variable X, denoted by _____, is determined using the formula: _____.

23. If a fair coin is tossed 1000 times, what is the expected number of heads?
    a) 50   b) ½   c) 1   d) 500

24. The mean of a discrete random variable represents:
    a) The value of the next outcome of the experiment.
    b) An actual value of the experiment.
    c) The sum of all the probabilities of the experiment.
    d) The long-run average outcome of the experiment.
    e) A non-weighted average of the experiment.

25. The expected value for a discrete random variable is called the mean.
    (T/F)

26. The standard deviation of a random variable is a measure of chance variation, that is, a measure of what is expected and what actually happens for a probability experiment.
    (T/F)

27. During tax season, the probability distribution of the number of calls per hour to the IRS office in Nassau County regarding tax filing questions is shown in the following table.

Number of Calls X	Probability P(X)	Number of Calls X	Probability P(X)
5	0.01	30	0.10
10	0.01	35	0.10
15	0.02	40	0.15
20	0.05	45	0.23
25	0.08	50	0.25

a) Determine the mean number of tax filing calls per hour to this IRS office.

b) Determine the probability that X will be within 5 of its mean value.

c) Find the standard deviation of X.

d) What is the probability that the number of calls will be within one standard deviation of the mean value?

e) What is the probability that the number of calls will be more than two standard deviations from the mean value?

28. The Department of Transportation(D.O.T) of a small town is studying the request of a civic association to install a traffic light at the busy intersection of Maple and Munster Streets within the town. Based upon the D.O.T's investigation, they devised the following probability distribution which models the number of accidents per month at this intersection.

Number of Accidents	2	3	4	5	6	7	8	9	10	11	12	13	14
Probability	.02	.04	.05	.10	.10	.05	.20	.05	.25	.06	.06	0	.02

The D.O.T's policy regarding the installation of a traffic light is that the monthly number of accidents must be greater than 8. Based upon this criteria, should the D.O.T. install a traffic light at this intersection?

29. Maria, a stock broker decides to consider different categories of risk options in the stock portfolio of her clients. Currently, the probability distribution of the number of risk options within the standard portfolio is shown in the following table, where the risk varies from 1 (the lowest) to 5 (the highest).

Risk of Investment X	1	2	3	4	5
Probability P(X)	0.05	0.15	0.20	0.40	0.20

Maria designs two alternative investment plans for her clients. These plans are illustrated within the following two tables.

Investment Plan #1

Risk of Investment X	1	2	3	4	5
Probability P(X)	0.15	0.25	0.35	0.15	0.10

Investment Plan #2

Risk of Investment X	1	2	3	4	5
Probability P(X)	0.20	0.15	0.50	0.10	0.05

Which investment plan should Maria give a client, if the client's strategy is to reduce the original portfolio the greatest amount in:
a) Overall average risk?
b) The probability of having stocks with a risk factor of more than 3?
c) The probability of having stocks with a risk factor of 3 or more?

30. Professor Par Kay, an economics professor at a local college, assigns grades in her *bread and butter* freshman introductory course using the following numerical scale: A = 4.0, B+ = 3.5, B = 3.0, C+ = 2.5, C = 2.0, D+ = 1.5, D = 1.0, and F = 0. Based upon previous class records, the probability distribution of the grades students receive in her introductory economics class is:

Grade

X	4.0	3.5	3.0	2.5	2.0	1.5	1.0	0
Probability								
P(X)	0.13	0.15	0.25	0.20	0.10	0.04	0.06	0.07

What is the probability that a student selected at random from her class will receive:
a) A grade of B or greater?
b) A failing grade, if D is the minimum passing grade?
c) A passing grade?
d) What is the average grade that a student receives in her class?

Section 5.5

31. For an experiment to be binomial, it must satisfy the following conditions:
a) There are n _____ trials.
b) The n identical trials are _____.
c) The outcome for each trial can be classified as either a _____ or a _____.
d) The probability of a _____ is the same for each trial.

32. Which of the following probability experiments cannot be modeled by a binomial distribution?
a) Tossing a biased coin 4 times.
b) Randomly selecting five 12 oz soda cans from a production line and measuring the amount of soda in each bottle.
c) Randomly selecting 6 cards with replacement from a deck of 52 playing cards.
d) Rolling a fair die 7 times.
e) A basketball player takes 8 foul shots.

33. The number $_nC_s$, determined by use of Table I, gives us the number of ways "s" successes can occur in "n" independent trials.

34. To calculate the probabilities for a binomial experiment, we use the binomial probability formula. This is symbolized as: P(s successes in **n** trials) = $_nC_s\, p^s\, q^{(n-s)}$

where: n = number of _____ trials
s = number of _____
n–s = number of _____

$_nC_s$ = number of _____ s successes can occur in **n** trials
p = probability of a _____
q = 1 – p = probability of a _____

35. For the binomial experiment of tossing a fair coin 4 times the number of ways to get 3 successes in 4 independent trials is: $_4C_3$ = _____. If you consider a head as a success, the four successes would be _____, _____, _____, and _____.

36. For a binomial experiment, where n = 5, s = 3, and p = ⅓, calculate:
a) P(3 successes in 5 trials) = P(3) = $_5C_3 \left(\frac{1}{3}\right)^3 \left(\frac{2}{3}\right)^2$
$$= \underline{\quad}\,\underline{\quad}\,\underline{\quad}$$
$$= \underline{\quad\quad}.$$
b) P(5 successes in 5 trials) = $_5C_5 \left(\frac{1}{3}\right)^5 \left(\frac{2}{3}\right)^0$
$$P(5) = \underline{\quad}\,\underline{\quad}\,\underline{\quad}$$
$$= \underline{\quad\quad}.$$

37. For a binomial experiment, if: P(s = 5) = $_7C_5 \left(\frac{1}{4}\right)^5 \left(\frac{3}{4}\right)^2$
then: n = _____, s = _____, p = _____, and q = _____.
The number of ways to get 5 successes in 7 trials is _____.
The number of successes is _____.
$_7C_5$ = _____.

38. A binomial probability distribution is an example of a _____ probability distribution.

39. In a binomial probability distribution, the probability associated for each of the possible values of the discrete random variable can be computed using the _____ _____ _____.

40. In a probability histogram, the probability of a value of the random variable X is equal to the _____ of the bar pertaining to the value of X.

41. The mean of a binomial distribution, denoted by _____, is given by the formula: _____.

42. The standard deviation of a binomial distribution, denoted by _____, is given by the formula: _____.

43. The procedure of using a small inexpensive sample of items which is randomly selected from a large shipment to decide whether to accept or to reject the entire shipment is called _____.

44. If in a binomial experiment n = 20 and p = 0.4 then μ_s =
a) 8 b) 10 c) 12 d) 20 e) 80

45. If in a binomial probability experiment n = 16 and p = 0.1 then σ_s =
a) 4
b) $\sqrt{16(0.1)}$
c) $\sqrt{16(0.1)(0.1)}$
d) $\sqrt{(0.1)(0.9)}$
e) $\sqrt{16(0.1)(0.9)}$

46. If the probability that a company rejects a shipment is 0.10, then the probability that the company will not reject the shipment is:
a) 0.05   **b)** 0.10   **c)** 0.50   **d)** 0.90
e) cannot be determined

47. In a binomial probability experiment, the probability of success, P(s), should be less than 0.5.
(T/F)

48. Acceptance sampling tests all the items in a population to infer acceptance of a sample from the population.
(T/F)

49. The probability that a company will not reject a shipment is the same as the probability that the company accepts the shipment.
(T/F)

50. If you guess at the answers to five multiple choice questions where each question has four choices, then what is the probability that:
a) You guess them all wrong?
b) You guess at least 4 correct?
c) You guess less than 3 correct?

51. The probability that a softball player named Casey gets a base hit during a single time at bat is 4/10. If he goes to bat 4 times in his next game (which is played in Mudville), determine:
a) The probability that he gets 4 hits.
b) The probability that he gets no hits, causing no joy in Mudville.
c) The probability that he gets 3 or more hits.

52. Matthew "The Magician" claims his hands are quicker than your eyes. To illustrate this he places a red ball under one of three cups, does some quick manipulations and asks you to tell which cup is covering the red ball. Since his hands are indeed faster than your eyes, calculate the probability that you do not guess the correct cup ten times in succession. (Calculate probability to three decimal places).

53. Each week during the football season, a New York newspaper has a contest that involves predicting the 10 winners of 10 specified football games. If Daniel randomly guesses the winner of each of these games, and if there are no ties, what is the probability that Daniel will guess all ten correct? (Assume each team has the same chance of winning.)

54. From past experience, Caryl, a golfer, knows that she will hit her drive into a sand trap from the green one-fourth of the time. Using this figure, what is the probability that she will hit the ball into a sand trap on exactly four of the first nine holes?

55. In the United States the probability that a person has chapped lips is 30%. On Charlene's next five dates, what is the probability that:
a) At least four of the dates have chapped lips?
b) Less than two have chapped lips?
c) None have chapped lips?

56. A national bank has determined that the probability of a default on one of their loans is 5%. If they approve seven loans during the next business day, what is the probability that:
a) There are no defaults?
b) There are at least six defaults?

57. Medical records show that 40% of all persons affected by a certain viral illness recover. A pharmaceutical company has developed a new vaccine for this illness. Ten people with this illness were selected at random and injected with the vaccine. Eight of the ten people recovered shortly after receiving the vaccine. Suppose that the vaccine was absolutely worthless:
a) What is the probability that at least eight of the ten people injected with the vaccine recover?
b) Based on your answer to part (a), do you think that the vaccine was helpful in the recovery of these people?

58. In Denmark the probability that a carton of a dozen eggs contains one rotten egg is $\frac{1}{20}$. If a boy named Hamlet buys 5 cartons of eggs, what is the probability that at least 1 carton contains a rotten egg (causing Hamlet to mumble: "Something is rotten in Denmark!")?

59. A slot machine has four windows. The wheel behind each window has the same five identical objects. They are: cherry, grape, peach, star and jackpot. After the handle is pulled, the four wheels revolve independently several times before coming to a stop. If the slot machine is played once, what is the probability that:
a) Four jackpots appear in the windows?
b) At most 1 grape appears in the windows?
c) Less than 3 stars appear in the windows?
d) Only fruits appear in the windows?

60. Four out of five patients who have an artery bypass heart operation are known to survive at least three years. Of five patients who recently had the operation, what is the probability that:
a) All five will survive at least 3 years?
b) At most two will *not* survive at least 3 years?
c) At least four will survive at least 3 years?

61. A psychologist claims that he has trained a rat named Algernon to select the correct path of a maze that leads to food 90% of the time. Based upon this assumption, what is the probability that Algernon will select the correct path six times in eight previously unknown mazes?

62. Anne Marie, a botanist, is studying a new hybrid Kentucky blue grass seed. It is known that these grass seeds have a 95% probability of germinating. If Anne Marie plants six seeds, what is the probability that:
a) Exactly four seeds will germinate?
b) At least five will germinate?
c) At most one will not germinate?

75. For each of the binomial probability experiments listed in problems 50 to 62:

a) Determine the binomial probability distribution.

b) Construct a probability histogram. Indicate the shape of the histogram and the value of p. What relationship do you notice between the shape and the value of p?

c) Calculate the binomial mean, μ_s, and the binomial standard deviation, σ_s.

76. Will Short, a fuse inspector for an automobile manufacturer, randomly selects and tests a sample of 20 fuses from a shipment of 10,000 fuses to decide whether to reject or not reject (accept) the entire shipment. If at least 10% of the fuses are defective within the sample, he will reject the entire shipment. Assuming that the defective fuses occur independently and historically, the percent of defective fuses is 15%, then:

a) Calculate the probability that the entire shipment will not be rejected (or accepted)?

b) Calculate the probability that the entire shipment will be rejected?

77. Hy Grad, a quality control engineer of an aerospace manufacturer, must determine if a new shipment of 10,000 protective tiles for the outer covering of a new space vehicle meet their specifications. If a tile can't withstand a heat resistance of at least 4,000 degrees fahrenheit then the tile is considered to be defective.

He randomly samples and tests 100 tiles from this shipment. Hy decides to reject the shipment if more than 1% of the sampled tiles are found to be defective.

a) Assuming the shipment contains 10% defective tiles, what is the probability that the entire shipment will not be rejected(or accepted)? the entire shipment will be rejected? Recalculate the probabilities of part (a), assuming the shipment contains:

b) 5% defective tiles.

c) 1% defective tiles.

d) What happens to the chance the shipment will be rejected as the percentage of defective tiles within the shipment decreases? Would the quality control engineer be satisfied with this relationship? Explain.

78. Ms. Kathleen Shape, the manager of a racquet sport complex, has ordered 1000 cans of low quality racquet balls. Based on prior orders, 20% are usually defective. Before accepting the shipment she decides to reject the shipment if 25% or more of a sample of 16 balls are defective.

a) What is the probability that Ms. Shape will accept the order of 1000 cans?

b) What is the probability that Ms. Shape will reject the order of 1000 cans?

CHAPTER REVIEW

79. A random variable can be classified as either a _____ or _____ random variable depending upon the numerical values that it can assume.

80. A discrete random variable is a random variable that can assume any value between any two possible values of the variable.
(T/F)

81. Determine which of the following random variables are discrete or continuous?

a) A person's chest size.

b) The number of customer's arriving at a credit union office during any hour.

c) The number of TV's sold at an appliance store during a given month.

d) The time required to travel to work.

e) The number of hats a person owns.

f) The actual amount of ice tea in a 12 oz. bottle.

g) The number of early arrivals at an airport on a given day.

h) The number of times *00* comes up on a particular roulette wheel during a certain day.

i) The number of points scored in a basketball game.

j) The number of inches of rainfall per month in San Francisco.

k) The number of air bags per car.

l) The number of people who visit Disney World each day.

m) The blood pressure of a middle-aged male.

n) The number of questions asked during a class test.

o) The amount of automobile gas consumed each week.

82. In general, the probability distribution of a discrete random variable can be shown by use of a _____, a _____ or a _____.

83. The sum of all the probabilities of a discrete probability distribution must always be equal to _____.

84. A probability distribution is a distribution which displays the frequencies associated with all the possible values of a random variable.
(T/F)

85. Let X be the number of defective radial tires obtained when randomly selected batch of eight tires is chosen from the production process. Using past quality control records of this production process, the probability distribution of X serves as a model of this production process and is shown in the following table.

Number of Defective Tires in the Batch X	0	1	2	3	4	5	6	7	8
Probability P(X)	0.85	0.10	0.03	0.01	0.005	0.002	0.002	0.001	0.000

What is the probability that a batch of eight tires randomly selected from this production process will have:

a) At most 2 defective tires?

b) At least 5 defective tires?

c) More than 5 defective tires?

d) If a batch of eight tires which were randomly selected from this production process had 7 defective tires, would you consider this an expected result or an unusual result?

e) If you are a quality control engineer in charge of monitoring this production process and this result occurred, what would this result mean to you?

86. At JMU in Virginia, 40% of the students participate in intramural athletics. If three students are selected at random, then let X represent the number of these students who participate in intramural athletics.

a) Construct a sample space of all the possible outcomes for this experiment.

b) Determine the probability of each one of the possible outcomes of the sample space.

c) Construct a probability distribution for the number of possible students who participate in intramural athletics.

d) What is the most likely value for X?

e) What is the probability that at least 1 of the 3 randomly selected students participate in intramural athletics?

f) What is the probability that at most 1 of the 3 randomly selected students participate in intramural athletics?

g) What is the probability that more than 1 of the 3 randomly selected students participate in intramural athletics?

h) What is the probability that none of the 3 randomly selected students participate in intramural athletics?

87. The mean value of a discrete random variable is what can be expected the next time the probability experiment is attempted. (T/F)

88. An investment analyst ranks a mutual fund by analyzing the type of investments made by the fund. According to the analyst's investigation of this fund, she constructs a probability distribution where X is the risk of the investment.

Risk of Investment X	1	2	3	4	5
Probability P(X)	0.15	0.30	0.15	0.25	0.15

a) Determine the average risk of this fund.

b) How would you classify this fund's risk, using the following classifications: lowest risk is 1, medium risk is 3, and highest risk is 5. Explain your answer.

89. Consider the experiment of tossing a fair coin until a tail appears, or until the coin has been tossed four times, whichever occurs first.

a) Construct a probability distribution for the number of heads.

b) What is the probability that less than three heads will occur?

c) What is the probability that at most three heads will occur?

d) What is the probability that at least three heads will occur?

e) What is the probability that more than three heads will occur?

f) What is the probability that a tail will occur on the first toss?

g) What is the probability that a tail will occur on the fourth toss?

h) What is the probability that a tail will not occur?

i) What is the average of number of times the coin will be tossed for this experiment?

j) What is the standard deviation of the number of times the coin will be tossed for this experiment?

90. The U.S. Census Bureau presented the following table pertaining to family size for the 1990 Census.

Size of Family	
Size of Family	**Number of Families**
2 persons	27,615
3 persons	15,298
4 persons	14,098
5 persons	5,965
6 persons	2,060
7 persons or more	1,285

Replace the last row of the table labelled 7 persons or more with just 7 persons, and let X be the size of family. If we imagine selecting one family at random, then:

a) Construct a probability distribution for X.

b) What is the probability of selecting a family containing 4 or more persons?

c) What is the probability of selecting a family containing 3 or less persons?

d) What is the probability of selecting a family containing more than 5 persons?

e) Construct a probability histogram for X.

f) Find the mean family size.

g) Find the standard deviation of family size.

91. The number and type of headache pain tablets taken by an individual can vary. Two types of headache pain tablets, aspirin and ibuprofen, are listed in the following table along with the probability for the number of tablets taken by an individual.

	Aspirin	**Ibuprofen**
X	**P(X)**	**P(X)**
1	0.4	0.6
2	0.5	0.3
3	0.1	0.1

For each of the discrete probability distributions:

a) Identify the values of the random variable.

b) Construct a probability histogram and determine its shape.

c) Calculate the sum of all the probabilities. What is the value of this sum? Did you expect this value? Explain.

d) What is the expected number of tablets for each type of pain tablet?

e) Calculate the standard deviation.

f) Is an individual more likely to take more than 2 aspirin or more than 2 ibuprofen? How did you arrive at your conclusion?

92. A disoriented fellow named Cello walked along a straight path as defined in the following way. He would either take one step left, not move or take 2 steps right. (see figure)

The probability distribution listed in the following table models his path.

Action	**X**	**P(X)**
move left	−1	0.2
no move	0	0.05
move right	1	0.75

For this probability distribution:

a) Identify the values of the random variable.

b) Construct a probability histogram and determine its shape.

c) Verify that the sum of all the probabilities is one.

d) What is the expected number of steps *and* in what direction does Cello move? Explain.

e) Calculate the standard deviation.

f) Is Cello likely to move more than 2 standard deviations to the left of 0? Explain.

g) Is Cello likely to move more than 2 standard deviations to the right of 0? Explain.

h) In which direction is Cello more likely to move more than 2 standard deviations from 0? Explain.

93. Each morning Dippen Donut serves an assortment of delicious donuts as well as other breakfast foods. The following probability distribution models the food ordered per customer each morning.

Number of Donuts Ordered	**Probability**
X	**P(X)**
0	0.15
1	0.40
2	0.30
3	0.15

For this probability distribution:

a) Identify the values of the random variable.

b) Construct a probability histogram and determine its shape.

c) Verify that the sum of all the probabilities is one.

d) What is the expected number of donuts ordered each morning?

e) Calculate the standard deviation.

f) How unusual is it for a customer to order more than 1 standard deviation number of donuts above the expected number of donuts ordered? Explain.

94. Craig, a young basketball player, has a 80% chance of making a free throw based on his performance over the season. If he attempts 10 free throws during his next game, then:

a) What is his expected number of misses?

b) What is his expected number of hits?

c) What is the probability that he hits all 10 free throws?

d) What is the probability that he misses all 10 free throws?

e) What is the probability that he hits at least 2 free throws?

f) What is the probability that he misses at most 1 free throw?

g) In the probability histogram of the probability distribution of making free throws, what is the height of the bar representing the probability of making 9 free throws?

h) In the probability histogram of the probability distribution of not making free throws, what is the height of the bar representing the probability of missing 4 free throws?

95. During the football season, the sportswriters Craig, Matthew and Debbie have a 0.2, 0.5, and 0.8 probability of predicting the correct winning team respectively. For the next five football games each sportswriter predicts:
  a) Construct a binomial probability distribution of the number of correct predictions for each sportswriter.
  b) Construct a probability histogram for each sportswriter.
  c) Identify the shape of each histogram. Based on the relationship between the shape of the histogram and the probability of making a correct prediction, what would be the shape of a histogram for a probability of 0.3? 0.7?
  d) Estimate the balance point for each histogram.
  e) Determine the mean number of correct predictions for each sportswriter.
  f) Find the standard deviation of the number of correct predictions for each sportswriter.
  g) What is the sum of all the probabilities of each binomial probability distribution? Did you expect these results? Explain.

96. One of the characteristics of a binomial distribution is that it involves probability experiments where each outcome can be classified in one of _____ possibilities.

97. In a binomial experiment, each trial must be:
  a) Mutually exclusive
  b) Dependent
  c) Independent
  d) Fixed

98. For a binomial experiment, n = 6 and s = 3, then: $_nC_s$ = $_6C_3$ = _____ . Therefore, the number of ways to get ____ successes in ____ independent trials is _____ .

99. For a binomial experiment, if p = 4/5, then q = _____ .

100. For a binomial distribution, the mean is denoted by the symbol:
  a) μ **b)** m   **c)** μ_x **d)** σ_x **e)** μ_s

101. For a binomial distribution, the standard deviation is denoted by the symbol:
  a) σ **b)** s   **c)** σ_x **d)** s_x **e)** σ_s

102. The mean of a binomial distribution can be determined by the formula:

  a) pq   **b)** npq   **c)** n(1–p)   **d)** np
  e) $\sqrt{np(1-p)}$

103. The standard deviation of a binomial distribution can be determined by the formula:
  a) pq   **b)** npq   **c)** n(1–p)   **d)** np
  e) $\sqrt{np(1-p)}$

104. A binomial probability experiment is an example of a discrete probability experiment.
  (T\F)

105. A *biased* coin is flipped 5 times. If the probability is 1/3 that it will land heads on any toss, calculate the probability that the coin:
  a) Lands heads all five times.
  b) Lands heads at least three times.
  c) Lands tails at most one time.

106. Candida and Sam, a young couple, plan to have five children. Assuming that the probability of having a boy is 1/2 determine:
  a) The probability of having 2 boys and 3 girls.
  b) The probability of having only 1 boy.
  c) The probability of having at least 4 boys.

107. If you roll a pair of fair dice, the probability that the sum is seven is 1/6. If the dice are rolled four times, what is the probability that:
  a) None of the outcomes are seven?
  b) All of the outcomes are seven?
  c) At most 1 of the outcomes is a seven?

108. Suppose an urn contains 10,000 balls, where 4,000 are red and 6,000 are blue. If five balls are randomly selected one at a time, with replacement, from this urn find the probability that there were:
  a) Exactly two blue balls selected.
  b) More than four red balls selected.
  c) At most two blue balls selected.
  d) No red balls selected.

109. Joe, the vegetable man, has ordered a truckload of grapefruits. He usually finds that 15% of the grapefruits are not acceptable for sale. Joe decides to reject the shipment if a sample of 20 grapefruits has at least 5 bad grapefruits.
  a) What is the probability that Joe will accept the truckload of grapefruits?
  b) What is the probability that Joe will reject the truckload of grapefruits?

WHAT DO YOU THINK?

110. *To Foul or Not to Foul—That is the Question*—A basketball team is losing by 3 points with only seconds left in the game. The losing team has the ball and is about to attempt a 3-point shot for a possible tie. *Should the winning team intentionally foul the shooter, thereby preventing the 3-point shot?* To answer this question, you must realize that when a basketball player is fouled while attempting a 3-point shot, the shooter is allowed to take 3 free-throws which count 1 point for each free-throw that is made. In addition, if the basketball player who is fouled while attempting the 3-point shot makes the shot, then the shot counts and the player is given one free-throw for a possible 4-point play.

Taking all these factors into consideration: *should the defensive team foul the shooter who is attempting the 3-point shot?* To answer this question, we need some information regarding the probability of a player making a 3-point shot and the chance of a player making a free-throw. According to the 2000 LYCOS Sports Almanac, the top 10 NBA players made approximately 44% of their 3-point shots, and 89 % of their free-throws. Assuming the best shooter takes the 3-point attempt, and using the Sports Almanac information, determine:

a) An estimate for a top NBA shooter making a free-throw and a 3-point shot?

b) The probability of the player making three consecutive free-throws, assuming independence?

c) The two possible outcomes of a 3-point shot, and their associated probabilities?

d) The expected or average value of a 3-point attempt?

e) The two possible outcomes of a free-throw, and their associated probabilities?

f) The expected or average value of a free-throw attempt?

g) The expected or average value of three free-throw attempts?

h) Compare the expected (or average value) of a 3-point attempt to the three free-throw attempts, and determine which has a greater value? Interpret this comparison.

i) What would your advice be to player defending the 3-point shooter—*to foul or not to foul*?

111. Examine the following U.S. Bureau of the Census table on Families by Size of Family: March 1998.

a) Identify the random variables within the table.

b) Discuss the type of random variable and the possible values for each variable.

c) Construct a probability distribution for the size of family for the categories: Total, Married-Couple families and Other families for United States, Metropolitan and Nonmetropolitan. Replace the seven or more persons family size with just seven persons.

d) Construct a probability histogram for each of the distributions described in part (c). Explain the differences or similarities for these histograms.

e) Determine the mean and standard deviation for each of the distributions discussed in part (c).

f) Compare the average family size for each distribution in part (e) and explain any differences between your results to the average size computed by the Census Bureau. Are there any discrepancies between your results and results of the Census Bureau? Do you think that this could be attributed to the fact that you changed the category *7 or more persons to just 7 persons?*

g) What do you think would happen if we replaced the category 7 or more persons by 8 persons? Re-calculate the average family size using 8 persons instead of 7 persons. How does this average result compare to the Census Bureau's average family size? Which result gave you a better estimate of the average family size, using 7 persons or 8 persons for the category 7 or more persons?

h) Do you think that a different value, like 9 or 10 or 11 or 12 persons, would provide a closer estimate to the Census Bureau's average family size? Try these values and explain what value you think the Census bureau might have used to compute their average family size?

112. Examine the following graphic entitled "Poverty and Literacy."

Statistical Snapshot

Poverty and Literacy

Economic status of adults at different levels of literacy as determined by their ability to understand and use written information.

Level of literacy: 1=least literate; 5=most literate
Source: U.S. Department of Education

Table 1. **Families, by Type, Age, Metropolitan-Nonmetropolitan Residence, and Race and Hispanic Origin of Householder: March 1998**

[Numbers in thousands except for averages and medians. For meaning of symbols, see text]

Characteristic	United States				Metropolitan				Nonmetropolitan			
		Other families				Other families				Other families		
	Total	Married-couple families	Male householder	Female householder	Total	Married-couple families	Male householder	Female householder	Total	Married-couple families	Male householder	Female householder
ALL FAMILIES												
Size of Family												
Families	70 880	54 317	3 911	12 652	56 346	42 773	3 174	10 399	14 533	11 543	737	2 253
Two persons	30 282	22 042	2 225	6 016	23 548	16 843	1 785	4 920	6 735	5 198	440	1 096
Three persons	16 231	11 639	964	3 628	13 010	9 236	796	2 977	3 221	2 403	168	651
Four persons	14 633	12 402	454	1 777	11 918	10 074	372	1 472	2 716	2 329	82	305
Five persons	6 555	5 633	167	756	5 276	4 495	131	649	1 279	1 138	35	106
Six persons	2 047	1 746	63	239	1 661	1 409	54	198	386	337	8	41
Seven or more persons	1 130	855	39	237	935	716	35	184	196	139	4	53
Total persons	225 360	175 770	11 178	38 412	180 781	139 927	9 191	31 663	44 579	35 843	1 987	6 749
Average per family	3.18	3.24	2.86	3.04	3.21	3.27	2.90	3.04	3.07	3.11	2.70	3.00

a) Identify the variables which are being presented within each graphic. Discuss each type of variable.
b) Describe the shape for each graphic. Explain what the shape indicates about the relationship between the variables presented.
c) Construct a probability distribution for the level of literacy for the adults using the information within the graphic entitled "Percentage in Poverty."
d) Name the type of graph being used to present the graphic entitled "Percentage in Poverty."
e) Find the mean literacy level for the adults in poverty. Interpret this result.
f) Describe the approximate average literacy level for the adults in poverty.
g) At approximately what literacy value do you think the graphic entitled "Percentage in Poverty" would represent the balance point of this graph? Explain your answer.
h) Find the standard deviation of the literacy levels for the adults in poverty. Interpret this result.
i) What percentage of the adults in poverty are within one standard deviation of the mean literacy level? What is the probability that an adult in poverty who is selected at random will fall within one standard deviation of the mean literacy level?
j) How do you think we could estimate the average median weekly wage from the information contained within the graphic entitled "Median Weekly Wage."
k) If an adult in poverty is selected at random, what is the probability that the adult will have a literacy level of at least 3? at most 1?
l) What inference can you draw from the graphic enti-tled "Percentage in Poverty" regarding the literacy level and the percentage in poverty?
m) What inference can you draw from the graphic enti-tled "Median Weekly Wage" regarding the literacy level and the median weekly wage?

113. The baseball World Series is a best-of–7 game series be-tween the American and National League Champions, that is, the series ending as soon as one team wins 4 games. If we assume that both teams are evenly matched, determine the probability that the World Se-ries will end:
a) In 7 games.
b) In 6 games.
c) In 5 games.
d) In 4 games.
e) Construct a probability histogram for the number of games the World Series will last.
f) Estimate the mean number of games that the World Series will last from the probability histogram.
g) Determine the expected number of games the World Series will last. Compare this result to the mean result found in Case Study 5.2 and explain why they are not the same? What is the difference between these two probability distributions?
h) Determine the standard deviation of the number of games the World Series will last. Compare this stan-dard deviation result to the result found in Case Study 5.2 and explain why they are not the same?
i) Determine the probability that the World Series will last at least 6 games?
j) Explain why the probability of the World Series ending in 6 games and 7 games are the same?

PROJECTS.

114. Randomly select 150 students to survey. Determine for each student the size of their respective family. Using these data,
a) Construct a probability distribution table.
b) Construct a probability histogram.
c) Determine the mean and standard deviation.
d) State the shape of the histogram.
Research the Bureau of the Census on the latest data pertaining to the U.S. family size. Using these data,
e) Construct a probability distribution table.
f) Construct a probability histogram.
g) Determine the mean and standard deviation.
h) State the shape of the histogram.
Compare your results to the Census Bureau's data.

115. Administer the following test to 32 students who have no previous knowledge about the material within each question.
a) Complete the table given below with your test results.
b) Construct a histogram using the data of the test results.
c) Compare the test results and the histogram of the test results to the binomial experiments table and histogram.
Test: Answer each question True or False.
1) If $f(x) = e^x$, x is a real number, then:
$$\int f(x)\, dx = f(x) + C,\text{ where C is a constant.}$$

2) Set A is an open set of a metric space, M, if for every x belonging to A, there exists a $\delta > 0$ such that the interval $(x - \delta, x + \delta) \varepsilon$ A.

3) In 1733, DeMoivre developed the equation for the T distribution.

4) For all values of x, $e^x = 1 + x + \dfrac{x^2}{2!} + \ldots + \dfrac{x^n}{n!} + \ldots$

5) If a function f(x) is differentiable at x_0, then it is continuous at x_0.

Test results:

Number of correct answers	Number of Students per correct answer
0	
1	
2	
3	
4	
5	

ANALYZING THE DATABASE USING TECHNOLOGY

The following exercises refer to the file DATABASE listed in Appendix A.

116. Using Technology, count the number of each discrete data value for the variable NB.

  a) Calculate the proportion of the sample that correspond to each data value.

  b) List the data values and their corresponding proportions and verify that this table is a discrete probability distribution.

  c) Find the mean, standard deviation and probability histogram of the probability distribution.

  d) Interpret the meaning of the values obtained for the mean and standard deviation in terms of the variable NB.

117. Using Technology, count the number of each discrete data value for the variable GFT.

  a) Calculate the proportion of the sample that correspond to each data value.

  b) List the data values and their corresponding proportions and verify that this table is a discrete probability distribution.

  c) Find the mean, standard deviation and probability histogram of the probability distribution.

  d) Interpret the meaning of the values obtained for the mean and standard deviation in terms of the variable GFT.

  e) What is the lower and upper dollar amounts that a student will spend on a gift if the value is to be within 1 standard deviation of the mean? What is the likelihood of this occurrence?

CHAPTER TEST

118. A random variable having only a limited number of values with breaks between successive possible values of the random variable is:

  a) discrete

  b) continuous

  c) numerical

  d) categorical

119. For each of the following situations, discuss the possible values of the indicated random variable and classify the random variable as discrete or continuous.

Situation	Random Variable
a) Airplane tickets	The number of seats on plane
b) Bicycle trip	The number of flat tires
c) Diet soda	The amount of ounces dispensed
d) Restaurant entree	The number of a particular type of entree ordered

120. For a probability distribution of a discrete random variable, the probability of any value of the random variable is always:

  a) Less than 0.5

  b) Greater than 0

  c) Less than 1.0

  d) Between 0 and 1.0 inclusive.

121. The mean of a discrete random variable is calculated by multiplying each possible value of the variable by its corresponding:

  a) Frequency

  b) Percentage

  c) Ratio

  d) Probability

122. According to the highway department in Praire City, Idaho, the number of passengers per car (including driver) commuting on highway 57 per evening is defined by the probability distribution

Number of Passengers X	Probability P(X)
1	0.35
2	0.35
3	0.15
4	0.10
5	0.05

For this probability distribution:
a) Identify the values of the random variable.
b) Construct a probability histogram and determine its shape.
c) Verify that the sum of all the probabilities is one.
d) What is the expected number of passengers each evening?
e) Calculate the standard deviation.
f) How unusual is it for a car to contain more than 2 passengers? Explain.

123. An experiment that has six possible outcomes cannot be classified as a binomial experiment. This statement is:
a) True   b) False   c) Cannot be determined

124. For a binomial experiment, if $_7C_6 = 7$, then the number of ways to get _____ successes in _____ independent trials is _____. The seven successes are: sssssf, _____, _____, _____, _____, _____, and _____ .

125. For a binomial experiment, where $p = \frac{1}{2}$, calculate: P(4 successes in 5 trials) = _____ .

126. If five cards are selected with replacement from a regular deck of 52 playing cards, what's the probability that:
a) None of the cards are clubs?
b) One of the five cards is a diamonds?
c) At least three of the cards are hearts?

127. Larry, an old basketball player, has a 70% chance of making a free throw based on his performance over the season. If he attempts 9 free throws during his next game, then what is the probability that:
a) He makes all nine free throws?
b) He misses all nine free throws?
c) He makes at least one free throw?
d) He will make the 9th free throw given that he has missed the first 8 free throws?

128. The probability that a stock analyst of the Wall Street firm DPT will convince one of his customers to take a "position" in a recommended stock is 40%. The analyst presents his recommendations to five customers. Assuming independence, what is the probability that:
a) All five will take a "position"?
b) None will take a "position"?
c) At most one will take a "position"?

129. A slot machine has four windows. The wheel behind each window has the same five identical objects. They are: cherry, grape, peach, star and jackpot. After the handle is pulled, the four wheels revolve independently several times before coming to a stop. If the slot machine is played once, what is the probability that:

a) Exactly three cherries appear in the windows?
b) At least three peaches appear in the windows?
c) Only 1 fruit appears in the windows?

130. Medical records indicate that 40% of the people have type O+ blood. What is the probability that of the next seven people donating blood that:
a) At least five have type O+ blood?
b) At most one has type O+ blood?
c) More than five do *not* have type O+ blood?

131. Determine which of the following random variables are discrete and which are continuous.
a) The number of people attending a jazz concert.
b) The actual number of liters of spring water in a gallon container.
c) The number of shares of stock owned by an investor in a mutual fund.
d) The age of an automobile.
e) The amount of time waiting on line to change a college student's schedule.
f) The number of pages in a statistics textbook.
g) The number of new clients opening up a charge card account.
h) The amount of time required to run a 10K race.
i) The number of broken bottles in a case of wine.
j) The price of a college textbook.

132. Michele, the quality control supervisor, at a radial tire manufacturer has her assistant, Lynn, select a batch of 4 radial tires at random times during the daily production process to check this manufacturing operation. Each batch of four tires are inspected to determine the number of defective tires. The assistant records one of five possible numbers: 0, 1, 2, 3, or 4 to indicate the number of defective tires within each batch.

   The following table represents their summary of the sampling results of this manufacturing process over a period of 12 months.

Number of Defective Tires Within a Batch	Percent of Defective Tires
0	71%
1	26%
2	2.5%
3	0.5%
4	0%

a) Identify the discrete random variable for this experiment, and the possible values of the random variable.
b) What probability would you associate with each possible value of this discrete random variable? Explain.
c) Construct a probability distribution for the discrete random variable X.
d) Construct a probability histogram for the discrete random variable X.
e) What is the probability that the next batch of radial tires selected from this production process will have 3 or more defective tires?

f) If you were the quality control supervisor and a randomly selected batch of radial tires had 4 defective tires, what might you conclude about the manufacturing process? Explain your answer.

133. Through careful record keeping over thousands of customers, MACBLIMP, a large fast food hamburger restaurant, has determined the probability distribution for the random variable, X, the number of premium sized hamburgers ordered per customers, as shown in Table 5.18.

TABLE 5.18

Number of Premium Sized Hamburgers per Customer X	Probability of the Number of Premium Sized Hamburgers per Customer P(X)
0	0.10
1	0.25
2	0.35
3	0.15
4	0.10
5	0.05

a) Construct a probability histogram for this probability distribution.

b) Determine the mean and standard deviation for this distribution.

c) What is the probability that a customer will order at least 2 premium sized hamburgers?

134. From an urn containing 8 marbles, four of which are colored red, two are colored white, and two blue. Four marbles are selected with replacement. Calculate the probability of:
a) Selecting four red marbles.
b) Selecting at least two blue marbles.

135. The mean of a binomial probability distribution, μ_s, can be calculated using the formula for the mean of a discrete probability distribution.
(T/F)

136. According to a survey, 80% of young women aged 17 to 23 are still living at home. If we assume this statistic is accurate for all young women in the age group, then for a sample of 4 women:
a) Determine the probability distribution for this binomial experiment.
b) Construct a probability histogram and describe its shape.
c) Find the binomial mean, μ_s, and the binomial standard deviation, σ_s.

137. Ms. Pix Els, a quality control engineer for a television manufacturer, must decide whether to accept or reject a shipment of five thousand 32" color picture tubes. She randomly samples and tests 100 of these tubes from the shipment. Ms. Els' criteria is to reject the entire shipment if more than 1% of the tubes tested are defective.
a) What is the probability that the entire shipment will **not be rejected** if 5% of the color tubes in this shipment are actually defective?
b) What is the probability that the entire shipment will **be rejected** if 5% of the color tubes in this shipment are actually defective?

Continuous Probability Distributions and the Normal Distribution

Contents

6.1   INTRODUCTION

In the previous chapter, the concept of a discrete probability distribution was introduced. In particular, the binomial probability distribution was examined as a model to many real world applications. Recall that *a discrete random variable can only assume a finite or countable number of values with a break between successive values of the variable.* For example, the number of free throws that a basketball player can make when attempting 12 free throws can be only one of thirteen values: 0, 1, 2, 3, . . . , 11, 12. Thus, it is impossible for a player to make 8½ free throws.

In this chapter, the concept of a continuous probability distribution will be examined. We will study a particular continuous probability distribution having a bell-shaped curve called the *normal probability distribution* or simply the *normal distribution*.

6.2   CONTINUOUS PROBABILITY DISTRIBUTIONS

As discussed in Chapter 5, a **continuous random variable** can assume an uncountable number of possible values between any two values of the variable. The values of a continuous random variable represent a measurement. For example, the amount of time a college student needs to get from one class to the next is an example of a continuous random variable. The variable time represents a measurement and its value can assume an uncountable number of possible values. For example, the amount of time a college student needs to travel between classes could possibly take 9.1 minutes or 9.01 minutes or even 9.001 minutes, etc. The accuracy to which the value of the variable can be measured depends upon the precision of the measuring device.

Suppose a continuous random variable X represents the amount of time a college student needs to travel between classes at a small eastern community college. Based on the results of a particular week, let's consider the probability distribution histogram representing the continuous variable X shown in Figure 6.1. The amount of time has been recorded to the nearest minute up to a maximum time of twenty minutes. There is a rectangle associated for each minute to get to class.

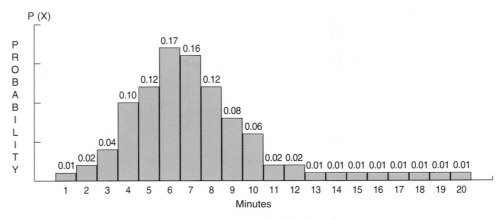

FIGURE 6.1

The height of each rectangle of the histogram in Figure 6.1 represents the probability that the student will take X minutes to get to the next class. For example, the probability that a student will take 5 minutes to get to the next class is 0.12, since the height of the rectangle corresponding to X = 5 is 0.12. Since each rectangle has a width of 1 minute, the area of each rectangle is equal to the probability of the X value occurring. For example, the area of the rectangle for X = 5 minutes is equal to the probability of X = 5 minutes, written as P(X = 5).

$$\text{Area of rectangle for X = 5 minutes} = (\text{base})(\text{height})$$
$$= (1)(0.12)$$
$$= 0.12$$
$$= P(X = 5).$$

Thus, **the area of the rectangle for X = 5 minutes is 0.12 and the probability associated with X = 5 minutes is also 0.12**.

Notice that the probability a student will require from 5 to 7 minutes to get to the next class is equal to the sum of the areas corresponding to the shaded rectangles associated with X = 5 minutes, X = 6 minutes, and X = 7 minutes. This is illustrated in Figure 6.2a. Thus,

$$\text{P(student requires from 5 to 7 min.)} = \text{sum of the areas of the rectangles for X = 5, X = 6, \& X = 7}$$
$$= P(X = 5) + P(X = 6) + P(X = 7)$$
$$= 0.12 + 0.17 + 0.16$$
$$= 0.45$$

You should also observe that *the sum of all the probabilities or the sum of all the areas of the rectangles equals one.* Thus,

P(student requires from 1 to 20 minutes to get to the next class) = the sum of the area of ALL the rectangles from 1 to 20
$$= 1.$$

Since time is a continuous random variable, it can assume any value between two possible values. If the time a student needs to get to the next class is measured to the nearest tenth of a minute, the amount of time can assume values such as 5 minutes or 5.1 minutes or 5.2 minutes etc. Thus, the probability histogram of Figure 6.2b will have more rectangles and each rectangle will have a narrower width as illustrated in Figure 6.2b. Although the histogram in Figure 6.2b has narrower rectangles, the total area of all these rectangles, which equals the sum of all the probabilities, is still one.

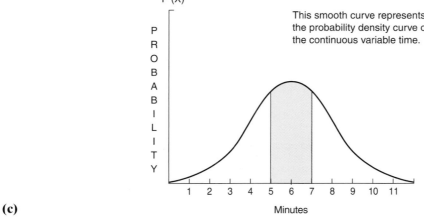

FIGURE 6.2

If we continue this process of measuring the continuous variable time (the amount of time a student needs to get to the next class) to a finer and finer degree of precision, such as a hundredth of a minute or a thousandth of a minute, etc. the number of rectangles will increase while the width of each rectangle gets narrower. As the widths get narrower, the top of the histogram begins to approach a smooth curve as shown in Figure 6.2c.

The smooth curve of the continuous variable time is called the *probability density curve* of the continuous variable time. The area under the probability density curve between two possible values of the continuous variable represents the probability that the value of the continuous variable will fall between these two values. Thus, the **probability** that the amount of time a student will take from 5 to 7 minutes to get to the next class is equal to the **area** under the probability density curve as illustrated in Figure 6.3.

Figure 6.3 illustrates that for a continuous probability distribution the probability assigned to an event, such as the event a student will take from 5 to 7 minutes to get to the next class, is equal to the area under the density curve satisfying the event. This probability assignment satisfies the characteristics of a probability distribution as discussed in Chapter 5. Let's now state the characteristics of a probability distribution for a continuous variable.

Characteristics of a Continuous Probability Distribution

1. The **probability** that the continuous random variable X will assume a value between two possible values X = a and X = b of the variable **is equal to the area** under the density curve between the values X = a and X = b.
2. The **total area** (or **probability**) under the density curve is equal to **1**.
3. The **probability** that the continuous random variable X will assume a value between **any two possible values** X = a and X = b of the variable is **between 0 and 1**.

Let's discuss these characteristics of a continuous probability distribution.

The first characteristic states that the probability a continuous random variable X will have a value between the possible values X = a and X = b is equal to the area under the density curve between these two values. This can be written as:

P(X = a to X = b) = the area under the curve between X = a and X = b.

This is illustrated in Figure 6.4.

The second characteristic indicates that the total area or probability under the density curve is 1 or 100% as shown in Figure 6.5.

The third characteristic states that the probability a continuous variable X will have a value between any two values X = a and X = b will be greater than 0 but less than 1 as illustrated in Figure 6.6.

FIGURE 6.3

FIGURE 6.4

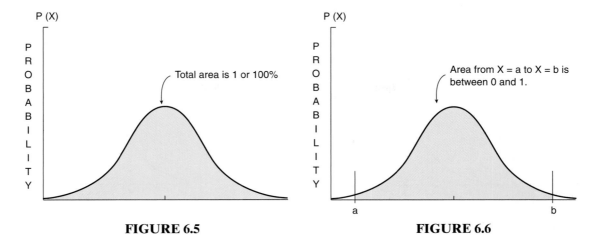

FIGURE 6.5   FIGURE 6.6

This can be written as:

$$0 < P(X = a \text{ to } X = b) < 1.$$

This third characteristic is true for a continuous variable since the largest possible probability is equal to the total area under the density curve which is 1 as indicated by the second characteristic. While the smallest possible probability is the probability assigned to an individual outcome of a continuous variable which is 0. That is, **the probability that a continuous variable will assume a specific value, such as X = a, is zero**, since the probability of a specific value corresponds to the area directly above the point X = a. This can be written as: **P(X = a) = 0**. Because the area of a single point is equal to the area above the point which is a line having no width there is no (or zero) area.

    Let's explain this idea of assigning a probability of zero to a specific value such as X = a by using the previous example pertaining to the amount of time a student needs to get to the next class. Specifically, the probability that a student will need from 4 to 5 minutes to get to the next class is equal to the area under the density curve between 4 and 5 minutes as illustrated in Figure 6.7a.

    The probability that a student will need from 4 to 4.5 minutes to get to the next class is the area under the density curve between 4 to 4.5 minutes as shown in Figure 6.7b.

    The probability that a student will need from 4 to 4.1 minutes to get to the next class is equal to the area under the density curve from 4 to 4.1 minutes as illustrated in Figure 6.7c.

FIGURE 6.7

(continues)

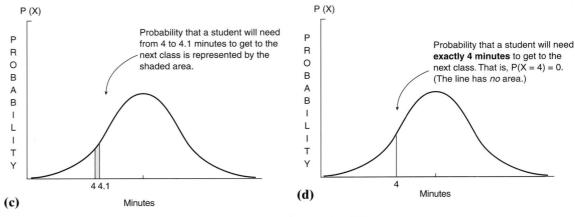

(c)

(d)

FIGURE 6.7 (continued)

As you can see from Figures 6.7a to 6.7c, as the number of minutes gets closer to the single value of 4 minutes (starting from 5 to 4.1 minutes), the areas are getting smaller and smaller. Continuing in this manner, you should begin to understand that the probability, which represents the area, that a student will need **exactly 4 minutes to get to the next class is 0**, since there is no (or zero) area associated with 4 minutes. This is illustrated in Figure 6.7d.

Because there is no probability associated with a single value of a continuous variable, then the probability that a continuous variable X assumes a value between a and b, written P(a < X < b), and the probability that a continuous variable X assumes a value from a to b, written P(a ≤ X ≤ b), are equal. Consequently, for a **continuous variable,**

$$P(a < X < b) = P(a \le X \le b),$$

since P(X = a) = 0 and P(X = b) = 0. For example, the probability that a student will need between 4 and 5 minutes to get to the next class, written P(4 < X < 5), is equal to the probability that a student will need from 4 to 5 minutes inclusive to get to the next class, written P(4 ≤ X ≤ 5), as shown in Figure 6.8.

In summary, the following probabilities are true for a continuous probability distribution.

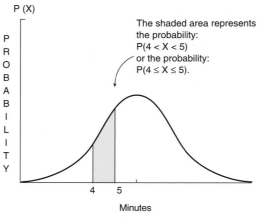

FIGURE 6.8

Probability Statements Associated with a Continuous Probability Distribution

1. The probability of obtaining a specific value X = a of a continuous variable is zero. That is,

$$P(X = a) = 0.$$

2. The probability that a continuous variable X assumes a value between a and b, written P(a < X < b), and the probability that a continuous variable X assumes a value from a to b, written P(a ≤ X ≤ b), are equal. That is,

$$P(a < X < b) = P(a \leq X \leq b).$$

In the next section, we will use these concepts and the characteristics of a continuous variable when we examine one of the most important continuous probability distributions called the normal distribution.

6.3   THE NORMAL DISTRIBUTION

If one uses the pinball demonstrator pictured in Figure 6.9, a collection of balls is released. As the balls fall through the different paths as shown in Figure 6.10, they are constantly hitting other balls and pins. Thus, the paths the balls follow are random. Because the paths are random one might expect to get a *radically different* figure each time the balls are released. However, this is not the case. In fact, a bell-shaped figure similar to the one pictured in Figure 6.11 occurs almost all of the time.

This occurrence was first observed by Sir Frances Galton, in a 1889 publication entitled *Natural Inheritance*, when he used a similar pinball machine to demonstrate that many unknown factors acting together yield a phenomena whose distribution is bell-shaped. The demonstration led to the discovery that the **normal distribution**, pictured in Figure 6.12, could be used as a model for this type of phenomena. The significance of this finding is that it provides an explanation of why many observable phenomena (common occurrences) in nature have *approximately **normal distributions***. It should be noted that the use of the word *normal* is based upon historical significance which just simply refers to

FIGURE 6.9

FIGURE 6.10

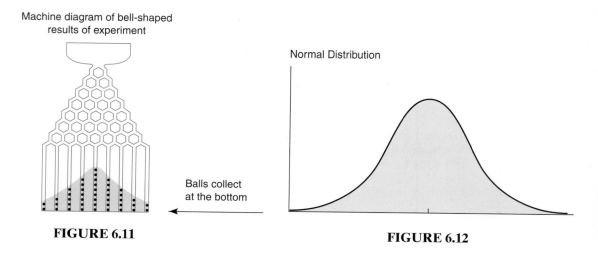

FIGURE 6.11   **FIGURE 6.12**

the shape of the distribution. It does not indicate that this particular distribution is more typical or more appropriate than any other distribution.

To understand why a phenomena can be modeled or approximated by a normal distribution let's consider the distribution of adult male heights. The distribution of adult male heights can be modeled or approximated by a normal distribution since each height is influenced by many random factors acting together. These factors include hereditary, environment, physiological and diet. Thus, we can think of the height of an adult male as the result of *a combination of many such factors.* Each factor is perceived as applying a small force or influence toward a male's height which can either increase or decrease the height of a male. Since so many factors influence a male's height, it would be extremely rare to expect **all these factors** exerting either all positive or all negative influences in one direction. Consequently, we rarely expect to find many male adults to be extremely short or exceptionally tall. Instead, we would expect to find more male adults whose heights are positively influenced by some of these factors and negatively influenced by the other factors. Thus, the heights of adult males would tend to be approximately a normal distribution with most of the males clustered around the average height, located at the center of the distribution, with fewer males that are either much shorter or much taller than the average height at the ends of the distribution. Thus, the distribution of adult male heights can be modeled or approximated by the normal bell-shaped curve shown in Figure 6.12.

Other examples of distributions that can be modeled or approximated by the normal distribution include IQ scores of individuals, adult weights, the diameters of tree trunks, blood pressures of men and women, scores on standardized exams measuring an individual's knowledge, tire wear, the size of red blood cells, the time required to get to work, and the actual amount of soda dispensed into a 2 liter soda bottle. The variables that have been observed to have an approximately normal distribution are continuous variables. Thus, *a normal distribution, also referred to as the normal probability distribution, is a distribution that represents the values of a continuous variable.* The importance of a normal distribution is that it serves as a *good model* in approximating many distributions of real-world phenomena. *If a continuous variable is said to be approximately normal, then the normal distribution can be used to model the continuous variable.* The graph of a normal distribution is called a *normal curve* which is a smooth symmetric bell-shaped curve with a single peak at the center. This is illustrated in Figure 6.12. It should be noted that not all bell-shaped curves represent normal distributions. In fact, we will discuss another bell-shaped distribution called a *t distribution* which is not a normal distribution in Chapter 8. In this chapter, however, we will study in detail the normal distribution.

A normal probability distribution, or simply the normal distribution, is a specific kind of bell-shaped curve with certain properties. Distributions that exhibit these properties all belong to the normal distribution family. Let's now discuss the properties of a normal distribution.

6.4 PROPERTIES OF A NORMAL DISTRIBUTION

In order to analyze distributions which are approximately normal, or that can be approximated by the normal distribution, we must discuss the properties that a normal distribution possesses.

Let's now summarize some of the more important properties of the normal distribution.

Properties of a Normal Distribution

The normal distribution and its graph, the normal curve, have the following properties which are illustrated in Figure 6.13.

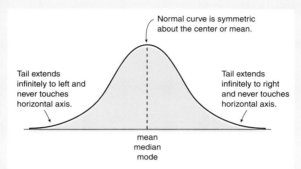

FIGURE 6.13

1. The normal curve is bell-shaped and has a single peak which is located at the center.
2. The mean, median and mode all have the same numerical value and are located at the center of the distribution.
3. The normal curve is symmetric about the mean.
4. The data values in the normal distribution are clustered about the mean.
5. In theory, the normal curve extends infinitely in both directions, always getting closer to the horizontal axis but never touching it. As the normal curve extends out away from the mean and gets closer to the horizontal axis, the area in the tails of the normal curve is getting closer to zero.
6. The total area under the normal curve is 1 which can also be interpreted as probability. Thus, the area under the normal curve represents 100% of all the data values.

Let's examine these properties assuming that a large distribution of IQ scores with a mean of 110 can be approximated by a normal distribution.

Property 1 indicates that the graph representing the distribution of IQ scores is bell-shaped and has a single peak at the center since the IQ scores are approximately a normal distribution. Thus, a graph of all the IQ scores can be modeled by a normal curve as shown in Figure 6.14.

As stated in **property 2**, the mean, median, and mode all have the same value and are located at the center of the normal distribution. Since the IQ scores are approximately a normal distribution, then the mean, median and mode are equal to 110 and are located at the center of the normal curve as illustrated in Figure 6.15.

By definition, the median is equal to the IQ score representing the middle value which is 110. Thus, the median is located at the center of the distribution and one half or 50% of the IQ scores are less than 110 because the median is 110. The mode represents the IQ score having the greatest frequency, thus the mode is also 110 and it is located at the peak which is located at the center of the distribution.

The **symmetric** property of the normal distribution, **property 3**, can be illustrated by examining Figures 6.16a and 6.16b.

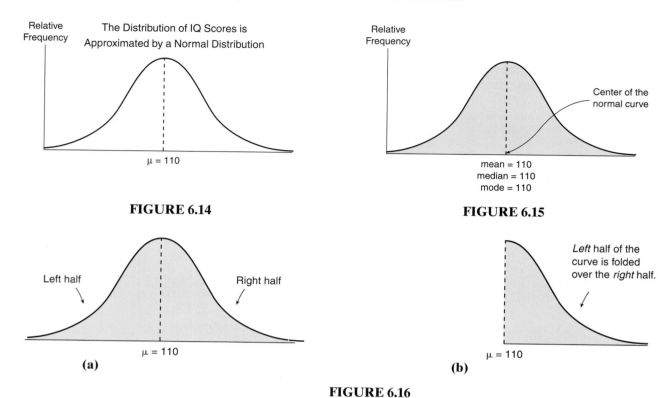

FIGURE 6.14

FIGURE 6.15

(a)

(b)

FIGURE 6.16

If the normal curve shown in Figure 6.16a is folded along the center which is located at the mean value of 110, then the two halves of the normal curve would be identical. This is illustrated by Figure 6.16b.

Figure 6.17 illustrates **property 4** which states that the data values in a normal distribution are clustered about the mean. In examining Figure 6.17, notice that greatest concentration of the area under of the normal curve is clustered around the center value of 110 which represents the mean.

Property 5 states in theory that the normal curve extends infinitely in both directions. This means that the graph of the mathematical formula representing a normal curve will result in a bell-shaped curve extending infinitely in both directions. This is illustrated in Figure 6.18.

However, in practical applications, a normal distribution is used as a model to represent a continuous variable such as the IQ of an individual. It is important to realize that it is impossible for an individual's IQ to approach infinity. For real-life applications, we will draw a normal curve extending infinitely in both directions; however, it is important to understand that the normal curve is serving as a model and the values of the continuous variable will not approach infinity.

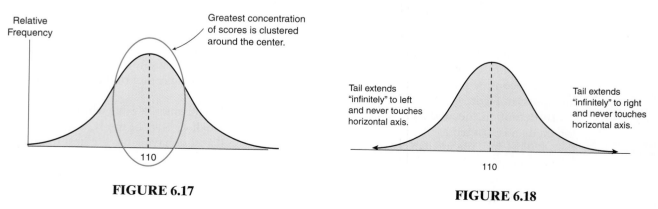

FIGURE 6.17

FIGURE 6.18

Property 6 states that the total area under the normal curve is 1. This is a geometric characteristic of the curve. For a normal distribution, the areas under a normal curve can be interpreted as probabilities. This is a characteristic of a continuous probability distribution.

The Standard Normal Curve

When we state that the distribution of a continuous variable is *approximately* normal, we are indicating that this continuous variable can be modeled by a normal distribution and its graph would be modeled by a normal curve. Thus, for each continuous variable that can be approximated by a normal distribution with a particular mean and standard deviation, there is a normal curve having the same mean and standard deviation which serves as a model of this variable. Consequently, there is *no single normal curve*, but rather *many normal curves* which are referred to as a **family of normal curves**. Let's examine this idea of a *family of normal curves*.

Consider three normal distributions representing the IQ scores of students at different colleges each of which has the *same mean of 110 but different standard deviations*. The standard deviations are $\sigma = 10$, $\sigma = 20$ and $\sigma = 30$. In Figure 6.19, the curve for each normal distribution is drawn. Although these normal curves vary in shape and size, notice that all three graphs in Figure 6.19 are *normal curves having the same center value* since their means are equal. Observe from Figure 6.19 that the normal distribution with the largest standard deviation, $\sigma = 30$, has a normal curve with greatest spread or dispersion, while the normal distribution with the smallest standard deviation, $\sigma = 10$, has a normal curve with the smallest spread or dispersion.

In Figure 6.19, notice for each pair of mean and standard deviation, there is a specific normal curve. There is a normal curve representing the IQ scores of the college where the mean is 110 and the standard deviation is 10. There is a different normal curve representing the IQ scores of the college whose mean is 110 and standard deviation is 20. Finally, there is a third normal curve representing the college IQ scores with a mean of 110 and a standard deviation of 30. Thus, for every particular combination of mean and standard deviation, a different normal curve can be generated. Figure 6.19 illustrates the idea of a **family of normal curves**.

In Figure 6.20, we illustrate three normal distributions representing the blood pressures of different aged males where the means vary from 120 to 130 to 140, but the standard deviation for each distribution is the same, $\sigma = 10$.

The normal distributions of blood pressures in Figure 6.20 have a different value at the center because the means are different. However, the normal distributions have the same variability since the standard deviations are equal. Much like a family of siblings where each can have a different shape and size, you can see by examining Figures 6.19 and 6.20 that there is a different normal curve for each mean and standard deviation. For this reason we say that there is a **family of normal curves**. Within this family of normal curves, there is only one normal distribution or curve for each combination of mean and standard deviation.

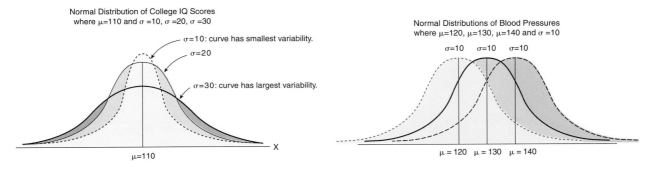

Normal Distribution of College IQ Scores
where $\mu=110$ and $\sigma=10$, $\sigma=20$, $\sigma=30$

$\sigma=10$: curve has smallest variability.
$\sigma=20$
$\sigma=30$: curve has largest variability.

$\mu=110$

Normal Distributions of Blood Pressures
where $\mu=120$, $\mu=130$, $\mu=140$ and $\sigma=10$

$\sigma=10$ $\sigma=10$ $\sigma=10$

$\mu=120$ $\mu=130$ $\mu=140$

FIGURE 6.19   **FIGURE 6.20**

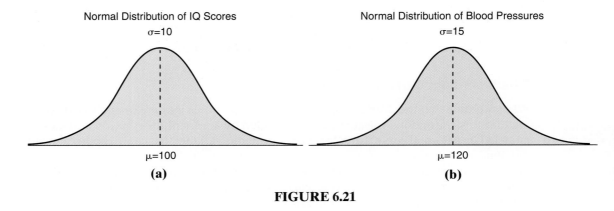

FIGURE 6.21

We have seen that there is a family of normal curves where each curve can have a different mean or a different standard deviation. Consequently, the number of possible normal curves is infinite. For example, there is a normal curve having a mean μ = 100 and standard deviation σ = 10 which models the IQ scores of college students. Another normal curve with a mean μ = 120 and standard deviation σ = 15 models the blood pressures of 20 year old males. These normal curves are illustrated in Figures 6.21a and 6.21b.

Let's examine the *similarity between the two normal curves* in Figures 6.22a and 6.22b. In Figure 6.22a, the proportion of area under the normal curve for the distribution of IQ scores between the μ = 100 and 110, which is one standard deviation above the mean, has been shaded. Similarly, in Figure 6.22b, an equivalent proportion of area under the normal curve for blood pressures between the μ = 120 and 135, which is also one standard deviation above the mean, has also been shaded. Although the shaded areas appear to be different, they represent the *same proportion of area under each normal curve*.

*This is also true for the proportion of area under every normal curve between the mean and the data value which is **one standard deviation above the mean** regardless of its mean and standard deviation.* In general, **for every normal curve the proportion of area under the curve between the mean and the data value which is one standard deviation above the mean is the same proportion of area**. It is also true that *the proportion of area under each normal curve between the mean and the data value which is **two standard deviations above the mean** represents the same proportion of area.* This is illustrated in Figures 6.23a and 6.23b for the distribution of IQ scores and blood pressures.

*The proportion of area under every normal curve between the mean and the data value which is **one standard deviation below the mean** is the same proportion of area.* This is illustrated in Figures 6.24a and 6.24b for the distribution of IQ scores and blood pressures.

FIGURE 6.22

FIGURE 6.23

FIGURE 6.24

In fact, **the proportion of area under any normal curve between the mean and the data value which is N standard deviations away from the mean is the same for all normal curves.** Consequently, when working with normal distribution applications it is possible only to have to work with one normal curve since each member of the family of normal distribution curves exhibit the same characteristics. Thus, although there are an infinite number of normal curves (or normal distributions), *there is one special member of the normal distribution family* that can used to serve as the normal distribution model for any application. This special normal distribution is referred to as the **standard normal distribution**. The **standard normal distribution** has a mean equal to zero, $\mu = 0$, and a standard deviation equal to one, $\sigma = 1$. The standard normal distribution model is shown in Figure 6.25.

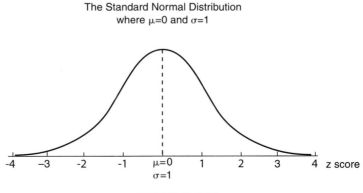

FIGURE 6.25

To utilize this standard normal distribution as a model for any normal distribution, it becomes necessary to convert any normal distribution to the standard normal distribution. This is accomplished by converting the values of the continuous variable to z scores. Recall from Chapter 3, the z score of a data value indicates the number of standard deviations that the data value deviates from the mean. The formula for the z score of a population data value is:

$$\text{z score of a data value x} = \frac{x - \mu}{\sigma} \; .$$

In essence, the z score formula helps us to convert any normal distribution to the standard normal distribution. This idea is illustrated in Figures 6.26a and 6.26b, where the normal distributions representing the IQ scores and the blood pressures of Figures 6.21a and 6.21b are shown with their respective z scores written underneath some of the values of the continuous variables, IQ scores and blood pressures.

As shown in Figures 6.26a and 6.26b, regardless of the values and units of any normal continuous variable, the z score formula can be used to transform any normal distribution to the standard normal distribution with a mean of 0 and a standard deviation of one. Thus, although both normal curves in Figures 6.26a and 6.26b represent different normal distributions, we can convert each normal curve to the standard normal curve by changing each data value to its z score. Consequently, the normal curves in Figures 6.26a and 6.26b can be modeled by the standard normal curve in Figure 6.27.

Since any normal distribution can be converted to the standard normal distribution, we only need to refer to one statistical table to find the area under any normal curve rather than an infinite number of tables for all the possible normal curves. This statistical table[1] is called the **Standard Normal Curve**

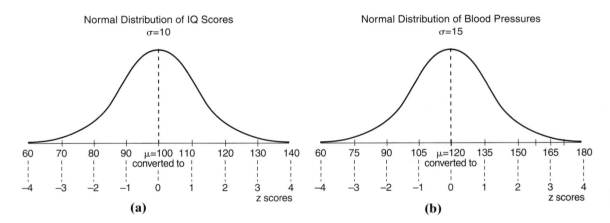

FIGURE 6.26

FIGURE 6.27

[1]The TI–83 Plus graphing calculator can find the area under a normal curve associated to a given z-score or raw score.

Area Table and will be referred to as **Table II in Appendix D: Statistical Tables**. Therefore, for any normal continuous variable, *Table II* can be used to find the area (or probability) which falls to the left of a particular z score associated with a normal curve. In Section 6.5, we will explain how to use *Table II: The Normal Curve Area Table* to determine the area or probability associated with any normal curve.

6.5 USING THE NORMAL CURVE AREA TABLE

The **Normal Curve Area Table, Table II,** located in **Appendix D: Statistical Tables** at the back of the text, gives the relationship between a z score and the proportion of area under the normal curve. In particular, when a z score is looked up in Table II, the proportion of area under the normal curve to the **left of this z score** is given. Let's now examine how to use Table II to find the different areas under a normal curve. Notice Table II, located in **Appendix D: Statistical Tables**, consists of two pages. One page pertains to the negative z scores while the other page pertains to the positive z scores. On each page there is a column labelled **z** within the table. When a z score is looked up in the table, it gives the proportion of area under the normal curve which is to the left of the z score.

For example, suppose we wanted to find the proportion of area under the standard normal curve to the left of the z score z = –1.28. The shaded area in Figure 6.28 illustrates the proportion of area to the left of z = –1.28. To determine this area, we need to locate z = –1.28 in Table II. To find this z score, look up –1.2 in the column labeled z on the page pertaining to the negative z scores. The second decimal place of z = –1.2**8** (i.e. the value 8) is found by moving across the row labeled –1.2 of the table until you reach the column labeled 8. The entry in Table II corresponding to z = –1.28 is 0.1003. This is illustrated in Figure 6.29. Thus, 0.1003 represents the proportion of area to the **left** of z = –1.28 as shown by the shaded area in Figure 6.28.

In general, the following procedure can be used to find the proportion of area under a normal curve to the left of a z score in Table II.

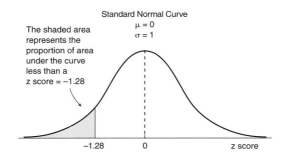

FIGURE 6.28

TABLE II: The Normal Curve Area Table

z	0	1	2	3	4	5	6	7	8	9
.									*	
.									*	
.									*	
-0.9									*	
-1.0									*	
-1.1									*	
-1.2	**								**0.1003**	
-1.3										
-1.4										
.										
.										
.										

FIGURE 6.29

> ## Procedure to Determine the Proportion of Area Under a Normal Curve to the Left of a z Score in Table II
>
> 1. Determine which page of Table II to use.
> 2. Using the appropriate page of the table, find the row corresponding to the z score under the column labeled z. This row is determined by looking for the integer value and the value of the first decimal place of the z score.
> 3. Locate the column corresponding to the z score. To determine this column, look for the value of the second decimal place of the z score by moving across the top row of the table until you find the column pertaining to the second decimal place.
> 4. The entry found in the table where the row and column determined in steps 3 and 4 intersect represents the proportion of area to the left of the z score.

EXAMPLE 6.1

Find the proportion of area under the normal curve:
a)   To the left of $z = -0.53$.
b)   To the left of $z = 2.56$.

Solution

a)   It's helpful to make a sketch of the normal curve and to shade in the proportion of area one needs to determine. In Figure 6.30, the proportion of area under the normal curve to the left of $z = -0.53$ is shaded. To determine this shaded area, look up the z score $z = -0.53$ in Table II using the procedure outlined above.
1. Since the z score is negative, use the page pertaining to the negative z scores.
2. Locate the row corresponding to the z score $z = \mathbf{-0.5}3$ by looking up **-0.5** under the column labeled z.
3. Locate the column corresponding to the second decimal place, 3, of the z score $z = -0.5\mathbf{3}$.
4. The entry in Table II corresponding to $z = -0.53$ is 0.2981. This is illustrated in Figure 6.31.

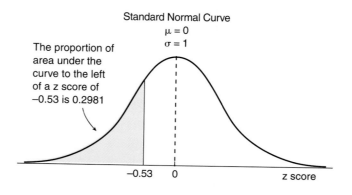

FIGURE 6.30

TABLE II: The Normal Curve Area Table

z	0	1	2	3	4	5	6	7	8	9
				*.						
.				*						
.				*						
.				*						
−1.0				*						
−0.9				*						
−0.8				*						
−0.7				*						
−0.6				*						
−0.5	*****************			0.2981						
.										
.										
.										

FIGURE 6.31

Thus, 0.2981 represents the proportion of area to the **left** of $z = -0.53$ as shown by the shaded area in Figure 6.30.

b) The proportion of area under the normal curve to the left of z = 2.56 has been shaded and is shown in Figure 6.32. To determine this shaded area, we need to look up the z score z = 2.56 in Table II.

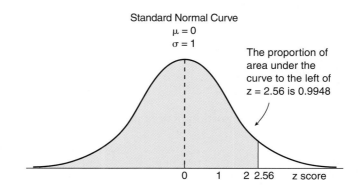

FIGURE 6.32

TABLE II: The Normal Curve Area Table

z	0	1	2	3	4	5	6	7	8	9
							*.			
.							*			
.							*			
.							*			
2.0							*			
2.1							*			
2.2							*			
2.3							*			
2.4							*			
2.5	**********************************						0.9948			
.										

FIGURE 6.33

Using the following procedure, we can locate z = 2.56 in Table II.
1. Since the z score is positive, use the page pertaining to positive z scores.
2. Locate the row corresponding to the z score z = **2.5**6 by looking up **2.5** under the column labeled z.
3. Locate the column corresponding to the second decimal place, 6, of the z score z = 2.5**6**.
4. The entry in Table corresponding to z = 2.56 is 0.9948. This is illustrated in Figure 6.33.

Thus, 0.9948 represents the proportion of area to the **left** of z = 2.56 as shown by the shaded area in Figure 6.32.

We can generalize the procedure to find the proportion of area to the left of a z score.

Procedure to Find the Proportion of Area to the Left of a z Score

---

Proportion of Area to the left of z = Entry in Table II corresponding to z

---

Example 6.2 illustrates how to use Table II to find areas under the normal curve to the ***right of a z score.***

EXAMPLE 6.2

Find the proportion of area under the normal curve:
a) To the right of z = −1.37.
b) To the right of z = 0.67.

Solution

a) In Figure 6.34, the proportion of area under the normal curve to the right of z = −1.37 has been shaded.

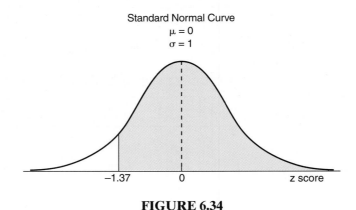

Standard Normal Curve
μ = 0
σ = 1

−1.37   0   z score

FIGURE 6.34

Find z = −1.37 in Table II. Using the techniques described, we find that the entry in Table II corresponding to z = −1.37 is 0.0853. This is illustrated in Figure 6.35.

TABLE II: The Normal Curve Area Table

z	0	1	2	3	4	5	6	7	8	9
								*		
•								*		
•								*		
•								*		
−1.1								*		
−1.2								*		
−1.3	** 0.0853
−1.4										
•										

FIGURE 6.35

Consequently, 0.0853 of the **total** area is to the left of z = −1.37. *Since the total proportion of area under the normal curve is 1, to find the proportion of area to the right of z = −1.37 subtract 0.0853 from 1.* Thus, the proportion of area to the *right* of z = −1.37 is:

$$\text{proportion of area to the } right \text{ of } z = -1.37 = 1 - 0.0853$$
$$= 0.9147.$$

This is illustrated in Figure 6.36.

b) The proportion of area under the normal curve to the right of z = 0.67 has been shaded and is shown in Figure 6.37. To determine this shaded area, we need to look up the z score z = 0.67 in Table II.

The proportion of area to the right of z = −1.37 is 0.9147

FIGURE 6.36   **FIGURE 6.37**

TABLE II: The Normal Curve Area Table

z	0	1	2	3	4	5	6	7	8	9
								*		
•								*		
•								*		
•								*		
0.1								*		
0.2								*		
0.3								*		
0.4								*		
0.5								*		
0.6	** 0.7486
•										

FIGURE 6.38

Using Table II, the entry corresponding to z = 0.67 is 0.7486. This is illustrated in Figure 6.38. Consequently, 0.7486 of the **total** area is to the left of z = 0.67.
To find the proportion of area to the right of z = 0.67 subtract 0.7486 from 1 since the total proportion of area under the normal curve is 1. Thus, the proportion of area to the *right* of z = 0.67 is:

$$\text{proportion of area to the } right \text{ of } z = 0.67 = 1 - 0.7486$$
$$= 0.2514.$$

This is illustrated in Figure 6.39.
We can now generalize the procedure to find the proportion of area to the right of a z score.

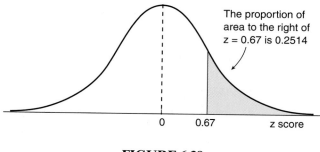

FIGURE 6.39

Another procedure which can be used to determine the proportion of area to the right of a z score is to utilize the symmetric property of the normal curve (property 3).

Procedure to Find the Proportion of Area to the Right of a z Score

1 – Proportion of Area to the left of z = Proportion of Area to the right of z

---

For example, using the alternate procedure to Part (a) of Example 6.2, the proportion of area to the right of z = –1.37 can be found by looking up the proportion of area to the left of z = 1.37, which is

---

Alternate Procedure to Find the Proportion of Area to the Right of a z Score

Proportion of Area to the right of z = Proportion of Area to the left of –z

---

0.9147. In Part (b) of Example 6.2, the proportion of area to the right of z = 0.67 can be found by looking up the proportion of area to the left of z = –0.67, which is 0.2514.
Example 6.3 illustrates how to use Table II to find areas under the normal curve **between two z scores**.

EXAMPLE 6.3

Find the proportion of area under the normal curve:
a) Between z = 0 and z = +1.5.
b) Between z = –1.96 and z = +1.96.
c) Between z = –1.25 and z = +1.0.

Solution

a) In Figure 6.40, the proportion of area under the normal curve between z = 0 and z = +1.5 has been shaded.

The procedure to determine this shaded region is outlined in the following two steps.

1. Determine the proportion of area to the left of z = 0 and the proportion of area to the left of z = 1.5. From Table II, the proportion of area to the left each z score is:

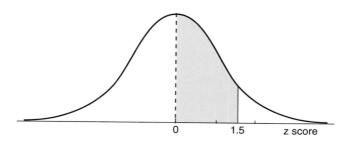

FIGURE 6.40

z Score	Proportion of Area to the Left
0	0.5000
1.5	0.9332

2. The proportion of area between the two z scores can be found by subtracting the **smaller area** from the **larger area**. Thus, *the proportion of area between z = 0 and z = 1.5 is*:

$$0.9332 - 0.5000 = 0.4332.$$

This is illustrated in Figure 6.41.

b) In Figure 6.42, the proportion of area between z = –1.96 and z = +1.96 has been shaded. To determine this shaded area, use the following two steps.

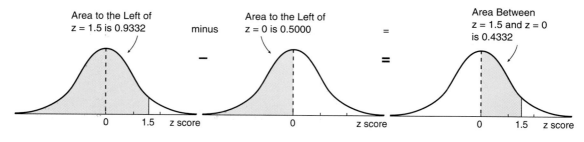

FIGURE 6.41

1. Determine the proportion of area to the left of z = –1.96 and the proportion of area to the left

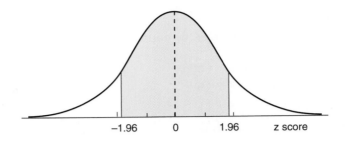

FIGURE 6.42

of $z = 1.96$. From TABLE II, the proportion of area to the left of each z score is:

z Score	Proportion of Area to the Left
−1.96	0.0250
1.96	0.9750

2. Subtract the **smaller area** from the **larger area**. Thus, *the proportion of area between z = 1.96 and z = −1.96 is*:

$$0.9750 - 0.0250 = 0.9500.$$

This is illustrated in Figure 6.43.

c)   In Figure 6.44, the proportion of area between $z = -1.25$ and $z = 1.0$ is shaded.

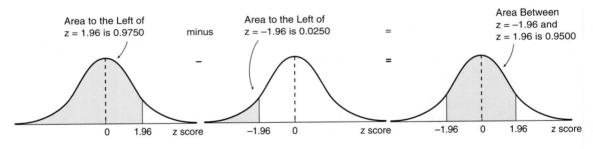

FIGURE 6.43

To determine this shaded region, perform the following two steps.

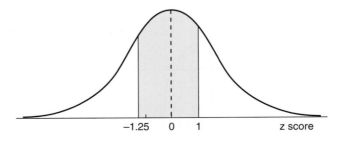

FIGURE 6.44

1. Determine the proportion of area to the left of each z score. From Table II, these proportions are:

z Score	Proportion of Area to the Left
−1.25	0.1056
1.00	0.8413

2. By subtracting the **smaller area** from the **larger area**, *the proportion of area between z = 1.00 and z = −1.25 is*:

$$0.8413 - 0.1056 = 0.7357.$$

This is illustrated in Figure 6.45.
We can now generalize the procedure to find the proportion of area between two z scores.

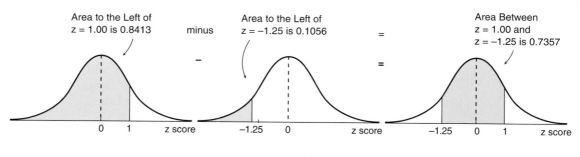

FIGURE 6.45

Since the normal curve represents a continuous variable, then the area associated with a particu-

---

Procedure to Find the Proportion of Area Between Two z Scores

Proportion of Area between two z scores = Proportion of Area to the left of larger z score *minus* Proportion of Area to the left of smaller z score

---

lar z score is zero. This is true because there is no area under a continuous curve and exactly over a z score. Therefore, we have the following rule.

Using the procedure to find the area between two z scores we can determine and verify the per-

---

Proportion of Area Associated to a Single z Score

Proportion of area for a particular z score equals zero.

---

centages associated with the Empirical Rule discussed in Chapter 3. The Empirical Rule states for a bell-shaped distribution that:

1. approximately 68% of the data values will lie within one standard deviation of the mean.

2.   approximately 95% of the data values will lie within two standard deviations of the mean.
3.   approximately all (99% to 100%) of the data values will lie within three standard deviations of the mean.

In Example 6.4, we will verify the results of the Empirical Rule for a normal distribution.

EXAMPLE 6.4

For a normal distribution, determine the percent of area under a normal curve within:
a)   One standard deviation of the mean.
b)   Two standard deviations of the mean.
c)   Three standard deviations of the mean.
d)   Why do the results of the Empirical Rule hold true for a normal distribution?

Solution

a)   The percent of area under a normal curve within one standard deviation of the mean is interpreted as the percent of area between the z scores $z = -1$ and $z = 1$. This is illustrated in Figure 6.46. To determine this shaded area, use the following two steps.
   1.   Find the proportion of area to the left of each z score. From Table II, these proportions are:

z Score	Proportion of Area to the Left
−1.00	0.1587
1.00	0.8413

   2.   Subtract the **smaller area** from the **larger area**. Thus, *the proportion of area between z = 1.00 and z = −1.00 is*:

$$0.8413 - 0.1587 = 0.6828.$$

To determine the percent of area between $z = 1.00$ and $z = -1.00$, multiply the proportion of area by 100%. Thus, the percent of area between $z = 1.00$ and $z = -1.00$ is:

$$\begin{aligned} \textit{percent of area between} \atop \textit{z = 1.00 and z = −1.00} &= \left(\textit{proportion of area between} \atop \textit{z = 1.00 and z = −1.00} \right) * \; 100\% \\ &= (0.6828)(100\%) \\ &= 68.28\% \end{aligned}$$

Thus, the percent of area under a normal curve within one standard deviation of the mean is 68.28%.
b)   The percent of area under a normal curve within two standard deviations of the mean is interpreted as the percent of area between the z scores $z = -2$ and $z = 2$. This is illustrated in Figure 6.47.

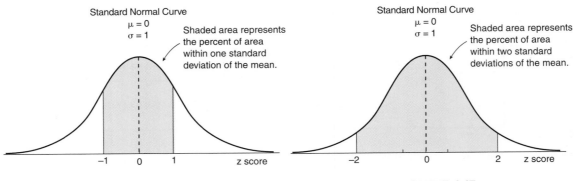

FIGURE 6.46   **FIGURE 6.47**

To determine this shaded area, use the following two steps.
1. Determine the proportion of area to the left of each z score. From Table II, these proportions are:

z Score	Proportion of Area to the Left
−2.00	0.0228
2.00	0.9772

2. Subtract the **smaller area** from the **larger area**. Thus, *the proportion of area between z = 2.00 and z = −2.00 is*:

$$0.9772 - 0.0228 = 0.9544.$$

To determine the percent of area between z = 2.00 and z = −2.00, multiply the proportion of area by 100%.

$$\textit{percent of area between z = 2.00 and z = −2.00} = (0.9544)(100\%)$$
$$= 95.44\%$$

Thus, the percent of area under a normal curve within two standard deviations of the mean is 95.44%.

c) The percent of area under a normal curve within three standard deviations of the mean is interpreted as the percent of area between the z scores z = −3 and z = 3. This is illustrated in Figure 6.48. To determine this shaded area, use the following two steps.
1. Determine the proportion of area to the left of each z score. From Table II:

z Score	Proportion of Area to the Left
−3.00	0.0013
3.00	0.9987

2. Subtract the **smaller area** from the **larger area**. Thus, *the proportion of area between z = 3.00 and z = −3.00 is*:

$$0.9987 - 0.0013 = 0.9974.$$

To change this proportion to percent, multiply the proportion of area by 100%. Thus:

$$\textit{percent of area between z = 3.00 and z = −3.00} = (0.9974)(100\%)$$
$$= 99.74\%$$

Thus, the percent of area under a normal curve within three standard deviations of the mean is 99.74%.

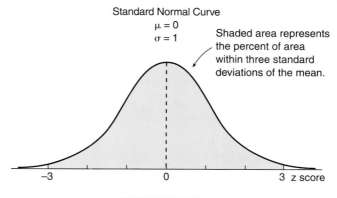

FIGURE 6.48

d) The results of the Empirical Rule hold true for bell-shaped curves. Since a normal curve is a bell-shaped curve, the results of the Empirical Rule are true for any normal distribution. _____ ∎

The results of Example 6.4 are very useful to remember when working with a normal distribution especially if you don't have Table II handy. These three results are stated below and illustrated in Figure 6.49.

In a Normal Distribution:

a) Approximately 68% of the area or data values under the normal curve is within one standard deviation of the mean. That is, approximately 68% of the area or data values falls between $\mu - 1\sigma$ and $\mu + 1\sigma$.

b) Approximately 95% of the area or data values under the normal curve is within two standard deviations of the mean. That is, approximately 95% of the area or data values falls between $\mu - 2\sigma$ and $\mu + 2\sigma$.

c) Approximately 100% of the area or data values under the normal curve is within three standard deviations of the mean. That is, approximately 100% of the area or data values falls between $\mu - 3\sigma$ and $\mu + 3\sigma$.

FIGURE 6.49

Finding a z-score Knowing the Proportion of Area to the Left

An important technique associated with the proportion of area and a z-score is to be able to **find** a z score **knowing** information about the proportion of area to the **left** of the z score.

EXAMPLE 6.5

For a normal distribution, find the z score(s) that cut(s) off:
a) The lowest 20% of area.
b) The highest 10% of area.
c) The middle 90% of the area.

Solution

a) The shaded proportion of area in Figure 6.50 represents the lowest 20% of the area in a normal distribution.

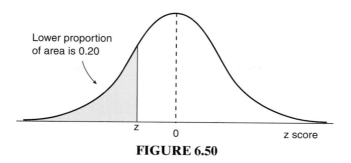

FIGURE 6.50

Notice that this area is positioned to the left of the mean: $\mu = 0$. Thus, this z score will be negative since it is below the mean: $\mu = 0$. To determine the z score that cuts off the lowest 20%, we must use Table II. Since Table II gives the relationship between z scores and the proportion of area to the left of a z score, knowing the proportion of area to the left of this unknown z score will enable us to determine this z score. We can calculate this z score by the using the following procedure.

Step 1 **Determine the proportion of area to the left of the z score, z.**

Since the z score cuts off the lowest 20%, then the proportion of area to the LEFT of the z score is 0.20.

Remark: To convert a percent to a decimal move the decimal point two places to the left. For example:

percent ⟶ **decimal**
20.00% (move decimal point two places to left) 0.2000

Step 2 **Locate the proportion of area in Table II which is closest to the area to the left of the z score and determine the z score corresponding to this proportion of area**.

In Table II find the proportion of area closest to 0.20. This is illustrated in Figure 6.51. Thus, the proportion of area closest to 0.2000 which can be found in Table II is 0.2005. The z score that is associated with 0.2005 is z = –0.84. Thus, the z score that cuts off the lowest 20% of area in a normal distribution is z = –0.84.

TABLE II: The Normal Curve Area Table

z	0	1	2	3	4	5	6	7	8	9
.					*					
.					*					
.					*					
−1.0					*					
−0.9					*					
−0.8	******************				0.2005	0.1977				
−0.7										
−0.6										
.										
.										
.										

FIGURE 6.51

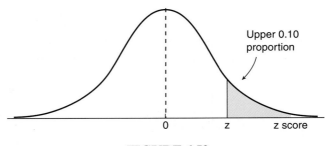

FIGURE 6.52

b)   The shaded proportion of area in Figure 6.52 represents the highest 10% of area in a normal distribution.

Step 1   **Determine the proportion of area to the left of the z score, z**
Notice that the proportion of area to the right of the z score that cuts off the highest 10% is 0.10 and it is positioned to the right of the mean: $\mu = 0$. Thus, the z score will be positive and has 0.10 of the proportion of area under the normal curve to the right of this z score. Remember in Table II, each z score is associated with the proportion of area to the **LEFT** of the z score. Thus, we need to compute the proportion of area to the **LEFT** of the z score to use Table II. To find the z score associated with the highest 10% or 0.10 proportion of area, we need to determine the proportion of area to the **LEFT** of the z score.

To compute the proportion of area to the LEFT, we subtract the proportion to the **RIGHT** of the z score from the **TOTAL AREA** under the normal curve which is 1. That is:

$$\begin{array}{ll} \text{proportion of area to} & = \quad \text{1.0000 minus proportion of area} \\ \text{the LEFT of z score} & \quad\quad \text{to the RIGHT of z score} \end{array}$$

$$= \quad 1.0000 - 0.10$$
$$= \quad 0.9000$$

Step 2   **Locate the proportion of area in Table II which is closest to the proportion of area that is to the left of the z score and determine the z score corresponding to this proportion of area**.
We must find the z score that corresponds to the proportion closest to 0.9000 in Table II. This is illustrated in Figure 6.53. The proportion of area closest to 0.9000 is 0.8997 and is highlighted in Figure 6.53. The z score that is associated with 0.8997 is $z = 1.28$. Thus the z score that cuts off the highest 10% of area in a normal distribution is $z = 1.28$.

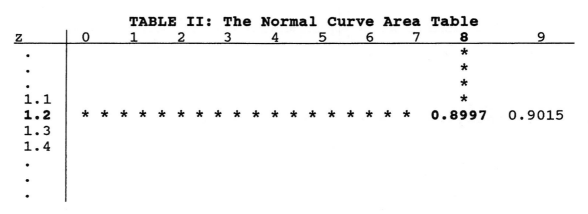

FIGURE 6.53

c)   In a normal distribution, z = 0 is located at the center. Therefore the middle 90% of the z scores will be centered about the z = 0, that is 45% of the z scores will be less than the z = 0 and 45% of the z scores will be greater than the z = 0. This is illustrated in Figure 6.54. By examining Figure 6.54, you should notice that the middle of the normal distribution means the proportion of area is **centered** about z = 0. Thus we are looking for two z scores, which we will symbolize as z_1 and z_2. To determine these z scores, we will follow the procedure outlined in part a of this problem.

Step 1   **Determine the proportion of area to the left of the each z score, z.**
To determine the proportion of area to the left of z_1, observe that 45% or 0.45 of the area is between the z score z_1 and the z = 0. Since the proportion of area to the left of z = 0 is 50% OR 0.50, then the remaining proportion of area to the left of z_1 is:

$$0.50 - 0.45 = 0.05.$$

This is illustrated in Figure 6.55.

Step 2   **Locate the proportion of area in Table II which is closest to the proportion of area that is to the left of the z score and determine the z score corresponding to this proportion of area.**
Since Table II in Appendix D gives the proportion of area to the left of a z score, we are looking for the area closest to 0.0500. The z score closest to 0.0500 can be found in Table II. This is illustrated in Figure 6.56.
Notice that the z scores −1.64 and −1.65 are each 0.0005 away from the proportion 0.0500. When this occurs *either* z score could be chosen. In this text, we will always use the z score **farthest from z = 0**, i.e. the z score with the greater absolute value. Thus, **z_1 = −1.65** is

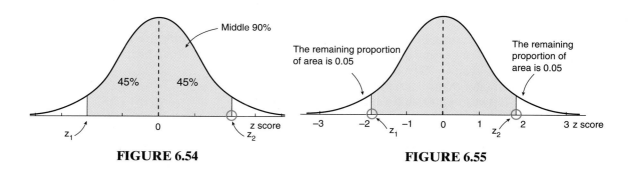

FIGURE 6.54   **FIGURE 6.55**

TABLE II: The Normal Curve Area Table

z	0	1	2	3	4	5	6	7	8	9
.						*				
.						*				
.						*				
−1.8						*				
−1.7						*				
−1.6	*	*	*	*	*	*	*	*	0.0505	**0.0495**	
−1.5										
−1.4										
.										
.										
.										

FIGURE 6.56

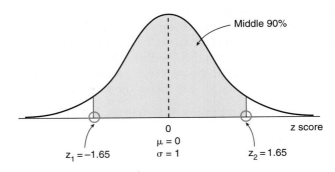

FIGURE 6.57

chosen to represent the z score that cuts off the lower proportion of 0.05 or the lowest 5%. Since the normal distribution is symmetric about z = 0, then the value of z_2 is also 1.65 standard deviations away from the mean of z = 0. However, since z_2 is greater than the mean of z = 0, then z_2 is positive and is equal to $z_2 = 1.65$. Therefore, the z scores that cut off the middle 90% of the normal distribution are $z_1 = -1.65$ and $z_2 = 1.65$. This is illustrated in Figure 6.57.

6.6 APPLICATIONS OF THE NORMAL DISTRIBUTION

Let's now consider some applied problems in which it will be assumed that the distributions under consideration can be approximated by a normal distribution.

EXAMPLE 6.6

Assume the distribution of tire wear for a radial brand of auto tire is approximately normal with μ = 48,000 miles and σ = 2,000 miles. Find the proportion of tires which would be expected to wear:
a) Less than 46,000 miles.
b) Greater than 49,000 miles
c) Between 47,000 miles and 51,000 miles.

Solution

Since this distribution is approximately normal, we will assume all of the properties of the normal distribution and use the normal curve as a sketch of the distribution of tire wear. This is shown in Figure 6.58a.
  In your examination of Figure 6.58a, notice that the mean is placed at the center of the normal curve below the z score line and corresponding to its z score of zero.
a) In Figure 6.58b, the shaded area represents the proportion of tires which would be expected to wear less than 46,000 miles.

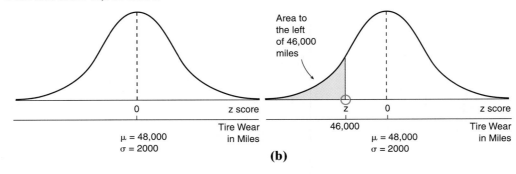

FIGURE 6.58

To determine the proportion of tires which would be expected to wear less than 46,000 miles we must find the portion of area to the left of 46,000 miles. To determine this, we first calculate the z score for 46,000 miles, using:

$$z = \frac{x - \mu}{\sigma}$$

Thus,

$$z = \frac{46,000 - 48,000}{2,000}$$

$$z = \frac{-2000}{2000} = -1$$

The proportion of area to the left of z = -1 is 0.1587. Therefore the proportion of tires which would be expected to wear less than 46,000 miles is 0.1587.

b) In Figure 6.59, the shaded area represents the proportion of tires which would expect to wear greater than 49,000 miles.

To find the proportion of tires which would be expected to wear greater than 49,000 miles, find the proportion of area to the right of 49,000 miles. To determine this, first calculate the z score of 49,000 miles.

$$z = \frac{49,000 - 48,000}{2,000} = 0.50$$

Remember that Table II gives the proportion of area to the left of 49,000 miles or z = 0.50, which is 0.6915. To find the proportion of area to the *right* of 49,000 miles, subtract 0.6915 from 1.0000. Therefore the proportion of tires which would expect to wear greater than 49,000 miles is 0.3085.

c) In Figure 6.60, the shaded area represents the proportion of tires which would expect to wear between 47,000 miles and 51,000 miles.

To find the area between 47,000 miles and 51,000 miles, first calculate their z scores.
For z of 47,000

$$z = \frac{47,000 - 48,000}{2,000} = -0.50$$

For z of 51,000

$$z = \frac{51,000 - 48,000}{2,000} = 1.50$$

FIGURE 6.59

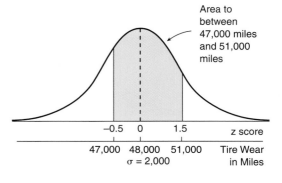

FIGURE 6.60

To find the proportion of area *between* the two z scores, determine each of the corresponding areas and then subtract the smaller area from the larger area.

Tire Wear (in miles)	z Score	Proportion of Area to the Left
47,000	–0.5	0.3085
51,000	1.5	0.9332

shaded area = larger area – smaller area
$$= 0.9332 - 0.3085$$
$$= 0.6247$$

Therefore, the proportion of tires that last between 47,000 miles and 51,000 miles is 0.6247.

EXAMPLE 6.7

A distribution of IQ scores is normally distributed with a mean of 100 and a standard deviation of 15. Find the proportion of IQ scores that are:
a) Less than 88.
b) Greater than 127.
c) Less than 70 or greater than 145.
d) Less than one standard deviation from the mean.
e) Within two standard deviations of the mean.

Solution

a) In Figure 6.61, the shaded area represents the proportion of IQ scores less than 88. To determine this area calculate z of 88.

$$z = \frac{88 - 100}{15} = -0.80$$

The proportion of IQ scores less than 88 is 0.2119.

b) In Figure 6.62, the shaded area represents the proportion of IQ scores greater than 127. To determine this area calculate the z of 127.

$$z = \frac{127 - 100}{15} = 1.80$$

The proportion of area to the left 127 is 0.9641. Therefore the proportion of IQ scores greater than 127 is equal to:

$$1.0000 - 0.9641 = 0.0359.$$

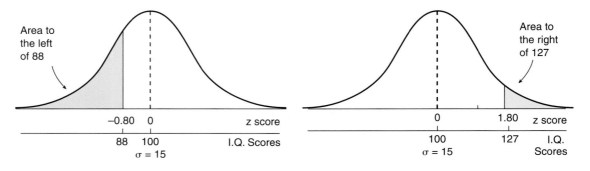

FIGURE 6.61   **FIGURE 6.62**

c) In Figure 6.63, the shaded area represents the proportion of IQ scores less than 70 or greater than 145.

    As can be seen in Figure 6.63, there are two separate areas to be determined. To calculate the *total* shaded area, calculate each area separately and add the two areas together. For the proportion of area less than 70, calculate the z of 70.

$$z = \frac{70 - 100}{15} = -2.00$$

Using Table II, the proportion of area less than 70 is 0.0228.
For the proportion of area greater than 145, calculate z of 145.

$$z = \frac{145 - 100}{15} = 3.00$$

    From Table II, the proportion of area to the right of 145 is 0.0013.
    Therefore the total shaded area is the sum of these two areas: $0.0013 + 0.0228 = 0.0241$. Thus the proportion of IQ scores less than 70 or greater than 145 is 0.0241.

d) In Figure 6.64, the shaded area represents the proportion of IQ scores within one standard deviation of the mean.

    Less than one standard deviation from the mean would include all IQ scores between $z = -1$ and $z = +1$ as shown in Figure 6.64. We need to determine the proportion of area between the z scores of -1 and +1.

    Using Table II, we have:

z Score	Proportion of Area to the Left
-1	0.1587
$+1$	0.8413

    To find the area between the z scores of -1 and $+1$ subtract the smaller area from the larger area.

$$
\begin{aligned}
\text{shaded area} &= \text{larger area - smaller area} \\
&= 0.8413 - 0.1587 \\
&= 0.6826.
\end{aligned}
$$

Therefore the proportion of IQ scores less than one standard deviation from the mean is 0.6826.

e) In Figure 6.65, the shaded area represents the proportion of IQ scores within two standard deviations of the mean.

    The IQ scores within two standard deviations from the mean would include all the IQ scores between $z = -2$ and $z = +2$ as shown in Figure 6.65. Let's determine the proportion of the area

FIGURE 6.63   **FIGURE 6.64**

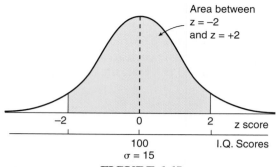

FIGURE 6.65

between the z scores of –2 and +2. Using Table II, we find the corresponding areas to the left of each z score:

z Score	Proportion of Area to the Left
–2	0.0228
+2	0.9772

Subtracting the smaller area from the larger area, the proportion of IQ scores within two standard deviations of the mean is 0.9544.

EXAMPLE 6.8

One thousand students took a standardized psychology exam. The results were approximately normal with $\mu = 83$ and $\sigma = 8$. Find the *number* of students who scored:
a) Less than 67.
b) Greater than 87.

Solution:

a) In Figure 6.66, the shaded area represents the proportion of students who scored less than 67.
    The z score of 67 is: $z = -2$. Using Table II, the proportion of area to the left of 67 is 0.0228.
    Thus, the number of students who scored less than 67 is:

$$0.0228 \text{ of } 1000 = (0.0228)(1000)$$
$$= 22.8$$

This is rounded off to 23 students.

b) In Figure 6.67, the shaded area represents the proportion of students who scored greater than 87.
    The z score of 87 is 0.50. From Table II, the proportion of the area to the left of $z = 0.50$ is 0.6915. Therefore the proportion of area to the right of 87 equals 0.3085.

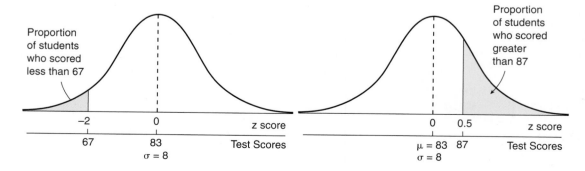

FIGURE 6.66   **FIGURE 6.67**

To find the *number* of students who scored greater than 87 multiply the proportion of area by the total number of students who took the exam. (The *area* to the right 87 represents the proportion of students in the distribution who scored greater than 87.) Thus, the number of students who scored greater than 87 is equal to:

$$0.3085 \text{ of } 1000 = (0.3085)(1000)$$
$$= 308.5.$$

We round this off to 309 students.

6.7 PERCENTILES AND APPLICATIONS OF PERCENTILES

Percentiles are widely used to describe the position of a data value within a distribution. Let's examine the definition of a **percentile rank** for a data value within a normal distribution.

> **DEFINITION**
> The **percentile rank** of a data value X within a normal distribution is equal to the percent of area under the normal curve to the left of the data value X. Percentile ranks are always expressed as a whole number.

EXAMPLE 6.9

Matthew earned a grade of 87 on his history exam. If the grades in his class were normally distributed with $\mu = 80$ and $\sigma = 7$, find Matthew's percentile rank on this exam.

Solution

The shaded area in Figure 6.68 represents the percentile rank of the grade 87.
To find the proportion of area to the left of 87 we must first calculate the z score of 87.

$$z = \frac{87 - 80}{7} = 1$$

From Table II, the proportion of area to the left of 87 is 0.8413. To convert a proportion to a percent move the decimal two places to the right. Thus, the proportion becomes 84.13%. Since percentile ranks are always expressed as whole numbers, 84.13% is rounded off to the nearest whole percent which is 84%. Therefore, the **percentile rank of 87 is 84**. Using Percentile notation, we can express this result as: **$87 = P_{84}$.**

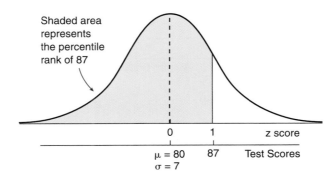

FIGURE 6.68

Matthew's grade of 87 has a percentile rank of 84 which means that his grade of 87 was better than 84% of the test grades.

Percentile rank is an important statistical measure that describes the position of a data value within a distribution. It can also be used to compare data values from different distributions. This is illustrated in Example 6.10.

EXAMPLE 6.10

Miss Brooke took two exams last week. Her grades and class results were as follows:

Exam	Her Grade	Class Mean (μ)	Class Standard Deviation (σ)
English	83	80	6
Math	77	74	5

Assuming the results of both exams to be normally distributed, use percentile ranks to determine on which exam Miss Brooke did better relative to her class.

Solution

a)   The shaded area in Figure 6.69 represents the percentile rank of Miss Brooke's English grade of 83. To determine this area, calculate the z score of 83.

$$z = \frac{83 - 80}{6} = 0.5$$

From Table II, the proportion of area to the left of 83 is 0.6915. This is expressed in percent form as 69.15%. Since percentile ranks are expressed in whole numbers, 69.15% rounded off to the nearest whole percent is 69. Therefore, the percentile rank of Miss Brooke's English grade is 69.

b)   The shaded area in Figure 6.70 represents the percentile rank of Miss Brooke's math grade of 77. To determine this area, compute the z score of 77.

$$z = \frac{77 - 74}{5} = 0.60$$

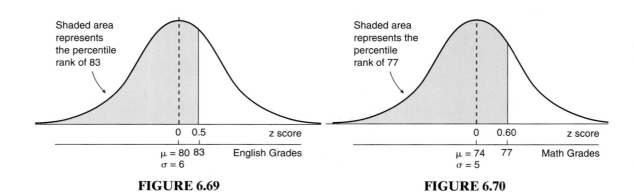

Shaded area represents the percentile rank of 83

$\mu = 80$ 83   English Grades
$\sigma = 6$

FIGURE 6.69

Shaded area represents the percentile rank of 77

$\mu = 74$ 77   Math Grades
$\sigma = 5$

FIGURE 6.70

The proportion of area corresponding to the z = 0.6 is 0.7257. This is 72.57%. Therefore, the percentile rank of her math exam grade is 73. The percentile rank of her math grade is larger than the percentile rank of her English grade. Thus, *relative* to her class, Miss Brooke did better on her math exam.

EXAMPLE 6.11

One of the entrance requirements at a local college is a percentile rank of at least 45 on the verbal SAT exam. Bill scored 470 on his verbal SAT exam. Does he meet the minimum requirement of this college, if the verbal SAT distribution is normally distributed with $\mu = 500$ and $\sigma = 100$?

Solution

The shaded area in Figure 6.71 represents the percentile rank of the SAT score 470.

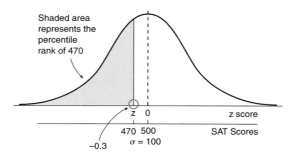

Shaded area represents the percentile rank of 470

FIGURE 6.71

Find the z score of 470.

$$z = \frac{470 - 500}{100} = -0.30$$

In Table II, the entry corresponding to the $z = -0.30$ is 0.3821 or 38.21%. Thus, the percentile rank of Bill's SAT score is 38. Therefore, Bill does not meet the entrance requirement.

EXAMPLE 6.12

An entrance requirement at an eastern university is a high school average in the top 25% of one's high school class. Craig would like to know if he qualifies for entrance into this college. His high school average is 85. If the high school averages of his class are normally distributed with a mean of 75 and a standard deviation of 10, does he meet the requirement?

Solution

Being in the top 25% of the graduating class means that Craig's average must be better than **at least 75%** of the graduating class. Therefore the percentile rank of Craig`s average must be at least 75. To determine if Craig qualifies for entrance into this college, find the percentile rank of Craig`s high school average and compare it to the minimum requirement of a percentile rank of 75. The shaded area in Figure 6.72 represents the percentile rank of Craig's high school average of 85.
    To determine this area, find the z score of 85.

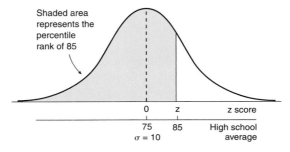

Shaded area represents the percentile rank of 85

FIGURE 6.72

$$z = \frac{85 - 75}{10} = 1$$

From Table II, the proportion of area corresponding to the z = 1 is 0.8413 which equals 84.13%. Therefore, the percentile rank of Craig's average is 84. Since Craig's percentile rank is greater than 75, he meets this entrance requirement.   ▪

CASE STUDY 6.1   College Boards

The information contained in the table of Figure 6.73 represents the percentile ranks of Achievement Tests administered by the College Board to high school seniors who are college-bound. An Achievement Test measures the specific knowledge of a subject.

Percentile ranks of Achievement Test Scores (for college-bound seniors)

Score	English		Mathematics			History		Sciences		
	Eng. Comp. EN-ES*	Literature LR	Math. Level I M1	Math Level II M2	Math Level IIC 2C	Amer. Hist. & Social Studies AH	Euro. Hist. & World Cult. EH	Biology BY	Chemistry CH	Physics PH
800	99+	99+	99+	92	92	99+	99+	99+	99	97
750	99	99+	99	79	79	98	98	97	94	90
700	96	95	93	60	59	93	93	89	86	80
650	87	85	83	39	41	84	83	76	73	66
600	75	70	67	20	19	71	70	61	57	50
550	60	54	48	9	8	54	53	43	40	32
500	41	38	30	4	4	36	34	27	24	16
450	25	23	15	2	1	20	18	15	12	6
400	13	12	5	1	..	8	6	7	4	1
350	5	5	1	1–	..	2	1	3	1	1–
300	1	1	1–	1–	..	1–	1–	1	1–	..
250	1–	1–	1–	..	..	1–	..	1–	..	..
200	..	..	..	..	..	..	..	..	..	..
Average Score	519	529	549	666	668	537	541	561	575	601

FIGURE 6.73

a) Do you think that the test results of a standardized achievement test would be approximately normally distributed when administered to a large group of students across the country?

b) If the Mathematics Achievement Test results for Level I were approximately normal, explain what this information would mean to you?

c) Examine the table in Figure 6.73 and determine the mean test score for the Mathematics Level I (M1), American History and Social Sciences (AH), and the Physics (PH) tests.

d) Approximate the median test score for each of these tests. If these test results are approximately normal, then what value would you expect the median test score to equal?

e) Let's assume that the standard deviation for each of the achievement tests in part (c) is approximately 100. For the mathematics Level I test, the American and Social Studies test, and the Physics test, approximate the percent of test scores that are within one, and two standard deviations of the mean.

f) For a normal distribution, what percentage of the data values are within one, two and three standard deviations of the mean.

g) Compare the results of parts (e) and (f).

h) Which exam(s) seem to approximate the percentages of a normal distribution? Do these results have any affect on the way you answered part (a)?

Another application involves finding the data value that is associated with a certain proportion of the area. This will be illustrated in the following problems.

EXAMPLE 6.13

Consider a normal distribution with a mean of 75 and $\sigma = 5$. Find the data value(s) in the distribution that:

a) Cut(s) off the top 25% of the data values.
b) Represents the 30th percentile.
c) Has a percentile rank of 55.
d) Cut(s) off the middle 40% of the data values.

Solution

a) The shaded area in Figure 6.74 represents the top 25% of the data values in a normal distribution.

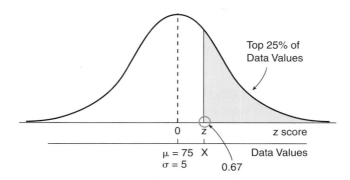

FIGURE 6.74

   To determine the data value that cuts off the top 25% of the data values, we must find the data value that has 25% of the data values greater than this value and 75% of the data values less than this value. Since Table II gives the relationship between z scores and the proportion of area to the left of a z score, then knowing the proportion of area to the left of this unknown z score will enable us to determine this z score. We can now begin to calculate this data value by the using the following procedure.

Step 1 **Determine the proportion of area to the left of the data value, X.**
   Since 25% is to the right of the data value, X, then 75% is to the left of the data value, X. Recall that 75% corresponds to a proportion of 0.7500.

Step 2 **Find the area in Table II which is closest to the area that is to the left of the data value and determine the z score corresponding to this area.**
   In Table II find the area closest to 0.75. This is illustrated in Figure 6.75.
   Thus, the closest area to 0.75 which can be found in the table is 0.7486. Thus, the corresponding z score for the data value X is 0.67. Therefore the data value X which cuts off the top 25% has a z score of 0.67.

Step 3 **Using the raw score formula, X = μ + (z)σ, convert the z score to a data value.**
   In order to convert the z score of 0.67 to a data value, we need to use the raw score formula:

$$X = \mu + (z)\sigma$$

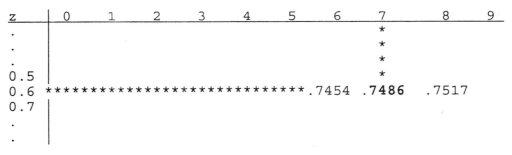

FIGURE 6.75

The data value for z = 0.67 is:

$$X = \mu + (z)\sigma$$
$$= 75 + (0.67)(5)$$
$$= 78.35$$

Therefore the data value which cuts off the top 25% in this normal distribution is 78.35.

b) To determine the data value that represents the 30th percentile, recall that the 30th percentile is the data value that has 30% of the distribution below it. We will follow the procedure outlined in part a of this question.

Step 1 **Determine the proportion of area to the left of the data value, X.**
We are looking for the data value X that has 30% or 0.30 of the area under the normal curve to the left of this data value.

Step 2 **Find the area in Table II which is closest to the area that is to the left of the data value and determine the z score corresponding to this area.**
We must find the z score that corresponds to the bottom 0.30 of area under the normal curve as illustrated in Figure 6.76.

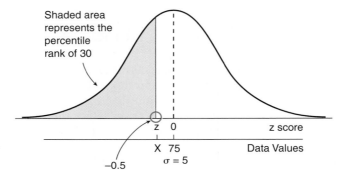

FIGURE 6.76

In Table II find the area closest to 0.30. This is illustrated in Figure 6.77.

TABLE II: Normal Curve Area Table

z	0	1	2	3	4	5	6	7	8	9
.			★							
.			★							
.			★							
-0.6			★							
-0.5	★★★★	.3050	.3015	.2981						
-0.4										
.										
.										

FIGURE 6.77

Thus, the closest area to 0.30 is 0.3015. The corresponding z score is –0.52.

Step 3 **Using the raw score formula, X = μ + (z)σ, convert the z score to a data value.**

Using the formula: X = μ + (z)σ, we can transform this z score to the data value X.

$$X = 75 + (-0.52)(5)$$
$$= 72.4.$$

Therefore the data value X which represents the 30th percentile in this distribution is 72.4.

c) To determine the data value that has percentile rank of 55, we will follow the procedure outlined in part a of this problem.

Step 1 **Determine the proportion of area to the left of the data value, X.**

The data value that has percentile rank of 55, cuts off the bottom 55% of the data values in the distribution. This is illustrated in Figure 6.78.

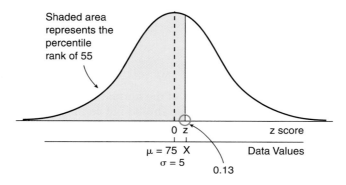

FIGURE 6.78

Step 2 **Find the area in Table II which is closest to the area that is to the left of the data value and determine the z score corresponding to this area.**

From Table II, the area closest to 0.55 is 0.5517, which corresponds to a z score of 0.13.

Step 3 **Using the raw score formula, $X = \mu + (z)\sigma$, convert the z score to a data value.**

$$X = 75 + (0.13)(5)$$
$$X = 75.65$$

Therefore, the data value that has a percentile rank of 55 is 75.65.

d) In a normal distribution, the mean is located at the center. Therefore the middle 40% of the data values will be centered about the mean, that is 20% of the data values will be less than the mean and 20% of the data values will be greater than the mean. This is illustrated in Figure 6.79.

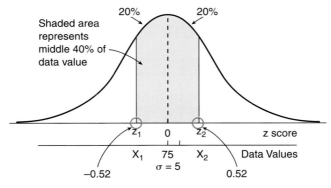

FIGURE 6.79

Notice in Figure 6.79 that we are looking for two data values, which we will symbolize as X_1 and X_2. To determine these data values, we will follow the procedure outlined in part a of this problem.

Step 1   Determine the proportion of area to the left of the data value, X.
To determine the proportion of area to the left of X_1, observe that 0.20 of the area is between the data value X_1 and the mean. Since the total proportion of area to the left of the mean is 0.50, then the remaining area to the left of X_1 is $0.50 - 0.20 = 0.30$.

Step 2   Find the area in Table II which is closest to the area that is to the left of the data value and determine the z score corresponding to this area.
In Table II the area closest to 0.30 is 0.3015. Its corresponding z score is -0.52.

Step 3   Using the raw score formula, $X = \mu + (z)\sigma$, convert the z score to a data value.

$$X_1 = 75 + (-0.52)(5)$$
$$X_1 = 72.4$$

To determine the value of X_2, we will use the symmetry property of the normal curve.

Step 1   Use the symmetry property of the normal curve to determine the z score of X_2.
In examining Figure 6.79, you should notice that the percent of area between the mean and z_1 is the same as the area between the mean and z_2. Using the symmetry property of the normal curve and the value of z_1 is -0.52, the value of z_2 is 0.52. Thus, the z score of X_2 is 0.52.

Step 2.   Using the raw score formula, $X = \mu + (z)\sigma$, convert the z score to a data value.

$$X_2 = 75 + (0.52)(5)$$
$$X_2 = 77.6$$

Therefore the middle 40% of the distribution is located between the two data values 72.4 and 77.6.   ■

We can now generalize the procedures to determine the data value that cuts off the bottom p% in a normal distribution and the data value that cuts off the top q% in a normal distribution.

Procedure to Find Data Value (or Raw Score) That Cuts Off Bottom p % Within a Normal Distribution

1. Change the percentage p to a proportion.
2. Using Table II, find the z score that has the area closest to this proportion. If there is a tie, choose the z score with the larger absolute value.
3. Substitute this z score into the raw score formula

$$X = \mu + (z)\sigma$$

to determine the data value that corresponds to this z score.

Procedure to Find Data Value (or Raw Score) That Cuts Off Top q % Within a Normal Distribution

1. Calculate the percentage of data values below the raw score by subtracting q from 100: $(100 - q)$.

Procedure to Find Data Value (or Raw Score) That Cuts Off Top q % Within a Normal Distribution (continued)

2. Change this percentage to a proportion.
3. Using Table II, find the z score that has the area closest to this proportion. If there is a tie, choose the z score with the larger absolute value.
4. Substitute this z score into the raw score formula

$$X = \mu + (z)\sigma$$

to determine the data value that corresponds to this z score.

EXAMPLE 6.14

In a large physical education class the grades on the final exam were normally distributed with $\mu = 80$ and $\sigma = 8$. Professor Stevenson assigns letter grades in the following way: the top 10% receive A's, the next 15% receive B's, the lowest 4% receive F's, the middle 50% receive C's, and the rest of the grades are D's. Find the numerical grades that correspond to each of the letter grades.

Solution

The information is interpreted in Figure 6.80.

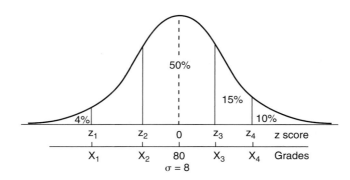

FIGURE 6.80

Using Figure 6.80, let us determine the test grades X_1, X_2, X_3, and X_4 that separate the letter grades.

To determine X_1:
1. Find the area to the left of X_1. This area is 4% or as a proportion 0.04.
2. Find the closest entry to 0.04 in Table II. The closest entry to 0.04 is 0.0401. The z score that corresponds to 0.0401 is −1.75.

To find the value of X_1, we can use the raw score formula:
$$X_1 = \mu + (z)\sigma$$
$$X_1 = 80 + (-1.75)(8)$$
$$X_1 = 66$$

Therefore, the grade which separates the F's from the D's is 66.

To determine X_2:
1. Find the proportion of area to the left of X_2. From the figure we see that 75% of the area is to the right of X_2. This means that the area to the left is 25% or 0.25.

2. The closest entry in Table II to 0.25 is 0.2514. The z score that corresponds to 0.2514 is –0.67. The formula to determine X_2 is:

$$X_2 = \mu + (z)\sigma$$
$$X_2 = 80 + (-0.67)(8)$$
$$X_2 = 74.64$$

Therefore, the test grade which separate grades C and D is 74.64.
To determine X_3:
1. The proportion of area to the left of X_3 is 0.75.
2. The closest entry in Table II is 0.7486. It has a z score of 0.67. Using the raw score formula, we have:

$$X_3 = \mu + (z)\sigma$$
$$X_3 = 80 + (0.67)(8)$$
$$X_3 = 85.36$$

The test grade which separate grades B and C is 85.36.
Finally, to determine X_4:
1. The proportion of area to the left of X_4 is 0.90.
2. The closest entry in Table II is 0.8997, which has a z score of 1.28. Using the raw score formula, we have:

$$X_4 = \mu + (z)\sigma$$
$$X_4 = 80 + (1.28)(8)$$
$$X_4 = 90.24$$

Thus the test grade which separate grades A and B is 90.24.

EXAMPLE 6.15

To determine the size of the annual Christmas bonus, Grace, the personnel and budget director of a telemarketing firm, decides to use annual sales per salesperson as the criterion. The salespeople in the top 20% of annual sales will receive $3000 in bonus, those in the next 30% will receive $2000 in bonus, those in the next 30% will receive $1000 and the rest will receive $500 in bonus. If the annual sales per salesperson is normally distributed with $\mu = \$120,000$ and $\sigma = \$15,000$ determine the annual sales required to obtain:
a) A bonus of $3000.
b) A bonus of $2000.

Solution

The relevant information is summarized in Figure 6.81.

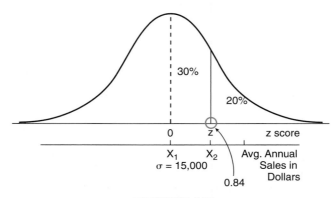

FIGURE 6.81

a) To determine X_2:
1. The percent of area to the left of X_2 is 80% which as a proportion is 0.80.
2. The closest entry in Table II to 0.80 is 0.7995 which has the z score of 0.84. Converting this z score to a raw score, we get $X_2 = \$132,600$.
   Thus, annual sales of at least $132,600 are required to get a $3000 bonus.
b) To determine X_1:
1. Notice that X_1 has 50% of the area to the left of it. Thus, X_1 is the mean.
2. Therefore, $X_1 = \$120,000$.
   Thus, annual sales of at least $120,000 are required to get at least a $2000 bonus.

EXAMPLE 6.16

A local community college decides to award scholarships based upon the results of a standardized achievement test. If this year's 5,000 test results are approximately normal with $\mu = 137$ and $\sigma = 15$, then determine the minimum test grade needed to win a scholarship if the top:
a) 20 students receive scholarships.
b) 30 students receive scholarships.

Solution

a) To find the minimum test grade needed to win a scholarship if the top 20 students receive scholarships, we must first determine the *proportion* of the students that will win scholarships. Since there are 20 students receiving scholarships out of 5,000 students, the proportion of scholarship winners equals:

$$\frac{20}{5000} = 0.0040$$

This is illustrated in Figure 6.82.

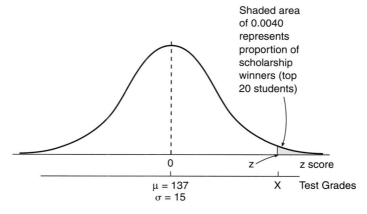

Shaded area of 0.0040 represents proportion of scholarship winners (top 20 students)

$\mu = 137$
$\sigma = 15$

FIGURE 6.82

To determine the test grade X which cuts off the top 0.0040 we need to determine the proportion of area to the left of the test grade X. Since 0.0040 is to the right of the test grade X, then 0.9960 is to the left of X. Using Table II, 0.9960 corresponds to a z score of 2.65.

In order to convert this z score into a test grade, we need to use the raw score formula:

$$X = \mu + (z)\sigma$$
$$X = 137 + (2.65)(15)$$
$$X = 176.75$$

Therefore, the minimum test grade needed to win a scholarship if the top 20 students will receive scholarships is 176.75.

b) To find the minimum test grade needed to win a scholarship if the top 30 students will receive scholarships, we must determine the *proportion* of the students that will win scholarships. Since 30 students out of 5,000 students will win scholarships, the proportion of scholarship winners equals:

$$\frac{30}{5000} = 0.0060$$

This is illustrated in Figure 6.83.

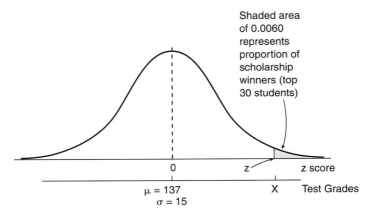

FIGURE 6.83

To find the value of the test grade X we need to determine the proportion of area to the left of the test grade X. Since 0.0060 is to the right of X, then the proportion to the left is 0.9940. Using Table II, 0.9940 corresponds to a z score of 2.51.
Using the raw score formula, we have:

$$X = \mu + (z)\sigma$$
$$X = 137 + (2.51)(15)$$
$$X = 174.65$$

Therefore, the minimum test grade needed to win a scholarship if the top 30 students will receive scholarships is 174.65.   ∎

6.8   PROBABILITY APPLICATIONS

In Section 6.2, we discussed the characteristics of a probability distribution for a continuous random variable. Since a normal distribution is an example of a continuous probability distribution, the characteristics for a continuous probability distribution hold for the normal distribution. Thus, for a normal distribution:

1. The probability that a normal variable X will assume a value between two possible values X_1 and X_2 equals the area under the normal curve between the values X_1 and X_2. This is illustrated in Figure 6.84.
2. The total area (or probability) under a normal curve is equal to 1. This is illustrated in Figure 6.85.
3. The probability that a normal variable X assumes a value between $X = X_1$ and $X = X_2$ is greater than or equal to 0 but less than or equal to 1. This is written as $0 \leq P(X_1 < X < X_2) \leq 1$. Since probability is expressed as a number from 0 to 1 this property emphasizes three important ideas:
    I.   The largest possible probability is 1, which is equal to the total area under a normal curve.
    II. The smallest possible probability is 0.

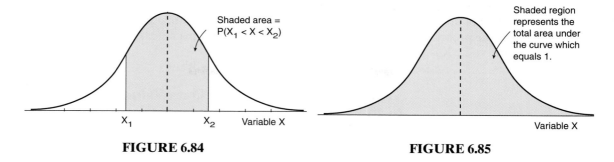

FIGURE 6.84   **FIGURE 6.85**

III. The probability that a variable will assume a specific value, say $X = X_1$, is 0 since the area associated with a specific value of the variable is 0. That is,

$$P(X = X_1) = 0.$$

This leads us to the following definition.

DEFINITION

The **probability of an Event E in a normal distribution** is defined to be:

P(Event E) = Proportion of area under the normal curve satisfying Event E.

This is illustrated in Figure 6.86.

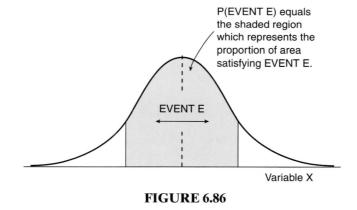

FIGURE 6.86

This leads to the following definition for the probability that a data value falls between two data values X_1 **and** X_2 within a normal distribution.

DEFINITION

Probability of a data value X falling between two data values: X_1 and X_2—The probability that a data value X selected at random from a normal distribution will fall between the two data values X_1 and X_2 is equal to the **proportion of area** between X_1 and X_2. This can be expressed as:

$P(X_1 \leq X \leq X_2)$ = Area under the normal curve between X_1 and X_2

Remember that a normal curve represents the distribution of a continuous variable, and the proportion of area under the normal curve that is associated with a particular data value is zero! Therefore, the probability of random selecting a data value from a normal distribution that is exactly equal to the value X is zero. This can be expressed as:

Probability of Selecting a Data Value Equal to the Value X_1 Within a Normal Distribution

$$P(\text{Data Value is } X_1) = 0$$

Let's apply these probability concepts to a normal distribution application.

EXAMPLE 6.17

Assume the distribution of the playing careers of major league baseball players can be approximated by a normal distribution with a mean of 8 years and a standard deviation of 4 years. Find the probability that a player selected at random will have a career that will last:
a) Less than 6 years
b) Longer that 14 years
c) Between 4 and 10 years.

Solution

a) The shaded area in Figure 6.87 represents the probability that a player's career will last less than 6 years.

   To determine the probability that a player selected at random will have a playing career that will last less than 6 years, determine the proportion of area to the left of 6 years. This is represented by the shaded area in Figure 6.87. To find the proportion of area to the left of 6 years, we need to use Table II. In order to use Table II, we must convert 6 years to a z score. The z score of 6 years is:

$$z = \frac{6-8}{4} = -0.5$$

From Table II, the proportion of area to the left of $z = -0.5$ is 0.3085. Therefore, the probability that a player's career will last less than 6 years is 0.3085.

b) The shaded area in Figure 6.88 represents the probability that a player's career will last longer than 14 years.

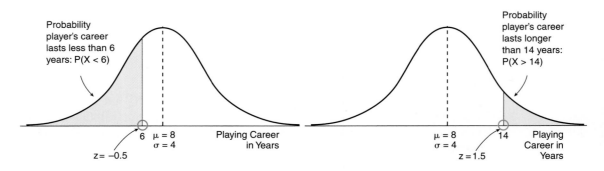

FIGURE 6.87   **FIGURE 6.88**

To determine the probability that a player selected at random has a career that lasts longer than 14 years, determine the proportion of area to the right of 14 years or the shaded area in Figure 6.88. To find the proportion of area to the right of 14 years, we need to use Table II. In order to use Table II, we must convert 14 years to a z score. The z score of 14 years is:

$$z = \frac{14-8}{4} = 1.5$$

From Table II, the proportion of area to the left of $z = 1.5$ is 0.9332. The proportion of area to the right of $z = 1.5$ is:

$$= 1 - 0.9332$$
$$= 0.0668$$

Therefore, the probability that a player's career lasts longer than 14 years is 0.0668.

c) The shaded area in Figure 6.89 represents the probability that a player's career will last between 4 and 10 years.

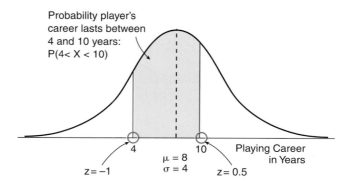

FIGURE 6.89

To determine the probability that a player selected at random will have a career that will last between 4 and 10 years, determine the proportion of area between 4 and 10 years. This is represented by the shaded area in Figure 6.89. To find the proportion of area between 4 and 10 years, we need to use Table II. To use Table II, we must convert both 4 years and 10 years to their respective z scores. The z scores of 4 and 10 years are:

$$z = \frac{4-8}{4} = -1$$

and

$$z = \frac{10-8}{4} = 0.5$$

From Table II, the proportion of area to the left of $z = -1$ is 0.1587, while the proportion of area to the left of $z = 0.5$ is 0.6915. Thus, the proportion of area between $z = 0.5$ and $z = -1$ is equal to the larger area (0.6915) minus the smaller area (0.1587):

proportion of area between $z = 0.5$ and $z = -1 = 0.6915 - 0.1587$
$$= 0.5328.$$

Therefore, the probability that a player's career will last between 4 and 10 years is 0.5328.

CASE STUDY 6.2   The Curve Moves Higher

Examine the two normal distributions in Figure 6.90 which appeared in a 1997 *New York Times* graphic entitled *The Curve Moves Higher.* Both normal distributions represent the IQ scores of American children as measured by the Stanford-Binet IQ test. The normal distribution labeled 1932 represent the IQ results of American children tested in 1932 while the 1997 normal distribution displays the IQ results of American children tested in 1997.

The Curve Moves Higher

As measured by the Stanford-Binet intelligence test, American children seem to be getting smarter. Scores of a group tested in 1932 fell along a bell-shaped curve with half below 100 and half above. Studies show that If children took that same test today, half would score above 120 on the 1932 scale. Very few of them would score in the "intellectually deficient" end, on the left side, and about one-fourth would rank in the "very superior" range.

1932   1997

Intellectually very superior

Intellectually deficient

55   70   85   100   115 120   130   145   160

Source: Ulric Neisser

FIGURE 6.90

a) What was the mean IQ score for both distributions?
b) Determine the median IQ score for both distributions.
c) State the modal IQ score for both distributions.
d) From the information contained within Figure 6.90, what IQ score was defined to be intellectually deficient using the 1932 standards? intellectually very superior?
e) Assuming the standard deviation for both distributions is 15, calculate the probability that a student would have scored within the intellectually deficient area for the 1932 group and then calculate it for the 1997 group.
f) Assuming the standard deviation for both distributions is 15, calculate the probability that a student would have scored within the intellectually very superior area for the 1932 group and then calculate it for the 1997 group.
g) Using the results of parts e and f, compare both distributions and explain the differences in intellectual ability as measured by the Stanford-Binet IQ test for both groups.
h) For the 1932 test, determine the percentile rank of the score 115. Now determine the percentile rank of the score 115 for the 1997 test. (Assume the standard deviation for both distributions is 15.) Explain what the difference between these percentile ranks would signify.
i) What IQ score on the 1932 test would represent the 3rd quartile? What IQ score on the 1997 test would represent the 3rd quartile? Explain what this signifies.
j) What IQ score on the 1997 test would be equivalent to the IQ score 70 on the 1932 test? How would you define intellectually deficient for the 1997 if you wanted to use the same standard applied for the 1932 group? (Assume the standard deviation for both distributions is 15.)
k) What IQ score on the 1997 test would be equivalent to the IQ score 130 on the 1932 test? How would you define intellectually very superior for the 1997 if you wanted to use the same standard applied for the 1932 group? (Assume the standard deviation for both distributions is 15.)

CASE STUDY 6.2   The Curve Moves Higher (continued)

l) If we assume that 100,000 American children took the 1932 IQ test, then how many children would you expect to fall within the area defined to be "intellectually very superior"?

m) Assuming that 100,000 American children took the 1997 IQ test, then how many children would you expect to fall within the area defined to be "intellectually very superior" according to the 1932 standards?

6.9   THE NORMAL APPROXIMATION TO THE BINOMIAL DISTRIBUTION

The normal distribution plays an important role in statistics because there are many probability distributions that can be approximated by a normal curve. In this section, we will examine how the normal distribution which represents a continuous probability distribution can serve as an approximation to the **binomial distribution** which represents a discrete probability distribution. However, before we consider this binomial approximation let us re-examine the binomial distribution which was introduced in Chapter 5.

In Chapter 5, we discussed how the binomial distribution serves as a model for a discrete random variable of a probability experiment which satisfies the following four conditions:

1. there are n identical trials.
2. the n identical trials are independent.
3. the outcome for each trial can be classified as either a success or a failure.
4. the probability of success, p, is the same for each trial.

If these conditions are met, then the probabilities of the binomial experiment can be computed using the binomial probability formula:

$$P(s \text{ successes in } n \text{ trials}) = {}_nC_s \, p^s \, q^{(n-s)}, \text{ where: } q = 1-p.$$

Consider the binomial experiment tossing a fair coin twice. For this binomial experiment, the number of trials or tosses is n = 2 and the probability of success (or a head) is p = ½. Using the binomial probability formula, we can compute the probability for all possible number of successes or heads. The binomial distribution for tossing a fair coin twice is illustrated in Figure 6.91.

Binomial Distribution for n = 2 and p = 1/2	
number of successes or heads "s heads"	Probability of "s" successes or heads $P(s \text{ heads}) = {}_nC_s \, p^s \, q^{(n-s)},$ where: q = 1-p
s = 2	${}_2C_2 \left(\frac{1}{2}\right)^2 \left(\frac{1}{2}\right)^0 = \frac{1}{4}$
s = 1	${}_2C_1 \left(\frac{1}{2}\right)^1 \left(\frac{1}{2}\right)^1 = \frac{2}{4}$
s = 0	${}_2C_0 \left(\frac{1}{2}\right)^0 \left(\frac{1}{2}\right)^2 = \frac{1}{4}$

FIGURE 6.91

FIGURE 6.92

Figure 6.91 represents the binomial distribution for n = 2 and p = ½. A histogram and frequency polygon of this binomial distribution is illustrated in Figure 6.92, where the vertical axis represents the probability of **s** successes and the horizontal axis represents the number of **s** successes. As you can observe in Figure 6.92, the histogram and the polygon for this binomial distribution is symmetric and the polygon formed by joining the midpoints of the rectangles is approximately bell-shaped.

In Figure 6.92 the *probability* for each success or head is represented by the *area* of the rectangle associated with this success. Observe that the probability of getting zero successes is represented by the rectangle starting at –0.5 and ending at 0.5. Since the width of this rectangle is 1 and the height or probability is ¼ then using the formula for the area of a rectangle we have:

$$\begin{aligned}\text{Area of rectangle} &= (\text{height})(\text{width}) \\ &= (¼)(1) \\ &= ¼.\end{aligned}$$

Therefore, the area of the rectangle represents the probability of getting zero successes or heads is ¼. Continuing in this manner, the area of the rectangle representing 1 success or head which represents the probability of getting one head is ½. Likewise, the area of the rectangle representing 2 successes or heads is ¼, which represents the probability of getting two heads.

Like all distributions we have studied the binomial distribution has a mean and standard deviation. Symbolically, the **mean of a binomial distribution** is expressed μ_s and is pronounced **mu sub s**. The **standard deviation of a binomial distribution** is expressed σ_s and is pronounced **sigma sub s**. To calculate the mean and standard deviation of a binomial, we use the following definitions:

DEFINITION
Mean of the Binomial Distribution—For a binomial distribution, the mean number of successes, denoted μ_s, is determined by the formula:

$$\mu_s = np$$

where: n = the number of trials
        p = the probability of a success in one trial

DEFINITION

Standard Deviation of the Binomial Distribution—In a binomial distribution, the standard deviation, denoted σ_s, is determined by the formula:

$$\sigma_s = \sqrt{np(1-p)}$$

where:
- n = the number of trials
- p = the probability of a success in one trial
- $1-p$ = the probability of a failure in one trial

For the binomial distribution illustrated in Figure 6.92 where $n = 2$ and $p = \frac{1}{2}$, the mean is:

$$
\begin{aligned}
\mu_s &= np \\
&= (2)(\frac{1}{2}) \\
&= 1 \text{ head}
\end{aligned}
$$

And the standard deviation of this binomial distribution is:

$$
\begin{aligned}
\sigma_s &= \sqrt{np(1-p)} \\
&= \sqrt{(2)(\frac{1}{2})(\frac{1}{2})} \\
&= \sqrt{0.5} \\
\sigma_s &\approx 0.71 \text{ heads}
\end{aligned}
$$

EXAMPLE 6.18

Using the binomial distribution where $n = 4$ and $p = \frac{1}{2}$ shown in Figure 6.93, compute the mean, μ_s, and the standard deviation, σ_s.

| Binomial Distribution for n = 4 and p = 1/2 ||
number of successes "s"	Probability of "s" successes $P(s \text{ heads}) = {}_nC_s\, p^s\, q^{(n-s)}$, where: $q = 1-p$
4	${}_4C_4\ (\frac{1}{2})^4\ (\frac{1}{2})^0 = \frac{1}{16}$
3	${}_4C_3\ (\frac{1}{2})^3\ (\frac{1}{2})^1 = \frac{4}{16}$
2	${}_4C_2\ (\frac{1}{2})^2\ (\frac{1}{2})^2 = \frac{6}{16}$
1	${}_4C_1\ (\frac{1}{2})^1\ (\frac{1}{2})^3 = \frac{4}{16}$
0	${}_4C_0\ (\frac{1}{2})^0\ (\frac{1}{2})^4 = \frac{1}{16}$

FIGURE 6.93

Solution

To compute mean, μ_s, use the formula:

$$\mu_s = np$$

If n = 4 and p = ½, then: $\mu_s = 2.$

To compute standard deviation, σ_s, use the formula:

$$\sigma_s = \sqrt{np(1-p)}$$

For n = 4, p = ½ and 1–p = ½,

$$\sigma_s = \sqrt{4\left(\frac{1}{2}\right)\left(\frac{1}{2}\right)}$$

$$\sigma_s = 1$$

The graph of this binomial distribution is illustrated in Figure 6.94.

FIGURE 6.94

In many applications of the binomial distribution the number of trials, n, is large. Figure 6.95 illustrates the effect of ***increasing the number of trials, n,*** on the shape of the binomial distribution with p = ½.

In Figure 6.95, notice that **as n *increases* the shape of the binomial distribution gets *closer* to the bell-shape of a normal distribution**. In fact, the binomial distribution *can* be approximated by a normal distribution with a mean μ_s = np and a standard deviation $\sigma_s = \sqrt{np(1-p)}$.

Binomial distributions with p=1/2

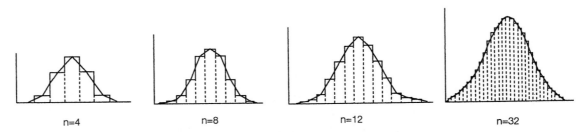

FIGURE 6.95

However, this approximation is reasonable only when the following conditions are *both* true:

$$np > 5 \text{ and } n(1-p) > 5.$$

Let's summarize these conditions.

Conditions of Normal Approximation of a Binomial Distribution

A binomial distribution with a probability of a success p and n trials can be approximated by a normal distribution with a mean $\mu_s = np$ and a standard deviation

$$\sigma_s = \sqrt{np(1-p)}$$

only when both:

$$np \text{ and } n(1-p) \text{ are greater than 5.}$$

Thus, if the number of trials, n, is sufficiently large to make *both np and n(1-p) greater than 5*, then the binomial distribution can be approximated by a normal curve where the mean is $\mu_s = np$ and the standard deviation is $\sigma_s = \sqrt{np(1-p)}$.

Under these conditions, the areas under the normal curve may be used to approximate the binomial probabilities. Let's illustrate the use of the normal approximation to a binomial distribution for tossing a fair coin 20 times.

Suppose we want to determine the probability of getting at least 14 heads in 20 tosses of a fair coin. The probability of at least 14 heads can be determined using the binomial probability formula:

$$P(s \text{ successes in } n \text{ trials}) = {}_nC_s\, p^s\, q^{(n-s)}$$

The probability of getting at least 14 heads is equal to the probability of getting 14 or more heads. Thus, we have:

P(at least 14 heads) = P(14 or more heads)
= P(14 heads)+ P(15 heads)+ P(16 heads)+ P(17 heads)+ P(18 heads)+ P(19 heads)+ P(20 heads)

Using the binomial probability formula to compute each of these probabilities, we have:
P(at least 14 heads) = P(14 heads)+ P(15 heads)+ P(16 heads)+ P(17 heads)+ P(18 heads)+ P(19 heads)+ P(20 heads)

$$= {}_{20}C_{14}(\tfrac{1}{2})^{14}(\tfrac{1}{2})^{6}+{}_{20}C_{15}(\tfrac{1}{2})^{15}(\tfrac{1}{2})^{5}+{}_{20}C_{16}(\tfrac{1}{2})^{16}(\tfrac{1}{2})^{4} +\ldots+{}_{20}C_{20}(\tfrac{1}{2})^{20}(\tfrac{1}{2})^{0}$$

P(at least 14 heads) ≈ 0.0370 + 0.0148 + 0.0046 + 0.0011 + 0.0002 + 0.00002 + 0.000001
≈ 0.0577.

Using the binomial probability formula to determine the result of 0.0577, you will experience these calculations to be both long and tedious.

Let's consider an easier approach which uses **the normal curve to approximate this binomial probability**. This approximation is reasonable since both np and n(1–p) are greater than 5. That is,

$$np = (20)(\frac{1}{2}) \text{ and } \qquad n(1-p) = (20)(\frac{1}{2})$$
$$= 10 \qquad\qquad\qquad = 10$$

To use the normal approximation, we need to calculate the mean, μ_s, and standard deviation, σ_s, of this binomial distribution using the formulas:

$$\mu_s = np \text{ and } \quad \sigma_s = \sqrt{np(1-p)},$$

$$\text{where } n = 20, \text{ and } p = \frac{1}{2}.$$

The mean is:

$$\mu_s = np$$
$$= (20)(\frac{1}{2})$$
$$= 10$$

and the standard deviation is:

$$\sigma_s = \sqrt{np(1-p)}$$
$$\sigma_s = \sqrt{20(\frac{1}{2})(\frac{1}{2})}$$
$$\sigma_s = \sqrt{5}$$
$$\sigma_s \approx 2.24$$

Thus, the binomial distribution where $n = 20$ and $p = \frac{1}{2}$ can be approximated by a normal distribution with mean: $\mu_s = 10$ and standard deviation: $\sigma_s = 2.24$. Examine Figure 6.96 which shows the binomial distribution for $n = 20$ and $p = \frac{1}{2}$ and the normal curve superimposed on this binomial distribution.

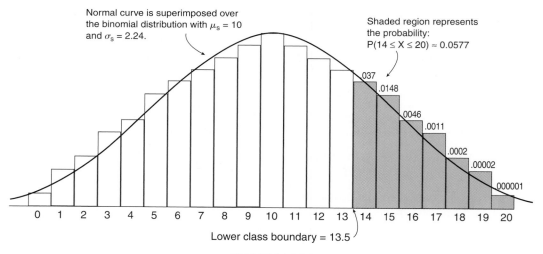

Normal curve is superimposed over the binomial distribution with $\mu_s = 10$ and $\sigma_s = 2.24$.

Shaded region represents the probability:
$P(14 \le X \le 20) \approx 0.0577$

.037
.0148
.0046
.0011
.0002
.00002
.000001

Lower class boundary = 13.5

FIGURE 6.96

In the probability histogram, as pictured in Figure 6.96, which represents the binomial distribution, the area of each rectangle equals the probability of the X value shown under the respective rectangle. The probability (or the area) of the X values 14 to 20 are shown above each of these rectangles. For example, the probability (or area of the rectangle) of X = 14 heads is 0.0370, while the probability (or area of the rectangle) of X = 15 heads is 0.0148 . . . and the probability (or area of the rectangle) X = 20 heads is 0.000001. Thus, the probability of at least 14 heads is the sum of these probabilities (or areas) which equals:

$$P(14 \leq X \leq 20) \approx 0.037 + 0.0148 + 0.0011 + 0.0002 + 0.00002 + 0.000001$$
$$\approx 0.0577.$$

Notice, in Figure 6.96, a normal curve with mean: $\mu_s = 10$ and standard deviation: $\sigma_s = 2.24$ has been superimposed over the binomial distribution. The normal curve can be used to obtain an approximation of these binomial probabilities without performing all the tedious calculations of the binomial formula.

The probability histogram of Figure 6.96 illustrates the binomial distribution where **the shaded region represents the probability of getting at least 14 heads**, since this region represents **the probability of 14 or more heads**. This area can be approximated by **the proportion of area under the normal curve to the *right of 13.5*** which is the lower class boundary of 14. Notice that we are finding the proportion of area to the right of 13.5, the boundary value of 14, and not to the right of 14. We are using the boundary value (13.5) rather than the actual value (14) because the Binomial Distribution is a discrete probability distribution and the Normal Distribution is a continuous probability distribution. We refer to the use of 13.5 rather than 14 as a **correction for continuity**. This **continuity correction** is due to the fact that we cannot find the probability of a specific value, like 14 heads, within a normal distribution. Therefore, the probability of exactly 14 heads corresponds to the proportion of area under the normal curve between the boundary values of 13.5 and 14.5. Therefore, any time we use the normal distribution to approximate a binomial probability, we must make a slight modification which is to either add or subtract 0.5 from the data value.

Therefore, the probability of at least 14 heads corresponds to the proportion of area under the normal curve which is to the right of 13.5. To determine the proportion of area to the right of 13.5, we must first compute the z score for x = 13.5. Using the z score formula,

$$z = \frac{x - \mu_s}{\sigma_s}$$

and substituting 13.5 for x, we have:

$$z = \frac{13.5 - 10}{2.24} = 1.56$$

From Table II, the proportion of area to the left of z = 1.56 is 0.9406. The proportion of area to the right of z = 1.56 is 0.0594.

This area of 0.0594 represents the normal approximation of the binomial probability of getting at least 14 heads in 20 tosses of a fair coin.

Let's compare the actual binomial probability of at least 14 heads to the normal approximation:

Binomial Calculation: **0.0577**

Normal Approximation: **0.0594**

Notice that the normal approximation (**0.0594**) is *very* **close** to the actual value (**0.0577**), since the difference between these two values is only **0.0017**.

When using the normal distribution to approximate binomial probabilities, the **class boundaries** of a data value are used to get a better approximation of the binomial probability. This is referred to a *continuity correction*, since the binomial distribution, which is a discrete distribution, is being corrected so that it can be approximated by the normal distribution, a continuous distribution.

Continuity Correction When Using the Normal Distribution to Approximate a Binomial Probability

When using the normal distribution to approximate a binomial probability, you must either add or subtract 0.5 from the data value depending upon the binomial probability question.

Let's summarize the procedure to approximate the binomial distribution using the normal distribution.

Normal Approximation Procedure to the Binomial Distribution

1. Determine the values of n, number of trials, and p, probability of a success, needed to solve the binomial probability problem.
2. Calculate the mean and standard deviation of the binomial distribution using the formulas:

$$\mu_s = np$$

$$\sigma_s = \sqrt{np(1-p)}$$

3. Draw a normal curve and a rectangle or rectangles that represent the number of successes. Shade the area under the normal curve representing the solution to the binomial probability problem.
4. Identify the class boundary or boundaries required for the solution to the binomial probability. The boundary value of the data value is found by either adding or subtracting 0.5 from the data value depending upon the binomial probability question.
5. Calculate the z score for each class boundary and use Table II to determine the proportion of area corresponding to the shaded proportion of area identified in step 4. This result represents the normal approximation to the binomial probability.

EXAMPLE 6.19

For each of the following binomial experiments, calculate the mean and standard deviation.
a)   n = 100 and p = 0.2
b)   n = 400 and p = 0.7

Solution

a)   For n = 100 and p = 0.2, the mean of this binomial experiment is:

$$\mu_s = np$$
$$= (100)(0.2)$$
$$\mu_s = 20$$

The standard deviation of this binomial experiment is:

$$\sigma_s = \sqrt{np(1-p)}$$
$$= \sqrt{(100)(0.2)(1-0.2)}$$
$$= \sqrt{(100)(0.2)(0.8)}$$
$$\sigma_s = 4$$

Thus the mean and standard deviation for this binomial experiment are $\mu_s = 20$ and $\sigma_s = 4$.
b)   For n = 400 and p = 0.7,

$$\mu_s = (400)(0.7)$$
$$\mu_s = 280$$

and:

$$\sigma_s = \sqrt{(400)(0.7)(0.3)}$$
$$\sigma_s \approx 9.17$$

Thus the mean and standard deviation for this binomial experiment are $\mu_s = 280$ and $\sigma_s \approx 9.17$.

EXAMPLE 6.20

Consider the binomial experiment of tossing a fair coin 100 times. Use the normal approximation to calculate the probability of getting:
a) At least 55 heads.
b) Between 40 and 60 heads.
c) Exactly 54 heads.
d) At most 45 heads.

Solution

To use the normal approximation to the binomial distribution, calculate the mean and standard deviation for the binomial distribution where $n = 100$, $p = \frac{1}{2}$, and $1 - p = \frac{1}{2}$.

The mean is:
$$\mu_s = np$$
$$= 50$$

The standard deviation is:

$$\sigma_s = \sqrt{np(1-p)}$$
$$= \sqrt{(100)(\tfrac{1}{2})(\tfrac{1}{2})}$$
$$= \sqrt{25}$$
$$\sigma_s = 5$$

Thus, the normal distribution with $\mu_s = 50$ and $\sigma_s = 5$ will be used to approximate these binomial probabilities.
a) To calculate the probability of getting at least 55 heads, we must determine the probability of getting 55 or more heads. This is illustrated in Figure 6.97.
      To approximate the probability of getting 55 or more heads use the lower boundary of 55 which is 54.5 and compute the z score of 54.5.

$$z = \frac{54.5 - 50}{5} = \frac{4.5}{5} = 0.90$$

Using Table II the area to the left of $z = 0.90$ is 0.8159. Thus, the area to the right of $z = 0.90$ is 0.1841. Therefore, the probability of at least 55 heads is approximately 0.1841.
b) To calculate the probability of getting **between** 40 and 60 heads, compute the probability of getting **more than** 40 heads and **less than** 60 heads. This is illustrated in Figure 6.98.
      To approximate the probability of getting **between 40 and 60 heads**, use the **upper boundary of 40**, which is **40.5**, and the **lower boundary of 60**, which is **59.5**. This is shown in Figure 6.98. To determine the shaded proportion of area in Figure 6.98 compute the z score of 40.5 and the z score of 59.5. We obtain:

z of 40.5 is –1.90
z of 59.5 is 1.90

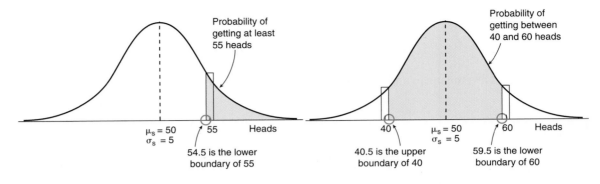

FIGURE 6.97   **FIGURE 6.98**

From Table II the proportion of area to the left of z = –1.9 is 0.0287, and the proportion of area to the left of z = 1.9 is 0.9713. Therefore, the area between z = –1.9 and z = 1.9 is 0.9713 – 0.0287 = 0.9426. Hence, the probability of getting between 40 and 60 heads is 0.9426.

c)   The probability of getting exactly 54 heads is approximated by the shaded proportion of area in Figure 6.99.

To approximate the **probability of exactly 54 heads, use the lower boundary of 54, which is 53.5, and the upper boundary of 54, which is 54.5**.

To determine the shaded area in Figure 6.99 compute the z score of 53.5 and the z score of 54.5. We obtain:

$$z \text{ of } 53.5 = 0.70$$
$$z \text{ of } 54.5 = 0.90$$

Using Table II the proportion of area to the left of z = 0.70 is 0.7580, and the proportion of area to the left of z = 0.90 is 0.8159. Thus, the area between z = 0.70 and z = 0.90 is 0.8159 – 0.7580 = 0.0579. Therefore, the probability of getting exactly 54 heads is approximately 0.0579.

d)   To calculate the probability of getting at most 45 heads, we must determine the probability of getting 45 or less heads. This is illustrated in Figure 6.100.

To approximate the probability of getting 45 or less heads use the upper boundary of 45 which is 45.5 and compute the z score of 45.5.

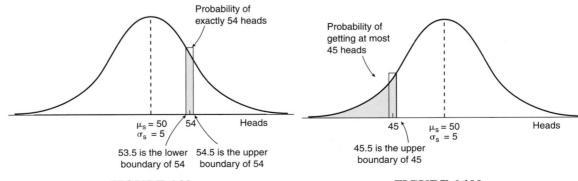

FIGURE 6.99   **FIGURE 6.100**

$$z = \frac{45.5 - 50}{5} = \frac{-4.5}{5} = -0.90$$

Using Table II the proportion of area to the left of z = – 0.90 is 0.1841. Therefore, the probability of at most 45 heads is approximately 0.1841.

In Example 6.20, we examined four different types of probability questions. For each question, we determined the boundary value required to find the appropriate proportion of area under the normal curve to approximate the binomial probability. Let's examine the different probability questions and the boundary values that were used to approximate the probability. Figure 6.101 shows the boundary value or values needed to determine the normal curve area to approximate the different binomial probability problems.

Binomial Probability Problem	Boundary Value Used to Solve Problem	Area Under Normal Curve corresponding to Binomial Probability
AT LEAST 55 HEADS	BOUNDARY VALUE is 54.5	Proportion of area TO THE RIGHT OF 54.5 (see Figure 6.97)
BETWEEN 40 AND 60 HEADS	LOWER BOUNDARY is 40.5 AND UPPER BOUNDARY is 59.5	Proportion of area BETWEEN 40.5 AND 59.5 (see Figure 6.98)
EXACTLY 55 HEADS	LOWER BOUNDARY is 54.5 AND UPPER BOUNDARY is 55.5	Proportion of area BETWEEN 54.5 AND 55.5 (see Figure 6.99)
AT MOST 45 HEADS	BOUNDARY VALUE is 45.5	Proportion of area TO THE LEFT OF 45.5 (see Figure 6.100)

FIGURE 6.101

EXAMPLE 6.21

An automobile salesperson is successful in selling new cars to 40% of the customers that visit the showroom. What is the probability that the salesperson will sell a new car to at least 30 of the next 50 customers?

Solution

This problem can be considered to be a binomial problem where the probability that the salesperson successfully sells a new car to the customer is 0.40, and the probability the salesperson does not sell a new car to the customer is: 1 – 0.4 = 0.60.

To determine if the normal approximation to the binomial distribution can be used to solve this problem, calculate np and n(1–p).

$$np = (50)(0.4) \qquad \text{and} \qquad n(1-p) = (50)(0.6)$$
$$= 20 \qquad\qquad\qquad\qquad\qquad = 30$$

Since np and n(1 – p) are both greater than 5 the normal approximation to the binomial distribution can be used to solve this problem.

The mean of the binomial distribution is:

$$\mu_s = np = 20$$

The standard deviation of the binomial distribution is:

$$\sigma_s = \sqrt{np(1-p)}$$
$$\sigma_s = \sqrt{12}$$
$$\sigma_s \approx 3.5$$

Thus, a normal distribution with $\mu_s = 20$ and $\sigma_s \approx 3.5$ will be used to obtain an approximation for the binomial probability of the salesperson selling a new car to at least 30 of the next 50 customers. This is illustrated in Figure 6.102.

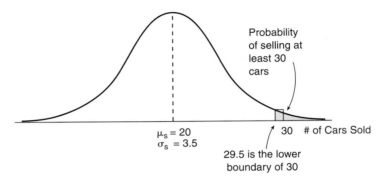

Probability of selling at least 30 cars

$\mu_s = 20$
$\sigma_s = 3.5$

30   # of Cars Sold

29.5 is the lower boundary of 30

FIGURE 6.102

To approximate the probability of selling at least 30 new cars, we need to calculate the probability of selling 30 or more cars. We will use the lower boundary of 30 which is 29.5 and find the proportion of area to the right of 29.5. This is illustrated by the shaded area in Figure 6.102.

To calculate the proportion of area to the right of 29.5, find the z score of 29.5 which is 2.71. In Table II, we find the proportion of area to the left of z = 2.71 is 0.9966.

Thus, the area to the right of z = 2.71 is 1– 0.9966 = 0.0034. Therefore, the probability that the salesperson successfully sells at least 30 new cars to his next 50 customers is approximately 0.0034.

EXAMPLE 6.22

Tom, a daily commuter to Wall Street, is late to work 20% of the time. Calculate the probability that in his next 40 trips to work Tom will be late at most 15 times.

Solution

Let's consider using the normal approximation to the binomial distribution for this problem, where the probability that Tom gets to work late is 0.20 and the probability that Tom does not get to work late is 0.80.

Calculate np and n(1 – p) to determine if both expressions are greater than 5.

$$\text{np} = (40)(0.20) \qquad \text{and} \qquad n(1-p) = (40)(0.80)$$
$$= 8 \qquad\qquad\qquad\qquad\qquad = 32$$

Since np and n(1 – p) are both greater than 5, the *normal* approximation to the binomial distribution can be used to solve this problem.

The *mean* of the *binomial* distribution is:

$$\mu_s = 8$$

The *standard deviation* of the *binomial* distribution is:

$$\sigma_s \approx 2.53$$

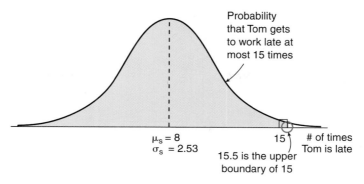

FIGURE 6.103

Thus, the normal distribution with $\mu_s = 8$ and $\sigma_s \approx 2.53$ will be used to obtain an approximation for the binomial probability that Tom gets to work late at most 15 times in his next 40 trips. This is illustrated in Figure 6.103.

To approximate this binomial probability, use the *upper* boundary of 15 which is 15.5 since we are trying to find the probability of 15 or less. Thus, this probability is determined by finding the proportion of area to the left of 15.5. Finding the z score of $15.5 = 2.96$ in Table II, the area to the left of $z = 2.96$ is 0.9985. Therefore, the probability that Tom gets to work late at most 15 times is approximately 0.9985.

EXAMPLE 6.23

A single fair die is rolled 36 times. Calculate the probability of getting:
a)   Exactly 7 sixes
b)   At least 10 fours

Solution

a)   For this binomial probability problem, we can use the normal approximation since np and n(1–p) are both greater than 5. Let's verify this.

Since the fair die is rolled 36 times, $n = 36$. For a fair die, the probability of getting a six in one roll is $\frac{1}{6}$.

Therefore,

$$np = 6 \text{ and } n(1 - p) = (36)(\tfrac{5}{6}) = 30.$$

The mean is: $\mu_s = 6$

The standard deviation is: $\sigma_s \approx 2.24$

Thus, a normal distribution with $\mu_s = 6$ and $\sigma_s \approx 2.24$ can be used to obtain an approximation for the binomial probability of getting 7 sixes in 36 rolls of a fair die. This is illustrated in Figure 6.104.

To approximate this binomial probability, use the lower boundary of 7 which is 6.5 and the upper boundary of 7 which is 7.5 since we are trying to find the proportion of area of exactly 7 sixes.

To determine the shaded area represented in Figure 6.101, we must compute the z scores for 6.5 and 7.5.

$$z \text{ of } 6.5 = 0.22 \text{ and } z \text{ of } 7.5 = 0.67$$

Using Table II the proportion of area to the left of $z = 0.22$ is 0.5871 and the proportion of area to the left of $z = 0.67$ is 0.7486. Therefore, the area between $z = 0.22$ and $z = 0.67$ is

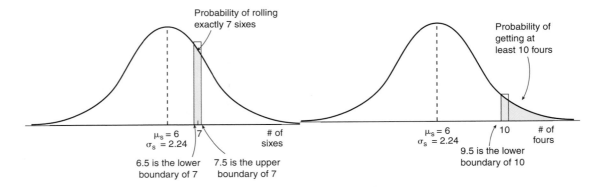

FIGURE 6.104   **FIGURE 6.105**

0.7486 – 0.5871 = 0.1615. Thus, the probability of getting exactly 7 sixes in 36 rolls of a fair die is approximately 0.1615.

b) As in Part a, this binomial probability problem has n = 36 trials or rolls. For a fair die, the probability of getting a four in one roll is: p = ⅙. Notice, these values for n and p are the same as those computed in Part a of this example, hence we can use the normal approximation to the binomial distribution where $\mu_s = 6$ and $\sigma_s \approx 2.24$.

Thus, the normal distribution illustrated in Figure 6.105 is used to obtain an approximation for the binomial probability of getting at least 10 fours in 36 rolls of a fair die.

This binomial probability can be approximated by determining the proportion of area to the right of the lower boundary 9.5 since we are trying to find the probability of 10 or more fours. To determine this area, compute the z score for 9.5.

$$z \text{ of } 9.5 = 1.56.$$

Using Table II, the proportion of area to the left of the z = 1.56 is 0.9406. The proportion of area to the right of z = 1.56 is 1 – 0.9406 = 0.0594. Therefore, the probability of getting at least 10 fours in 36 rolls of fair die is approximately 0.0594.   ∎

CASE STUDY 6.3

In Case Study 4.6, the article entitled "Trial By Mathematics" which appeared in *Time* magazine on April 26, 1968 discussed a robbery committed by an interracial couple. The couple accused of the crime had been convicted because the likelihood of a couple having the known characteristics of the robbers had been established at 1 in 12 million. In the couples' appeal, the judge assumed the probability p of a couple having all the characteristics of the robbers to be: p = 1/12,000,000. Assume that there does exist another such couple where each of the N couples in the population serve as a trial of a binomial experiment. The judge then calculated the probability that another couple has the same characteristics of the convicted couple for the value of N = 12,000,000.

a) Would the normal distribution be a good approximation to the binomial distribution? What values of N, p, and (1 – p) would you use, if you could use the normal approximation?

b) What is the mean and standard deviation of this binomial distribution?

c) If you used the normal approximation to the binomial distribution, what boundary value would you use to calculate the probability that two or more such couples within the population of N couples satisfying the characteristics of the robbers?

CASE STUDY 6.3 (continued)

d) Using the normal distribution, what did you get for the probability that two or more such couples satisfy the characteristics of the robbers? How does this compare to the judges' calculation of approximately 41%?

e) Calculate this probability again for the following different values of N couples (in millions): 15, 20, 25, 30, 40, 50, 75, and 100. Compare your results using the normal approximation to the results of Table 5.17 in Chapter 5 which represent the probabilities calculated using the binomial distribution. Are the results of the normal approximation close to the binomial distribution? What happens to the difference between the normal approximation and the binomial distribution as the value of N gets larger?

6.10   USING TECHNOLOGY

In this chapter we have explored the characteristics of the normal distribution and some of its applications. Using MINITAB or EXCEL we can *simulate* a sample of data values that approximates the graph of the normal distribution. In MINITAB, a histogram of 100 z scores was randomly generated to approximate a normal distribution. This is shown in Figure 6.106.

Similarly using EXCEL, a histogram of 100 z scores was randomly generated to approximate a normal distribution. This is shown in Figure 6.107.

The shapes of the histograms pictured in Figures 6.106 and 6.107 appear to be approximately normal. Most of the data values are within two standard deviations of the mean. In fact for these samples, 98% of the data values are within two standard deviations of the mean. Remember, in a normal distribution 95% of the data values are within two standard deviations of the mean. Can you find any other differences between the histograms pictured in Figures 6.106 and 6.107 and the properties of the normal distribution? What do you think will happen if we used MINITAB and EXCEL to produce graphs for samples of data values where the number of values is larger than 100? What do you think contributes to the differences between the characteristics of the distributions of data values and the characteristics of the normal distribution?

In Chapter 5, computer software was used to produce a table of probability values and a distribution for a binomial experiment. In Section 6.9, we examined how the normal distribution is used to approximate a binomial distribution. MINITAB and EXCEL can be used to produce a binomial distribution along with a table of binomial probability values.

The MINITAB graph shown in Figure 6.108a and the subsequent MINITAB table of probability values in Figure 6.108b of a binomial experiment was generated for which n = 32 and p = 0.5.

FIGURE 6.106

FIGURE 6.107

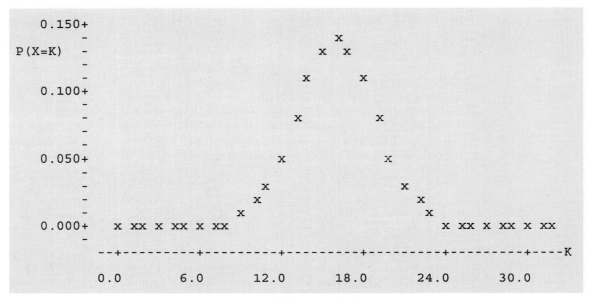

FIGURE 6.108a

ROW	K	P(X=K)
1	0	0.000000
2	1	0.000000
3	2	0.000000
4	3	0.000001
5	4	0.000008
6	5	0.000047
7	6	0.000211
8	7	0.000784
9	8	0.002449
10	9	0.006531
11	10	0.015020
12	11	0.030041
13	12	0.052571
14	13	0.080879
15	14	0.109765
16	15	0.131718
17	16	0.139950
18	17	0.131718
19	18	0.109765
20	19	0.080879
21	20	0.052571
22	21	0.030041
23	22	0.015020
24	23	0.006531
25	24	0.002449
26	25	0.000784

FIGURE 6.108b (continues)

27	26	0.000211
28	27	0.000047
29	28	0.000008
30	29	0.000001
31	30	0.000000
32	31	0.000000
33	32	0.000000

FIGURE 6.109b (continued)

Similarly, an EXCEL graph shown in Figure 6.109a and the subsequent EXCEL table of probability values in Figure 6.109b of a binomial experiment was generated for which n = 32 and p = 0.5.

Notice that the shape of the graphs in Figures 6.108a and 6.109a approximate the shape of the normal distribution for the binomial experiment where n = 32 and p = 0.5.

FIGURE 6.109a

Number of Successes	Prob(s)
0	2.32831E-10
1	7.45058E-09
2	1.15484E-07
3	1.15484E-06
4	8.37259E-06
5	4.68865E-05
6	0.000210989
7	0.000783674
8	0.002448983
9	0.00653062
10	0.015020426
11	0.030040853
12	0.052571493
13	0.080879219
14	0.109764654
15	0.131717585
16	0.139949934

FIGURE 6.109b (continues)

17	0.131717585
18	0.109764654
19	0.090978219
20	0.052571492
21	0.030040853
22	0.015020426
23	0.00653062
24	0.002448983
25	0.000783674
26	0.000210989
27	4.68865E-05
28	8.37259E-06
29	1.15484E-06
30	1.15484E-07
31	7.45058E-09
32	2.32831E-10

FIGURE 6.109b (continued)

The TI-83 Plus graphing calculator has a built-in capability of computing the area under the normal curve and displaying the result graphically.

Figure 6.110 displays the shaded area under the normal curve to the left of z = 1. The TI-83 Plus computes this area to be approximately 0.8413.

Figure 6.111 displays the shaded area under the normal curve between the lower z score of z = –1.5 and the higher z score of z = 1. The TI-83 Plus computes this area to be approximately 0.7745.

Figure 6.112 displays the shaded area under the normal curve to the right of z = 1.5. The TI-83 computed this area to be approximately 0.0668.

FIGURE 6.110

FIGURE 6.111

FIGURE 6.112

KEY TERMS

Continuous Random Variable   377
Continuous Probability
   Distribution   380
Normal Distribution   383
Standard Normal Curve   387
Percentiles   411

Percentile Rank   411
Probability   422
Binomial Distribution   427
Mean of a Binomial Distribution   428
Standard Deviation of a Binomial
   Distribution   429

Class Boundaries   433
Normal Approximation to a Binomial
   Distribution   431

EXERCISES

Section 6.2

1. The variable *gender* is not a continuous random variable because it can assume two distinct values. (T/F)

2. The variable *airplane flight times between New York and Los Angeles* is a continuous random variable because time can assume many possible values. (T/F)

3. The sum of all the areas of the rectangles in a probability distribution histogram representing a continuous random variable is always equal to one. (T/F)

4. The smooth curve of the continuous variable X is called the normal distribution. (T/F)

5. The normal distribution is an example of a probability density curve. (T/F)

6. The probability that a continuous variable will assume a specific value, such as X = a, is always zero. (T/F)

7. If the process of measuring a continuous variable is to a finer and finer degree of precision then:
   a) The number of rectangles used to estimate the curve will decrease
   b) The width of each of the rectangles used to estimate the curve will get narrower
   c) The height of the rectangles used to estimate the curve will approach a line
   d) All of the above are correct

8. Which is not a characteristic of a continuous probability distribution?
   a) The probability that the continuous random variable X will assume a value between two possible values, X = a and X = b, is equal to the area under the density curve between X = a and X = b.
   b) The total area under the curve is one.
   c) The probability that the continuous variable X will assume a value between any two values X = a and X = b is between 0 and 1.
   d) The probability that the continuous variable X will assume a value of 0 is 1.

Section 6.3

9. Explain why many observable phenomena have shapes that are approximated by a normal distribution.

10. For each of the following continuous variables estimate whether or not their respective shapes are approximately normally distributed.
    a) The time it takes to travel from JFK International Airport in New York to Logan International Airport in Chicago.
    b) The amount of dollars earned for selling advertising space in the New York Times from 1970 to 1996.
    c) The number of pages in an elementary statistics book.
    d) The number of bacteria present in a culture after one hour.
    e) The weight in pounds of one day old Doberman puppies.
    f) The amount of electricity used to run your refrigerator.

Section 6.4

11. List the properties of a normal distribution.

12. Draw a standard normal distribution from z = –4 to z = 4. On the normal curve, show the proportion of data values that fall between each integer z score.

13. Use the properties of the normal distribution to answer the questions relating to the normal distribution in the following figure.

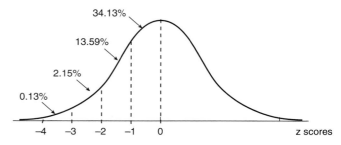

a) What proportion of the distribution is less than a z-score of –3?
b) What proportion of the distribution is less than a z-score of –1?
c) What proportion of the distribution is less than a z-score of 0?
d) What proportion of the distribution is less than a z-score of 2?
e) What proportion of the distribution is less than a z-score of 4?
f) What proportion of the distribution is greater than a z-score of 0?
g) What proportion of the distribution is greater than a z-score of –1?
h) What proportion of the distribution is greater than a z-score of 2?
i) What proportion of the distribution is greater than a z-score of –3?
j) What proportion of the distribution is greater than a z-score of 4?
k) What proportion of the distribution is between a z-score of –1 and 1?

l) What proportion of the distribution is between a z-score of –2 and 2?

m) What proportion of the distribution is between a z-score of –3 and 3?

n) What proportion of the distribution is between a z-score of –4 and 4?

14. The data values in a normal distribution tend to cluster about the _____.

15. In a normal distribution, the mean is located at the _____ of the distribution.

16. The proportion of area under the normal curve which is to the left of the mean is equal to _____.

17. In a normal distribution if the median is 100, then the mean is _____.

18. In a normal distribution, the percent of data values to the left of z = –0.53 is the same as the percent of data values to the right of z = _____.

19. In a normal distribution, the percent of area to the left of z = –1 is _____. Therefore, the percent of area to the right of z = –1 is _____.

20. The shaded area to the right of z = 0 is equal to the shaded area to the left of z = 0.
(T/F)

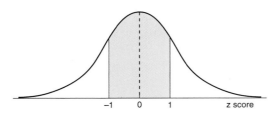

21. The shaded area A1 is equal to the shaded are A2.
(T/F)

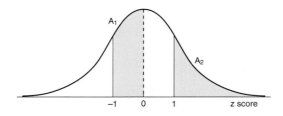

22. The z score of 0 divides the normal distribution into two equal parts.
(T/F)

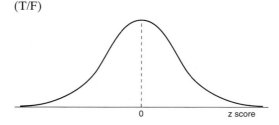

23. The area to the left of a z score of 1 equals the area to the right of a z score of 1.
(T/F)

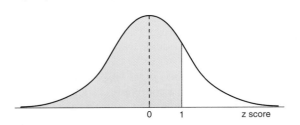

24. The area between the z scores –1 and –2 is equal to the area between the z scores +1 and +2.
(T/F)

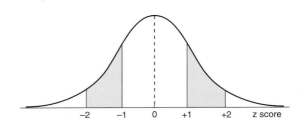

25. The total area under the normal curve is infinite.
(T/F)

Section 6.5

26. In a normal distribution find the proportion of area:
a) Less than a z score of 1.78.
b) Between the z scores of –2.09 and +0.53.
c) Greater than the z score of 2.19.

27. In a normal distribution find the proportion of area:
a) Less than a z score of +2.50.
b) Between the z scores of –1.33 and +0.5.
c) Greater than the z score of –1.30.

28. In a normal distribution find the percent of area:
a) Less than a z score of –1.65.
b) Between the z scores of –3 and 3.
c) Greater than the z score of 2.33.

29. In a normal distribution find the percent of area:
a) Between the z scores of –1.96 and 1.96.
b) Between the z scores of –2.58 and 2.58.

30. In a normal distribution find the proportion of area:
a) Less than a z score of 4.
b) Between the z scores of –4 and +4.
c) Greater than the z score of –4.

31. In a normal distribution find the z score(s) that:
a) Cuts off the bottom 0.40 of the z scores.
b) Cuts off the top 0.01 of the z scores.
c) Cuts off the middle 90% of the z scores.

32. In a normal distribution find the z score(s) that:
 a) Cuts off the bottom 10% of the z scores.
 b) Cuts off the top 1% of the z scores.
 c) Cuts off the middle 95% of the z scores.

Section 6.6

33. In a normal distribution with $\mu = 90$ and $\sigma = 15$ find the proportion of data values which are:
 a) Less than 106.
 b) Between 78 and 107.
 c) Greater than 100.

34. The amount of soda that a filling machine dispenses into a 32 ounce bottle is approximately a normal distribution with $\mu = 32$ oz. and $\sigma = 0.5$ oz. Find the proportion of bottles that are expected to contain:
 a) Less than 31.6 oz.
 b) Between 31 oz. and 32.7 oz.
 c) More than 33 oz.

35. The Motor Vehicle Commissioner reports that the weight of passenger cars is normally distributed with $\mu = 2700$ lbs. and $\sigma = 300$ lbs. Determine:
 a) The proportion of cars weighing less than 3500 lbs.
 b) The proportion of cars weighing more than 2200 lbs.
 c) The proportion of cars weighing either less than 2100 lbs. or more than 3800 lbs.

36. According to the latest computer internet usage survey of 1500 high school students, the amount of social time per day a student spends on the internet is approximately normally distributed with $\mu = 210$ minutes and $\sigma = 45$ minutes.

 Determine:
 a) The proportion of students that spend less than 176 minutes on the internet.
 b) The number of students that spend between 150 and 300 minutes on the internet.
 c) The percent of students that spend more than 4 hours on the internet.
 d) The minimum computer usage time spent on the internet by the top 5% of the users.
 e) The maximum computer usage time spent on the internet by the lowest 400 users.

37. Bruce, an accountant, determines that the mean time required to prepare a tax return using the computer package "Tax Pro" is normally distributed with a mean of 2.8 hours and a standard deviation of 0.7 hours. If Bruce will prepare 800 tax returns during the year, then approximately how many will Bruce complete in less than 3 hours and 45 minutes?

38. Debbie, an architect, is designing the interior doors to a new squash club. She wants the doors to be high enough so that 90% of the men using the doors will have at least a one foot clearance. Assuming the heights to be normally distributed with a mean of 69 inches and a standard deviation of 4 inches, how high must Debbie design the doors to satisfy her requirements?

39. Matthew, an experimental psychologist, indicates that the age at which a child learns to walk is normally distributed with a mean age of 10.9 months with a standard deviation of 0.5 months. If Matthew classifies an early walker as a child who is among the youngest 10% to walk, then by what age must a child walk to be identified as an early walker?

40. According to bank records, the amount of daily cash withdrawals from a Long Beach bank is normally distributed with a mean of $75,000 and a standard deviation of $10,000. How much cash should the bank have on hand in order to cover the daily withdrawals 90% of the time?

41. The production process at an automobile manufacturing company uses ball bearings whose service life is approximately normally distributed with a mean of 820 hours and a standard deviation of 40 hours. If the maintenance supervisor decides to replace the ball bearings before no more than 1% have worn out, what is the maximum time the ball bearings can be in operation before being replaced?

42. The length of time required to complete a college placement exam is normally distributed with a mean of 90 minutes and a standard deviation of 10 minutes. How much time should the college proctor allow the students for the exam if he would like:
 a) 95% of the students to complete the exam?
 b) 90% of the students to complete the exam?
 c) 99% of the students to complete the exam?

Section 6.7

43. In a normal distribution, if the percent of data values greater than the data value 60 is 84.13 then, the percentile rank of 60 is_____.

44. In a normal distribution if the percentile rank of a data value is 50, then the data value is equal to the _____, and its z score is equal to _____.

45. In a normal distribution what is the percentile rank of the data value which is:
 a) Two standard deviations greater than the mean?
 b) One standard deviation less than the mean?
 c) One-half a standard deviation greater than the mean?

46. In a normal distribution with $\mu = 250$ and $\sigma = 20$ find the percentile rank of the following data values:
 a) 286.
 b) 265.
 c) 225.

47. In a normal distribution with $\mu = 80$ and $\sigma = 10$, if a data value is the 70th percentile, then the data value has a value of _____.

48. In a normal distribution with $\mu = 75$ and $\sigma = 15$ the data value with a percentile rank of 77 is:
 a) 77   **b)** 75   **c)** 80   **d)** 86.1

49. In a normal distribution with $\mu = 300$ and $\sigma = 40$ find the data value equal to:
  a) P_{85}.
  b) P_{35}.
  c) P_{70}.
  d) The first decile.
  e) The third quartile.
  f) The sixth decile.

50. Three hundred first year law students at a local law school had a mean of 150 on the LSAT, the law boards, with a standard deviation of 10. Assuming these results are approximately normally distributed, determine:
  a) The percentile rank of the LSAT score 163.
  b) The percentile rank of the LSAT score 135.
  c) The LSAT score that cuts off the top 2% of the LSAT scores (to the nearest whole number).
  d) The LSAT score that cuts off the top 50 LSAT scores (to the nearest whole number).
  e) The LSAT score that represents the 6th decile (to the nearest whole number).
  f) The LSAT score that represents the first quartile (to the nearest whole number).
  g) The LSAT score that represents the third quartile (to the nearest whole number).
  h) The LSAT score that represents the 15th percentile (to the nearest whole number).
  Suppose one of these first year law student's is selected at random, and you have to guess the student's LSAT score. If you guess it correctly to within 12 points, then you will be given ten dollars.
  i) what LSAT score should you guess and what is your chance of winning the ten dollars?

Section 6.8

51. In a normal distribution find the probability that a data value picked at random has a z score:
  a) Less than $z = -1.16$.
  b) Between $z = 1.0$ and $z = +0.5$.
  c) Greater than $z = 1.75$.

52. In a normal distribution which has $\mu = 900$ and $\sigma = 350$ find the probability that a data value picked at random is:
  a) Less than 500.
  b) Between 800 and 1200.
  c) Greater than 1100.

53. A marketing research agency states that the number of responses received from 2,000 mailed questionnaires is normally distributed with a mean of 1400 and a standard deviation of 80. If Craig, a market researcher, plans to mail out 2,000 questionnaires for a consumer product study, what is the probability that Craig will receive at least 1500 responses?

54. Recently, Ms. Piper bought a tire for her car. The manufacturer claimed that the tire wear is normally distributed with $\mu = 56{,}000$ miles and $\sigma = 4{,}000$ miles. What is the probability:

  a) That Ms. Piper's tire lasts less than 50,000 miles?
  b) That Ms. Piper's tire lasts between 60,000 and 70,000 miles?
  c) That Ms. Piper's tire lasts at least 60,000 miles?

55. An automatic machine process produces ball bearings whose diameters are normally distributed with $\mu = 0.075''$ and $\sigma = 0.004''$. Find the probability that a ball bearing selected at random will have a diameter:
  a) Less than $0.071''$.
  b) Greater than $0.083''$.
  c) Between $0.077''$ and $0.087''$.

56. According to the manufacturer of Crackle natural peach flavored iced tea drinks, the net amount of iced tea in a glass bottle is normally distributed with a mean of 12 ounces and a standard deviation of 0.018 ounces. What is the probability that a bottle selected at random from the manufacturing process contains:
  a) Less than 11.98 ounces?
  b) Between 11.96 and 12.01 ounces?
  c) Greater than 12.03 ounces?
  d) If the maximum amount of iced tea that a standard bottle can hold is 12.05 ounces, then what is the probability that a bottle selected at random was overfilled?

57. It is estimated that on a given night at a harness racing track Aaron, a typical gambler, will lose on the average $65.00 with a standard deviation of $25.00. If the distribution of losses is normally distributed, what is the probability that a typical harness racing bettor will:
  a) Lose more than $100?
  b) Break even or make money?
  c) If two friends that bet independently spend an evening at the track what is the probability that they both lose more than $80? (Hint: Use the multiplication rule for independent probability events in Chapter 4.)

58. The amount of time required for Jain to travel to and from home and the office can be approximated by a normal distribution with $\mu = 55$ minutes and $\sigma = 10$ minutes.
  a) If Jain leaves home at 7:45 a.m., what is the probability that she will arrive at the office no later than 9:00 a.m.?
  b) If coffee is served at the office between 8:45–9:00 a.m., what is the probability that Jain will miss the coffee break (arrives after 9:00 a.m.) if she leaves home at 8:05 a.m.?
  c) If Jain has an appointment with a client at the office promptly at 9:05 a.m., what is the probability she will make the appointment if she leaves home promptly at 8:15 a.m.?

Section 6.9

59. The normal distribution is a good approximation of the binomial distribution when both np and n(1–p) are greater than _____.

60.
a) For a binomial distribution with n = 10 and p = ⅕, would the normal distribution be a good approximation to the binomial distribution? _____.
b) For a binomial distribution with n = 8 and p = ¾, would the normal distribution be a good approximation to the binomial distribution? _____.

61. The frequency polygon of a binomial distribution looks more like a _____ distribution as the number of trials, n, gets larger.

62. For a binomial distribution, the formula for:
a) The mean of the binomial distribution, μ_s, is _____
 _____.
b) The standard deviation of the binomial distribution, σ_s, is _____.

63. For a binomial distribution, if n = 100 and p = ½, then:
a) $\mu_s = np =$ _____.
b) $\sigma_s = \sqrt{np(1-p)} =$ _____.

64. For a binomial distribution with n = 200 and p = 0.37 what is the value of μ_s?
a) 74   **b)** 200   **c)** 37   **d)** 100

65. For a binomial distribution with n = 120 and p = 0.4 what is the value of σ_s?
a) 0.24   **b)** 28.8   **c)** 5.37   **d)** 14.4

66. To get a good approximation of a binomial probability problem by using the normal approximation, real boundaries should be applied.
(T/F)

67. Use the normal distribution to approximate the following binomial probabilities:
a) If n = 100 and p = 0.5, then find the probability that the number of successes "s" is:
  1. Greater than 60, i.e. P(s > 60).
  2. Equal to 60, i.e. P(s = 60).
  3. Greater than or equal to 60, i.e. P(s ≥ 60).
  4. Less than 60 or greater than 60, i.e. P(s < 60 or s > 60).
b) If n = 100 and p = 0.1, then find the probability that the number of successes "s" is:
  1. Equal to 10, i.e. P(s = 10).
  2. Less than 7, i.e. P(s<7).
  3. Greater than or equal to 7, i.e. P(s ≥ 7).
  4. Less than 7 or greater than or equal to 7, i.e. P(s < 7 or s ≥ 7).

68. For the binomial experiment of tossing a fair coin 400 times, use the normal distribution to approximate the probability that:
a) The coin lands heads at least 217 times.
b) The coin lands tails between 180 and 195 inclusive.
c) The coin lands heads exactly 200 times.
d) The coin lands heads less than 185 or more than 210.

69. If a pitcher has 0.25 probability of striking out a batter what's the probability that this pitcher strikes out 18 or more of the next 40 batters he faces?
a) 0.0031   **b)** 0.05   **c)** 0.01   **d)** 0.9969

70. A multiple choice test consists of 100 questions, each with five possible answers. If a student must answer at least 33 questions correctly in order to pass, what is the probability that the student passes the test? (Assume the student guesses at all the answers).

71. Over the past year, 60% of the patients waiting to see Dr. Hawkeye, an ophthalmologist, for their scheduled appointment have had to wait at least 45 minutes. What is the probability that out of the next 600 patients:
a) More than 390
b) Less than 340
will have to wait at least 45 minutes for their scheduled appointments?

72. According to a study by Dow Jones & Co., the best time to buy stocks is on a Monday afternoon since the chance of the market rising is 0.43 while the best time to sell is on a Friday since the chance of the market rising is 0.58. Use the results of this study to determine the probability that over the next 100 trading weeks, the market will:
a) Rise on a Monday afternoon at least 55 times.
b) Rise on a Friday at most 45 times.
c) Not rise on Friday more than 40 times.
d) Not rise on a Monday afternoon less than 60 times.

73. A baseball slugger hits a home run once out of every fifteen times he bats, that is, the probability that he will hit a home run at any given time at bat is ¹⁄₁₅. If he bats 450 times in a season, what is the probability that he hits:
a) At least 40 home runs?
b) Between 15 and 30 home runs (inclusive)?
c) More than 49 home runs?

74. Last year, the records of a Brooklyn college show that 80% of their graduates who were recommended to U.S. medical schools were admitted. If the records of 100 of these Brooklyn college graduates who were recommended to U.S. medical schools were randomly selected from the school's files, determine the probability that:
a) At least 90 of these graduates were admitted to a U.S. medical school.
b) At most 15 of these graduates were not admitted to a U.S. medical school.

75. Medical records show that 25% of all people suffering from "hardening of the arteries" have side effects from a certain type of medication. If 200 people suffering from "hardening of the arteries" are given this medication, what is the probability that:
a) No more than 35 will have side effects?
b) At least 160 will not have side effects?

76. Clinical records indicate that 20% of the outpatients in a facility for emotional disorders have been treated in this facility for at least 3 years. What is the probability that a sample of 400 outpatients from this facility will include:
a) Not more than 60 patients who have been treated at least 3 years?

b) No fewer than 90 patients who have been treated at least 3 years?

77. The Best Fit Screw Company institutes the following quality control procedure to improve the quality of the screws it uses. Before a shipment of screws is accepted a sample of 100 screws is selected and tested for defects. If more than six of the screws are found to be defective, the shipment is rejected.
   a) If a shipment is 20 percent defective, what is the probability that it will be accepted?

b) If a shipment is 10 percent defective, what is the probability that it will be accepted?

78. A money market fund company reports that next to individual retirement accounts (IRA's), the tax-shelter most frequently used by their shareholders is the uniform gifts to minors account. If 10% of their shareholders are custodians of an account for a minor, then what is the probability that out of the next 40,000 shareholders opening new accounts no more than 4100 will be custodian accounts for a minor?

> ## CHAPTER REVIEW

---

79. Use the properties of the normal distribution to answer the questions relating to the normal distribution in the following figure.

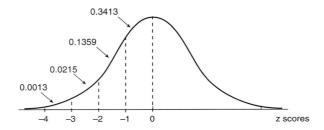

   a) What proportion of the distribution is less than a z-score of –4?
   b) What proportion of the distribution is less than a z-score of –2?
   c) What proportion of the distribution is less than a z-score of 0?
   d) What proportion of the distribution is less than a z-score of 1?
   e) What proportion of the distribution is less than a z-score of 3?
   f) What proportion of the distribution is less than a z-score of 5?
   g) What proportion of the distribution is within 1 standard deviation of the mean?
   h) What proportion of the distribution is within 2 standard deviations of the mean?
   i) What proportion of the distribution is within 3 standard deviations of the mean?

80. The shaded areas (A1 and A2) are equal. (T/F)

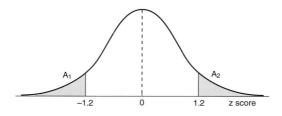

81. The shaded area to the right of a z score of –1 is greater than the area to the left of z score of –1. (T/F)

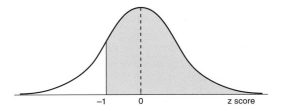

82. For a normal distribution the percent of area between z = 1 and z = –1 is approximately 68.26. Therefore the percent of data values between z = –1 and z = 1 is approximately _____.

83. In a normal distribution, the proportion of data values between z = 0 and z = –2 is the same as the proportion of data values between z = _____ and z = _____.

84. The percent of data values in a normal distribution that are located within:
   a) One standard deviation of the mean (that is, between z = +1 and z = –1) is approximately _____.
   b) Two standard deviations of the mean (that is, between z = 2 and z = –2) is approximately _____.
   c) Three standard deviations of the mean (that is, between z = +3 and z = –3) is approximately _____.

85. In a normal distribution find the z score(s) that:
   a) Cuts off the bottom 84% of the z scores.
   b) Cuts off the top 10% of the z scores.
   c) Cuts off the middle 50% of the z scores.

86. In a normal distribution find the z score(s) that:
   a) Cuts off the bottom 12% of the z scores.
   b) Determines the third decile.
   c) Determines the first quartile.
   d) Cuts off the top 5% of the z scores.
   e) Cuts off the middle 60% of the z scores.

87. In a normal distribution if the mean is 75 then the median is:
   a) 0   **b)** 50   **c)** 75   **d)** Insufficient information

88. Consider the following information for two normal distributions A and B.

A	B
$\mu = 50$	$\mu = 75$
$\sigma = 10$	$\sigma = 20$

For distribution A, the percent of data values between 50 and 60 is_____. For distribution B, 34.13 percent of data values are between 55 and _____.

89. In a normal distribution find the proportion of area:
a) Less than a z score of –1.65.
b) Between the z scores of 1.03 and +2.81
c) Greater than the z score of 0.30.

90. In a normal distribution with $\mu = 50$ and $\sigma = 10$ the proportion of data values greater than 65 is:
a) 0.0668   **b)** 0.6915   **c)** 0.9332   **d)** 0.1587

91. During the past season the number of points scored per game by the local High School football team was approximately normally distributed with $\mu = 18$ and $\sigma = 10$.

Use the normal distribution to answer the following questions:
a) If one assumes this season's play is indicative of next season's play then estimate the percent of next season's games that the team will score more than 31 points?
b) If the team plays 30 games in approximately how many would they score more than 6 points?
c) What's the probability that the team will score at least 22 points in any given game?

92. The production process at an automobile manufacturing company uses ball bearings whose service life is approximately normally distributed with a mean of 820 hours and a standard deviation of 40 hours. If the maintenance supervisor decides to replace the ball bearings before no more than 5% have worn out, what is the maximum time the ball bearings can be in operation before being replaced?

93. At a local high school 5000 juniors and seniors recently took an aptitude test. The results of the exam were normally distributed with $\mu = 450$ and $\sigma = 50$. Calculate the following:
a) The percent of students that scored over 575.
b) The number of students that scored less than 425.
c) The probability of a student selected at random having scored between 400 and 510.

94. A machine manufactures a special nut whose diameter is found to be normally distributed with $\mu = 1.5$ inches and $\sigma = 0.10$ inches. The specifications, for this special nut, call for the diameters to be within the limits of 1.4 plus or minus 0.30 inches. If a nut does not meet this specification, it is considered to be defective. What percentage of the nuts this machine manufactures will be considered to be defective?

95. An entrance requirement for a certain University is a percentile rank of at least 85 on the Math SAT exam.

Ten applicants are chosen at random and their Math SAT scores are listed below. If the Math SAT scores are normally distributed with $\mu = 500$ and $\sigma = 100$. Determine which of the ten applicants fail to meet the entrance requirement.

Applicants	Math SAT Score
1. Tina	590
2. Steven	640
3. Christopher	625
4. Michael	575
5. Craig	700
6. Allison	520
7. Nick	730
8. Meow	595
9. Matthew	650
10. Ryan	615

96. A new drug developed to immobilize wild life is administered to a herd of four hundred buffaloes which must be transported to another grazing area for environmental reasons. The buffaloes reaction time to this drug is approximately normal with a mean of 17.4 seconds and a standard deviation of 3.4 seconds. What is the probability that a buffalo selected at random will have a reaction time to the drug:
a) Less than 15 seconds?
b) Greater than 20 seconds?
c) Between 13 and 23 seconds?
Determine:
d) What is the maximum time required for the ten most *susceptible* buffaloes to react to this drug?

97. The normal distribution can be used as a good approximation to the binomial distribution if np and $n(1 - p)$ are both greater than:
a) 10   **b)** 5   **c)** 0.5   **d)** 25

98. For the binomial distribution with $n = 30$ and $p = ⅕$, would the normal distribution be a good approximation to the binomial distribution?_____.

99. For a binomial distribution with $n = 800$ and $p = 0.45$, calculate the value of:
a) μ_s?
b) σ_s?

100. Use the normal distribution to approximate the following binomial probabilities: If $n = 10,000$ and $p = 0.8$, then find the probability that the number of successes "s" is:
a) Greater than 8060, i.e $P(s > 8060)$.
b) Greater than or equal to 8060, i.e. $P(s \geq 8060)$.
c) Less than 7960, i.e. $P(s < 7960)$.
d) Equal to 7960, i.e. $P(s = 7960)$.
e) Between 7960 and 8060, i.e. $P(7960 < s < 8060)$.

101. If a fair coin is tossed 100 times what is the probability that the coin lands heads more than 60 times?
a) 0.9821   **b)** 0.05   **c)** 0.0179   **d)** 0.95

102. A recent survey showed that only 17% of the married women in the labor force have husbands who were earning over $55,000 annually. If a random sample of 100 married women is selected from the labor force, what is the probability that:

a) More than 25 have husbands earning over $55,000 annually?

b) Less than 76 have husbands earning less than $55,000 annually?

103. Jacqueline, a sales representative of Day News, a Nassau County newspaper, makes 200 calls a day trying to persuade potential customers to subscribe to Day News. If she has a 30% chance of selling a new subscription, what is the probability that Jacqueline will sell:

a) At least 78 new subscriptions for the day?

b) Fewer than 40 new subscriptions for the day?

104. The accountant firm of a major credit card company reports that 30% of all the company's delinquent accounts will eventually require legal action to collect the payment due. If this statement is accurate, what is the probability that of the 10,000 delinquent accounts due:

a) At least 3100 accounts will require legal action?

b) At most 6940 accounts will not require legal action?

105. A New York municipal court cites "incompatibility" as the legal cause for 80 percent of all divorce cases. If one hundred divorce cases are randomly selected from the court files, what is the probability that:

a) Not more than 72 cite incompatibility as the grounds for divorce?

b) At least 85 cite incompatibility as the grounds for divorce?

c) Less than 15 do *not* cite incompatibility as the grounds for divorce?

106. Medical researchers at a Boston university report that 20% of babies born to American mothers this year will be delivered by cesarean sections. What is the probability that out of the next 300 deliveries:

a) Not more than 85 will be cesarean sections?

b) At least 260 will not be cesarean sections?

107. A study released by the Bureau of Justice Statistics found that eight out of 10 young adults paroled from prison are rearrested for serious crimes within six years. If 1600 cases of young parolees are reviewed after six years, then what is the probability that:

a) More than 1300 were rearrested for a serious crime?

b) Less than 1320 were rearrested for a serious crime?

WHAT DO YOU THINK?

108. The bar graph in the following figure represents the ages of the *Forbes* magazine's 400 Richest People in the United States for 1992. To be ranked on this list, you had to be worth at least $265 million.

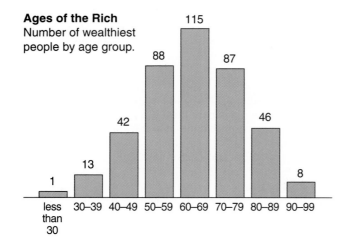

The 400 Wealthiest

Ages of the Rich
Number of wealthiest people by age group.

less than 30: 1
30–39: 13
40–49: 42
50–59: 88
60–69: 115
70–79: 87
80–89: 46
90–99: 8

a) What variable is being displayed in this histogram?

b) Is this variable: discrete or continuous?

c) What shape does this histogram have?

d) What do you think the shape of the histogram representing the ages of all the people living in the USA would look like? Explain.

e) Would you expect the mean age or median age of all the people living in the USA to be larger? Explain.

f) In a normal distribution, what is the relationship between the values of the mean, median and the mode?

g) Using the information contained in the histogram, what age would you use to represent the typical age of each class if you wanted to calculate the mean age?

h) Omitting the class "less than 30", calculate the mean, median and modal age (to the nearest whole number). How do these results compare to part (f)? Using the histogram and omitting the "less than 30" class, approximate the percentage of rich people that are:

i) From 50 to 65 years old and from 65 to 79 years old?

j) From 50 to 79 years old?

k) From 40 to 89 years old?

l) From 31 to 65 years old?

m) From 65 to 99 years old?

n) Omitting the class "less than 30", calculate the standard deviation of the ages of the richest 399 people using part (g). Using this information and assuming the distribution of ages of the richest people is approximately normal, answer the questions of parts (i) to (m).

o) Compare your answers from parts (i) to (m) to the results of part (n). Do you think that it is appropriate to make use of the normal distribution to answer questions regarding the distribution of the wealthiest people? Explain. What is the probability of selecting a person from the distribution of wealthiest people who is:

p) From 70 to 79 years old?

q) At least 50 years old?

r) At most 69 years old?

s) Calculate the same probabilities using the normal distribution as your model for the distribution of the ages and compare your results to parts (p) to (r).

109. The following graphic entitled "Mind Over Muscle" appeared in *The New York Times* on November 19, 1995.

The horizontal bars within the graphic represent the number of people who finished the 1995 New York City Marathon for each ten-minute period starting with 2 hours. Notice that the horizontal bar graph can be approximated by a bell-shaped curve.

a) Re-read the introduction to Section 6.3. Using this information, explain why you think the finishing times for the marathon would approximate a bell-shape curve.

b) Notice in the bar graph that there are five bars identified by black tips that do not conform to the bell-shaped curve. What are the times associated with these bars? The author of the article believes that runners strive to run the marathon on the "fast side of the closest round time". That is, a runner pushes to run a 3:57 rather than 4:02 or a 4:58 rather than a 5:03. Do you agree with this explanation? What do you think is the reason for these five spikes?

110. An article entitled "Student Finds Penny IS Tail-Heavy" appeared in *The Washington Post* on November 27, 1965. The article gives an account of a high

Mind Over Muscle

Running up 13,000-foot volcanoes? Yes, that's a pretty good way to squeeze out your best performance at the New York City Marathon. It worked for German Silva of Mexico, the men's winner last Sunday. But what really lights a runner's fire is the magic of round numbers.

You hear it all the time: "If I can just get under four hours," " Break three hours and I can die in peace." Runners carry these mantras around for months, even years.

Now, statistics would dictate that if you grouped the finishing times in 10-minute chunks, you'd see a tidy bell curve—the rarefied ranks of the speedy bulging smoothly toward the bulk of 4:15 runners in the middle, then falling off just as smoothly.

But no, runners gleefully defy statistics. Hundreds of them regularly leap to the fast side of the closest round time. A 4:02 runner pushes for a 3:57; a 5:03 is pulled by 4:58. This year at the four-hour barrier, the one most accessible to the average runner, the bell curve cracked.

New York runners often say, "Well, I lost 7 minutes at the start, so I *really* did . . . " But it's what the clock says that imbeds itself in their souls. Just try telling them a 3:00:10 is the same as a 2:59:50.

Hubert B. Herring

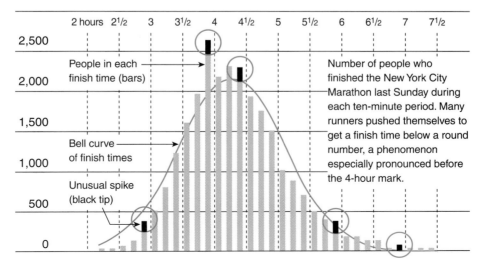

The New York Times

school senior named Edward who flipped a penny 17,950 times. He determined that the penny was tail-heavy. According to the story, a student flipped a penny 17,950 times and he recorded 464 more heads than tails. From his experiment, he proclaimed that the United States Mint produces tail-heavy pennies.

a) Can this be considered a binomial experiment? If it is, then what are the values of n, p, and $(1 - p)$?

b) Can you use the normal approximation to the binomial distribution to determine probabilities associated with this experiment? Explain.

c) How many heads and tails did Edward get during his experiment?

d) If we define p to be the probability of getting a head, then what is the expected mean number of heads for this experiment? How does the mean number of heads compare to the result in part (c)?

e) If a coin is fair, would you expect the number of times a coin lands heads to be equal to the mean number of heads found in part (d)? If not, then how many heads might you expect the coin to deviate from this expected mean number?

f) The number of heads can be 9,207 or 9,208, but it can't be any value in between. Is the number of heads a discrete or continuous variable? Since the normal distribution represents values between whole numbers, does it represent a discrete or continuous variable? Why are you able to use the normal distribution to approximate the binomial distribution? Do any adjustments have to be made to perform this approximation? If so, what are these adjustments?

g) What is the probability that a coin will land at least 9,207 heads in 17,950 tosses, using the normal approximation?

h) Is this probability small or large? If the event is rare, then would you expect the probability of the event to be small or large? What can you say about this event?

i) Do you think that the coin is fair or biased?

j) What did you use as the boundary value to calculate the probability in part (g)? Explain why it is necessary to use a boundary value rather than the actual value of 9,207, when using the normal approximation to the binomial distribution?

PROJECTS

111. a) Randomly select 36 females and record their heights (or weights).

b) Construct a frequency table, a histogram and a frequency polygon using your data.

c) Calculate the mean and standard deviation of your data.

d) Find the percent of heights (or weights) that are within 1 standard deviation of the mean.

e) For a normal distribution which has the same mean and standard deviation obtained in part (c) calculate the percent of data values within one standard deviation of the mean.

f) Compare the results of parts (d) and (e).

g) Repeat parts (a) through (f), using samples of size 64, 100, and 200.

112. Consider the uniform distribution pictured in the histogram below.

a) On twenty-one small pieces of paper write the numbers 0 through 20, one number to a piece of paper.

b) Place these pieces of paper into a container.

c) Select ten numbers from the container with replacement and record the result of each selection.

d) Calculate the sum of the ten numbers selected.

e) Repeat steps (c) and (d) until 100 sums have been calculated.

f) Construct a histogram and frequency polygon using an interval width of 5 for the 100 sums.

g) Compare their general shape to that of the normal distribution.

113. Use the random number generator within a technological tool such as MINITAB, EXCEL, or TI–83 Plus Calculator to produce approximately normally distributed data values for N = 10, 100, 200 and 500 data values. Use $\mu = 0$ and $\sigma = 1$. Construct a histogram for each distribution.

a) Describe the shape of each histogram.

b) Does the shape of the histogram change as the sample size increases? Explain.

c) Repeat parts (a) and (b). Are the results the same as before? Explain.

Numbers

d) What do you believe would be the shape of the resulting histogram if N = 100,000?

114. Use the random number generator within a technological tool such as MINITAB, EXCEL, or TI–83 Plus Calculator to produce approximately normally distributed data values for N = 10, 100, 200 and 500 data values. Use $\mu = 500$ and $\sigma = 100$. Construct a histogram for each distribution.

a) Describe the shape of each histogram.

b) Does the shape of the histogram change as the sample size increases? Explain.

c) Repeat parts (a) and (b). Are the results the same as before? Explain.

d) For each histogram calculate the proportion of data values that are within two standard deviations of the mean.

e) Compare the results obtained in part (d) to the actual proportion of data values that are within two standard deviations of the mean in a normal distribution.

f) As the sample size is increased, did the proportion of data values within two standard deviations of the mean for the samples, get closer to or farther from the proportion of data values that are within two standard deviations of the mean for a normal distribution?

115. Use a technological tool to produce a binomial distribution along with a table of binomial probability values for the binomial experiment where n = 100 and p = 0.5.

a) Using this information, calculate $P(s \leq 45)$.

b) Compare this probability value to the one obtained by using the normal approximation to the binomial distribution. Are these results very close? Did you expect this to happen? Explain.

116. a) Repeat problem 115 for n = 200, 300 and 400.

b) 1) for n = 200, calculate $P(s \leq 90)$.
Compare this probability value to one obtained by using the normal approximation to the binomial distribution.
2) for n = 300, calculate $P(s \leq 135)$.
Compare this probability value to one obtained by using the normal approximation to the binomial distribution.
3) for n = 400, calculate $P(s \leq 180)$.
Compare this probability value to one obtained by using the normal approximation to the binomial distribution.

c) By analyzing the previous results, write a conclusion regarding the normal approximation to the binomial distribution as n increases?

117. In the casino game roulette the probability of success for the outcome "black" is approximately 0.474. Use a technological tool to generate a table of successes along with the probability of success for choosing "black" and to construct a graph of each distribution for the game being played:

a) n = 10 times

b) n = 100 times

c) n = 1000 times

d) What happens to the probability of success in the game as the number of times the game is played increases?

ANALYZING THE DATABASE USING TECHNOLOGY

The following exercises refer to the file DATABASE listed in Appendix A. Using a technological tool, answer each exercise.

118. Determine the mean and standard deviation for the variable AVE.

a) Using a technological tool, obtain the probability of getting an average less than 78.

b) Sort and display the data values for the variable AVE and find the proportion of data values below 78.

c) Compare the results of parts (a) and (b).

119. Determine the mean and standard deviation for the variable GPA.

a) Using a technological tool, obtain the probability of getting an average less than 3.00.

b) Sort and display the data values for the variable GPA and find the proportion of data values less than 3.00.

c) Compare the results of parts (a) and (b).

CHAPTER TEST

120. In a normal distribution approximately two-thirds of the data values are within _____ standard deviation(s) of the mean.

a) 3   **b)** 1   **c)** 2   **d)** 1 and ½

121. In a normal distribution find the proportion of area:

a) Less than a z score of –0.50.

b) Between the z scores of –0.33 and +1.5

c) Greater than the z score of 2.88.

122. If two hundred thousand families in a local community have annual incomes which are normally distributed with a mean of $32,500 and a standard deviation of $5,000, then determine the following:

a) The proportion of families with incomes greater than $38,000.

b) The percent of families with incomes between $30,000 and $39,000.

c) The number of families who have incomes less than $29,000.

d) The family income that represents the 8th decile.

e) The family income that represents the 1st quartile.

f) The family income that represents the 65th percentile.

g) The family income that cuts off the lowest 200 incomes.

h) The family income that cuts off the highest 100 incomes.

i) The maximum family income eligible for food stamps if the five hundred families with the lowest incomes in this community are eligible for food stamps.

123. A woman wrote to Dear Abby the following letter.

Dear Abby,

   When my son first married his wife, she would spend a couple of weeks with him and then go visit her parents across the state for a week or so. This pattern kept up for more than a year. My son knew his wife dated other men while on her visits home.

   Last June she went for a visit with her folks and stayed almost six weeks. 253 days after the night of her return, she gave birth to a full-term healthy son. According to my information, 270 days must elapse after insemination, or 275 to 280 days after the first day of monthly period. Taking all this into consideration, she would have been impregnated while on her visit at her home.

   I don't think my son is aware of these facts. Should I mention to him that even though he is the legal father of the baby he may not be the biological father? Or would it be better not to say anything?
        —His Mom.

Although Dear Abby approached the problem from a nonstatistical view (she told the mom to mind her own business), we can use the normal distribution to provide an answer using a statistical approach. If we assume that completed pregnancies are normally distributed with a mean of 270 days and a standard deviation of 16 days, then calculate the probability that a pregnancy lasts:

a) At most 253 days. (i.e. the wife could've gotten pregnant after she returned home)

b) Longer than 295 days. (i.e. the wife could've been pregnant before she left = 253 days + 6 weeks = 295 days)

c) Between 253 and 295 days.

d) What do you think are the chances that the wife was impregnated by her husband? Explain.

124. Suppose the systolic blood pressure for an adult male above age 55 is normally distributed with a mean of 145 and a standard deviation of 20. If a sixty year old male is selected at random, what is the probability that his blood pressure is:

a) Between 140 and 160?

b) Greater than 170?

c) If 4000 adult males above age 55 have their blood pressure checked, then how many would you expect to have a blood pressure less than 130?

d) Volunteers from a Red Cross mobile unit that is checking blood pressures decide to recommend for additional medical diagnosis only those males above age 55 whose blood pressures are at the third quartile. What would be the minimum systolic blood pressure required to be recommended for additional medical diagnosis?

125. If the amount of soda which a dispensing machine puts into a two liter bottle is normally distributed with $\sigma = 0.5$ oz. find the mean amount of soda which the machine will put into a two liter bottle if only 65.54% of the bottles the machine filled will have less than 67.6 oz. of soda.

126. The lifetime of a car battery is found to be normally distributed with $\mu = 5$ years and $\sigma = \frac{3}{4}$ year. If the company which manufactures this battery is only willing to replace 5% of these batteries under its guarantee how many months should they guarantee their batteries?

127. If the grades of a math exam are normally distributed with $\sigma = 5$ find the mean grade on this exam, if 90 equals P_{92}.

128. Use the properties of the normal distribution to answer the questions relating to the normal distribution shown in the following figure.

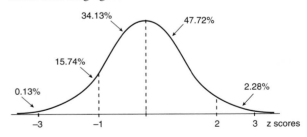

a) What proportion of the distribution is less than a z-score of 2?

b) What proportion of the distribution is between a z-score of −1 and 0?

c) What proportion of the distribution is greater than a z-score of 1?

d) What proportion of the distribution is less than a z-score of −1?

e) What proportion of the distribution is between a z-score of 1 and 2?

f) What proportion of the distribution is between a z-score of −1 and −2?

g) What proportion of the distribution is between a z-score of –2 and –3?

129. The binomial distribution can be approximated by a normal distribution if either np or n(1 – p) is greater than 5.
(T/F)

130. Assuming that the probability that someone will respond positively to a survey question is 0.40 what is the chance that more than half of the 150 people surveyed will respond positively?

a) 0.40   **b)** 0.20   **c)** 0.50   **d)** 0.0049

131. The probability that a camcorder battery lasts three years is 0.80. What is the probability that between 330 and 340 of the next 400 batteries sold last three years?

132. An airline company knows that 90% of the people making flight reservations for a certain flight will show up for the flight. What is the probability that out of the next 10,000 people making flight reservations:

a) 9075 or less will show up for the flight?
b) At least 9030 of them will show up for the flight?
c) Exactly 1000 will not show up for the flight?

133. From past experience a restaurant owner knows that 80% of the drinks ordered will be alcoholic. For the next 400 drinks ordered:

a) How many would be expected to be alcoholic?
b) What is the probability that at least 300 drinks will be alcoholic?

On a *good* weekend the owner sells at least $990 worth of alcoholic drinks at $3.00 per drink.

c) If 400 drinks are ordered next weekend what is the probability that next weekend is good?
d) The owner estimates that 25,600 drinks will be sold during the next year. He knows that for every 30 alcoholic drinks sold he uses one bottle of liquor. If each bottle of liquor costs him $9.00, how much money should he budget to be 95% confident his liquor costs are covered?

CHAPTER 7

Sampling and Sampling Distributions

Contents

7.1   THE SAMPLING DISTRIBUTION OF THE MEAN

As previously mentioned, populations are generally either quite large, have an unlimited number of data values, (that is, infinite) or partly unobtainable. Since a population can rarely be studied completely, a sample randomly selected from the population serves as a convenient and economical procedure to estimate the characteristics of a population. One population characteristic we are interested in estimating is the mean of a population. For example,

- an internist uses samples to estimate the average cholesterol level in a patient's body,
- an economist uses samples to estimate the average interest rate for short-term bonds,
- a tire manufacturer uses samples to estimate the average wear of their new radial tire,
- a light-bulb manufacturer uses samples to estimate the average life of each type of bulb they produce,
- a pool owner uses samples to determine the average pH reading of her pool,
- a pharmaceutical company uses samples to estimate the average time its new pain relieving drug will be effective,
- a college student uses samples to estimate the average textbook cost for all the college students.

In each of these situations, sample information is being used to estimate the mean of a population. When the population mean is being estimated using sample data, the mean of the sample will probably not be equal to the mean of the population. In fact, if a few samples were randomly selected from the same population, *it is very likely that none of these sample means would be exactly equal to the mean of the population.*

Consider, for example, a soft-drink company who manufactures a 2 liter bottle of their new diet drink. Due to variations in the manufacturing process, some bottles will probably contain slightly less than 2 liters while others will contain slightly more. Because of the imperfections in the dispensing process, we really have no idea of what the "true" mean amount of soda, μ, is for the population of soda bottles. The only possible way we could determine the true population mean, μ, is to remove and open every bottle from the production line and determine the amount of soda within each bottle. Practically speaking, however, it is virtually impossible to do this. In such instances, **inferential statistics** is used to estimate the mean of the population. A sample of the bottles are randomly selected from the production line and the mean amount of soda for this sample is computed. Assume a random sample of 15 bottles yields the following amounts of soda.

Amount of soda, in liters, for the random sample of 15 bottles

1.93	1.95	1.94	1.96	2.03
1.96	2.02	1.93	2.04	2.01
2.01	2.01	1.96	1.93	2.02

The sample mean, $\bar{x}$, for these 15 bottles is:

$$\bar{x} = \frac{1.93 + 1.95 + 1.94 + \ldots + 2.02}{15} = 1.98 \text{ liters}$$

It is reasonable to use this sample information to estimate the mean amount of soda for all the bottles manufactured by this company. Thus, the **sample mean of $\bar{x}$ = 1.98 liters** would serve as an **estimate** of the **true mean amount of soda, μ, of the population**. When we use the sample mean, $\bar{x}$, of 1.98 liters as an estimate of the true population mean, μ, we are using inferential statistics, that is, using sample information, $\bar{x}$, to draw an inference about a population parameter, μ.

However, once we use a sample mean to estimate the mean of a population, it is natural to ask the question: *how good of an estimate do we have?* That is, *how close is $\bar{x}$ to μ?* Is it possible that this sample mean, $\bar{x}$, is identically equal to the true population mean, μ? In essence, we are asking: how likely is it that a sample of 15 bottles would yield a mean equal to the mean amount of soda for all the bottles manufactured?

We would have to say it is probably very unlikely that this sample mean would be equal to the population mean. In fact, if we were to select 5 more samples of 15 bottles from the production line, more likely than not, these 5 sample means would not only differ from the population mean, μ, but would probably also differ from one another. That is, all 5 sample means would most likely have a different value for $\bar{x}$, since the samples would contain different bottles randomly selected from the same production line. Therefore, in answer to our question, it is rather unlikely to expect the sample mean, $\bar{x}$, to be identically equal to the population mean, μ.

At this point, you should begin to understand that although there is only one value for the true mean amount of soda for all the bottles manufactured by this company, there are many different values for the mean amount of soda from the samples selected from this population. Therefore, *the estimates of a true population mean will vary from sample to sample due to the data values randomly selected within each sample, that is, by chance alone.* Different samples selected from the same population will possibly yield different sample results because they contain different data values. For example, by chance alone, a sample may contain mostly bottles that are below the mean amount of soda or mostly bottles containing amounts of soda above the mean amount of soda. Consequently, since the samples of bottles vary from one another, by chance alone, the estimates of the true population mean amount of soda will vary.

Suppose we selected a sample and calculated the sample mean to be 1.98 liters. *Our estimate of the true population mean would be 1.98 liters.* However, suppose you selected another sample from the same production line and computed the sample mean to be 2.03 liters. *Your estimate of the same population mean would be 2.03 liters.* A third person selecting a sample from the same production line would most likely obtain a different sample mean result and consequently, a different estimate of the same population mean. *These variations in the estimates of the population mean from sample to sample are due to chance and are called* **sampling errors.** This sampling error is due to the luck of the sampling selection, that is, the random selection of the sample data values chosen from the population. For example, assume, hypothetically, that the true population mean amount of soda is 2 liters. If we used our first sample mean of 1.98 liters to estimate the population mean, our estimate would result in an error. The difference between our estimate of the true population mean (1.98 liters) and the true population mean (2 liters) represents the sampling error. That is,

$$\text{sampling error} = \text{sample mean} - \text{population mean}$$
$$= 1.98 \text{ liters} - 2 \text{ liters}$$
$$= -0.02 \text{ liters.}$$

On the other hand, your estimate of this same population mean would be 2.03 liters which was based on the random selection of another sample from the same population. This estimate would also result in an error. In this instance, the sampling error is:

$$\text{the sampling error} = \text{sample mean} - \text{population mean}$$
$$= 2.03 \text{ liters} - 2 \text{ liters}$$
$$= 0.03 \text{ liters.}$$

These sampling errors are attributed to the fact that the samples contained a different collection of randomly selected bottles from the same production line. So, by chance alone, these different sampling errors occurred. The sampling errors are not the result of any errors which can occur during the:

	selection process (i.e. not selecting a representative sample of bottles),
or	measuring process (i.e. incorrectly measuring the amount of soda per bottle),
or	recording process (i.e. incorrectly recording the amount soda per bottle),
or	computation process (i.e. incorrectly calculating the sample mean amount of soda).

These type of errors are called **nonsampling errors.**

Sampling errors are simply errors due to chance or the luck of the selection process.

DEFINITION 7.1

Sampling error is the difference between the value of a sample statistic, such as the sample mean, $\bar{x}$ and the value of the corresponding population parameter, such as the population mean, μ.

Thus, the sampling error for the mean is:

sampling error = sample mean – population mean

assuming the sample is random and there are no nonsample errors.

In symbols,

sampling error of the mean = $\bar{x} - \mu$.

EXAMPLE 7.1

Suppose the population of seven college students on the Student Government Association (SGA) have the following ages:

$$23, 19, 20, 21, 18, 19, 25$$

a) Compute the population mean age, μ, of all the students on the SGA.
    If a random sample of 3 students was selected from this population having the ages: $19, 21$, and 18, then
b) Compute the sample mean age for this sample.
c) Determine the sampling error if this sample were used to estimate the population mean age.
    If a random sample of 3 students was selected from this population having the ages: $23, 21$, and 25, then
d) Compute the sample mean age for this sample.
e) Determine the sampling error if this sample were used to estimate the population mean age.
f) Interpret the meaning of this sampling error.

Solution

a) The population mean age, μ, is:

$$\mu = \frac{23 + 19 + 20 + 21 + 18 + 19 + 25}{7} \approx 20.71 \text{ years}$$

b) The sample mean, $\overline{x}$, of the ages $19, 21$, and 18 is:

$$\overline{x} = \frac{19 + 21 + 18}{3} \approx 19.33 \text{ years}$$

c) If a sample mean of 19.33 is used to estimate the population mean of 20.71, then the sampling error would be:

$$\text{sampling error} = \overline{x} - \mu.$$
$$= 19.33 - 20.71$$
$$= -1.38 \text{ years}$$

d) The sample mean, $\overline{x}$, of the ages $23, 21$, and 25 is:

$$\overline{x} = \frac{23 + 21 + 25}{3} = 23 \text{ years}$$

e) If a sample mean of 23 is used to estimate the population mean of 20.71, then the sampling error would be:

$$\text{sampling error} = \overline{x} - \mu.$$
$$= 23 - 20.71$$
$$= 2.29 \text{ years}$$

f) Sampling error represents the error that would be made in estimating the population mean using the mean of a sample selected from this population. This error is due to chance alone. That is, by chance alone, a sample mean of 23 was selected from this population of ages. Thus, if we were to use a sample mean of 23 to estimate the population mean of 20.71, then, by chance alone, our estimate would have an error of 2.29 years.

Sampling error is inevitable because we are using a chosen number of data values which are randomly selected, by chance, from the population. In practice, we will select only one sample from the population to estimate the mean of the population. However, keep in mind, this chosen sample is only one of many possible samples which could have been selected from the population. The value of the sample mean, $\bar{x}$ is dependent upon the sample of data values selected, so the sample mean does not have a constant value like the population mean. That is, a population can have only one mean. Yet, *depending upon which sample is selected from a population, the mean of a sample can vary from sample to sample as different samples of the same size are randomly chosen from the same population.* Thus, the sample mean is a **random variable** because it is dependent upon the particular data values which are randomly selected from the population. In order for us to determine how closely a sample mean estimates the mean of a population, it is necessary for us to have some prior knowledge about all the possible sample means which could have been selected and how these sample means are distributed. That is, we are interested in examining the distribution of all the possible values of the sample mean, $\bar{x}$, for a population. Such a distribution is called the **distribution of sample means**, or more commonly referred to as the **sampling distribution of the mean**.

> **DEFINITION 7.2**
> The **sampling distribution of the mean** is a probability distribution which lists the sample means from all possible samples of the same sample size selected from the same population along with the probability associated with each sample mean.

Let's illustrate the idea of a sampling distribution of the mean by constructing such a distribution. This illustration is, of course, hypothetical because in practice the population would be much larger and we would be unable to obtain all the values of the population.

Suppose the prices of 7 statistical calculators sold in a college bookstore represent the population. The data values of this population are:

$$\$30, \$32, \$34, \$36, \$38, \$40, \$42.$$

For this population, the mean price and standard deviation of these prices are: $\mu = \$36$ and $\sigma = \$4$. Figure 7.1 illustrates how these population values were computed.

```
Population of calculator prices and its characteristics:
   the population mean, μ, and standard deviation, σ
```

X	X − μ	(X − μ)²
30	30−36 = −6	(−6)² = 36
32	32−36 = −4	(−4)² = 16
34	34−36 = −2	(−2)² = 4
36	36−36 = 0	(0)² = 0
38	38−36 = 2	(2)² = 4
40	40−36 = 4	(4)² = 16
42	42−36 = 6	(6)² = 36

$$\mu = \frac{\Sigma X}{N} = \frac{252}{7} \qquad \sigma = \sqrt{\frac{\Sigma(X-\mu)^2}{N}} = \sqrt{\frac{112}{7}} = \sqrt{16}$$

$$\mu = 36 \qquad\qquad \sigma = 4$$

FIGURE 7.1

We will construct a sampling distribution of the mean by selecting all possible samples of size 2 that can be selected **without replacement** from the population of prices. The total number of possible samples of size 2 can be determined using Table I in Appendix D: Statistical Tables. Since there are 7 prices which comprise the population and we are going to select samples of size 2, the total number of possible samples that can be selected without replacement is equal to $_7C_2$. From Table I in Appendix D, we have:

$$\text{total number of possible samples of size } 2 = {_7C_2} = 21.$$

Thus, there are 21 distinct samples of size 2. These 21 samples and their respective means are shown in Figure 7.2.

All Possible Samples of Size 2 and Their Sample Means

Sample	Data Values of Selected Sample	Sample Mean, $\bar{x}$
1	$30, $32	$\bar{x} = \dfrac{30 + 32}{2} = \$31$
2	$30, $34	$\bar{x} = \dfrac{30 + 34}{2} = \$32$
3	$30, $36	$\bar{x} = \dfrac{30 + 36}{2} = \$33$
4	$30, $38	$\bar{x} = \dfrac{30 + 38}{2} = \$34$
5	$30, $40	$\bar{x} = \dfrac{30 + 40}{2} = \$35$
6	$30, $42	$\bar{x} = \dfrac{30 + 42}{2} = \$36$
7	$32, $34	$\bar{x} = \dfrac{32 + 34}{2} = \$33$
8	$32, $36	$\bar{x} = \dfrac{32 + 36}{2} = \$34$
9	$32, $38	$\bar{x} = \dfrac{32 + 38}{2} = \$35$
10	$32, $40	$\bar{x} = \dfrac{32 + 40}{2} = \$36$
11	$32, $42	$\bar{x} = \dfrac{32 + 42}{2} = \$37$
12	$34, $36	$\bar{x} = \dfrac{34 + 36}{2} = \$35$
13	$34, $38	$\bar{x} = \dfrac{34 + 38}{2} = \$36$
14	$34, $40	$\bar{x} = \dfrac{34 + 40}{2} = \$37$
15	$34, $42	$\bar{x} = \dfrac{34 + 42}{2} = \$38$
16	$36, $38	$\bar{x} = \dfrac{36 + 38}{2} = \$37$
17	$36, $40	$\bar{x} = \dfrac{36 + 40}{2} = \$38$
18	$36, $42	$\bar{x} = \dfrac{36 + 42}{2} = \$39$
19	$38, $40	$\bar{x} = \dfrac{38 + 40}{2} = \$39$
20	$38, $42	$\bar{x} = \dfrac{38 + 42}{2} = \$40$
21	$40, $42	$\bar{x} = \dfrac{40 + 42}{2} = \$41$

FIGURE 7.2

Figure 7.2 illustrates that different samples will yield different values of the sample mean. For example, the sample mean can be as small as $31 or as large as $40, depending upon the sample chosen. If a sample is chosen by simple random sampling, then each sample has an equal chance of being selected. Each of the 21 possible samples shown within Figure 7.2 has a probability of ½₁ of being randomly selected. Since there are two samples out of 21 possible samples that yield a sample mean of $33, then the probability is ²⁄₂₁ that a sample randomly selected from these 21 samples will yield a sample mean of $33. Similarly, the probability is ²⁄₂₁ that the sample randomly selected from these 21 samples will yield a sample mean of $34. From the information in Figure 7.2, we can construct a probability distribution of these sample means which lists all the possible values which the sample mean $\bar{x}$ can assume along with the probabilities of each of these sample means occurring.

Figure 7.3 represents a probability distribution of the sample means since it lists all the possible sample means and their corresponding probabilities. Since the data values of this probability distribution are the means of all the possible samples, this probability distribution represents the sampling distribution of the mean for random samples of size 2.

A histogram of the sampling distribution of the mean shown in Figure 7.3 is illustrated in Figure 7.4.

An examination of the sampling distribution in Figure 7.4 reveals information about the variations, due to chance, of the mean of random samples of size 2 selected from the population of prices. For instance, the probability that a sample mean will be within $1 of the population mean of μ = $36 is 9/21. This is because a sample mean of $35, $36 or $37 will fall within $1 of the population mean and their corresponding probabilities add up to ⁹⁄₂₁.

```
        Sampling Distribution of the Mean
            for random samples of size 2

     Value of              Probability of selecting
 Sample Mean, x̄              Sample Mean, x̄
        31                       1/21
        32                       1/21
        33                       2/21
        34                       2/21
        35                       3/21
        36                       3/21
        37                       3/21
        38                       2/21
        39                       2/21
        40                       1/21
        41                       1/21
```

FIGURE 7.3

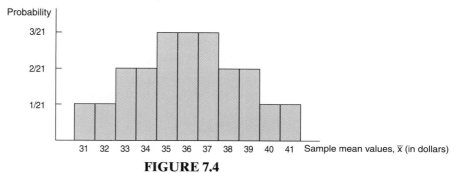

FIGURE 7.4

That is,

$$P\binom{\text{sample mean will be}}{\text{within \$1 of } \mu = \$36} = P\binom{\text{sample mean}}{\text{is \$35}} + P\binom{\text{sample mean}}{\text{is \$36}} + P\binom{\text{sample mean}}{\text{is \$37}}$$

$$= \quad \sqrt[3]{21} \quad + \quad \sqrt[3]{21} \quad + \quad \sqrt[3]{21}$$

$$= \quad \sqrt[9]{21}.$$

If we didn't know the population mean, then we would consider selecting a sample at random from the population and computing its mean to estimate the population mean. The sampling distribution can provide us with an idea of how large of a sampling error we could make. Example 7.2 illustrates this concept.

EXAMPLE 7.2

Using the sampling distribution of the mean given in Figure 7.2, what is the probability that a sample randomly selected from the population of calculator prices will result in a sampling error in estimating the population mean of $2 or less?

Solution

Since the population mean is $36, then selecting a sample mean from $34 to $38 would result in a sampling error of $2 or less. That is, the sample mean will deviate from the population mean of $36 by $2 or less. According to the sampling distribution of the mean given in Figure 7.3, the probability of selecting a sample mean from $34 to $38 is equal to the sum of the probabilities associated to these sample means. That is:

$$P(\text{sample mean from \$34 to \$38}) = P(\$34) + P(\$35) + P(\$36) + P(\$37) + P(\$38)$$

$$= \sqrt[2]{21} + \sqrt[3]{21} + \sqrt[3]{21} + \sqrt[3]{21} + \sqrt[2]{21}$$

$$= \sqrt[13]{21}.$$

Thus, the probability that a sample mean will result in a sampling error of $2 or less is equal to $^{13}\!/_{21}$.

In describing the main characteristics of a distribution, we typically determine its mean, standard deviation, and describe the shape of the distribution. Before we discuss the mean and standard deviation of the sampling distribution of the mean we will introduce the notation for these measures.

Notation for the Mean of the Sampling Distribution of the Mean

The **mean of the sampling distribution of the mean** is denoted by $\mu_{\bar{x}}$, read mu sub x bar.
   Thus,

$$\mu_{\bar{x}} = \text{mean of all the sample means of the sampling distribution}$$

Notation for the Standard Deviation of the Sampling Distribution of the Mean

The **standard deviation of the sampling distribution of the mean** is denoted by $\sigma_{\bar{x}}$, read sigma sub x bar.
   Thus,

$$\sigma_{\bar{x}} = \text{standard deviation of all the sample means of the sampling distribution}$$

To compute these measures for the sampling distribution of the mean shown in Figure 7.3, we will use the definitions of the population mean and population standard deviation discussed in the probability distribution chapter where the variable X is replaced by $\overline{x}$.

For the sampling distribution of the mean shown in Figure 7.3, the mean of the sampling distribution of the mean is: $\mu_{\overline{x}} = \$36$, and the standard deviation of the sampling distribution of the mean is: $\sigma_{\overline{x}} \approx \$2.58$. Figure 7.5 contains the calculations of $\mu_{\overline{x}}$ and $\sigma_{\overline{x}}$.

Figure 7.6 summarizes the characteristics of the sampling distribution of the mean and the analogous characteristics of the population of prices.

```
           Calculation of Mean and Standard Deviation of the
                   Sampling Distribution of the Mean

 x̄     P(x̄)      x̄P(x̄)      x̄-μx̄      (x̄-μx̄)²           (x̄-μx̄)²P(x̄)

 31    1/21       31/21     31-36=-5    (-5)²=25      (25)(1/21)  = 25/21
 32    1/21       32/21     32-36=-4    (-4)²=16      (16)(1/21)  = 16/21
 33    2/21       66/21     33-36=-3    (-3)²= 9      ( 9)(2/21)  = 18/21
 34    2/21       68/21     34-36=-2    (-2)²= 4      ( 4)(2/21)  =  8/21
 35    3/21      105/21     35-36=-1    (-1)²= 1      ( 1)(3/21)  =  3/21
 36    3/21      108/21     36-36= 0    ( 0)²= 0      ( 0)(3/21)  =   0
 37    3/21      111/21     37-36= 1    ( 1)²= 1      ( 1)(3/21)  =  3/21
 38    2/21       76/21     38-36= 2    ( 2)²= 4      ( 4)(2/21)  =  8/21
 39    2/21       78/21     39-36= 3    ( 3)²= 9      ( 9)(2/21)  = 18/21
 40    1/21       40/21     40-36= 4    ( 4)²=16      (16)(1/21)  = 16/21
 41    1/21       41/21     41-36= 5    ( 5)²=25      (25)(1/21)  = 25/21
```

$$\mu_{\overline{x}} = \Sigma \overline{x} \cdot P(\overline{x}) \qquad \Sigma(\overline{x}-\mu_{\overline{x}})^2 \cdot P(\overline{x}) = 140/21 \approx 6.67$$

$$= 756/21 \qquad\qquad \sigma_{\overline{x}} = \sqrt{\Sigma(\overline{x}-\mu_{\overline{x}})^2 \cdot P(\overline{x})} \approx \sqrt{6.67}$$

$$\mu_{\overline{x}} = \$36 \qquad\qquad \sigma_{\overline{x}} \approx \$2.58$$

FIGURE 7.5

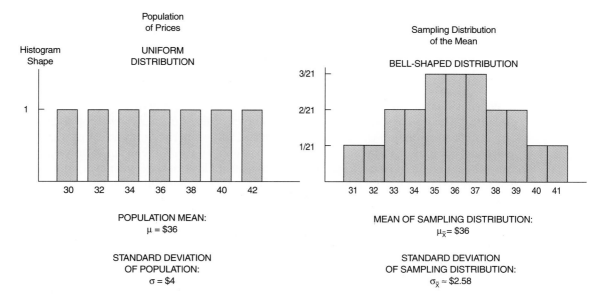

Histogram Shape

Population of Prices — UNIFORM DISTRIBUTION

Sampling Distribution of the Mean — BELL-SHAPED DISTRIBUTION

POPULATION MEAN:
$\mu = \$36$

MEAN OF SAMPLING DISTRIBUTION:
$\mu_{\overline{x}} = \$36$

STANDARD DEVIATION OF POPULATION:
$\sigma = \$4$

STANDARD DEVIATION OF SAMPLING DISTRIBUTION:
$\sigma_{\overline{x}} \approx \$2.58$

FIGURE 7.6

From Figure 7.6, observe some of the important relationships between the population and the sampling distribution of the mean for this example.

1. The mean of the sampling distribution of the mean, $\mu_{\bar{x}}$, equals the mean of the population, μ.
2. The standard deviation of the sampling distribution of the mean, $\sigma_{\bar{x}}$, is less than the population standard deviation, σ.
3. The shape of the sampling distribution of the mean and the shape of the population are different. The sampling distribution of the mean has a more normal curve shape.

These observations illustrate some very important and fundamental concepts of the sampling distribution of the mean. We will discuss these further in the following sections.

Before we continue, it is important to understand and be able to distinguish between the mean and standard deviation of a population, a sample, and the sampling distribution of the mean. In earlier chapters, we described a population by its mean, μ, and standard deviation, σ. A sample was described by its mean, $\bar{x}$, and standard deviation, s. Now in this chapter, we have discussed the mean and standard deviation of the sampling distribution of the mean. Figure 7.7 contains the symbols for the mean and standard deviation of a population, a sample and the sampling distribution of the mean.

**Notation for Mean and Standard Deviation for a Population,
a Sample and the Sampling Distribution of the Mean**

	Population	**Sample**	**Sampling Distribution of the Mean**
Description:	collection of all data values	portion of data values randomly selected from the population	means of all possible samples of size n randomly selected from the population
Mean:	μ	$\bar{x}$	$\mu_{\bar{x}}$
Standard Deviation:	σ	s	$\sigma_{\bar{x}}$

FIGURE 7.7

7.2   THE MEAN AND STANDARD DEVIATION OF THE SAMPLING DISTRIBUTION OF THE MEAN

In the previous section, we examined the concept of the sampling distribution of the mean, using a hypothetical situation of selecting all possible samples of size 2 from a known population of 7 data values. This unrealistic situation was used to demonstrate that when randomly selecting a sample from a population and computing its mean, the value of this sample mean is the mean of only one of many possible samples that might have been selected. In practical applications, we will never know all the data values of a population and it will be impractical or impossible to randomly select all the possible samples of a particular sample size from the population. Consequently, in inferential statistics, we never construct a sampling distribution rather we conceive of the situation of selecting all possible samples of a particular size from a population containing an infinite number of data values. Such a sampling distribution is referred to as a **Theoretical Sampling Distribution**. Since the theoretical sampling distribution is a sampling distribution obtained by theoretical results we must rely on statisticians to provide the theory and formulas needed to help us determine the characteristics of the Theoretical Sampling Distribution of the mean. In this section, we will examine how to determine the mean and standard deviation of the Theoretical Sampling Distribution of the mean by sampling from a list of means.

Mean of the Sampling Distribution of the Mean

As discussed earlier, the mean of all the sample means of the sampling distribution is called the mean of the sampling distribution of the mean and is denoted by $\mu_{\bar{x}}$, read mu sub x bar.

Statistical theory tell us that if we were to take all the possible samples of the same size n from a population, the mean of all the sample means, $\mu_{\bar{x}}$, will be equal to the mean of the population, μ.

> ### DEFINITION 7.3
> **Mean of the Sampling Distribution of the Mean, $\mu_{\bar{x}}$** The mean of the sample means of all possible samples of size n is called the mean of the sampling distribution of the mean, denoted by $\mu_{\bar{x}}$. It is equal to the mean of the population from which the samples were selected. In symbols, this is expressed as:
>
> $$\mu_{\bar{x}} = \mu$$

Standard Deviation of the Sampling Distribution of the Mean

The standard deviation of the sampling distribution of the mean, however, is not equal to the standard deviation of the population. As we illustrated in Figure 7.6, the standard deviation of the sampling distribution of the mean is smaller than the standard deviation of the population. That is, **the sampling distribution of the mean is less dispersed than the population from which the samples were selected**. According to statistical theory, the standard deviation of the sampling distribution of the mean, denoted by $\sigma_{\bar{x}}$, is equal to the standard deviation of the population, σ, divided by the square root of the sample size, n. The standard deviation of the sampling distribution of the mean is commonly referred to as the **Standard Error of the Mean**.

> ### DEFINITION 7.4
> **Standard Deviation of the Sampling Distribution of the Mean or Standard Error of the Mean, denoted by $\sigma_{\bar{x}}$** The standard error of the mean is the standard deviation of the sample means of all possible samples of size n of the sampling distribution, denoted by $\sigma_{\bar{x}}$. The standard error of the mean is equal to the standard deviation of the population, σ, divided by the square root of the sample size n. That is,
>
> $$\text{standard error of the mean} = \frac{\text{population standard deviation}}{\sqrt{\text{sample size}}}$$
>
> In symbols, this is expressed as:
>
> $$\sigma_{\bar{x}} = \frac{\sigma}{\sqrt{n}}$$

Example 7.3 illustrates the use of these formulas to calculate the mean and standard error of the sampling distribution of the mean.

E X A M P L E   7 . 3

According to a study of TV viewing habits, the average number of hours a teenager watches MTV per week is $\mu = 17.9$ hours with a standard deviation of $\sigma = 3.8$ hours. If a sample of 64 teenagers is randomly selected from the population, then determine the mean and standard error of the mean of the sampling distribution of the mean.

Solution

Since a random sample of 64 teenagers is being selected from the population, then the sampling distribution of the mean consists of all possible samples of size n = 64. According to statistical theory, the mean of the sampling distribution of the mean, $\mu_{\bar{x}}$, is equal to the population mean, μ. That is, $\mu_{\bar{x}} = \mu$. Since the population mean is $\mu = 17.9$ hours, then the mean of the sampling distribution of the mean is equal to 17.9. Thus, $\mu_{\bar{x}} = 17.9$ hours.

The standard deviation of the sampling distribution of the mean or the standard error of the mean, $\sigma_{\bar{x}}$, is equal to the standard deviation of the population, σ, divided by the square root of the sample size n. That is,

$$\sigma_{\bar{x}} = \frac{\sigma}{\sqrt{n}}.$$

Since the population standard deviation is $\sigma = 3.8$ and the sample size is n = 64, then the standard error of the mean is:

$$\sigma_{\bar{x}} = \frac{\sigma}{\sqrt{n}}$$

$$\sigma_{\bar{x}} = \frac{3.8}{\sqrt{64}}$$

$$\sigma_{\bar{x}} = \frac{3.8}{8}$$

$$\sigma_{\bar{x}} \approx 0.48$$

In Example 7.4, we will discuss what happens to the standard error of the mean when the size of the sample is increased.

EXAMPLE 7.4

The registrar at a large University states that the mean grade point average of all the students is $\mu = 2.95$ with a population standard deviation of $\sigma = 0.20$.

a) Determine the mean and standard error of the sampling distribution if the sampling distribution of the mean consists of all possible sample means from samples of size 25.

b) Determine the mean and standard error of the sampling distribution if the sampling distribution of the mean consists of all possible sample means from samples of size 100.

c) What effect did increasing the sample size have on the mean and standard error of the sampling distribution?

d) In which sampling distribution of the mean, the one with sample size 25 or the one with sample size 100, would you have a better chance of selecting a sample mean which is closer to the population mean grade point average? Explain

Solution

a) According to statistical theory, $\mu_{\bar{x}} = \mu$. Since the population mean is $\mu = 2.95$, then the mean of the sampling distribution of the mean is equal to 2.95. Thus, $\mu_{\bar{x}} = 2.95$. The formula for the standard error of the mean, is,

$$\sigma_{\bar{x}} = \frac{\sigma}{\sqrt{n}}.$$

Since the population standard deviation is $\sigma = 0.20$ and the sample size is n = 25, then the standard error is:

$$\sigma_{\bar{x}} = \frac{\sigma}{\sqrt{n}}$$

$$\sigma_{\bar{x}} = \frac{0.20}{\sqrt{25}}$$

$$\sigma_{\bar{x}} = \frac{0.20}{5}$$

$$\sigma_{\bar{x}} = 0.04 .$$

b) The mean of the sampling distribution of the mean, $\mu_{\bar{x}}$, is equal to the population mean, μ, regardless of the sample size; therefore, the mean of the sampling distribution of the mean is still equal to 2.95. Therefore, $\mu_{\bar{x}} = 2.95$. The standard error of the mean, $\sigma_{\bar{x}}$, however, is affected by the sample size since $\sigma_{\bar{x}}$ is equal to the standard deviation of the population, σ, divided by the square root of the sample size n. That is,

$$\sigma_{\bar{x}} = \frac{\sigma}{\sqrt{n}} .$$

The population standard deviation is still $\sigma = 0.20$ but the sample size has increased to n = 100. Thus, the standard error of the mean is:

$$\sigma_{\bar{x}} = \frac{\sigma}{\sqrt{n}}$$

$$\sigma_{\bar{x}} = \frac{0.20}{\sqrt{100}}$$

$$\sigma_{\bar{x}} = \frac{0.20}{10}$$

$$\sigma_{\bar{x}} = 0.02 .$$

c) The results of parts (a) and (b) are shown in the following table.

Sample Size n	Mean of the Sampling Distribution $\mu_{\bar{x}}$	Standard Error of the Sampling Distribution $\sigma_{\bar{x}}$
n = 25	$\mu_{\bar{x}} = 2.95$	$\sigma_{\bar{x}} = 0.04$
n = 100	$\mu_{\bar{x}} = 2.95$	$\sigma_{\bar{x}} = 0.02$

Observe from this table, the mean of the sampling distribution was not affected as the sample size increased from n = 25 to n = 100. This will always be true. That is, *the mean of the sampling distribution is not affected by the sample size.* However, the standard error of the sampling distribution will be affected as the sample size increases. Examining the table, we observe as the sample size increased from 25 to 100, the standard error of the sampling distribution decreased from 0.04 to 0.02. *In general, as the sample size increases, the standard error of the sampling distribution will decrease.*

d) Since the sampling distribution of the mean for all possible samples of size n = 100 has a smaller standard deviation, $\sigma_{\bar{x}} = 0.02$, then *you have a better chance of selecting a sample mean closer to the population mean grade point average from this sampling distribution.* This is true because a smaller standard deviation indicates that samples of size n = 100 will have less dispersion about the mean than samples of size n = 25. In the sampling distribution containing samples of size n = 100, the sample means will be relatively closer to the mean of the population. This will provide us with a better chance of selecting a sample mean that is closer to the population mean grade point average.

Interpretation of the Standard Error of the Mean

The standard deviation of the sampling distribution of the mean is referred to as the Standard Error of the Mean because it is a measure of how much a sample mean is likely to deviate from the population mean, that is, it is a measure of the average sampling error.

Recall when a sample is randomly selected from the population and its mean, $\bar{x}$, is used as an estimate of the population mean, μ, the difference between the sample mean, $\bar{x}$, and the population mean, μ, represents the sampling error. For any distribution, the standard deviation of the distribution provides an approximate measure of the average deviation of the data values from the mean. Thus, in a sampling distribution of the mean, the standard deviation of the sampling distribution of the mean, $\sigma_{\bar{x}}$, will roughly indicate the average deviation of the sample means, $\bar{x}$, from the population mean, μ, or average sampling error. Consequently, the standard deviation of the sampling distribution of the mean, $\sigma_{\bar{x}}$, is a measure of the average sampling error and is referred to as the Standard Error of the Mean.

If the *Standard Error of the Mean, $\sigma_{\bar{x}}$,* is a small number, then the sampling distribution *of the mean has relatively little dispersion* and the *sample means will be relatively close to the population mean.* In such instances, a sample mean which is randomly selected from the sampling distribution will have a relatively large probability of not deviating considerably from the population mean. Consequently, **there is a good chance of a small sampling error in estimating the population mean when $\sigma_{\bar{x}}$ is a small number**.

On the other hand, if the *Standard Error of the Mean, $\sigma_{\bar{x}}$,* is a large number, then *the sampling distribution of the mean has a relatively large dispersion* and the *sample means will be relatively far from the population mean.* In such instances, a sample mean that is randomly selected from the sampling distribution will have a relatively large probability of deviating considerably from the population mean. Consequently, **there is a good chance of a large sampling error in estimating the population mean when $\sigma_{\bar{x}}$ is a large number**.

EXAMPLE 7.5

At a large community college the mean IQ score of the student body is 107 with a standard deviation of 20. Suppose a random sample of size n is selected from the student body, compute the standard error of the mean, $\sigma_{\bar{x}}$, for samples of size:

a)   n = 4
b)   n = 25
c)   n = 400
d)   What happens to the standard error of the mean as the sample size increases?
e)   Answer the following question based on the results of parts (a) to (c).
     If you were going to select a random sample from this population of IQ scores, which sample size (n = 4, n = 25 or n = 100) would give you a better chance of being closer to the population mean IQ score? Explain.

Solution

The standard error of the mean is determined by the formula:

$$\sigma_{\bar{x}} = \frac{\sigma}{\sqrt{n}}$$

a)   Since the standard deviation of the population, σ, is 20 and the sample size, n, is 4, then the standard error of the mean is:

$$\sigma_{\bar{x}} = \frac{\sigma}{\sqrt{n}}$$

$$\sigma_{\bar{x}} = \frac{20}{\sqrt{4}}$$

$$\sigma_{\bar{x}} = 10$$

b) For $\sigma = 20$ and n = 25, the standard error of the mean is:

$$\sigma_{\bar{x}} = \frac{\sigma}{\sqrt{n}}$$

$$\sigma_{\bar{x}} = \frac{20}{\sqrt{25}}$$

$$\sigma_{\bar{x}} = 4$$

c) For a sample size of n = 400 and a population standard deviation, σ, of 20 then the standard error of the mean is:

$$\sigma_{\bar{x}} = \frac{\sigma}{\sqrt{n}}$$

$$\sigma_{\bar{x}} = \frac{20}{\sqrt{400}}$$

$$\sigma_{\bar{x}} = 1$$

d) As the sample size **increases** from n = 4 to n = 100, the standard error of the mean, $\sigma_{\bar{x}}$, **decreases** from $\sigma_{\bar{x}} = 10$ to $\sigma_{\bar{x}} = 1$.

e) A sample size of n = 100 would give you a better chance of being closer to the population mean IQ score because the standard error of the mean has the smaller value of $\sigma_{\bar{x}} = 1$. As the standard error of the mean, $\sigma_{\bar{x}}$, **decreases**, then the sample means will become **closer** to the population mean, and thus **increase** the chances of selecting a sample with a mean IQ score being closer to the population mean IQ score. ∎

7.3 THE FINITE CORRECTION FACTOR

In our previous discussion of the standard error of the mean or the standard deviation of the sampling distribution *of the mean*, $\sigma_{\bar{x}}$, we used the formula:

$$\sigma_{\bar{x}} = \frac{\sigma}{\sqrt{n}}$$

to compute its value. *This formula holds true for when the population contains an infinite number of data values,* (that is, it contains an unlimited number of data values) *or when sampling from a finite population with replacement* (that is, after a data value is selected from the population, it is placed back into the population before the next data value is chosen).

In many practical applications, the populations contain a finite number of data values and the sampling is done without replacement (that is, each data value sampled from the population is not re-placed). *If sampling without replacement is being done from a finite population, then the formula to compute the standard deviation of the sampling distribution of the mean must be modified.* This modification is referred to as the *finite correction factor.* The following formula represents the exact formula for the standard deviation of the sampling distribution of the mean when sampling without replacement from a finite population, N.

Formula for the Standard Deviation of the Sampling Distribution of the Mean for a Finite Population

For a finite population, the formula for the standard deviation of the sampling distribution of the mean, $\sigma_{\bar{x}}$, is:

(continues)

Formula for the Standard Deviation of the Sampling Distribution of the Mean for a Finite Population (continued)

$$\sigma_{\bar{x}} = \frac{\sigma}{\sqrt{n}} \cdot \sqrt{\frac{N-n}{N-1}}.$$

Where:

σ is the standard deviation of the population
n is the sample size
N is the population size

the term

$$\sqrt{\frac{N-n}{N-1}}$$

is called the finite correction factor

■
EXAMPLE 7.6

In a large lecture college psychology class containing 250 students, the mean test grade on the first exam was $\mu = 75$ with a population standard deviation $\sigma = 12$. If the college instructor samples n students from this population without replacement and finds their mean test grade, then determine the standard deviation of the sampling distribution of the mean for the following samples of size n.

a) n = 9
b) n = 49
c) n = 100

Solution

For each sample size the sampling is being done without replacement from a finite population; therefore, we need to apply the formula for the standard deviation of the sampling distribution of the mean for a finite population:

$$\sigma_{\bar{x}} = \frac{\sigma}{\sqrt{n}} \cdot \sqrt{\frac{N-n}{N-1}}$$

a) For a sample size of n = 9 students, a population standard deviation of $\sigma = 12$, and a population size of N = 250, the standard deviation of the sampling distribution of the mean is:

$$\sigma_{\bar{x}} = \frac{\sigma}{\sqrt{n}} \cdot \sqrt{\frac{N-n}{N-1}}$$

$$\sigma_{\bar{x}} = \frac{12}{\sqrt{9}} \cdot \sqrt{\frac{250-9}{250-1}}$$

$$\sigma_{\bar{x}} = \frac{12}{3} \cdot \sqrt{\frac{241}{249}}$$

$$\sigma_{\bar{x}} \approx 4 \cdot \sqrt{0.968}$$

$$\sigma_{\bar{x}} \approx 4 \cdot (0.984)$$

$$\sigma_{\bar{x}} \approx 3.94$$

Thus, for a sample size of n = 9, the standard deviation of the sampling distribution of the mean is approximately 3.94.

b) For a sample size of n = 49 students, a population standard deviation of $\sigma = 12$, and a population size of N = 250, the standard deviation of the sampling distribution of the mean is:

$$\sigma_{\bar{x}} = \frac{\sigma}{\sqrt{n}} \bullet \sqrt{\frac{N-n}{N-1}}$$

$$\sigma_{\bar{x}} = \frac{12}{\sqrt{49}} \bullet \sqrt{\frac{250-49}{250-1}}$$

$$\sigma_{\bar{x}} = \frac{12}{7} \bullet \sqrt{\frac{201}{249}}$$

$$\sigma_{\bar{x}} \approx (1.71) \bullet \sqrt{0.807}$$

$$\sigma_{\bar{x}} \approx (1.71) \bullet (0.898)$$

$$\sigma_{\bar{x}} \approx 1.54$$

Therefore, for a sample size of n = 25, the standard deviation of the sampling distribution of the mean is approximately 1.54.

c) For a sample size of n = 100 students, a population standard deviation of $\sigma = 12$, and a population size of N = 250, the standard deviation of the sampling distribution of the mean for a finite population without replacement is

$$\sigma_{\bar{x}} = \frac{\sigma}{\sqrt{n}} \bullet \sqrt{\frac{N-n}{N-1}}$$

$$\sigma_{\bar{x}} = \frac{12}{\sqrt{100}} \bullet \sqrt{\frac{250-100}{250-1}}$$

$$\sigma_{\bar{x}} = \frac{12}{10} \bullet \sqrt{\frac{150}{249}}$$

$$\sigma_{\bar{x}} \approx (1.2) \bullet \sqrt{0.602}$$

$$\sigma_{\bar{x}} \approx (1.2) \bullet (0.776)$$

$$\sigma_{\bar{x}} \approx 0.93$$

For a sample size of n = 100 students, the standard deviation of the sampling distribution of the mean is approximately 0.93.   ▬

In Example 7.6, when the sample size was n = 9, the finite correction factor

$$\sqrt{\frac{N-n}{N-1}}$$

was approximately 0.984, which is very close to 1. As the sample size increased to n = 100, the finite correction factor decreased to a value of approximately 0.776. Thus, as shown from this example, when the sample size, is small, n = 9, relative to the population size, N = 250, the finite correction factor is very close to 1. In such instances, the standard deviation of the sampling distribution of the mean, $\sigma_{\bar{x}}$, is approximately equal to the formula:

$$\frac{\sigma}{\sqrt{n}}$$

since

$$\sqrt{\frac{N-n}{N-1}} \approx 1 \, .$$

In practice, if the sample size, n, is small *relative* to the population size, N, then the finite correction factor,

$$\sqrt{\frac{N-n}{N-1}} \, ,$$

is approximately equal to 1, and thus can be ignored. The general rule used to determine whether the sample is small in relation to the population is:

the sample size, n, is less than 5% of the population size, N.

That is,

$$\frac{\text{sample size}}{\text{population size}} \text{ is less than } 5\%.$$

In symbols, this condition is written:

$$\frac{n}{N} < 5\%.$$

Consequently, we can establish the following general rule for the standard deviation of the sampling distribution when sampling from a finite population.

General Rule for Computing the Standard Deviation of the Sampling Distribution of the Mean When Sampling From a Finite Population

When sampling without replacement from a finite population, and the sample size, n, is less than 5% of the population size, N, then we can use the formula:

$$\sigma_{\bar{x}} = \frac{\sigma}{\sqrt{n}}$$

to determine the standard deviation of the sampling distribution of the mean.

In most applications, *the sample size, n, is relatively small with respect to the population size, N. Consequently, we will generally assume this is true and use the formula*

$$\sigma_{\bar{x}} = \frac{\sigma}{\sqrt{n}}$$

to compute the standard deviation of the sampling distribution of the mean or the standard error of the mean. This will be the procedure used within this chapter and the remainder of the text, unless the problem states otherwise.

7.4   THE SHAPE OF THE SAMPLING DISTRIBUTION OF THE MEAN

As previously discussed, the sampling distribution of the mean is a distribution of the values of all the possible sample means. Suppose a consumer group selects a random sample of 100 bulbs to test a leading manufacturer's claim that their new bulb More Lite will last an average of 5400 hours. Although, the consumer group will only select one sample of bulbs from the population of bulbs and calculate the mean of the sample, you should realize that this selected sample occurred by chance. This means that the chosen light bulbs were randomly selected, and other samples of the same size, n = 100 bulbs, could just as easily been chosen, each one of which would have yielded its own sample mean. Now, let's conceive of continuing to select random samples of the same size, n = 100 bulbs, from the population of More Lite bulbs manufactured by this company, and computing the mean life for each sample. This is continued until we have completely exhausted the selection of all the possible samples of size n = 100 bulbs from the population. The distribution of all these possible sample means from samples of size n = 100 would represent the sampling distribution of the mean. Of course, in practice, it would be impossible or impractical to construct such a sampling distribution of the mean. In this sense, the sampling distribution of the mean is a theoretical distribution. In general, when we refer to the sampling distribution of the mean we are actually referring to a theoretical probability distribution which relates the value of each possible sample to the probability that such a sample mean will occur.

In practice, since only one sample will be selected from the population, it is impossible to construct the actual sampling distribution of the mean for a population containing an infinite number of data values. Thus, we must rely on statisticians to provide us with the necessary theorems to enable us to construct a theoretical sampling distribution of the mean. We have already discussed the formulas to help us determine the mean, $\mu_{\bar{x}}$, and standard deviation, $\sigma_{\bar{x}}$, of the sampling distribution of the mean if we know the population mean and standard deviation. To completely describe the essential characteristics of the sampling distribution of the mean, we need to determine its shape. We will now present and discuss two important theorems in inferential statistics that will enable us to determine the shape of the sampling distribution of the mean. The first theorem will discuss the shape of the sampling distribution of the mean when sampling from a normal population. The second theorem, called the **Central Limit Theorem**, will provide us with information about the shape of the sampling distribution of the mean when sampling from a population with an unknown shape.

Sampling From a Normal Population

If all possible samples of size n are selected from a population that is normally distributed, then the shape of the sampling distribution of the mean will also be normally distributed regardless of the sample size. This is stated in Theorem 7.1.

THEOREM 7.1 The Shape of the Sampling Distribution When Sampling From a Normal Population

---

If the population being sampled is a normal distribution, then the sampling distribution of the mean is a normal distribution regardless of the sample size, n.

The sampling distribution of the mean will be a normal distribution even for samples of size n = 2 provided the population from which the samples are drawn is a normal distribution. This is illustrated in Figure 7.8.

Figure 7.8 shows the population from which the samples are selected is a normal distribution. The resulting shapes of the sampling distribution of the mean for different sample sizes ranging from

Shape of the Sampling Distribution of the Mean for Different Sample Sizes, n, Selected from a Normal Population

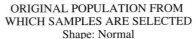

ORIGINAL POPULATION FROM
WHICH SAMPLES ARE SELECTED
Shape: Normal

Sampling distribution of the mean for samples of size:

(a) n = 2 shape: normal	(b) n = 10 shape: normal	(c) n = 20 shape: normal	(d) n = 30 shape: normal	(e) n = 100 shape: normal

FIGURE 7.8

n = 2 to n = 100 are also normal as illustrated in Figures 7.8 (a) to (e). Observe, in Figure 7.8, as the sample size increases from n = 2 to n = 100, the dispersion of the sample means within the sampling distributions decreases.

Using the formulas to compute the mean and standard deviation of the sampling distribution discussed in the previous sections, we can now completely describe the sampling distribution of the mean, (that is, determine the mean, standard error and the shape of the sampling distribution), when sampling from a normal population whose mean is μ and a standard deviation is σ. Let's now summarize these characteristics of the sampling distribution of the mean for a normally distributed population.

Characteristics of the Sampling Distribution of the Mean When Sampling From a Normal Population Whose Mean is μ and Standard Deviation is σ

If all possible samples of size n are selected from a normal population, then the sampling distribution of the mean has the following three characteristics.

1) The sampling distribution of the mean is a normal distribution, regardless of the sample size, n.

2) The mean of the sampling distribution of the mean, $\mu_{\bar{x}}$, is equal to the mean of the population, μ. Symbolically, this is written:

$$\mu_{\bar{x}} = \mu.$$

3) The standard error of the sampling distribution of the mean, $\sigma_{\bar{x}}$, is equal to the standard deviation of the population, σ, divided by the square root of the sample size, n. Symbolically, this is written:

$$\sigma_{\bar{x}} = \frac{\sigma}{\sqrt{n}}.$$

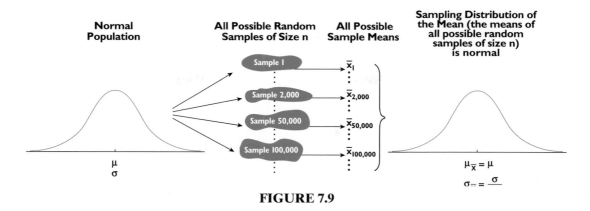

FIGURE 7.9

Figure 7.9 illustrates the conceptual idea of the sampling distribution of the mean, its characteristics, and the relationship to the characteristics of a normal population.

Example 7.9 shows how to determine the characteristics of the sampling distribution of the mean when sampling from a normal population.

EXAMPLE 7.7

At a large New England college, the grade point average (GPA) of all attending students is normally distributed with a mean of $\mu = 2.95$ and a population standard deviation of $\sigma = 0.32$. A sample is randomly selected from this population and its sample mean, $\bar{x}$, is calculated. Determine the mean, $\mu_{\bar{x}}$, the standard error, $\sigma_{\bar{x}}$ and identify the shape of the sampling distribution of the mean for samples of size:

a) n = 9
b) n = 49
c) n = 100

Solution

In each case the sampling distribution of the mean will be a normal distribution since the samples were randomly selected from a normal population. The mean of the sampling distribution of the mean is determined by the formula: $\mu_{\bar{x}} = \mu$. Since the population mean is $\mu = 2.95$, the mean of the sampling distribution of the mean is also equal to 2.95. That is, $\mu_{\bar{x}} = 2.95$. These results hold for each sample size. However the standard error of the sampling distribution of the mean, $\sigma_{\bar{x}}$, depends on the sample size and will be calculated for each.

a) Since the sample size is n = 9, and the population standard deviation is $\sigma = 0.32$, then the standard error of the sampling distribution of the mean is determined by the formula:

$$\sigma_{\bar{x}} = \frac{\sigma}{\sqrt{n}}.$$

Substituting, n = 9 and $\sigma = 0.32$ into this formula, we have:

$$\sigma_{\bar{x}} = \frac{0.32}{\sqrt{9}}$$

$$\sigma_{\bar{x}} = \frac{0.32}{3}$$

$$\sigma_{\bar{x}} \approx 0.11.$$

Therefore, the sampling distribution of the mean will be a normal distribution with a mean of $\mu_{\bar{x}} = 2.95$ and a standard error of $\sigma_{\bar{x}} \approx 0.11$.

(b) For a sample size of n = 49, and a population standard deviation of $\sigma = 0.32$, then the standard error of the sampling distribution of the mean is calculated by the formula:

$$\sigma_{\bar{x}} = \frac{\sigma}{\sqrt{n}} \, .$$

Substituting, n = 49 and $\sigma = 0.32$ into this formula, we obtain:

$$\sigma_{\bar{x}} = \frac{0.32}{\sqrt{49}}$$

$$\sigma_{\bar{x}} = \frac{0.32}{7}$$

$$\sigma_{\bar{x}} \approx 0.05$$

Thus, the sampling distribution of the mean will be a normal distribution with a mean of $\mu_{\bar{x}} = 2.95$ and a standard error of $\sigma_{\bar{x}} \approx 0.05$.

(c) For a sample size of n = 100, and a population standard deviation of $\sigma = 0.32$, then the standard error of the sampling distribution of the mean is obtained using the formula:

$$\sigma_{\bar{x}} = \frac{\sigma}{\sqrt{n}} \, .$$

Substituting, n = 100 and $\sigma = 0.32$ into this formula, we obtain:

$$\sigma_{\bar{x}} = \frac{0.32}{\sqrt{100}}$$

$$\sigma_{\bar{x}} = \frac{0.32}{10}$$

$$\sigma_{\bar{x}} \approx 0.03$$

Consequently, the sampling distribution of the mean will be normally distributed with a mean of $\mu_{\bar{x}} = 2.95$ and a standard error of $\sigma_{\bar{x}} \approx 0.03$. _____ ∎

Sampling from A Non-Normal Population

Theorem 7.1 assumes that when sampling from a normal population, the sampling distribution of the mean will also be a normal distribution. However, there are many statistical applications where the population will not be normally distributed. In fact, there are applications where the shape of the population will be unknown. In such instances, how can we determine the shape of the sampling distribution of the mean, if the population is not a normal distribution or has an unknown shape? In these situations, we rely on the most important theorem of inferential statistics called the **Central Limit Theorem**.

THEOREM 7.2   The Central Limit Theorem

For any population, the sampling distribution of the mean approaches a normal distribution as the sample size n becomes large. This is true regardless of the shape of the population being randomly sampled.

The Central Limit Theorem is a very important theorem in inferential statistics because it tells us that the sampling distribution of the mean will always approach the same distribution shape, a normal bell-shaped distribution, as the sample size n becomes larger, regardless of the population shape. Thus, according to the Central Limit Theorem, the sampling distribution of the mean can be approximated by a normal distribution as long as the sample size is large enough regardless of the shape of the population distribution from which the sample is randomly selected. In essence, since the **population can have any shape, it is not even necessary to know the shape of the population provided the sample size is large enough**. Since in most statistical applications the shape of the population is usually not known, this emphasizes the importance of the Central Limit Theorem in the field of statistical inference.

How large the sample size n should be to justify the use of the normal curve as an approximation of the sampling distribution of the mean depends on the shape of the population being sampled. The closer the shape of the sampled population is to a normal or bell-shaped distribution, the smaller the sample size n required for the sampling distribution of the mean to be closely approximated by a normal distribution. **Extremely skewed populations will require a relatively larger sample size n** for the sampling distribution of the mean to achieve a close approximation of the normal distribution. That is, more data values need to be randomly selected for the sample when the population shape is far from a normal population.

Figure 7.10 illustrates the use of the Central Limit Theorem for populations of different shapes and different sample sizes.

In Figure 7.10, the sampling distribution of the mean is shown for samples of size n = 2, n = 5, and n = 30 from four different population shapes: uniform, bimodal, extremely skewed to the right and normal. Notice, for samples of size n = 5, the sampling distribution of the mean for all four populations is beginning to approach a normal distribution. For a sample size of n = 30, regardless of the shape of the population, the sampling distributions of the mean are close to a normal distribution. We cannot say precisely how large a sample size, n, is needed to apply the Central Limit Theorem since, in practice, we usually do not know the shape of the population being sampled. Consequently, there is a need for a useful general rule of thumb to follow when a sample is large enough to apply the Central

Application of Central Limit Theorem: Sampling Distribution of the Mean for Various Population Shapes and Different Sample Sizes

FIGURE 7.10

Limit Theorem. The general rule widely accepted and used by statisticians is that the sampling distribution of the mean can be approximated by a normal distribution provided the sample size n is greater than 30 regardless of the shape of the population.

General Rule for Applying the Central Limit Theorem: The n greater than 30 Rule

For most applications, a sample size n greater than 30 is considered large enough to apply the Central Limit Theorem. Thus, the sampling distribution of the mean can be reasonably approximated by a normal distribution whenever the sample size n is greater than 30.

Although, we will use this general rule as our definition of a large sample throughout this text, remember, the Central Limit Theorem states that the larger the sample size, the better the normal approximation of the sampling distribution of the mean. Consequently, in practical applications, this **n greater than 30 rule** for a large sample should be applied with caution. That is, a larger sample size may be required for a good approximation when the population is far from a normal bell-shaped distribution.

Using the result of the Central Limit Theorem, and the formulas for the mean and standard error of the sampling distribution, we can state the characteristics of the sampling distribution of the mean when sampling from a non-normal population in Theorem 7.3.

THEOREM 7.3   Characteristics of the Sampling Distribution of the Mean When Sampling From a Non-normal Population

If the following three conditions are satisfied:
* given any infinite population with mean, μ, and standard deviation, σ, and
* all possible random samples of size n are selected from the population to form a sampling distribution of the mean, and
* the sample size, n, is large (greater than 30),

then:
1) the sampling distribution of the mean is **approximately normal**.
2) the mean of the sampling distribution of the mean is equal to the mean of the population. This is expressed as:

$$\mu_{\bar{x}} = \mu$$

3) the standard error of the sampling distribution of the mean is equal to standard deviation of the population divided by the square root of the sample size. Symbolically, this is written as:

$$\sigma_{\bar{x}} = \frac{\sigma}{\sqrt{n}}$$

Figure 7.11 illustrates the concept of the sampling distribution of the mean, its characteristics, and the relationship to the characteristics of a normal population.

To illustrate Theorem 7.3, consider selecting all possible random samples of *size n* = 100 from each of the populations shown in Figure 7.12. Thus, each of the resulting sampling distributions of the mean will be approximately normal with their respective mean and standard error shown in Figure 7.12.

FIGURE 7.11

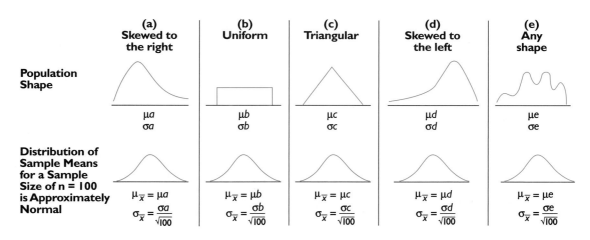

FIGURE 7.12

EXAMPLE 7.8

GRAM-HAM Bell, a telephone company, states that the average length of time of long-distance telephone calls is $\mu = 21.3$ minutes with a standard deviation of $\sigma = 3.8$ minutes. Determine the mean and the standard error of the sampling distribution of the mean and describe the shape of the sampling distribution of the mean when the sample size is:

a) $n = 36$
b) $n = 100$
c)   Compare the sampling distributions of the mean for the sample size of $n = 36$ and $n = 100$.
d)   If you had to estimate the mean of the population by either randomly selecting a sample of size $n = 36$ or a sample size of $n = 100$ from the population, then which sample size would give you a better chance of obtaining a smaller sampling error? Explain.

Solution

a)   The mean of the sampling distribution of the mean is equal to the population mean and is determined by the formula: $\mu_{\bar{x}} = \mu$. Since the population mean is $\mu = 21.3$ minutes, then the mean of the sampling distribution is:

$$\mu_{\bar{x}} = \mu = 21.3 \text{ minutes}$$

Thus, the mean of the sampling distribution of the mean is: $\mu_{\bar{x}} = 21.3$ minutes.

The standard error of the sampling distribution of the mean is equal to the population mean divided by the square root of the sample size. That is,

$$\sigma_{\bar{x}} = \frac{\sigma}{\sqrt{n}}$$

For a population standard deviation of $\sigma = 3.8$ minutes, and a sample size of $n = 36$, the standard error of the sampling distribution of the mean is:

$$\sigma_{\bar{x}} = \frac{\sigma}{\sqrt{n}}$$

$$\sigma_{\bar{x}} = \frac{3.8}{\sqrt{36}}$$

$$\sigma_{\bar{x}} = \frac{3.8}{6}$$

$$\sigma_{\bar{x}} \approx 0.63 \text{ minutes}$$

Although, the shape of the population of length of times of long-distance telephone calls is unknown, the sampling distribution of the mean is approximately a normal distribution because a sample size of $n = 36$ (n greater than 30) can be considered as a large enough sample to apply the Central Limit Theorem.

The sampling distribution of the mean is illustrated in Figure 7.13.

b)   The mean of the sampling distribution of the mean is equal to the population mean, that is, $\mu_{\bar{x}} = \mu$. Since the population mean is $\mu = 21.3$ minutes, then the mean of the sampling distribution is:

$$\mu_{\bar{x}} = \mu = 21.3 \text{ minutes}$$

Thus, the mean of the sampling distribution of the mean is: $\mu_{\bar{x}} = 21.3$ minutes.

The standard error of the sampling distribution of the mean is

$$\sigma_{\bar{x}} = \frac{\sigma}{\sqrt{n}} \quad .$$

For a population standard deviation of $\sigma = 3.8$ minutes, and a sample size of $n = 100$, the standard error of the sampling distribution of the mean is:

$$\sigma_{\bar{x}} = \frac{\sigma}{\sqrt{n}}$$

$$\sigma_{\bar{x}} = \frac{3.8}{\sqrt{100}}$$

$$\sigma_{\bar{x}} = \frac{3.8}{10}$$

$$\sigma_{\bar{x}} \approx 0.38 \text{ minutes}$$

Although, the shape of the population of length of times of long-distance telephone calls is unknown, the sampling distribution of the mean is approximately a normal distribution because a sample size of $n = 100$ (n greater than 30) can be considered as a large enough sample to apply the Central Limit Theorem.

The sampling distribution of the mean is illustrated in Figure 7.14.

c)   Comparing the characteristics of the sampling distributions shown in Figures 7.15 and 7.16, we should notice that both sampling distributions can be approximated by a normal distribution since the sample sizes are greater than 30. Also, notice that the mean of both sampling distribu-

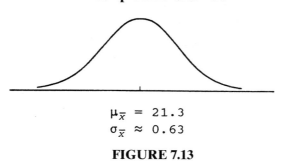

Sampling Distribution of the Mean for a Sample Size of n = 36

$$\mu_{\bar{x}} = 21.3$$
$$\sigma_{\bar{x}} \approx 0.63$$

FIGURE 7.13

Sampling Distribution of the Mean for a Sample Size of n = 100

$$\mu_{\bar{x}} = 21.3$$
$$\sigma_{\bar{x}} \approx 0.38$$

FIGURE 7.14

tions are equal to 21.3 minutes regardless of the sample size. However, the standard error of the sampling distribution for a sample size of n = 100 is smaller than the standard deviation of the sampling distribution for a sample size of n = 36.

d) Since the standard error of the sampling distribution of the mean for a sample size of n = 100 ($\sigma_{\bar{x}} \approx 0.38$) is smaller than the standard error of the sampling distribution of the mean for a sample size of n = 36 ($\sigma_{\bar{x}} \approx 0.63$), then you should select a random sample of size n = 100. A smaller standard deviation of the sampling distribution or standard error of the mean indicates a relatively smaller dispersion among the sample means and thus, the sample means will be relatively closer to the population mean.

Consequently, there is a good chance of a small sampling error in estimating the population mean where the standard error of the sampling distribution is smaller. ■

Let's now summarize the different possible cases discussed when working with the sampling distribution of the mean. Figure 7.15 contains the assumptions along with the appropriate characteristics of the sampling distribution of the mean.

Assumptions:

Infinite Population

or

Sampling with Replacement from a Finite Population

or

Population Size, N, is Large Relative to the Sample Size, n, (i.e., n < 0.05N)

Case I: Sampling from a Normal Population, Regardless of Sample Size, n

	Population	Sampling Distribution of the Mean
Mean:	μ	$\mu_{\bar{x}} = \mu$
Std Dev:	σ	$\sigma_{\bar{x}} = \dfrac{\sigma}{\sqrt{n}}$
Shape:	Normal	Normal

FIGURE 7.16 (continues)

Assumptions:

Case II: Sampling from a Non-Normal Population and the Sample Size, n, is Large (That is, n > 30)

	Population	Sampling Distribution of the Mean
Mean:	μ	$\mu_{\bar{x}} = \mu$
Std Dev:	σ	$\sigma_{\bar{x}} = \dfrac{\sigma}{\sqrt{n}}$
Shape:	Non-Normal	Normal when n > 30

Assumptions:
Finite Population

Sampling without Replacement from a Non-Normal Population and Sample Size, n, is Large Relative to the Population Size, N (i.e. n>0.05N)

	Population	Sampling Distribution of the Mean
Mean:	μ	$\mu_{\bar{x}} = \mu$
Std Dev:	σ	$\sigma_{\bar{x}} = \dfrac{\sigma}{\sqrt{n}} \bullet \sqrt{\dfrac{N-n}{N-1}}$
Shape:	Non-Normal	Normal when n > 30

FIGURE 7.16 (continued)

7.5 CALCULATING PROBABILITIES USING THE SAMPLING DISTRIBUTION OF THE MEAN

Using the Central Limit and the characteristics of the sampling distribution of the mean discussed in Section 7.4, we can now illustrate how to calculate probabilities using the sampling distribution of the mean. To calculate these probabilities, we will need to determine a z score of the sample mean and use Table II: The Normal Curve Area Table. As discussed in an earlier chapter, the z score formula for a data value x is:

$$z \text{ of data value} = \frac{\text{data value} - \text{population mean}}{\text{population standard deviation}}.$$

Symbolically, the z score formula was:

$$z \text{ of } x = \frac{x - \mu}{\sigma}$$

However, in this chapter, since we are working with the sampling distribution of the mean, the data values are sample means, $\bar{x}$, thus, the z score formula becomes:

$$z \text{ score of a sample mean} = \frac{\text{sample mean} - \text{mean of the sampling distribution}}{\text{standard error of the sampling distribution}}$$

Consequently, when working with the sampling distribution of the mean, the z score formula is now symbolized as:

$$z \text{ of } \bar{x} = \frac{\bar{x} - \mu_{\bar{x}}}{\sigma_{\bar{x}}}$$

Example 7.14 demonstrates how to calculate probabilities using the sampling distribution of the mean using this z score formula and Table II: The Normal Curve Area Table.

EXAMPLE 7.9

At a large public state college in Virginia, the mean Verbal SAT score of all attending students was μ = 600 with a population standard deviation of σ = 65. If a random sample of 100 students is selected from the population of students, determine:

a)   The probability that mean Verbal SAT score of the selected sample will be less than 615.
b)   The probability that mean Verbal SAT score of the selected sample will be within 10 points of the population mean.

Solution

Since a random sample of n = 100 students is being selected from the population, then, according to the Central Limit Theorem, the sampling distribution of the mean can be approximated by a normal distribution because the sample size (n = 100) is greater than 30. To answer parts (a) and (b) we need to determine the mean and standard error of the sampling distribution of the mean using Theorem 7.3. From Theorem 7.3, the mean of the sampling distribution of the mean, $\mu_{\bar{x}}$, is equal to the population mean. Thus, the mean of the sampling distribution is:

$$\mu_{\bar{x}} = \mu$$

$$\mu_{\bar{x}} = 600.$$

The standard error of the sampling distribution of the mean is equal to the population standard deviation divided by the square root of the sample size. Therefore, the standard error of the sampling distribution is:

$$\sigma_{\bar{x}} = \frac{\sigma}{\sqrt{n}}$$

$$\sigma_{\bar{x}} = \frac{65}{\sqrt{100}}$$

$$\sigma_{\bar{x}} = \frac{65}{10}$$

$$\sigma_{\bar{x}} = 6.5$$

Figure 7.17 shows the characteristics of the sampling distribution of the mean: an approximately normal distribution with mean $\mu_{\bar{x}}$ = 600, and a standard error $\sigma_{\bar{x}}$ = 6.5.

a)   To determine the probability that the mean Verbal SAT score of the selected sample will be less than 615, we will use the sampling distribution of the mean illustrated in Figure 7.17. To calculate the probability that the sample of 100 students will be less than 615, we need to find the area to the left of 615. The shaded area shown in Figure 7.18 to the left of 615 represents the probability that the selected sample mean will be less 615.

To find this shaded area to left of 615, we must first calculate the z score of 615. Since the data values of the sampling distribution are sample means, $\bar{x}$, the z score formula becomes:

$$z \text{ score of a sample mean} = \frac{\text{sample mean} - \text{mean of the sampling distribution}}{\text{standard error of the sampling distribution}}$$

FIGURE 7.17

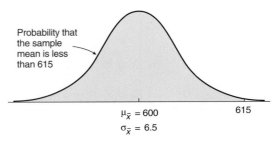

FIGURE 7.18

The z score formula is now symbolized as:

$$z \text{ of } \overline{x} = \frac{\overline{x} - \mu_{\overline{x}}}{\sigma_{\overline{x}}}$$

Substituting $\overline{x} = 615$, $\mu_{\overline{x}} = 600$ and $\sigma_{\overline{x}} = 6.5$, into this z score formula, we have:

$$z \text{ of } 615 = \frac{615 - 600}{6.5}$$

$$z \text{ of } 615 \approx 2.31$$

From Table II: Normal Curve Area Table in Appendix D, the area to the left of z = 2.31 is 0.9896. Therefore, the probability of selecting a sample of 100 students whose mean Verbal SAT score will be less than 615 is 0.9896.

(b) To determine the probability that the mean Verbal SAT of the selected sample will be within 10 points of the population mean, we need to find the sample means that are within 10 points of the mean. Since the mean is 600, the sample means which are 10 points away from the mean are:

$$600 - 10 = 590 \text{ and } 600 + 10 = 610.$$

Thus, to find the probability that the mean Verbal SAT of the selected sample will be within 10 points of the population mean, we need to determine the area between 590 and 610. This probability is represented by the shaded area in Figure 7.19.

To find the shaded area in Figure 7.19, we must find the z scores of 590 and 610, using the z score formula:

$$z \text{ of } \overline{x} = \frac{\overline{x} - \mu_{\overline{x}}}{\sigma_{\overline{x}}}, \ \mu_{\overline{x}} = 600 \text{ and } \sigma_{\overline{x}} = 6.5.$$

FIGURE 7.19

The z score of $\bar{x} = 590$ is:

$$z \text{ of } 590 = \frac{590 - 600}{6.5}$$

$$z \text{ of } 590 \approx -1.54$$

While the z score of $\bar{x} = 610$ is:

$$z \text{ of } 610 = \frac{610 - 600}{6.5}$$

$$z \text{ of } 610 \approx 1.54$$

To determine the area between 590 and 610, we must look up the z scores corresponding to these sample means. From Table II: Normal Curve Area Table in Appendix D, the area to the left of z = –1.54 is 0.0618, while the area to the left of z = 1.54 is 0.9382. To determine the area between 590 and 610, we must subtract the area to the left of z = –1.54 from the area to the left of z = 1.54. Thus, we have:

area between 590 and 610	=	area to the left of z = 1.54	–	area to the left of z = –1.54
	=	0.9382	–	0.0618
	=	0.8764		

Therefore, the probability that mean Verbal SAT score of the selected sample will be within 10 points of the population mean is 0.8764.

EXAMPLE 7.10

The population mean weight of newborn babies for a western suburb is 7.4 lbs. with a standard deviation of 0.8 lbs. What is the probability that a sample of 64 newborns selected at random will have a mean weight greater than 7.5 lbs.?

Solution

To determine the probability that a random sample of 64 babies will have a mean weight greater than 7.5 lbs, we must compute the characteristics of the sampling distribution. Since a random sample of n = 64 babies is being selected from the population, then, according to the Central Limit Theorem, the sampling distribution of the mean can be approximated by a normal distribution because the sample size (n = 64) is greater than 30. The mean of the sampling distribution of the mean is equal to the population mean. Therefore, mean of the sampling distribution is:

$$\mu_{\bar{x}} = \mu$$

$$\mu_{\bar{x}} = 7.4 \text{ lbs}$$

The standard error of the sampling distribution of the mean is:

$$\sigma_{\bar{x}} = \frac{\sigma}{\sqrt{n}}$$

$$\sigma_{\bar{x}} = \frac{0.8}{\sqrt{64}}$$

$$\sigma_{\bar{x}} = 0.1$$

Figure 7.20 shows the characteristics of the sampling distribution of the mean: an approximately normal distribution with mean $\mu_{\bar{x}} = 7.4$, and a standard error $\sigma_{\bar{x}} = 0.1$.

To find the probability that the sample mean will be greater than 7.5 lbs. we must find the area to the *right* of 7.5 lbs. The shaded area in Figure 7.21 illustrates the probability that the selected sample mean will be greater than 7.5 lbs.

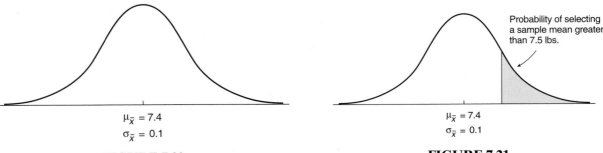

$\mu_{\bar{x}} = 7.4$
$\sigma_{\bar{x}} = 0.1$

FIGURE 7.20

$\mu_{\bar{x}} = 7.4$
$\sigma_{\bar{x}} = 0.1$

Probability of selecting
a sample mean greater
than 7.5 lbs.

FIGURE 7.21

To determine the shaded area in Figure 7.21, compute the z score of 7.5 using the z score formula:

$$z \text{ of } \bar{x} = \frac{\bar{x} - \mu_{\bar{x}}}{\sigma_{\bar{x}}}, \ \mu_{\bar{x}} = 7.4 \text{ and } \sigma_{\bar{x}} = 0.1.$$

The z score of $\bar{x} = 7.5$ is:

$$z = \frac{7.5 - 7.4}{0.1} = 1$$

Using Table II: Normal Curve Area Table in Appendix D, the area to the left of z = 1 is 0.8413. To obtain the area to the right, subtract the area to the left from 1. Thus, the area to the right of 7.5 lbs is equal to:

$$1 - 0.8413 = 0.1587.$$

Therefore, the probability of randomly selecting a sample of 64 newborns whose mean weight is greater than 7.5 lbs. is 0.1587.

EXAMPLE 7.11

The population of the ages of all U. S. college students is skewed to the right with a mean age of 27.4 years and a standard deviation of 5.8 years. Determine the probability that a random sample of 49 students selected from the population will have a sample mean age within one year of the population mean age?

Solution

Since the sample size is 49 (greater than 30), then according to the Central Limit Theorem, the sampling distribution of the mean can be approximated by a normal distribution, regardless of the shape of the population. The mean of this sampling distribution is equal to:

$$\mu_{\bar{x}} = \mu$$
$$\mu_{\bar{x}} = 27.4 \text{ years}$$

and, its standard error is equal to:

$$\sigma_{\bar{x}} = \frac{\sigma}{\sqrt{n}}$$
$$\sigma_{\bar{x}} = \frac{5.8}{\sqrt{49}}$$
$$\sigma_{\bar{x}} \approx 0.83$$

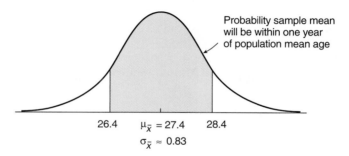

FIGURE 7.22

To determine the probability that the sample mean will be within one year of the population mean age, we must find the sample ages which are 1 year less than the population mean age of 27.4 years (that is: 27.4 – 1 = 26.4 years) and 1 year greater than the population mean age of 27.4 (that is: 27.4 + 1 = 28.4 years). Thus, we need to find the probability that the selected sample will have a mean between 26.4 years and 28.4 years. This probability is represented by the shaded area shown in Figure 7.26.

To determine this shaded area we must compute the z scores for 26.4 years and 28.4 years. Substituting $\mu_{\bar{x}} = 27.4$ and $\sigma_{\bar{x}} = 0.83$ into the z score formula, we can compute the z scores of 26.4 and 28.4. Thus:

$$\text{z of } 26.4 = \frac{26.4 - 27.4}{0.83} \text{ and z of } 28.4 = \frac{28.4 - 27.4}{0.83}$$

$$\text{z of } 26.4 = -1.20 \text{ and z of } 28.4 = 1.20$$

Using Table II: Normal Curve Area Table in Appendix D, the area to the left of z = –1.20 is 0.1151, while the area to the left of z = 1.20 is 0.8849. To obtain the area between 26.4 and 28.4 we must subtract the smaller area, 0.1151, from the larger area, 0.8849, which is:

$$0.8849 - 0.1151 = 0.7698.$$

Therefore, the probability that a random sample of 49 students selected from the population will have a sample mean age within one year of the population mean age is 0.7698. ▬▬▬▬■

CASE STUDY 7.1   Average Annual Income for Families with Children

Examine the information on the "Average Annual Income For Families With Children" in Figure 7.12, which appeared in the *New York Times*.
  a) Define the population for Figure 7.22(a). What do you believe is the shape of the population? Explain.
  For the population stated in Figure 7.22(a):
  b) If all possible samples of size 100 are selected from the population of Figure 7.22(a) and the mean is computed for these samples, what distribution shape would you expect for the resulting distribution?
  c) What is the name of the resulting distribution?
  d) what value would you expect the mean of the resulting distribution to be?
  e) If the population standard deviation were σ, then what would be the standard deviation of the distribution containing the mean from all of the possible samples?
  For the population stated in Figure 7.22(b):
  f) Define the population and what do you think is the shape of this population? Explain.

CASE STUDY 7.2　Average Annual Income for Families with Children (continued)

FIGURE 7.23

g) If all possible samples of size 64 are selected from the population of Figure 7.23(b) and the means are computed for these samples, what distribution shape would you expect for the resulting distribution?

h) What is the name of the resulting distribution?

i) What value would you expect the mean of the resulting distribution to be?

j) If the population standard deviation were σ, then what would be the standard deviation of the distribution containing the mean from all of the possible samples?

For the population stated in Figure 7.23(c):

k) Define the population and what do you think is the shape of this population? Explain.

l) If all possible samples of size 36 are selected from the population of Figure 7.23(c) and the mean is computed for these samples, what distribution shape would you expect for the resulting distribution?

m) What is the name of the resulting distribution?

n) What value would you expect the mean of the resulting distribution to be?

o) If the population standard deviation were σ, then what would be the standard deviation of the distribution containing the mean from all of the possible samples?

7.6　THE EFFECT OF SAMPLE SIZE ON THE STANDARD ERROR OF THE MEAN

Let's examine the effect of an increase in the sample size, n, on the standard error of the mean, $\sigma_{\bar{x}}$.

EXAMPLE 7.11

Consider the distribution of 5 feet 9 inch American males whose mean weight is 160 lbs. with a standard deviation of 10 lbs. Determine the mean, $\mu_{\bar{x}}$, and standard error, $\sigma_{\bar{x}}$, for the sampling distribution of the mean for samples of size 36, 100, 400 and 1600.

Solution

For each we shall use the formulas for

$$\mu_{\bar{x}} = \mu \text{ and } \sigma_{\bar{x}} = \frac{\sigma}{\sqrt{n}},$$

the population mean $\mu = 160$ and the population standard deviation of $\sigma = 10$.

a) For a sample size of n = 36, then the mean and standard error of the sampling distribution are:

$$\mu_{\bar{x}} = 160 \qquad \sigma_{\bar{x}} = \frac{10}{\sqrt{36}}$$

$$\sigma_{\bar{x}} = 1.67$$

b) For a sample size of n = 100, then the mean and standard error of the sampling distribution are:

$$\mu_{\bar{x}} = 160 \qquad \sigma_{\bar{x}} = \frac{10}{\sqrt{100}} = 1$$

c) For a sample size of n = 400, then the mean and standard error of the sampling distribution are:

$$\mu_{\bar{x}} = 160 \text{ and } \sigma_{\bar{x}} = \frac{10}{\sqrt{400}} = 0.5$$

d) For a sample size of n = 1600, then the mean and standard error of the sampling distribution are:

$$\mu_{\bar{x}} = 160 \text{ and } \sigma_{\bar{x}} = \frac{10}{\sqrt{1600}} = 0.25$$

Using the results of Example 7.11, notice as the sample size increases from n = 36 to n = 1600, the standard error of the mean decreases from $\sigma_{\bar{x}} = 1.67$ to $\sigma_{\bar{x}} = 0.25$. This relationship is illustrated in Figure 7.24.

Also, notice that as the sample size increases the sample means become more clustered about the mean, $\mu_{\bar{x}}$. Figure 7.25 illustrates that the size of the interval of sample means containing the middle 99% of the sample means decreases as the sample size increases.

FIGURE 7.24

FIGURE 7.25

For instance when n = 36, 99% of the sample means lie within the interval 155.69 to 164.31. Whereas when n = 1600, 99% of the sample means lie within the smaller interval 159.35 to 160.65.

Suppose you didn't know the mean weight for 5 foot 9 inch American males discussed previously and you were going to estimate the population mean by selecting a random sample from the population of 5 foot 9 inch American males. Using Figure 7.25, which sample size would you use if you wanted to be 99% confident that the sample mean estimate would be within one pound of the actual population mean?

You should choose a sample size of n = 1600 since 99% of the sample means are within one pound of the actual population mean. In fact for this sample size, the sample mean is within 0.65 lbs. of the actual population mean. Thus, we can now summarize the effect of the sample size on the standard error of the sampling distribution of the mean and the accuracy of using a sample mean to estimate the population mean.

The Effect of the Sample Size on the Standard Error of the Sampling Distribution of the Mean

As the sample size increases, the standard error of the sampling distribution of the mean decreases. In general, when using a sample mean to estimate a population mean, **as the sample size increases the more confidence you have in the accuracy of the sample mean as an estimate of the population mean**.

7.7   THE SAMPLING DISTRIBUTION OF THE PROPORTION

Our discussion so far in this chapter has centered around the mean of a population. However, sometimes we are interested in the **proportion** or fraction of a population that possesses a particular characteristic.

> **DEFINITION 7.5**
> A **proportion** is a fraction, ratio or percentage that indicates the part of a population or sample that possesses a particular characteristic.

For example, statisticians, pollsters or researchers might be interested in inferences about the proportion of:

1. U.S. adults who wear seat belts.
2. individuals not catching a cold who take large doses of vitamin C.
3. children who live with only one parent within the U.S.
4. people who will vote for the Democratic candidate in the upcoming senate election.
5. defective computer memory chips produced using a new innovative manufacturing process.
6. patients that recover from a certain illness who are treated with a new drug.

In each of these cases, we are interested in the proportion of a population. To determine this proportion, it becomes necessary to count the number of data values within the population that possess a particular characteristic. In the earlier sections of this chapter, we worked with data that was measurable. Now we will be working with non-measurable data, that is, data that can only be counted. For example, the population data will be categorized and counted according to a particular characteristic such as wearing seat belts, taking vitamin supplements, living with only one parent, voting for a particular candidate, gender, race, religion, marital status, educational level, state of health, and so on. When dealing with count data, the **proportion** or **fraction** of a finite **population** that possesses each of these characteristics can be determined using the following definition. This proportion is a parameter because it represents a population value.

DEFINITION 7.6

The **population (or true) proportion** of a finite population is the ratio of the number of occurrences (or observations) in the population that possess the particular characteristic to the population size. The population proportion, denoted by p, can be expressed by the formula:

$$p = \frac{X}{N}$$

where: p = population proportion
  X = number of occurrences (or observations) in the population possessing the
     particular characteristic
  N = population size

The population proportion is often expressed in an equivalent percentage form.

The concept of a proportion is similar to the probability of a success of a binomial distribution discussed in Chapter 5. This is because the probability of a success for a binomial experiment represents the proportion of the population that possesses a particular characteristic. Example 7.12 illustrates the calculation of a population proportion.

EXAMPLE 7.12

In the 1999 New York City Marathon, there were 31,785 runners who finished the race. The following table shows the number of finishers by their sex.

Sex	Number who finished the race
Men	22625
Women	9160

Determine the population proportion (to 4 decimal places) of:
a) men who completed the marathon.
b) women who completed the marathon.

Solution

a) The proportion of all runners who completed the marathon who were men is:

$$p = \frac{\text{number of men runners who completed the marathon}}{\text{total number of all runners who completed marathon}}$$

$$p = \frac{X}{N} = \frac{22625}{31785}$$

$$p = 0.7118$$

The population proportion of men who completed the marathon is 0.7118 or 71.18%.
b) The proportion of all runners who completed the marathon who were women is:

$$p = \frac{\text{number of women runners who completed the marathon}}{\text{total number of all runners who completed marathon}}$$

$$p = \frac{X}{N} = \frac{9160}{31785}$$

$$p = 0.2882$$

The population proportion of women who completed the marathon is 0.2882 or 28.82%. _____ ■

There are many instances where it is either impractical or impossible to calculate the population proportion. For example, suppose you wanted to determine the proportion of blue colored plain M&M's manufactured by the Mars Corporation. Since it is virtually impossible to determine the actual population proportion of blue M&M's manufactured by Mars Corporation (although it might be fun trying to accomplish this task), it becomes necessary to **estimate the population proportion of blue M&M's**. In such instances, a random sample is selected and the proportion of the sample, symbolized by $\hat{p}$ and read as p-hat, is used to estimate the true population proportion, p. The sample proportion represents a statistic and is computed using the following definition.

DEFINITION 7.7

The **sample proportion** is the ratio of the number of occurrences (or observations) in the sample that possess the particular characteristic to the sample size.

Thus, the sample proportion, denoted by $\hat{p}$ (read p-hat), can be expressed by the formula:

$$\hat{p} = \frac{x}{n}$$

where: $\hat{p}$ = sample proportion
   x = number of occurrences (or observations) in the sample possessing the particular characteristic
   n = sample size

EXAMPLE 7.13

A poll conducted by the International Mass Retail Association claimed that 756 Americans say they own an answering machine. If a random sample of 1200 Americans was polled, then determine the proportion of Americans within the sample who own an answering machine.

Solution

The proportion of Americans within the sample who own an answering machine is:

$$\hat{p} = \frac{\text{number of Americans who own an answering machine}}{\text{sample size}}$$

$$\hat{p} = \frac{x}{n}$$

$$\hat{p} = \frac{756}{1200} = 0.63$$

Thus, the sample proportion of Americans who own an answering machine is 0.63 or 63%._____ ■

The concept of a population and a sample proportion are discussed within Case Study 7.2.

CASE STUDY 7.2 Population and Sample Proportion

Examine the two snapshots entitled "Least Senior States" and "Drivers Who Buckle Up" shown in Figure 7.26.

FIGURE 7.26a   FIGURE 7.26b

a) What variable is being represented within each snapshot?
b) Is the variable numeric or categorical? Explain.
c) Identify the populations being represented within each snapshots.
d) For the proportions stated within each snapshot, explain why you believe the proportion is a population proportion or a sample proportion. Write the symbol you would use for each proportion.

Let's return to the task of estimating the population proportion of blue M&M's. Suppose a sample of 500 M&M plain candies is randomly selected and is found to contain 43 blue M&M's. Using this sample data, the sample proportion of blue M&M's is:

$$\hat{p} = \frac{\text{number of blue M \& Ms within the sample}}{\text{total number of M \& Ms within the sample}}$$

$$\hat{p} = \frac{x}{n} = \frac{43}{500}$$

$$\hat{p} = 0.086$$

Consequently, the proportion of blue M&M's within the sample is 0.086 or 8.6%. Keep in mind that this sample proportion of 8.6% blue M&M's is a **statistic** and serves as an **estimate** of the unknown population parameter p, the population proportion of blue M&M's. At this time, it is appropriate to ponder the following question: Do you think that 8.6% is the exact proportion of blue M&M's within the population? Probably not! And what would happen if we decided to take a second sample to estimate the population proportion? Do you think that we would obtain the same result? That is, if a second random sample of 500 M&M's was selected from this same population, do you think this second sample would contain exactly 8.6% blue M&M's? In all likelihood, we would expect a second sample to yield a different proportion of blue M&M's. Let's consider taking a third sample. Would you expect a third sample to contain the same proportion of blue M&M's as either the first or second sample? Hopefully, you should begin to realize that the proportion of blue M&M's can vary from sample to sample even though there is only one true value for the proportion of blue M&M's for all the plain M&M's manufactured. Thus, just by chance alone, the estimate of a population proportion will vary from sample to sample due to the data values randomly selected within each sample. Therefore, the sample proportion is called a random variable because it is dependent upon the particular data values which are randomly selected from the population. For example, by chance alone, a sample may vary from containing no blue M&M's to one containing only blue M&M's. In order for us to determine how close a sample proportion estimates the population proportion, it is necessary for us to have information about **all** the possible sample proportions which can be selected from the population and how these sample proportions are distributed. Such a distribution of all sample proportions is referred to as the **sampling distribution of the proportion**.

DEFINITION 7.8

The sampling distribution of the proportion is a probability distribution which lists all the possible values of the sample proportions of the same sample size selected from a population along with the probability associated with each value of the sample proportion.

In Example 7.14, we will construct a sampling distribution of the proportion to facilitate the understanding of this concept.

EXAMPLE 7.14

Suppose a small bag of plain M&M's contains 2 brown, 1 red, 1 yellow, 1 blue, 1 green and 1 orange. We will assume this bag represents our population. Suppose we take all possible samples of 5 M&M's each.

a) Determine the population proportion p of brown M&M's.

b) Determine the total number of samples of size 5 that can be selected from this population.

c) Construct a frequency distribution table containing all the possible samples of size 5 and the proportion of brown M&M's for each of those samples.

Solution

a)   The population proportion of brown M&M's is:

$$p = \frac{\text{number of brown M\&Ms within the population}}{\text{population size}}$$

$$p = \frac{X}{N} = \frac{2}{7} = 0.2857$$

b)   The number of samples of size 5 that can be selected from a population containing 7 M&M's can be computed using the combination formula: $_nC_s$. Since n = 7 and s = 5 we have $_7C_5 = 21$. (This counting technique is discussed in Section 4.3.) Thus, there are 21 possible samples of size 5 that can be selected from the population of 7 M&M's.

c)   The 21 possible samples of size 5 are illustrated in the following table.

All Possible Samples of Size 5 and the Sample Proportion of Brown M&M's for Each Sample.

All Samples of size 5	Sample Proportion of Brown M&M's Using the Formula: $\hat{p} = \dfrac{x}{n}$
brown, brown, red, yellow, blue	$\hat{p} = \dfrac{x}{n} = \dfrac{2}{5} = 0.40$
brown, brown, red, yellow, orange	$\hat{p} = \dfrac{x}{n} = \dfrac{2}{5} = 0.40$
brown, brown, red, yellow, green	$\hat{p} = \dfrac{x}{n} = \dfrac{2}{5} = 0.40$
brown, brown, yellow, blue, green	$\hat{p} = \dfrac{x}{n} = \dfrac{2}{5} = 0.40$
brown, brown, yellow, blue, orange	$\hat{p} = \dfrac{x}{n} = \dfrac{2}{5} = 0.40$
brown, brown, red, yellow, green	$\hat{p} = \dfrac{x}{n} = \dfrac{2}{5} = 0.40$
brown, brown, blue, green, orange	$\hat{p} = \dfrac{x}{n} = \dfrac{2}{5} = 0.40$
brown, brown, green, orange, red	$\hat{p} = \dfrac{x}{n} = \dfrac{2}{5} = 0.40$
brown, brown, green, orange, yellow	$\hat{p} = \dfrac{x}{n} = \dfrac{2}{5} = 0.40$
brown, brown, green, orange, red	$\hat{p} = \dfrac{x}{n} = \dfrac{2}{5} = 0.40$
brown, red, yellow, blue, green	$\hat{p} = \dfrac{x}{n} = \dfrac{1}{5} = 0.20$
brown, red, yellow, blue, green	$\hat{p} = \dfrac{x}{n} = \dfrac{1}{5} = 0.20$
brown, red, yellow, blue, orange	$\hat{p} = \dfrac{x}{n} = \dfrac{1}{5} = 0.20$
brown, red, yellow, blue, orange	$\hat{p} = \dfrac{x}{n} = \dfrac{1}{5} = 0.20$
brown, red, blue, green, orange	$\hat{p} = \dfrac{x}{n} = \dfrac{1}{5} = 0.20$
brown, red, blue, green, orange	$\hat{p} = \dfrac{x}{n} = \dfrac{1}{5} = 0.20$
brown, yellow, blue, green, orange	$\hat{p} = \dfrac{x}{n} = \dfrac{1}{5} = 0.20$

brown, yellow, blue, green, orange	$\hat{p} = \dfrac{x}{n} = \dfrac{1}{5} = 0.20$
brown, red, yellow, green, orange	$\hat{p} = \dfrac{x}{n} = \dfrac{1}{5} = 0.20$
brown, red, yellow, green, orange	$\hat{p} = \dfrac{x}{n} = \dfrac{1}{5} = 0.20$
red, yellow, blue, green, orange	$\hat{p} = \dfrac{x}{n} = \dfrac{0}{5} = 0$

Using this table we can construct the following frequency distribution table of the sample proportions.

sample proportion of brown M&M's: $\hat{p}$	frequency
0.40	10
0.20	10
0	1

Before we discuss the characteristics of the sampling distribution of the proportion, we will define the notation for the mean and standard deviation of the sampling distribution of the proportion.

Notation for the Mean of the Sampling Distribution of the Proportion

The mean of the sampling distribution of the proportion is denoted by $\mu_{\hat{p}}$, read mu sub p hat. Thus,

$$\mu_{\hat{p}} = \text{mean of all the sample proportions of the sampling distribution}$$

Notation for the Standard Deviation of the Sampling Distribution of the Proportion
Also Known as the Standard Error of the Proportion

The standard deviation of the sampling distribution of the proportion or the standard error of the proportion is denoted by $\sigma_{\hat{p}}$, read sigma sub p hat. Thus,

$$\sigma_{\hat{p}} = \text{standard deviation of all the sample proportions of the sampling distribution}$$

Using this notation, we will now present the characteristics of the sampling distribution of the proportion. The mean of the sampling distribution of the proportion is equal to the population proportion, p. You should recall that this result is similar to the relationship between the mean of the sampling distribution of the mean which was equal to the population mean.

The Mean of the Sampling Distribution of the Proportion

The mean of the sampling distribution of the proportion, $\mu_{\hat{p}}$, is equal to the population proportion, p.
  Thus,

$$\mu_{\hat{p}} = p$$

The standard deviation of the sampling distribution of the proportion is referred to as the standard error of the proportion because it is a measure of how much a sample proportion is likely to deviate from the population proportion. It is also a measure of the average sampling error which was discussed in Section 7.2 with respect to the sampling distribution of the mean.

The Standard Deviation of the Sampling Distribution of the Proportion also Known as the Standard Error of the Proportion

The standard deviation of the sampling distribution of the proportion or the standard error of the proportion, $\sigma_{\hat{p}}$, is defined as:

$$\sigma_{\hat{p}} = \sqrt{\frac{p(1-p)}{n}}$$

This formula for the standard error of the proportion is appropriate provided that the sample size is small as compared to the population size. Recall from Section 7.3, the general rule used to determine whether the sample is small in relation to the population is:

the sample size, n, is less than 5% of the population size, N.

That is,

$$\frac{sample\ size}{population\ size} \text{ is less than 5\%.}$$

In symbols, this condition is written:

$$\frac{n}{N} < 5\%.$$

If this condition doesn't hold true, then the finite correction factor as discussed in Section 7.3 should appear in the formula for the standard error of the proportion. That is, the formula for the standard error of the proportion becomes:

$$\sigma_{\hat{p}} = \sqrt{\frac{p(1-p)}{n}}\sqrt{\frac{N-n}{N-1}}.$$

In this chapter, we will assume when working with the sampling distribution of the proportion that the population is large relative to sample size so **we will not apply the finite correction factor** except for Example 7.16.

EXAMPLE 7.15

According to a survey in *Men's Health Magazine,* (about) 37% of adults aged 18 to 54 have taken a herbal diet supplement. If $\hat{p}$ represents the proportion of adults aged 18 to 54 within a random sample of 200 such adults, then:

a) State the mean of the sampling distribution of the proportion using the appropriate notation.
b) State the standard error of the proportion using the appropriate notation.

Solution

a) Let's define p as the proportion of all adults aged 18 to 54 who have taken a herbal diet supplement. Thus,

$$p = 0.37$$

and

$$1 - p = 1 - 0.37 = 0.63.$$

The mean of the sampling distribution of the proportion is:

$$\mu_{\hat{p}} = p$$

$$\mu_{\hat{p}} = 0.37$$

b) Using the information, p = 0.37, 1 − p = 0.63 and the sample size, n, is 200 then the standard error of the proportion is:

$$\sigma_{\hat{p}} = \sqrt{\frac{p(1-p)}{n}}$$

$$= \sqrt{\frac{(.37)(0.63)}{200}}$$

$$\sigma_{\hat{p}} = 0.0341 \text{ (to 4 decimal places)}$$

In Example 7.16, we will illustrate the use of the finite correction factor when computing the standard deviation of the sampling distribution of the proportion.

EXAMPLE 7.16

Using the information contained in the frequency distribution table found in part (c) of Example 7.14, then:

a) Compute the mean and standard deviation of all the sample proportions of brown M&M's determined in part (c) of Example 7.14.
b) Using the formulas for the mean and standard deviation of the sampling distribution of the proportion, compute the mean and standard deviation of the sampling distribution constructed in Example 7.14.
c) Compare parts (a) and (b).

Solution

a) The following table represents the frequency distribution table of all the possible sample proportions of brown M&M's determined in Example 7.14.

Sample Proportion of Brown M&M's: $\hat{p}$	Frequency
0.40	10
0.20	10
0	1

The mean of all the sample proportions of brown M&M's is determined by the formula:

$$\text{mean} = [\Sigma(\hat{p}*\text{frequency})]/(\text{sum of the frequencies})$$

Thus, the mean of all the sample proportions of brown M&M's is:

$$\text{mean} = \frac{(0.40)(10)+(0.20)(10)+0(1)}{21} = 0.2857 \text{ (to 4 decimal places)} = \mu_{\hat{p}}$$

The standard deviation of all the sample proportions of brown M&M's is determined by the formula:

$$\text{standard deviation} = \sqrt{[\{\Sigma(\hat{p}-\text{mean})^2*\text{frequency})\}/(\text{sum of the frequencies})]}$$

The standard deviation of the all the sample proportions of brown M&M's is:

$$\text{standard deviation} = \sqrt{\{(0.40-0.2857)^2*10 + (0.20-0.2857)^2*10 + (0-0.2857)^2*1)/21\}}$$

$$\text{standard deviation} = 0.1166 \text{ (to 4 decimal places)} = \sigma_{\hat{p}}$$

b) Using the formula for the mean of the sampling distribution of the proportion and the result from part (a) of Example 7.20, we have:

From Example 7.20 part (a), the population proportion of brown M&M's is:

$$p = \frac{X}{N} = \frac{2}{7} = 0.2857$$

Using the formula for the mean of the sampling distribution of the proportion, we have:

$$\mu_{\hat{p}} = p$$

$$\mu_{\hat{p}} = 0.2857$$

Since $\dfrac{n}{N}$ is greater than 5%, the **finite correction factor formula** for the standard deviation of the sampling distribution of the proportion must be used.

For $p = 0.2857$, $N = 7$ and $n = 5$, we have:

$$\sigma_{\hat{p}} = \sqrt{\frac{p(1-p)}{n}}\sqrt{\frac{N-n}{N-1}}$$

$$= \sqrt{\frac{(0.2857)(1-0.2857)}{5}}\sqrt{\frac{7-5}{7-1}}$$

$$\sigma_{\hat{p}} = 0.1166 \text{ (to 4 decimal places)}$$

c) The results for parts (a) and (b) are the exactly the same. ■

The purpose of Example 7.16 was to verify the formulas for the mean and the standard deviation of the sampling distribution of the proportion. We will always use the formulas for the mean and standard deviation of the sampling distribution of the proportion because, in practice, we will be sampling from a very large or infinite population which makes it impractical or impossible to construct the sampling distribution of the proportion.

CASE STUDY 7.3   Top States for Caesarean Delivery

Examine the snapshot entitled "Top States for Caesarean Delivery" shown in Figure 7.27.

Statistical Snapshot

Top States for Caesarean Deliveries

In 1998, 21% of all births in the USA were by Caesarean delivery.
States that had the highest percentage of Caesarean deliveries:

State	Percentage
Mississippi	27%
Louisiana	26%
New Jersey	25%
Arkansas	25%
West Virginia	24%
Alabama	24%
Texas	24%
South Carolina	23%
Delaware	23%
New York	23%

Source: March 2000 National Vital Statistics

FIGURE 7.27

a) What variable is being represented within the snapshot?

b) Is this variable numeric or categorical? Explain.

c) If we define the population to be all births in the USA for the year 1998, then state whether each of the percentages shown in Figure 7.27 represent a population or a sample proportion.

d) Using your answer to part (c), rewrite each percentage as a decimal and use the appropriate notation to represent this proportion.

e) Explain why this would not be considered a sampling distribution of the proportion for the population stated in part (c).

f) Explain how you might go about constructing an appropriate sampling distribution of the proportion for the stated population. Within your explanation, identify how you would select each sample, your sample size, and so on.

g) For the sampling distribution of the proportion you identified in part(f), state the value of the mean and standard error of the proportion using the information shown in the snapshot and the information you presented in part(f). Use appropriate notation when stating these values.

Sampling Error of the Proportion

You should realize that Example 7.14 is unusual because very rarely will we ever have any knowledge of the actual value of the population proportion. In fact that is why we need to select a random sample to estimate the value of the population proportion. Consequently, whenever we estimate the population proportion we will be subjected to committing a sampling error.

Recall from Section 7.1 that sampling errors are simply errors due to chance or the luck of the selection process. That is, *we can expect the estimates of a population proportion to vary from sample to sample just due to chance only.* This difference between the sample proportion, $\hat{p}$, and the value of the corresponding population proportion, p, is called the sampling error of the proportion.

> **DEFINITION 7.9**
>
> **Sampling error of the proportion** is the difference between the value of a sample statistic, such as the sample proportion, $\hat{p}$, and the value of the corresponding population proportion, p.
>
> Thus, the *sampling error for the proportion* is:
>
> **sampling error = sample proportion – population proportion**
>
> assuming the sample is random and there are no nonsample errors.
>
> In symbols,
>
> **sampling error of the proportion = $\hat{p}$ – p.**

Recall in Example 7.15, the population proportion of brown M&M's was p = 0.2857. However, if we were to randomly select any of the 21 possible samples of size 5 to estimate this population proportion then we would make a sampling error. For example, suppose we had selected one of the samples with proportion

$\hat{p} = 0.40$ then the *sampling error for the proportion* would be:

sampling error = sample proportion – population proportion
                 = 0.40 – 0.2857
sampling error = 0.1143

Thus, we would make a sampling error of 0.1143 if the sample proportion of 0.40 was used to estimate the population proportion of brown M&M's which is p = 0.2857. What would be the sampling error if we had selected a sample with proportion $\hat{p} = 0.20$? Hopefully, you computed the sampling error to be –0.0857! Why is the sampling error negative?

Interpretation of the Standard Error of the Proportion

Let's now discuss how to interpret the standard error of the proportion. Since the standard error of the proportion is a measure of the average sampling error, then if the *standard error* of the proportion, $\sigma_{\hat{p}}$, is a small number, then the sampling distribution of the proportion has relatively little dispersion and the sample proportions will be relatively close to the population proportion. In such instances, a sample proportion which is randomly selected from the sampling distribution will have a relatively large probability of not deviating considerably from the population proportion. Consequently, there is a good chance of a *small* sampling error in estimating the population proportion when $\sigma_{\hat{p}}$ is a *small* number.

On the other hand, if the standard error of the proportion, $\sigma_{\hat{p}}$, is a **large** number, then the sampling distribution of the proportion has relatively larger dispersion and the sample proportions will be relatively far from the population proportion. In such instances, a sample proportion which is randomly selected from the sampling distribution will have a relatively large probability of deviating considerably from the population proportion. Consequently, there is a good chance of a *large* sampling error in estimating the population proportion when $\sigma_{\hat{p}}$ is a large number.

Shape of the Sampling Distribution of the Proportion

The shape of the sampling distribution of the proportion is determined from the central limit theorem. As discussed in Section 7.4, the Central Limit Theorem allowed us to conclude that the sampling distribution of the mean can be approximated by a normal distribution whenever the sample size is large (i.e. greater than 30). We can now apply the central limit theorem to the sampling distribution of the proportion to obtain a statement about its shape. This is stated in Theorem 7.4.

THEOREM 7.4 Central Limit Theorem for the Sampling Distribution of the Proportion

If a random sample of size n is selected from a population with a population proportion p, then the sampling distribution of the proportion can be approximated by a normal distribution whenever the sample size is sufficiently large. A sample size n can be considered sufficiently large whenever np and $n(1-p)$ are both greater than 5. That is,

$$np > 5$$

and

$$n(1-p) > 5.$$

You should recall that these were the same conditions that were required for the normal approximation of the binomial distribution as discussed in Section 6.9.

EXAMPLE 7.17

According to the U.S. Census Bureau, 20% of men aged from 25 to 29 are still living at home. Assume this proportion is true for the population of all men aged 25 to 29. If a random sample of size 100 is selected from this population, then determine whether the sampling distribution of the proportion can be approximated by a normal distribution.

Solution

Since p is defined to be the proportion of all men aged 25 to 29 who still live at home, then:

$$p = 0.20$$

and

$$1 - p = 1 - 0.20 = 0.80.$$

According to the central limit theorem, we need to calculate the value of np and $n(1-p)$ to determine if they are both greater than 5. Since $n = 100$, $p = 0.20$ and $1 - p = 0.80$, we have:

$$np = 100(0.20) = 20$$

and

$$n(1-p) = 100(0.80) = 80.$$

Since both np and $n(1 - p)$ are greater than 5, then according to the central limit theorem the sampling distribution of the proportion can be approximated by a normal distribution.

Using the result of the Central Limit Theorem for the sampling distribution of the proportion and the formula for its mean and standard error, we state the characteristics of the sampling distribution of the proportion in Theorem 7.5.

THEOREM 7.5 Characteristics of the Sampling Distribution of the Proportion

If the following three conditions are satisfied:
- given a large population with population proportion p
- all possible random samples of size n are selected from the population to form the sampling distribution of the proportion, and,
- the sample size, n, is sufficiently large, i.e. $np > 5$ and $n(1 - p) > 5$,

then:
1) the sampling distribution of the mean can be approximated by a normal distribution
2) the mean of the sampling distribution of the proportion is equal to the population proportion, p.
   This is expressed as:

$$\mu_{\hat{p}} = p$$

3) the standard deviation of the sampling distribution of the proportion or the standard error of the proportion, $\sigma_{\hat{p}}$, is:

$$\sigma_{\hat{p}} = \sqrt{\frac{p(1-p)}{n}}$$

Figure 7.28 illustrates the conceptual idea of the sampling distribution of the proportion, its characteristics, and the relationship to the characteristics of the population.

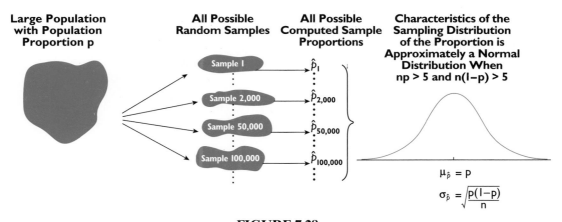

FIGURE 7.28

EXAMPLE 7.18

According to the National Highway Traffic Safety Administration, 70% of all motor vehicle drivers within the state of California use their seat belts. Assume this proportion is true for the population of all motor vehicle drivers in California who use their seat belts. If a random sample of size 200 is selected from this population, then determine the:

a) Mean of the sampling distribution of the proportion
b) Standard error of the proportion (to 4 decimal places)
c) Shape of the sampling distribution of the proportion

Solution

a) Let p defined to be the proportion of all motor vehicle drivers within the state of California who use their seat belts. Since p = 0.70 then the mean of the sampling distribution of the proportion is:

$$\mu_{\hat{p}} = p$$
$$\mu_{\hat{p}} = 0.70$$

b) The standard error of the proportion, $\sigma_{\hat{p}}$, is:

$$\sigma_{\hat{p}} = \sqrt{\frac{p(1-p)}{n}}$$

$$\sigma_{\hat{p}} = \sqrt{\frac{(0.70)(1-0.70)}{200}}$$

$$\sigma_{\hat{p}} = \sqrt{\frac{(0.70)(0.30)}{200}}$$

$$\sigma_{\hat{p}} = 0.0324$$

c) Since the values of np and n(1 – p) are

$$np = 200(0.70) = 140$$

and

$$np = 200(0.30) = 60$$

are both greater than 5, then the sampling distribution of the proportion can be approximated by a normal distribution with mean $\mu_{\hat{p}} = 0.70$, and standard error of the proportion $\sigma_{\hat{p}} = 0.0324$. This is illustrated in Figure 7.29.

Sampling Distribution of the Proportion
is Approximately Normal

$$\mu_{\hat{p}} = 0.70$$

$$\sigma_{\hat{p}} = 0.0324$$

FIGURE 7.29

Calculating Probabilities Using the Sampling Distribution of the Proportion

Later in this text we will need to make an inference or draw a conclusion about a population proportion. We will usually select only one random sample from the population and draw our inference or conclusion on the basis of this one sample. In the following examples, we will show how the sampling distribution of the proportion can be used to calculate probabilities about the value of a sample proportion $\hat{p}$ based upon the results of only one random sample.

EXAMPLE 7.19

According to Princeton Survey Research, 47% of drivers in the Midwest who say they drive at or below the speed limit. Assume this percentage represents the true population proportion of all Midwest drivers who drive at or below the speed limit. Determine the probability that more than 53% in a random sample of 200 Midwest drivers will say they drive at or below the speed limit.

Solution

Let p be defined to be the proportion of all drivers in the Midwest say they drive at or below the speed limit. Thus

$$p = 0.47.$$

Using Theorem 7.5, the mean of the sampling distribution of the proportion is:

$$\mu_{\hat{p}} = p = 0.47.$$

The standard error of the proportion (or the standard deviation of the sampling distribution) $\sigma_{\hat{p}}$, is computed by the formula:

$$\sigma_{\hat{p}} = \sqrt{\frac{p(1-p)}{n}}$$

Since n = 200, p = 0.47 and 1 - p = 0.53, we have:

$$\sigma_{\hat{p}} = \sqrt{\frac{0.47(0.53)}{200}}$$

$$\sigma_{\hat{p}} \approx 0.0353 \text{ (to 4 decimal places)}$$

According to the central limit theorem, since

$$np = 200(0.47) = 94$$

and

$$n(1-p) = 200(0.53) = 106$$

are both greater than 5, we can conclude that the sampling distribution of the proportion is approximately a normal distribution. Thus the sampling distribution of the proportion for this example is shown in Figure 7.30.

To calculate the probability that more than 53% in a random sample of 200 Midwest drivers will say they drive at or below the speed limit we must determine the shaded area under the normal curve to the right of $\hat{p} = 0.53$. This is illustrated in Figure 7.31.

Since the sampling distribution of the proportion is approximately normal, we can use the use Table II: The Normal Curve Area Table to obtain the probability associated with the shaded area in Figure 7.35. To compute this probability, we will need to determine a z score of the sample proportion $\hat{p} = 0.53$. As discussed in Chapter 3, the z score formula for a data value x is:

$$z \text{ of data value } = \frac{data\ value - mean}{standard\ deviation}.$$

In this section, since we are working with the sampling distribution of the proportion, the data values are sample proportions, $\hat{p}$, thus, the z score formula becomes:

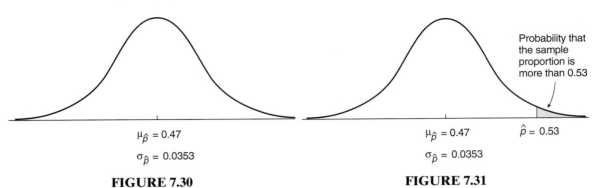

Sampling Distribution of the Proportion
is Approximately Normal

$\mu_{\hat{p}} = 0.47$

$\sigma_{\hat{p}} = 0.0353$

FIGURE 7.30

$\mu_{\hat{p}} = 0.47$

$\sigma_{\hat{p}} = 0.0353$

$\hat{p} = 0.53$

Probability that
the sample
proportion is
more than 0.53

FIGURE 7.31

$$z \; score \; of \; a \; = \frac{sample \; proportion - mean \; of \; the \; sampling \; distribution}{standard \; deviation \; of \; the \; sampling \; distribution}.$$

Therefore, when working with the sampling distribution of the proportion, the z score formula is now symbolized as:

$$z \; of \; \hat{p} = \frac{\hat{p} - \mu_{\hat{p}}}{\sigma_{\hat{p}}}.$$

Thus, the z score of $\hat{p} = 0.53$ is:

$$z = \frac{0.53 - 0.47}{0.0353}$$

$$z \; of \; \hat{p} = 0.53 \; is \; 1.70$$

From Table II, the Normal Curve Area Table found in Appendix D: Statistical Tables, the area to the left of z = 1.70 is 0.9554. The area to the right of z = 1.70 is 1 − 0.9554 = 0.0446.

Therefore, the probability that more than 53% in a random sample of 200 Midwest drivers will say they drive at or below the speed limit is 0.0446.   ∎

EXAMPLE 7.20

According to a survey by the Better Sleep Council, (nearly) one-third of people admit to dozing off at their workplace. Assume this proportion represents the true population proportion of all workers who doze off at their workplace. If a random sample of 100 workers is selected from this population, then determine the probability that the proportion of workers who admit to dozing off at work falls between 0.24 and 0.42.

Solution

Let p be defined to be the proportion of all workers who doze off at their workplace. Thus,

$$p \approx 0.33.$$

Using Theorem 7.5, the mean of the sampling distribution of the proportion is:

$$\mu_{\hat{p}} = p = 0.33.$$

The standard error of the proportion (or the standard deviation of the sampling distribution), $\sigma_{\hat{p}}$, is computed by the formula:

$$\sigma_{\hat{p}} = \sqrt{\frac{p(1-p)}{n}}$$

For n = 100, p = 0.33 and 1 − p = 0.67, we have:

$$\sigma_{\hat{p}} = \sqrt{\frac{0.33(0.67)}{100}}$$

$$\sigma_{\hat{p}} \approx 0.0470 \text{ (to 4 decimal places)}$$

According to the central limit theorem, since

$$np = 100 \, (0.33) = 33$$

and

$$n(1-p) = 100 \, (0.67) = 67$$

are both greater than 5, we can conclude that the sampling distribution of the proportion is approximately a normal distribution. Thus the sampling distribution of the proportion for this example is shown in Figure 7.32.

To calculate the probability that the proportion of workers within the sample who admit to dozing off at work falls between 0.24 and 0.42, we must determine the shaded area under the normal curve between $\hat{p} = 0.24$ and $\hat{p} = 0.42$. This is illustrated in Figure 7.33.

Since the sampling distribution of the proportion is approximately normal, we will use Table II: The Normal Curve Area Table to obtain the probability associated with the shaded area in Figure 7.33. To compute this probability, we will need to determine a z score for the sample proportions: $\hat{p} = 0.24$ and $\hat{p} = 0.42$. Thus, the z scores are:

$$z = \frac{0.24 - 0.33}{0.0470} \quad \text{and} \quad z = \frac{0.42 - 0.33}{0.0470}$$

z of $\hat{p} = 0.24$ is −1.91 and z of $\hat{p} = 0.42$ is 1.91

From Table II: the Normal Curve Area Table, the area associated with each of these z scores is:

z score	area to the left
−1.91	0.0281
1.91	0.9719

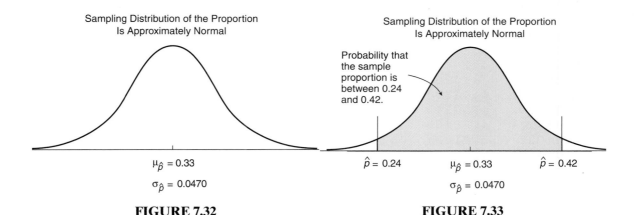

Sampling Distribution of the Proportion Is Approximately Normal	Sampling Distribution of the Proportion Is Approximately Normal
$\mu_{\hat{p}} = 0.33$	Probability that the sample proportion is between 0.24 and 0.42.
$\sigma_{\hat{p}} = 0.0470$	$\hat{p} = 0.24$ $\mu_{\hat{p}} = 0.33$ $\hat{p} = 0.42$ $\sigma_{\hat{p}} = 0.0470$

FIGURE 7.32   **FIGURE 7.33**

Subtract the smaller area from the larger area to compute the shaded area shown in Figure 7.33. This result is:

$$0.9719 - 0.0281 = 0.9438.$$

Therefore, the probability is 0.9438 that between 0.24 and 0.42 of the workers in a random sample of 100 workers will admit to dozing off at work.   ∎

7.8   USING TECHNOLOGY

The Central Limit Theorem and its consequences are perhaps some of the most important results in elementary statistics.

An advantage of using technology such as MINITAB, EXCEL or the TI-83 Plus is that it usually enables us to simulate concepts that would otherwise be difficult to understand. The following output of 200 means each representing a sample of size 49 was generated in MINITAB from a uniform distribution where $\mu = 4$ and $\mu = 2$. The output simulates Theorems 7.2 and 7.3 that are stated within Section 7.4.

MINITAB OUTPUT OF THE 200 MEANS FOR THE SIMULATION

C3

3.65306	3.79592	3.75510	4.36735	3.81633	4.32653	4.04082
4.73469	4.59184	3.93878	4.02041	3.69388	3.91837	3.87755
4.12245	4.32653	3.26531	4.40816	3.97959	3.53061	4.69388
4.14286	3.85714	4.04082	3.97959	4.22449	3.38776	4.44898
3.79592	3.89796	4.06122	4.30612	3.65306	3.73469	4.44898
3.71429	3.93878	4.16327	3.93878	4.48980	4.48980	3.93878
3.55102	3.91837	3.87755	3.59184	4.38775	4.26531	4.14286
4.00000	4.24490	4.30612	4.16327	3.69388	4.22449	4.08163
4.04082	3.53061	3.75510	4.02041	4.26531	4.04082	3.81633
3.73469	4.48980	3.61224	3.87755	4.04082	4.79592	4.00000
4.00000	3.51020	4.14286	4.12245	4.04082	4.06122	4.10204
3.87755	4.02041	3.93878	4.28571	3.75510	4.10204	3.93878
4.14286	3.97959	4.04082	3.69388	4.34694	3.89796	3.95918
3.73469	3.89796	4.06122	4.26531	4.38775	4.30612	4.12245
3.63265	3.77551	3.65306	3.83673	4.08163	4.32653	3.97959
3.46939	4.12245	4.36735	3.75510	3.57143	3.91837	4.18367
3.73469	3.79592	4.28571	4.40816	4.16327	3.89796	3.59184
4.12245	3.69388	3.97959	4.18367	3.57143	3.42857	4.30612
4.42857	4.51020	4.42857	3.75510	3.79592	3.40816	4.46939
3.51020	3.81633	4.18367	3.77551	3.91837	3.63265	4.18367
4.08163	4.24490	3.67347	4.20408	3.97959	4.14286	3.73469
4.28571	4.14286	4.10204	3.69388	3.40816	4.16327	4.00000
4.00000	4.44898	3.79592	3.83673	4.44898	3.75510	3.77551
3.97959	4.57143	3.73469	3.65306	4.00000	3.93878	4.10204
3.85714	4.08163	3.87755	3.93878	3.97959	4.20408	3.83673
4.04082	3.91837	3.63265	3.67347	3.97959	3.95918	3.69388
3.97959	4.20408	3.85714	3.79592	3.83673	4.20408	4.44898
4.20408	3.97959	3.44898	4.32653	3.83673	4.34694	3.57143
4.34694	4.04082	4.28571	3.67347			

FIGURE 7.34

MINITAB OUTPUT OF A HISTOGRAM OF THE SAMPLE MEANS

Histogram of C3   N = 200
Each * represents 2 obs.

Midpoint	Count	
3.2	1	*
3.4	6	***
3.6	27	**************
3.8	42	*********************
4.0	51	**************************
4.2	39	********************
4.4	28	**************
4.6	4	**
4.8	2	*

FIGURE 7.35

MINITAB OUTPUT OF THE SUMMARY STATISTICS FOR THE SIMULATION

	N	MEAN	MEDIAN	TRMEAN	STDEV	SEMEAN
C3	200	3.9966	3.9796	3.9951	0.2895	0.0205

	MIN	MAX	Q1	Q3
C3	3.2653	4.7959	3.7806	4.1990

FIGURE 7.36

By examining the histogram you should see that:

1. the shape of the resulting sampling distribution of the mean is approximately normal.
2. the summary statistics indicate the mean of the sampling distribution is 3.9966 while the STDEV is 0.2895.

Are these results consistent to the results of Theorems 7.2 and 7.3? Explain.

According to Theorems 7.2 and 7.3, the distribution of sample means constructed using random samples selected from this uniform population has the following characteristics:

1. The sampling distribution of the mean is approximately normal.
2. $\mu_{\bar{x}} = \mu$
   $\mu_{\bar{x}} = 4$

3. $\sigma_{\bar{x}} = \dfrac{\sigma}{\sqrt{n}}$

   $\sigma_{\bar{x}} = \dfrac{2}{\sqrt{49}}$

   $\sigma_{\bar{x}} = 0.2857$

Therefore since the mean for this simulation of 200 sample means is 3.9966 and the estimate of the population standard deviation is 0.2895 you can see that the simulation is indeed very close. This illustrates the results of the Central Limit Theorem. In practice such simulations are usually carried out many more thousands of times.

A similar simulation was conducted using EXCEL. The histogram in Figure 7.41a and the summary statistics in Figure 7.41b represent 200 random samples of size 49 selected from a uniform distribution population where $\mu = 4$ and $\mu = 2$.

Are these results consistent to the results of Theorems 7.2 and 7.3? Explain.

Another simulation of the Central Limit Theorem using the TI-83 Plus was conducted. The histogram in Figure 7.42 represents the uniform distribution of the population values 1 to 50. The population parameters were $\mu = 25.5$ and $\sigma = 14.43$.

Using the TI-83 Plus, 100 random samples of size 36 was selected from this population. A histogram of the resulting sampling distribution of the mean is shown in Figure 7.43.

The resulting descriptive statistics of the sampling distribution of the mean is shown in Figure 7.44.

How do these values compare to the expected values of the sampling distribution of the mean? Explain why there might be any differences between the expected values and the computed values.

**Histogram of Sample Means
Sample Size = 49**

FIGURE 7.37a

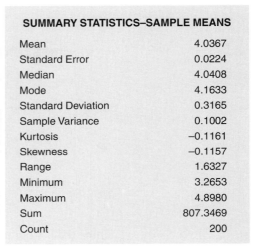

SUMMARY STATISTICS–SAMPLE MEANS	
Mean	4.0367
Standard Error	0.0224
Median	4.0408
Mode	4.1633
Standard Deviation	0.3165
Sample Variance	0.1002
Kurtosis	−0.1161
Skewness	−0.1157
Range	1.6327
Minimum	3.2653
Maximum	4.8980
Sum	807.3469
Count	200

FIGURE 7.37b

FIGURE 7.38

FIGURE 7.39

RESULTS OF THE
SAMPLING DIST
OF THE MEAN

MEAN OF SAMPLE
MEANS = 24.95
STD ERROR= 2.41

FIGURE 7.40

SECTION EXERCISES

Section 7.1

1. An error that occurs during the selection, measuring, recording or computation process of sampling is called an _____ error.

2. The variation in a sample estimate of the population mean is called _____ _____.

3. The sampling error of the mean is equal to $\bar{x}$ – _____.

4. The sampling distribution of the mean is a probability distribution which lists all the possible values of the _____ _____ of the same sample size selected from a population along with the _____ associated with each value of the sample mean.

5. The mean of all the sample means of the sampling distribution of the mean is symbolized as _____.

6. The standard deviation of all the sample means of the sampling distribution of the mean is symbolized as _____.

7. The difference between the population mean and a sample mean is called the:
   a) Standard deviation
   b) Variance
   c) Sampling error
   d) Finite correction factor

8. The sampling distribution of the mean is made up of the means of *many* random samples of size n selected from an infinite population.
   (T/F)

9. Suppose the following ten I.Q. scores represent a population of I.Q. scores:

   123, 130, 106, 117, 127, 103, 118, 133, 124, 131

   a) Compute the population mean I.Q. score, μ.
   For each of the following random samples of I.Q. scores selected from this population

   i) compute the sample mean.
   ii) determine the sampling error if this sample were used to estimate the population mean.
   b) 130, 103, 133
   c) 124, 118, 117
   d) 127, 124, 106

10. The following list of hourly wages represent the population of all employees working at a small local computer store CompAmerica:

    $10, $8, $9.50, $7.50, $12, $15

    a) Calculate the mean hourly wage for all the employees.
    b) Determine all the possible samples of size n = 2 that can be selected from this population without replacement.
    c) Compute all the possible sampling errors that could be made if any of these samples were used to estimate the population mean. In addition, determine the probability of making such an error.

11. Consider the finite population of six individuals who are identified by the first letters of their surnames:

    M, A, T, H, E, W. If we are going to randomly select two people from this group to form a committee, then:
    a) Identify all 15 possible pairs of people that can be randomly selected such as: MA, MT, MH, etc.
    b) Determine the probability of selecting one of these pairs of people.
    c) If each letter is assigned the following number: M is assigned #1, A is assigned #2, T is assigned #3, H is assigned #4, E is assigned #5, AND W is assigned #6, then list the two pairs of people who would be randomly selected using the following random numbers: 94879 16831.

12. Consider the following population of data values:

    49, 53, 57, 61, 65, 69, 73

a) Find the population mean, μ, and the population standard deviation, σ.

b) Construct the sampling distribution of the mean for random samples of size n = 2 from this population *with replacement* by listing all the possible sample means along with the probability associated with each sample mean.

c) Calculate $\mu_{\bar{x}}$ and $\sigma_{\bar{x}}$ using the information in part (b). Compare these values to the population values computed in part(a). Discuss your observations.

d) Compute all the possible sampling errors that could be made if any of these samples were used to estimate the population mean. In addition, determine the probability of making such an error.

Section 7.2

13. a) The mean of a sample is symbolized by _____.
    b) The mean of the population is symbolized by _____.
    c) The standard deviation of the population is symbolized by _____.
    d) The mean of the sampling distribution of the mean is symbolized by_____.
    e) The standard error of the sampling distribution of the mean is symbolized by _____.

14. The sampling distribution of the mean is made up of the means of _____ possible random samples of size n selected from a population.

15. The mean of the sampling distribution of the mean, denoted by _____ and is equal to the mean of the _____ from which the samples were selected. In symbols, this is expressed as: _____.

16. The standard deviation of the sampling distribution of the mean is called the _____ _____ of the mean.

17. The standard error of the mean is the _____ _____of all the sample means of size n of the sampling distribution, denoted by _____ . The standard error of the mean is equal to the standard deviation of the population, σ, divided by the square root of the _____ _____. In symbols, this is expressed as: _____.

18. If random samples of size 25 are selected from a population with a mean of 45 and a standard deviation of 15, then the mean of all the sample means will be:
    a) 9   b) 45   c) 60   d) 15

19. If random samples of size 16 are selected from a population with a mean of 80 and a standard deviation of 20, then the standard error of the mean will be:
    a) 5   b) 16   c) 4   d) 20

20. Suppose a random sample of size n = 64 is selected from a population with mean, μ, and standard deviation, σ.

    For each of the following values of μ and σ, find the value of $\mu_{\bar{x}}$ and $\sigma_{\bar{x}}$.
    a) $\mu = 20$, and $\sigma = 2$
    b) $\mu = 90$, and $\sigma = 5$

c) $\mu = 150$, and $\sigma = 10$
d) $\mu = 200$, and $\sigma = 50$

21. Find the mean, $\mu_{\bar{x}}$, of the sampling distribution of the mean and the standard error, $\sigma_{\bar{x}}$, of the mean if the population from which the random samples are selected has $\mu = 100$ and $\sigma = 9$ where the sample size, n, is:
    a) 9   b) 81   c) 100   d) 400

22. Suppose you are sampling from a population with $\mu = 850$ and $\sigma = 95$. If a random sample of size n = 81 is selected from this population, determine the mean and variance of the sampling distribution of the mean.

23. Suppose a random sample of size n is selected from a population with $\mu = 470$ and $\sigma^2 = 625$. For each of the following values of n, state the mean and standard error of the sampling distribution of the mean.
    a) 25   b) 36   c) 81   d) 200   e) 1,000

Section 7.3

24. When sampling without replacement from a finite population, the formula to compute the standard deviation of the sampling distribution of the mean is: _____.

25. When sampling without replacement from a finite population, and the sample size, n, is less than 5% of the population size, N, then a _____ _____ factor must be used. In such instances, the standard error of the sampling distribution of the mean can be computed using the formula: _____.

26. The finite correction factor is approximately one when _____.

27. According to a survey of all the 900 families living in Soap Town, USA, the mean length of time the families keep a T.V. set is 98 months with a standard deviation of 9 months.

    If a sample of 36 families is randomly selected from this town without replacement and the mean length of time the families keep a TV for this sample is computed, then:
    a) Determine the standard error of the mean.
    b) What is the value of the finite correction factor?
    c) Compute the ratio of n/N. Is this value less than 5% of the population size? If it is, what should this indicate about the value of the finite correction factor?

28. The total attendance at a three day rock concert in Lumberstock, New York was 10,000. According to a survey of all the people in attendance, the mean amount of time they slept was 4.7 hours with a standard deviation of 2.8 hours. If a random sample of 100 of those attending the concert is selected, then:
    a) Determine the standard error of the mean.
    b) Find the value of the finite correction factor.
    c) Calculate the value of the ratio n/N. Is this value less than 5% of the population size? If it is, what should this tell you about the value of the finite correction factor?

Section 7.4

29. The Central Limit Theorem states that the sampling distribution of the mean can be closely approximated by a _____ distribution if the sample size is _____ . That is, usually greater than _____ .

30. The importance of the Central Limit Theorem is that it guarantees that the sampling distribution of the mean is approximately normal as long as the sample size is large enough regardless of the _____ of the population from which the samples were selected.

31. If all possible random samples of size 100 are selected from an infinite population whose mean is 130 and standard deviation is 10, then:
a) The sampling distribution of the mean is approximately _____ . This a result of the _____ _____ Theorem.
b) The mean of the sampling distribution of the mean is _____ . In symbols, we write: $\mu_{\bar{x}}$ = _____.
c) The standard error of the mean is _____ . In symbols, we have: $\sigma_{\bar{x}}$ = _____.

32. The sampling distribution of the mean is normal for all sample sizes, even as small as n = 2, if the original population, from which the samples were selected, is a _____ distribution.

33. Describe the characteristics (its mean, standard error and shape) of the sampling distribution of the mean if sampling is done from a normal population where μ = 110, and σ = 10 for samples of size:
a) n = 4
b) n = 25
c) n = 100

34. If the standard error of the mean, $\sigma_{\bar{x}}$, is a small number, then the sampling distribution of the mean has relatively _____ dispersion and the sample means will be relatively _____ to the population mean.

35. If random samples of size 10 are selected from a normal distribution, then the sampling distribution of the mean will be:
a) Unknown
b) Any shape
c) Uniform
d) Normal

36. If random samples of size 20 are selected from a distribution of unknown shape, then the sampling distribution of the mean will be:
a) Unknown
b) Any shape
c) Uniform
d) Normal

37. If random samples of size 50 are selected from a uniform distribution, then the sampling distribution of the mean will be:
a) Unknown
b) Any shape

c) Uniform
d) Normal

38. The sampling distribution of the mean will be approximately normal when n is less than 30. (T/F)

39. For each of the following parts, you are given the approximate *population* shape, the population mean, the population standard deviation and are asked to form a sampling distribution of the mean by selecting all possible random samples of size n. Determine the:
1) Approximate shape (normal or unknown) for the sampling distribution of the mean
2) Mean of the sampling distribution of the mean, $\mu_{\bar{x}}$
3) Standard error of the mean, $\sigma_{\bar{x}}$.

a) shape: uniform
mean, μ = 160
standard deviation,
σ = 8
sample size, n = 64

b) shape: triangular
mean, μ = 16
standard deviation,
σ = 3
sample size, n = 81

a   b

c) shape: any shape
mean, μ = 4000
standard deviation,
σ = 200
sample size, n = 25

d) shape: normal
mean, μ = 1200
standard deviation,
σ = 400
sample size, n = 16

a   b

e) shape: unknown
μ = 32
σ = 5
n = 100

f) shape: bimodal
μ = 500
σ = 100
n = 400

a   b

g) shape: any shape
μ = 20,000
σ = 4500
n = 225

h) shape: unknown
μ = 8
σ = 1.6
n = 16

a   b

i) shape: normal
   $\mu = 1000$
   $\sigma = 100$
   $n = 4$

j) shaped: skewed
   $\mu = 24,000$
   $\sigma = 6000$
   $n = 9$

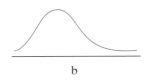

a   b

40. Suppose you are sampling from a normal population with $\mu = 525$ and $\sigma = 100$, what is the smallest sample size (greater than one) required for the sampling distribution of the mean to be normal?

Section 7.5

41. When working with the sampling distribution of the mean, the formula used for the z score is _____.

42. The mean systolic blood pressure of young female adults is 125 with a standard deviation of 24. Find the probability that a random sample of 100 young female adults will have a mean systolic blood pressure:
   a) Less than 122.
   b) Between 121 and 127.
   c) Greater than 126.

43. The mean age of New York City legal secretaries is 24 years with $\sigma = 3$ years. If a sample of 36 secretaries is selected at random, what is the probability that the sample mean age is:
   a) Less than 25?
   b) Between 24 and 26?
   c) Greater than 28?

44. The population of IQ scores from a large community college has a mean of 110 with a standard deviation of 10. Find the probability that a random sample of size
   a) 36
   b) 81
   c) 100
   selected from this population will have a sample mean between 108 and 112.
   d) What happens to the probability as the sample size increases? How would this help someone who is interested in estimating the population mean?

45. The mean weight of newborn babies in a Long Island Community is 7.5 lbs. with a standard deviation of 1.4 lbs. What is the probability that a random sample of 49 babies has a mean weight of at least 7.2 lbs?

46. A new TREK model mountain bike has a mean selling price of $725 in the eastern section of the U.S. Suppose the standard deviation of the selling prices of the bike is $85. If a random sample of the 64 bikes is selected

from this population, what is the probability that the sample mean price for a TREK 800 bike will fall between $675 and $750?

47. The mean weekly family entertainment for a New York County is $45.70 with a population standard deviation of $6.45. Calculate the probability that a random sample of size 81 selected from this population will yield a sample mean greater than $47?

48. At a sports arena, twelve professional wrestlers squeeze into an elevator on the third floor going down to the wrestling ring for the Royal Rumble. The weights of the professional wrestlers is normally distributed with $\mu = 265$ lbs and $\sigma = 30$ lbs. If the elevator's weight capacity is 3400 lbs, calculate the probability that the elevator will not be able to carry the 12 wrestlers to the Royal Rumble?

49. Miss Peld, a statistics instructor, announces to her class that the number of words per page in their 800 page statistics textbook is normally distributed with $\mu = 437$ wpp and $\sigma = 46$ wpp. Angelo, a statistics student, decides to test Miss Peld's claim by randomly selecting 16 pages from the textbook and determining the mean number of words per page. What is the probability that the mean number of words per page for Angelo's sample will be greater than 460?

50. A random sample of 100 is taken from an infinite population where $\mu = 72$ and $\sigma = 8$. If the sample mean is used to estimate the population mean, what is the probability the sampling error will be less than 0.50? (That is, the sample mean will be greater than 71.5 but less than 72.5?)

51. An automotive parts manufacturer randomly samples 49 parts and inspects them for defects each day to insure its production process is in control. If the process is in control, the daily population output of 10,000 parts is expected to have a mean of 8 defective parts with a standard deviation of 2.94. The quality control department defines the production process to be out of control if the random sample of 49 parts contains more than 9 defective parts. In such instances, the manufacturer will need to retool. What is the probability that the manufacturer will need to retool by mistake?

52. A light bulb manufacturer wishes to estimate the mean life of its new light bulb. The manufacturer randomly samples 144 of these new bulbs. What is the probability that the manufacturer's estimate obtained by the mean of this sample will be within 40 hours of the population mean if we assume the standard deviation of all the new bulbs is 250 hours?

53. The birthrate for a county in Kentucky is stated to be 1.45 per women. Assume the population standard deviation is 0.30. If a random sample of 400 women is selected from this county, what is the probability that the mean birthrate of the sample will fall between 1.20 and 1.70?

54. Last year, the mean batting average of all major league baseball players was .275 with a standard deviation of .018. What is the probability that the mean of a random sample of 36 baseball players is at most .280?

55. During the month of December, the mean telephone bill for families in a Tucson, Arizona community was $48 with a standard deviation of $9. If a random sample of 36 families is selected at random from this community, what is the probability that the telephone bills for the month of December for the sampled families would have a mean between $45.50 and $50.50?

56. A manufacturer of automobile batteries states that their "slow die" battery has a mean life of 50 months with a standard deviation of 6 months. If a consumer protection group randomly samples 49 of these batteries, what is the probability that the mean life of the consumer group's sample will be at most 52 months (assuming the manufacturer's claim is true)?

57. The Environmental Protection Agency's (E.P.A.) rating of an automobile manufacturer`s Z car is 27 m.p.g with a standard deviation of 6 m.p.g.. Suppose the Miami Police Department has randomly purchased a sample of 36 Z cars from this manufacturer. If the police officers have driven these cars exclusively in the city and have recorded a mean average of 24 m.p.g., then:
a) What are the chances of getting a random sample mean of at most 24 m.p.g.?
b) Would you question the E.P.A.'s rating for this model car based upon this sample result? Explain.

58. A light bulb manufacturer states that its energy saver 60 watt light bulb has a mean life of 1850 hours with a standard deviation of 240 hours. If random samples of size 64 of these light bulbs are selected and tested, then within what interval (centered about the mean) would you expect 95% of these sample means to fall?

59. The mean IQ score of a tribe of American Indians is 110 with a standard deviation of 14. If the distribution of sample means is formed for random samples of size 49 between what two sample means centered at the mean will:
a) 90% of all sample means lie?
b) 95% of all sample means lie?
c) 99% of all sample means lie?

60. The production characteristics for a small engine part are as follows: mean is 2.36", standard deviation is 0.04" and normally distributed.
a) What percent of these parts fail to meet the engineering specifications of 2.35" plus or minus 0.1"?
b) If sixteen of these parts are selected at random what is the probability that the average length is less than 2.35"?
c) A quality control procedure requires that a random sample of size 4 be selected and that the sample mean be in the interval 2.32" to 2.38". If not, then

the case of parts is declared defective. What percent of these samples will fail to meet this test?

61. If the mean length of the parts made by an old cutting machine is 6.74 inches with a standard deviation of 0.12 inches then:
a) What is the probability that a random sample of 36 of these parts will have a mean length greater than 6.75 inches?
b) An acceptance sampling procedure requires that the mean length for a random sample of 144 of these parts be between 6.725 inches and 6.755 inches. What is the probability of the sample mean not being in this interval?

Section 7.6

62. As the sample size increases, the standard error of the mean _____.

63. The standard deviation of the sampling distribution of the mean gets smaller as the size of the sample
a) Increases
b) Remains the same
c) Decreases
d) Not enough information

64. The sampling distribution of the mean will have _____ dispersion as the population.
a) Less
b) The same
c) More

65. As the sample size increases, the standard error of the mean
a) Increases
b) Decreases
c) Remains the same
d) Cannot be determined

66. For a particular country club of 500 members, the standard deviation of the ages is 16. If a survey is conducted to estimate the mean age by randomly sampling 81 members from this population without replacement, then determine the standard error of the mean.

67. The standard error of the mean will be reduced by 50%, if the sample size is:
a) Doubled
b) Tripled
c) Quadrupled
d) Halved

68. At a midwestern college, the mean height of all the women students is 5' 3" with a standard deviation of 2.4". Determine the mean, $\mu_{\bar{x}}$, and standard error, $\sigma_{\bar{x}}$, for the sampling distribution of the mean for samples of size:
a) 49
b) 81
c) 144
d) 900

e) What affect does increasing the sample size have on the standard error of the mean? Explain.

Section 7.7

69. The Central Limit Theorem of the sampling distribution of the proportion states that the sampling distribution of the proportion can be approximated by a normal distribution whenever the sample size is sufficiently _____ . That is, when _____ > 5 and _____ > 5.

70. When working with the sampling distribution of the proportion, the formula used for the z score is _____.

71. A _____ is a fraction, ratio or percentage that indicates the part of a population or sample that possesses a particular characteristic.

72. The formula to compute the population (or true) proportion of a finite population is _____ .

73. The formula to compute the sample proportion is _____ .

74. The notation for the mean of the sampling distribution of the proportion is _____.

75. The notation for the standard deviation of the sampling distribution of the proportion is _____.

76. The formula for the mean of the sampling distribution of the proportion is _____.

77. The formula for the standard error of the proportion is _____.

78. The formula to compute the sampling error for the proportion is: sampling error = _____ – _____ .

79. If 14 out of every 35 people in the population interviewed answered yes to the survey question, then the population proportion, p, would be:
a) 0.14   **b)** 0.20   **c)** 0.50   **d)** 0.40

80. If a random sample of size 40 is selected from an infinite population with a proportion of women equal to 0.25, what is the standard error of the proportion of women?
a) 0.0610   **b)** 0.0801   **c)** 0.0685   **d)** 0.0488

81. If the sample size is increased, then the standard deviation of the sampling distribution of the proportion will:
a) Decrease
b) Increase
c) Remain the same
d) Not enough information

82. The formula for $\mu_{\hat{p}}$ is given by:
a) $\mu_{\hat{p}} = np$
b) $\mu_{\hat{p}} = p$
c) $\mu_{\hat{p}} = p/n$
d) $\mu_{\hat{p}} = n(1-p)$

83. Determine the sample proportion, $\hat{p}$, (to 4 decimal places) for each of the following statements.
a) Thirty out of 100 incoming freshman do not meet the minimum college requirements in reading.
b) A family counselor finds that 180 out of 200 patients are lonely because they have forgotten how to have fun.

c) Four out of 37 stock investors purchase stocks based upon presumed inside information (i.e. a hot tip).

84. Determine the mean and standard error of the sampling distribution of the proportion and whether or not the sampling distribution of the proportion can be approximated by a normal distribution, if:
a) p = 0.40, and n = 50
b) The population proportion is 0.65 and the sample size is 200.
c) A random sample of 400 was selected from a population composed of 70% democratic.

85. Suppose a small bag of plain M&M's contains 2 brown, 2 red, 1 yellow, 1 blue, 1 green and 1 orange. We will assume this bag represents our population. Suppose we take all possible samples of 3 M&M's each.
a) Determine the population proportion p of red M&M's.
b) Determine the total number of samples of size 3 that can be selected from this population.
c) Construct a frequency distribution table containing all the possible samples of size 3 and the proportion of red M&M's for each of those samples.
d) Compute the mean and standard deviation of all the sample proportions of red M&M's.
e) Using the formulas for the mean and standard deviation of the sampling distribution of the proportion, compute the mean and standard error of the sampling distribution. (Hint: use the finite correction factor when computing the standard deviation.)
f) Compare parts (d) and (e).

86. According to a National Sleep Foundation Survey, 70% of adults say it takes more than 30 minutes to fall asleep at night. Let's assume that this percentage is true for the population of all U.S. adults. If a random sample of 250 adults is selected from this population, then determine the probability that the sample proportion, $\hat{p}$, of adults who take more than 30 minutes to fall asleep will be:
a) Less than 0.66.
b) Greater than 0.74.
c) Between 0.64 and 0.76.

87. According to the Princeton Survey Research Group, 42% of U.S. drivers who live in the South say they drive at or below the speed limit. Assume this proportion is true for the population of all U.S. drivers living in the South. If a random sample of 300 drivers is selected from this population, then determine the probability that the sample proportion, $\hat{p}$, of drivers living in the South who say they drive at or below the speed limit is:
a) At most 39%.
b) At least 47%.
c) Between 36% to 49%.

88. A large New York law firm states that 80% of their cases are settled out of court. What is the probability that out of the next 200 cases that:
a) At least 75% will be settled out of court?
b) At least 90% will be settled out of court?
c) At least 25% will **not** be settled out of court?

89. If the sample size, n, is increased, then the mean of the sampling distribution of the mean:
a) Increases
b) Remains the same
c) Decreases
d) Not enough information

90. As the sample size increases the standard error of the mean, $\sigma_{\bar{x}}$, also increases.
(T/F)

91. The symbol used to represent the standard deviation of the sampling distribution of the mean is
a) $\sigma_{\bar{x}}$ b) σ c) s   d) $\bar{x}$

92. The theorem that states "For any population, the sampling distribution of the mean approaches a normal distribution as the sample size n becomes large, regardless of the shape of the population being randomly sampled, is called the _____ _____ Theorem.

93. If all possible random samples of size n are selected from an infinite population with a mean, μ, and a standard deviation, σ, then:
a) The mean of the sampling distribution of the mean, denoted $\mu_{\bar{x}}$, is equal to the _____ of the population from which the samples were selected. This is symbolized: $\mu_{\bar{x}}$ = _____.
b) The standard error of the mean, denoted σ, is equal to the population standard deviation divided by the square root of the sample _____. This is symbolized: $\sigma_{\bar{x}}$ = _____.

94. If all possible random samples of size n are selected from an infinite population with a standard deviation of σ then, the standard deviation of the sampling distribution of the mean, $\sigma_{\bar{x}}$, will equal

$$\frac{\sigma}{\sqrt{n}}$$

only if *n* is greater than 30.
(T/F)

95. An infinite population has a $\mu = 120$ and $\sigma = 15$. A random sample of size n = 16 is selected from the population. Determine the mean, $\mu_{\bar{x}}$, and the standard error of the mean, $\sigma_{\bar{x}}$.

96. A very large population has a mean = 1540 and a variance of 40,000. A random sample of n = 100 is selected from the population. Find the mean, $\mu_{\bar{x}}$, of the sampling distribution of the mean and the standard error, $\sigma_{\bar{x}}$, of the mean.

97. The general rule widely accepted and used by statisticians is that the sampling distribution of the mean can be approximated by a normal distribution provided the sample size n is greater than 30 regardless of the shape of the population.
(T/F)

98. A report on the annual contribution of the 2,000 members of a local rubbish union stated that the mean contribution to their trash fund was $\mu = \$455$ with a standard deviation $\sigma = \$92$. If a sample of n union members is randomly selected from this union without replacement and the mean contribution for this sample is computed, then determine the standard error of the sampling distribution of the mean for the following samples of size n.
a) n = 16
b) n = 81
c) n = 400
d) Explain what happens to the value of the finite correction factor as the sample size increases.

99. A small calculus class of 8 students received the following scores on their midterm: 91, 84, 73, 82, 69, 66, 78, 87.

Assuming these scores represent a population, then:
a) Compute the population mean test score, μ.

For each of the following random samples of test scores selected from this population
i) compute the sample mean.
ii) determine the sampling error if this sample were used to estimate the population mean.
b) 84, 69, 87
c) 91, 82, 73
d) 66, 91, 66

100. The heights of 4000 male athletes have a mean of 72" and a standard deviation of 2". If all possible random samples of size 64 are taken from this population, determine:
a) The mean and standard error of the sampling distribution of the mean.
b) The percent of sample means that fall between 71.75" and 72.25".
c) The probability a sample mean is less than 71.35".
d) Below what sample mean can we expect to find the lowest 20% of all the sample means?

101. According to a National Health Survey, the mean cholesterol level for men aged 18 to 24 is 197. Assuming that this is the mean of the population of cholesterol levels for men aged 18 to 24 with a standard deviation of $\sigma = 20$, then determine the mean and standard error of the sampling distribution of the mean for samples of size:
a) n = 49
b) n = 400
c) What effect did increasing the sample size have on the mean and standard error of the sampling distribution?

102. A college instructor has determined that the mean time it takes all the students to complete the final exam is $\mu = 92.5$ minutes with a standard deviation of $\sigma = 17.6$ minutes. Determine the mean and the standard error of the sampling distribution of the mean and describe the shape of the sampling distribution of the mean when the sample size is:

a) n = 49
b) n = 144

103. Determine the sample proportion, $\hat{p}$, (to 4 decimal places) for each of the following statements.
  a) A nationwide survey of 1200 people found that 800 favored the death penalty for murder.
  b) A government agency has determined that 1850 out of a sample of 5000 student borrowers have defaulted on their federal student loans.

104. Determine the mean and standard error of the sampling distribution of the proportion and whether or not the sampling distribution of the proportion can be approximated by a normal distribution, if:
  a) p = 0.10, and n = 30
  b) The population proportion is 0.80 and the sample size is 100.
  c) A random sample of 150 was selected from a population composed of 20% unemployed people.

105. A National Survey conducted by The Social Science Research Center at Old Dominion University found that 56% of all drivers admitted they run red lights. Assume this proportion is true for the population of all U.S. drivers. If a random sample of 500 drivers is selected from this population, then determine the probability that the sample proportion, $\hat{p}$, of drivers who admit to running red lights is:
  a) Less than 59%.
  b) Between 53% and 58%.
  c) Greater than 61%.
  What would be the sampling error if we had selected a sample:
  d) With proportion $\hat{p}$ = 59% of drivers who admit to running a red light.
  e) With proportion $\hat{p}$ = 51% of drivers who admit to running a red light.
  f) Is it possible for the sampling error to be negative? Explain.

106. The following table summarizes the responses of a cross section of 9000 Americans aged 16 and over regarding the following two questions:

  Question #1: " If a man doesn't want his wife to take a job, should she respect his wishes?"

  Question #2: "Do you think it is or is not all right for a man and a woman to live together without getting married?

	Question #1		Question #2	
	YES	NO	ALL RIGHT	NOT ALL RIGHT
TOTAL	4790	4210	4388	4612
REGION				
Northeast	710	1090	1026	774
Southeast	990	810	728	1072
Midwest	970	830	791	1009
Southwest	1210	590	687	1113
Far West	910	890	1156	644
SEX				
Women	2365	2060	1946	2479
Men	2425	2150	2442	2133
MARITAL STATUS				
Single	902	1363	1593	672
Married	1243	1042	915	1370
Widowed	1482	643	396	1729
Separated/ Divorced	1163	1162	1484	841
EDUCATION				
High School Incomplete	1422	793	778	1437
High School Graduate	1343	892	915	1320
Some beyond High School	1122	1133	1262	993
College Graduate	903	1392	1433	862

Determine the sample proportion, $\hat{p}$, for each of the following:
  a) Northeast Americans responding yes to question #1.
  b) Southwestern Americans responding yes to question #1.
  c) Single Americans responding no to question #1.
  d) Widowed Americans responding no to question #1.
  e) Those Americans who did not complete high school responding yes to question #1.
  f) College graduates responding yes to question #1.
  g) Midwest Americans responding not all right to question #2.
  h) Far West Americans responding all right to question #2.
  i) Women responding all right to question #2.
  j) Married Americans responding not all right to question #2.
  k) Separated/divorced Americans responding not all right to question #2.
  l) College graduates responding all right to question #2.

107. According to a Gallup Poll, 60% of adults say they experience heartburn. Assume this proportion is true for the population of all adults. If a random sample of 300 adults is selected from this population, then determine the probability that:
  a) Less than 172 adults within the sample experience heartburn.
  b) More than 191 adults within the sample experience heartburn.
  c) Between 164 to 198 adults within the sample experience heartburn.
  What would be the sampling error if we had selected a sample:
  d) With proportion $\hat{p}$ = 59% of adults who experienced heartburn.
  e) With proportion $\hat{p}$ = 51% of adults who experienced heartburn.
  f) Is it possible for the sampling error to be negative? Explain.

WHAT DO YOU THINK?

108. The following article entitled "Order of the Draft Drawing" which appeared in the New York Times shows the order in which birth dates were selected during the 1969 draft lottery. On December 1, 1969 the lottery was held in the Selective Service headquarters in Washington, D.C. to determine the draft status of all 19 year-old males for the Vietnam Conflict. The 366 possible birth dates were inserted within a small capsule. The capsules were placed in a stationary drum beginning with January, then February and so on until all the birth dates of December were placed in the drum last. The first capsule drawn would have the highest draft priority, and so on.

Order of the Draft Drawing

Special to The New York Times

WASHINGTON, *Dec. 1–Following is the order in which birth dates were drawn tonight in the draft lottery.*

1	Sept. 14	48	Aug. 8	95	Dec. 24	142	Aug. 12	189	Feb. 17	236	Feb. 24	283	Oct. 3
2	April 24	49	Sept. 2	96	Dec. 18	143	Nov. 17	190	July 18	237	Oct. 11	284	July 10
3	Dec. 30	50	July 7	97	Nov. 8	144	Feb. 2	191	April 29	238	Jan. 14	285	Feb. 29
4	Feb. 14	51	Nov. 7	98	July 17	145	Aug. 4	192	Oct. 20	239	Mar. 28	286	Aug. 25
5	Oct. 18	52	Jan. 25	99	Nov. 29	146	Nov. 18	193	July 31	240	Dec. 19	287	July 30
6	Sept. 6	53	Dec. 22	100	Dec. 31	147	Apr. 7	194	Jun. 9	241	Oct.19	288	Oct. 17
7	Oct. 24	54	Aug. 5	101	Jan. 5	148	Apr. 16	195	Sept. 24	242	Sept. 12	289	July 27
8	Sept. 7	55	May 16	102	Aug. 15	149	Sept. 25	196	Oct. 24	243	Oct. 21	290	Feb. 22
9	Nov. 22	56	Dec. 5	103	May 30	150	Feb. 11	197	May 9	244	Oct. 3	291	Aug. 21
10	Dec. 6	57	Feb. 23	104	June 19	151	Sept. 29	198	Aug. 14	245	Aug. 26	292	Feb. 18
11	Aug. 31	58	Jan. 19	105	Dec. 8	152	Feb. 13	199	Jan. 3	246	Sept. 18	293	Mar. 5
12	Dec. 7	59	Jan. 24	106	Aug. 9	153	July 22	200	Mar. 19	247	June 22	294	Oct. 14
13	July 8	60	June 21	107	Nov. 16	154	Aug. 17	201	Oct. 23	248	July 11	295	May 13
14	April 11	61	Aug. 29	108	March 1	155	May 6	202	Oct. 4	249	June 1	296	May 27
15	July 12	62	April 21	109	June 23	156	Nov. 21	203	Nov. 19	250	May 21	297	Feb. 3
16	Dec. 29	63	Sept. 20	110	June 6	157	Dec. 3	204	Sept. 21	251	Jan. 3	298	May 2
17	Jan. 15	64	June 27	111	Aug. 1	158	Sept. 11	205	Feb. 27	252	April 23	299	Feb. 28
18	Sept. 28	65	May 10	112	May 17	159	Jan. 2	206	June 10	253	April 6	300	Mar. 12
19	Nov. 1	66	Nov. 12	113	Sept. 15	160	Sept. 22	207	Sept. 14	254	Oct. 16	301	June 3
20	June 4	67	July 25	114	Aug. 6	161	Sept. 2	208	April 26	255	Sept 17	302	Feb. 20
21	Aug. 10	68	Feb. 12	115	July 3	162	Dec. 23	209	June 30	256	Mar. 23	303	July 26
22	June 28	69	June 13	116	Aug. 23	163	Dec. 13	210	Feb. 4	257	Sept. 28	304	Dec. 17
23	July 24	70	Dec. 21	117	Oct. 22	164	Jan. 30	211	Jan. 31	258	Mar. 24	305	Jan. 1
24	Oct. 3	71	Sept. 10	118	Jan. 23	165	Dec. 4	212	Feb. 16	259	Mar. 13	306	Jan. 7
25	Feb. 19	72	Oct. 12	119	Sept. 23	166	Mar. 16	213	Mar. 8	260	April 17	307	Aug. 13
26	Dec. 14	73	June 17	120	July 14	167	Aug. 28	214	Feb. 5	261	Aug. 3	308	May 28
27	July 21	74	April 27	121	Jan. 14	168	Aug. 7	215	Jan. 4	262	April 28	309	Nov. 26
28	June 3	75	May 19	122	Mar. 7	169	Mar. 13	216	Feb. 10	263	Sept. 9	310	Nov. 5
29	Mar. 2	76	Nov. 6	123	Dec. 28	170	Mar. 26	217	Mar. 30	264	Oct. 27	311	Aug. 19
30	Mar. 21	77	Jan. 28	124	April 12	171	Oct. 15	218	April 10	265	Mar. 22	312	April 8
31	May 24	78	Dec. 27	125	Oct. 2	172	July 23	219	April 9	266	Nov. 4	313	May 11
32	April 1	79	Oct. 31	126	Nov. 13	173	Dec. 26	220	Oct. 10	267	Mar. 3	314	Dec. 12
33	Mar. 17	80	Nov. 9	127	Nov. 14	174	Nov. 30	221	Jan. 12	268	Mar. 27	315	Sept. 30
34	Nov. 2	81	April 4	128	Dec. 18	175	Sept. 13	222	Jan. 25	269	April 5	316	April 22
35	May 7	82	Sept. 5	129	Dec. 1	176	Oct. 25	223	Mar. 25	270	July 29	317	Mar. 9
36	Aug. 24	83	April 3	130	May 15	177	Sept. 19	224	Jan. 6	271	April 2	318	Jan. 13
37	May 31	84	Dec. 25	131	Nov. 15	178	May 14	225	Sept. 1	272	June 12	319	May 23
38	Oct. 30	85	June 7	132	Nov. 25	179	Feb. 25	226	May 29	273	April 15	320	Dec. 18
39	Dec. 11	86	Feb. 1	133	May 12	180	June 13	227	July 19	274	June 16	321	May 8
40	May 3	87	Oct. 6	134	June 11	181	Feb. 8	228	June 2	275	Mar. 4	322	July 15
41	Dec. 10	88	July 28	135	Dec. 20	182	Nov. 23	229	Oct. 29	276	May 4	323	Mar. 10
42	July 13	89	Feb. 18	136	Mar. 11	183	May 20	230	Nov. 24	277	July 9	324	Aug. 11
43	Dec. 9	90	April 18	137	June 25	184	Sept. 3	231	April 14	278	May 13		
44	Aug. 14	91	Feb. 7	138	Oct. 13	185	Nov. 15	232	Sept. 4	279	July 4		
45	Aug. 2	92	Jan. 26	139	Mar. 6	186	Jan. 21	233	Sept. 27	280	Jan. 20		
46	Nov. 11	93	July 1	140	Jan. 18	187	July 20	234	Oct. 7	281	Nov. 28		
47	Nov. 27	94	Oct. 28	141	Aug. 13	188	July 5	235	Jan. 17	282	Nov. 10		

325	Jan. 10	346	April 12
326	May 22	347	Feb. 6
327	July 6	348	Nov. 3
328	Dec. 2	349	Jan. 29
329	Jan. 11	350	July 2
330	May 1	351	April 25
331	July 14	352	Aug. 27
332	Mar. 18	353	June 29
333	Aug. 30	354	Mar. 14
334	Mar. 21	355	Jan. 27
335	June 9	356	June 14
336	April 19	357	May 26
337	Jan. 22	358	June 24
338	Feb. 9	359	Oct. 1
339	Aug. 22	360	June 20
340	April 24	361	May 25
341	June 18	362	Mar. 29
342	Oct. 9	363	Feb. 21
343	Mar. 25	364	May 5
344	Aug. 26	365	Feb. 26
345	April 20	366	June 3

Following is the order of the alphabet to be applied to the first letter of the last names in determining the order of call for inductees with the same birth dates:
J, G, D, X, N, O, Z, T, W, P, Q, Y, U, C, F, I, K, H, S, L, M, A, R, E, B, V

Theoretically, if the capsules were adequately mixed, then the resulting draft order should have been random with respect to each month. For example, a birth date in December should have the same chance of being selected early in the draft as a birth date for any other month, such as January. Examine the list of birth dates within the previous article which represents the order of the 1969 draft drawing.

a) For the first 122 birth dates selected in the 1969 draft lottery, determine the frequency for each birth month.

b) If the selection process represented a random selection, then determine the expected frequency per month for the first 122 selections.

c) Based on the results of the first two parts, do you believe this draft lottery represented a random selection? Explain. What do you think might have contributed to this result?

109. Each of the following statements represent an excerpt from different studies which indicate how the sample for the study was selected. For each sampling procedure, indicate whether you think the procedure to select the sample results is biased or unbiased. Explain the reason for your answer, in some cases you may wish to answer "not enough information given." In such cases, explain why.

a) "A market research survey was mailed to a random sample of 250 owners of new automobiles. A total of 85 completed surveys was received yielding a return rate of 34%."

b) "Forty-six rats, all coming from one of several litters, were separated from their mother when they were three weeks old. One half (Group A) were put into individual cages; the other half (Group B) were left together to see what effect a rat's early environment has on its behavior later in life."

c) "A total of 356 persons were interviewed, 160 men and 196 women, to test whether men have nightmares as often as women."

d) "The subjects in this sample were 90 children, ranging in age from 6 to 12, who were selected from a list of students attending an elementary school. Three children were selected at random from each of the classes within the school."

e) "A telephone survey was conducted to determine current attitudes toward birth control education in the public high schools. The respondents were 1,345 men and women of voting age; all were white"

f) "A total of 199 persons, all complaining of frequent headaches, agreed to participate in a study to compare the effectiveness of four different headache remedies. The participants were divided into four groups (I, II, III, and IV)."

110. The article entitled "Poll Involved Queries to 1,540" describes the procedure used to select adults for a New York Times/CBS News Public Opinion Poll.

Poll Involved Queries to 1,540

The latest New York Times/CBS News Poll is based on telephone interviews conducted from Jan. 11 through Jan. 15 with 1,540 adults around the United States.

The sample of telephone exchanges called was selected by a computer from a complete list of exchanges in the country. The exchanges were chosen in such a way as to insure that each region of the country was represented in proportion to its population. For each exchange, the telephone numbers were formed by random digits, thus permitting access to both listed and unlisted residential numbers.

The results have been weighted to take account of household size and to adjust for variations in the sample relating to region, race, sex, age and education.

In theory, it can be said that in 95 cases out of 100 the results based on the entire sample differ by no more than 3 percentage points in either direction from what would have been obtained by interviewing all adult Americans. The error for smaller subgroups is larger, depending on the number of sample cases in the subgroup.

The theoretical errors do not take into account a margin of additional error resulting from the various practical difficulties in taking any survey of public opinion.

Read the procedure that was used to conduct this public opinion poll.

a) Define the population for this poll.

b) What do you think are some problems with selecting a random sample of adults for a national poll using a telephone interview?

c) What does the statement "the exchanges were chosen in such a way as to insure that each region of the country was represented in proportion to its population" mean? What is the purpose of doing this?

d) What does the statement "the results have been weighted to take account of household size and to adjust for variations in the sample relating to region, race, sex, age and education"? Why do you believe is the purpose for doing this?

e) How would you translate the statement "95 cases out of 100 the results based on the entire sample differ by no more than 3 percentage points in either direction from what would be obtained by interviewing all adult Americans"?

PROJECTS

111. a) Take a set of 50 blank plastic chips and write the following numbers on the chips:

Number on Chips	Frequency
10	6
9	5
8	6
7	4
6	7
5	7
4	4
3	5
2	5
1	1

b) Construct a histogram for the above distribution using a class width of 1.

c) Calculate:
  1) the mean (μ) of the population.
  2) the standard deviation (σ) of the population.

d) Place the 50 chips in a box. Shake the box rigorously and randomly choose 20 samples of size 9 with replacement. (Be sure to shake the box each time before a new sample is chosen) For *each* sample chosen, calculate the sample mean, $\bar{x}$, and indicate the results in the table below.

Sample	$\bar{x}$
1	
2	
3	
.	
.	
.	
20	

e) Using the 20 sample means, construct a histogram and frequency polygon.

f) Calculate the mean of all the sample means, $\mu_{\bar{x}}$, and the standard deviation of the sample means, $\sigma_{\bar{x}}$. Place these values in the following table.

g) Calculate the expected mean of the sample means, and the expected standard deviation of the sample means using the formulas:

$$\mu_{\bar{x}} = \mu, \text{ and } \sigma_{\bar{x}} = \frac{\sigma}{\sqrt{n}}.$$

Place these values in the following table.

Computed Values	Expected Values
$\mu_{\bar{x}} =$	$\mu_{\bar{x}} = \mu$
$\sigma_{\bar{x}} =$	$\sigma_{\bar{x}} = \dfrac{\sigma}{\sqrt{n}}$

h) Compare the computed values to the expected values of $\mu_{\bar{x}}$ and $\sigma_{\bar{x}}$.

i) Repeat the above procedure for twenty random samples of size 25 with replacement. Compare and interpret the results of both experiments.

112. The formulas of $\mu_{\bar{x}}$ and $\sigma_{\bar{x}}$ are dependent upon the values of the population mean, μ, and population standard deviation, σ, and the size, n, of the sample selected. Given the population: 1, 2, 3, 4, 5.

a) Calculate μ and σ for this population.

b) Form a distribution by selecting *with replacement* all samples of size n = 2.

c) Calculate the mean of each sample found in part (b).

d) Form a sampling distribution of the mean from the sample means found in part (c).

e) Find the mean and standard deviation of the sample means found in part (c). (i.e. find $\mu_{\bar{x}}$ and $\sigma_{\bar{x}}$)

f) Form a distribution by selecting *without replacement* all samples of size n = 2.

g) Calculate the mean of each sample found in part (f).

h) Form a sampling distribution of the mean from the sample means found in part (g).

i) Find the mean and standard deviation of the sample means found in part (g).

j) Compute the theoretical values for $\mu_{\bar{x}}$ and $\sigma_{\bar{x}}$ using the formulas for the mean and standard deviation of the sampling distribution of the mean.

k) Compare the results of parts (e) and (j).

l) Compare the results of parts (i) and (j). Notice that the results of parts (i) and (j) will not be equal unless the finite correction factor is applied. Verify. Explain why the finite correction factor is necessary for parts (i) and (j).

ANALYZING THE DATABASE USING TECHNOLOGY.

The following exercises refer to the file DATABASE listed in Appendix A. Using a technological tool, answer each exercise.

113. For each of the following variables:
  a) AGE
  b) AVE
  c) STY
  d) CUM
  e) GFT
  i) compute the mean and standard deviation.
  ii) select a random sample of 20 student records.
  iii) compute the mean and standard deviation of each of these random samples.
  iv) compute the sampling error for mean.

114. For each of the following variables:
   a) AGE
   b) HS
   c) WK
   i) compute the mean and standard deviation.
   ii) construct a table of 10 random samples, where each sample contains 20 data values.
   iii) calculate the mean for each of the 10 random samples.

   iv) Form a distribution of the 10 sample means by recording the mean of each random sample within the table.
   Determine the mean and standard error for this distribution of sample means.
   v) Compare the results of part (iv) to the original mean and standard deviation computed in part (i). Explain any *differences* in the statistics in light of the theorems and properties discussed in this chapter.

CHAPTER TEST

115. To apply the Central Limit Theorem for means the shape of the original population must be known. (T/F)

116. The sampling distribution of the mean will be approximately normally distributed when the sample size is greater than:
   a) 25   **b)** 30   **c)** 50   **d)** 100

117. A random sample of size n = 8 is selected from a population. Under what conditions will the sampling distribution of the mean be a normal distribution?

118. According to the registrar at a local community college, the average mathematics S.A.T. for all the students is 475. A random sample of 100 students selected from this student body yields an average math S.A.T. score of 490. Determine the sampling error if this sample were used to estimate the population mean mathematics S.A.T. score.

119. For a normally distributed population, what sample size is required to insure that the sampling distribution of the mean is also normally distributed?
   a) n = 2   **b)** n = 10   **c)** n = 30   **d)** n = 31

120. Recently, it was reported that a baby born in 2000 is expected to live to a mean age of 74 years. If the standard deviation for this population is 10 years, use the Central Limit Theorem to answer questions about a sampling distribution of the mean formed by taking from the population of babies born in 2000, all possible random samples of size 100.
   a) Find $\mu_{\bar{x}}$
   b) Determine $\sigma_{\bar{x}}$
   c) Can this sampling distribution of the mean be approximated by a normal distribution?
   d) If a random sample of 100 babies born in 2000 were selected, what is the probability that these babies will live to at least a mean age 72? to at least a mean age 80?
   e) If the population of life expectancies for those born in 2000 is approximately normal, what is the probability that a baby born in 2000 will live to:
   at least age 72?
   at least age 80?
   f) Why are the answers to parts (d) and (e) different?

121. Consider the following population of data values:
$$29, 31, 33, 35, 37, 39, 41$$
   a) Find the mean, μ, and the standard deviation, σ.
   b) Construct the sampling distribution of the mean for random samples of size n = 2 from this population with replacement by listing all the possible sample means along with the probability associated with each sample mean.
   c) Calculate $\mu_{\bar{x}}$ and $\sigma_{\bar{x}}$ using the information in part (b). Compare these values to the population values computed in part(a). Discuss your observations.
   d) Compute all the possible sampling errors that could be made if any of these samples were used to estimate the population mean. In addition, determine the probability of making such an error.

122. Suppose a population is infinite with $\sigma = 90$. Calculate the standard error of the mean for random samples of size:
   a) 64
   b) 100
   c) 144
   d) 1000
   e) 10,000
   f) Explain what happens to the standard error of the mean as the sample size, n, increases?
   g) If you wanted to estimate the mean of the population, which of the previous sample sizes would you use to minimize the sampling error? Explain.

123. At a university sports complex, eleven football players squeeze into the elevator on the seventh floor. The weights of the university's football players is normally distributed with $\mu = 235$ lbs and $\sigma = 30$ lbs. If the elevator's weight capacity is 2500 lbs, calculate the probability that the elevator will not be able to carry this heavy load?

124. The mean tire life of a certain brand of radial tires is 40,000 miles with a standard deviation of 2000 miles. If the life of this brand of tires is normally distributed then:
   a) What is the probability a tire will last longer than 38,000 miles?
   b) What is the probability that the mean life of a random *sample* of 100 tires is greater than 40,400 miles?

c) What is the probability that the mean life of a random *sample* of 400 tires is less than 40,200 miles?

125. An automotive battery company claims its new battery DYHARD has a mean life of 60 months. Assume the population standard deviation is 9 months. A consumer group selects a random sample of 144 batteries and tests them.
   a) Assuming the manufacturer's claim is true, determine the mean, standard error, and the shape of the sampling distribution of the mean.
   b) How likely is it that the consumer group's sample will have a mean life less than 57 months if the claim is true?
   c) Based on the sample result in part (b), do you believe that the consumer group has enough statistical evidence to state that the manufacturer's claim is false? Explain.

126. If you are sampling from a normal population, would it be advantageous to take a large sample? Explain.

127. Air travel from JFK New York to Sarasota, Florida takes an average 150 minutes with $\sigma = 8$ minutes. Use the Central Limit Theorem to determine the characteristics and to answer questions about a sampling distribution of the mean formed by selecting from this population random samples of size 64.
   a) Find $\mu_{\bar{x}}$.
   b) Determine $\sigma_{\bar{x}}$.
   c) Can this sampling distribution of the mean be approximated by a normal distribution?
   d) What is the probability that a random sample of 64 flights from JFK to Sarasota will average (mean average) more than 10 minutes late?
   e) If the population of air travel time from JFK to Sarasota is normally distributed, what is the probability that a flight from JFK to Sarasota is more than 10 minutes late?
   f) Why are the answers to parts (d) and (e) different?

128. Suppose you are sampling from a population with a population variance $\sigma^2 = 1600$. If you would want the standard error of the mean to be at most 8, what is the minimum sample size you should use?

129. For the following population shapes where the population standard deviation is known,
   (I)   a normal population
   (II)   a bell-shaped population: close to a normal
   (III) a slightly skewed population
   (IV)   a highly skewed population

determine which type of population shape would require:
   a) The smallest sample size
   b) The largest sample size
to use the normal distribution as an approximation of the sampling distribution of the mean?

130. A CNN survey reported that 803 of women drivers and 874 of men drivers pump their own gas. If this survey was based upon a random sample of 1005 male drivers and a random sample of 1100 female drivers, then determine the sample proportion of (and state result using the appropriate notation):
   a) Male drivers who pump their own gas.
   b) Male drivers who do not pump their own gas.
   c) Women drivers who pump their own gas.
   d) Women drivers who do not pump their own gas.

131. Suppose a population is infinite with $p = 0.54$. Calculate the standard error of the proportion for random samples of size:
   a) 100
   b) 200
   c) 400
   d) 800
   e) 1200
   f) Explain what happens to the standard error of the proportion as the sample size, n, increases?
   g) Assuming you didn't know the population proportion and you wanted to estimate p, which of the previous sample sizes would you use to minimize the sampling error? Explain.

132. According to a Fox News/Opinion Dynamics Poll, 44% of adults believe there is intelligent life on other planets. Let's assume that this percentage is true for the population of all U.S. adults. If a random sample of 200 adults is selected from this population, then determine the probability that the sample proportion, $\hat{p}$, of adults who believe there is intelligent life on other planets is:
   a) Between 46% and 51%.
   b) At least 50%.
   Determine the probability that:
   c) At most 95 adults sampled will indicate they believe in aliens.
   d) More than 105 adults sampled will indicate they believe in aliens.
   Determine the sampling error if we had selected a sample:
   e) With proportion $\hat{p} = 49\%$ of adults who believe there is intelligent life on other planets.

Estimation

Contents

8.1 INTRODUCTION

"What time is it?"

The response to this question is an **estimate** of the actual time. Estimates like this are made everyday. In fact, occasions arise in business, in social science, in medicine and in science when it becomes necessary to estimate a population parameter such as the population mean, the population proportion or the population standard deviation. For instance:

- A sociologist is interested in the mean age of women when delivering their first child.
- The census bureau is trying to determine the proportion of American workers who use computers at work.
- A quality control engineer wants to monitor the variability of the sugar content of soft drinks.
- An environmentalist needs to know the mean amount of toxins in the city's water supply.
- A student is interested in the proportion of students who pass a statistics course with a particular instructor.
- A commuter wishes to know the variability of the amount of time necessary to travel to work using mass transit.
- A company president wants to determine the proportion of people that would purchase a new line of shavers.

In each of these examples, the researcher is trying to determine the *true* or *actual population parameter*. In practical applications, the true population parameter is unattainable since populations are large and it would be either impractical or impossible to obtain the entire population data to calculate the true population parameter. In such instances, it becomes necessary to select a random sample from the population and use the sample data to estimate the population parameter. The process of using sample data to make an inference about a population parameter is called statistical inference. In this chapter, we will discuss one major area of statistical inference called **estimation**.

8.2   POINT ESTIMATE OF THE POPULATION MEAN AND THE POPULATION PROPORTION

In this section, we will introduce procedures that enable us to estimate the population mean or the population proportion using information from a sample. A procedure that assigns a numerical value to a population parameter based upon sample information is called estimation.

> **DEFINITION 8.1**
> **Estimation** is the statistical procedure which uses sample information to estimate the value of a population parameter such as the population mean, population standard deviation or population proportion.

Suppose a sociologist is interested in determining the population mean age of southern California women when delivering their first child. How would the sociologist obtain an *estimate* of the mean age of this population?

The sociologist could *randomly* select a sample of the birth records of first time mothers from the southern California area. Using this sample of records, the sample mean age of the first time mothers can be calculated. This *sample mean* is used to *estimate* the population mean age of first time mothers. Such an estimate is called a **point estimate of the population mean**.

> **DEFINITION 8.2**
> **Point Estimate** is a sample estimate of a population parameter, such as, a population mean or population proportion. The point estimate is expressed by a single number.

CASE STUDY 8.1   Average Shower Time

Examine the snapshot entitled "Long, hot shower?" shown in Figure 8.1. Notice that there are estimates for the average U.S. shower time for all adults, men, women, 18–24 age group and 45–54 age group. These averages represent *point estimates* of the *true* population shower times for these different population groups.

From this snapshot, it is estimated that men spend an average of 11.4 minutes taking a shower while women spend an average of 13 minutes in the shower.

On the other hand, adults aged 18–24 spend an average of 16.4 minutes taking a shower while adults aged 45–54 spend an average of 10.4 minutes in the shower.

Overall, an adult spends an average of 12.2 minutes taking a shower. This average represents **a point estimate** of the mean shower time of **all U. S. adults**.

CASE STUDY 8.1   Average Shower Time (continued)

FIGURE 8.1

CASE STUDY 8.2   Do You Believe in Aliens?

Examine the pie chart graphics shown in the snapshot of Figure 8.2. The graphic provides an estimate of the proportion of U.S. men and women who believe in aliens.

FIGURE 8.2

According to the information contained within the snapshot in Figure 8.2, the *point estimate* of the **proportion** of **all U.S. men** who believe in intelligent life on other planets is 54% while the *point estimate* of the **proportion** of **all U.S. women** who believe in intelligent life on other planets is 33%.

In Case Studies 8.1 and 8.2, a point estimate was used to estimate a population parameter. In Case Study 8.1, the population mean was estimated by a sample mean, while in Case Study 8.2, the population proportion was estimated by a sample proportion. **A sample mean, $\bar{x}$, is one method used to obtain a point estimate of the population mean, μ; while the sample proportion, $\hat{p}$, is used to obtain a point estimate of the population proportion, p. The sample mean and the sample proportion formulas are called estimators.** Any sample statistic formula that is used to estimate a population parameter is called an estimator.

> **DEFINITION 8.3**
> An **Estimator** is a method or formula used in estimating a population parameter.

It is important to distinguish between an *estimate* and an *estimator*. If a sample mean is used to **estimate** the population mean, then the **numerical value obtained** from the sample mean formula is the **estimate** while the **estimator** is the **sample mean *formula*** which was used to compute this point estimate.

EXAMPLE 8.1

The Student Government Association (SGA) at Nassau Community College is interested in estimating the mean number of hours that all full-time students work during a school week. If the SGA randomly samples 200 students and calculates the sample mean number of hours students work to be 22.4 hours, then determine the:
a) Population
b) Population parameter being estimated
c) Estimator used to estimate the population parameter
d) Point estimate for the population parameter.

Solution

a) The population is all full-time students attending Nassau Community College.
b) The population parameter to be estimated is the **population mean** number of hours that a full-time student works during a school week.
c) The estimator is the *sample mean formula* used to calculate the **mean number of hours** a full-time student works during a school week for the **sample of 200 students**.
d) The point estimate for the population mean number of hours is 22.4 hours.

A question that needs to be addressed at this point is:

How do we know that the sample mean, $\bar{x}$, is a good estimator for the population mean, μ?

The criteria for a **good estimator** are:

- Unbiasedness
- Efficiency
- Consistency
- Sufficiency

We will **only** consider the criteria of *unbiasedness*. An estimator of a population parameter is said to be **unbiased** if the mean of the point estimates obtained from the independent samples selected from the population will *approach* the true value of the population parameter as more and more samples are selected.

Based on our discussion in Chapter 7, the sample mean is an unbiased estimator of the population mean because the mean of all the sample means is equal to the mean of the population. It can also be shown that the sample proportion, $\hat{p}$, possesses the four criteria discussed above to be a good estimator of the population proportion, p.

8.3 INTERVAL ESTIMATION

In the previous section, we considered the concept of a point estimate. In practice, we will only select **one** sample to compute a point estimate. However, we must realize that the sample we select is **only one** of the many possible samples that could have been selected from the population.

For example, if you were interested in estimating the mean GPA of the population of 26,000 community college students attending Nassau Community College, you would *randomly* select a sample of students and calculate the mean GPA of the sample. Suppose you determine that the mean GPA for the selected sample is 2.63. Although this **point estimate** of 2.63 would represent our best guess for the true population mean GPA, you should realize that this estimate of 2.63 is *probably* **not going to be exactly equal to the true population mean**! In fact, if you selected a second random sample of students and calculated the mean GPA of this second sample, you probably would have arrived at a result that is *different* from the first sample mean GPA of 2.63.

Since samples do vary, one major disadvantage of using one sample mean as a point estimate of the population mean is that we don't know how close or far the point estimate is from the *true* population mean. Thus, when using a point estimate to estimate a population parameter, we are not sure of the extent of the *error* involved in the estimate.

An estimate of a population parameter would be more useful if we could provide a measure of the error associated with the estimate of a population parameter. In fact many opinion polls contain a measure of the extent of error associated with estimating a population parameter. Case Study 8.3 illustrates the idea of a "sampling error" associated with a point estimate of a population proportion. This error is referred to as the **margin of error**.

CASE STUDY 8.3 Do Politicians Take Advantage of Us?

The Opinion Poll conducted by an Independent Poll in Figure 8.3 indicates that 67% is a point estimate for the proportion of the people who say that they feel that politicians in power take advantage of the general population.

Statistical Snapshot

Public Opinion of Politicians

Percentage of people who say they feel those in power try to take advantage of the general population:

67%*

*Opinion poll result from a sample size of 983. The margin of error is plus or minus three percentage points

FIGURE 8.3

CASE STUDY 8.3   Do Politicians Take Advantage of Us? (continued)

Notice the statement attached to the point estimate of 67% includes a warning that the sample result of 67% in estimating the true population proportion has a **margin of error** *of plus or minus of 3 percentage points*. This "margin of error" is due to "sampling error" because not everyone in the population has been polled! The sampling error means that if a second random sample were selected from this population and a point estimate of the population proportion is determined, we would **expect** this sample proportion to be different from 67%.

Since the proportion of a sample can vary from sample to sample, then the point estimates determined from different samples can yield **different estimates for the population proportion**. Thus, the margin of error of ±3 percentage points reflects the sampling error in estimating the true population proportion. So, we interpret the opinion poll as stating that the true population proportion lies within the interval of: 67% ± 3%. The interval is estimating that the true population proportion will lie between:

$$(67\% - 3\%) \text{ to } (67\% + 3\%)$$

or,

$$64\% \text{ to } 70\%$$

This **range of percentage values from 64% to 70% is referred to as an interval estimate of the true population proportion**. Thus, an interval estimate uses a point estimate in constructing a range of values within which one can be reasonably sure that the true population parameter will lie. In particular, the interval estimate consists of two components:

1) **67%:** the value of the sample proportion which represents a point estimate of the population proportion.
2) **3 percentage points:** the margin of error which represents the range allowed for the anticipated sampling error.

From Case Study 8.3, we can see that an **interval estimate** is a technique that uses a point estimate along with an associated sampling error to construct an interval to estimate a population parameter.

DEFINITION 8.4

Interval Estimate is an estimate that specifies a *range of values* within which the population parameter is likely to fall.

Let's go back to the previous example of trying to estimate the population mean GPA of Nassau Community College students using the point estimate of 2.63. If we instead stated our estimate as: the mean GPA may lie between the values: 2.43 and 2.83, then the range of values from 2.43 to 2.83 would represent an interval estimate of Nassau's mean GPA.

In comparison to a point estimate which uses a single value to estimate the population parameter and is very unlikely to be exactly equal to the population parameter, an interval estimate uses a range of values to estimate the population parameter. A probability level can be assigned to the interval estimate which will indicate how confident we are that the interval will include the value of the population parameter. The probability level that is associated with an interval estimate is referred to as the confidence level. This type of interval estimate is called a confidence interval. In Section 8.4, we will examine how to construct a confidence interval for estimating the mean of a population.

8.4 INTERVAL ESTIMATION: CONFIDENCE INTERVALS FOR THE POPULATION MEAN

Let's illustrate the procedure to construct an interval estimate of a population mean by considering an example. Suppose we want to determine an interval estimate for the mean GPA of Nassau Community College students.

The first step of the procedure in constructing an interval estimate of a population mean is to select a random sample and calculate the sample mean, $\bar{x}$. Suppose a random sample of 36 students was selected from the population of Nassau students and the sample mean is determined to be: $\bar{x} = 2.63$. Remember, though, this sample mean is only one of many possible sample means that could have been determined. That is, this is one of the possible sample means within the sampling distribution of the mean. Since the sample size, n, is greater than 30 (for this example, n = 36), then according to Theorem 7.2: The Central Limit Theorem, the sampling distribution of the mean is approximately normal with:

$$\mu_{\bar{x}} = \mu$$

$$\sigma_{\bar{x}} = \frac{\sigma}{\sqrt{n}} \, ,$$

The Sampling Distribution of the Mean is illustrated in Figure 8.4.

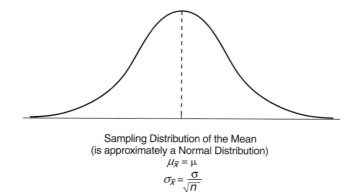

Sampling Distribution of the Mean
(is approximately a Normal Distribution)
$\mu_{\bar{x}} = \mu$
$\sigma_{\bar{x}} = \dfrac{\sigma}{\sqrt{n}}$

FIGURE 8.4

Within this normal distribution of sample means, we would expect 95% of the sample means, $\bar{x}$, to lie within 1.96 standard deviations[1] of the Population Mean. Therefore, we expect 95% of the sample means to lie between the values:

population $-$ (1.96)(standard deviation) and population mean $+$ (1.96)(standard deviation)

This can be expressed as:

$$\mu - (1.96)\sigma_{\bar{x}} \quad \text{and} \quad \mu + (1.96)\sigma_{\bar{x}}$$

Using

$$\sigma_{\bar{x}} = \frac{\sigma}{\sqrt{n}} \, ,$$

we can then rewrite the values between which we would expect 95% of the sample means to fall. These values are expressed as:

[1] Please note: The standard deviation used in this statement refers to the standard deviation of the sampling distribution of the mean, $\sigma_{\bar{x}}$.

$$\mu - (1.96)\frac{\sigma}{\sqrt{n}} \text{ and } \mu + (1.96)\frac{\sigma}{\sqrt{n}}$$

These two values are illustrated in Figure 8.5.

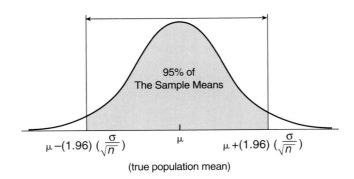

95% of
The Sample Means

$\mu - (1.96)\left(\frac{\sigma}{\sqrt{n}}\right)$ μ $\mu + (1.96)\left(\frac{\sigma}{\sqrt{n}}\right)$

(true population mean)

FIGURE 8.5

If the sample mean, $\bar{x}$, that we select from the population, happens to be one of the sample means that falls within the 95% region illustrated in Figure 8.5, and we construct an interval around the sample mean by:

subtracting 1.96 standard deviations from the sample mean, $\bar{x}$,

expressed as:

$$\bar{x} - (1.96)\frac{\sigma}{\sqrt{n}}$$

and

adding 1.96 standard deviations to the sample mean, $\bar{x}$,

expressed as:

$$\bar{x} + (1.96)\frac{\sigma}{\sqrt{n}}$$

then the interval, written as:

$$\bar{x} - (1.96)\frac{\sigma}{\sqrt{n}} \text{ to } \bar{x} + (1.96)\frac{\sigma}{\sqrt{n}}$$

will contain the *true* population mean, μ. This is illustrated in Figure 8.6.

However, if the sample mean, $\bar{x}$, that we select is a sample mean that comes from one of the regions outside the 95% region illustrated in Figure 8.6, then the interval constructed using the formula:

$$\bar{x} - (1.96)\frac{\sigma}{\sqrt{n}} \text{ to } \bar{x} + (1.96)\frac{\sigma}{\sqrt{n}}$$

will not contain the true population mean. This is illustrated in Figure 8.7.

FIGURE 8.6

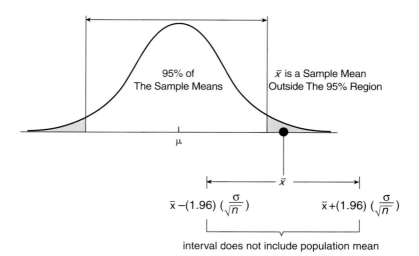

FIGURE 8.7

Therefore, if all possible samples of size n (for n greater than 30) are selected, and an interval is constructed using the formula:

$$\bar{x} - (1.96)\frac{\sigma}{\sqrt{n}} \text{ to } \bar{x} + (1.96)\frac{\sigma}{\sqrt{n}}$$

for each possible sample mean, then 95% of such intervals are expected to contain the true population mean, μ. This interval is referred to as a **95% Confidence Interval for the Population Mean**, and is defined as follows.

DEFINITION

95% Confidence Interval for the Population Mean, μ, where the Population Standard Deviation is Known.

A 95% Confidence Interval for the population mean, **μ**, (with known population standard deviation) is an interval expected to capture the true population mean, **μ**, 95% of the time and is constructed by the formula:

$$\bar{x} - (1.96)\frac{\sigma}{\sqrt{n}} \text{ to } \bar{x} + (1.96)\frac{\sigma}{\sqrt{n}}$$

where:

$\bar{x}$ is the sample mean,

σ is the population standard deviation,

n   is the sample size greater than 30

Thus, constructing a 95% Confidence Interval to estimate the population mean GPA of Nassau students, for which the sample mean, $\bar{x} = 2.63$ for n = 36 students, is obtained using the formula:

$$\bar{x} - (1.96)\frac{\sigma}{\sqrt{n}} \text{ to } \bar{x} + (1.96)\frac{\sigma}{\sqrt{n}}$$

If we assume that the population standard deviation, σ, is 0.6, then a 95% confidence interval is:

$$\bar{x} - (1.96)\frac{\sigma}{\sqrt{n}} \text{ to } \bar{x} + (1.96)\frac{\sigma}{\sqrt{n}}$$

$$(2.63) - (1.96)\frac{0.6}{\sqrt{36}} \text{ to } (2.63) + (1.96)\frac{0.6}{\sqrt{36}}$$

$$(2.63) - (1.96)\frac{0.6}{6} \text{ to } (2.63) + (1.96)\frac{0.6}{6}$$

$$(2.63) - (1.96)(0.1) \text{ to } (2.63) + (1.96)(0.1)$$

$$2.43 \text{ to } 2.83$$

Therefore, a 95% Confidence Interval is: 2.43 to 2.83. That is, we estimate the mean GPA of all Nassau Community College students to fall within the interval: 2.43 to 2.83.

The interval 2.43 to 2.83 is called the confidence interval, and the endpoints of the interval are called the confidence limits. The smaller endpoint of the confidence interval is called the lower confidence limit, while the larger endpoint of the confidence interval is referred to as the upper confidence limit.

DEFINITION

The endpoints of a confidence interval are called the **confidence limits** of the interval. The smaller endpoint of the interval is referred to as the **lower confidence limit**. The larger endpoint of the interval is referred to as the **upper confidence limit.**

For this interval, the lower confidence limit is 2.43, while 2.83 represents the upper confidence limit. The probability value expressed as a percentage which is associated with the confidence interval is called the confidence level or degree of confidence.

DEFINITION
The **Confidence Level** of a confidence interval is the probability value, expressed as a percentage, that is associated with an interval estimate. The probability value represents the chance that the procedure used to construct the confidence interval will give an interval that will include the population parameter. Thus, the higher the probability value, the greater the confidence that the interval estimate will include the population parameter.

The confidence level for the interval: 2.43 to 2.83 is 95%. This confidence level of 95% indicates that: in the long run, the percentage of all intervals constructed using this procedure will probably contain the population mean 95% of the time. In fact, if we were to repeat this process of constructing such an interval for all possible samples, we would be confident that 95% of all possible intervals constructed would include the population mean.

Because of this, the interval 2.43 to 2.83 is referred to as a 95% Confidence Interval. This statement doesn't indicate whether one particular interval, like the interval, 2.43 to 2.83, will actually contain the true population parameter. It indicates that we are 95% confident that the true population mean is contained in the interval 2.43 to 2.83.

Furthermore, it is interpreted to mean: that if a 95% confidence interval for the population mean was constructed for each possible sample of size n selected from the population, we would expect that 95% of these confidence intervals to include the population mean and 5% of these confidence intervals not to include the population mean.

In Figure 8.8, a 95% confidence interval is shown for four different possible samples. Notice from Figure 8.8 that if a sample mean falls within the 95% shaded area (like $\bar{x}_1$ and $\bar{x}_3$) then the confidence interval will contain the population mean. While if the sample mean falls outside this 95% region(like $\bar{x}_2$ and $\bar{x}_4$), then the confidence interval will not contain the population mean. Again, keep in mind that a 95% confidence interval doesn't tell you whether a particular interval will contain the population mean. But rather it means that: in the long run, the percentage of all intervals constructed using this procedure will probably contain the population mean 95% of the time.

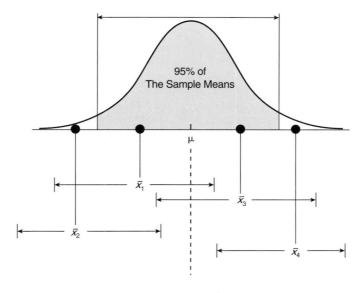

FIGURE 8.8

Although, any confidence level can be chosen to construct a confidence interval, the most common confidence levels are: 90%, 95% and 99%. The formulas to construct a 90% and 99% Confidence Intervals are similar to a 95% Confidence Interval formula except for the value of the z score which is used in the formula. In a 90% Confidence Interval, the z score: 1.65 is used to construct the interval estimate, while in a 99% Confidence Interval, the appropriate z score is: 2.58 in constructing this interval estimate. Thus, formulas for a 90% and 99% Confidence Intervals are defined as follows.

DEFINITION
90% Confidence Interval for the Population Mean, μ, where the Population Standard Deviation is Known. A 90% Confidence Interval for the population mean, **μ**, (with known population standard deviation) is an interval that is expected to capture the population mean, **μ**, 90% of the time and is constructed by the formula:

$$\bar{x} - (1.65)\frac{\sigma}{\sqrt{n}} \text{ to } \bar{x} + (1.65)\frac{\sigma}{\sqrt{n}}$$

where:

$\bar{x}$ is the sample mean
σ is the population standard deviation
n   is the sample size greater than 30.

Similarly, we can define a **99% Confidence Interval for the Population Mean to be**:

DEFINITION
99% Confidence Interval for the Population Mean, μ, where the Population Standard Deviation is Known. A 99% Confidence Interval for the population mean, **μ**, (with known population standard deviation) is an interval that is expected to capture the population mean, **μ**, 99% of the time and is constructed by the formula:

$$\bar{x} - (2.58)\frac{\sigma}{\sqrt{n}} \text{ to } \bar{x} + (2.58)\frac{\sigma}{\sqrt{n}}$$

where:

$\bar{x}$ is the sample mean
σ is the population standard deviation
n   is the sample size greater than 30

Notice that in the formula for a 90% confidence interval, the values, −1.65 and 1.65, represent the appropriate z-scores associated with a 90% Confidence Interval, while the z-scores, −2.58 and +2.58, are used to construct a 99% Confidence Interval. The z-scores, −1.65 and +1.65, are used for a 90% confidence interval, since the sampling distribution of the mean, which is approximately a normal distribution for a sample size greater than 30 and a known population standard deviation, has approximately 90% of the sample means within 1.65 standard deviations of the true population mean. Similarly, 99% of the sample means are expected to lie within 2.58 standard deviations of the population mean. This is illustrated in Figure 8.9.

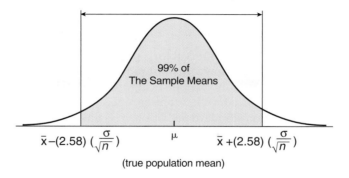

FIGURE 8.9

Let's calculate a 99% confidence interval for the population mean GPA for Nassau students, using $\bar{x} = 2.63$, n= 36 and $\sigma = 0.6$. From the definition of a 99% confidence interval, we have:

$$\bar{x} - (2.58)\frac{\sigma}{\sqrt{n}} \text{ to } \bar{x} + (2.58)\frac{\sigma}{\sqrt{n}}$$

Substituting the sample mean, $\bar{x} = 2.63$, sample size, n = 36 and the standard deviation, $\sigma = 0.6$, we have:

$$(2.63) - (2.58)\frac{0.6}{\sqrt{36}} \text{ to } (2.63) + (2.58)\frac{0.6}{\sqrt{36}}$$

$$(2.63) - (2.58)\frac{0.6}{6} \text{ to } (2.63) + (2.58)\frac{0.6}{6}$$

$$(2.63) - (2.58)(0.1) \text{ to } (2.63) + (2.58)(0.1)$$

$$2.37 \text{ to } 2.89$$

Thus, a 99% confidence interval is 2.37 to 2.89.

That is, we are 99% confident that the mean GPA of all Nassau Community College students falls within the interval:

$$2.37 \text{ to } 2.89$$

In summary: we have computed both a 95% confidence interval and a 99% confidence interval for the population mean GPA of the Nassau Community College students to be:

95% Confidence Interval:	Width of Interval is:
2.43 to 2.83	$2.83 - 2.43 = 0.40$
99% Confidence Interval:	Width of Interval is:
2.37 to 2.89	$2.89 - 2.37 = 0.52$

You should notice that as the confidence level increases from 95% to 99%, the width of the confidence interval also increases.

In general, as the confidence level increases, the width of the confidence interval also increases.

Constructing a Confidence Interval for a Population Mean: When the Population Standard Deviation is Unknown

In constructing a Confidence Interval for a population mean, it was assumed that the standard deviation of the population was known. In most practical applications, the population standard deviation is rarely known. Therefore, a more realistic approach in constructing an interval estimate of the true population mean is to consider the situation where the **population standard deviation is unknown**.

When the population standard deviation, σ, is unknown, the sample standard deviation, s, is used to estimate the population standard deviation. When we estimate σ, we cannot be confident that our estimated confidence interval will contain the population mean, μ. Sometimes, the confidence interval will not contain μ not because the sample mean is off, but because the estimate of the **width** of the confidence interval is off. This uncertainty with the width of the confidence interval is due to the fact that the z score can no longer be used to construct a confidence interval for a population mean when the population standard deviation is unknown.

In the early 1900's, W. S. Gosset faced a similar problem when he worked for Guinness Breweries as a chemist. He had to make conclusions about the mean quality of various brews where the population standard deviation was unknown. Gosset's work led him to the discovery that when s, the sample standard deviation, was used to approximate the population standard deviation, σ, and was substituted for σ into the formula for the *z statistic*

$$z = \frac{\bar{x} - \mu_{\bar{x}}}{\sigma / \sqrt{n}}$$

the new statistic

$$\frac{\bar{x} - \mu_{\bar{x}}}{s / \sqrt{n}}$$

generated by Gosset was **not** normally distributed. However, Gosset showed that this new statistic which he called a *t statistic* possessed a distribution that was similar to a normal distribution but was more varied. In fact, the smaller the sample size, n, the greater the spread in the distribution for *t*. Gosset published his work on the *t distribution* in 1908. Since the policy of the Guinness Brewing Company required that he not publish his discoveries under his own name, he used the pen name "Student." His unique choice of this pen name has resulted in the *t score* statistic

$$t = \frac{\bar{x} - \mu_{\bar{x}}}{s / \sqrt{n}}$$

also being called a *Student's t score*, and the *t distribution* also called *"Student's t" distribution* in his honor.

Thus, the *t* **Distribution** rather than the normal distribution is used to construct confidence intervals for the population mean under the following conditions.

Conditions to Use The t Distribution When Constructing a Confidence Interval for the Mean of a Population

The *t* **Distribution** is used to construct a confidence interval for the population mean when the following conditions hold:
- The population standard deviation, σ, is unknown, and is estimated by the sample standard deviation, s.
- The population from which the sample is selected is approximately a normal distribution (or bell-shaped).

The *t* Distribution

Before we discuss the procedure to construct a confidence interval for the population mean using the *t* distribution, we need to discuss the properties of a *t* distribution.

You should notice that a *t* statistic is very similar to the z statistic. A z score

$$z = \frac{\bar{x} - \mu_{\bar{x}}}{\sigma / \sqrt{n}}$$

measures the difference between the sample mean, $\bar{x}$, and its mean $\mu_{\bar{x}}$ in units of the standard error

$$\frac{\sigma}{\sqrt{n}},$$

while the *t* score

$$t = \frac{\bar{x} - \mu_{\bar{x}}}{s / \sqrt{n}}$$

measures the difference between the sample mean, $\bar{x}$, and its mean $\mu_{\bar{x}}$ in units of the **estimated standard error**

$$\frac{s}{\sqrt{n}}.$$

The properties of a *t* distribution are similar to the normal distribution in some respects. Both distributions are symmetric bell-shaped curves about the mean and never touch the horizontal axis. The total area under the *t* curve is 1.0 or 100% as is the case with the normal curve. For small samples, the *t* distribution is more dispersed than the standard normal distribution. That is, it has more area in the tails and less in the center than the normal distribution. Thus, in appearance, a *t* distribution is lower and flatter than the normal distribution. This is due to the extra variability caused by substituting the varying sample standard deviations s for the fixed value parameter σ. However as the sample size increases, the *t* distribution approaches the standard normal distribution. This reflects the fact that as the sample size increases, the value of s approaches the value of σ. The *t* distribution is composed of a family of *t* curves, where there is a different *t* curve for each sample size. Thus, the area under a particular *t* curve is dependent upon the concept of **degrees of freedom (df)**. The degrees of freedom for this t statistic is equal to the sample size minus one, that is,

$$df = n - 1.$$

The number of degrees of freedom can be thought of as the number of observations within the sample that can be chosen freely. For example, suppose that a sample of n = 5 observations has a mean of 120. This sample would have (5 − 1) or 4 degrees of freedom since the 5 deviations must always have a sum of 0. That is,

$$(x_1 - 120) + (x_2 - 120) + (x_3 - 120) + (x_4 - 120) + (x_5 - 120) = 0.$$

Therefore, if we know any 4 of these 5 deviations then the remaining deviation **cannot** be free to vary. So we subtract 1 from 5 because we lose one degree of freedom since we think of 4 of these deviations as being **free to change**. Hence, the number of degrees of freedom for this sample is:

degrees of freedom: df = n − 1 = 5 − 1 = 4.

DEFINITION

Degrees of Freedom of a statistic are the number of free choices used in computing the statistic. The degrees of freedom, denoted by *df*, for each sample of size n, is one less than the sample size. Thus, for a sample of size n, the degrees of freedom are given by formula:

$$df = n - 1$$

FIGURE 8.10

Figure 8.10 shows the relationship between the normal distribution and two particular *t* distributions of sample sizes n = 5 and n = 12, or degrees of freedom *df* = 4 and *df* = 11, respectively.

Notice, from Figure 8.10, the *t* distributions are **flatter and more dispersed** than the normal distribution, and, as the degrees of freedom *increase* the *t* distribution is getting closer to the normal distribution. For most practical purposes, whenever the degrees of freedom are greater than 30, the *t* and normal distributions are considered to be sufficiently close.

Let's summarize the properties of the *t* distribution.

Properties of the *t* Distribution

- The *t* distribution is bell-shaped and is symmetric about t = 0.
- The *t* distribution is more varied and flatter than the standard normal distribution.
- There is a different *t* distribution for each sample size. A particular *t* distribution is specified by giving the degrees of freedom, $df = n - 1$.
- As the number of degrees of freedom increases, the *t* distribution approaches the standard normal distribution. They are sufficiently close when the degrees of freedom are greater than 30.

When the *t* **Distribution** is used to construct a confidence interval for the population mean, then the formulas for a 90%, 95% and a 99% confidence interval will include :

- the sample standard deviation, s, rather than the population standard deviation, σ, and
- *t* scores rather than z scores.

Since the *t* distribution is composed of a family of *t* curves that are dependent upon degrees of freedom, the table representing the area associated with the *t* distribution is given with degrees of freedom. Hence, to determine the specific *t* score to use for a confidence interval formula, the degrees of freedom, *df*, associated with the *t* score must be determined using the formula: *df = n – 1*. Knowing the degrees of freedom, *df*, and the confidence level, then the appropriate *t* score for a confidence interval is found using Table III: Critical values for the *t* Distribution found in Appendix D.

Substituting s for σ, and replacing the z score by the appropriate *t* score, we can now define a **90%, 95% or a 99% Confidence Interval for the Population Mean,** *where the population standard deviation is unknown.*

DEFINITION

90% Confidence Interval for the Population Mean, μ, where Population Standard Deviation is Unknown A 90% Confidence Interval for the population mean, **μ**, when the population standard deviation is *unknown*, is constructed by the formula:

$$\bar{x} - (t_{95\%})\frac{s}{\sqrt{n}} \text{ to } \bar{x} + (t_{95\%})\frac{s}{\sqrt{n}}$$

where:

$\bar{x}$	is the sample mean
n	is the sample size
$t_{95\%}$	is the positive critical *t* score with $df = n - 1$ that corresponds to a **one-tailed test at $\alpha = 5\%$**
s	is the sample standard deviation.

DEFINITION

95% Confidence Interval for the Population Mean, μ, where Population Standard Deviation is Unknown A 95% Confidence Interval for the population mean, **μ**, when the population standard deviation is *unknown*, is constructed by the formula:

$$\bar{x} - (t_{97.5\%})\frac{s}{\sqrt{n}} \text{ to } \bar{x} + (t_{97.5\%})\frac{s}{\sqrt{n}}$$

where:

$\bar{x}$	is the sample mean
n	is the sample size
$t_{97.5\%}$	is the **positive** critical *t* score with $df = n - 1$ that corresponds to a **two-tailed test at $\alpha = 5\%$**
s	is the sample standard deviation.

DEFINITION

99% Confidence Interval for the Population Mean, μ, where Population Standard Deviation is Unknown A 99% Confidence Interval for the population mean, **μ**, when the population standard deviation is *unknown*, is constructed by the formula:

$$\bar{x} - (t_{99.5\%})\frac{s}{\sqrt{n}} \text{ to } \bar{x} + (t_{99.5\%})\frac{s}{\sqrt{n}}$$

where:

$\bar{x}$	is the sample mean
n	is the sample size
$t_{99.5\%}$	is the **positive** critical *t* score with $df = n - 1$ that corresponds to a **two-tailed test at $\alpha = 1\%$**
s	is the sample standard deviation.

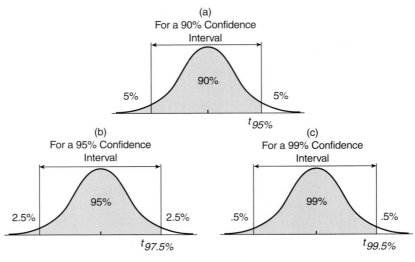

FIGURE 8.11

Notice that the *t* score for a 90% confidence interval is found in Table III under the column listed $t_{95\%}$, while the appropriate *t* score for a 95% confidence interval is found under the column heading $t_{97.5\%}$, and the *t* score for a 99% confidence interval is found under the column for $t_{99.5\%}$. The subscript for each of these t scores refers to the area under the t distribution that is to the LEFT of each positive *t* score. This is illustrated in Figure 8.11.

In Figure 8.11a, for a 90% confidence interval, the area to the left of the positive *t* score is 95%, therefore, this *t* score is referred to as: $t_{95\%}$. From Figure 8.11b, for a 95% confidence interval, the area to the left of the positive *t* score is 97.5%, therefore, this *t* score is referred to as: $t_{97.5\%}$. Examining Figure 8.11c, for a 99% confidence interval, the area to the left of the positive *t* score is 99.5%, therefore, this *t* score is referred to as: $t_{99.5\%}$.

EXAMPLE 8.2

A random sampling of 16 students was selected from the student body at a local college to determine the average amount of money that students carry with them. If the sample mean, $\bar{x}$, was equal to $28, with a sample standard deviation of s=6, then construct a:
a) 95% Confidence Interval for estimating the mean amount of money all students carry on them.
b) 99% Confidence Interval for estimating the mean amount of money all students carry on them.

Solution

a) Since the population standard deviation is unknown and is estimated by s, then the formula to compute a 95% Confidence Interval for the population mean is:

$$\bar{x} - (t_{97.5\%})\frac{s}{\sqrt{n}} \text{ to } \bar{x} + (t_{97.5\%})\frac{s}{\sqrt{n}}$$

To determine a 95% Confidence Interval, we need to determine the appropriate *t* score by finding the degrees of freedom using the formula: df = n − 1. For a sample size of 16, we have: df = 16 − 1 = 15. Using Table III, the appropriate *t* score is found under the column $t_{97.5\%}$ and along the row for 15 degrees of freedom. Thus, the t score, $t_{97.5\%}$, for 15 degrees of freedom is: 2.13. Using the following values:

$$\bar{x} = 28, t_{97.5\%} \text{ (with } df = 15) = 2.13, s = 6 \text{ and n} = 16$$

in the formula for a 95% Confidence Interval, we have:

$$(28) - (2.13)\frac{6}{\sqrt{16}} \text{ to } 28 + (2.13)\frac{6}{\sqrt{16}}$$

$$(28) - (2.13)\frac{6}{4} \text{ to } 28 + (2.13)\frac{6}{4}$$

$$(28) - (2.13)(1.50) \text{ to } 28 + (2.13)(1.50)$$

$$(28) - (3.20) \text{ to } 28 + (3.20)$$

$$24.81 \text{ to } 31.20$$

Thus, a 95% Confidence Interval for the mean amount of money all students carry on them is: $24.81 to $31.20.

b) To construct a 99% Confidence Interval for the population mean, where the population standard deviation is **unknown**, use the formula:

$$\bar{x} - (t_{99.5\%})\frac{s}{\sqrt{n}} \text{ to } \bar{x} + (t_{99.5\%})\frac{s}{\sqrt{n}}$$

To determine a 99% Confidence Interval, we need to determine the appropriate *t* score by finding the degrees of freedom using the formula: df = n − 1. For a sample size of 16, we have: df = 16 − 1 = 15. Using Table III, the appropriate *t* score is found under the column $t_{99.5\%}$ and along the row for 15 degrees of freedom. Thus, the t score, $t_{99.5\%}$, for 15 degrees of freedom is: 2.95. Using the following values:

$$\bar{x} = 28, t_{99.5\%} \text{ (with } df = 15) = 2.95, s = 6 \text{ and } n = 16$$

in the formula for a 99% Confidence Interval, we have:

$$(28) - (2.95)\frac{6}{\sqrt{16}} \text{ to } 28 + (2.95)\frac{6}{\sqrt{16}}$$

$$(28) - (2.95)\frac{6}{4} \text{ to } 28 + (2.95)\frac{6}{4}$$

$$(28) - (2.95)(1.50) \text{ to } 28 + (2.95)(1.50)$$

$$(28) - (4.43) \text{ to } 28 + (4.43)$$

$$\$23.58 \text{ to } \$32.43$$

Thus, a 99% Confidence Interval for the mean amount of money all students carry on them is: $23.58 to $32.43.

EXAMPLE 8.3

A professor in the English department would like to estimate the average number of typing errors per page in term papers for all students enrolled in liberal arts English courses. For a random sample of 36 term papers, the professor found the mean number of typing errors per page was 4.6 with s = 1.4. Find the 90% Confidence Interval for the mean number of typing errors per page for all students enrolled in liberal arts English courses.

Solution

Since the population standard deviation is **unknown** and is estimated by s, then the formula to compute a 90% Confidence Interval for the population mean is:

$$\bar{x} - (t_{95\%})\frac{s}{\sqrt{n}} \text{ to } \bar{x} + (t_{95\%})\frac{s}{\sqrt{n}}$$

To determine a 90% Confidence Interval, we need to determine the appropriate t score by finding the degrees of freedom using the formula: df = n -- 1. For a sample size of 36, we have: df = 36 – 1 = 35. Using Table III, the appropriate t score is found under the column $t_{95\%}$. Since $df = 35$ does not appear in the table and is exactly halfway between $df = 30$ and $df = 40$, we will choose the t score value that is farthest from zero. Thus in this case we will choose the t score for 30 degrees of freedom. Thus, the t score, $t_{95\%}$, for 30 degrees of freedom is: 1.70. Using the following values:

$$\bar{x} = 4.6, \; t_{95\%} \; (\text{with } df = 30) = 1.70, \text{s} = 1.4 \text{ and n} = 36$$

in the formula for a 90% Confidence Interval, we have:

$$(4.6) - (1.70)\frac{1.4}{\sqrt{36}} \text{ to } 4.6 + (1.70)\frac{1.4}{\sqrt{36}}$$

$$(4.6) - (1.70)\frac{1.4}{6} \text{ to } 4.6 + (1.70)\frac{1.4}{6}$$

$$(4.6) - (1.70)(0.35) \text{ to } 4.6 + (1.70)(0.35)$$

$$(4.6) - (0.60) \text{ to } 4.6 + (0.60)$$

$$4 \text{ to } 5.20$$

Thus, a 90% Confidence Interval for the mean number of typing errors per page for all students enrolled in liberal arts English courses is: 4 to 5.20.

8.5 INTERVAL ESTIMATION: CONFIDENCE INTERVALS FOR THE POPULATION PROPORTION

Very often, you see the results of an opinion poll stated in a newspaper or a magazine. Polls are conducted to determine the proportion or percentage of people who favor a particular issue like gun control, the proportion of people who favor a certain candidate, the percentage of people who prefer a particular soft drink, the proportion of people who don't drink and drive. In each instance, the purpose of the opinion poll is to estimate the proportion or percentage of a population with a particular characteristic or opinion.

For example, suppose an opinion poll is conducted to determine the proportion of all American adults who disapprove of a new Congressional law. If an opinion poll of 1500 American adults indicates that 1170 adults disapprove of the new law, we can use this sample information to estimate the proportion of **all** American adults who disapprove of the new law by calculating the sample proportion, $\hat{p}$. This sample proportion of people is determined by the formula:

$$\hat{p} = \frac{\text{number of adults disapproving of the new Congressional law}}{\text{total number of adults polled}}$$

Thus,

$$\hat{p} = \frac{1170}{1500}$$

or

$$\hat{p} = 0.78 \text{ or } 78\%$$

Since this opinion poll has determined that 78% of the American adults polled disapprove of the new Congressional law, then we can use this sample proportion as a point estimate of the proportion of all American adults who disapprove of the new law. Thus, the question becomes: is it reasonable to conclude from this sample proportion, $\hat{p}$, that 78% of all American adults disapprove of the new law?

That is, how confident can one be that this poll of 1500 American adults reflects the true feelings of the entire population of American adults or the population proportion, p?

Suppose a second opinion poll was conducted for another 1500 adults, would one expect the same percentage of American adults to disapprove of the new law? Probably not! In fact, if more and more samples were selected, the sample proportion, $\hat{p}$, would vary from sample to sample. Some of these sample proportions will be smaller than the population proportion, p, and some will be larger. Therefore, this sample proportion, $\hat{p}$, which serves as a point estimate of the population proportion, p, does not indicate how accurate this estimate is.

Thus, in order to provide a level of confidence in our estimate of the population proportion, we need to construct an interval estimate of the population proportion, p. To construct an interval estimate of the population proportion, we need to examine the distribution of all possible sample proportions. This distribution is referred to as the sampling distribution of the proportion.

A detailed discussion regarding the sampling distribution of the proportion was previously discussed in Section 7.9. The **Characteristics of the Sampling Distribution of the Proportion, p,** are:

- the sampling distribution of the proportion is approximately normal when the size of the sample n is large, that is, when both np and $n(1-p)$ are greater than 5.
- the mean of the sampling distribution of the proportion, denoted $\mu_{\hat{p}}$, is: $\mu_{\hat{p}} = p$
- the standard deviation of the sampling distribution of the proportion (or the standard error of the proportion), denoted $\sigma_{\hat{p}}$, is:

$$\sigma_{\hat{p}} = \sqrt{\frac{p(1-p)}{n}}$$

In the same way that the sample mean was used to construct a confidence interval for the population mean, the sample proportion, $\hat{p}$, will be used to construct 90%, 95% and a 99% confidence intervals for the population proportion, p.

When constructing an interval estimate of the population proportion, the actual value of the population proportion, p, is **not known**. Since the best estimate that we have for the population proportion, p, is the sample proportion, $\hat{p}$, we will use the sample proportion, $\hat{p}$, as an estimate of the population proportion, p, in the formula for $\sigma_{\hat{p}}$.

When we replace the population proportion, p, by the sample proportion, $\hat{p}$, in the formula for the standard deviation of the sampling distribution of the proportion, $\sigma_{\hat{p}}$, we have an **estimate of the standard deviation of the sampling distribution of the proportion** (also referred to as an **estimate of the standard error of the proportion**) and it is denoted by the symbol: $s_{\hat{p}}$.

DEFINITION

The Estimate of Standard Deviation of the Sampling Distribution of The Proportion, $s_{\hat{p}}$ (also referred to as the **estimate of the standard error of the proportion**) The value of $s_{\hat{p}}$, is an estimate of the standard deviation of the sampling distribution of the proportion, $\sigma_{\hat{p}}$, and is calculated by the formula:

$$s_{\hat{p}} = \sqrt{\frac{\hat{p}(1-\hat{p})}{n}}$$

where:

$\hat{p}$ is the sample proportion.
n is the sample size.

EXAMPLE 8.4

Determine an estimate of the standard error of the sampling distribution of the proportion, $\sigma_{\hat{p}}$, using the formula for $s_{\hat{p}}$, if a random sample of 49 data values has a sample proportion of: $\hat{p} = 0.4$.

Solution

An estimate of $\sigma_{\hat{p}}$ is found using the formula for $s_{\hat{p}}$, which is:

$$s_{\hat{p}} = \sqrt{\frac{\hat{p}(1-\hat{p})}{n}}$$

Substitute the value of the sample proportion: $\hat{p} = 0.4$ and the sample size: n = 49 into the formula for $s_{\hat{p}}$, we have:

$$s_{\hat{p}} = \sqrt{\frac{(0.4)(0.6)}{49}}$$

$$s_{\hat{p}} = \sqrt{0.0049}$$

$$s_{\hat{p}} = 0.07$$

Under the assumption that the sampling distribution of the population proportion, p, is approximately a normal distribution, $\hat{p}$ serves as a *point estimate of the population proportion,* and $s_{\hat{p}}$ serves as an estimate of the standard error of the sampling distribution of the proportion, we can use the reasoning that was developed in constructing confidence intervals for population means to construct confidence intervals for the population proportion. Thus, we can define the *90%, 95% and 99% confidence intervals for the population proportion, p* as follows.

DEFINITION
Confidence Intervals for the Population Proportion, p, Where n is Large
1. A 90% Confidence Interval for the Population Proportion, p, is constructed by the formula:
$$\hat{p} - (1.65)\,s_{\hat{p}} \quad \text{to} \quad \hat{p} + (1.65)\,s_{\hat{p}}$$
2. A 95% Confidence Interval for the Population Proportion, p, is constructed by the formula:
$$\hat{p} - (1.96)\,s_{\hat{p}} \quad \text{to} \quad \hat{p} + (1.96)\,s_{\hat{p}}$$
3. A 99% Confidence Interval for the Population Proportion, p, is constructed by the formula:
$$\hat{p} - (2.58)\,s_{\hat{p}} \quad \text{to} \quad \hat{p} + (2.58)\,s_{\hat{p}}$$

where:

$\hat{p}$ is the point estimate of the population proportion,

$s_{\hat{p}}$ is the estimate of the standard error of the sampling distribution of the proportion, and is computed by the formula:

$$s_{\hat{p}} = \sqrt{\frac{\hat{p}(1-\hat{p})}{n}}$$

n   is the sample size

EXAMPLE 8.5

A sociologist reports that from a study of 1000 respondents, 65% of the respondents believe that the best place to meet a "suitable" companion is by taking an evening class.

(Source: Bruskin-Goldring Research Poll 2-13-92)

Find a:
a)   95% confidence interval for the population proportion, p.
b)   99% confidence interval for the population proportion, p.

Solution

a)   To find a confidence interval for a population proportion, p, we must first calculate $s_{\hat{p}}$ using the formula:

$$s_{\hat{p}} = \sqrt{\frac{\hat{p}(1-\hat{p})}{n}}$$

Since the point estimate of the sample proportion, $\hat{p} = 0.65$, and n = 1000, then

$$s_{\hat{p}} = \sqrt{\frac{(0.65)(0.35)}{1000}}$$

$$s_{\hat{p}} = 0.015$$

A 95% Confidence Interval for the population proportion p is found by:

$$\hat{p} - (1.96)\, s_{\hat{p}} \quad \text{to} \quad \hat{p} + (1.96)\, s_{\hat{p}}$$

substituting in the formula, we have:

$$(0.65) - (1.96)(0.015) \text{ to } (0.65) + (1.96)(0.015)$$

$$0.621 \text{ to } 0.679$$

Therefore, a 95% confidence interval for the population proportion p that believe the best place to meet a "suitable" companion by taking an evening class is:

$$62\% \text{ to } 68\%$$

That is, we are 95% confident that the *true* population proportion p is between 62% and 68%.

b)   A 99% Confidence Interval for the population proportion, p, is found by:

$$\hat{p} - (2.58)\, s_{\hat{p}} \quad \text{to} \quad \hat{p} + (2.58)\, s_{\hat{p}}$$

substituting in the formula, we have:

$$(0.65) - (2.58)(0.015) \text{ to } (0.65) + (2.58)(0.015)$$

$$0.611 \text{ to } 0.689$$

Therefore, a 99% confidence interval for the population proportion p that believe the best place to meet a "suitable" companion by taking an evening class is:

$$61\% \text{ to } 69\%$$

That is, we are 99% confident that the *true* population proportion p is between 61% and 69%.

8.6   DETERMINING SAMPLE SIZE AND THE MARGIN OF ERROR

In the previous two sections, we developed the formulas to construct a confidence interval for a population mean and a population proportion. In those sections, we arbitrarily chose a sample size. In practice, it is important to determine an appropriate sample size for a desired confidence level. Selecting a sample size larger than necessary will involve a greater cost. Thus, we must answer the question, "how does one decide on how large a sample size, n, is required?"

One factor that affects the sample size, n, is the *level of precision* that is required. If a high level of precision (that is, a better estimate or more accuracy) is required for the confidence interval, then the sample size must be increased since a larger sample will decrease the sampling error. Therefore, the more precision you need for a confidence interval, the larger the sample size you will be required to take.

Let's examine some procedures that are used to determine the sample size for a specified precision level and confidence level. First, we will consider the procedure for determining the sample size for estimating a population mean.

Sample Size for Estimating a Population Mean, μ

A confidence interval for the population mean, μ, where the population standard deviation, σ, is known has the form:

$$\bar{x} \pm (z\ score)(\frac{\sigma}{\sqrt{n}})$$

Thus, the confidence interval for a specific level of confidence has two components:

1. $\bar{x}$: which represents a point estimate of the population mean

2. $(z\ score)(\frac{\sigma}{\sqrt{n}})$: which represents the **margin of error**

This **margin of error** is the maximum possible error of estimate for the population mean using the sample mean, $\bar{x}$. We will denote the margin of error by E.

DEFINITION
Margin of Error for Estimating the Population Mean, where the Population Standard Deviation is Known The margin of error, denoted by E, for the population mean is the maximum possible error of estimate for the population mean, μ, using the sample mean, $\bar{x}$. The formula to determine this margin of error is:

$$E = (z)(\frac{\sigma}{\sqrt{n}})$$

where:

E = margin of error
z = z score corresponding to the level of confidence
σ is the population standard deviation
n is the sample size which is greater than 30

The margin of error, E, represents one-half the width of the confidence interval as illustrated in Figure 8.12.

For a fixed sample size and population standard deviation, as the level of confidence is increased, the margin of error also increases. This is illustrated in Table 8.1.

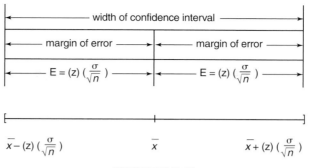

FIGURE 8.12

TABLE 8.1

Level of Confidence	z score	Margin of Error
90%	1.65	$(1.65)(\frac{\sigma}{\sqrt{n}})$
95%	1.96	$(1.96)(\frac{\sigma}{\sqrt{n}})$
99%	2.58	$(2.58)(\frac{\sigma}{\sqrt{n}})$

The size of the margin of error determines the precision or accuracy of the estimate of the population mean. A precise estimate has a small margin of error. We would like our estimate of the population mean to be precise and also to have a high level of confidence. However, as shown in Table 8.1, as the confidence level increases from 90% to 99%, the margin of error increases which causes a decrease in the precision level.

In examining the margin of error formula, you should notice that there are three quantities within the formula. These quantities are the z score, the population standard deviation, and the sample size. All three have an effect on the margin of error, but, since the population standard deviation represents the variability of **all** the data values, it is a fixed value over which we have no control. On the other hand, the z score and the sample size are quantities over which we have control.

Our objective will be to reduce the margin of error without reducing the confidence level, so that the precision of the estimate of the population mean can be improved. If we hold the confidence level fixed, a simple way to reduce the margin of error is to increase the sample size. This is true because the sample size is in the denominator of the margin of error formula; therefore, as the sample size increases the margin of error will decrease. This concept is illustrated in Example 8.6.

EXAMPLE 8.6

During the past year, the flight times between two cities was reported to have a population standard deviation of 20 minutes. Determine the margin of error for estimating the mean flight time between the two cities for a confidence level of 95% for each of the following sample sizes:
a) 36
b) 64
c) 100

d) Compare the results of the previous three parts and state what happens to the margin of error as the sample size is increased.

Solution

To calculate the margin of error, we use the formula:

$$E = (z)\left(\frac{\sigma}{\sqrt{n}}\right)$$

Since the population standard deviation is given to be 20 minutes, then $\sigma = 20$. For a 95% level of confidence, the z score is: 1.96. Substituting these values into the margin of error formula, we have:

$$E = (1.96)\left(\frac{20}{\sqrt{n}}\right)$$

a) For a sample size of 36, the margin of error is:

$$E = (1.96)\left(\frac{20}{\sqrt{36}}\right)$$
$$E \approx (1.96)(3.33)$$
$$E \approx 6.53 \text{ minutes}$$

b) For a sample size of 64, the margin of error is:

$$E = (1.96)\left(\frac{20}{\sqrt{64}}\right)$$
$$E = (1.96)(2.5)$$
$$E = 4.9 \text{ minutes}$$

c) For a sample size of 100, the margin of error is:

$$E = (1.96)\left(\frac{20}{\sqrt{100}}\right)$$
$$E = (1.96)(2)$$
$$E = 3.92 \text{ minutes}$$

d) Notice from previous parts, as the sample size increased from 36 to 100, the margin of error, E, decreased from 6.53 minutes to 3.92 minutes. Thus, a smaller margin of error can be achieved by increasing the sample size. ∎

As illustrated in Example 8.6, selecting a larger sample size for a fixed confidence level will reduce the margin of error. As the margin of error is decreased, the width of the confidence interval will also be reduced. This will result in an increase in the precision or accuracy of estimating the population mean.

Since the margin of error and the size of a sample are related, we can develop a formula that determines the required sample size, n, for a predetermined margin of error (or precision requirement) and confidence level. Using the margin of error formula and solving for n, we can obtain a formula that will determine the sample size for a given margin of error.

**The Formula to Determine the Sample Size
for a Given Margin of Error in Estimating The Population Mean, μ**

For a given confidence level, a known population standard deviation, and a given margin of error, the formula to determine the sample size, n, to satisfy these requirements in estimating the population mean is:

$$n = \left[\frac{z\sigma}{E}\right]^2$$

If the resulting value of n is not a whole number, the next largest whole number should be taken for the required sample size.

where:

n = the required sample size for the specified conditions
E = predetermined margin of error
z is the z score corresponding to the level of confidence
σ is the population standard deviation

E X A M P L E   8 . 7

A light-bulb manufacturer wants to determine how large a random sample the quality control department should take to be 99% confident that the sample mean will be within 25 hours of estimating the population mean.

Determine the sample size required to satisfy these requirements if we assume that the population standard deviation is 250 hours.

Solution

To determine the sample size, n, for the given conditions, we need to use the formula:

$$n = \left[\frac{z\sigma}{E}\right]^2$$

For a confidence level of 99%, the z score is 2.58. The population standard deviation is given to be 250 hours, therefore, $\sigma = 250$. Since the quality control department wants to be within 25 hours of the population mean, then the margin of error is 25 hours. Substituting this information into the sample size formula, we have:

$$n = \left[\frac{(2.58)(250)}{25}\right]^2$$

$$n = 665.64$$

Thus, the sample size required to meet the requirements of the quality control department is 666.

If the population standard deviation, σ, is unknown, then the conventional procedure is to take a preliminary sample (of any size greater than 30) and to find the sample standard deviation, s. The value of s is used to replace the value of σ in the formula for the sample size. However, it should be noted that when s is used to estimate the value of σ, then the sample size determined using s may yield a margin of error that can be either smaller or larger than the predetermined margin of error. Why?

Sample Size for Estimating a Population Proportion, p

A confidence interval for the population proportion, p, where the sample size is large, and the population proportion, p, is unknown, and is estimated by the sample proportion, $\hat{p}$, has the form:

$$\hat{p} \pm (z \text{ score})\left(\sqrt{\frac{\hat{p}(1-\hat{p})}{n}}\right)$$

Thus, the confidence interval for a specific level of confidence has two components:

1. $\hat{p}$: which represents a point estimate of the population proportion

2. $(z \text{ score})\left(\sqrt{\frac{\hat{p}(1-\hat{p})}{n}}\right)$: which represents the margin of error

To determine this margin of error, we need to know the value of the sample proportion, $\hat{p}$, and the z score corresponding to the confidence level. This margin of error is the maximum possible error of estimate for the population proportion using the sample proportion, $\hat{p}$.

We will denote the margin of error by E. Opinion Polls usually express the point estimate, the sample proportion, of the poll as a percentage and the margin of error of the poll as percentage points. Care must be taken to distinguish between percentages and percentage points. Percentage refers to a proportion value multiplied by 100%, while percentage points represent units on the percent scale. The margin of error for opinion polls is always stated as a certain number of percentage points, and not as a percentage.

DEFINITION
Margin of Error for Estimating the Population Proportion for a Large Sample The margin of error, denoted by E, for the population proportion is the maximum possible error of estimate for the population proportion, p, using the sample proportion, $\hat{p}$. The formula to determine the margin of error is:

$$\mathbf{E = (z)}\left(\sqrt{\frac{\hat{p}(1-\hat{p})}{n}}\right)$$

where:

E   = margin of error
z   = z score corresponding to the level of confidence
$\hat{p}$ is a sample proportion
n   is a large sample size

This margin of error, E, represents one-half the width of the confidence interval as illustrated in Figure 8.13.

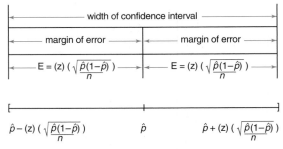

FIGURE 8.13

EXAMPLE 8.8

The Nielsen television ratings used a random sample of 2,000 homes to estimate with 95% confidence that 45% of the proportion of all homes watched a football game on Monday Night Football. Determine the margin of error for the Nielsen's estimate of the proportion of all homes watching this football game on Monday Night Football.

Solution

To calculate the margin of error, we use the formula:

$$E = (z)\sqrt{\frac{\hat{p}(1-\hat{p})}{n}}$$

For a 95% level of confidence, the z score is: 1.96. Since a random sample of 2,000 homes was selected, then n = 2,000. Given that the sample proportion of homes watching the football game is 45%, then $\hat{p}$ = 0.45, and $1 - \hat{p} = 1 - 0.45 = 0.55$. Substituting these values into the margin of error formula, we have:

$$E = (1.96)(\sqrt{\frac{(0.45)(0.55)}{2,000}})$$

$$E = (1.96)(\sqrt{\frac{(0.2475)}{2,000}})$$

$$E = (1.96)(\sqrt{(0.0001238)})$$

$$E = (1.96)(0.0111)$$

$$E \approx 0.0218$$

Thus, the margin of error is approximately 0.0218. This can also be expressed as approximately **2.18 percentage points.**

As shown earlier in this section, when estimating the mean of a population, the margin of error decreases as the sample size increases. This also holds true when estimating a population proportion. As the margin of error is decreased, then the precision or accuracy of estimating the population proportion will increase.

Since the margin of error and the size of a sample are related, we can develop a formula that determines the required sample size, n, for a predetermined margin of error (or precision requirement) and confidence level. Using the margin of error formula and solving for n, we can obtain a formula that will determine the sample size for a given margin of error when estimating a population proportion, p. When the margin of error formula is solved for n, we get:

$$n = \frac{z^2(\hat{p})(1-\hat{p})}{E^2}$$

CASE STUDY 8.4   Phone Survey Methods

The following *New York Times* article entitled "Method Used in Taking Survey in Phone Interview" describes the technique used in selecting the sample for a *New York Times*/CBS News Public Opinion Poll.
   a) How many people were selected for this poll?
   b) Name some procedures that the pollsters did when selecting the sample to insure that it was representative of the population?

(continues)

CASE STUDY 8.4   Phone Survey Methods (continued)

Method Used in Taking Survey in Phone Interview

The latest New York Times/CBS News Poll is based on telephone interviews conducted from last Wednesday through last Sunday with 1,536 adult men and women around the United States. Of this total, 542 said that they were Democrats, 495 said they were Republicans and 499 said they were independents.

The sample of telephone exchanges called was selected by a computer from a complete list of exchanges in the country. The exchanges were chosen in a way that would insure that each region of the country was represented in proportion to its population. For each exchange, the telephone numbers were formed by random digits, thus permitting access to both listed and unlisted residential numbers.

The results have been weighted to take account of household size and to adjust for variations in the sample relating to region, race, sex, age and education.

Higher Rate for Republicans

Republicans were sampled at a higher rate than others to insure a sufficiently large number from that party. The groups of voters, by party identification, were then weighted to reflect their proper proportion in the voting population.

In theory, one can say with 95 percent certainty that the results based on the entire sample differ by no more than 3 percentage points in either direction from what would have been obtained by interviewing all adult Americans. The error for smaller subgroups is larger, depending on the number of sample cases in the subgroup.

The theoretical errors do not take into account a margin of additional error resulting from the various practical difficulties in taking any survey of public opinion.

FIGURE 8.14

c) Explain what is meant by the statement: "in theory, one can say with 95% certainty that the results based on the entire sample differ by no more than 3 percentage points in either direction from what would have been obtained by interviewing all adult Americans"? What confidence interval are they referring to within this statement? What is the margin of error for this poll? What is the population of people for this poll?

d) What additional errors are the pollsters referring to in the statement: "the theoretical errors do not take into account a margin of additional errors resulting from the various practical difficulties in taking any survey of public opinion"?

The Formula to Determine the Sample Size for a Given Margin of Error in Estimating The Population Proportion, p

For a given confidence level, a point estimate of the population proportion, $\hat{p}$, and a given margin of error, the formula to determine the sample size, n, to satisfy these requirements in estimating the population proportion is:

$$n = \frac{z^2(\hat{p})(1-\hat{p})}{E^2}$$

If the resulting value of n is not a whole number, the next largest whole number should be taken for the required sample size.

where:

n = the required sample size for the specified conditions
E = predetermined margin of error
z = the z score corresponding to the level of confidence
$\hat{p}$ = a point estimate of the population proportion

Thus, to calculate for a sample size, n, we need to determine the values for z, E and $\hat{p}$. The value for z is the z score that corresponds to the confidence level used in estimating the population proportion, while the value for E is the predetermined margin of error for estimating the population proportion. However, the value of $\hat{p}$, the sample proportion, is *unknown* since we would need to select a sample to determine $\hat{p}$.

Thus, our problem is: the formula for the sample size requires that we have a value for $\hat{p}$, but in order for us to determine this value for $\hat{p}$, we need to decide upon how large a sample to select which is the purpose of using this sample size formula.

Consequently, we don't have a value for $\hat{p}$, and thus, we cannot use the formula for the sample size, n. We can alleviate this problem in one of two ways:

1. Take a pilot sample (of any sample size that is sufficiently large) and calculate $\hat{p}$ for this sample, or use the value of $\hat{p}$ from a previous sample. This value of $\hat{p}$ is used to find the sample size, n.
2. Determine the maximum possible product of $\hat{p}$ and $1 - \hat{p}$, and simply replace $\hat{p}$ and $1 - \hat{p}$ with values that produce the maximum possible product of $\hat{p}$ and $1 - \hat{p}$. This procedure generates the **conservative estimate of the sample size.**

To help find this conservative estimate of the sample size, we need to determine the maximum product of $\hat{p}$ and $1 - \hat{p}$.

Table 8.2 displays the product of $\hat{p}$ and $1 - \hat{p}$ for values of $\hat{p}$ from 0.1 to 0.9.

TABLE 8.2   Table of Values of $\hat{p}, (1 - \hat{p})$, and Their Product

$\hat{p}$	$(1 - \hat{p})$	$(\hat{p})(1 - \hat{p})$
0.1	0.9	0.09
0.2	0.8	0.16
0.3	0.7	0.21
0.4	0.6	0.24
0.5	0.5	0.25
0.6	0.4	0.24
0.7	0.3	0.21
0.8	0.2	0.16
0.9	0.1	0.09

From Table 8.2, you should notice that the maximum value of the product of $\hat{p}$ and $1 - \hat{p}$ occurs when $\hat{p}$ is equal to 0.5. Thus, the maximum possible product of $\hat{p}$ and $1 - \hat{p}$ will be 0.25, no matter what value of $\hat{p}$ is chosen. Therefore, $\hat{p}$ will always be less than $\hat{p} = 0.25$. Substituting 0.25 for the product:$(\hat{p})(1 - \hat{p})$ into the formula for the sample size, n, we obtain:

$$n = \frac{z^2 (0.25)}{E^2}$$

This formula for the sample size, n, based upon using 0.5 for the value of $\hat{p}$ will give a conservative estimate of the sample size. This is referred to as a conservative estimate because it gives the maximum sample size regardless of the possible value of $\hat{p}$.

Conservative Estimate of Determining the Sample Size for a Given Margin of Error in Estimating The Population Proportion, p

For a given confidence level, and a given margin of error, the formula to determine the conservative sample size, n, to satisfy these requirements in estimating the population proportion is:

$$n = \frac{z^2 (0.25)}{E^2}$$

If the resulting value of n is not a whole number, the next largest whole number should be taken for the required sample size.

where:

n = the required sample size for the specified conditions
E = predetermined margin of error
z is the z score corresponding to the level of confidence

EXAMPLE 8.9

An automobile club would like to estimate the proportion of all drivers who wear seat belts while driving. If the automobile club wants the margin of error to be within 2 percentage points of the true population proportion for a 99% confidence interval, then determine:
a)   A conservative estimate for the sample size.
b)   An estimate of the sample size if a previous study showed that 65% wear seat belts.

Solution

a)   To determine a conservative estimate for the sample size of drivers who wear seat belts, we use the formula:

$$n = \frac{z^2 (0.25)}{E^2}$$

To calculate the sample size, n, using this formula, we need to determine the z score and a margin of error for these requirements. A confidence level of 99%, uses the z score, z = 2.58. Since the automobile club wants to be within 2 percentage points, then the margin of error is: E = 0.02. Substituting these values into the formula for n, we have:

$$n = \frac{(2.58)^2 (0.25)}{(0.02)^2}$$

$$n = \frac{1.6641}{0.0004}$$

$$n = 4160.25$$

Since the resulting value of n is not a whole number, the next largest whole number is taken to be: 4161. Thus, the automobile club's conservative estimate of the sample size is 4161 drivers. Therefore, if the club wants to be within two percentage points of the population proportion of drivers who wear seat belts, and 99% confident of their estimate, they should take a sample of 4161 drivers.

b) To determine an estimate of the sample size, n, using a sample proportion, $\hat{p}$, determined from a previous study, we use the formula:

$$n = \frac{z^2(\hat{p})(1-\hat{p})}{E^2}$$

To calculate the sample size, n, using this formula, we need to determine the z score, a margin of error for these requirements, and a sample proportion, $\hat{p}$. A confidence level of 99%, uses a z score, $z = 2.58$. Since the automobile club wants to be within 2 percentage points, then the margin of error is: $E = 0.02$. From the previous study, we can use 0.65 for the value for $\hat{p}$, so $\hat{p}=0.65$ and $1-\hat{p}=0.35$. Substituting these values into the formula for the sample size, n, we have:

$$n = \frac{(2.58)^2(0.65)(0.35)}{(0.02)^2}$$

$$n = \frac{1.5143}{0.0004}$$

$$n = 3785.75$$

Since the resulting value of n is not a whole number, the next largest whole number is taken: 3786. Thus, if the automobile club takes a sample of 3786 drivers, then the estimate of the population of all drivers that wear seat belts will be within 2 percentage points of the population proportion.

———————————■

In Example 8.9, it is important to realize that the sample size of 3786 drivers was determined using the sample proportion, $\hat{p}=0.65$, and that the automobile club wanted to be within 2 percentage points of the population proportion. However, you should realize that if the sample proportion for the new sample of 3786 drivers happens to be greater than 0.65, the margin of error will not be within the requirement of 2 percentage points.

Therefore, if you want to be cautious and more conservative in your estimate, you may want to select a sample size that is greater than 3786 drivers. For example, perhaps you would use the sample size of 4161 that was determined in *part a* of Example 8.9.

Summary of Confidence Intervals

Table 8.3 contains a summary of the confidence intervals and the appropriate conditions.

TABLE 8.3   Summary of Confidence Intervals

Parameter Being Estimated	Conditions of Estimate	Point Estimate	Confidence Interval	Sampling Distribution is:
μ	Known σ	$\bar{x}$	$\bar{x}-(z)(\frac{\sigma}{\sqrt{n}})$ to $\bar{x}+(z)(\frac{\sigma}{\sqrt{n}})$ where : $z = 1.65$ for 90% $z = 1.96$ for 95% $z = 2.58$ for 99%	Approximately a Normal Distribution

(continues)

TABLE 8.3   (continued)

Parameter Being Estimated	Conditions of Estimate	Point Estimate	Confidence Interval	Sampling Distribution is:
μ	Unknown σ	$\bar{x}$	$\bar{x}-(t)(\frac{s}{\sqrt{n}})$ to $\bar{x}+(t)(\frac{s}{\sqrt{n}})$ where: $t=t_{95\%}$ for 90% $t=t_{97.5\%}$ for 95% $t=t_{99.5\%}$ for 99%	A t Distribution with: df = n − 1
p	$n\hat{p}>5$ and $n(1-\hat{p})>5$	$\hat{p}$	$\hat{p}-(z)(s_{\hat{p}})$ to $\hat{p}+(z)(s_{\hat{p}})$ where: $z=1.65$ for 90% $z=1.96$ for 95% $z=2.58$ for 99% $s_{\hat{p}}=\sqrt{\frac{\hat{p}(1-\hat{p})}{n}}$	Approximately a Normal Distribution

8.7   USING TECHNOLOGY

In this chapter we have studied the methods of constructing confidence intervals about population parameters and have discussed the following three cases.

1. Confidence intervals about a population mean, μ, where the population standard deviation, σ, is known.
2. Confidence intervals about a population mean, μ, where the population standard deviation, σ, is unknown.
3. Confidence intervals about a population proportion, p, where $n\hat{p}>5$ and $n(1-\hat{p})>5$.

Confidence intervals can be easily be constructed using MINITAB, EXCEL software or the TI-83 Plus calculator.

For example, suppose 100 data values are collected and inputed into a MINITAB worksheet. If the population standard deviation, σ, is 10, the MINITAB output display for the 95% confidence interval for this sample data as shown in Figure 8.15.

MINITAB output:

	N	MEAN	STDEV	SE MEAN	95.0 PERCENT C.I.
THE ASSUMED SIGMA = 10.0					
C1	100	50.52	9.92	1.00	(48.56, 52.48)

FIGURE 8.15

If you examine the output in Figure 8.15, you should notice that a 95% confidence interval for a population mean for the sample of 100 data values is listed under the heading 95.0 PERCENT C.I. The values 48.56 and 52.48 are the confidence limits for the 95% confidence interval.

An estimate of the population mean when the population standard deviation, σ, is unknown can also be produced. The MINITAB output for a 90% confidence interval for a population mean for 16 sample data stored in C1 of a MINITAB worksheet is displayed in Figure 8.16.

MINITAB output:

SIGMA unknown

	N	MEAN	STDEV	SE MEAN	90.0 PERCENT C.I.
C1	16	3.0352	0.2870	0.0717	(2.9094, 3.1610)

FIGURE 8.16

Examine the output in Figure 8.16. What is the 90% confidence interval? How many data values are in the sample? What is the sample mean? the sample standard deviation? the standard error of the mean? How is the SE MEAN calculated?

Finally, using MINITAB we can construct a 99% confidence interval for the population proportion where the sample size is 350 and the sample proportion is 0.80.

The MINITAB output is shown in Figure 8.17.

	N	MEAN	STDEV	SE MEAN	99.0 PERCENT C.I.
C1	350	0.8000	0.4006	0.0214	(0.7445, 0.8555)

FIGURE 8.17

Examine the output in Figure 8.17. What is the 99% confidence interval for the population proportion, p? What is the margin of error? What is the 99% confidence interval for this point estimate?

When using EXCEL, the software returns the margin of error for a given alpha level (α), population standard deviation (σ) and sample size (n). For example, if the alpha level is 5%, the population standard deviation is 5 and the sample size is 50, EXCEL returns the margin of error 1.3859. The user must then create the 95% confidence interval using the sample mean.

On the other hand, EXCEL does create confidence interval descriptives for both population means and population proportions directly from sample data where the population standard deviation is unknown. Figures 8.18a and 8.18b display the EXCEL confidence interval output for a sample of 100 randomly generated numbers from 1 to 100. It should be noted that the sample was produced using a feature of EXCEL called a random number generator. The 100 numbers where selected from a normal distribution with a mean = 50 and standard deviation = 10. Figures 8.18a and 8.18b contain the results that show the 90% and 95% confidence interval using these 100 sample data values. Within the table, the "Confidence Level (90%)" or "Confidence Level (95%)" displays the Margin of Error for the confidence interval.

Similarly, the 90% and 99% confidence interval statistics for a population proportion has been generated using a sample size of 350 and a sample proportion of 0.80. Figures 8.19a and 8.19b display the EXCEL output. Notice again, the "Confidence Level (90%)" and "Confidence Level (99%)" represents the Margin of Error for the confidence Interval. For all confidence interval analysis, EXCEL leaves the calculation for the Confidence Interval up to the EXCEL user.

90% Confidence Interval for Population Mean where Population Standard Deviation is Unknown	
Mean	49.60
Standard Error	1.09
Standard Deviation	10.86
Count	100
Confidence Level(90.0%)	1.80

(a)

95% Confidence Interval for Population Mean where Population Standard Deviation is Unknown	
Mean	49.60
Standard Error	1.09
Standard Deviation	10.86
Count	100
Confidence Level(95.0%)	2.15

(b)

FIGURE 8.18

90% Confidence Interval for Population Proportion	
Mean	0.80
Standard Error	0.0011
Standard Deviation	0.0204
Count	350
Confidence Level(90.0%)	0.0018

(a)

99% Confidence Interval for Population Proportion	
Mean	0.80
Standard Error	0.0011
Standard Deviation	0.0204
Count	350
Confidence Level(99.0%)	0.0028

(b)

FIGURE 8.19

The TI-83 Plus calculator can also simplify the construction of confidence intervals for a population mean or a population proportion. Notice in Figure 8.20a the TI-83 Plus calculator refers to a confidence interval about a population mean where the population standard deviation is known as a **ZInterval.** The input screen for such an interval requires you to enter the population standard deviation, σ, and the sample results $\bar{x}$ and n. Notice in Figure 8.20a, the population standard deviation has been entered as 10 while the sample results were entered as: $\bar{x}$ = 50.52, and n = 100. To obtain a 95% confidence interval the confidence level, labeled C-Level, has been entered as .95. Within the input screen, the word *Stats* is highlighted because the sample information, $\bar{x}$ and n, was entered. Figure 8.20b displays the TI-83's output for the 95% confidence interval for this information.

Notice in Figure 8.20b, the TI-83 displays the 95% confidence interval as (48.56,52.48). The values 48.56 and 52.48, enclosed within the parentheses, represent the lower and upper 95% confidence limits respectively. The display also includes the sample mean and sample size. What is the standard error of the mean? Why do you think this screen is entitled a **ZInterval**?

A confidence interval of the population mean when the population standard deviation, σ, is unknown can also be constructed using the TI-83 Plus. This confidence interval is identified as a TInterval. The input screen for a 90% confidence interval for a population mean for 20 sample data stored in List L2 is displayed in Figure 8.21a. The word DATA is highlighted in Figure 8.21a because the sample data, stored in List L2, was entered into the TI-83 Plus rather than the sample results as shown in Figure 8.20a.

Figure 8.21b displays the 90% confidence interval. Why do you think this confidence interval is entitled a **TInterval**? Explain what the values 18.94 and 28.76 represent. How many data values were in the sample? What is the value of the sample standard deviation and the sample mean? State the margin of error for this confidence interval.

```
ZInterval
 Inpt:Data Stats
 σ:10
 x̄:50.52
 n:100
 C-Level:.95
 Calculate
```

FIGURE 8.20a

```
ZInterval
 (48.56,52.48)
 x̄=50.52
 n=100
```

FIGURE 8.20b

FIGURE 8.21a

FIGURE 8.21b

FIGURE 8.22a

FIGURE 8.22b

To construct a 99% confidence interval for the proportion, p, of red M&M's within a population where a random sample of 350 M&M's containing 38 red M&M's, the appropriate TI-83 Plus input screen for this information is shown in Figure 8.22a. Why do you think the this confidence interval is labeled **1-PropZInt** in Figure 8.22a?

Using the output in Figure 8.22b, what is the point estimate for the population proportion of red M&M's? State the sample proportion of red M&M's. What is the margin of error? What are the limit values for the 99% confidence interval? Explain what this confidence interval indicates about the proportion of red M&M's within the population.

KEY TERMS

Estimate   529
Estimation   530
Point Estimate   530
Point Estimate of the Population
   Proportion, p   530
Estimator   532
Unbiased   532
Good Estimator   532
Interval Estimate   534
Margin of Error   533
90% Confidence Interval for the
   Population Mean, μ 540
95% Confidence Interval for the
   Population Mean, μ 538
99% Confidence Interval for
   Population Mean, μ 540

t Distribution   542
Degrees of Freedom, *df*   543
Sampling Distribution of the
   Proportion   549
Estimate of the Standard Deviation
   of the Sampling Distribution of
   the Proportion or the Estimate of
   the Standard Error of the
   Proportion, $s_{\hat{p}}$ 549
90% Confidence Interval for
   Population Proportion, p   550
95% Confidence Interval for
   Population Proportion, p   550
99% Confidence Interval for
   Population Proportion, p   550
Precision   552

Conservative Estimate of the
   Sample Size   560
Confidence Limits   538
Confidence Level   539

> **SECTION EXERCISES**

Section 8.2

1. The mean, proportion or standard deviation of a population is called a population _____ .

2. To estimate a population parameter, a random _____ is selected from the population.

3. The statistical procedure where sample information is used to estimate the value of a population parameter such as the population mean, population standard deviation or population proportion is called _____ .

4. A sample estimate using a single number to estimate a population parameter, such as, a population mean or population proportion is called a _____ estimate.

5. A method that is used to obtain a point estimate of the population proportion, p, is the _____ .

6. An estimator of a population parameter is said to be _____ , if the mean of the point estimates obtained from the independent samples selected from the population will approach the true value of the population parameter as more and more samples are selected.

7. Which symbol represents a point estimate of the population mean?
   a) p   **b)** $\mu_{\hat{p}}$ **c)** $\hat{p}$ **d)** $\bar{x}$ **e)** $E\mu$

8. Which symbol represents a point estimate of the population proportion?
   a) p   **b)** $\mu_{\hat{p}}$ **c)** $\hat{p}$ **d)** $\bar{x}$ **e)** $E\mu$

9. An example of an estimator is the formula for the standard error of the proportion.
   (T/F)

10. One major disadvantage of using a sample mean point estimate to estimate the true population mean is that we are never sure how far the point estimate is from the true population mean.
    (T/F)

Section 8.3

11. The margin of error usually given in an opinion poll is due to _____ error because not everyone in the population was selected for the poll.

12. An _____ estimate is an estimate that specifies a range of values that the population parameter is likely to fall within.

13. The first step of the procedure in constructing an interval estimate of a population parameter is to select a random sample and calculate a _____ estimate.

14. When constructing a 99% confidence interval for the population mean where the population standard deviation is not known, the sample standard deviation is used to construct such an interval.
    (T/F)

15. State the four criteria required for a good estimator.

16. A CNN/Gallup Poll of 496 adults nationwide stated that 39% of respondents nationally say the federal government has become so large and powerful it poses an immediate threat to the rights and freedoms of ordinary citizens. Percentage of various demographic groups who hold that opinion were:

    CNN/Gallup Poll Results

    Sex:

Men:	35%
Women:	41%

    Education:

No College:	45%
Some College:	40%
College Grad:	26%

    If the margin of error was ± 5 percentage points, then: give an interval estimate for the percentage of:
    a) Men who fear big government.
    b) Women who fear big government.
    c) Adults with no college education who fear big government.
    d) Adults with some college education who fear big government.
    e) College graduates who fear big government.

17. If an interval estimate of the mean life, in miles, of radial tires is 63,040 to 66,960, then determine the margin of error.

Section 8.4

18. The 95% confidence interval for the population mean, **μ**, where the population standard deviation is **known** and the sample size is greater than 30, is constructed by the formula: _____ to _____ .

19. The 99% confidence interval for the population mean, **μ**, where the population standard deviation is **known** and the sample size is greater than 30, is constructed by the formula: _____ to _____ .

20. The 90% confidence interval for the population mean, **μ**, when the population standard deviation is **unknown**, is constructed by the formula: _____ to _____ .

21. The 99% confidence interval for the population mean, **μ**, when the population standard deviation is **unknown**, is constructed by the formula: _____ to _____ .

22. The confidence level of a confidence interval is the _____ value, expressed as percentage, that is associated with an interval estimate, which represents the chance that the _____ used to construct the confidence interval will give an interval that will include the population _____ . Thus, the higher the probability

value, the greater the _____ that the interval estimate will include the population parameter.

23. The *t* Distribution is used to construct a confidence interval for the population mean when the following conditions hold.
   a) The population standard deviation, σ is _____, and is estimated by the _____ .
   b) The population from which the sample is selected is approximately a _____ distribution.

24. According to a CNN random sample of 64 couples, the mean length of dating before marriage is 540 days with a sample standard deviation of 90 days.
   a) Construct a 90% confidence interval to estimate the mean number of dating days for the population.
   b) State the lower and upper confidence limits for this interval.

25. If a sample of size 36 is selected, then the degrees of freedom for the *t* distribution is:
   a) 30   **b)** 37   **c)** 6   **d)** 35

26. To insure that the sampling distribution of the mean can be approximated by the normal distribution, the sample size must be less than 30.
   (T/F)

27. Degrees of freedom is a concept used to determine critical *t* scores.
   (T/F)

28. Which formula is used in the calculation of a confidence interval for the mean when the population standard deviation is **unknown**?
   a) $\dfrac{\sigma}{\sqrt{n}}$

   b) $\dfrac{s}{\sqrt{n}}$

   c) $\sqrt{np(1-p)}$

   d) $E\mu$
   e) np

29. Which formula is used to calculate the estimate of the standard error of the proportion?
   a) $\dfrac{\sigma}{\sqrt{n}}$

   b) $\dfrac{s}{\sqrt{n}}$

   c) $\sqrt{np(1-p)}$

   d) $\sqrt{\dfrac{\hat{p}(1-\hat{p})}{n}}$

   e) np

30. When constructing a 99% confidence interval for the population proportion p for a sample size n, it is assumed that both np and n(1 – p) are greater than 5.
   (T/F)

31. The gasoline consumption of Chevy vans is known to be approximately normally distributed. If a random sample of 25 vans had a mean of 31.7 mpg for highway driving with s = 2.9 mpg., then construct a 95% confidence interval for the mean gasoline consumption of these Chevy vans.

32. The registration time for students at a community college is approximately normally distributed. If a random sample of 49 students has a mean registration time of 92 minutes with a standard deviation of 11.2 minutes, construct a 90% confidence interval for the mean registration time at this community college.

33. A sociologist is interested in estimating the educational level of a community. She randomly interviews 25 adult residents of the community and determines the number of years they attended school. Her sample had a mean of 12.5 years with s = 3.8 years. Use a 95% confidence interval to estimate the educational level of all the adults living in this community.

34. The mean cholesterol level of a random sample of 36 adults aged 45–54 was 215 milligrams of cholesterol with s = 19.84. Construct a 95% confidence interval for the mean cholesterol level of all adults aged 45–54.

35. LITESON, a manufacturer of lighting products, randomly selects a sample of 64 new energy-saving 38 watt light bulbs to estimate the mean amount of hours for these bulbs. Construct a 99% confidence interval to estimate the mean life of all these energy-saving bulbs if the sample mean is 2425 hours with s = 137 hours.

36. A survey of 40 NFL players found the average weight to be 245.3 pounds with s = 15.7 lbs, with an average height of 6 feet 2 inches with s = 3.8 inches. Find:
   a) A 95% confidence interval to estimate the mean weight of all NFL players.
   b) A 90% confidence interval to estimate the mean height of all NFL players.

Section 8.5

37. The value of $s_{\hat{p}}$, which is an estimate of the standard error of the population proportion, $\sigma_{\hat{p}}$, is determined by the formula: $s_{\hat{p}} = $ _____

38. The 95% confidence interval for the population proportion is constructed by the formula: _____ to
_____ .

39. Which formula is used in the calculation of a confidence interval for the population proportion?
   a) p   **b)** $\mu_{\hat{p}}$ **c)** $\hat{p}$ **d)** $\bar{x}$ **e)** $E\mu$

40. When the sampling distribution of the population proportion is approximated by a normal distribution, which z-score is used to construct the 95% confidence interval?
   a) 0.95   **b)** 1.65   **c)** 1.96   **d)** 2.33   **e)** 2.58

For problems 41 to 46, when computing $s_{\hat{p}}$, round off to four decimal places.

41. Determine a 90%, 95% and 99% confidence interval for the following sample data:
   a) $\hat{p} = 0.30$, and n=100
   b) $\hat{p} = 0.30$, and n = 1600
   c) $\hat{p} = 0.30$, and n = 100,000
   d) Explain the relationship between the width of each confidence interval and the margin of error as the sample size increases.

42. According to a CNN Opinion Poll of 500 economists, 43% stated that they felt the stock market would get worse before the end of the year. Construct a 99% confidence interval to estimate the population proportion of economists who feel that the stock market will get worse before the end of the year.

43. A recent Gallup Poll determined that 1278 of 1800 American adults interviewed were in favor of tougher laws to combat crime. Find a 99% confidence interval for the true population proportion of American adults who are in favor of tougher laws to combat crime.

44. According to an independent poll of 1160 people, the Internal Revenue Service (IRS) provided the wrong answers to 198 people who called to ask a question pertaining to their tax return during the recent tax season. Construct a 90% confidence interval to estimate the proportion of all times that the IRS fails to provide a correct answer to a tax question.

45. A Department of Transportation survey of 1480 American drivers stated that 873 drivers wear seat belts. Construct:
   a) A 95% confidence interval to estimate the true proportion of all American drivers that wear seat belts.
   b) A 99% confidence interval to estimate the true proportion of all American drivers that wear seat belts.

46. A National Health Survey of 1640 women determined that 574 women indicated that they are trying to lose weight at any given time, while 468 out of 1560 men stated that they are constantly trying to maintain their weight. Construct:
   a) A 95% confidence interval to estimate the true proportion of all women who are trying to lose weight at any given time.
   b) A 90% confidence interval estimate the true proportion of all men who are constantly trying to maintain their weight.

47. Given the statement: *a 95% confidence interval for the proportion of people owning an answering machine is: 45% ± 3 percentage points,* explain why the following interpretation of this 95% confidence interval statement is incorrect.

This confidence interval is interpreted to mean that you are 95% certain that the true proportion of all people that own an answering machine is within 3 percentage points of 45%.

Section 8.6

48. To increase the precision of a confidence interval with a fixed confidence level, you must _____ the sample size.

49. A confidence interval for a specific level of confidence consists of two components: a point estimate of the _____, and the _____ of error.

50. The margin of error for a confidence interval to estimate the population mean represents the _____ possible error of estimate for the population mean using the _____ .

51. The margin of error is denoted by the symbol _____. The margin of error represents one-half the _____ of the confidence interval.

52. As the level of confidence is increased, where the sample size and population standard deviation remain fixed, the margin of error _____ .

53. To reduce the margin of error while holding the confidence level fixed, then the sample size must be _____ .

54. The width of a confidence interval is twice the _____ .

55. For a given confidence level, a known population standard deviation, and a given margin of error, the formula to determine the sample size, n, to satisfy these requirements in estimating the population mean is: n = _____ .

56. For a given confidence level, a point estimate of the population proportion, $\hat{p}$, and a given margin of error, the formula to determine the sample size, n, to satisfy these requirements in estimating the population proportion is: n = _____ .

57. When determining the margin of error, the sample standard deviation is the one measure you can control. (T/F)

58. Determine a **conservative estimate** of the sample size for estimating the population proportion using a 95% confidence interval where the margin of error is to be:
   a) 0.01
   b) 0.10
   c) Explain one advantage in computing **conservative estimate**.

59. A manufacturing company wants to estimate the proportion of defective squash balls that are produced by a machine to be within 0.03 of the population proportion for a 99% confidence level. How large of a sample size, n, must the company select to accomplish this using the **conservative estimate** of the sample size formula?

60. **a)** How large a sample is required if one would like to be 95% confident that the estimate of the population mean height of Americans will be within 0.5 inches of the population mean? (Assume that the population standard deviation is 6 inches.)

b) How large a sample is required for a 99% confidence interval of the population mean height of Americans? (Assume that the population standard deviation is 6 inches.)

61. How many times would a fair coin have to be randomly tossed to be 99% confident that between 40% and 60% of the tosses will land heads?

62. An opinion poll estimates the percentage of voters who favor candidate P to be 48% with a margin of error of 3

percentage points. Candidate P is not pleased with this poll and decides to take another poll that will have a higher precision level of 2 percentage points for the margin of error. If the candidate is willing to accept a 95% confidence level, then determine:

a) The number of voters that should be interviewed for this new poll.

b) The cost of the new poll, if the cost per interview is $1.50.

CHAPTER REVIEW

63. A sample mean, $\bar{x}$, is one method that is used to obtain a _____ estimate of the population mean, μ.

64. Any sample statistic that is used to estimate a population parameter is called an _____ .

65. A point estimate is a procedure that is used to estimate the value of a population parameter. (T/F)

66. An estimator is considered unbiased because as more and more samples are selected from the population, the mean of the point estimates obtained from the independent random samples approach the true value of the population parameter. (T/F)

67. An interval estimate uses a range of values and a probability level to indicate how confident one is that the interval will **not** contain the population parameter. (T/F)

68. A Gallup survey of 1000 adults stated 49% of American adults suffer sleep-related problems such as insomnia. In addition, 52% of women say they have sleeping difficulties while only 45% of men stated they had sleeping difficulties. Whereas 40% of adults say they sometimes doze off when bored. The margin of error was 3 percentage points for this survey. Using this information, state an interval estimate for each of the stated percentages within this Gallup survey.

69. The 90% confidence interval for the population mean, μ, where the population standard deviation is **known** and the sample size is greater than 30, is constructed by the formula: _____ to _____ .

70. The 95% confidence interval for the population mean, μ, when the population standard deviation is **unknown,** is constructed by the formula: _____ to _____ .

71. A 95% confidence interval for a population mean doesn't tell you whether a particular _____ will contain the population mean. But rather it means that: in the long run, the percentage of _____ intervals constructed using this procedure will probably contain the population mean _____ of the time.

72. The sampling distribution of the mean is a *t* distribution if the standard deviation of the _____ is unknown

and the population from which the sample is selected is a _____ distribution.

73. The *t* distribution is generally less dispersed than the normal distribution. (T/F)

74. Which formula is used in the calculation of a confidence interval for the mean when the population standard deviation is **known**?

a) $\dfrac{\sigma}{\sqrt{n}}$

b) $\dfrac{s}{\sqrt{n}}$

c) $\sqrt{np(1-p)}$

d) $\sqrt{\dfrac{\hat{p}(1-\hat{p})}{n}}$

e) np

75. A random sample of 100 American workers showed that the average number of hours an employee works per week is 36.3 with the sample standard deviation equal to 4.2 hours. Find a 95% confidence interval for the mean number of hours that all American employees work per week.

76. A sociology professor is interested in estimating the mean number of hours that a day student spends per week studying. The professor randomly selects 400 day students and calculates that the sample mean number of hours spent on studying is 18.5 hrs with s = 4. Determine the:

a) Population

b) Population parameter being estimated

c) Estimator used to estimate the population parameter

d) Point estimate

e) Margin of error for the 90%, 95%, and 99% confidence level

f) 90% confidence interval for the population mean, μ

g) 95% confidence interval for the population mean, μ

h) 99% confidence interval for the population mean, μ

77. The Student Government Association President wants to estimate the mean amount of dollars spent on textbooks and supplies per semester by a full-time student.

The President randomly selects 625 full-time students and calculates the mean amount of dollars they spent on textbooks and supplies per semester to be $247 with s=35. Determine the:
a) Population
b) Population parameter being estimated
c) Estimator used to estimate the population parameter
d) Point estimate
e) Margin of error for the 90%, 95%, and 99% confidence level
f) 90% confidence interval for the population mean, μ
g) 95% confidence interval for the population mean, μ
h) 99% confidence interval for the population mean, μ

78. A special fat reducing diet is tested on 28 middle aged males. The results of the test indicated that the mean amount of weight loss was 14 lbs with s = 2.5. Determine a 99% Confidence Interval for the diet. What is the margin of error associated with this estimate?

79. The properties of a *t* distribution are:
a) The graph of a *t* distribution is _____ .
b) The *t* distribution is symmetric about the _____

_____ .
c) The *t* distribution is more varied and flatter than the standard _____ distribution.
d) There is a different *t* distribution for each _____ size. A particular *t* distribution is specified by giving the degrees of _____, where *df* = ____.
e) As the number of degrees of freedom increases, the *t* distribution approaches the _____ distribution. They are sufficiently close when the degrees of freedom are greater than ____.

80. The formula used to determine the *df* with one sample is:
a) $df = n$ b) $df = n + 1$ c) $df = n - 1$ d) $df = n$

81. The 90% confidence interval for the population proportion is constructed by the formula: _____ to _____ .

82. A random sample of n college students is selected from the student body to estimate the mean IQ score of the student population. Assuming that the sample mean is 108, and the population standard deviation is equal to 15, construct a 95% confidence interval for samples of size:
a) 36
b) 100
c) 400
d) Determine the width of the confidence intervals found in parts a, b & c.
e) What is the effect on the width of the confidence interval as the sample size is increased while the confidence level remains the same?

For problems 83 to 87, when computing $s_{\hat{p}}$, round off to four decimal places.

83. DPT Enterprises, Inc. is about to market a new kind of shaver, a shaver with six blades. In order to determine if

they should proceed with their manufacturing plans, the marketing department of the company decides to survey a cross section of the potential buyers as to their feelings regarding their purchasing of the new shaver. The results of the survey were:

152 potential buyers said they would buy the shaver
sample size = 7569

Determine the:
a) Population
b) Population parameter being estimated
c) Estimator used to estimate the population parameter
d) Point estimate
e) Margin of error for the 90%, 95%, and 99% confidence level
f) 90% confidence interval for the population proportion.
g) 95% confidence interval for the population proportion.
h) 99% confidence interval for the population proportion.

84. Suppose you are the polling consultant for a state senator. You find that a straw poll of 625 registered voters indicates that 263 registered voters name drugs within the schools as the most important issue facing the inner city schools. Determine a 95% confidence interval for the proportion of all voters who hold this opinion. What is the margin of error associated with this estimate?

85. *PCDAY* computing magazine recently published that Microhard word processing software now has 24% of the nation's word processing market. Determine the:
a) Population
b) Population parameter being estimated
c) Estimator used to estimate the population parameter
d) Point estimate
e) 90% confidence interval and margin of error for the population proportion if the sample size used is:
1) 100
2) 400
3) 1024
f) 95% confidence interval and margin of error for the population proportion if the sample size used is:
1) 100
2) 400
3) 1024
g) 99% confidence interval and margin of error for the population proportion if the sample size used is:
1) 100
2) 400
3) 1024.
h) Discuss what happens to the margin of error as the sample size increases for each confidence level.
i) Discuss what happens to the margin of error as both the sample size and confidence level increase.

86. According to a nationwide survey of 1254 adults conducted by U.S. Health Care Financing Administration,

915 adults said they suffered from headache pain, and 702 reported that they suffered from backache pain. Find:

a) A 90% confidence interval for the true proportion of all adults that suffer from headache pain.

b) A 95% confidence interval for the true proportion of all adults that suffer from backache pain.

87. A Roper Starch survey of 1350 men aged 18 years and older found that 486 men were single, while a random sample of 1560 women aged 18 years and older showed that 624 were single. Construct:

a) A 95% confidence interval to estimate the true proportion of all single women that are 18 years or older.

b) A 99% confidence interval to estimate the true proportion of all single men that are 18 years or older.

88. A random sample of 49 college male students indicates that the mean pulse rate, while at rest, is 68.3 beats per minute. Assuming the population standard deviation is 9.6 beats per minute, determine:

a) A 95% confidence interval for the mean pulse rate, while at rest, for the population of college male students.

b) The width of this 95% confidence interval.

c) The margin of error for this 95% confidence interval.

d) How large a sample of college students would one need to select to be 95% confident that the margin of error is within 1 heart beat of the mean pulse rate for all college male students?

89. The quality-control department of an electrical manufacturer estimated the mean lifetime of their new miser 60-watt bulb by randomly selecting 64 bulbs and determined the sample mean lifetime to be: $\bar{x} = 1817$ hours. If the population standard deviation of these miser bulbs is 240 hours, then:

a) Determine the margin of error for a 99% confidence interval.

b) What is the width of this 99% confidence interval?

c) Within how many hours can the manufacturer conclude that they are 99% confident that the sample mean lifetime of 1817 hours is from the population mean lifetime of these new miser bulbs?

90. The formula used to calculate the margin of error when estimating the population mean, where the population standard deviation is known, is: E = _____ .

91. The margin of error formula used to determine the maximum possible error of estimate for the population proportion using the sample proportion, $\hat{p}$, is: E = _____ .

92. For a given confidence level, and a given margin of error, the formula to determine the **conservative** sample size, n, to satisfy these requirements in estimating the population proportion is: n = _____ .

93. A medical student is interested in estimating with a 90% confidence level the proportion of babies that are born between the hours of: 6AM and 6PM, called a "*morning baby.*" If the student wants the margin of error to be within 4 percentage points, determine:

a) A **conservative estimate** for the sample size required to meet these requirements.

b) An estimate of the sample size required to satisfy these conditions, if a previous sample showed the proportion of morning babies to be 0.62.

WHAT DO YOU THINK?

94. The following article entitled "Survey Finds High Fear of Crime" discusses the results of a Gallup Poll on crime.

Survey Finds High Fear of Crime

Fear of crime continues to pervade American society, especially in urban areas, where 76 percent of women fear walking alone at night in their neighborhood, according to the latest Gallup Poll.

Over all, 45 percent of Americans are afraid to go out alone at night within a mile of their homes, the researchers reported. Thirteen percent had that fear in the day. Sixty-two percent of the women surveyed had that fear, as did 26 percent of the men.

The survey also found that crime had affected an average of 25 percent of American households in the last 12 months.

Comparing surveys over the last decade, the poll reported that the incidence of crime and fear of crime had remained about the same.

Another statistic that has remained constant is the number of people who do not feel safe at home at night. Sixteen percent said they felt unsafe, as did 16 percent in 1991, 15 percent in 1987 and 20 percent in 1985. The difference in these figures is statistically insignificant because the survey's margin of error is plus or minus three percentage points.

The one area in which a marked change was found was the number of people who thought there was "more crime in this area than there was a year ago". In 1992, 47 percent felt there was more crime than there had been a year before, in contrast to 37 percent in the latest poll.

The poll said its findings showed that "the actual crime situation in this country is more serious than official Government figures" indicate because "many incidents are not reported to the police."

The findings were based on interviews conducted in person with 1,555 adults from Jan. 28-31.

a) Define the population for this survey.

b) What type of estimate does the percentage value of 76% represent? What population parameter is it being used to estimate? Explain.

c) What was the margin of error for this survey? How would you interpret this margin of error?

d) State an interval that you believe might contain the true population proportion of Americans who are afraid to go out alone at night within one mile of their homes. How did you construct such an interval?

e) What is meant by the statement "the difference in these figures is statistically insignificant because the survey's margin of error is plus or minus three percentage points"?

f) State a sample point estimate for the proportion of women who are afraid to go out alone at night within a mile of their homes. State an interval estimate for the proportion of women who are afraid to go out alone at night within a mile of their homes. What is the difference between these two estimates?

95. The following *New York Times* section entitled "Pulse/ Working Mothers" presents the results of four questions conducted by the Gallup Poll.

  a) Define the population for this survey.

b) In question #1, what type of estimate does the percentage value 67% represent? What population parameter is being estimated? Explain.

c) Calculate the margin of error for question #1 using a z score of 1.96. How does this compare to the margin of error for the poll?

d) Construct a 95% confidence interval for the "yes" response to question #1. How would you interpret this result? What is the width of this confidence interval? How does this compare to the margin of error?

e) Determine a 95% confidence interval for the population proportion of women who feel it is very important to share child-rearing responsibilities with another adult. What is the width of this confidence interval? How does this compare to the margin of error? Explain.

f) Give a point estimate of the women who feel that conditions for working mothers would improve if more women were elected to prominent Federal government positions. Determine a 95% confidence interval using this point estimate. What is the width of this interval?

g) State an interval that you believe, with 95% confidence, might contain the true population proportion

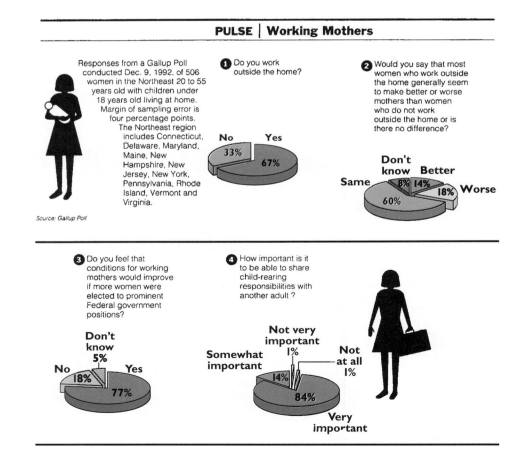

PULSE | Working Mothers

Responses from a Gallup Poll conducted Dec. 9, 1992, of 506 women in the Northeast 20 to 55 years old with children under 18 years old living at home. Margin of sampling error is four percentage points. The Northeast region includes Connecticut, Delaware, Maryland, Maine, New Hampshire, New Jersey, New York, Pennsylvania, Rhode Island, Vermont and Virginia.

Source: Gallup Poll

1 Do you work outside the home?

No 33%   Yes 67%

2 Would you say that most women who work outside the home generally seem to make better or worse mothers than women who do not work outside the home or is there no difference?

Same 60%   Don't know 8%   Better 14%   Worse 18%

3 Do you feel that conditions for working mothers would improve if more women were elected to prominent Federal government positions?

Don't know 5%   No 18%   Yes 77%

4 How important is it to be able to share child-rearing responsibilities with another adult?

Somewhat important 14%   Not very important 1%   Not at all 1%   Very important 84%

of women who feel that most women who work outside the home generally seem to make worse mothers than women who do not work outside the home. What is the width of this interval? How does this width compare to the margin of error?

h) State a point estimate for the proportion of women who feel it is somewhat important to share child-

rearing responsibilities with another adult? Determine a 95% and a 99% confidence interval using this point estimate. What is the width of each of these intervals? What can you conclude about the relationship between the width of the confidence intervals and the degree of confidence?

PROJECTS

96. Find an example of an interval estimate that is published in a newspaper or magazine. Identify the:
  a) Population
  b) Population parameter being estimated
  c) Estimator used to estimate the population parameter
  d) Point estimate
  e) Sample size
  f) Margin of error

97. Poll your fellow students on an issue of concern for your school. For your poll, identify the:
  a) Population
  b) Population parameter being estimated
  c) Estimator used to estimate the population parameter
  d) Point estimate
  e) Margin of error
  f) 90% confidence interval for the population parameter
  g) 95% confidence interval for the population parameter
  h) 99% confidence interval for the population parameter

98. Randomly select a page from this text and count the number of words on the page.
  a) Estimate the number of words in this book using this information.
  b) Construct a 95% confidence interval using this information.

99. Use a random sample of students at your school to estimate the population of students at the school that are:
  a) Female.
  b) Male.
  Using this information, construct a 95% confidence interval for the percentage of all students that are:
  c) Female.
  d) Male.

100. Use a technological tool to find the 90%, 95%, and 99% confidence intervals for the population mean for the sample data randomly selected from the population whose standard deviation is 20, if the data values are:

$$104 \ 75 \ 59 \ 73 \ 71 \ 74 \ 39$$
$$93 \ 84 \ 80 \ 62 \ 120 \ 50 \ 80$$
$$56 \ 62$$

  a) What is the point estimate?
  b) For each confidence interval determine the margin of error.

101. Use a technological tool to find the 90%, 95%, and 99% confidence intervals for the population mean for the random sample of data values selected from the population.

$$2.91 \ 2.34 \ 1.94 \ 3.33 \ 3.95$$
$$2.55 \ 2.67 \ 2.87 \ 2.95 \ 2.78$$
$$3.56 \ 3.68 \ 2.88 \ 3.05 \ 2.68$$
$$3.55 \ 2.98 \ 1.94 \ 2.47 \ 2.88$$

  a) What is the point estimate?
  b) For each confidence interval determine the margin of error.

102. Use a technological tool to find the 90%, 95%, and 99% confidence intervals for the population proportion for a random sample of 400 data values selected from a population that yields a point estimate of 0.6. For each confidence interval determine the margin of error.

103. Suppose that you randomly sample 20 times from a population whose data values are approximately normal with a mean of 500 and a standard deviation of 100.
  a) If you were to form a 95% confidence interval for your 20 random samples, how many of the confidence intervals would you expect to include the true population mean value of 500?
  b) What would be the margin of error for your simulation if the sample size was 400?
  c) Use a technological tool to simulate the selection of 20 random samples of size 400 from a normal distribution whose mean is 500 and whose standard deviation is 100.
  d) For each of the 20 random samples generated in part (c), calculate the 95% confidence interval using a technological tool.
  e) How many of the 20 confidence intervals contained the true population mean of 500? How does this compare to your answer to part (a)? Explain.

The following exercises refer to the file DATABASE listed in Appendix A. Using a technological tool, answer each exercise.

104. For the variable names: GPA, AVE, WRK, STY, GFT.
   a) Construct 90%, 95% and 99% confidence intervals for each of the variables.
   b) Interpret each of the confidence intervals in terms of the population means to which they are inferring.

105. For the variable names: SEX, EYE, HR, MAJ.
   a) Construct 90%, 95% and 99% confidence intervals for each portion of the population proportion contained within each variable.
   b) Interpret each of the confidence intervals in terms of the population proportion to which they are inferring.

106. The numerical value obtained from the sample mean (or sample proportion) formula is referred to as an _____ of the population mean (or sample proportion). The sample mean (or sample proportion) formula which is used to find a point estimate of the population mean (or population proportion) is called an _____ .

107. The 95% confidence interval for the population mean suggests that 5% of these confidence intervals constructed for all possible sample means will not contain the true population mean.
(T/F)

108. A poll conducted for the National Heart, Lung and Blood Institute determined that 49% of adults know their own cholesterol level. If the survey's margin of error was 2.5 percentage points, then:
   a) State an interval estimate for the percentage of adults who know their cholesterol level.
   b) If 1,583 adults were surveyed, then state whether the interval estimate of part (a) is either a 90%, 95% or 99% interval estimate. Explain your reasoning.

109. Determine a 90%, 95% and 99% confidence interval and the margin of error for the following sample data:
   a) $\bar{x} = 78, s = 4$ and $n = 16$
   b) $\bar{x} = 78, s = 4$ and $n = 36$
   c) $\bar{x} = 78, s = 4$ and $n = 49$
   d) $\bar{x} = 78, s = 4$ and $n = 100$
   e) What happens to the width of each confidence interval and the margin of error as the sample size increases?

110. In general, as the confidence level increases, the width of the confidence interval _____ .

111. For a sample of size n, the degrees of freedom is equal to the sample size minus _____ . In symbols, $df = $ _____ .

112. A *New England Journal of Medicine* diet study stated that an interval estimate of total caloric intake per day for the control group was 1581 to 3127. While the interval estimate of total caloric intake per day for the treatment group was 1555 to 3409.

   a) Determine the margin of error for each group.
   b) Which group has the wider interval estimate? How does this compare to the size of the margin of error?
   c) Is there a relationship between the width of an interval estimate and the margin of error? Explain.

113. Using the information: a random sample of 36 students averaged 9.06 hours of sleep on the weekend with a sample standard deviation of 1.08 hours, construct:
   a) A 90% confidence interval
   b) A 95% confidence interval
   c) A 99% confidence interval
   for the population mean amount of time students sleep on the weekend
   d) Determine the width of each confidence interval by subtracting the lower confidence limit from the upper confidence limit.
   e) Compare and discuss the relationship of the width of each confidence interval with the confidence level.
   f) What happens to the width as the confidence level increases?

114. Which of the following is *not* a property of the *t* distribution?
   a) Less dispersed than the normal distribution
   b) Symmetric with respect to t = 0
   c) Bell-shaped
   d) Different *t* distribution for each sample size

115. A random sample of 16 college students living within a dorm had a mean monthly telephone bill of $52.79 with s = $8.64. Construct a 90% confidence interval for the mean monthly telephone bill for all students living in the college dorm.

116. The 99% confidence interval for the population proportion is constructed by the formula: _____ to _____ .

117. When the sampling distribution of the population proportion is approximated by a normal distribution, which z-score is used to construct the 99% confidence interval?
   a) 0.95   **b)** 1.65   **c)** 1.96   **d)** 2.33   **e)** 2.58

118. A CNN telephone survey of 1050 married adults indicated that 724 adults preferred to celebrate their anniversary by eating at a romantic restaurant. Construct a 90% confidence interval to estimate the true proportion of all married adults who prefer to celebrate their anniversary by eating at a romantic restaurant.

119. As the sample size increases, the margin of error increases.
(T/F)

120. A political activist wants to estimate the proportion of all college students who are registered to vote. Determine:
a) A **conservative estimate** of the sample size that would produce a margin of error of 3 percentage points for a 95% confidence interval.
b) An estimate for the size of a sample for a 95% confidence interval, if a previous sample indicated that the proportion of college students who are registered to vote was 28%.

CHAPTER 9

Introduction to Hypothesis Testing

Contents

9.1 INTRODUCTION

Hypothesis testing is an important statistical decision-making tool that has applications in a variety of fields such as education, economics, medicine, psychology, marketing, sociology, management, etc. The following situations represent typical instances where a decision is required and the hypothesis testing procedure can be applied to help with this decision.

- A new drug is being tested to determine its effectiveness and safety. These results will be compared to the effectiveness of the drug currently in use. Based on the comparison of the test results, a decision will be made either to market the new drug or to continue marketing the present drug.
- The college registrar is testing a new registration procedure. The effectiveness of the new procedure is to be determined by comparing data collected under the existing system with the data collected using the new registration system. The registrar's decision as to which procedure to use will depend upon the analysis of the test results.
- A new manufacturing procedure is being tested to determine its effectiveness in reducing the number of defective finished products. These test results will be compared to the number of defective products under the present manufacturing procedure. Based on the comparison of the test results, a decision will be made to either implement the new procedure or to retain the present procedure.
- The developer of a special reflective coating for windows claims that this coating applied to the windows of a house will reduce air conditioning costs by at least 40%. Before a manufacturer will agree to purchase the manufacturing and marketing rights of this product a test will be conducted to determine if this product is as effective as claimed by its developer. Based on the test results the manufacturer will decide if it should purchase the special reflective coating.
- Many companies use "**acceptance sampling**" to determine if the quality of parts received from suppliers meet their specifications. Before the company accepts the supplier's shipment of parts, a sample of the parts is selected from the shipment and tested to determine if the parts meet the specifications. Based on the analysis of the test results, the company will either accept or reject the supplier's shipment.

9.2 HYPOTHESIS TESTING

Hypothesis testing is an example of inferential statistics. Since sample information is used to draw a conclusion about the population from which the sample was selected. For example, suppose an automotive club researcher decides to test the claim that "70% of Americans use seat belts" made by the National Highway Traffic Safety Administration by using a sample selected from the population. The National

Highway's claim states that the population proportion of Americans who use a seat belt is 70%. If the researcher samples 1500 Americans and determines 67.5% indicate that they use a seat belt, then based on this statistical result can the researcher conclude that National Highway's claim about the population proportion is too high? A hypothesis test is an appropriate statistical technique to use to answer this question because the researcher is using a sample proportion to draw a conclusion about the population proportion of Americans who use a seat belt. The hypothesis testing procedure will enable the researcher to determine if the sample proportion of 67.5% is significantly less than the stated population proportion of 70% or whether this difference happened just by chance alone.

It is also important to realize that we cannot be 100% certain about the conclusions we draw about the population based upon one sample since a different sample selected from the same population could conceivably lead one to draw a different conclusion about the same population. Consequently, it is necessary to use probability to help explain how reliable our conclusions are. The inferences we make will be most reliable when the sample data is randomly selected from the population. Therefore, when we apply the hypothesis testing procedure we will always assume that the sample data was randomly selected from the population.

In this chapter, we will examine the reasoning used in the hypothesis testing procedure. The essence of hypothesis testing is to evaluate the evidence provided by a sample regarding a claim made about a population parameter. The following simplified example regarding sex prediction illustrates the reasoning associated with a hypothesis test.

EXAMPLE 9.1   Hypothesis Test of Sex Prediction

A doctor asserts she has a method that is 75% accurate in predicting, several months before birth, the sex of an unborn child. She is challenged to convince us that her claim is true. To test her claim, she predicts the sex of 36 unborn children and is correct in 17 of her predictions. Do we have any basis to support the doctor's claim?

Solution

We cannot support the doctor's claim, since we can argue that if her claim of 75% accuracy is true, she would almost never guess ONLY 17 out of 36 newborns. The reasoning behind rejecting her claim is supported by the extremely small probability that she would correctly predict as few as 17 out of 36 newborns if she really can predict the sex 75% of the time. The probability of such an occurrence is only 0.0002. In other words, if her claim of 75% is true, then we would expect her to correctly predict as few as 17 out of 36 newborns only twice in 10,000 times over the long run. This extremely small probability convinces us that her claim cannot be supported and should be rejected. _____■

The basic idea behind hypothesis testing as illustrated by this example is simply a sample result that would rarely happen if a claim were true is good evidence to reject the claim. Clearly, we started to suspect the doctor's claim when the outcome of 17 correct predictions out of 36 newborns was shown to be a very unusual or rare event. (That is, a probability of 0.0002!) Thus, the more unusual or rare the sample outcome, the more doubtful we are that the sample outcome couldn't just happen by chance alone. In such instances, we believe that the sample outcome is enough evidence "beyond a reasonable doubt" to reject the claim!

Null and Alternative Hypotheses

A hypothesis test begins by stating the hypotheses or claims of the statistical test. There are two hypotheses that are formulated. One is referred to as the **null hypothesis** while the other is called the **alternative hypothesis**. The null hypothesis is a statement which hypothesizes a value for a population parameter. While the alternative hypothesis is a statement that claims the population parameter is a value **different** than the value stated within the null hypothesis. In the hypothesis testing procedure we try to gather evidence to reject the null hypothesis and thus assert the alternative hypothesis.

In many ways, the hypothesis testing procedure is similar to the U.S. judicial process. In our development of hypothesis testing we will draw an analogy to the judicial process to provide a rationale and better understanding of the procedure used in the statistical testing of a hypothesis.

Within the judicial system, once an individual has been accused of committing a crime, a trial is conducted to determine if there is enough evidence to convict the individual. Throughout the trial, the fundamental assumption is that the individual is innocent. However, it is the objective of the prosecutor to present enough evidence to convince the jury to reject the assumption of innocence and find the individual guilty as charged.

In hypothesis testing the researcher is confronted with a similar problem. The researcher begins by formulating a fundamental assumption referred to as the null hypothesis. Similar to the judicial system where it is the prosecutor's task to present evidence to cause the rejection of the assumption of innocence, in the hypothesis testing procedure it is the objective of the researcher to present sample data (evidence) to cause the rejection of the null hypothesis.

Thus, the only way the prosecutor can obtain the objective of a guilty verdict is by convincing the jury to reject the assumption of innocence. This last statement is the essence of hypothesis testing.

In the hypothesis testing procedure, the researcher formulates *two hypotheses:* the **null hypothesis** and an **alternative hypothesis**. The alternative hypothesis is stated in such a way that by *rejecting the null hypothesis* the researcher is able to support his or her belief, the alternative hypothesis. The null hypothesis is symbolized by H_o and the alternative hypothesis is symbolized by H_a. Let's now define these two hypotheses.

DEFINITION 9.1

Null Hypothesis, symbolized by H_o, is the statement being tested which states a value for a population parameter and is initially **assumed to be true**. The null hypothesis is stated as to indicate **"no change"** in the status quo or **"no difference"** or **"no relationship"**. It is formulated for the sole purpose of trying to reject it by seeking evidence against it.

Within the hypothesis testing procedure, the researcher will be testing whether the claim stated about the population parameter within the null hypothesis is reasonable based upon the sample information. If the sample information leads to the rejection of the null hypothesis, then this will convince the researcher to accept the alternative hypothesis. The alternative hypothesis is a statement about the population parameter that the researcher is trying to find evidence to support it.

DEFINITION 9.2

Alternative Hypothesis, symbolized by H_a, is a statement about the value of a population parameter which is different from the valued stated in the null hypothesis. The alternative hypothesis is stated to indicate that the status quo is **"not true"** or **"there is a difference"** or **"there is a relationship."** The alternative hypothesis is suspected to be true and is supported by the rejection of the null hypothesis.

The alternative hypothesis is always stated in a manner whereby the rejection of the null hypothesis will lead to the acceptance of the alternative hypothesis.

EXAMPLE 9.2

State the null hypothesis and the alternative hypothesis for the following study.

A national poll states that 60% of the U.S. population believe that the Space Shuttle program should be continued. A researcher who decides to test this statement would like to show that more than 60% of the U.S. population believe the Space Shuttle program should be continued.

Solution

The researcher would like to find evidence to support that more than 60 percent of the U.S. population believe the Space Shuttle program should be continued. This statement about the population parameter is the *alternative* hypothesis, H_a. In order to support the alternative hypothesis, H_a, the researcher must *test* and *try to gather evidence to reject* the statement that 60 percent of the U.S. population believe the Space Shuttle program should be continued. Since this statement about the Space Shuttle program represents "no change" in the status quo, then this is the *null* hypothesis, H_o. The null and alternative hypotheses are:

H_o: The proportion of the U.S. population who believe the Space Shuttle program should be continued is 60%.

H_a: The proportion of the U.S. population who believe the Space Shuttle program should be continued is **more than 60 percent**.

EXAMPLE 9.3

State the null hypothesis and the alternative hypothesis for the following research.

A college newspaper claims that full-time college students work an average of 20 hours a week. A marketing professor who believes this claim is too high decides to conduct a study to test the newspaper's claim.

Solution

The professor would like to find evidence to show that full-time college students work less than an average of 20 hours per week. This statement about the population parameter is the *alternative* hypothesis, H_a. In order to support the alternative hypothesis, H_a, the professor must *test* and *try to gather evidence to reject* the statement that full-time college students work an average of 20 hours per week which represents the status quo. This is the *null* hypothesis, H_o. The hypotheses are:

H_o: The population average number of hours that full-time college students work **is 20 hours per week**.

H_a: The population average number of hours that full-time college students work **is less than 20 hours per week**.

In the **Examples 9.2 and 9.3**, each **alternative** hypothesis contained words such as: **more than** or **less than**. These words indicate the *direction* of the difference from the value of the population parameter as stated in the null hypothesis. Such hypotheses are called ***directional*** alternative hypotheses.

DEFINITION 9.3

A **directional alternative hypothesis** is an alternative hypothesis that considers **only one specified direction of difference** away from the value stated in the null hypothesis. A directional alternative hypothesis is stated using words equivalent to: **less than** or **greater than**.

EXAMPLE 9.4

State the null hypothesis and the alternative hypothesis for the following research.

A new environmentally safe organic fertilizer developed by a botanist is claimed to have no effect on the average yield of 50 vegetables per plant. The U.S. Agriculture Department wants to test the botanist's claim against the suspicion the new fertilizer *has an effect* on the average yield of 50 vegetables per plant.

Solution

The hypothesis to be tested is: the new fertilizer has no effect on the average yield of 50 vegetables per plant. This is referred to as the *null* hypothesis, H_o. Since the Agriculture Department would like to test whether the average yield **has been** effected (i.e., decreased or increased), both possibilities must be considered when stating the alternative hypothesis. This is done by stating the alternative hypothesis as: **using the new fertilizer the average yield per plant is not 50 vegetables.** So the hypotheses are:

H_o: The new fertilizer has no effect on the population average yield of 50 vegetables per plant.

H_a: Using the new fertilizer the population average yield per plant **is not** 50 vegetables.

When we need to consider **both** directions for the alternative hypothesis, that is, when phrases such as: too high, too low, more than, less than, etc. are **not** explicitly used or implied then the alternative hypothesis is a ***nondirectional*** alternative hypothesis.

> **DEFINITION 9.4**
>
> A **nondirectional alternative hypothesis** is a hypothesis that considers **both directions** away from the value specified in the null hypothesis. A **nondirectional** alternative hypothesis is stated using phrases equivalent to: **is not**, or **is not equal to**.

After the hypotheses are formulated the researcher's task is to design a procedure to test the null hypothesis. This statistical procedure consists of five steps and is referred to as the **hypothesis testing procedure.**

Hypothesis Testing Procedure

The hypothesis testing procedure consists of the five steps.

Step 1   Formulate the hypotheses.
Step 2   Determine the model to test the null hypothesis.
Step 3   Formulate a decision rule.
Step 4   Analyze the sample data.
Step 5   State the conclusion.

To help you understand the logic of the hypothesis testing procedure, we will outline the hypothesis testing procedure and illustrate how it is similar to the procedure followed within the judicial system.

A Comparison of the Hypothesis Tesing Procedure to the Judicial System

Hypothesis Testing Procedure	Application of Hypothesis Testing Procedure to the Judicial System
Step 1 Formulate the hypotheses. State the null hypothesis, H_o, and alternative hypothesis, H_a.	**Step 1 H_o:** *Individual is innocent.* This statement represents the status quo. **H_a:** *Individual is guilty.* The statement the prosecutor will try to convince the jury to accept by presenting evidence to **reject the null hypothesis.**
Step 2 Determine the model to test the null hypothesis. In this step the researcher identifies an appropriate distribution to serve as a model and calculates its mean and standard error. The mean and standard error values are referred to as the **expected results** of the test and are computed based upon the **assumption that the null hypothesis is true.**	**Step 2** The model is how the trial will be conducted. This includes the selection of a jury and the strategies formulated by both the defense attorney and the prosecutor. **This trial is based upon the assumption that the accused is presumed to be innocent** (i.e. the null hypothesis is assumed to be true).
Step 3 Formulate a decision rule. A decision rule is a statement formulated by the researcher which defines the criteria necessary for the rejection of the null hypothesis.	**Step 3** Each juror, in his/her own mind, will determine how much evidence is required to convict the individual. (i.e. reject the assumption of innocence)
Step 4 Analyze the sample data. After the data has been collected, the researcher analyzes the sample data by calculating the **test statistic**. A **test statistic** is a quantity computed from sample information that is used to make a decision about the null hypothesis.	**Step 4** The jury must analyze the evidence presented by both the prosecutor and the defense attorney.

Step 5 State the conclusion. The researcher compares the **test statistic** to the **decision rule** and determines the conclusion. The conclusion is either:
a) **Reject the Null Hypothesis, H_o**
    OR
b) **Fail to Reject the Null Hypothesis, H_o.**
	Step 5 The jury determines whether the evidence presented at the trial is enough beyond a reasonable doubt to convict the individual. Their verdict is either:
	a) **Individual is guilty** (this is equivalent to: **reject the null hypothesis**)
	    OR
	b) **Individual is not guilty** (this is equivalent to: **fail to reject the null hypothesis**)

When a researcher draws a conclusion using the hypothesis testing procedure an important question to be considered is: will this procedure always lead to the correct conclusion? Unfortunately, the answer is no. Let's explore why by examining the possible outcomes of a trial. Everyone should be aware that the jury's verdict at the end of a trial is not always correct. The possible outcomes of a trial are shown in Figure 9.1.

By examining Figure 9.1 we see that there are four possible outcomes. In two of these outcomes the correct decision is rendered but in the other two outcomes the wrong decision is reached. These wrong decisions are to *convict* an innocent person or to *free* a guilty person. When the jury convicts an

Possible Outcomes of a Trial	Truth: Person is	
Jury's Verdict:	Not Guilty	Guilty
Guilty	Wrong Decision	Correct Decision
Not Guilty	Correct Decision	Wrong Decision

FIGURE 9.1

innocent person they've committed an error. In statistics, this type of error is referred to as a **Type I error**. The error the jury commits when setting a guilty person free in statistics is referred to as a **Type II error**. A good procedure tries to *minimize* the probabilities of making both types of errors or incorrect decisions. In hypothesis testing the errors a researcher can make which are similar to the incorrect decisions of a jury are summarized in Figure 9.2.

Possible Outcomes to a Statistical Hypothesis Test	Reality:	
Conclusion:	H_o is True	H_o is False
Reject H_o	Type I Error	Correct Decision
Fail to Reject H_o	Correct Decision	Type II Error

FIGURE 9.2

In examining Figure 9.2 notice that there are two types of errors that a researcher can make when performing a hypothesis test. These errors are referred to as a *Type I Error* and a *Type II Error*.

DEFINITION
A **Type I Error** is the error that is made when a **true null hypothesis is incorrectly rejected**.

For example, suppose a researcher is testing the null hypothesis that "70% of Americans use seat belts." A Type I error would occur if 70% of Americans use a seat belt is true for the entire population but the researcher *wrongfully* rejects this null hypothesis because a sample with a proportion much less than 70% was selected from the population.

DEFINITION 9.5
A **Type II Error** is the error that is made when a **false null hypothesis is not rejected**.

Let's return to the example where the researcher is testing the null hypothesis that 70% of Americans use seat belts. A Type II Error occurs when this null hypothesis is actually false (that is, 70% of Americans do not use seat belts) yet the researcher selects a sample, just by chance, with a proportion that is extremely close to 70% and *incorrectly* concludes that the null hypothesis (70% of Americans use seat belts) should not be rejected.

Consequently, when performing a hypothesis test, it is necessary to attempt to minimize the effects of a Type I and Type II Error. Such techniques will be discussed in Section 9.3.

Now, we will illustrate the hypothesis testing procedure through the following two examples.

EXAMPLE 9.5

Suppose you have a favorite coin which you use to make decisions everyday. For example, you might ask, "should I attend my statistics class tomorrow? Heads, I attend, tails I don't." Over a period of time, you notice that you have a perfect attendance record and you begin to question the fairness of your favorite coin. How would you go about testing whether or not your favorite coin is biased? You would need to obtain a sample of the behavior of your favorite coin and draw a conclusion concerning its possible bias. In essence, you would need to conduct a hypothesis test to determine whether your favorite coin is biased (i.e. the probability of heads, p, is not equal to $\frac{1}{2}$: $p \neq \frac{1}{2}$). We will illustrate the hypothesis testing procedure to test your favorite coin for bias.

To help us concentrate just on the concepts of hypothesis testing, the calculations for the mean, standard error (SE) and distribution model usually calculated in step 2 and the calculations for the decision rule(s) usually calculated in step 3 are deliberately omitted within this discussion. You will **NOT** be responsible for these calculations within this chapter. However, these calculations will be discussed and included in subsequent chapters.

Solution

Step 1   Formulate the hypotheses.
We will **assume** that the coin is fair. Thus, the probability of a head, p, is $\frac{1}{2}$: $p = \frac{1}{2}$. This statement represents the null hypothesis.

Null Hypothesis, H_o: $p = \frac{1}{2}$ (coin is fair).

Since we suspect that our favorite coin is not fair then we state the alternative hypothesis as:

Alternative Hypothesis, H_a: $p \neq \frac{1}{2}$ (coin is biased).

Step 2   Determine the model to test the null hypothesis.
To test the null hypothesis we need to sample the behavior of our favorite coin. We will do this by tossing the coin 100 times. *Assuming the null hypothesis is true,* we expect the sampling distribution to have the following characteristics:
1) approximately a normal distribution
2) mean = 0.50
3) standard error: SE = 0.05
These results are shown in Figure 9.3.

Step 3   Formulate the decision rule.
Before one can formulate a decision rule, it is necessary to define a criteria for the rejection of the null hypothesis. This criteria will **always** be based upon the assumption that the null hypothesis is **true**.

Based upon the assumption that the coin is fair, one would expect a sample of 100 tosses to land heads about *50* times. We might decide to consider an *unusual* sample as a statistical result containing more than 60 heads or fewer than 40 heads. For each case, we would con-

Sampling distribution model
is approximately normal

mean = 0.50
standard error = 0.05

FIGURE 9.3

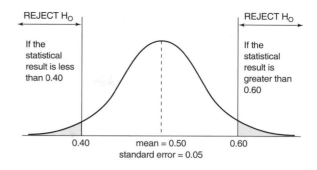

REJECT H$_O$ — If the statistical result is less than 0.40

REJECT H$_O$ — If the statistical result is greater than 0.60

0.40   mean = 0.50   0.60
standard error = 0.05

FIGURE 9.4

clude that the coin is biased. Thus, we would write our *decision rule* as: *reject the null hypothesis,* H$_o$, if, the statistical result is either *more than 60% heads or less than 40% heads.* This decision rule is illustrated in Figure 9.4.

Step 4 Analyze the sample data.
The coin is tossed 100 times and the proportion of heads is recorded. This proportion is referred to as the **statistical result**.

Suppose the coin lands heads 67 times in 100 tosses. The statistical result is:

$$\text{sample proportion} = 67/100 = 0.67$$

Step 5 State the conclusion.
Compare the statistical result to the *decision rule* and determine the conclusion.

For a sample proportion of 0.67, the conclusion is: reject the null hypothesis. This is illustrated in Figure 9.5.

The rejection of the null hypothesis means that one does *not* agree with the assumption that the coin is fair. Therefore, this leads to conclusion that the coin is biased. Thus, in statistical terms, a rejection of the null hypothesis leads to the acceptance of the alternative hypothesis. Furthermore, a rejection of the null hypothesis means that the *difference* between the statistical result and the expected result (the mean) is significant enough to support the alternative hypothesis. We can then say that this difference is **statistically significant**.

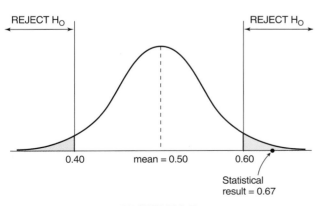

REJECT H$_O$

REJECT H$_O$

0.40   mean = 0.50   0.60

Statistical result = 0.67

FIGURE 9.5

FAIL TO REJECT H$_O$
If the statistical result falls within 0.40 and 0.60

0.40   mean = 0.50   0.60

FIGURE 9.6

If the statistical result fell between 0.40 and 0.60, the conclusion is *not* to reject the null hypothesis or, in other words, to *fail to reject* the null hypothesis since the statistical result is not greater than 0.60 or less than 0.40. This is illustrated in Figure 9.6.

When the statistical result does *not* fall within the rejection region of the decision rule, the conclusion is stated as: *fail to reject* the null hypothesis.

The interpretation of the conclusion (i.e. fail to reject the null hypothesis) means that, according to the decision rule, the statistical result is *not* significantly different from the mean. Therefore, although there is a difference, this difference is **not statistically significant** (not large enough) to conclude that the coin is biased. We are attributing this difference to chance alone. That is, if the coin is truly fair, we would not expect the coin to always land heads 50% of the time for every sample of 100 tosses. We would expect some of the statistical results to vary from 50% heads. This sample variability is often referred to as "**variability due to chance alone**."

In general, when the researcher *fails* to reject the null hypothesis, this means that the difference between the **statistical result** and the **expected result** (the mean) is **not statistically significant**. ▬

Let us use the hypothesis testing procedure to test the claim about VCR's stated in Example 9.6.

EXAMPLE 9.6

A video cassette recorder manufacturer claims that 90% of its video cassette recorders (VCR's) operate three years before repairs are necessary. A consumer group feels that the 90% figure is too high and decides to test the claim.

Solution

Step 1   Formulate the hypotheses.
The claim being tested is that the proportion of all VCR's that operate three years before needing repair is 90%. Since this statement represents the status quo, the null hypothesis is:

H_o: the population proportion of VCR's that operate three years before needing repair is 90%: $p = 0.90$.

On the other hand, the consumer group believes that the 90% figure is too high, thus the alternative hypothesis is stated as:

H_a: the population proportion of VCR's that operate three years before needing repair is *less than 90%*: $p < 0.90$.

Step 2   Determine the model to test the null hypothesis.
To test the null hypothesis the consumer group randomly selects 100 people who have owned one of the manufacturer's video recorders for at least three years. Assuming the *null* hypothesis is true we would expect 90% of the video recorders to last three years before needing repair with a standard error, SE, of 3% or 0.03.

(Note: As indicated in Example 9.5 all calculations necessary to obtain the mean, standard error (SE), model distribution and decision rule(s) are deliberately omitted to simplify the presentation).

The sampling distribution which is approximately normal with the expected results shown in Figure 9.7 serves as the model.

Step 3   Formulate the decision rule.
Based upon the assumption that the manufacturer's claim is correct one would expect 90%

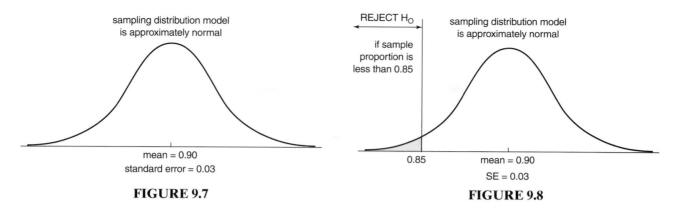

FIGURE 9.7   **FIGURE 9.8**

of the video recorders to have lasted three years before needing repair. Suppose the consumer group formulates its decision rule to be: **reject the null hypothesis if less than 85% of the VCR's have operated at least three years before needing repair.** Thus, if the sample proportion is less than 0.85, then the consumer group will reject the null hypothesis. This decision rule is illustrated in Figure 9.8.

Step 4   Analyze the sample data.
The 100 selected people are interviewed to determine how long their VCR's operated before needing repair.
   If the statistical result is:
87% of the VCR's operated at least three years before needing repair. Thus, the sample proportion of VCR's needing repair is 87% or 0.87.

Step 5   State the conclusion.
For a statistical result of 0.87, the conclusion is *fail to reject* H_o since the sample proportion of 0.87 is greater than the decision rule of 0.85. This is illustrated in Figure 9.9.

FIGURE 9.9

Our conclusion is *fail to reject* H_o since the sample proportion is *not* significantly less than the mean. Consequently, our conclusion (*fail to reject* H_o) means that the manufacturer's claim is not supported.

9.3   THE DEVELOPMENT OF A DECISION RULE

The objective of a hypothesis test is to use sample data to decide if one should reject or fail to reject the null hypothesis. Researchers often use a predetermined decision rule to decide whether the sample data supports or refutes the null hypothesis. To decide whether to reject H_o or fail to reject H_o,

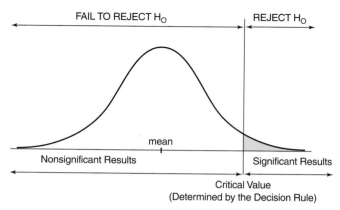

FAIL TO REJECT H_O   REJECT H_O

mean

Nonsignificant Results   Significant Results

Critical Value
(Determined by the Decision Rule)

FIGURE 9.10

the researcher compares the statistical result to the value(s) of the decision rule, referred to as the critical value(s). We examine this idea of a decision rule further through the use of Figure 9.10.

According to the decision rule pictured in Figure 9.10 one *rejects* the null hypothesis if the statistical result is *greater than* the critical value. One *fails to reject* the null hypothesis if the statistical result is *less than* the critical value. Any statistical result falling *beyond* the critical value (shown by the shaded region) is referred to as a ***significant*** result because it leads to the *rejection* of the null hypothesis. For the decision rule illustrated in Figure 9.10, any statistical result less than the critical value is referred to as a *nonsignificant result* since it leads one to *fail to reject the null hypothesis*.

The shaded area to the right of the critical value is referred to as the ***level of significance***, since any statistical result falling within this shaded area is considered *significantly* greater than the expected result (the mean) and will lead to a rejection of the null hypothesis. Let's now define the level of significance.

DEFINITION 9.7

The **level of significance** (definition one) is the probability of a statistical result falling beyond the critical value, assuming that the null hypothesis is true. The level of significance is represented by the lower-case Greek letter α, pronounced alpha.

This is illustrated in Figure 9.11.

FAIL TO REJECT H_O   REJECT H_O

Level of
significance, α

mean

Nonsignificant Results   Critical   Significant Results
Value

FIGURE 9.11

EXAMPLE 9.7

Using the decision rule from Example 9.6, illustrated in Figure 9.12, determine the level of significance, α.

FIGURE 9.12

Solution

For this decision rule, the level of significance, α, is the area to the left of the critical value of 0.85 because any sample proportion falling below 0.85 is considered a significant result. This sampling distribution is approximated by the normal distribution. We can determine the level of significance by computing the z score of 0.85 and by using Table II: The Normal Curve Area Table.

$$z = \frac{0.85 - 0.90}{0.03} = -1.67$$

Using TABLE II the area to the left of z = –1.67 is 0.0475 or 4.75%. Therefore the level of significance is 4.75%, written $\alpha \approx 4.75\%$.

EXAMPLE 9.8

The decision rule in Example 9.5 is illustrated in Figure 9.13. Determine the significance level for this decision rule.

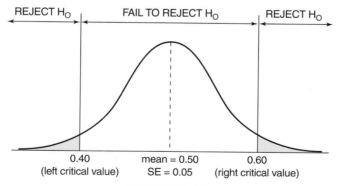

FIGURE 9.13

Solution

From the diagram in Figure 9.13, the decision rule has two areas which must be considered in the evaluation of the significance level. These areas are: the area that exceeds the right critical value of

0.60, and the area that is less than the left critical value of 0.40. If the statistical result falls into **either** one of the shaded areas then this result is **considered significant enough to reject the null hypothesis**.

The level of significance, $\boldsymbol{\alpha}$, is the **sum** of the two shaded areas in Figure 9.13. We can determine the level of significance by computing the z scores of 0.40 and 0.60. The z score of 0.40 is:

$$z = \frac{0.40 - 0.50}{0.05} = -2.00$$

From Table II, the area to the left of z = –2.00 is 0.0228 or 2.28%. Calculating the z score of 0.60, we get:

$$z = \frac{0.60 - 0.50}{0.05} = 2.00$$

From Table II, the area to the left of z = 2.00 is 0.9772 or 97.72%. Therefore the area to the right of z = 2.00 is 2.28%. (see Figure 9.14)

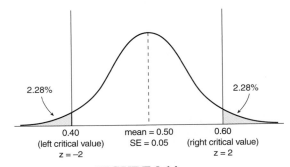

FIGURE 9.14

Since the significance level, $\boldsymbol{\alpha}$, represents the two shaded areas illustrated in Figure 9.14, then α is equal to the sum of these two shaded areas. Thus, we have:

$\boldsymbol{\alpha}$ = the area to the left of 0.40 plus the area to the right of 0.60
$\boldsymbol{\alpha}$ = area to the left of z = –2 plus area to the right of z = 2
$\boldsymbol{\alpha}$ = 2.28% + 2.28%
$\boldsymbol{\alpha}$ = 4.56%

Let's take another look at Type I and Type II errors and their relationship to the significance level, $\boldsymbol{\alpha}$. Recall that a Type I error is made when a true null hypothesis is incorrectly rejected. Therefore **whenever** the null hypothesis is rejected the possibility of a Type I error occurs. Consequently, a Type I error will occur whenever the null hypothesis is true *and* a statistical result falls beyond the critical value, leading to the rejection of the true null hypothesis. This is illustrated in Figure 9.15.

FIGURE 9.15

As can be seen from the diagram in Figure 9.15, when the null hypothesis is true the probability of committing a Type I error equals the level of significance, α.

Thus an alternative definition of the level of significance can be defined as follows:

> **DEFINITION 9.8**
>
> The **level of significance** (definition two) is the probability of committing a Type I error or the probability of rejecting a true null hypothesis.

The decision rule determines the level of significance. Thus, by choosing different decision rules the level of significance can be increased or decreased. Since the level of significance is the probability of committing a Type I error one might ask: "why not choose a decision rule that will have the *smallest* possible significance level"? Example 9.9 addresses this question.

EXAMPLE 9.9

Suppose a hypothesis test is conducted to determine if a coin is biased. If the coin is tossed 100 times consider the following three decision rules that are illustrated in Figures 9.16, 9.17 and 9.18.

Solution

FIGURE 9.16

FIGURE 9.17

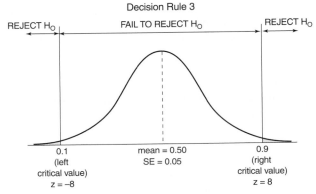

FIGURE 9.18

Notice in Decision Rule 1 illustrated in Figure 9.16, a coin will be considered biased if the sample proportion of heads is either *less than 0.40 or greater than 0.60*. In Decision Rule 2 illustrated in Figure 9.17, a coin will be considered biased if the sample proportion is either *less than 0.35 or greater than 0.65*. And finally, using Decision Rule 3 illustrated in Figure 9.18, a coin is considered biased if the sample proportion is *less than 0.1 or greater than 0.9*.

Notice as the critical values for the decision rules are chosen ***farther*** from the mean of 0.50, the significance level, represented by the shaded areas, ***decreases***. Since no one ever knows whether the coin being tossed is fair or biased, let's consider how choosing the critical values of our decision rule farther from the mean value affects the probabilities of a Type I and Type II error for a coin that is in *reality* fair (possibility #1) verses biased (possibility #2).

Possibility #1:   Coin is Fair

Assuming the coin being tossed is *fair,* then the effect of choosing the critical values **farther** from the mean ***decreases*** the chance of concluding that a fair coin is **biased**. Thus, the chance of committing a *Type I has decreased.*

Possibility #2:   Coin is Biased

Assuming the coin being tossed is *biased,* then the effect of choosing the critical values farther from the mean *decreases* the chance of concluding that the coin is biased. Thus, the chance of concluding that this biased coin is actually fair *has increased.* Therefore, the chance of committing a *Type II error has increased.*

To illustrate the relationship between choosing the critical values farther from the mean and the chance of committing a Type II error let's consider tossing a ***biased*** coin (possibility #2) 100 times. If the coin lands heads 85 times out of 100 tosses (i.e. the sample proportion is 0.85) let's examine the possible conclusions for each of the three previously stated decision rules shown in Figures 9.16, 9.17 and 9.18.

Using the Decision Rule 1 (Figure 9.16) and Decision Rule 2 (Figure 9.17) we would conclude that the coin is biased since the sample proportion 0.85 falls beyond the right critical value. This happens to be the correct decision.

However using Decision Rule 3 (Figures 9.18), which have the critical values farther from the mean, would lead to the *incorrect conclusion that the biased coin is fair,* since the sample proportion 0.85 *does not* fall beyond the right critical value of 0.90.

Now let's reconsider the question posed prior to Example 9.9: "why not choose a decision rule that will have the smallest possible significance level"?

We can conclude from the previous discussion that *as the significance level decreases the chance of committing a Type II error increases.* Figure 9.19 illustrates this relationship. The probability of committing a Type II error will be denoted by the lower-case Greek letter ß, pronounced beta.

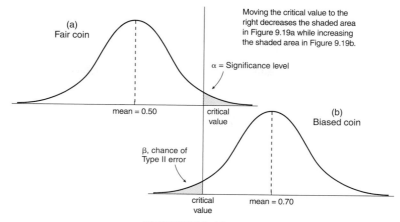

FIGURE 9.19

Before we begin, you should note that in Figure 9.19b, 0.70 will be used as the mean of the biased coin. However, *any* value other than 0.50 could have been used to represent the mean of the biased coin.

By carefully examining Figure 9.19, we observe that as the critical value line is moved to the right, the significance level, α, decreases *but* the chance of committing a Type II error, β, *increases*. On the other hand, if the critical value line is moved to the left, the significance level, α, increases while the chance of committing a Type II error, β, *decreases*.

Now that we have examined the relationship between the significance level, α, and the probability of committing a Type II error, β, one might ask: "what *is* an appropriate value for the significance level"?

As can be seen from the previous discussion, if the significance level, α, is chosen too small then this increases the risk of committing a Type II error. Usually a significance level, α, of less than 1% is generally not used. On the other hand, values greater than 10% are generally not chosen for the significance level, α, since this would allow for a greater chance of committing a Type I error. Consequently in practice the two most commonly used values for the significance level, α, are 1% and 5%.

After the researcher has selected a suitable significance level, the critical z-score value(s) of the decision rule can be found in Table II.[1]

In the following examples we will illustrate the technique used to identify the critical z-score value(s) for the decision rule.

EXAMPLE 9.10

A consumer testing agency is conducting a hypothesis test to determine the validity of an advertised claim made by the Eye Saver Light Bulb Co. that the mean life of its new 60 watt bulb is 1800 hours. To test this claim the agency randomly selects 400 bulbs. Determine the critical z-score value(s) for the decision rule if:

a)   The consumer agency believes the claim is too high and selects a significance level of 5%.
b)   The consumer agency wants to test the claim using a nondirectional test and selects a significance level of 5%.

Solution to Example 9.10(a):

a)   To determine the decision rule, we will use the first three steps in the hypothesis testing procedure.

---

[1]Assuming the Distribution is Normal. Other Distributions will be discussed in subsequent chapters.

Step 1 Formulate the hypotheses.
The null hypothesis is:

H_o: The population mean life of the new 60 watt bulb is 1800 hrs: $\mu = 1800$.

Since the consumer agency believes that the claim is *too high*, the alternative hypothesis is:

H_a: The population mean life of the new 60 watt bulb is *less than* 1800 hrs: $\mu < 1800$.

Step 2 Determine the model to test the null hypothesis.
(Note: all calculations necessary to obtain the mean and standard error (SE) are deliberately omitted to simplify the presentation). To test this claim, the consumer agency randomly selects 400 bulbs from the population.

Assuming the null hypothesis is true implies that the mean life for samples of 400 bulbs is 1800 hrs with a standard error of 5 hrs.

The sampling distribution which is approximately normal with the expected results shown in Figure 9.20 serves as the model.

Step 3 Formulate the decision rule.
First, we must determine whether we have a directional or nondirectional alternative hypothesis. Since the alternative hypothesis is the mean life is *less than* 1800 hours, we have a *directional alternative hypothesis*. Therefore the critical z-score value of the decision rule will be located to the *left* of the mean. This is illustrated in Figure 9.21.

In this example the consumer agency selected a significance level of 5%. The significance level of 5% is represented by the shaded region in Figure 9.22. Using this information we can determine the critical z score, written as z_c. Since we have a normal distribution and the area to the left of the critical z score, z_c, is 5%. Using Table II, we can find the value of z_c associated with the area 0.05. The value for z_c is -1.65. This is illustrated in Figure 9.22.

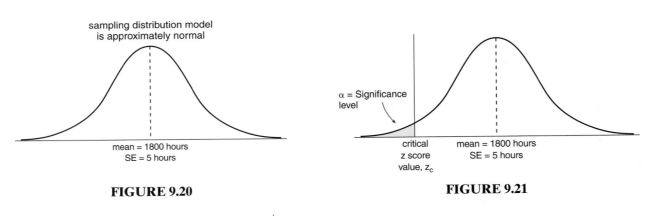

sampling distribution model
is approximately normal

mean = 1800 hours
SE = 5 hours

FIGURE 9.20

α = Significance
level

critical   mean = 1800 hours
z score   SE = 5 hours
value, z_c

FIGURE 9.21

Significance
Level, α = 5%

$z_c = -1.65$ mean = 1800 hours
SE = 5 hours

FIGURE 9.22

For the critical z-score, z_c –1.65, we formulate the following decision rule: **reject the null hypothesis if the z-score of the sample mean life is less than the critical z-score of –1.65.** This is illustrated in Figure 9.23.

FIGURE 9.23

Notice from Figure 9.23, the z score of the sample mean enables us to make a decision about the null hypothesis. The z score of the sample mean is commonly referred to as the **test statistic**.

DEFINITION 9.9
The **test statistic** is a quantity computed from sample information that is used to decide whether to reject or fail to reject the null hypothesis.

In this chapter, the test statistic is determined by the formula:

$$z = \frac{\text{sample statistic} - \text{mean}}{\text{SE}}$$

Since the region for rejecting the null hypothesis is only on the left side (or in the left tail) of the sampling distribution this type of hypothesis test is referred to as a ***one-tailed test***, abbreviated **1TT**.

One-Tailed Test, 1TT

A **one-tailed test** is conducted when the alternative hypothesis is directional.

A one-tailed test is illustrated in Figure 9.24.

DIRECTIONAL ALTERNATIVE HYPOTHESIS	HYPOTHESIS TESTING MODEL

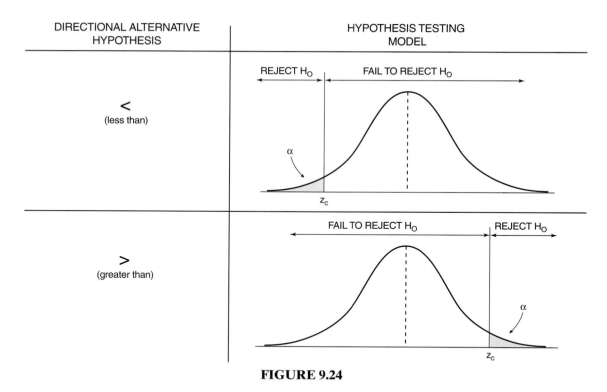

FIGURE 9.24

b)   As in part (a), we will use the first three steps in the hypothesis testing procedure to determine the decision rule.

Step 1   Formulate the hypotheses.
The null hypothesis is:

H_o: The population mean life of the new 60 watt bulb is 1800 hrs: $\mu = 1800$.

Since the consumer agency wants to test the null hypothesis using a nondirectional test, the alternative hypothesis is:

H_a: The population mean life of the new 60 watt bulb is *not* 1800 hrs: $\mu \neq 1800$.

Step 2   Determine the model to test the null hypothesis.
(Note all calculations necessary to obtain the mean and standard error (SE) are deliberately omitted to simplify the presentation). To test the null hypothesis the consumer agency randomly selects 400 bulbs. Assuming the null hypothesis is true implies that the mean life for all samples of 400 bulbs is 1800 hrs with a standard error(SE) of 5 hrs. The sampling distribution which is approximately normal with the expected results shown in Figure 9.25 serves as the model.

Step 3   Formulate the decision rule.
First we must determine whether we have a directional or nondirectional alternative hypothesis. Since the alternative hypothesis is nondirectional we must determine *two* critical z-score values, one located to the left of the mean and one located to the right of the mean. The critical z-score value located to the left of the mean is referred to as the **left critical z-score value**, denoted z_{LC}, and the critical value located to the right of the mean is referred to as the **right critical z-score value**, denoted z_{RC}. This is illustrated in Figure 9.26.
Since the significance level for this example is 5%, then the sum of the two shaded regions in Figure 9.26 must total 5%. The conventional procedure is to **divide the significance**

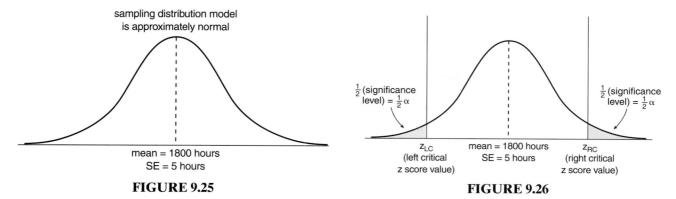

FIGURE 9.25   **FIGURE 9.26**

level *equally* between these two shaded regions. Therefore the area of each shaded region is half the significance level (i.e. ½ **α**). Since the significance level is 5% the area in each shaded region (or tail) is:

$$\tfrac{1}{2}\alpha = \tfrac{1}{2}(5\%)$$
$$= 2.5\%$$

This is illustrated in Figure 9.27.

The decision rule requires two critical z-score values: the left critical value (referred to as the **left critical z score**, denoted z_{LC}) and the right critical value (referred to as the **right critical z score**, denoted z_{RC}). Using the information in Figure 9.27 and Table II, we can find the value of the two critical z scores, z_{LC} and z_{RC}.

To find z_{LC} we must determine the z score which has 2.5% or 0.025 of the area to the left. From Table II, $z_{LC} = -1.96$. Similarly to find z_{RC} we must determine the z score which has 97.5% or 0.9750 of the area to the left. From Table II, $z_{RC} = +1.96$. This is illustrated in Figure 9.28.

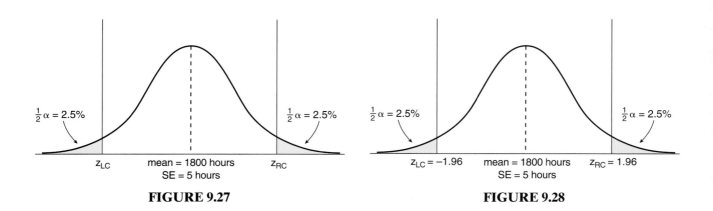

FIGURE 9.27   **FIGURE 9.28**

Using these critical z score values we formulate the decision rule: **reject the null hypothesis if the z score of the sample mean life (the test statistic) is either less than the left critical z score value of –1.96 or more than the right critical z score value of 1.96.** This is illustrated in Figure 9.29.

FIGURE 9.29

In the previous example there were two regions on the normal curve for rejecting the null hypothesis. One rejection region was in the left tail and the other rejection region was in the right tail of the curve. This type of hypothesis test is referred to as a **two-tailed test**, abbreviated **2TT**.

Two-Tailed Test, 2TT

A **two-tailed test** is conducted when the alternative hypothesis is nondirectional.

   In a two-tailed test, the level of significance, α, is divided equally between the two tails. Therefore, the area in each tail is half the significance level, $\frac{1}{2}\,\alpha$.

A two-tailed test is illustrated in Figure 9.30.

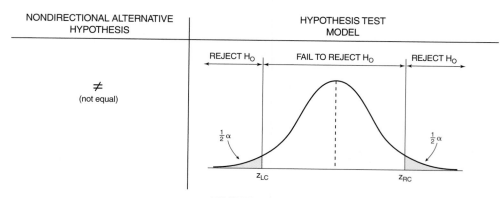

FIGURE 9.30

EXAMPLE 9.11

A national department store chain has determined that in previous years 60% of its customers used the department store's special holiday credit card to make Christmas purchases. This year because of changing economic conditions the department store management would like to determine if the 60% figure is too low. To test the 60% figure, 150 customers are randomly selected during the week of December 10th and asked whether they were using the store's special holiday credit card. Determine the decision rule for the hypothesis test. Use a significance level of 1%.

Assume the sampling distribution is approximately normal with a mean of 0.60 and a standard error of: $SE = 0.04$.

Test the null hypothesis:

> H_o: The population proportion of the customers who use the special holiday credit card is 60%: $p = 0.60$.

Against the alternative hypothesis:

> H_a: The population proportion of customers who use the special holiday credit card is *more than 60%*: $p > 0.60$

Solution

Since the first two steps of the hypothesis testing procedure are given we begin with Step 3.

Step 3   Formulate the decision rule.

We have a directional alternative hypothesis since it is written as *more than 60%* of the customers use the special holiday credit card. Therefore the critical value will be located to the *right* of the mean. This is illustrated in Figure 9.31.

Using the information in Figure 9.31 and Table II: the Normal Curve Area Table, we can determine the critical z score, z_c. Since the percent of the area to the left of z_c is 99% then critical z score is $z_c = 2.33$.

The decision rule is: reject the null hypothesis if the z score of the sample proportion (test statistic) is *more* than the critical z score of 2.33. This is illustrated in Figure 9.32.

FIGURE 9.31

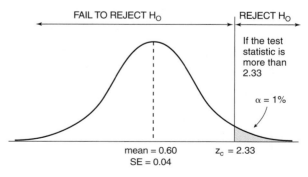

FIGURE 9.32

From the previous examples, we can now generalize the procedure to formulate the decision rule.

Procedure to Formulate the Decision Rule

a) Determine the type of alternative hypothesis. (directional or nondirectional).
b) Determine the type of test (1TT or 2TT).
c) Identify the significance level ($\alpha = 5\%$ or $\alpha = 1\%$).
d) Construct the appropriate hypothesis test model.
e) Find the critical z score(s) using Table II for the appropriate level of significance.
f) State the decision rule.

Tables 9.3 and 9.4 summarize the procedure for formulating the decision rule for the significance levels of 5% and 1%.

Formulating the Decision Rule Using 5% Significance Level

Type of Alternative Hypothesis, H_a	Directional (less than) <	Directional (greater than) >	Nondirectional (not equal to) ≠
Type of Test	One-tailed (1TT)	One-tailed (1TT)	Two-tailed (2TT)
Hypothesis Test Model	REJECT H₀ / FAIL TO REJECT H₀; $\alpha = 5\%$; $z_c = -1.65$, mean	FAIL TO REJECT H₀ / REJECT H₀; mean, $z_c = 1.65$; $\alpha = 5\%$	REJECT H₀ / FAIL TO REJECT H₀ / REJECT H₀; $\frac{1}{2}\alpha = 2.5\%$, $\frac{1}{2}\alpha = 2.5\%$; $z_{LC} = -1.96$, mean, $z_{RC} = 1.96$
Critical Z Score(s)	$z_C = -1.65$	$z_C = 1.65$	$z_{LC} = -1.96$ and $z_{RC} = 1.96$
Decision Rules	Reject H_O, if the test statistic is less than −1.65	Reject H_O, if the test statistic is greater than 1.65	Reject H_O, if the test statistic is either less than −1.96 or greater than 1.96

TABLE 9.3

Formulating the Decision Rule Using 1% Significance Level

Type of Alternative Hypothesis, H_a	Directional (less than) <	Directional (greater than) >	Nondirectional (not equal to) $\neq$
Type of Test	One-tailed (1TT)	One-tailed (1TT)	Two-tailed (2TT)
Hypothesis Test Model	REJECT H$_0$ FAIL TO REJECT H$_0$ $\alpha = 1\%$ $z_c = -2.33$ mean	FAIL TO REJECT H$_0$ REJECT H$_0$ $\alpha = 1\%$ mean $z_c = 2.33$	REJECT H$_0$ FAIL TO REJECT H$_0$ REJECT H$_0$ $\frac{1}{2}\alpha = 0.5\%$ $\frac{1}{2}\alpha = 0.5\%$ $z_{LC} = -2.58$ mean $z_{RC} = 2.58$
Critical Z Score(s)	$z_C = -2.33$	$z_C = 2.33$	$z_{LC} = -2.58$ and $z_{RC} = 2.58$
Decision Rules	Reject H_O, if the test statistic is less than −2.33	Reject H_O, if the test statistic is greater than 2.33	Reject H_O, if the test statistic is either less than −2.58 or greater than 2.58

TABLE 9.4

Now that we have completed the introduction to hypothesis testing, let us summarize the hypothesis testing procedure.

Hypothesis Testing Procedure

Step 1   Formulate the two hypotheses, H_o and H_a.

Step 2   Determne the model to test the null hypothesis, H_o.
Under the assumption H_o is true, calculate the expected results: (**These results will be discussed in the subsequent chapters.**)
a) Identify the appropriate sampling distribution used as the hypothesis testing model.
b) Mean of the sampling distribution
c) Standard error (SE) of the sampling distribution

(continues)

Hypothesis Testing Procedure (continued)

Step 3   **Formulate the Decision Rule**:

a) Determine type of alternative hypothesis, directional or nondirectional.
b) Determine type of test, 1TT or 2TT.
c) Identify the significance level, $\alpha = 1\%$ or $\alpha = 5\%$.
d) Construct the appropriate hypothesis test model.
e) Find the critical z score(s) using Table II for the appropriate level of significance.
f) State the decision rule.

Step 4   **Analyze the sample data.**
Collect the necessary sample data to calculate the test statistic using the formula

$$z = \frac{\text{sample statistic} - \text{mean}}{\text{SE}}$$

Step 5   **State the conclusion.**
Compare the test statistic to the decision rule and either:
a) **Reject H$_o$ and accept H$_a$ at** α,

or

b) **Fail to reject H$_o$ at** α.

Example 9.12 illustrates the use of the hypothesis testing procedure to perform a hypothesis test.

EXAMPLE 9.12

Last year, 75% of adults within the USA stated that they believed a college degree was very important. This year a national poll randomly selected 1,020 American adults and found that 794 adults believed that a college degree is very important. Can you conclude that the percent of adults within the USA who believe a college degree is very important has significantly increased this year? Use mean = 0.75 and standard error: SE = 0.0136 to perform a hypothesis test at $\alpha = 5\%$ to answer this question.

Solution

We will use the hypothesis testing procedure to perform this hypothesis test. The first step is to formulate the hypotheses.

Step 1   Formulate the two hypotheses, H$_o$ and H$_a$.
The hypothesis being tested is that 75% of the adults within the USA believe a college degree is important. Therefore, the null hypothesis is:

H$_o$: The population proportion of adults within the USA who believe a college degree is important is 75%: $p = 0.75$.

Since we are trying to show that the percent of adults who believe a college degree is important *has increased,* the alternative hypothesis is:

H$_a$: The population proportion of adults within the USA who believe a college degree is important is *more than 75%:* $p > 0.75$.

The second step involves determining the model to test the null hypothesis.

Step 2 Determine the model to test the null hypothesis, H_o.

To test the null hypothesis, a national poll of 1,020 American adults were randomly selected to determine their belief about the importance of a college degree. Under the assumption H_o is true, we need to calculate the expected results. As we have mentioned repeatedly throughout Chapter 9, the expected results are given so we can concentrate on the concepts of the hypothesis testing procedure. Thus, the sampling distribution is approximately normal with a mean = 0.75 and a standard error, SE = 0.0136. These expected results are shown in Figure 9.33.

Now that we have calculated the expected results based upon the assumption that the null hypothesis is true, we need to formulate a decision rule.

Step 3 Formulate the decision rule.
  a) Determine type of alternative hypothesis.
      Since the alternative hypothesis is in the form of a *more than statement,* it is a directional hypothesis.
  b) Determine the type of test.
      A directional alternative hypothesis is a one tail test (1TT). Since it is in the form of a *more than statement,* the critical value will be located to the *right* of the mean.
  c) Identify the significance level.
      The significance level is $\alpha = 5\%$.
  d) Construct the appropriate hypothesis test model.
      This is illustrated in Figure 9.34.
  e) Calculate the critical z score using Table II:
      Using the information in Figure 9.34 and Table II: the Normal Curve Area Table, we can determine the critical z score, z_c. Since the percent of the area to the left of z_c is 95%, then $z_c = 1.65$.

      The decision rule is: reject the null hypothesis if the z score of the sample proportion (test statistic) is *more* than the critical z score of 1.65. This is illustrated in Figure 9.35.

      Now that the decision rule has been formulated, we need to calculate the test statistic.

Step 4 Analyze the sample data.

The experiment is the process of collecting the sample information from the population. The national poll of 1,020 randomly selected American adults represents the sample data. Since 794 adults within the sample said that a college degree is very important, then the sample proportion is: 794/1020 ≈ 0.7784. The test statistic for the sample proportions;

$$z = \frac{0.7784 - 0.75}{0.0136}$$

$$z = 2.09 \text{ (test statistic)}$$

FIGURE 9.33

FIGURE 9.34

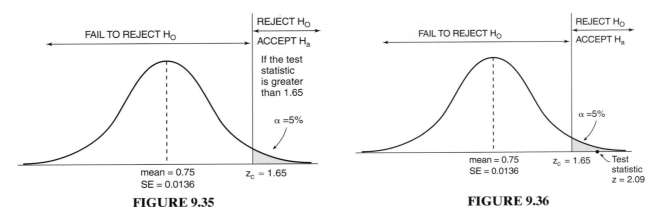

mean = 0.75
SE = 0.0136 $z_c \approx 1.65$

FIGURE 9.35

mean = 0.75 $z_c = 1.65$
SE = 0.0136

FIGURE 9.36

If we compare the test statistic to the decision rule, we can draw a conclusion.

Step 5   State the conclusion.
Since the test statistic 2.09 is greater than the critical z score of 1.65 then the conclusion is *reject H_o and accept H_a at α = 5%*. This is illustrated in Figure 9.36.
Therefore, more than 75% of adults within USA believe a college degree is very important at α = 5%.

CASE STUDY 9.1   Trying to Kick the Habit

Using the information contained in the snapshot entitled "Trying to Kick the Habit" shown in Figure 9.37, answer the following questions.

FIGURE 9.37

a) Define the population of people being illustrated in Figure 9.37.
b) Define the variable(s) being discussed in the snapshot in Figure 9.37. If you use the information pertaining to the year 1989 as representing the status quo, and the information regarding the year 1995 as the direction you believe the percentages for each category are headed, then:
c) Formulate a null hypothesis and an alternative hypothesis for each of the four categories shown in Figure 9.37.
d) Indicate the type of alternative hypothesis.

CASE STUDY 9.1 Trying to Kick the Habit (continued)

e) Determine the type of test (i.e. 1TT or 2TT), and on which side of the curve the critical z values would be positioned.
f) Describe how you would select an appropriate sample to test the null hypothesis.
g) When calculating the expected results in step 2 of the hypothesis testing procedure, what assumption are you making? Explain why it is necessary to make this assumption.
h) For the hypothesis test you outlined regarding Acupuncture, what would be the conclusion to your test if the test statistic were to fall to the left of your critical z score value?
i) For the hypothesis test you outlined regarding Hypnosis, what would be the conclusion to your test if the test statistic were to fall to the right of your critical z score value?

CASE STUDY 9.2

Using the information contained in the snapshot entitled "Skyrocketing Cable Rates" shown in Figure 9.38, answer the following questions assuming you are a researcher who feels that cable rates are increasing.

FIGURE 9.38

a) What variable is being shown by the graph in Figure 9.38? If you use the information regarding cable rates for the year 1992 as representing the status quo, and the implied direction of the graph as your belief about what cable rates will be doing then:
b) Formulate a null hypothesis and an alternative hypothesis.
c) Indicate the type of alternative hypothesis.
d) Determine the type of test (i.e. 1TT or 2TT), and on which side of the curve the critical z score value would be positioned.
e) Describe how you would select an appropriate sample to test the null hypothesis.

CASE STUDY 9.2 (continued)

   f) When calculating the expected results in step 2 of the hypothesis testing procedure, what assumption are you making? Explain why it is necessary to make this assumption.

   g) For your hypothesis test, what would be the conclusion to your test if the test statistic were to fall to the right of your critical z score value?

9.4   p-VALUES FOR HYPOTHESIS TESTING

When performing a hypothesis test, the last step or step 5 of the hypothesis testing procedure requires that the test statistic be compared to the critical z score value z_c of the decision rule to determine whether to either reject the null hypothesis or fail to reject the null hypothesis. In Example 9.12, a one-tailed test(1TT) on the right side was performed to determine if we could reject the null hypothesis at a 5% level of significance. In step 5 of the hypothesis test, the test statistic of 2.09 was compared to the critical z score $z_c = 1.65$. Since the test statistic was *greater than* the critical z score, $z_c = 1.65$, the *null hypothesis H_o was rejected at the 5% level of significance* (that is, $\alpha = 5\%$). This is illustrated in Figure 9.39.

A question that might be asked is: *could we have rejected the null hypothesis for a different significance level, such as $\alpha = 4\%$ or $\alpha = 3\%$ or $\alpha = 2\%$ or even $\alpha = 1\%$?*

For example, if the significance level of Example 9.12 was $\alpha = 4\%$, would the null hypothesis still have been rejected? To answer this question, we need to determine the critical z score z_c for a significance level of $\boldsymbol{\alpha = 4\%}$, and a 1TT on the right side. Since the percent of area to the right of the critical z score z_c is 4%, then the percent of area to the left of the critical z score, z_c, is 96%. Using Table II: the Normal Curve Area Table, the nearest area is 0.9599, thus the critical z score is: $z_c = 1.75$.

Since the test statistic of z = 2.09 **is still greater than** this critical z score of $z_c \approx 1.75$ for a significance level of 4%, the null hypothesis is rejected at the significance level of $\boldsymbol{\alpha = 4\%}$. This is illustrated in Figure 9.40.

Using this same procedure to determine the critical z-score z_c for each of the significance levels $\boldsymbol{\alpha = 3\%}$ and $\boldsymbol{\alpha = 2\%}$, we obtain a critical z score of $z_c \approx 1.88$ for $\boldsymbol{\alpha = 3\%}$, and a critical z score of $z_c \approx 2.05$ for $\boldsymbol{\alpha = 2\%}$. Since the test statistic of z = 2.09 is still greater than both of the critical z scores, $z_c \approx 1.88$ (for $\boldsymbol{\alpha = 3\%}$) and $z_c \approx 2.05$ ($\boldsymbol{\alpha = 2\%}$), then the null hypothesis is rejected at each of these significance levels. This is illustrated in Figure 9.41(a) and Figure 9.41(b) respectively.

FIGURE 9.39

FIGURE 9.40

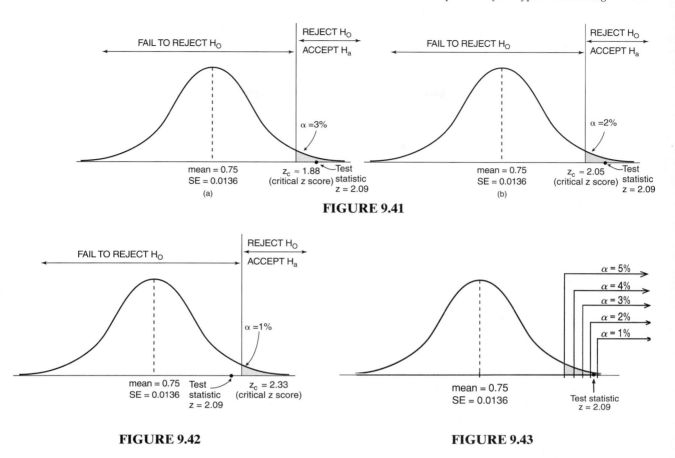

FIGURE 9.41

FIGURE 9.42

FIGURE 9.43

However, at the significance level of $\alpha = \mathbf{1\%}$, the null hypothesis **is not rejected**, since the test statistic z = 2.09 is now **less than** the critical z score of z_c = 2.33. This is illustrated in Figure 9.42.

Examining the results for the different significance levels, we can begin to obtain an estimate to the answer of the question: *how large would the significance level, α, have to be to reject the null hypothesis?* Answer: the null hypothesis of Example 9.12 can be rejected using a significance level of α = 2% or greater. This is illustrated in Figure 9.43.

From Figure 9.43, we should notice it is possible to use a significance level smaller than 2% but greater than 1% that would still allow us to reject the null hypothesis. In essence, we are looking for the *true level of significance* for this hypothesis test or the ***smallest value*** of α for which the null hypothesis can be rejected. The smallest value of α is called the **probability-value** or **p-value of a hypothesis test**. The p-value of a hypothesis test is also referred to as the **observed significance level of a hypothesis test**. The p-value of a hypothesis test is usually expressed in decimal form rather than a percent. We will express the p-value as both a decimal and a percent.

DEFINITION 9.10

The **p-value**, or observed significance level, of a hypothesis test is the **smallest level of significance** (α) at which the null hypothesis H_o can be rejected using the test statistic.

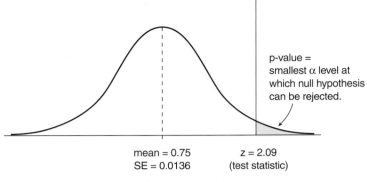

FIGURE 9.44

To find the smallest value of α at which the null hypothesis of Example 9.12 can be rejected, that is, the p-value, it is necessary to find the area to the right of the test statistic of 2.09. This is illustrated in Figure 9.44.

Using Table II: The Normal Curve Area Table, the area to the left of $z \approx 2.09$ is 0.9817, thus the area to the right which represents the p-value is:

$$\text{p-value} = 1 - 0.9817 = 0.0183.$$

Thus, the p-value of this hypothesis test is 0.0183 or 1.83%. Consequently, the smallest value of α at which the null hypothesis of Example 9.12 can be rejected is 1.83%. This is illustrated in Figure 9.45.

Therefore, we say that this test statistic of 2.09 is "extremely significant," since the p-value or probability of observing a sample proportion of 0.7784 is only 0.0183 or 1.83%. **Reporting the p-value of a hypothesis test is more informative than stating the conclusion of a hypothesis test.** Suppose instead of stating the conclusion of the hypothesis test in Example 9.12 as reject the null hypothesis at α = 5%, the p-value of 0.0183 or 1.83% was reported. This knowledge about the p-value of the hypothesis test conveys more information to the reader. It tells the reader that the null hypothesis can be rejected at α = 4% and that it can be rejected even at smaller values of α such as α = 2%. In fact, this p-value of 0.0183 or 1.83% indicates that the null hypothesis can be rejected at values of α as small as α = 1.83%. Compare the content information indicated by the statement "the p-value is 0.0183 or 1.83%" with the very limited information contained by the statement "reject the null hypothesis at α = 5%".

Computer software programs, like MINITAB, carry out hypothesis tests by calculating the p-value for you. In fact, many researcher articles containing statistical tests publish p-values. Thus,

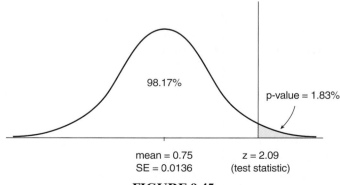

FIGURE 9.45

instead of selecting a significance level, α, before conducting the experiment as outlined in the hypothesis testing procedure, the researcher or the computer software reports the p-value of the hypothesis test along with the statistical result. It is left to the reader to interpret the significance of the hypothesis test. That is, the reader must determine whether to reject the null hypothesis based upon the reported p-value. Usually, the null hypothesis is rejected if the p-value is less than the significance level, α, that the reader decides to choose. Thus, the smaller the p-value, the stronger the evidence against the null hypothesis provided by the statistical result. To decide whether to reject the null hypothesis when the p-value of a hypothesis test is reported, you can use the following guideline.

Deciding Whether to Reject the Null Hypothesis when a p-Value is Reported

Compare the p-value of the hypothesis test to the chosen significance level, α, that you are willing to tolerate. If the p-value is less than or equal to α, then the hypothesis test is significant at a selected significance level, α. That is,

$$\text{if p-value} \le \alpha,$$

then reject H_0 at significance level, α.

Remember, however, that a p-value conveys more information than than just reporting whether or not to reject the null hypothesis at a given significance level, α. Thus, the p-value indicates how unusual the statistical result is assuming that the null hypothesis is true. Therefore, the p-value will provide an indication as to whether or not the statistical result is very significant to not significant. The following rules of thumb established by researchers will help you to interpret p-values regarding the significance of the statistical result.

Interpreting p-Values

1. If the p-value is less than 0.01 (or 1%), the statistical result is **very significant**.
2. If the p-value is between 0.01 (or 1%) and 0.05 (or 5%), the statistical result is **significant**.
3. If the p-value is between 0.05 (or 5%) and 0.10 (or 10%), the statistical result is **marginally or not significant**.
4. If the p-value is greater than 0.10 (or 10%), the statistical result is **not significant**.

EXAMPLE 9.13

A statistical hypothesis test was conducted using a significance level of $\alpha = 5\%$. If the p-value of this test is equal to 0.06 (or 6%), can the null hypothesis be rejected?

Solution

Since the p-value of a hypothesis test is the smallest level of significance (α) at which the null hypothesis H_0 can be rejected, then for this test the null hypothesis can not be rejected because the p-value of 0.06 (or 6%) is greater than the significance level of $\alpha = 5\%$.

EXAMPLE 9.14

The null hypothesis of a statistical hypothesis test was rejected at a significance level of $\alpha = 5\%$. If the p-value of this test is equal to 0.025 (or 2.5%), then what is the smallest value of α for which the null hypothesis can be rejected?

Solution

Since the p-value of a hypothesis test is the smallest level of significance (α) at which the null hypothesis H_o can be rejected, then the smallest value of α is equal to 2.5%.

Procedure to Calculate the p-Value of a Hypothesis Test

Let's discuss how to compute the p-value of a hypothesis test for the following three possible cases.

Case One: A one-tailed test on the left side
For a one-tailed test on the left side, the p-value of a hypothesis test is equal to the percent of area in the tail to the left of the test statistic of the test. This is illustrated in Figure 9.46.

Case Two: A one-tailed test on the right side
For a one-tailed test on the right side, the p-value of a hypothesis test is equal to the percent of area in the tail to the right of the test statistic of the test. This is illustrated in Figure 9.47.

Case Three: A two-tailed test
For a two-tailed test, the p-value of a hypothesis test is equal to *twice* the percent of area in the one tail beyond the direction of the test statistic of the test. This is illustrated in Figure 9.48.

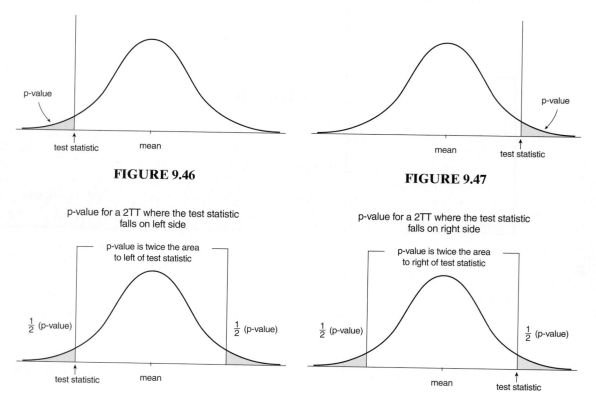

FIGURE 9.46   **FIGURE 9.47**

FIGURE 9.48

EXAMPLE 9.15

Use the information contained within the given hypothesis test to answer the following questions. The first two steps of the hypothesis testing procedure are given.

A consumer testing agency is conducting a hypothesis test to determine the validity of an advertised claim made by the Eye Saver Light Bulb Co. that the mean life of its new 60 watt bulb is 1800 hours. The consumer agency believes the claim is too high and randomly selects 400 bulbs to test the company's claim and determines the mean life of these 400 bulbs to be 1788 hours.

Step 1 Formulate the hypotheses.

H_o: The population mean life of the new 60 watt bulb is 1800 hrs: $\mu = 1800$ hrs.
H_a: The population mean life of the new 60 watt bulb is *less than* 1800 hrs: $\mu < 1800$ hrs.

Step 2 Determine the model to test the null hypothesis.

To test the null hypothesis, the consumer agency randomly selects 400 bulbs. Assuming the null hypothesis is true implies that the mean life for all possible samples of 400 bulbs is 1800 hrs with a standard error (SE) of 5 hrs.

The sampling distribution is approximately normal with the expected results shown in Figure 9.49 serve as the model.
a) Calculate the p-value of this hypothesis test.
b) Can the consumer agency reject the null hypothesis at $\alpha = 5\%$? at $\alpha = 1\%$?
c) What is the smallest level of significance at which the null hypothesis H_o can be rejected?

Solution

a) To calculate the p-value, we need to find the area to the left of the sample mean of 1788 hours, since this is a 1TT on the left side. This is illustrated in Figure 9.50.

To determine this area find the z score of 1788. This is the test statistic. Using the z score formula, the test statistic is:

$$z \text{ of } 1788 = \frac{1788 - 1800}{5} = -2.40.$$

Using Table II: The Normal Curve Area Table, the area to the left of $z = -2.40$ is 0.0082. Thus the p–value is 0.0082 or 0.82%.
b) Yes it can be rejected at both significance levels, since the p-value of 0.0082 or 0.82% is less than both 5% and 1%.
c) The smallest level of significance at which the null hypothesis can be rejected is equal to the p-value which is 0.0082 (or 0.82%).

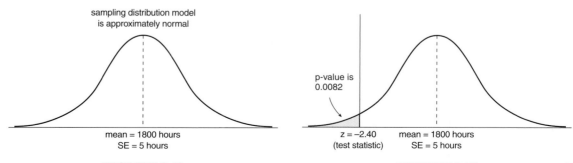

sampling distribution model
is approximately normal

mean = 1800 hours
SE = 5 hours

FIGURE 9.49

p-value is
0.0082

z = –2.40   mean = 1800 hours
(test statistic)   SE = 5 hours

FIGURE 9.50

Now that we have completed the p-value approach to hypothesis testing, let us summarize the procedure.

---

p-Value Approach to the Hypothesis Testing Procedure

Step 1   Formulate the two hypotheses, H_o and H_a.

Step 2   Determine the model to test the null hypothesis, H_o.
Under the assumption H_o is true, calculate the expected results: **(These results will be discussed in the subsequent chapters.)**
 a) Identify the appropriate sampling distribution used as the hypothesis testing model.
 b) Mean of the sampling distribution.
 c) Standard error (SE) of the sampling distribution.

Step 3   Formulate the Decision Rule:
 a) Determine type of alternative hypothesis, directional or nondirectional.
 b) Determine type of test, 1TT or 2TT.
 c) Identify the significance level, $\alpha = 1\%$ or $\alpha = 5\%$.
 d) Construct the appropriate hypothesis test model.
 e) State the decision rule as: *Reject H_o if the p-value of the test statistic is less than α.*

Step 4   Analyze the sample data.
Collect the necessary sample data to calculate the test statistic. Determine the p-value of the test statistic.

Step 5   Determine the conclusion.
Compare the p-value of the test statistic to the decision rule and either:
 a) **Reject H_o and accept H_a at α,**
 or
 b) **Fail to reject H_o at α.**

9.5   USING TECHNOLOGY

Using statistical software is generally the way a researcher analyzes hypotheses tests. These software packages have many different models of hypothesis tests. Although each model is specific to the distribution from which a sample is found, they have one common thread—each reports the **significance of the test using a p-value**.

For example, the MINITAB output below represents a directional hypothesis test where the alternative hypothesis is the population mean is less than 80. The MINITAB output is shown in Figure 9.51.

	N	MEAN	STDEV	SE MEAN	Z	P VALUE
C1	49	78.160	4.988	0.714	−2.58	0.0051

FIGURE 9.51

Such an output would indicate that the null hypothesis is rejected and the alternative hypothesis is accepted. This is indicated because of the p-value, 0.0051. In fact, such a low p-value gives strength to the rejection of the null hypothesis!

TI-83 Plus calculator output screens display a nondirectional and directional hypothesis test. Figure 9.52a represents an output screen for a nondirectional hypothesis test where the alternative hypothesis is $p \neq 0.30$ with a p-value of 0.5127. Figure 9.52b represents an output screen for a directional hypothesis test where the alternative hypothesis is $\mu < 80$ with a p-value of 1.17 E-4. Identify the test statistic in each figure. Which of these ouput screens indicate a rejection of the null hypothesis for $\alpha = 1\%$?

FIGURE 9.52a   FIGURE 9.52b

KEY TERMS

Null Hypothesis, H_o 579
Alternative Hypothesis, H_a 579
Directional Alternative
   Hypothesis   580
Nondirectional Alternative
   Hypothesis   581
Hypothesis Testing Procedure   581
Type I Error   583
Type II Error   583

Statistically Significant   585
Test Statistic   595
Expected Result (mean)   586
Critical z Score, z_c 594
Level of Significance, α 591
Chance of Type II Error, β 593
Left Critical z Score, z_{LC} 596
Right Critical z Score, z_{RC} 596
One-Tailed Test, 1TT   595

Two-Tailed Test, 2TT   598
p-Value   607
Very Significant p-Value   609
Significant p-Value   609
Marginal or Not Significant
   p-Value   609
Not Significant p-Value   609

SECTION EXERCISES

Section 9.2

1. The null hypothesis is the hypothesis to be tested that is initially assumed to be _____ and formulated for the sole purpose of trying to _____. The null hypothesis is symbolized as _____.

2. The alternative hypothesis is the hypothesis which is supported by the rejection of the _____ hypothesis. The alternative is symbolized as _____.

3. When a false null hypothesis is accepted, one has committed a Type _____ error.

4. If a false alternative hypothesis is accepted, then:
    a) A Type I error has been made
    b) A Type II error has been made
    c) No error has been made

5. A Type I error is an error that is made when a true null hypothesis is incorrectly rejected.
    (T/F)

6. A rejection of the null hypothesis means that the difference between the test statistic and the _____ result, the mean, is statistically _____.

7. If the null hypothesis is rejected then the alternative hypothesis is:
   a) Accepted
   b) Rejected
   c) Neither accepted nor rejected

8. "Statistically significant" means that the sample statistic is different enough from the expected result to support the alternative hypothesis.
   (T/F)

Section 9.3

9. The level of significance is the probability of committing a Type _____ error.

10. The Greek letter used to symbolize a Type II error is _____.

11. Whenever the alternative hypothesis is directional we have a _____ tailed test.

12. In a two-tailed test, the significance level is divided _____ between the two tails. Therefore, for $\alpha = 1\%$, the percent of the area in each tail is_____.

13. The critical z score for a one-tailed test at $\alpha = 5\%$ is either _____ or _____.

14. The two critical z scores for a two-tailed test at $\alpha = 1\%$ are _____ and _____.

15. In a hypothesis test, if the test statistic does not fall beyond the critical z score, then the conclusion is stated as _____ H_o.

16. If a nondirectional alternative hypothesis is being tested then:
   a) A one-tailed test is performed
   b) A two-tailed test is performed
   c) Not enough information is given

17. When the test statistic does not fall beyond the critical z score(s) then the decision is to "fail to reject H_o." What type of error may have been made?
   a) No error
   b) Type I error
   c) Type II error

18. As the significance level increases, the chance of committing a Type II error decreases.
   (T/F)

19. The decision rule is usually determined after a suitable significance level is chosen.
   (T/F)

20. A directional alternative hypothesis results from a two-tailed test.
   (T/F)

For problems 21–26, state the null and alternative hypotheses assuming you are the individual or agency performing the hypothesis test. Also indicate whether these tests are directional or nondirectional.

21. The Department of Consumer Affairs is going to conduct a study to determine if the following claim made by Weight Examiners Inc. is an exaggeration. "The mean weight loss during the first 10 days is 12 pounds!"

22. The Environmental Protection Agency is going to conduct a series of tests to determine if V & D Inc. is exceeding the allowable pollutant levels. The allowable pollutant level is a mean of 13 ppm.

23. According to a research study linking maternal smoking and childhood asthma, 10% of the children whose mothers smoked during pregnancy are asthmatic. A local official from a public health agency has doubts about this statement and decides to test this claim against her suspicion that it is not 10%.

24. The National Education Association (NEA) states that the national mean salary of public school teachers in the United States is $45,890. A teacher's union wants to show the their mean salary is less than the national mean.

25. A consumer protection group is interested in testing a new energy-saving refrigerator because of their suspicion that the new refrigerator uses more than the advertised mean consumption of 4.9 kilowatts hours of electricity per day.

26. According to the National Center for Education Statistics, the national average daily rate of attendance for kindergarten through 12th grade is 94%. The school superintendent of a city school district believes her district has a daily average attendance rate that is higher than the national average.

For problems 27–29, you are given the null hypothesis (H_o), the alternative hypothesis (H_a), a diagram indicating the sampling distribution model, the mean, standard error(SE), critical z score(s) and a test statistic.

27. $H_o: \mu = 100$
       $H_a: \mu \neq 100$

a) State the decision rule.
b) Do you reject the null hypothesis?
c) Do you accept the alternative hypothesis?

28. $H_o: p = 0.50$
  $H_a: p > 0.50$

FAIL TO REJECT H_O | REJECT H_O
ACCEPT H_a

mean = 0.50
standard error = 0.025

(critical z score)

Test statistic
z = 2.49

a) State the decision rule.
b) Do you reject the null hypothesis?
c) Do you reject the alternative hypothesis?

29. $H_o: \mu = 114$
  $H_a: \mu < 114$
  a) State the decision rule. If the test statistic is z=2, then:
  b) Do you reject the null hypothesis?
  c) Do you accept the alternative hypothesis?

REJECT H_O
ACCEPT H_a

FAIL TO REJECT H_O

$z_c = -2.33$
(critical z score)

mean = 114
standard error = 7

If the test statistic is z = −3, then:

d) Do you reject the null hypothesis?
e) Do you accept the alternative hypothesis?

For the problems 30–32, use the given information to:
   a) Label each diagram with critical z score(s), reject and fail to reject areas and the test statistic.
   b) Determine the conclusion.
   c) Is the test statistic statistically significant?

30. $H_o: p = 0.90$
  $H_a: p > 0.90$
  Decision Rule: Reject H_o if test statistic is greater than z = 2.33.
  The test statistic is z = 2.

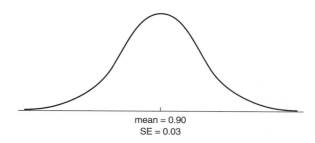

mean = 0.90
SE = 0.03

31. $H_o: \mu = 190$
  $H_a: \mu \neq 190$

  Decision Rule: Reject H_o if the test statistic is either less than −1.96 or greater than 1.96.
  The test statistic is z = 2.2.

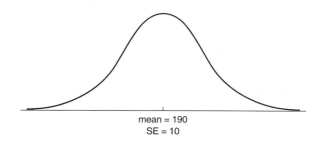

mean = 190
SE = 10

32. $H_o: \mu = 14.5$
  $H_a: \mu < 14.5$

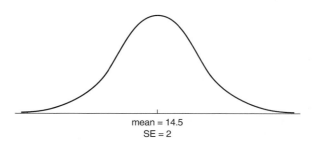

mean = 14.5
SE = 2

Decision Rule: Reject H_o if the test statistic is less than −1.65.
The test statistic is z = −1.9.

For problems 33–35, use problems 30–32 and:

a) Determine the chance of a Type I error.

For problems 36–39, the null and alternative hypotheses, the mean and standard error(SE), the significance level, α, and a diagram are given.

Calculate the critical z score(s) and formulate the decision rule. Label the diagram with the mean, standard error(SE), significance level, critical z score(s) and reject and fail to reject areas. Answer the appropriate questions.

36. $H_o: \mu = 2500$
$H_a: \mu > 2500$
Mean = 2500
Standard Error(SE) = 100
Significance Level, $\alpha = 5\%$

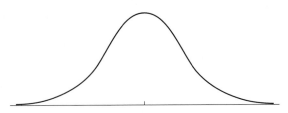

a) If the test statistic is:
1) 2.15   **2)** 1.00   **3)** –1.00   **4)** –13
then determine the conclusion.
b) Which of these results are statistically significant?

37. $H_o: \mu = 18$
$H_a: \mu < 18$
Mean = 18
Standard Error(SE) = 3
Significance Level, $\alpha = 1\%$

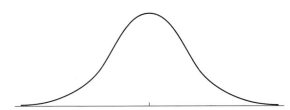

a) If the test statistic is:
1) –2   **2)** 1.00   **3)** –2.35   **4)** 3.33
then determine the conclusion.
b) Which of these results are statistically significant?

38. $H_o: p = 0.80$
$H_a: p < 0.80$
Mean = 0.80

Standard Error(SE) = 0.02
Significance Level, $\alpha = 1\%$

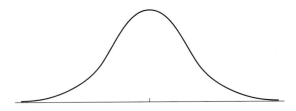

a) If the test statistic is:
1) –2.74   **2)** –0.58   **3)** –2.03   **4)** –2.68
then determine the conclusion.
b) Which of these results are statistically significant?

39. $H_o: p = 0.40$
$H_a: p \neq 0.40$
Mean = 0.40
Standard Error(SE) = 0.0315
Significance Level, $\alpha = 5\%$

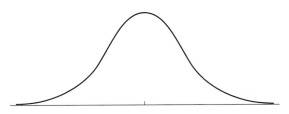

a) If the test statistic is:
1) –1.85   **2)** 2.36   **3)** –2.49   **4)** 1.34
then determine the conclusion.
b) Which of these results are statistically significant?

Section 9.4

40. The p-value, or observed significance level, of a hypothesis test is the _____ level of significance at which the null hypothesis H_o can be rejected using the test statistic.

41. When interpreting p-values, a rule of thumb that can be followed is:
a) If the p-value is less than 1%, the test statistic is _____ significant.
b) If the p-value is between 1% and 5%, the test statistic is _____ .
c) If the p-value is between 5% and 10%, test statistic is _____ significant.
d) If the p-value is greater than 10%, the test statistic is _____ significant.

42. The p-value, or observed significance level is the largest level of significance, α, at which the null hypothesis H_o can be rejected.
(T/F)

43. P-values can be represented as either percents or decimals.
(T/F)

44. If the p-value for a test statistic is greater than 10%, the test statistic is not significant.
(T/F)

45. An unemployment agency claims that the mean age of recipients of unemployment benefits is 37 years. A trade union association believes this claim is not correct. The association randomly interviews 400 recipients of unemployment benefits and obtains a mean age of 35 years. The researcher computes the decision rule for this test to be: reject H_o if the test statistic is greater than 1.96 or less than –1.96 years. Use the following model to perform this hypothesis test, and:
a) State the null and alternative hypotheses.
b) Label the diagram with the critical z-scores, z_c, reject and fail to reject areas, and the test statistic.

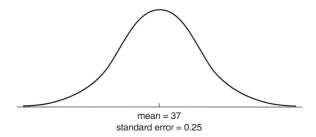

mean = 37
standard error = 0.25

c) Determine the p-value for the test statistic.
d) State your conclusion.

46. According to a recent census report 50% of U.S. families earn more than $20,000 per year. A sociologist from a northeastern university believes this percent is too low. He randomly selects 100 families and determines that 64 have incomes of more than $20,000. The decision rule is to reject H_o if the test statistic is more than 2.33.
a) State the null and alternative hypotheses.
b) Label the diagram with the critical z-scores, z_c, reject and fail to reject areas, and the test statistic.

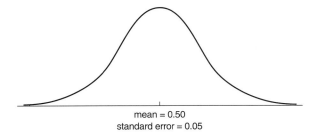

mean = 0.50
standard error = 0.05

c) Determine the p-value for the test statistic.
d) State your conclusion.

For problems 47–50:

a) Formulate the null and alternative hypotheses.
b) Use the mean, standard error(SE), and significance level, α, given in the problem to calculate the critical z-score value(s) and formulate the decision rule.
c) Label the diagram with the mean, standard error (SE), significance level, reject and fail to reject areas.
d) Determine the p-value for the test statistic.
e) Use the test statistic to determine the conclusion.
f) State whether the test statistic is statistically significant.
g) Answer the questions in each problem.

47. An independent research group is interested in showing that the percent of babies delivered by Cesarean Section is increasing. Last year, 20% of the babies born were delivered by Cesarean Section. The research group randomly inspects the medical records of 100 recent births and finds that 25 of the births were by Cesarean Section. Can the research group conclude that the percent of births by Cesarean section has increased? Use mean = 0.20, standard error(SE) = 0.04 and $\alpha = 5\%$.

48. According to the latest figures unemployment is at 8.7%. The Congressman from the third district believes that the unemployment rate is lower in his district. To test his belief he interviews 200 residents of his district and finds 9 of them to be unemployed. Is the Congressman's belief correct? Use mean = 0.087, standard error(SE) = 0.0199 and $\alpha = 5\%$.

49. According to the norms established for a mathematics achievement test fifth graders should have a mean score of 88. If 64 randomly selected fifth graders from a local school district average 89.4, can the district superintendent conclude that her fifth graders are above the norm? Use mean = 88, standard error(SE) = 1.2 and $\alpha = 1\%$.

50. A beverage company has a machine that is supposed to fill soda bottles with two liters of soda. To check that the machine is operating correctly, (i.e., not under filling or overfilling the bottles), a sample of 81 bottles was selected and the contents of each bottle was determined. The sample mean was 1.93 liters of soda. Does this indicate that the machine is improperly filling the bottles? Use mean = 2.0 liters, standard error(SE) = 0.02 liter and $\alpha = 1\%$.

51. The Federal Aviation Agency(FAA) claims that 10% of all U. S. airline flights are delayed at least 15 minutes. The Air Transport Association(ATA) who believes the claim is too high decides to test this claim. The ATA selects a random sample of 1000 U. S. airline flights and determines that 98 flights were delayed at least 15 minutes. Use a mean = 0.10 and a standard error(SE) = 0.0095.
a) What is the p-value for this hypothesis test?
b) Can the null hypothesis be rejected at $\alpha = 1\%$?

c) What is the smallest level of significance that the null hypothesis can be rejected?

52. The college newspaper at Rich Man's College states the average time that students study per week is 8.5 hours. A skeptical student decides to test the claim to determine if the claim is true. The student selects a random sample of 400 students from the student body and determines the average study time of the sample to be 9.2 hours. Use a mean = 8.5 and a standard error(SE) = 0.12.

a) What is the p-value for this hypothesis test?
b) Can the null hypothesis be rejected at $\alpha = 5\%$?
c) What is the smallest level of significance for which the null hypothesis can be rejected?

CHAPTER REVIEW

53. In the hypothesis testing procedure, the main objective of the researcher is to present enough data to show that the null hypothesis is not correct.
(T/F)

54. If a false null hypothesis is rejected then
a) A Type I error has been made
b) A Type II error has been made
c) No error has been made

55. If the test statistic is beyond the critical z-score, z_c, then the result is considered:
a) To be a Type I error
b) Statistically significant
c) To be a Type II error

56. When the difference between the sample statistic and the expected result is *not* statistically significant the researcher concludes that the null hypothesis is true.
(T/F)

57. The Greek letter used to symbolize the level of significance is _____.

58. Whenever the alternative hypothesis is nondirectional we have a _____ tailed test.

59. The general formula used to calculate a test statistic, $z =$ _____ .

60. The two critical z scores for a two-tailed test at $\alpha = 5\%$ are _____ and _____.

61. The critical z score for a one-tailed test at $\alpha = 1\%$ is either _____ or _____.

62. When the test statistic falls beyond the critical z-score(s) then the decision is to:
a) Reject H_o, and accept H_a
b) Fail to reject H_o
c) Seek more information

63. When a directional hypothesis is being tested and the critical z-score is to the right of the mean then the alternative hypothesis must be of the form:
a) Less than
b) More than
c) Not equal to

64. When a nondirectional hypothesis is being tested then and the significance level is 5% then the critical z scores are:

a) ± 1.96
b) ± 2.58
c) ± 1.65

65. The level of significance is the probability of a test statistic supporting the null hypothesis.
(T/F)

66. In a hypothesis test, the null hypothesis is rejected if the p-value is _____ or _____ the significance level, α. Thus, the smaller the p-value, the stronger the evidence against the _____ hypothesis provided by the test statistic.

67. **a)** If the p-value of a statistical hypothesis test is equal to 3%, can the null hypothesis be rejected at $\alpha = 5\%$?
b) For this test, the smallest significance level in which the null hypothesis can be rejected is _____.

68. In a two-tailed test, the p-value of a hypothesis test is equal to _____ the percent of area in the tail beyond the direction of the test statistic of the test.

For problems 69 & 70, state the null and alternative hypotheses assuming you are the individual or agency performing the hypothesis test. Also indicate whether these tests are directional or nondirectional.

69. In a recent issue of Psychology for Tomorrow researchers report that 20% of the wives who hold full-time jobs now earn more than their husbands. A sociologist from the midwest believes this claim is too high and decides to test the claim.

70. A national magazine recently claimed that 3 out of every 10 women between the ages of 16 and 40 years have a form of herpes virus. Researchers representing the New World Medical Society believe the claim is not true and decide to test the claim.

71. You are given the null hypothesis (H_o), the alternative hypothesis (H_a), a diagram indicating the sampling distribution model, the mean, standard error(SE), critical z-score(s) and a test statistic.

$H_o: \mu = 12$
$H_a: \mu < 12$

a) State decision rule.
If the test statistic is z = –2, then:
b) Do you reject the null hypothesis?
c) Do you accept the alternative hypothesis?
If the test statistic is z = 3, then:
d) Do you reject the null hypothesis?
e) Do you accept the alternative hypothesis?

72. Use the given information to:
a) Label the diagram with critical z-score(s), reject and fail to reject areas and the test statistic.
b) Determine the conclusion.
c) Is the test statistic statistically significant?
H_o: p = 0.80
H_a: p < 0.80
Decision Rule: Reject H_o if the test statistic is less than $z_c = -1.65$.
The test statistic is z = –1.88.

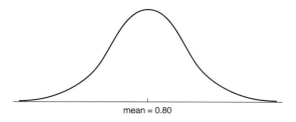

73. Use the information in problem 72 to calculate the chance of a Type I error.

For problems 74–75, the null and alternative hypotheses, the mean and standard error(SE), the significance level, α, and a diagram are given.

Calculate the critical z-score(s) and formulate the decision rule. Label the diagram with the mean, standard error(SE), significance level, critical z-score(s) and reject and fail to reject areas. Answer the appropriate questions.

74. H_o: $\mu = 90$
H_a: $\mu \neq 90$
Mean = 90
Standard Error(SE) = 10
Significance Level, $\alpha = 5\%$

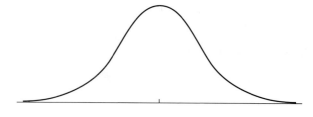

a) If the test statistic is:
1) – 0.7   **2)** – 1.10   **3)** 2.00   **4)** 1.30
then determine the conclusion.
b) Which of these results are statistically significant?

75. H_o: p = 0.30
H_a: p > 0.30
Mean = 0.30
Standard Error(SE) = 0.0229
Significance Level, $\alpha = 5\%$

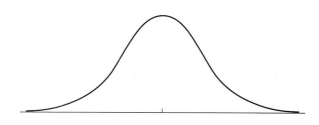

a) If the test statistic is:
1) 0.93   **2)** 1.61   **3)** 0.91   **4)** – 0.09
then determine the conclusion.
b) Which of these results are statistically significant?

76. According to a recent insurance company claim an American family of four spends a mean of $2000 per year for medical care. The medical association believes this claim is too high. They randomly survey 3600 families and find the mean expenditure to be $1990. Their decision rule is to reject H_o if the test statistic is less than $z_c = -2$.

Use the following model to perform this hypothesis test, and:
a) State the null and alternative hypotheses.
b) Label the diagram with the critical z-score(s), reject and fail to reject areas, and the test statistic.

c) Determine the p-value for the test statistic.

d) State your conclusion.

77. A psychiatrist wants to determine if a small amount of alcohol decreases the reaction time in adults. The mean reaction time for a specified test is 0.20 seconds. A sample of 64 people were given a small amount of alcohol and their reaction time averaged 0.17 seconds. Does this sample result support the psychiatrist's hypothesis? Use mean = 0.20 sec., standard error(SE) = 0.01 sec. and $\alpha = 1\%$.

a) Formulate the null and alternative hypotheses.

b) Use the mean, standard error(SE), and significance level, α, given in the problem to calculate the critical z-score(s) and formulate the decision rule.

c) Label the diagram with the mean, standard error(SE), significance level, reject and fail to reject areas.

d) Determine the p-value for the test statistic.

e) Use the test statistic to determine the conclusion.

f) State whether the test statistic is statistically significant.

g) Answer the question.

>>> WHAT DO YOU THINK?

78. Examine the graph entitled "Back to School."

Statistical Snapshot

Back to School

Percentage of people interested in continuing their education:

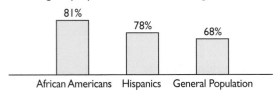

Source: Opinion Research Corporation, survey of 508 minority members and a survey of 1,009 members of the general population

a) What different populations are being represented within the snapshot?

If we assume the stated figures within the graph represent the population parameters for each population, then determine:

b) The null hypothesis for each percentage figure within the graph.

c) An alternative hypothesis if you believe that the figure is too high for the general population, but too low for the African American population, and the Hispanic population.

d) Indicate the type of alternative hypothesis for each population.

e) Determine the type of test (i.e. 1TT or 2TT), and on which side of the curve the critical z-score would be positioned.

f) Describe how you would select an appropriate sample to test the null hypothesis.

g) When calculating the expected results in step 2 of the hypothesis testing procedure, what assumption are you making? Explain why it is necessary to make this assumption.

h) Is there an overlap between the members of the three populations shown in the snapshot? If so, then explain why you think that the percentage for the general population can be smaller than the percentages of the other populations that are represented within the general population?

79. Examine the graph entitled "Spending for the Holidays."

Statistical Snapshot

Spending for the Holidays

Men claim they'll spend an average $653 this holiday season; women, $580. Spending plans by age groups:

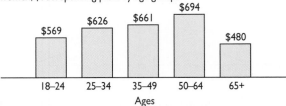

Source: Opinion Research Corporation, survey of 508 minority members and a survey of 1,009 members of the general population

a) What different populations are being represented within the snapshot?

b) Does the average amount of money spent by each age group represent both males and females?

c) What claim do the men make regarding their spending during the holidays?

d) What claim do the women make regarding their spending during the holidays?

e) How many people were surveyed to determine their spending plans for the holiday? Do you have any information regarding their break down with respect to their age and sex? Why do think that information might be helpful in interpreting the results stated in the snapshot?

If you are planning to test the statement about what men spend for the holidays and your belief is that the figure within the graph is too high, what would:

f) The null and alternative hypotheses be for your test.

g) Indicate the type of alternative hypothesis for each population.

h) Determine the type of test (i.e. 1TT or 2TT), and on which side of the curve the critical z-score would be positioned.

i) Describe how you would select an appropriate sample to test the null hypothesis.

j) When calculating the expected results in step 2 of the hypothesis testing procedure, what assumption are you making? Explain why it is necessary to make this assumption to test the null hypothesis.

k) For the hypothesis test you outlined regarding the amount men spend for the holidays, what would the conclusion be to your test if the test statistic fell to the left of your critical z-score?

If you are planning to test the statement about what women spend for the holidays and your belief is that the figure within the graph is too low, what would:

l) The null and alternative hypotheses be for your test.

m) Indicate the type of alternative hypothesis for each population.

n) Determine the type of test (i.e. 1TT or 2TT), and on which side of the curve the critical z-score would be positioned.

o) Describe how you would select an appropriate sample to test the null hypothesis.

p) When calculating the expected results in step 2 of the hypothesis testing procedure, what assumption are you making? Explain why it is necessary to make this assumption to test the null hypothesis.

q) For the hypothesis test you outlined regarding the amount women spend for the holidays, what would the conclusion be to your test if the test statistic fell to the right of your critical z-score?

If you are planning to test the statement about what people within the age group 25–34 spend for the holidays and your belief is that the figure within the graph is too low, what would:

r) The null and alternative hypotheses be for your test.

s) Indicate the type of alternative hypothesis for each population.

t) Determine the type of test (i.e. 1TT or 2TT), and on which side of the curve the critical z-score would be positioned.

u) Describe how you would select an appropriate sample to test the null hypothesis.

v) When calculating the expected results in step 2 of the hypothesis testing procedure, what assumption are you making? Explain why it is necessary to make this assumption to test the null hypothesis.

w) For the hypothesis test you outlined regarding the amount people aged 25–34 spend for the holidays, what would the conclusion be to your test if the test statistic fell to the right of your critical z-score?

PROJECTS

80. Read a research article from a professional journal in a field such as medicine, education, marketing, science, social science, etc. Write a summary of the research article which includes the following:

a) Name of article, author and journal (include volume, number and date).

b) The statement of the research problem.

c) The null and alternative hypotheses.

d) How the experiment was conducted (include the sample size and the sampling technique).

e) Determine the test statistic and the level of significance.

f) State the conclusion in terms of the null and alternative hypotheses.

81. Select a claim found in a magazine, newspaper or stated on television or radio. Formulate an opinion regarding this claim, and devise a hypothesis testing procedure to test the claim. Be sure to include the following:

a) The source from which you found this claim.

b) The null and alternative hypotheses.

c) Define the population and how you would go about selecting a sample from this population.

d) State the method you would use to obtain your data from the sample.

ANALYZING THE DATABASE USING TECHNOLOGY

The following exercises refer to the file DATABASE listed in Appendix A. Using a technological tool, answer each exercise.

82. For each variable, conduct a hypothesis test. Test the null hypothesis that the population mean is: $\mu = k$ against a nondirectional alternative hypothesis. Have your instructor help you interpret the output.

a) k = 18 for the variable AGE.

b) k = 85 for the variable AVE.

c) k = 8 for the variable STY.

d) k = 2.75 for the variable GPA.

e) k = 100 for the variable GFT.

83. For each variable, conduct a hypothesis test. Test the null hypothesis that the population mean is: $\mu = k$ against a directional alternative hypothesis. Have your instructor help you interpret the output.

a) k = 18 for the variable AGE and perform a greater than test.

b) k = 85 for the variable AVE and perform a less than test.

c) k = 8 for the variable STY and perform a greater than test.

d) k = 2.75 for the variable GPA and perform a greater than test.

e) k = 100 for the variable GFT and perform a less than test.

Have your instructor help you interpret the output.

CHAPTER TEST

84. If the null hypothesis is rejected then the alternative hypothesis is accepted. (T/F)

85. When a true null hypothesis is rejected, one has committed a Type _____ error.

86. If a test statistic is statistically significant, then the _____ hypothesis is accepted.

87. As the significance level decreases the chance of committing a Type I error _____, while the chance of committing a Type II error _____.

88. In a hypothesis test, if the test statistic falls beyond the critical z-score, then the conclusion is stated as _____ H_o and _____ H_a.

89. The significance level, α, is the probability of:

a) Rejecting a false null hypothesis

b) Making a Type II error

c) Rejecting a true null hypothesis

90. As the significance level decreases, the chance of committing a Type I error decreases. (T/F)

91. Reporting a p-value of 0.89% indicates that the null hypothesis can be rejected at values of α as small as α = _____ %.

92. If a null hypothesis is rejected at $\alpha = 1\%$ then the p-value for the test statistic must be less than 0.01. (T/F)

For problems 93–94, state the null and alternative hypotheses assuming you are the individual or agency performing the hypothesis test. Also indicate whether these tests are directional or nondirectional.

93. The National Safety Council has recently stated that only 11% of all licensed drivers wear seat belts. A research team believes this claim is too low and decides to test it.

94. The U.S. Navy is going to conduct a series of tests to determine if an automatic opening device for parachutes meets the manufacturer's claim of a mean opening time of 6 seconds.

95. You are given the null hypothesis (H_o), the alternative hypothesis (H_a), a diagram indicating the sampling distribution model, the mean, standard error(SE), critical value(s) and a statistical result.

H_o: p = 0.20

H_a: p $\neq$ 0.20

a) State the decision rule.

b) If the test statistic is – 0.03, state your conclusion.

c) If the test statistic is 2.23, state your conclusion.

d) If the test statistic is 1.95, state your conclusion.

96. The null and alternative hypotheses, the mean and standard error(SE), the significance level, α, and a diagram are given. Calculate the critical value(s) and formulate the decision rule. Label the diagram with the mean, standard error(SE), significance level, critical z value(s) and reject and fail to reject areas. Answer the appropriate questions.

H_o: $\mu = 520$

H_a: $\mu > 520$

Decision Rule: Reject H_o if the test statistic is greater than – 2.33.

The test statistic is 2.9.

97. A manufacturer wants to advertise a product in *Playperson* magazine. The product is specifically designed for a person aged 21 through 35 years. The magazine has stated that 70% of its subscribers are in this age group. The marketing supervisor for the manufacturer believes the claim is too high and randomly surveys 100 of the magazine's subscribers and determines that 64 are in this age group. The decision rule is reject H_o if the test statistic is less than -1.75.

a) State the null and alternative hypotheses.

b) Label the diagram with the critical z-score(s), reject and fail to reject areas, and the test statistic.

mean = 0.70
standard error = 0.0458

c) Determine the p-value for the test statistic.

d) State your conclusion.

98. A pharmaceutical company claims to have developed a new antibiotic which is more effective against type A bacteria than its current product. The current product is 90% effective against type A bacteria. To test its claim a random sample of 400 individuals who were infected with this bacteria are treated with the new antibiotic and 380 recover. Do these results support the pharmaceutical company's claim?

Use mean = 0.90, standard error(SE) = 0.015 and $\alpha = 1\%$.

a) Formulate the null and alternative hypotheses.

b) Use the mean, standard error(SE), and significance level, α, given in the problem to calculate the critical z score(s) and formulate the decision rule.

c) Label the diagram with the mean, standard error(SE), significance level, reject and fail to reject areas.

d) Determine the p-value for the test statistic.

e) Use the test statistic to determine the conclusion.

f) State whether the test statistic is statistically significant.

g) Answer the question.

CHAPTER 10

Hypothesis Test Involving a Population Proportion

Contents

10.1 INTRODUCTION

Are the following claims startling? What are your feelings about these claims?

EXAMPLE 10.1

The Bureau of Statistics claims that 75% of new small businesses will go bankrupt within ten months.

Success

Failure

FIGURE 10.1

EXAMPLE 10.2

A sociologist claims that two out of three couples that wed this year will divorce within five years.

Newlyweds

Divorce Court

FIGURE 10.2

EXAMPLE 10.3

Educational Research Associates (ERA) claims that at least 40% of the male graduates of the State University have a reading level below 9th grade.

Entering

Graduating

FIGURE 10.3

In each of the previous claims, the population characteristic described is based upon count data. That is, individuals in the population are categorized and counted according to a particular characteristic like sex, race, religion, marital status, educational level, political affiliation, state of health, etc. When dealing with count data, the **proportion of the population** that possess each of these characteristics can be determined.

DEFINITION 10.1

The **population (or true) proportion** is the ratio of the number of occurrences (or observations) in the population that possess the particular characteristic to the population size.

Thus, the population proportion, denoted by p, can be expressed by the formula:

$$p = \frac{X}{N}$$

where: p = population proportion
X = number of occurrences (or observations) n the population possessing the particular characteristic
N = population size

The population proportion is often expressed in an equivalent percentage form.

For example, according to the registration records of the 26,000 students attending a large state community college, 6,240 students were enrolled in a psychology course. Thus, the proportion of community college students enrolled in a psychology course is:

$$p = \frac{\text{number of students enrolled in a psychology course}}{\text{total number of students}}$$

$$= \frac{6,240}{26,000}$$

$$= 0.24$$

The population proportion, p = 0.24, can also be expressed as 24%. Therefore, we can state that: 24% of the community college students are enrolled in a psychology course.

However, there are many instances where it is either impractical or impossible to calculate the population proportion. For example, suppose you wanted to determine the proportion of red colored M & M's manufactured by the Mars Corporation. Since it is impractical to determine the population (or true) proportion of red colored M & M's, it becomes necessary to *estimate* the population proportion. To estimate this proportion, we would have to select a random sample of M & M candies and calculate the proportion of red colored M & M's within the sample. If there were 500 M & M's in the sample and 150 were red, then we would have $^{150}\!/_{500}$ or 30% red colored M & M's. This result is called a **sample proportion.**

DEFINITION 10.2

The **sample proportion** is the ratio of the number of occurrences (or observations) in the sample that possess the particular characteristic to the sample size.

Thus, the sample proportion, denoted by $\hat{p}$ (read p-hat), can be expressed by the formula:

$$\hat{p} = \frac{x}{n}$$

where: $\hat{p}$ = sample proportion

x = number of occurrences (or observations) in the sample possessing the particular characteristic

n = sample size

The sample proportion of 30% red colored M & M's is a statistic that can be used to estimate the unknown population value p, population proportion of red colored M & M's. Keep in mind, however, if a second random sample of M & M's were selected and the proportion of red colored M & M's determined, we would most likely obtain a different sample proportion of red M & M's. Since different samples consist of different items from the population, we expect the different samples to provide different values for the sample proportion. Therefore, if we are interested in either estimating or testing claims about a population proportion, it becomes necessary to examine the distribution of all possible values of the sample proportion. This distribution is referred to as the sampling distribution of the proportion.

In this chapter, we will be applying the general hypothesis testing procedure discussed in Chapter 9 to test a claim made about a population proportion. For instance, considering Example 10.3, suppose that you believe the claim: 40% of the State University male graduates having a reading level below 9th grade is too high. How would you go about statistically testing this claim while trying to support your point of view?

To test this claim you would select a random sample of size n from the population and compute the sample proportion of State University male graduates that have a reading level below 9th grade. This sample proportion, $\hat{p}$, is compared to the claimed value for the population proportion, p, to determine if the difference between the sample proportion and the population proportion is statistically significant. If the difference between the sample proportion and the population proportion is statistically significant then your belief about the State University male graduates is too high would be statistically supported.

The statistical procedure needed to perform this hypothesis test involves the general five step hypothesis testing procedure developed in Chapter 9 where the sampling distribution of the proportion will be used as the hypothesis testing model. The sampling distribution of the proportion has the same properties as the Binomial Distribution which was discussed in Chapter 5. These properties will be discussed in Section 10.2.

CASE STUDY 10.1   Mutual Funds

Examine the pie chart information contained in the snapshot entitled "Mutual funds bearing loads" shown in Figure 10.4. The pie chart presents the different type of mutual funds along with the number of funds belonging to each type.

Statistical Snapshot

Mutual Funds Bearing Loads

Of the 3,037 stock and bond mutual funds available, a little more than half charge a sales fee, or load, which is charges as a percentage of the amount invested.

1,476   No-load (no sales fee)

100   237   Low-load (sales fee: 0.1%–3.9%)

Full-load (sales fee: 6.1%–8.5%)   1,224   Mid-load (sales fee: 4%–6%)

Source: Lipper Analitical Services

FIGURE 10.4

a) Define the population represented by the pie chart?
b) What variable is represented by the pie chart?
c) Is this variable numeric or categorical? Explain.
d) What is the total number of funds represented by the pie chart?
e) Is this variable numeric or categorical? Explain.
f) Determine the proportion of no-load mutual funds represented by the pie chart.
g) Determine the proportion of full-load mutual funds represented within the pie chart.
h) Determine the proportion of low-load mutual funds represented within the pie chart.
i) Determine the proportion of mid-load mutual funds represented within the pie chart.
j) What percent of the mutual funds represented by the pie chart have no sales fee?
k) What percent of the mutual funds represented by the pie chart have a sales fee from 0.1% to 6%?

10.2   THE SAMPLING DISTRIBUTION OF THE PROPORTION

Let us now discuss the characteristics of the model needed to perform a hypothesis test involving a population proportion: **the sampling distribution of the proportion.**

Theorem 10.1   The Characteristics of the Sampling Distribution of The Proportion

If all possible random samples of size n are selected from an infinite or large binomial population[1] having a population proportion p and, the sample proportion, $\hat{p}$, is computed for each of these samples, then:

(continues)

[1]A binomial population is a population where the scores included can be classified into one of two categories. (See Section 5.5 for more information)

a) the **sampling distribution of the proportion** is approximately normal when **both** np and n(1 − p) are greater than 5.

b) The **mean of the sampling distribution of the proportion**, denoted $\mu_{\hat{p}}$, is: $\mu_{\hat{p}} = p$

c) The **standard deviation of the sampling distribution of the proportion**, denoted $\sigma_{\hat{p}}$, is:[2]

$$\sigma_{\hat{p}} = \sqrt{\frac{p(1-p)}{n}}$$

This standard deviation is commonly referred to as **the standard error of the proportion.**

Theorem 10.1 is illustrated in Figure 10.5.

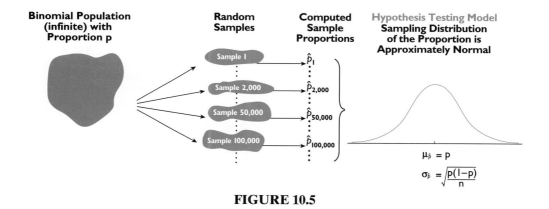

FIGURE 10.5

Let's apply the results of Theorem 10.1 to the following problem.

EXAMPLE 10.4

If 75% of new small businesses fail within 10 months, what's the probability that a random sample of 100 newly formed small businesses will have a proportion of at least 80% failures within 10 months?

Solution

From Theorem 10.1, the mean of the sampling distribution of the proportion is: $\mu_{\hat{p}} = p$. Since the population proportion p is 75% or 0.75, then: $\mu_{\hat{p}} = 0.75$.

---

[2]If we are sampling without replacement from a finite binomial population then the exact formula for $\sigma_{\hat{p}}$ is:

$$\sigma_{\hat{p}} = \sqrt{\frac{p(1-p)}{n}}\sqrt{\frac{N-n}{N-1}}$$

where:

N is the population size and n is the sample size. If the sample size, n, is less than 5% of the population size, N, then it is appropriate to use:

$$\sigma_{\hat{p}} = \sqrt{\frac{p(1-p)}{n}}$$

Using n = 100, p = 0.75 and 1 − p = 0.25, the standard error of the proportion, $\sigma_{\hat{p}}$, is:

$$\sigma_{\hat{p}} = \sqrt{\frac{p(1-p)}{n}}$$

$$\sigma_{\hat{p}} = \sqrt{\frac{0.75(0.25)}{100}}$$

$$\sigma_{\hat{p}} = 0.0433$$

The sampling distribution of the proportion is approximately a normal distribution since:

$$\text{np} = (100)(0.75) \qquad \text{and} \qquad n(1-p) = (100)(0.25)$$
$$= \quad 75 \qquad\qquad\qquad\qquad = \quad 25$$

are both greater than 5. The sampling distribution of the proportion is illustrated in Figure 10.6.

sampling distribution of the proportion
(is approximately a normal distribution)

FIGURE 10.6

Since the sampling distribution of the proportion is approximately a normal distribution, we need to calculate a z score to find the shaded area in Figure 10.6. The z score formula for the sampling distribution of the proportion is given by:

$$z \; of \; \hat{p} = \frac{\hat{p} - \mu_{\hat{p}}}{\sigma_{\hat{p}}}$$

Thus, the z score of 0.80 is

$$z = \frac{0.80 - 0.75}{0.0433}$$

$$z \; of \; 0.80 = 1.15$$

From Table II, the Normal Curve Area Table found in Appendix D: Statistical Tables, the area to the right of z = 1.15 is 0.1251. Therefore, the probability of a sample of 100 newly formed businesses will have at least 80% failures within 10 months is 0.1251.

EXAMPLE 10.5

E.R.A. claims that 40% of the male graduates of the State University System have a reading level below the 9th grade. What is the probability that less than 38% of a random sample of 270 male State University graduates will have a reading level below 9th grade?

Solution

From Theorem 10.1, we obtain the mean of the sampling distribution of the proportion using: $\mu_{\hat{p}} = p$.

$$\text{Thus, } \mu_{\hat{p}} = 0.40$$

Since $n = 270$, $p = 0.40$ and $1 - p = 0.60$, the standard error of the proportion is:

$$\sigma_{\hat{p}} = \sqrt{\frac{p(1-p)}{n}}$$

Thus,

$$\sigma_{\hat{p}} = \sqrt{\frac{0.40(0.60)}{270}}$$

$$\sigma_{\hat{p}} = 0.0298$$

Because np and n(1 – p) are both greater than 5, then the sampling distribution of the proportion is approximately a normal distribution. This is illustrated in Figure 10.7.

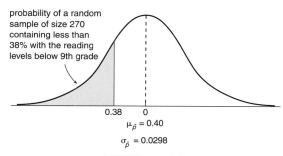

**sampling distribution of the proportion
(is approximately a normal distribution)**

probability of a random sample of size 270 containing less than 38% with the reading levels below 9th grade

0.38   0
$\mu_{\hat{p}} = 0.40$
$\sigma_{\hat{p}} = 0.0298$

FIGURE 10.7

Since we are dealing with a normal distribution, we need to calculate a z score of 0.38 to determine the shaded area illustrated in Figure 10.7.

$$z = \frac{0.38 - 0.40}{0.0298} = -0.67$$

From Table II, the area to the left of $z = -0.67$ is 0.2514. Therefore, the probability that less than 38% of the State University's male graduates have a reading level below 9th grade is 0.2514.

10.3   HYPOTHESIS TESTING INVOLVING A POPULATION PROPORTION

Now that we have discussed the sampling distribution of the proportion model, let's develop the **hypothesis testing procedure for hypotheses involving a population proportion** using the five step general hypothesis testing procedure discussed in Chapter 9. Throughout this chapter, we will be assuming that the sampling distribution of the proportion satisfies the conditions of Theorem 10.1.

Hypothesis Testing Procedure Involving a Population Proportion

Step 1   Formulate the two hypotheses, H_o and H_a.
            Null Hypothesis:
            The null hypothesis has the following form:

Null Hypothesis Form:

H_o: The population proportion, p, is claimed to be **equal to** the proportion p_o.
This is symbolized as:

$$H_o: \ p = p_o$$

Alternative Hypothesis:
Since the alternative hypothesis, H_a, can be stated as either *greater than*, *less than*, or *not equal to* the numerical value, μ_o, then the alternative hypothesis can have one of three forms:

Form (a): Greater Than Form For H_a

H_a: The population proportion, p, is claimed to be **greater than** the numerical value, p_o.
This is symbolized as:

$$H_a: \ p > p_o$$

Form (b): Less Than Form For H_a

H_a: The population proportion, p, is claimed to be **less than** the numerical value, p_o.
This is symbolized as:

$$H_a: \ p < p_o$$

Form (c): Not Equal Form For H_a

H_a: The population proportion, p, is claimed to be **not equal** to the numerical value, p_o.
This is symbolized as:

$$H_a: \ p \neq p_o$$

Step 2   Determine the model to test the null hypothesis, H_o.
Under the assumption H_o is true, calculate the expected results. Since we are testing a hypothesis about a population proportion using a sample proportion, $\hat{p}$, we use as our model the sampling distribution of the proportion and should choose a sample size which will make both np and n(1 – p) greater than 5.
Using Theorem 10.1 and under the assumption H_o is true (i.e. $p = p_o$), then:
the **expected results** are:
a)   The sampling distribution of the proportion is *approximately normal* and serves as the hypothesis testing model.
b)   The mean of the sampling distribution of the proportion is:

$$\mu_{\hat{p}} = p_o,$$

(i.e. the mean $\mu_{\hat{p}}$ equals the claimed population proportion, p_o.)
c) The standard error of the proportion is:

$$\sigma_{\hat{p}} = \sqrt{\frac{p_o(1-p_o)}{n}}$$

This hypothesis testing model is illustrated in Figure 10.8

Hypothesis Testing Model

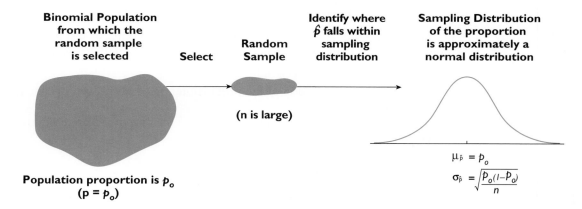

FIGURE 10.8

In theory, the binomial population being sampled must be infinite to use the standard error formula:

$$\sigma_{\hat{p}} = \sqrt{\frac{p(1-p)}{n}}$$

However, it is appropriate to use this formula when the population is *finite* and the population size, N, is large relative to the sample size, n. The rule used to determine whether the population is large relative to the sample size is: the sample size, n, is less than 5% of the population size, N.
That is, $n/N < 5\%$.

Step 3 Formulate the decision rule.
a) Determine the type of alternative hypothesis: directional or non-directional.
b) Determine the type of test: 1TT or 2TT.
c) Identify the significance level: $\alpha = 1\%$ or $\alpha = 5\%$.
d) Using Table II, find the critical z score(s) z_c.
e) Construct the hypothesis test model.
f) State the decision rule.

Step 4 Analyze the sample data.
Randomly select the necessary sample data from the binomial population and calculate the sample proportion, $\hat{p}$, using the formula:

$$\hat{p} = \frac{\text{number of occurrences possessing particular characteristic}}{\text{sample size}}$$

Calculate the z score of the sample proportion using the formula:

$$z = \frac{\hat{p} - \mu_{\hat{p}}}{\sigma_{\hat{p}}}$$

This is referred to as the **test statistic**.

Step 5   State the conclusion.

Compare the test statistic, z, to the critical z score(s), z_c, of the decision rule and draw one of the following conclusions:

a)   b)

Reject H_o and   or   **Fail to reject H_o**
Accept H_a at α   **at α**

In summary the procedure just outlined to perform a hypothesis test involving a population proportion, p, contains three refinements to the general hypothesis testing procedure developed in Chapter 9. They are:

I. The sampling distribution of the proportion is used as the appropriate hypothesis testing model.

II. The properties of the sampling distribution of the proportion are used to calculate the expected values.

III. The formula: $z = \dfrac{\hat{p} - \mu_{\hat{p}}}{\sigma_{\hat{p}}}$ is used to calculate the test statistic, z.

EXAMPLE 10.6

An advertising agency developed the theme for the commercials for the day time soap: *The Nights of Our Lives* on the assumption that 80% of its viewers are women. The ad agency would consider changing the theme of the commercials if the proportion of women viewers is significantly lower than 80%.

To test this population proportion, the ad agency conducted a random survey of 400 viewers of this show and determined that 311 of these viewers were women. Based upon this sample proportion, should the ad agency change the theme of the commercials at $\alpha = 5\%$?

Solution

Step 1   Formulate the hypotheses.

H_o: The population proportion of women viewers who watch the day time soap *The Nights of Our Lives* is 0.80.

In symbols, we have:

H_o: p = 0.80

Since the advertising agency is interested in determining if the population proportion is *lower than* 0.80, then the alternative hypothesis is directional and is stated as:

H_a: The population proportion of women viewers who watch the day time soap *The Nights of Our Lives* is *less than* 0.80.

In symbols, we have:

H_a: p < 0.80

Step 2   Determine the model to test the null hypothesis, H_o.

Under the assumption H_o is true, calculate the expected results. Using Theorem 10.1 and the assumption H_o is true, the expected results are:

a) The sampling distribution of the proportion is approximately a normal distribution since both np and n(1 – p) are greater than 5.
b) For p = 0.80, then the mean of the sampling distribution of the proportion is: $\mu_{\hat{p}} = 0.80$
c) Since n = 400, p = 0.80 and 1 – p = 0.20, then the standard error of the proportion is:

$$\sigma_{\hat{p}} = \sqrt{\frac{p(1-p)}{n}}$$

$$\sigma_{\hat{p}} = \sqrt{\frac{0.80(0.20)}{400}}$$

$$\sigma_{\hat{p}} = 0.02$$

Figure 10.9 illustrates the sampling distribution of the proportion as the Hypothesis Testing model.

**sampling distribution of the proportion
(is approximately a normal distribution)**

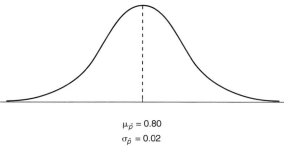

$\mu_{\hat{p}} = 0.80$
$\sigma_{\hat{p}} = 0.02$

FIGURE 10.9

Step 3 Formulate the decision rule.
a) The alternative hypothesis is *directional* since the ad agency wants to determine if the proportion of women viewers is significantly *lower* than 0.80.
b) The type of hypothesis test is *one-tailed* on the left side.
c) The significance level is: $\alpha = 5\%$.
d) The critical z score, z_c, for a one-tailed test on the left side with $\alpha = 5\%$ is –1.65.
e) Figure 10.10(a) illustrates the decision rule for this hypothesis test.

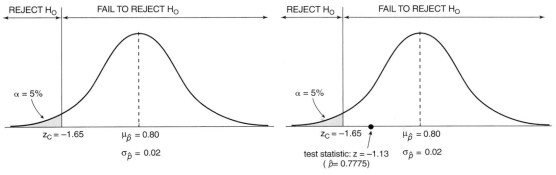

FIGURE 10.10(a)   **FIGURE 10.10(b)**

The decision rule is:

f)   Reject H_o if the test statistic, z, is less than -1.65.

Step 4   Analyze the sample data.

First, using the survey data, compute the sample proportion, $\hat{p}$

$$\hat{p} = \frac{\text{number of women within the survey who watch the soap}}{\text{sample size}}$$

$$\hat{p} = \frac{311}{400}$$

$$\hat{p} = 0.7775$$

Second, compute the test statistic, z, using: $z = \dfrac{\hat{p} - \mu_{\hat{p}}}{\sigma_{\hat{p}}}$ for $\hat{p} = 0.7775$, $\mu_{\hat{p}} = 0.80$ and $\sigma_{\hat{p}} = 0.02$, the test statistic is:

$$z = \frac{0.7775 - 0.80}{0.02} \approx -1.13.$$

Step 5   State the conclusion.

From Figure 12.10(b), since the test statistic z = -1.13 is **not** less than the critical z score $z_c = -1.65$ then we fail to reject H_o at $\alpha = 5\%$. Therefore, the ad agency *should not* change the theme of the commercials for *The Nights of Our Lives*.

EXAMPLE 10.7

The IRS stated that last year 20% of the Federal Income Tax Returns contained arithmetic errors. A random sample of 500 of this year's Federal Returns found 130 returns with arithmetic errors. Can the IRS conclude that the proportion of Federal Returns containing arithmetic errors has significantly changed at $\alpha = 5\%$?

Solution

Step 1   Formulate the hypotheses.

H_o: For this year, the population proportion of Federal Income Tax Returns with arithmetic errors is 0.20.

In symbols, we have:

H_o: p = 0.20

H_a: For this year, the population proportion of Federal Income Tax Returns with arithmetic errors is **not** 0.20.

In symbols, we have:

H_a: $p \neq 0.20$

Step 2   Determine the model to test the null hypothesis, H_o.

Under the assumption H_o is true and using Theorem 10.1, the expected results are:

a)   The sampling distribution of the proportion is approximately a normal distribution since both np and n(1 – p) are greater than 5.

b)   Since p = 0.20, then the mean is: $\mu_{\hat{p}} = 0.20$.

c)   For n = 500, p = 0.20 and 1 – p = 0.80, then the standard error is:

$$\sigma_{\hat{p}} = \sqrt{\frac{p(1-p)}{n}}$$

$$\sigma_{\hat{p}} = 0.0179$$

Figure 10.11 illustrates the sampling distribution of the proportion which serves as the hypothesis testing model.

sampling distribution of the proportion
(is approximately a normal distribution)

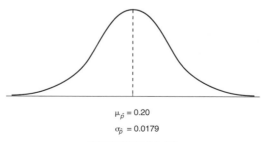

$\mu_{\hat{p}} = 0.20$

$\sigma_{\hat{p}} = 0.0179$

FIGURE 10.11

Step 3 Formulate the decision rule.
  a) The alternative hypothesis is **non-directional** since the IRS is trying to determine if the proportion of Federal Returns containing arithmetic errors for this year is **significantly different** from 0.20.
  b) The type of hypothesis test is two-tailed.
  c) The significance level is: $\alpha = 5\%$.
  d) The critical z scores, z_{LC} and z_{RC}, for a two-tailed test with $\alpha = 5\%$ are $z_{LC} = -1.96$ and $z_{RC} = +1.96$.
  e) Figure 10.12(a) illustrates the decision rule for this hypothesis test.

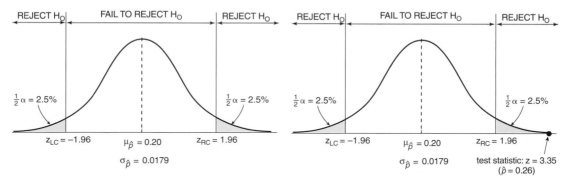

FIGURE 10.12(a)   **FIGURE 10.12(b)**

The decision rule is:
  f) Reject H_o if the test statistic, z, is either *less than* $z_{LC} = -1.96$ or *greater than* $z_{RC} = 1.96$.

Step 4 Analyze the sample data.
First, compute the sample proportion, $\hat{p}$

$$\hat{p} = \frac{\text{number of returns in the sample containing arithmetic errors}}{\text{sample size}}$$

$$\hat{p} = \frac{130}{500}$$

$$\hat{p} = 0.26$$

Second, compute the test statistic, z for, $\hat{p} = 0.26$.

$$z = \frac{0.26 - 0.20}{0.0179} \approx 3.35$$

Step 5   State the conclusion.

As shown in Figure 10.12(b), since the test statistic z = 3.35, is *greater than* the right critical z score z_{RC} = 1.96, we reject H_o and accept H_a at α = 5%. Therefore, the IRS can conclude that the proportion of this year's Federal Returns containing arithmetic errors has signifi-cantly changed at α = 5%.

EXAMPLE 10.8

A biochemist has developed a new drug which he claims is more effective in the treatment of a skin disorder than the existing drug. Using the existing drug only 30 percent of the people contracting this skin disorder recover completely. To test his claim, he administers this new drug to a sample of 300 people who have contracted this skin disorder. The biochemist determines that 110 patients in his sample show a complete recovery. Based upon this sample result, can the biochemist conclude at α = 1% that his new drug is more effective than the existing drug in the treatment of this skin disorder?

Solution

Step 1   Formulate the hypotheses.

H_o: The population proportion of people who completely recover from this skin disorder using the new drug is 0.30.

In symbols, we have:

H_o: p = 0.30

H_a: The population proportion of people who completely recover from this skin disorder using the new drug is *greater than* 0.30.

In symbols, we have:

H_a: p > 0.30

Step 2   Determine the model to test the null hypothesis, H_o.

Under the assumption H_o is true, and using Theorem 10.1, the expected results are:

a) The sampling distribution of the proportion is approximately a normal distribution since both np and n(1 – p) are greater than 5.

b) Since p = 0.30 the mean is: $\mu_{\hat{p}}$ = 0.30.

c) For n = 300, p = 0.30 and 1-p = 0.70, the standard error is:

$$\sigma_{\hat{p}} = \sqrt{\frac{p(1-p)}{n}}$$

$$\sigma_{\hat{p}} = 0.0265$$

Figure 10.13 illustrates the sampling distribution of the proportion as the hypothesis testing model.

Step 3   Formulate the decision rule.

a) The alternative hypothesis is *directional* since the biochemist wants to determine if the proportion of patients completely recovering using the new drug is *greater than* 0.30.

b) The type of hypothesis test is one-tailed on the right side.

c) The significance level is: α = 1%.

d) The critical score, z_c, for a one-tailed test on the right side with α = 1% is 2.33.

**sampling distribution of the proportion
(is approximately a normal distribution)**

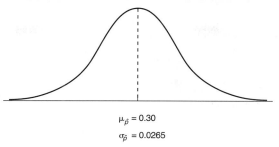

$\mu_{\hat{p}} = 0.30$

$\sigma_{\hat{p}} = 0.0265$

FIGURE 10.13

e)   Figure 10.14(a) illustrates the decision rule for this hypothesis test.

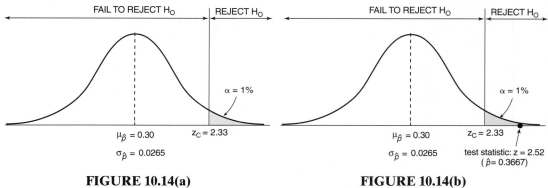

FIGURE 10.14(a)   **FIGURE 10.14(b)**

The decision rule is:
f)   Reject H_o if the test statistic, z, is greater than $z_c = 2.33$.

Step 4   Analyze the sample data.
First, compute the sample proportion, $\hat{p}$.

$$\hat{p} = \frac{\text{number of people in the sample who recover using new drug}}{\text{sample size}}$$

$$\hat{p} = \frac{110}{300}$$

$$\hat{p} = 0.3667$$

Second, compute the test statistic, z, for $\hat{p} = 0.3667$.
$z \approx 2.52$

Step 5   State the conclusion.
As shown in figure 10.14(b), since the test statistic, $z = 2.52$, is greater than the critical z score, $z_c = 2.33$, we reject H_o and accept H_a at $\alpha = 1\%$. Therefore, the biochemist can conclude that his new drug is more effective than the existing drug in the treatment of this skin disorder at a significance level of 1%.

Examine the information contained in the snapshot entitled "Percentage of female workers who are executives or managers" shown in Figure 10.15

    a) What parameter is represented by the graph in Figure 10.15?
    b) What type of graph is used in Figure 10.15 to present the percentage values?
    c) Define the population described in Figure 10.15?
    d) What variable is represented by the graph?
    e) Is this variable numeric or categorical? Explain.
    f) According to Figure 10.15, what proportion of female workers were executives or managers during 1972?
    g) According to Figure 10.15, what was the population proportion of female executives or managers for 1982?

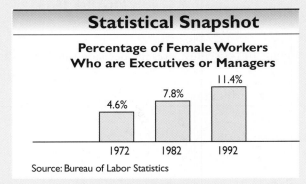

FIGURE 10.15

    h) According to Figure 10.15, what is the population proportion of female executives or managers for 1992? Using the information for 1992, design a hypothesis test assuming you believe that the trend shown in Figure 10.15 will continue to the present time. Within your test, state:
    i) The null hypothesis, using the information pertaining to 1992 as the status quo.
    j) An alternative hypothesis.
    k) Is the alternative hypothesis directional or nondirectional? Is this a 1TT or a 2TT? Explain.
    l) Which population parameter are you assuming you know to perform this hypothesis test? What is the value of this parameter?
    m) State the name of the sampling distribution that will serve as the model for this test? Is this sampling distribution a normal distribution? Explain.
    n) What is the mean of this sampling distribution? What is the standard error of the sampling distribution?
    o) Which tail of the curve would you place the critical value for your hypothesis test?
    p) If you decide to use a significance level of 5%, then write the critical value formula required to perform the test and determine the critical value.
    q) If the test statistic (or sample result) falls to the left of the critical z score of your test, what is the conclusion to this test? Could you agree that the proportion of the population of female executives or managers significantly changed? If you can, then explain the type of significant change you can conclude from the test. What can you conclude about the population proportion?
    r) If the test statistic (or sample result) falls to the right of the critical z score of your test, what is the conclusion to this test? Could you agree that the proportion of the population of female executives or managers has significantly changed? If you can, then explain the type of significant change you can conclude from the test. What can you conclude about the population proportion?
    s) If the p-value of the hypothesis test is 4% (or 0.04), then can you reject the null hypothesis at $\alpha = 5\%$? at $\alpha = 1\%$? For each significant level, does this indicate that the percentage of the female executives or managers has significantly changed? Explain what you can conclude regarding the population proportion for each significant level?
    t) If the p-value of the hypothesis is 0.90% (or 0.0090) and $\alpha = 1\%$, could you conclude that the percentage of female executive or managers has significantly changed? Explain.

Summary of Test Statistic Approach to Hypothesis Test Involving a Population Proportion

The following outline is a summary of the 5 step hypothesis testing procedure for a hypothesis test involving one population propoprtion.

Step 1   Formulate the two hypotheses, H_o and H_a.
Null Hypothesis, H_o: $p = p_o$
Alternative Hypothesis, H_a: has one of the following three forms:
H_a: $p < p_o$ or H_a: $p > p_o$ or H_a: $p \neq p_o$

Step 2   Determine the model to test the null hypothesis, H_o.
Under the assumption H_o is true, the expected results are:
a) The sampling distribution of the proportion is approximately normal when both np and $n(1-p)$ are greater than 5.
b) The mean of the Sampling Distribution of The Proportion, denoted $\mu_{\hat{p}}$, is: $\mu_{\hat{p}} = p$
c) the standard error of the proportion, denoted $\sigma_{\hat{p}}$, is:

$$\sigma_{\hat{p}} = \sqrt{\frac{p(1-p)}{n}}$$

Step 3   Formulate the decision rule.
a) Alternative hypothesis: directional or non-directional.
b) Type of test: 1TT or 2TT.
c) Significance level: $\alpha = 1\%$ or $\alpha = 5\%$.
d) Find the critical z score(s), z_c.
e) Construct the hypothesis test model.
f) State the decision rule.

Step 4   Analyze the sample data.
a) Compute the sample proportion, $\hat{p}$, using the formula:

$$\hat{p} = \frac{\text{number of occurrences possessing particular characteristic}}{\text{sample size}}$$

b) Compute test statistic, z, using: $z = \dfrac{\hat{p} - \mu_{\hat{p}}}{\sigma_{\hat{p}}}$

Step 5   State the conclusion.
Compare the test statistic, z, to the critical z score(s), z_c, of the decision rule and draw one of the following conclusions:
either: (a) Reject H_o and Accept H_a at α
or (b) Fail to Reject H_o at α

Table 10.1 contains a condensed summary of the hypothesis testing procedure involving a population proportion.

TABLE 10.1   Summary of Hypothesis Test for Testing the Value of a Population Proportion

Form of the Null Hypothesis	Conditions of Test	Test Statistic Formula	Sampling Distribution is:
$p = p_o$	$np > 5$ and $n(1 - p) > 5$	$z = \dfrac{\hat{p} - \mu_{\hat{p}}}{\sigma_{\hat{p}}}$ where $\mu_{\hat{p}} = p$ $\sigma_{\hat{p}} = \sqrt{\dfrac{p(1 - p)}{n}}$	Approximately a Normal Distribution

10.4 p-VALUE APPROACH TO HYPOTHESIS TESTING INVOLVING POPULATION PROPORTION USING THE TI-83 PLUS CALCULATOR

The p-value approach will require refinements in steps 3, 4 and 5 of the hypothesis testing procedure. In step 3, the decision rule will be stated as: Reject the H_o if the p-value of the test statistic is less than α. In step 4, the p-value will be determined using the TI-83 Plus calculator. While in step 5, the conclusion of the hypothesis test is determined by comparing the p-value to the level of significance, α.

Let's reexamine the hypothesis test shown in example 10.8 using a p-value approach with the aid of the TI-83 Plus Calculator.

EXAMPLE 10.9

A biochemist has developed a new drug which he claims is **more effective** in the treatment of a skin disorder than the existing drug. Using the existing drug only 30 percent of the people contracting this skin disorder recover completely. To test his claim, he administers this new drug to a sample of 300 people who have contracted this skin disorder. The biochemist determines that 110 patients in his sample show a complete recovery.

Based upon this sample result, can the biochemist conclude at $\alpha = 1\%$ that his new drug is more effective than the existing drug in the treatment of this skin disorder?

Solution

Step 1   *Formulate the hypotheses.*

H_o: The population proportion of people who completely recover from this skin disorder using the new drug is 0.30.

In symbols, we have:

H_o: $p = 0.30$

H_a: The population of people who completely recover from this skin disorder using the new drug is *greater than* 0.30.

In symbols, we have:
H_o: $p > 0.30$

Step 2   *Determine the model to test the null hypothesis, H_o.*
Under the assumption H_o is true, and using Theorem 10.1, the expected results are:

a) The Sampling Distribution of The Proportion is approximately a normal distribution since both np and n(1 − p) are greater than 5.
b) Since p = 0.30 the mean is: $\mu_{\hat{p}} = 0.30$.
c) For n = 300, p = 0.30 and 1 − p = 0.70, the standard error is:

$$\sigma_{\hat{p}} = \sqrt{\frac{p(1-p)}{n}}$$

$$\sigma_{\hat{p}} = 0.0265$$

Figure 10.16 illustrates the Sampling Distribution of The Proportion Hypothesis Testing model.

**sampling distribution of the proportion
(is approximately a normal distribution)**

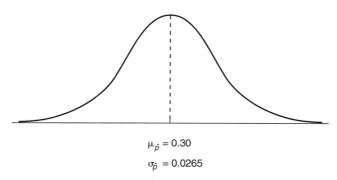

$\mu_{\hat{p}} = 0.30$

$\sigma_{\hat{p}} = 0.0265$

FIGURE 10.16

Step 3 *Formulate the decision rule.*
a) the alternative hypothesis is *directional* since the biochemist wants to determine if the proportion of patients completely recovering using the new drug is *greater than* 0.30.
b) the type of hypothesis test is one-tailed on the right side.
c) the significance level is: α = 1%.
d) Figure 10.17 illustrates the decision rule for this hypothesis test.

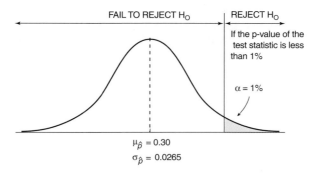

FIGURE 10.17

The decision rule is:
e) Reject H_o if the p-value of the test statistic is less than $\alpha = 1\%$.

Step 4 *Analyze the sample data.*
Determine the p-value of the test statistic by entering the sample data into the TI-83 Plus calculator. The TI-83 Plus calculator output screen is shown in figure 10.18.

FIGURE 10.18

From the output screen, the p-value of the test statistic $z \approx 2.52$ is 0.0059. Using this p-value we can position the test statistic on the hypothesis testing model in Figure 10.19.

FIGURE 10.19

Step 5 *State the conclusion.*
Since the p-value (0.0059) of the test statistic is less than 1%, our conclusion is reject H_o and accept H_a at a p-value of 0.0059. Therefore, the biochemist can conclude that his new drug is more effective than the existing drug in the treatment of this skin disorder at a significance level of 1%.

Now we will summarize this procedure.

Summary of the p-Value Approach to Hypothesis Testing Involving a Population Using the TI-83 Plus Calculator

Step 1   *Formulate the two hypothesis, H_o and H_a.*
Null Hypothesis, H_o: $p = p_o$
Alternative Hypothesis, H_a: has one of the following three forms:
H_a: $p < p_o$ or H_a: $> p_o$ or H_a: $p \neq p_o$

Step 2   *Determine the model to test the null hypothesis, H_o.*
Under the assumption H_o is true, the expected results are:
a)   the Sampling Distribution of The Proportion is approximately normal when **both** np and n(1 – p) are greater than 5.
b)   the mean of the Sampling Distribution of The Proportion, denoted $\mu_{\hat{p}}$, is: $\mu_{\hat{p}} = p$
c)   the standard error of the proportion denoted $\sigma_{\hat{p}}$, is:

$$\sigma_{\hat{p}} = \sqrt{\frac{p(1-p)}{n}}$$

Step 3   *Formulate the decision rule.*
a)   alternative hypothesis: directional or non-directional.
b)   type of test: 1TT or 2TT.
c)   significance level: $\alpha = 1\%$ or $\alpha = 5\%$.
d)   construct the appropriate hypothesis test model.
e)   state the decision rule as *Reject H_o if the p-value of the test statistic is less than α.*

Step 4   **Analyze the sample data.**
Enter the necessary sample data into the TI-83 Plus calculator to determine the p-value of the test statistic.

Step 5   **Determine the conclusion.**
Compare the p-value of the test statistic to the decision rule and either:
a)   **Reject H_o and accept H_a at α,**
or
b)   **Fail to reject H_o at α.**

10.5   USING TECHNOLOGY

In this chapter we have explored hypothesis tests involving a population proportion. In MINITAB to conduct a hypothesis test of a population proportion, p, we use the ZTEST command. A MINITAB output of a ZTEST for a nondirectional alternative hypothesis test, where the population proportion p = 0.7 is stated as MU, the population standard deviation of the proportion is denoted as SIGMA and the random sample of data values are listed in C1 is displayed in Figure 10.20.

MINITAB OUTPUT

TEST OF MU = 0.7000 VS MU N.E. 0.7000
THE ASSUMED SIGMA = 0.458

	N	MEAN	STDEV	SE MEAN	Z	P VALUE
C1	40	0.5500	0.5038	0.0725	−2.07	0.039

FIGURE 10.20

For this output what is the null hypothesis? the alternative hypothesis? Notice that the sample contained 40 data values and that the p-value for the sample is 0.039. Is the null hypothesis rejected?

A MINITAB output for a 1TT test on the left involving a population proportion p = 0.80 and the random sample data is contained in C1 is shown in Figure 10.21.

MINITAB OUTPUT

TEST OF MU = 0.8000 VS MU L.T. 0.8000
THE ASSUMED SIGMA = 0.400

	N	MEAN	STDEV	SE MEAN	Z	P VALUE
C1	400	0.7800	0.4148	0.0200	−1.00	0.16

FIGURE 10.21

Examine the output. Do the sample results in C1 indicate that the alternative hypothesis is accepted?

TI-83 Plus calculator output screens display a nondirectional and directional hypothesis test. Figure 10.22a represents an output screen for a nondirectional hypothesis 1-proportion z-test where the alternative hypothesis is $p \neq 0.70$ with a p-value of 0.0384. Figure 10.22b represents an output screen for a directional hypothesis 1-proportion z-test where the alternative hypothesis is $p < 0.80$ with a p-value of 0.1587. For each test, identify the number of standard deviations the sample proportion deviates from the mean. Which of these output screens indicates a rejection of the null hypothesis at $\alpha = 5\%$?

FIGURE 10.22a

FIGURE 10.22b

SECTION EXERCISES

Section 10.1

(Round off ALL answers to four decimal places.)

1. The symbol p represents the proportion of the _____ possessing the particular characteristic.

2. The symbol $\hat{p}$ represents the proportion of the _____ and is computed using the formula:

$$\hat{p} = \frac{\text{number of occurrences possessing particular characteristic}}{\text{sample size}}$$

3. Determine the sample proportion, $\hat{p}$, for each of the following statements.
   a) Thirty out of 100 incoming freshman do not meet the minimum college requirements in reading.
   b) A nationwide survey of 1200 people found that 800 favored the death penalty for murder.
   c) A family counselor finds that 180 out of 200 patients are lonely because they have forgotten how to have fun.
   d) A government agency has determined that 1850 out of a sample of 5000 student borrowers have defaulted on their federal student loans.
   e) Four out of 37 stock investors purchase stocks based upon presumed inside information (i.e. a hot tip).

4. The following table summarizes the responses of a cross section of 9000 Americans aged 16 and over regarding the following two questions:

   Question #1: " If a man doesn`t want his wife to take a job, should she respect his wishes?"

   Question #2: "Do you think it is or is not all right for a man and a woman to live together without getting married?

	Question #1		Question #2	
	YES	NO	ALL RIGHT	NOT ALL RIGHT
TOTAL	4790	4210	4388	4612
REGION				
Northeast	710	1090	1026	774
Southeast	990	810	728	1072
Midwest	970	830	791	1009
Southwest	1210	590	687	1113
Far West	910	890	1156	644
SEX				
Women	2365	2060	1946	2479
Men	2425	2150	2442	2133
MARITAL STATUS				
Single	902	1363	1593	672
Married	1243	1042	915	1370
Widowed	1482	643	396	1729
Separated/ Divorced	1163	1162	1484	841
EDUCATION				
High School Incomplete	1422	793	778	1437
High School Graduate	1343	892	915	1320
Some beyond High School	1122	1133	1262	993
College Graduate	903	1392	1433	862

Determine the sample proportion, $\hat{p}$, for each of the following:

a) Northeast Americans responding yes to question #1.
b) Southwestern Americans responding yes to question #1.
c) Single Americans responding no to question #1.
d) Widowed Americans responding no to question #1.
e) Those Americans who did not complete high school responding yes to question #1.
f) College graduates responding yes to question #1.
g) Midwest Americans responding not all right to question #2.
h) Far West Americans responding all right to question #2.
i) Women responding all right to question #2.
j) Married Americans responding not all right to question #2.
k) Separated/divorced Americans responding not all right to question #2.
l) College graduates responding all right to question #2.

Section 10.2

(Round off ALL answers to four decimal places.)

5. The sampling distribution of the proportion has the following characteristics:
   a) The mean of the sampling distribution of the proportion, $\mu_{\hat{p}}$, is given by the formula: $\mu_{\hat{p}} =$ _____
   b) The standard error of the proportion is given by the formula: $\sigma_{\hat{p}} =$ _____
   c) The sampling distribution of the proportion is approximately normal when both _____ and _____ are greater than 5.

6. The sampling distribution of the proportion is approximately normal when either np or n(1 – p) is greater than 5.
   (T/F)

7. In calculating $\mu_{\hat{p}}$, we use the formula np where n is the sample size and p is the sample proportion. (T/F)

8. Determine the mean and standard error of the sampling distribution of the proportion. Can the sampling distribution of the proportion be approximated by a normal distribution, if:
   a) $p = 0.40$, and $n = 50$?
   b) $p = 0.10$, and $n = 30$?
   c) The population proportion is 0.65 and the sample size is 200?
   d) The population proportion is 0.80 and the sample size is 100?
   e) A random sample of 400 was selected from a population composed of 70% democratic?

9. If the population proportion is 0.25 and the sample size is 500, then determine the probability that the sample proportion, $\hat{p}$, is:
   a) Greater than 0.29
   b) Less than 0.27
   c) Between 0.22 and 0.30
   d) At most 0.20
   e) At least 0.26

10. A large New York law firm states that 80% of their cases are settled out of court. What is the probability that out of the next 200 cases that:
    a) At least 75% will be settled out of court?
    b) At least 90% will be settled out of court?
    c) At least 25% will not be settled out of court?

Section 10.3

(Round off ALL answers to four decimal places.)

11. To perform a hypothesis test involving a population proportion, the sampling distribution of the _____ is used as the hypothesis testing model.

12. The null hypothesis of a hypothesis test involving a population proportion is stated as: The population proportion, symbolized _____ , is _____ to the proportion p_o. In symbols, $H_o: p = p_o$.

13. The alternative hypothesis of a hypothesis test involving a population proportion has one of the following three forms:
    a) the population proportion, symbolized _____ , is greater than the proportion p_o. In symbols, $H_a: p$ ___ p_o.
    b) The _____ proportion, p, is less than the proportion p_o. In symbols, $H_a: p$ ___ p_o.
    c) The population _____ , p, is not equal to the proportion p_o. In symbols, $H_a: p$ ___ p_o.

14. The formula for $\mu_{\hat{p}}$ is given by:
    a) $\mu_{\hat{p}} = np$
    b) $\mu_{\hat{p}} = p$
    c) $\mu_{\hat{p}} = p/n$
    d) $\mu_{\hat{p}} = n(1-p)$

15. If the alternative hypothesis is $H_a: p > p_o$, then the researcher is trying to show:
    a) p is less than p_o
    b) p equals p_o
    c) p is not equal to p_o
    d) p is greater than p_o

16. The formula for the test statistic, z, for a hypothesis test involving a population proportion is: z = _____ .

17. In a hypothesis test the value used for p in calculating $\mu_{\hat{p}}$ and $\sigma_{\hat{p}}$ is obtained from:
    a) The statistical result
    b) The alternative hypothesis
    c) The null hypothesis
    d) The standard error

18. To determine the conclusion of a hypothesis test involving a population proportion, the test statistic is computed and compared to the _____ value(s).

For problems 19 to 28:

   a) State the Null and Alternative Hypotheses.
   b) Calculate the expected results for the hypothesis test assuming the null hypothesis is true and determine the hypothesis test model.
   c) Formulate the decision rule.
   d) Determine the test statistic.
   e) Determine the conclusion and answer the question(s) posed in the problem, if any.
   f) Round off all calculations to four decimal places.

19. A car manufacturer claims that less than 10% of their cars have major defective parts. A skeptical consumer believes the claim is too low and randomly surveys 100 owners of the manufacturer's cars and finds 16 cars had major defective parts. Would this indicate that the manufacturer's claim was incorrect at $\alpha = 5\%$?

20. A gasoline lawn mower manufacturer claims that their power lawn mowers start up on the first try 95% of the time. A consumer's protection group feels the manufacturer claim is too high and randomly selects 200 of the manufacturer's mowers and finds that 178 start on the first try. Would this indicate that the manufacturer was indeed exaggerating at $\alpha = 1\%$?

21. A survey conducted by an Institute for Social Research claims that 40% of the American people say life in the United States is getting worse. Would one disagree with this claim at $\alpha = 5\%$ if an independent poll of 400 Americans shows that 175 believe life in the U.S. is getting worse?

22. In 1996, 18% of the fire alarms in Hyde Park were false alarms. This year in a random sample of 200 fire alarms 30 were false alarms. Using a 5% significance level has the rate of false alarms decreased since 1996?

23. According to a study released by a New York newspaper 25% of Long Island shoppers are being charged sales tax on non-taxable items in supermarkets because of the

complexity of the state's tax law. Mr. Jessel, a consumer advocate, decides to test this claim against his suspicion that the claim is too low. In a random survey of supermarket shoppers, Mr. Jessel finds that 65 out of 200 shoppers were improperly charged tax on their purchases. Does this sample result support Mr. Jessel's claim at $\alpha = 1\%$?

24. The Federal Trade Commission claims that Presidential Nuts, Inc., located in Plains, Ga., puts too many peanuts in their mixed nuts. Presidential Nuts Inc. claims that their mixed nuts contain only 20% peanuts. To test this claim, the Federal Trade Commission sampled 400 nuts at random and found 102 were peanuts. Does this finding support the claim made by the Federal Trade Commission at $\alpha = 1\%$?

25. A census bureau study of divorce rates reports that 68% of the men who wed before age 22 were divorced within 20 years. The Institute of Family Relations decided to test the validity of this report by randomly selecting and reviewing 250 marriages where the men wed before age 22. If 186 of these marriages ended in divorce within 20 years, can the Institute of Family Relations conclude the census bureau's claim is incorrect at $\alpha = 5\%$?

26. The market research component of a shaver company will not allow mass production of a new shaver unless they can get a test market acceptance rate of at least 85%. If the test market survey of their latest five blade shaver received 320 favorable responses out of a random sample of 400 interviews, should the company mass produce their new five blade shaver at $\alpha = 1\%$?

27. According to the latest National Crime Poll 75% of all women fear walking alone at night in their neighborhoods. A sociologist feels that this proportion is too high for women living in a middle class suburb on Long Island. To test her claim, the sociologist randomly samples 250 women living in this Long Island suburb and determines that 162 fear walking alone at night in their neighborhoods. Does this sample data support the sociologist's claim at $\alpha = 5\%$?

28. A national survey on "The Evolving Role of the Secretary in the Information Age" reported that 60% of the secretaries experienced eye strain when using word processors with a CRT display screen. An executive secretary decided to test this claim. She randomly surveys fifty secretaries who work with a CRT and determines that 35 experience eye strain. Based upon this sample data can the executive secretary reject the national claim at $\alpha = 1\%$?

Section 10.4

For problems 29 to 38, use questions 19 to 28 of Section 10.3 exercises and apply the p-value approach to hypothesis testing using the TI-83 Plus calculator. For each of these problems, use the 5 step procedure to perform a hypothesis test at both $\alpha = 1\%$ and $\alpha = 5\%$. Include the following within your test:

a) State the null and alternative hypotheses.

b) Calculate the expected results for the experiment assuming the null hypothesis is true and state the hypothesis test model.

c) Formulate the decision rule.

d) Identify the test statistic and its p-value.

e) State the conclusion and anwer any question(s) posed in the problem for each alpha level.

f) Determine the smallest level of significance for which the null hypothesis can be rejected.

>>>> **CHAPTER REVIEW**

(Roundoff ALL answers to four decimal places.)

39. The population proportion is the number of occurrences of a particular characteristic in a population. (T/F)

40. The sample proportion, $\hat{p}$, is the ratio of the number of occurrences of a particular characteristic to the sample size n. (T/F)

41. If 14 out of every 35 people in the population interviewed answered yes to the survey question, then the population proportion, p, would be:
    a) 0.14   **b)** 0.20   **c)** 0.50   **d)** 0.40

42. The sampling distribution of the proportion has properties similar to the Binomial Distribution. (T/F)

43. The mean of the sampling distribution of the proportion is determined from the sample proportion, $\hat{p}$. (T/F)

44. If random samples of size 80 are selected from an infinite binomial population with a proportion of minority members of 0.37, then what would be the mean of the sampling distribution?
    a) 0.37   **b)** 0.80   **c)** 0.50   **d)** Can not determine

45. If random samples of size 40 are selected from an infinite binomial population with a proportion of women equal to 0.25, what would be the standard error of the proportion?
    a) 0.0610   **b)** 0.0801   **c)** 0.0685   **d)** 0.0488

46. If the population proportion is 0.7 and the sample size is 300, then determine the probability that the sample proportion, $\hat{p}$, is:
    a) Greater than 0.67
    b) Between 0.65 and 0.73
    c) Less than 0.74
    d) At least 0.64
    e) At most 0.69

47. The hypothesis testing model for a hypothesis test involving a population proportion is the sampling distribution of the _____ .

48. The sampling distribution of the proportion is approximately a normal distribution when:
   a) n>30
   b) always
   c) np>5 and n(1 – p)>5
   d) np>5 or n(1 – p)>5

49. When formulating the null hypothesis involving a population proportion p, it is assumed that $p = p_0$ where p_0 represents the claimed population proportion.
(T/F)

50. If the alternative hypothesis is expressed as $p<p_0$, then the rejection of H_0 will statistically indicate that the population proportion is significantly less than p_0.
(T/F)

51. When performing a hypothesis test about a population proportion, the expected results are determined under the assumption that _____ .

52. The value for $\mu_{\hat{p}}$ used in the hypothesis testing procedure is based upon the assumption that H_0 is true.
(T/F)

53. When doing a hypothesis test involving a population proportion, p, the z-score of the sample proportion is referred to as the statistical result.
(T/F)

For problems 54 to 58:

   a) State the Null and Alternative Hypotheses.
   b) Calculate the expected results for the hypothesis test assuming the null hypothesis is true and determine the hypothesis test model.
   c) Formulate the decision rule.
   d) Determine the test statistic.
   e) Determine the conclusion and answer the question(s) posed in the problem, if any.
   f) Round off all calculations to four decimal places.

54. Past experience has shown that 40% of the students fail a University entrance exam in English. If 50 out of 100 students from a certain city failed, would one be justified in concluding that the students from this city are inferior in English using $\alpha = 5\%$?

55. The production manager claims to have devised a new production process which will significantly lower the percent of defective parts manufactured. The present process produced defective parts at a rate of 10%. If a trial run using the new process produces 70 defects in a sample of 800, can one conclude that this new process is more effective at $\alpha = 5\%$?

56. A study conducted by the National Cancer Institute found that 15% of all cancer patients treated with synthetic human interferon had their tumors shrink to less than half their original size. Medical researchers at a Western Medical School decide to test this claim at $\alpha = 1\%$. If the researchers find that interferon caused the tumors to shrink to less than half their previous size in 14 of 80 patients, then can one reject the National Cancer Institutes claim?

57. The personnel director for a Florida based insurance company believes that her new hiring procedure will result in a better employee retainment. The present hiring technique resulted in a 60% employee retainment for those employees that have been with the company for more than six months. If the company samples 200 employees that have been hired under the new procedure and 126 are still with the company after six months does this indicate that the personnel director's claim is correct using $\alpha = 5\%$?

58. A recent survey indicated that 60% of the people who own a personal computer use it to play video games. HAL, a personal computer manufacturer, decides to test this claim against the suspicion that it is lower than 60%. In a random sample of 100 personal computer owners, 52 indicate they use their computer to play video games. Does this sample support the manufacturer's claim at $\alpha = 1\%$?

▶▶▶ WHAT DO YOU THINK?

59. Examine the pie chart entitled "The projected 2005 U.S. labor force" in Figure 10.23. The pie chart presents the projected group of workers who will comprise the U. S. labor force according to the U. S. Bureau of Labor Statistics.

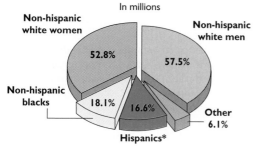

Statistical Snapshot

Projected 2005 U.S. Labor Force

In millions

* Hispanics can be of any race
Source: Bureau of Labor Statistics

FIGURE 10.23

a) Define the population.
b) What variable is presented by the pie chart?
c) Is this variable numeric or categorical? Explain
d) What proportion of the labor force projected for 2005 is non-hispanic white men?
e) What proportion of the labor force projected for 2005 is non-hispanic blacks?
f) What proportion of the labor force projected for 2005 is Hispanic?
g) What proportion of the labor force projected for 2005 is listed as other?

According to the U.S. Bureau of Labor Statistics, the present proportion of U. S. workers is 43% is white men; 35% is white female: 11% is Black; 8% is Hispanic, and 3% is Asians, native americans and others.

h) What is the percentage shift in the labor force for the white male worker?
i) What is the percentage shift in the labor force for the white black worker?
j) What is the percentage shift in the labor force for the white female worker?
k) What is the percentage shift in the labor force for the hispanic worker?
l) What is the percentage shift in the labor force for the worker categorized as other?

m) Which group within the labor force will have greatest percentage increase?
n) Which group within the labor force will have smallest percentage increase?
o) Which group within the labor force will have smallest percentage decrease?
p) What parameter is represented by the pie chart for each group?

For each group of U.S. worker presented within the pie chart, design a hypothesis test for the present that includes:

q) A null hypothesis. Use the information pertaining to the present labor force as the status quo.
r) An alternative hypothesis. Use the pie chart information as your guide as to what you believe to be the direction of the proportion with regard to the present value of the true population parameter.
s) Is the alternative hypothesis directional or nondirectional? Is this a 1TT or a 2TT? Explain.
t) Which population parameter are you assuming you know to perform this hypothesis test? What is the value of this parameter?
u) State the name of the sampling distribution that will serve as the model for this test? Is this sampling distribution a normal distribution? Explain.
v) What is the mean of this sampling distribution? What is the standard error of the sampling distribution?
w) Which tail of the curve would you place the critical z score value for your hypothesis test?
x) If you decide to use a significance level of 5% for each hypothesis test, then calculate the test statistic.
y) If the test statistic falls to the right of the critical z-score for the U. S. hispanic worker hypothesis test, what is the conclusion to this test? Could you agree that the proportion of the population of U. S. hispanic workers has significantly changed at $\alpha = 5\%$? If you can, then explain the type of significant change you can conclude from the test.
z) If the p-value of the hypothesis test is 6% (or 0.06), then can you reject the null hypothesis for non-hispanic white men at $\alpha = 5\%$? Does this indicate that the percentage of the non-hispanic white male worker within the U. S. labor force has significantly changed? Explain what you can conclude regarding the population proportion? If the p-value of the hypothesis is 2.90% (or 0.0290) and $\alpha = 2\%$, could you conclude that the percentage of the non-hispanic white male worker within the U. S. labor force has significantly changed? Explain.

60. Read the article "Agency says 59% of us buckle up" shown in Figure 10.24.

Statistical Snapshot

Agency says 59% of us buckle up

Safety campaigns have helped boost national seat belt use to 59%, the Transportation Department reported. Safety belt use ranges from 28% in Rhode Island to 85% in Hawaii. A survey of 19 cities showed seat belt use increased to 54% from 50% after a summerlong campaign. Belt use in cities is usually lower. "We are beginning to bring 'hard-core' non-users into the fold," said Transportation Secretary Samuel Skinner. He said each percentage point gain represents nearly 2 million people. Seat belts saved an estimated 4,800 lives in 1990.

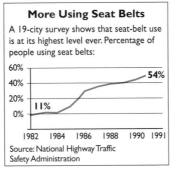

More Using Seat Belts

A 19-city survey shows that seat-belt use is at its highest level ever. Percentage of people using seat belts:

Source: National Highway Traffic Safety Administration

FIGURE 10.24

a) Explain why the percentage figure within the title of the article (59%) is different from the percentage figure (54%) shown in the graph for the year 1991?

b) What variable is presented by the graph?

c) Is this variable numeric or categorical? Explain.

d) Is this variable discrete or continuous? Explain. Using the stated percentage values within the article (59%, 28%, 85%, and 54%) as representing the status quo values for each population, and assuming your position is that you believe that the stated values are too high for the values 59% and 85%, while your belief is that the values of 28% and 54% are too low, then:

e) Define the population for each stated percentage value.

f) State the null and alternative hypotheses.

g) State the type of alternative hypothesis.

h) State whether this hypothesis test is a 1TT or a 2TT.

i) State the name of the sampling distribution which will serve as the model for this test. Is this sampling distribution a normal distribution? Explain.

j) Indicate the population parameter you are assuming is true to perform your hypothesis test. State the value of this population parameter.

k) State the mean of this sampling distribution. Determine the standard error of the sampling distribution.

l) Explain which tail of the curve that the critical z score value of the test is placed for the hypothesis test. If you decide to use a significance level of 5% for each hypothesis test, then write the test statistic formula required to perform the test and determine the critical z score.

m) If the test statistic falls to the right of the critical z score for the hypothesis test pertaining to the Rhode Island percentage, what is the conclusion to this test? Could you agree that the proportion of the population has significantly changed at $\alpha = 5\%$? If you can, then explain the type of significant change you can conclude from the test.

n) If the p-value of the hypothesis test pertaining to the 59 percentage value is 5.3% (or 0.053), then can you reject the null hypothesis for this test at $\alpha = 5\%$? Could you conclude that the proportion of people using seat belts for this population has significantly changed? Explain.

o) If the p-value of the hypothesis test pertaining to the 54 percentage value is 1.90% (or 0.0190) and $\alpha = 2\%$, could you conclude that the percentage of people within the population that uses seat belts has significantly changed? Explain.

PROJECTS

61. Hypothesis Testing Project.

A. Selection of a topic

   1. Select a reported fact or claim about a population proportion made in a local newspaper, magazine or other source.

   2. Suggested topics:

      a) Home team advantage: Randomly select any two weeks of a football, baseball, basketball or hockey season and record the following:

         1. total number of games played during the two weeks selected.

         2. the number of games the home team won.

Test the null hypothesis: $p = \frac{1}{2}$ against the alternative: $p > \frac{1}{2}$ (i.e. home team advantage).

   b) Males equal females? Select a random sample of at least 30 families. For these families record the number of male and female children. Test the null hypothesis: $p = \frac{1}{2}$ against the alternative hypothesis: $p \neq \frac{1}{2}$.

   c) In the first national election where eighteen year olds were allowed to vote, the United States Census Bureau claimed that 48% of the eligible voters in the 18–20 year age group voted. Perform a hypothesis test to check if this claim is still valid.

B. Use the following procedure to test the claim selected in Part A.

1. State the claim, and identify the population referred to in the statement of the claim, also indicate the source.

2. State your opinion regarding the claim (i.e. do you feel it is too high, too low, or simply don't agree with the claim) and clearly identify the population you plan to sample to test your opinion.

3. State the null and alternative hypotheses.

4. Develop and state a procedure for selecting a random sample from your population. Indicate the technique you are going to use to obtain your sample data.

5. Compute the expected results, indicate the hypothesis testing model, and choose an appropriate level of significance.

6. Find the critical z-score(s) and state the decision rule.

7. Perform the experiment and calculate the test statistic, z.

8. Construct a hypothesis testing model and place the test statistic on the model.

9. Formulate the appropriate conclusion and interpret the conclusion with respect to your opinion (as stated in step 2).

62. Read a research article from a professional journal in a field such as medicine, education, marketing, science, social science, etc. Write a summary of the research article that includes the following:

   A. Name of article, author and journal (include volume number and date).

   B. Statement of the research problem.

   C. The null and alternative hypotheses.

   D. How the experiment was conducted (give the sample size; and the sampling technique).

   E. Determine the test statistic and the level of significance.

   F. State the conclusion in terms of the null and alternative hypotheses.

ANALYZING THE DATABASE USING TECHNOLOGY

The following exercises refer to the file DATABASE listed in Appendix A. Using a technological tool answer each exercise.

63. For the variable name: SEX

   The chairman of the math department belives that the proportion of female students is 0.5.

   Test the claim that the proportion of female students is *not* 0.5.

   State the null and alternative hypotheses for this test.

   Is the null hypothesis rejected? Identify the p value and interpret.

   State the conclusion.

64. For the variable name: MAJ

   The Vice President of Finance believes that the proportion of Liberal Arts students is at least 60%. Test this claim if you believe that the claim is *too high*.

   State the null and alternative hypotheses for this test.

   Is the null hypothesis rejected? Identify the p value and interpret.

   State the conclusion.

CHAPTER TEST

(Roundoff ALL answers to four decimal places.)

65. Determine the sample proportion, $\hat{p}$, for each of the following statements.

   a) A nationwide survey of 1500 people found that 730 use seat belts.

   b) A researcher finds that 280 out of 400 health club members take a daily multi-vitamin.

66. Determine the mean and standard error of the sampling distribution of the proportion. Can the sampling distribution of the proportion be approximated by a normal distribution, if a random sample of 150 was selected from a population composed of 20% unemployed people?

67. If the sample size is increased, then the standard error of the proportion will:

   a) Decrease
   b) Increase
   c) Remain the same
   d) Can't tell

68. When performing a hypothesis test involving a population proportion the null hypotheses, H_o, is always stated as:

   a) $H_o: p \neq p_o$
   b) $H_o: p > p_o$
   c) $H_o: p < p_o$
   d) $H_o: p = p_o$

69. If the experimenter believes that the claimed population proportion value p_o is too high, then his alternative hypothesis is stated as:
   a) $H_a: p \neq p_o$
   b) $H_a: p > p_o$
   c) $H_a: p < p_o$
   d) $H_a: p = p_o$

70. The medical officer at a Southwestern University states that 40% of all dental students have contracted the H–2 virus. For a random sample of twenty students, what is the probability that:
   a) at least 50% will have contracted the virus?
   b) less than 25% will have contracted the virus?
   c) between 30% to 60% will have contracted the virus?

   For problems 61 to 63:

   a) state the Null and Alternative Hypotheses.
   b) calculate the expected results for the hypothesis test assuming the null hypothesis is true and determine the hypothesis test model.
   c) formulate the decision rule.
   d) determine the test statistic.
   e) determine the conclusion and answer the question(s) posed in the problem, if any.
   f) round off all calculations to four decimal places.

71. An avid football fan decides to test her claim that the home team has an advantage in a *pick'em* game. To test the claim that the proportion of pick'em games the home team wins is 0.50, the fan randomly selects 40 football games that are rated *pick'em* and finds that the home team was the winning team 23 times. Can the football fan conclude that her claim is correct at $\alpha = 5\%$?

72. Based on a recent survey, the New York Off-Track Betting Corporation (O.T.B.) stated that 57% of its single-male bettors earned over \$38,000 per year. If 300 randomly selected single male O.T.B. bettors were interviewed and 178 earned over \$38,000 per year, would one disagree with the O.T.B.'s claim at $\alpha = 5\%$?

73. An educational psychologist claims that 80% of the recent high school graduates that enter college do so primarily because of parental pressure. Researchers from the California University system believe this claim is too high when applied to entering freshman in the California University system. The researchers randomly sample 1600 of their most recent entering freshman and find that 1248 entered college primarily because of parental pressure. Does this sample result significantly support the researcher's belief at $\alpha = 1\%$?

Hypothesis Test Involving a Population Mean

Contents

11.1 INTRODUCTION

The general concept of hypothesis testing was introduced in Chapter 9. In this chapter we will examine in detail the procedure to test hypotheses (or claims) made about a population mean **using information obtained from a sample drawn from the population**.

To illustrate the use of this procedure, consider the following story about the Precision Tool and Die Company, which was the principal employer in a southern Nevada town. This company has been credited with building up the town not only from an economic point of view, but also in a physical sense, since they supplied precision manufactured screws used to assemble many of the town's building projects. In fact, today the company still boasts: "we're the company that screwed up this town."

The success of this company can be attributed to the quality control department whose motto is: "we manufacture only precision screws." The quality control manager is responsible for testing every batch of screws before they leave the plant to insure they meet the manufacturer's specifications.

For example, if the quality control manager needed to determine if the entire batch of 4" screws have been manufactured to the required length specification, she would randomly select a sample of the screws and compute the mean length of this sample. Her decision to either reject or not reject the entire batch is based upon a comparison of the mean of this sample to the manufacturer's length specification. If the difference between the sample mean length and the manufacturer's length specification is **statistically significant**, then the entire batch will be rejected. On the other hand, if the difference is **not statistically significant**, then the manager is **confident** that the entire batch meets the required length specification based upon the sample tested and the entire batch would not be rejected.

In this chapter, we will examine the statistical procedure used by the quality control manager to make her decision. The underlying theorems which support this statistical test are the Central Limit Theorem and the Theorem on the Properties of Sampling Distributions (discussed in Chapter 7). The development of the hypothesis testing procedure concerning a population mean will incorporate these theorems into the general hypothesis testing procedure outlined in Chapter 9. Let's now develop the hypothesis testing procedure involving a population mean.

11.2   HYPOTHESIS TESTING INVOLVING A POPULATION MEAN

We are now going to outline the hypothesis testing procedure for testing the mean of a population by modifying the general five step hypothesis testing procedure developed in Chapter 9. The first step of the hypothesis testing procedure is to formulate the null and alternative hypotheses. Let's examine how to state these hypotheses for a test involving a population mean.

Step 1   Formulate the two hypotheses, H_o and H_a.
Null Hypothesis: In general, the null hypothesis has the following form.

Null Hypothesis Form

H_o: The mean of the population, μ, is claimed to be equal to a numerical value which will be symbolized as: μ_o.
   Thus, the null hypothesis can be symbolized as:

$$\mathbf{H_o}: \mu = \mu_o$$

Alternative Hypothesis:
   Since the alternative hypothesis, H_a, can be stated as either *greater than, less than,* or *not equal* to the numerical value, μ_o, then the alternative hypothesis can have one of three forms:

Form (a): Greater Than Form For H_a

H_a: The mean of the population, μ, is claimed to be **greater than** the numerical value, μ_o.
This is symbolized as:

$$\mathbf{H_a}: \mu > \mu_o$$

Form (b): Less Than Form For Ha

H_a: The mean of the population, μ, is claimed to be **less than** the numerical value, μ_o.
This is symbolized as:

$$\mathbf{H_a}: \mu < \mu_o$$

Form (c): Not Equal Form For Ha

H_a: The mean of the population, μ, is claimed to be **not equal** to the numerical value, μ_o.
This is symbolized as:

$$\mathbf{H_a}: \mu \neq \mu_o$$

Step 2   Determine the model to test the null hypothesis, H_o.
   Two important design considerations are choosing a sample size, n, and determining the sampling distribution model. Since we are testing a hypothesis about a population mean using a sample mean, $\bar{x}$, we use as the hypothesis test model the sampling distribution of the mean and its properties, which were discussed in Chapter 7. Using this information, we can draw the following conclusions.

Under the following assumptions that:
a) The null hypothesis, H_o, is true, i.e. $\mu = \mu_o$, and,
b) The standard deviation of the population, σ, is **known**, and,
c) The sample size, n, is greater than 30,

then we can conclude that:
a) The sampling distribution of the mean is approximately **normal** and serves as the hypothesis test model,
b) The mean of the sampling distribution of the mean is:

$$\mu_{\bar{x}} = \mu_o$$

(i.e. the mean, $\mu_{\bar{x}}$, is equal to the claimed population mean, μ_o).
c) The standard error of the mean, $\sigma_{\bar{x}}$, is:

$$\sigma_{\bar{x}} = \frac{\sigma}{\sqrt{n}}$$

$\sigma_{\bar{x}}$ is also the standard deviation of the sampling distribution of the mean. This is illustrated in Figure 11.1.

Hypothesis Testing Model

Hypothesis Testing Model

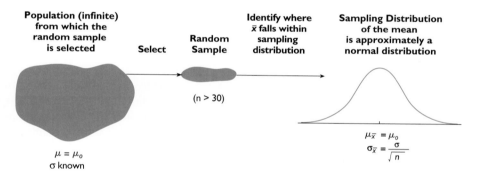

FIGURE 11.1

In theory, the population being sampled must be infinite to use the standard error of the mean formula:

$$\sigma_{\bar{x}} = \frac{\sigma}{\sqrt{n}}$$

However it is appropriate to use this formula when the population is *finite* and the population size, N, is large relative to the sample size, n. The rule used to determine whether the population is large relative to the sample is: the sample size, n, is less than 5% of the population size, N. That is, $\frac{n}{N} < 5\%$.

Step 3   Formulate the decision rule.
a) Determine the type of alternative hypothesis (i.e., is the alternative hypothesis **directional** or **nondirectional**?)
b) Determine the type of hypothesis test (i.e., is the test **1TT** or **2TT**?)
c) Identify the significance level (i.e., is $\alpha = 1\%$ or $\alpha = 5\%$?)
d) Find the critical z score(s), z_c, using Table II.

e) Construct the appropriate **hypothesis testing model**.

f) State the decision rule.

Step 4   Analyze the sample data.

a) Compute the sample mean, $\bar{x}$.

b) Compute the test statistic, z, using: $z = \dfrac{\bar{x} - \mu_{\bar{x}}}{\sigma_{\bar{x}}}$

Step 5   State the conclusion.

Compare the test statistic to the **critical z score**, z_c, of the decision rule and draw one of the following conclusions:

(a)		(b)
Reject H₀ and	or	**Fail to reject H₀**
Accept Hₐ at α		**at α**

In summary, the procedure just outlined to perform a hypothesis test involving a population mean, μ, where the **population standard deviation, σ, is known** and **n is greater than 30**, contains three refinements to the general hypothesis testing procedure developed in Chapter 9. They are:

I   The sampling distribution of the mean is used as the appropriate hypothesis testing model.

II   The properties of the sampling distribution of the mean are used to calculate the expected values.

III   The formula: $z = \dfrac{\bar{x} - \mu_{\bar{x}}}{\sigma_{\bar{x}}}$ is used to calculate the test statistic, z.

Example 11.1 demonstrates the use of the hypothesis testing procedure to test a population mean.

EXAMPLE 11.1

An automatic opening device for parachutes has a stated mean release time of 10 seconds with a population standard deviation of 3 seconds. A local parachute club decides to test this claim against the alternative hypothesis that the release time is not 10 seconds. The club purchases 36 of these devices and finds that the mean release time is 8.5 seconds. Does this sample result indicate that the opening device does not have a mean release time of 10 seconds? Use $\alpha = 1\%$.

Solution

Step 1   Formulate the hypotheses.

H₀: The population mean release time is 10 seconds.

This is symbolized as: $H_o: \mu = 10$ secs.

Hₐ: The population mean release time *is not* 10 seconds.

This is symbolized as: $H_a: \mu \neq 10$ secs.

Step 2   Determine the model to test the null hypothesis, H₀.

To test the null hypothesis, the club decides to purchase 36 parachutes.

Since the sample size, n, is greater than 30, we can use the Central Limit Theorem. Using the results of this theorem, the sampling distribution of the mean is a normal distribution and *serves as the hypothesis testing model.*

Assuming the null hypothesis is true, the *expected results* for the sampling distribution of the mean are:

$$\mu_{\bar{x}} = \mu$$

$$\mu_{\bar{x}} = 10 \text{ seconds}$$

and

$$\sigma_{\bar{x}} = \frac{\sigma}{\sqrt{n}}$$

$$\sigma_{\bar{x}} = \frac{3}{\sqrt{36}}$$

$$\sigma_{\bar{x}} = 0.50 \text{ seconds}$$

Figure 11.2 illustrates the sampling distribution of the mean hypothesis testing model.

Step 3 Formulate the decision rule.
    a) The alternative hypothesis is nondirectional.
    b) The type of test is two-tailed, 2TT.
    c) The significance level is: $\alpha = 1\%$.

The Sampling Distribution of the Mean (is a normal distribution)

$\mu_{\bar{x}} = 10$ sec.
$\sigma_{\bar{x}} = 0.50$ sec.

FIGURE 11.2

    d) Using Table II: The Normal Curve Area Table, for a 2TT at $\alpha = 1\%$. The two critical z scores, z_{LC} and z_{RC}, are:

$$z_{LC} = -2.58 \text{ and } z_{RC} = 2.58$$

    e) Figure 11.3(a) illustrates the decision rule for this hypothesis test.

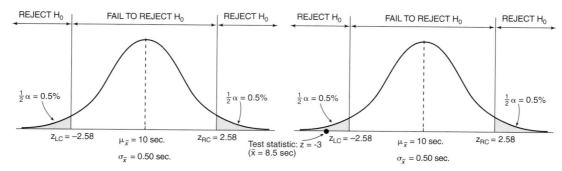

FIGURE 11.3(a)   **FIGURE 11.3(b)**

The decision rule is:
    f) Reject the null hypothesis if the test statistic, z, is less than −2.58, or more than 2.58.

Step 4 Analyze the sample data.
    a) The **sample mean** is: $\bar{x} = 8.5$ seconds.

    b) Compute the test statistic, z, using $z = \frac{\bar{x} - \mu_{\bar{x}}}{\sigma_{\bar{x}}}$. For $\bar{x} = 8.5$, $\mu_{\bar{x}} = 10$ and $\sigma_{\bar{x}} = 0.5$, the test statistic is $z = -3$.

Step 5   State the conclusion.

From Figure 11.3(b), since the test statistic $z = -3$ is less than the critical z score $z_{LC} = -2.58$; we *reject* H_o and *accept* the alternative hypothesis, H_a, at $\alpha = 1\%$. Therefore, the mean release time for the automatic opening device is **significantly different** than 10 seconds.

EXAMPLE 11.2

A tire manufacturer advertises that its brand of radial tires has a mean life of 40,000 miles with a population standard deviation of 1,500 miles.

A consumer's research team decides to investigate this claim after receiving several complaints from people who believe this advertisement is false (i.e. the mean life of 40,000 miles is too high).

If the research team tests 100 of these radial tires and obtains a sample mean tire life of 39,750, is the advertisement legitimate? Use $\alpha = 5\%$.

Solution

Step 1   Formulate the hypotheses.

H_o: The population mean tire life is 40,000 miles.

This is symbolized as: $H_o: \mu = 40{,}000$ miles
H_a: The population mean tire life is less than 40,000 miles.

This is symbolized as: $H_a: \mu < 40{,}000$ miles

Step 2   Determine the model to test the null hypothesis, H_o.

Under the assumption that the null hypothesis is true and the sample size, n, is 100, then the *expected results* are:

$$\mu_{\bar{x}} = \mu$$
$$\mu_{\bar{x}} = 40{,}000 \text{ miles}$$

and

$$\sigma_{\bar{x}} = \frac{\sigma}{\sqrt{n}}$$
$$\sigma_{\bar{x}} = 150 \text{ miles}$$

From the Central Limit Theorem, the sampling distribution of the mean is approximately normal and serves as the hypothesis testing model. This is illustrated in Figure 11.4.

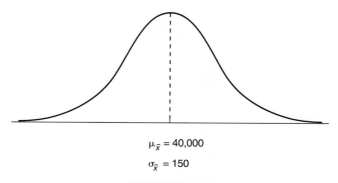

$\mu_{\bar{x}} = 40{,}000$

$\sigma_{\bar{x}} = 150$

FIGURE 11.4

Step 3   Formulate the Decision Rule.
a) The alternative hypothesis is directional, since the research team is trying to show that the mean tire life is too high.
b) The type of test is one-tailed on the left side.
c) The significance level is: $\alpha = 5\%$.
d) For a one-tailed test on the left side at $\alpha = 5\%$, the critical z score, z_c, using Table II, (the Normal Curve Area Table), is: $z_c = -1.65$.
e) Figure 11.5(a) illustrates the decision rule for this hypothesis test.

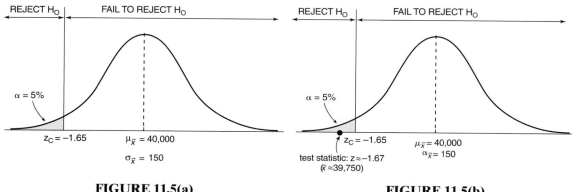

FIGURE 11.5(a)   **FIGURE 11.5(b)**

The decision rule is:
f) Reject the null hypothesis if the test statistic is less than $z_c = -1.65$.

Step 4   Analyze the sample data.
a) The sample mean is: $\bar{x} = 39{,}750$ miles.
b) Compute the test statistic, z. The test statistic is $z \approx -1.67$.

Step 5   State the conclusion.
From Figure 11.5(b), since the test statistic $z = -1.67$ is less than the critical z_c of -1.65 we *reject* H_o *and accept* H_a at $\alpha = 5\%$. Thus, the research team can conclude that the advertisement was *not* legitimate.   ∎

11.3   INTRODUCTION TO THE t DISTRIBUTION

There are many practical instances when one performs a hypothesis test involving a population mean, μ, where **the population standard deviation, σ, is unknown**.
For example:

- An automobile manufacturer claims that its new subcompact averages 50 mpg for highway driving.
- A cereal company claims that their family-sized cereal box has an average net weight of 15 oz.
- An archaeologist claims that the dinosaur species Tyrannosaurus Rex has an average length of 50 feet.

In such instances, when the population standard deviation is unknown, it becomes necessary to obtain a good estimate of the population standard deviation. A good estimate of the population standard deviation is determined by using the standard deviation of a random sample selected from the population. The following formula is used to estimate the population standard deviation. This formula will be referred to as the definition formula for the sample standard deviation, s.

Formula to Estimate the Population Standard Deviation

Definition Formula for the Sample Standard Deviation:

$$s = \sqrt{\frac{\sum (x - \bar{x})^2}{n-1}}$$

where: s = sample standard deviation
$\bar{x}$ = sample mean
n = sample size

When the sample size, n, is **large**, then s is considered to be a **good estimator for** σ because the bias in s is very small. That is, s is just as likely to be larger than the population standard deviation as it is to be smaller. This concept is similar to an unbiased coin which is just as likely to come up heads as tails on any toss.

Consequently, **whenever the population standard deviation, σ, is unknown, then the standard error of the mean must also be estimated**. Since s serves as a good estimate of the population standard deviation, σ, then the estimate of the standard error of the mean will make use of s. This estimate of the standard error of the mean is symbolized by $s_{\bar{x}}$ and is computed by the following formula.

Formula to Estimate the Standard Error of the Mean

$$s_{\bar{x}} = \frac{s}{\sqrt{n}}$$

where:

$s_{\bar{x}}$ = estimate of the standard error of the mean, $\sigma_{\bar{x}}$
s = estimate of the population standard deviation, σ
n = sample size

Thus, when s is used to estimate σ, then $s_{\bar{x}}$ is used to estimate $\sigma_{\bar{x}}$.

When we are confronted with having to estimate the population standard deviation when performing a hypothesis test involving a population mean, we need to use a distribution developed by a statistician named William S. Gosset called the **Student's t distribution** or simply, the t distribution rather than the normal distribution as our model for the sampling distribution of the mean. Gosset's research work was done while he was employed by the famous Guinness Brewery in Ireland and was published under his pen-name "Student." Gosset's development of the t distribution allows us to test hypotheses involving a population mean when the population standard deviation, σ, is unknown. Let's examine this *t* distribution.

The *t* Distribution

If samples of size n are randomly selected from a **normal or approximately normal popula-tion** with an unknown standard deviation, then when σ is approximated by s the test statistic

$$z = \frac{\bar{x} - \mu_{\bar{x}}}{\sigma/\sqrt{n}} \text{ becomes } \frac{\bar{x} - \mu_{\bar{x}}}{s/\sqrt{n}} \text{ and is called a t score.}$$

The distribution of all the t scores is referred to as the t distribution.

It is important to realize that when you are performing a hypothesis test involving a population mean where the population is normal and s is used as an estimator of the unknown population standard deviation, then the distribution of the test statistic $t = \frac{\bar{x} - \mu_{\bar{x}}}{s/\sqrt{n}}$ is a *t* distribution. Let's now examine the properties of a *t* distribution.

In general the *t* distribution is similar to the normal distribution in that it is **symmetric about the mean and bell-shaped**. However, the *t* distribution is more dispersed than a normal distribution, that is, it has more area in the tails and less in the center than the normal distribution. Thus, in appearance, a *t* curve is lower and flatter than the normal curve. The *t* distribution is composed of a family of *t* curves, where there is a different *t* curve for each sample size. Thus, the area under a particular *t* curve is **depen-dent upon the size of the sample, n**, or the value of: **n – 1**, known as the concept of **degrees of freedom**.

DEFINITION 11.1

The **degrees of freedom**, denoted by *df*, for each sample of size n, is one less than the sample size. Thus, for a sample of size n, the degrees of freedom are given by formula:

$$df = n - 1$$

Figure 11.6 shows the relationship between the normal distribution and two particular *t* distribu-tions of sample sizes n = 5 and n = 12, or degrees of freedom *df* = 4 and *df* = 11, respectively.

Notice, from Figure 11.6, the *t* distributions are **flatter and more dispersed** than the normal distri-bution, and, as the sample size or the degrees of freedom *increase* the *t* distribution is getting closer to

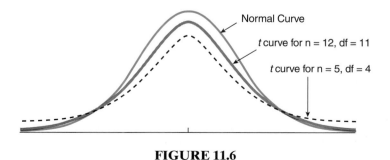

FIGURE 11.6

the normal distribution. In fact, as the number of degrees of freedom (or the sample size) increases, the *t* distribution begins to approach the normal distribution until the two distributions are virtually identical. For most practical purposes, whenever the degrees of freedom are greater than 30, the *t* and normal distributions are considered to be sufficiently close.

Let's summarize the properties of the *t* distribution.

Properties of the *t* Distribution

- The *t* distribution is bell-shaped.
- The *t* distribution is symmetric about the mean.
- There is a different *t* distribution for each sample size, n, or degrees of freedom, *df* = n − 1.
- As the number of degrees of freedom increases, the *t* distribution approaches the normal distribution. They are sufficiently close when the degrees of freedom are greater than 30.

Since the *t* distribution is composed of a family of *t* curves that are dependent upon degrees of freedom, the table representing the area associated with the *t* distribution is given with degrees of freedom. The *t* distribution table is different than the normal distribution table in that it lists the critical *t* scores, denoted t_c, for significance levels of 5% and 1% which are needed to perform a hypothesis test. These critical *t* scores, t_c, are found in Table III: Critical Values for the *t* Distribution in Appendix D: Statistical Tables. Let's examine Table III and discuss how to use it.

11.4   USING TABLE III: CRITICAL VALUES FOR THE *t* DISTRIBUTION

To find the **critical *t* score**, t_c, in Table III needed to perform a hypothesis test, you need the following information:

- The significance level, α.
- Type of hypothesis test. (i.e. 1TT or 2TT)
- Degrees of freedom, *df*.

Example 11.3 illustrates how to use Table III, given the previous information.

EXAMPLE 11.3

Use Table III to determine the critical *t* score, t_c, for a hypothesis test where:
1) $\alpha = 1\%$.
2) one-tailed test on the right side.
3) *df* = 16.

Solution

To determine the critical *t* score on the right side, t_c, examine Table III. A portion of Table III is shown in Table 11.1.

TABLE 11.1   Table III: Critical Values for the t Distribution

	One Tail			Two Tail	
	Critical	Critical		Critical	Critical
	t	t		t	t
	left	right		left	right
df	(t_c)	(t_c)		(t_{LC})	(t_{RC})
		$t_{99\%}$			$t_{99.5\%}$
1		*			
2		*			
3		*			
.		*			
.		*			
.		*			
15		*			
16	* * * * * * * * * * * * * * * * * *	2.58			
17					
.					
.					
.					
Normal Distribution					

$\alpha = 1\%$

From Table 11.1, the critical *t* score on the right side, t_c, is 2.58, because it is found under the column for one tail test at $\alpha = 1\%$, critical *t* right and in the row for $df = 16$.

EXAMPLE 11.4

Find the critical *t* score, t_c, for the *t* distribution in Figure 11.7 if:
1) $\alpha = 5\%$
2)   One-tailed test on the left side.
3) $df = 30$.

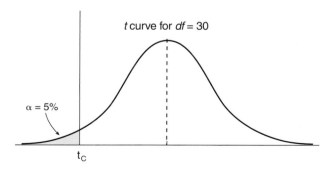

FIGURE 11.7

Solution

From Table III, the $t_c = -1.70$ since it is in the column for one tail test at $\alpha = 5\%$, critical *t* left and in the row for $df = 30$.

EXAMPLE 11.5

Find the critical *t* scores, t_{LC} and t_{RC}, for a two-tailed test, $\alpha = 5\%$ and $df = 9$ as illustrated in Figure 11.8.

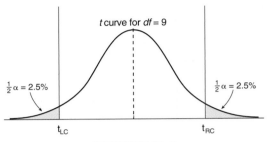

t curve for *df* = 9

$\frac{1}{2}\alpha = 2.5\%$ $\frac{1}{2}\alpha = 2.5\%$

t_{LC} t_{RC}

FIGURE 11.8

Solution

From Table III, the critical *t* scores are $t_{LC} = -2.26$ and $t_{RC} = 2.26$.

EXAMPLE 11.6

Using the information in Figure 11.9, find the critical *t* score, t_c.

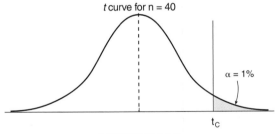

t curve for n = 40

$\alpha = 1\%$

t_C

FIGURE 11.9

Solution

Before Table III can be used, the degrees of freedom must be calculated using $df = n - 1$. For n = 40, $df = 39$. Since there is no row for 39 degrees of freedom in Table III, we use the row for 40 degrees of freedom because it is *closest* to 39 *df*. Therefore, for $\alpha = 1\%$, $t_c = 2.42$.

EXAMPLE 11.7

Using the information in Figure 11.10, find the critical *t* scores, t_{LC} and t_{RC}.

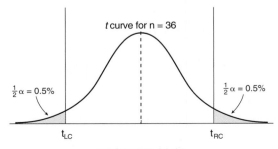

t curve for n = 36

$\frac{1}{2}\alpha = 0.5\%$ $\frac{1}{2}\alpha = 0.5\%$

t_{LC} t_{RC}

FIGURE 11.10

Solution

Before Table III can be used, the degrees of freedom *and* the significance level must be determined. The degrees of freedom for n = 36 is: *df* = 35. The level of significance, α, is determined by adding together the two shaded areas in Figure 11.10. Thus, α = 1%. In Table III there is **no** row corresponding to *df* = 35. Since *df* = 35 falls exactly between *df* = 30 and *df* = 40 we will use the t_c score that is *farthest* from *t* = 0. Thus we use the *t* scores corresponding to *df* = 30. Therefore, t_{LC} = –2.75 and t_{RC} = 2.75.

Procedure to Locate a Critical t Score in Table III

To locate a critical *t* score in Table III, use the following procedure.
1. Select the appropriate α value column.
2. Identify the type of hypothesis test:
   one or two tail test
3. Select the appropriate *df* row using the following guidelines:
   (i)   If the *df* value is found in the table, use this row to locate the critical *t* score.
   (ii) If the exact *df* value does not appear in the table, then choose the row corresponding to the closest *df* value to locate the critical t score.
   (iii) If the *df* value does not appear in the table but falls exactly halfway between two *df* values, then choose the row that corresponds to the critical *t* score that is farthest from the *t* score: *t* = 0.

11.5   HYPOTHESIS TESTING: POPULATION STANDARD DEVIATION UNKNOWN

The *t* distribution is important in hypothesis tests involving a population mean where the population is approximately normal and the population standard deviation is *unknown*. In these instances the population standard deviation, σ, is estimated by s, the sample standard deviation, and the distribution of the test statistic is a *t* distribution. Therefore, the *t* distribution is used in hypothesis testing under the following conditions.

When the Distribution of the Test statistic: $\frac{\bar{x} - \mu_{\bar{x}}}{s_{\bar{x}}}$ is a t Distribution

The *t* distribution is used in performing a hypothesis test involving the population mean, when the following two conditions are true:
1. The population is approximately normal
2. The population standard deviation is unknown

The five step hypothesis testing procedure has to be modified when performing a hypothesis test involving a population mean when the *t* distribution serves as the model for the distribution of the test statistic. Let's discuss these minor changes in the hypothesis testing procedure.

Hypothesis Testing Procedure Changes When the Distribution of the Test Statistic is a t Distribution

In performing a hypothesis test where the distribution of the test statistic is a *t* distribution, the hypothesis testing procedure using a *t* distribution is similar to the hypothesis testing procedure using a normal distribution. The same five step procedure is used with the only differences being:

1. $\sigma_{\bar{x}}$ has been estimated by $s_{\bar{x}}$, where

$$s_{\bar{x}} = \frac{s}{\sqrt{n}}$$

2. The test statistic z is replaced by the test statistic t. The formula for the test statistic is:

$$t = \frac{\bar{x} - \mu_{\bar{x}}}{s_{\bar{x}}}.$$

3. The use of the *t* distribution in place of the normal distribution for the test statistic and serves as the hypothesis testing model.
4. The critical z score, z_c, is replaced by a critical t score, t_c. Critical t scores are found in Table III: Critical Values for the t Distribution.

Let's now consider a few examples of hypothesis testing involving a population mean where the *t* distribution serves as the model for the sampling distribution of the mean.

EXAMPLE 11.8

An automobile manufacturer claims that their economy car averages 55 mpg for highway driving. An engineer representing a leading automotive magazine believes this claim is too high. To test the manufacturer's claim, the engineer randomly selects sixteen of the economy cars and finds that they averaged 53 mpg with s = 2.5 mpg. Does this sample result indicate that the manufacturer's claim is too high at $\alpha = 1\%$?

Solution

Step 1   Formulate the hypotheses.

H_o: The population mean mpg for the economy car is 55.

In symbols, $H_o: \mu = 55$ mpg.

H_a: The population mean mpg for the economy car is less than 55.
In symbols, $H_a: \mu < 55$ mpg.

Step 2   Determine the model to test the null hypothesis, H_o.
To test the null hypothesis, a random sample of n = 16 cars was selected and tested. **Since σ is unknown, it is necessary to estimate σ using s, thus, the distribution of the test statistic is a *t* distribution** and serves as the hypothesis testing model.
For the sampling distribution of the mean, the expected results are:

$$\mu_{\bar{x}} = \mu$$

$$\mu_{\bar{x}} = 55 \text{ mpg}$$

and, **since s is an estimate for σ, it is necessary to estimate $\sigma_{\bar{x}}$ using the formula:**

$$s_{\bar{x}} = \frac{s}{\sqrt{n}}$$

$$s_{\bar{x}} = \frac{2.5}{\sqrt{16}}$$

$$s_{\bar{x}} = 0.125 \text{ mpg}$$

For n = 16, the degrees of freedom, df, is 15.
Thus, the test statistic distribution with df = 15 is illustrated in Figure 11.11.

The distribution of the test statistic with *df* = 15 (is a *t* Distribution)

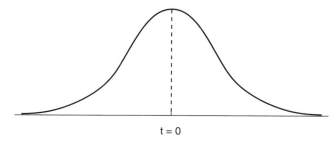

t = 0

FIGURE 11.11

Step 3   Formulate the decision rule.
   a) The alternative hypothesis is directional since the engineer believes that the manufac-
        turer's claim is *too high*.
   b) The type of hypothesis test is one-tailed (1TT) on the left side.
   c) The significance level is: $\alpha = 1\%$.
   d) Using Table III, the critical t score, t_c, for a one-tailed test on the left side with $\alpha = 1\%$ and
        df = 15, is: $t_c = -2.60$.
   e) Figure 11.12(a) illustrates the decision rule for this hypothesis test.

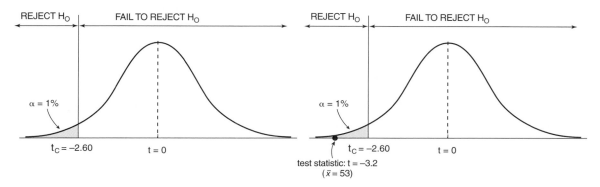

FIGURE 11.12(a)   **FIGURE 11.12(b)**

The decision rule is:

f) reject the null hypothesis if the test statistic t is less than $t_c = -2.60$.

Step 4 Analyze the sample data.

a) The sample mean is: $\bar{x} = 53$ mpg

b) Compute the test statistic, t, using $t = \dfrac{\bar{x} - \mu_{\bar{x}}}{s_{\bar{x}}}$.

For $\bar{x} = 53$, $\mu_{\bar{x}} = 55$ and $s_{\bar{x}} = 0.125$, $t = -3.2$.

Step 5 State the conclusion.

Using Figure 11.12(b), since the test statistic $t = -3.2$ is less than the critical t score $t_c = -2.60$, we reject H_o and accept H_a at $\alpha = 1\%$. Thus, the sample mean is *significantly different* than the manufacturer's claim of 55 mpg. Therefore, the engineer can conclude that the manufacturer's claim is too high at $\alpha = 1\%$.   ∎

EXAMPLE 11.9

A medical research team decides to study whether pressure exerted on a person's upper arm will increase bleeding time. The average bleeding time for a pricked finger where no pressure is applied to the upper arm is 1.6 minutes. To test their claim the research team randomly selects 64 subjects. They find that the average bleeding time is 1.9 minutes with s = 0.80 minutes when 50 mm of pressure is applied to the upper arm.

Does this sample result support the claim that pressure applied to the upper arm will increase bleeding time? (use $\alpha = 5\%$)

Solution

Step 1 Formulate the hypotheses.

H_o: The population mean bleeding time when 50 mm of pressure is applied to the upper arm is 1.6 minutes.

In symbols, H_o: $\mu = 1.6$ minutes.

H_a: The population mean bleeding time when 50 mm of pressure is applied to the upper arm is greater than 1.6 minutes.

In symbols, H_a: $\mu > 1.6$ minutes.

Step 2 Determine the model to test the null hypothesis, H_o.

To test the null hypothesis, a random sample of n = 64 subjects was selected and tested. **Since σ is unknown, s was used to estimate σ, and s was found to be 0.8 minutes.**

Under the assumption H_o is true, the sampling distribution of the mean has the expected results:

$$\mu_{\bar{x}} = \mu \qquad \text{and} \qquad s_{\bar{x}} = \dfrac{s}{\sqrt{n}}$$

$$\mu_{\bar{x}} = 1.6 \text{ minutes} \qquad\qquad s_{\bar{x}} = 0.1 \text{ minutes}$$

The distribution of the test statistic is a *t* distribution with *df* = 63 and serves as the hypothesis testing model. This is illustrated in Figure 11.13.

Step 3 Formulate the decision rule.

a) The alternative hypothesis is directional since the research team believes that pressure applied to the upper arm will *increase* bleeding time.

b) The type of hypothesis test is one-tailed on the right side.

c) The significance level is: $\alpha = 5\%$.

The distribution of the test statistic with *df* = 63 (is a *t* distribution)

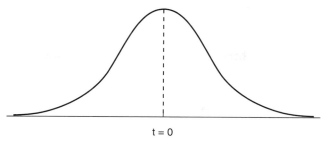

t = 0

FIGURE 11.13

d) For a one-tailed test on the right side with $\alpha = 5\%$ and $df = 63$, we need to find the critical *t* score on the right, t_c, in Table III using the closest *df* table entry. From Table III, $t_c = 1.67$
e) Figure 11.14(a) illustrates the decision rule for this hypothesis test.

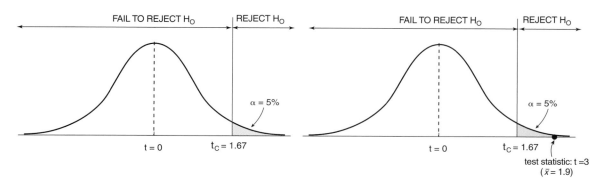

| FAIL TO REJECT H$_O$ | REJECT H$_O$ | | FAIL TO REJECT H$_O$ | REJECT H$_O$ |

$\alpha = 5\%$

t = 0 $t_C = 1.67$

$\alpha = 5\%$

t = 0 $t_C = 1.67$

test statistic: t =3
($\bar{x}$ = 1.9)

FIGURE 11.14(a)   **FIGURE 11.14(b)**

The decision rule is:
f) Reject the null hypothesis if the test statistic, t, is greater than $t_c = 1.67$.

Step 4 Analyze the sample data.
a) The sample mean is: $\bar{x} = 1.9$ minutes.
b) Compute the test statistic, t. The test statistic is $t = \dfrac{1.9-1.6}{0.1} = 3$.

Step 5 State the conclusion.
Using Figure 11.14(b), since the test statistic t = 3 is *greater than* the t score, $t_c = 1.67$, we reject H$_o$ and accept H$_a$ at $\alpha = 5\%$.
Therefore, the sample mean is statistically significant and the research team can conclude that pressure applied to the upper arm will increase bleeding time at $\alpha = 5\%$. ■

E X A M P L E   1 1 . 1 0

American Computer Machines, a large computer firm, has branch offices in several major cities of the world. From past experience, ACM knows that its employees relocate on the average once every ten years. Due to recent population trends, the company wants to determine if the average relocation time has changed (that is, is the average relocation time *different* from ten years?). To determine if a change has occurred, a random sample of twenty-five employees were interviewed and it was found that their mean relocation time was 9.5 years with s = 4.5 years.

Does this sample result indicate a change has occurred in the mean relocation time? (use $\alpha = 5\%$)

Solution

Step 1   Formulate the hypotheses.

H_o: The population mean relocation time is 10 years.

In symbols, $H_o: \mu = 10$ years.

H_a: The population mean relocation is not 10 years.

In symbols, $H_a: \mu \neq 10$ years.

Step 2   Determine the model to test the null hypothesis, H_o.
To test the null hypothesis, a random sample of n = 25 employees were interviewed. **Since σ is unknown, s was used to estimate σ and determined to be 4.5 years**. Under the assumption H_o is true, the expected results for the sampling distribution of the mean are:

$$\mu_{\bar{x}} = 10 \text{ years}$$

and

$$s_{\bar{x}} = 0.9 \text{ years}$$

The hypothesis testing model is the distribution of the test statistic which is a *t* distribution with *df* = 24. This is illustrated in Figure 11.15.

The distribution of the test statistic with *df* = 24 (is a *t* Distribution)

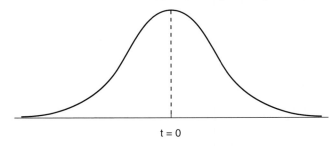

t = 0

FIGURE 11.15

Step 3   Formulate the Decision Rule.
a) The alternative hypothesis is *nondirectional* since the company is testing whether the mean relocation time has decreased or increased.
b) The type of hypothesis test is two-tailed.
c) The significance level is: $\alpha = 5\%$.
d) Using Table III, the critical values for a two-tailed test with $\alpha = 5\%$ and $df = 24$ are:

$$t_{LC} = -2.06 \text{ and } t_{RC} = 2.06$$

e) Figure 11.16(a) illustrates the decision rule for this hypothesis test.
The decision rule is:
f) Reject the null hypothesis if the test statistic t is either less than –2.06 or greater than 2.06.

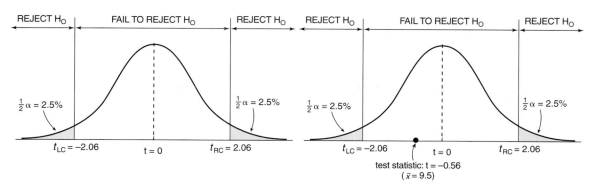

FIGURE 11.16(a)   **FIGURE 11.16(b)**

Step 4   Analyze the sample data.

a) The sample mean is: $\bar{x} = 9.5$ years.

b) The test statistic $t = \dfrac{9.5-10}{0.9} \approx -0.56$.

Step 5   State the conclusion.

Using Figure 11.16(b), since the test statistic $t = -0.56$ falls between the critical t scores of -2.06 and 2.06, we *fail to reject* H_o at $\alpha = 5\%$.

Although there is a *difference* between the sample mean of 9.5 years and the hypothesized mean of 10 years, this difference is **not statistically significant**. Therefore, the company cannot conclude that the mean relocation time of 10 years has changed. ■

EXAMPLE 11.11

The IRS claims that the mean amount of time it takes to transfer tax information from a tax return to a computer record is 35 minutes. Before they will invest into a new system, they decide to do a test run to determine if the new system is significantly better than the present system.

Four hundred tax returns are randomly selected and the data is transferred using the new system. The mean amount of time it takes to transfer the data from a tax return to a computer record is 34.3 minutes with $s = 4.2$ minutes. Based upon this sample result should the IRS invest in the new system? (use $\alpha = 5\%$).

Solution

Step 1   Formulate the hypotheses.

In hypothesis testing problems dealing with a comparison between a present (or existing) system and a new system, the null hypothesis is *always* stated as: the mean of the new system is *equal* to the mean of the present (or existing) system. The null hypothesis is stated in this form because if the null hypothesis is rejected, then this would *indicate* the new system is significantly better than the present system.

On the other hand, if the null hypothesis *cannot* be rejected, then the new system is *not* considered to be significantly better. Thus, in this instance, the present system would *not* be replaced by the new system. Therefore, the null hypothesis is:

H_o: Under the new transfer system, the population mean time to transfer a tax return to a computer record is 35 minutes.

In symbols, H_o: $\mu = 35$ minutes.

H_a: Under the new transfer system, the population mean time to transfer a tax return to a computer record is less than 35 minutes.

In symbols, H_a: $\mu < 35$ minutes.

Step 2   Determine the model to test the null hypothesis, H_o.

To test the null hypothesis, a random sample of n = 400 tax returns were transferred to computer records using the new transfer system. Since the population standard deviation, σ, is unknown, s was used to estimate σ. The value of s was determined to be 4.2 minutes. Under the assumption H_o is true, the expected results for the sampling distribution of the mean are:

$$\mu_{\bar{x}} = 35 \text{ minutes}$$

and

$$s_{\bar{x}} = 0.21 \text{ minutes}$$

The hypothesis testing model is the distribution of the test statistic with $df = 399$ which is a t distribution. This is illustrated in Figure 11.17.

distribution of the test statistic with df = 399 (is a t Distribution)

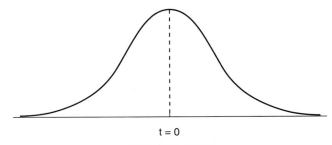

t = 0

FIGURE 11.17

Step 3   Formulate the decision rule.
  a) The alternative hypothesis, H_a, is directional.
  b) The type of hypothesis test is one-tailed on the left side.
  c) The significance level is: $\alpha = 5\%$.
  d) The critical t score for a one-tailed test on the left side with $\alpha = 5\%$ and $df = 399$ is found in Table III. It is $t_c = -1.65$.
  e) Figure 11.18(a) illustrates the decision rule for this hypothesis test.

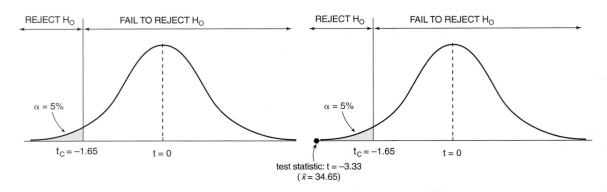

FIGURE 11.18(a)   **FIGURE 11.18(b)**

The decision rule is:

f)   Reject the null hypothesis if the test statistic t is less than $t_c = -1.65$.

Step 4   Analyze the sample data.

a)   The sample mean is: $\bar{x} = 34.3$ minutes.

b)   The test statistic $t = \dfrac{34.65 - 35}{0.21} \approx -3.33$.

Step 5   State the conclusion.

Using Figure 11.18(b), since the test statistic $t = -3.33$ falls below the critical t score of -1.65, we reject H_o and accept H_a at $\alpha = 5\%$. Thus, there is a significant difference between the sample mean time of 34.3 minutes and the expected mean time of 35 minutes. Therefore, the IRS should consider investing into the new data transferring system.

CASE STUDY 11.1   Costs of Visiting the Doctor

The snapshot entitled "Cost to visit doc skyrockets" shown in Figure 11.19 shows the average cost of a visit to the doctor for the years 1983 and 1992.

For each year shown in Figure 11.19,

a)   Define the population.

b)   Define the variable being displayed.

c)   Is the variable—discrete or continuous?

d)   For the year 1982, what does value $25.11 indicate about the population?

e)   For the year 1992, what does value $46.43 indicate about the population?

Assuming you are an individual who believes the value for the year 1992 is **too low**, and decides to perform a hypothesis test to test this value of $46.43.

f)   What is the null and alternative hypothesis for this test? Is the alternative hypothesis directional or nondirectional? Explain.

g)   Which population parameter are you assuming you know? What is the value of this parameter?

h)   Which population parameter are you missing? How would you go about obtaining an estimate of this parameter?

i)   What is the name of the sampling distribution that will serve as the model to this test? Is the distribution of the test statistic a normal or a t distribution, if we assume that the distribution of doctor costs is a normal distribution? Explain.

j)   What is the mean of this sampling distribution? What formula would you use to estimate the standard error of the sampling distribution?

k)   Which tail of the curve would the critical t score value of the test be placed?

FIGURE 11.19

CASE STUDY 11.1   Costs of Visiting the Doctor (continued)

l) If the test statistic falls to the right of the critical t score value, what is the conclusion to this test? Would this result indicate the average cost for a visit to the doctor is more or less than $46.43? Explain.

m) If the p-value of the hypothesis test is 3.96% (or 0.0396), then can you reject the null hypothesis at $\alpha = 1\%$? What would you say about the average cost for a visit to the doctor? Explain.

n) If the p-value of the hypothesis is 0.98% (or 0.0098) and $\alpha = 1\%$, could you conclude that the average cost for a visit to the doctor is more than $46.43? Explain.

CASE STUDY 11.2   How Many Sick Days Do We Take?

The study of the sick days conducted by the National Center for Health Statistics was based on a survey of 117,000 households containing a total of 303,000 persons.

Figure 11.20 displays a table containing some of findings of the study.

a) The statement "Women averaged 5.5 lost work days per year" pertains to what population?

b) What parameter is being mentioned within the statement? Define the variable being displayed. Is the variable—discrete or continuous?

c) According to the study the men averaged 4.3 lost work days per year. Can you speculate on some reasons as to why women might average more sick days per year than men?

d) If you were to conduct a hypothesis test to determine if the stated claim is too high, what would be the null and alternative hypotheses? Is the alternative hypothesis directional or nondirectional? Explain.

e) Which population parameter are you assuming you know? What is the value of this parameter?

f) Which population parameter are you missing? How would you go about obtaining an estimate of this parameter?

g) What is the name of the sampling distribution that will serve as the model to this test? Is the distribution of the test statistic a normal or a *t* distribution, if we assume that the distribution of sick days is a normal distribution? Explain.

h) What is the mean of this sampling distribution? What formula would you use to estimate the standard error of the sampling distribution?

i) Which tail of the curve would the critical t score value of the test be placed?

j) If the test statistic falls to the left of the critical t score value, what is the conclusion to this test? Would this result indicate the average number of sick days for women is more or less than 5.5? Explain.

k) If the p-value of the hypothesis test is 4.50% (or 0.0450), then can you reject the null hypothesis at $\alpha = 5\%$? What would you say about the average number of sick days for women? Explain.

l) If the p-value of the hypothesis is 1.76% (or 0.176) and $\alpha = 1\%$, could you conclude that the average number of sick days for women is more than 5.5? Explain.

Statistical Snapshot

A Sick Survey

The National Center for Health Statistics released a study yesterday comparing the amount of sick days taken by working men and women. Among its findings:

- Women average 5.5 lost work days per year, compared with 4.3 for men.
- 11.2 percent of women took eight or more sick days per year, while 7 percent of men had that many.
- By job, the fewest lost work days were 3.0 for men in the professions 3.3 for women.

- 78.5 percent of working women reported visiting a doctor during one year compared with 61.8 percent of male workers.
- 9.4 percent of women reported a hospital stay, compared with 7.5 percent of men. But the average hospital stay was 6.1 days for men and 5.4 for women.

Source: The Associated Press

FIGURE 11.20

Summary of Test Statistic Approach to Hypothesis Testing Involving a Population Mean

The following outline is a summary of the 5 step hypothesis testing procedure for a hypothesis test involving one population mean.

Step 1 Formulate the two hypotheses, H_o and H_a.

Null Hypothesis, H_o: $\mu = \mu_o$

Alternative Hypothesis, **H_a**: has one of the following three forms:

H_a: $\mu < \mu_o$ or H_a: $\mu > \mu_o$ or H_a: $\mu \neq \mu_o$

Step 2 Determine the model to test the null hypothesis, H_o.

Under the assumption H_o is true, the expected results are:

a) The distribution of the test statistic is the hypothesis testing model and is either:

    (i) approximately a normal distribution, if the standard deviation of the population is known and the sample size is greater than 30,

    or

    (ii) a t Distribution with degrees of freedom: $df = n - 1$ if the standard deviation of the population is unknown.

b) The mean of the sampling distribution of the mean is given by the formula:

$$\mu_{\bar{x}} = \mu_o$$

(since H_o is true :i.e. $\mu = \mu_o$)

c) For a normal distribution: the standard error of the mean, denoted by $\sigma_{\bar{x}}$ is:

$$\sigma_{\bar{x}} = \frac{\sigma}{\sqrt{n}}$$

or

for a t distribution: the estimate of the standard error of the mean, written $s_{\bar{x}}$, is given by the formula:

$$s_{\bar{x}} = \frac{s}{\sqrt{n}}$$

Step 3 Formulate the decision rule.

a) Alternative hypothesis: directional or non-directional.

b) Type of test: 1TT or 2TT.

c) Significance level: $\alpha = 1\%$ or $\alpha = 5\%$.

d) Critical score:

for a normal distribution: z_c is found in Table II.

for a t distribution: t_c is found in Table III where df = n–1.

e) Construct the hypothesis testing model.

f) State the decision rule.

Step 4 Analyze the sample data.

a) Compute the sample mean: $\bar{x}$.

b) for a normal distribution: test statistic is: $z = \frac{\bar{x} - \mu_{\bar{x}}}{\sigma_{\bar{x}}}$.

for a t distribution: test statistic is: $t = \frac{\bar{x} - \mu_{\bar{x}}}{s_{\bar{x}}}$.

Step 5 State the conclusion.

Compare the test statistic to the critical score of the decision rule and state the conclusion:

either: (a)   Reject H_o and Accept H_a at α

or   (b)   Fail to Reject H_o at α

Table 11.2 contains a condensed summary of the hypothesis tests involving a population mean.

TABLE 11.2   Summary of Hypothesis Tests for Testing the Value of a Population Mean

Form of the Null Hypothesis	Conditions of Test	Test Statistic Formula	Distribution of the test statistic is a:
$\mu = \mu_o$	KNOWN σ and $n > 30$	$z = \dfrac{\bar{x} - \mu_{\bar{x}}}{\sigma_{\bar{x}}}$ where: $\sigma_{\bar{x}} = \dfrac{\sigma}{\sqrt{n}}$	Normal Distribution
$\mu = \mu_o$	UNKNOWN σ	$t = \dfrac{\bar{x} - \mu_{\bar{x}}}{s_{\bar{x}}}$ where: $s_{\bar{x}} = \dfrac{s}{\sqrt{n}}$	t Distribution where: df $= n - 1$

11.6 p-VALUE APPROACH TO HYPOTHESIS TESTING INVOLVING A POPULATION MEAN USING THE TI-83 PLUS CALCULATOR

The p-value approach will require refinements in steps 3, 4 and 5 of the hypothesis testing procedure. In step 3, the decision rule will be stated as: Reject the H_o if the p-value of the test statistic is less than α. In step 4, the p-value will be determined using the TI-83 Plus calculator. While in step 5, the conclusion of the hypothesis test is determined by comparing the p-value to the level of significance, α.

Let's reexamine the hypothesis test shown in Example 11.11 using the p-value approach with the aid of the TI-83 Plus calculator.

EXAMPLE 11.12

The IRS claims that the mean amount of time it takes to transfer tax information from a tax return to a computer record is 35 minutes. Before they will invest into a new system, they decide to do a test run to determine if the new system is significantly better than the present system.

Four hundred tax returns are randomly selected and the data is transferred using the new system. The mean amount of time it takes to transfer the data from a tax return to a computer record is 34.3 minutes with s = 4.2 minutes. Based upon this sample result should the IRS invest in the new system? (use $\alpha = 5\%$).

Solution

Step 1   Formulate the hypotheses.

In hypothesis testing problems dealing with a comparison between a present (or existing) system and a new system, the null hypothesis is *always* stated as: the mean of the new system is *equal* to the mean of the present (or existing) system. The null hypothesis is stated in this form because if the null hypothesis is rejected, then this would *indicate* the new system is significantly better than the present system.

On the other hand, if the null hypothesis *cannot* be rejected, then the new system is *not* considered to be significantly better. Thus, in this instance, the present system would *not* be replaced by the new system. Therefore, the null hypothesis is:

H_o: Under the new transfer system, the population mean time to transfer a tax return to a computer record is 35 minutes.

In symbols, H_o: $\mu = 35$ minutes.

H_a: Under the new transfer system, the population mean time to transfer a tax return to a computer record is less than 35 minutes.

In symbols, H_a: $\mu < 35$ minutes.

Step 2   Determine the model to test the null hypothesis, H_0.
To test the null hypothesis, a random sample of n = 400 tax returns were transferred to computer records using the new transfer system. Since the population standard deviation, σ, is unknown, s was used to estimate σ. The value of s was determined to be 4.2 minutes. Under the assumption H_0 is true, the expected results for the sampling distribution of the mean are:

$$\mu_{\bar{x}} = 35 \text{ minutes}$$
$$\text{and}$$
$$s_{\bar{x}} = 0.21 \text{ minutes}$$

The hypothesis testing model is the distribution of the test statistic which is a t distribution with $df = 399$. This is illustrated in Figure 11.21.

distribution of the test statistic (is a *t* distribution with *df* = 399)

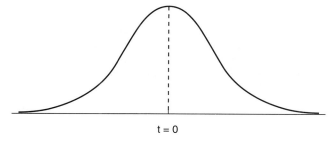

t = 0

FIGURE 11.21

Step 3   Formulate the decision rule.
  a) The alternative hypothesis, H_a, is directional.
  b) The type of hypothesis test is one-tailed on the left side.
  c) The significance level is: $\alpha = 5\%$.
  d) Figure 11.22 illustrates the decision rule for this hypothesis test.
  e) The decision rule is: Reject H_0 if the p-value of the test statistic is less than $\alpha = 5\%$.

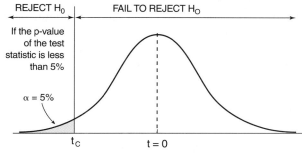

FIGURE 11.22

Step 4   Analyze the sample data.
Determine the p-value of the test statistic by entering the sample data into the TI-83 Plus calculator. The output screen of the TI-83 Plus calculator is shown in Figure 11.23.

FIGURE 11.23

From the output screen, the p-value of the test statistic $t \approx -3.33$ is approximately 4.692 E-4. The p-value of 4.692 E-4 can also be written as 0.0004692. Using this p-value we can now position the test statistic on the hypothesis testing model shown in Figure 11.24.

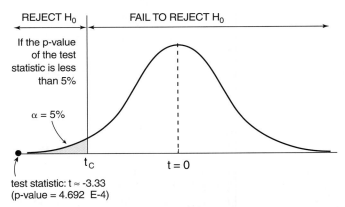

FIGURE 11.24

Step 5   State the conclusion.
Since the p-value (4.692 E-4) of the test statistic is less than $\alpha = 5\%$, we reject H_0 and accept H_a at a p-value of 4.692 E-4. Thus, there is a significant difference between the sample mean time of 34.3 minutes and the expected mean time of 35 minutes. Therefore, the IRS should consider investing into the new data transferring system.

Now we will summarize this procedure.

Summary of the p-Value Approach to Hypothesis Testing Involving a Population Mean Using the TI-83 Plus Calculator

Step 1   Formulate the two hypotheses, H_0 and H_a.
Null Hypothesis, $H_o: \mu = \mu_o$
Alternative Hypothesis, H_a: has one of the following three forms:
$H_a: \mu < \mu_o$ or $H_a: \mu > \mu_o$ or $H_a: \mu \neq \mu_o$

Step 2   Determine the model to test the null hypothesis, H_o.
Under the assumption H_o is true, the expected results are:
a) the distribution of the test statistic is either:
    (i) approximately a normal distribution, if the standard deviation of the population is known and the sample size is greater than 30,
    or.
    (ii) a t Distribution with degrees of freedom: $df = n-1$ if the standard deviation of the population is unknown.
b) the mean of the sampling distribution of the mean is given by the formula:

$$\mu_{\bar{x}} = \mu_0$$

(since H_o is true: i.e. $\mu = \mu_o$)

c) for a normal distribution: the standard error of the mean, denoted by $\sigma_{\bar{x}}$, is:

$$\sigma_{\bar{x}} = \frac{\sigma}{\sqrt{n}}$$

or
for a t distribution: the estimate of the standard error of the mean, written $s_{\bar{x}}$, is given by the formula:

$$s_{\bar{x}} = \frac{s}{\sqrt{n}}$$

Step 3   Formulate the decision rule.
a) alternative hypothesis: directional or non-directional.
b) type of test: 1TT or 2TT.
c) significance level: $\alpha = 1\%$ or $\alpha = 5\%$.
d) construct the hypothesis test model.
e) state the decision rule as: *Reject H_o if the p-value of the test statistic is less than α.*

Step 4   Analyze the sample data.
Enter the necessary sample data into the TI-83 Plus calculator to determine the p-value of the test statistic.

Step 5   Determine the conclusion.
Compare the p-value of the test statistic to the decision rule and either:
a) Reject H_o and accept H_a at α,
or
b) Fail to reject H_o at α.

11.7 USING TECHNOLOGY

In this chapter we have developed hypotheses tests involving a population mean. A MINITAB output (Figure 11.25) of a ZTEST for a nondirectional alternative hypothesis test, where the mean = 20 and population standard deviation = 4. A sample of 36 data values labeled as C1 was used to conduct this test.

MINITAB OUTPUT

TEST OF MU = 20.000 VS MU N.E. 20.000
THE ASSUMED SIGMA = 4.00

	N	MEAN	STDEV	SE MEAN	Z	P VALUE
C1	36	18.413	4.546	0.667	−2.38	0.018

FIGURE 11.25

Notice that the test of the population mean, $\mu = 20$ verses μ not equal to 20 is significant for an $\alpha = 2\%$ or higher since the p-value for the sample in C1 is 0.018. In most social science applications, p-values less than 0.05 are considered significant.

A MINITAB output (Figure 11.26) for a 1TT t-test on the right involving a population mean, where mean = 70 and the sample data is contained in C1 is:

MINITAB OUTPUT

TEST OF MU = 70.000 VS MU G.T. 70.000

	N	MEAN	STDEV	SE MEAN	T	P VALUE
C1	25	71.470	4.540	0.908	1.62	0.059

FIGURE 11.26

In this example notice that the output indicates that the alternative hypothesis, H_a, is that the population mean is greater than 70. By examining the p-value for this test you should notice that is 0.059. Since this p-value is greater than 0.05, the sample data would **not** indicate a rejection of the null hypothesis. Thus, a conclusion from this output would be that the we fail to reject H_o, although there is a difference between the sample mean (i.e. sample mean, $\bar{x} = 71.470$) and the population mean (i.e. population mean, $\mu = 70$) the difference is **not statistically significant** at $\alpha = 5\%$.

TI-83 Plus calculator output screens display a nondirectional and directional hypothesis test. Figure 11.27(a) represents an output screen for a nondirectional hypothesis z-test where the alternative hypothesis is $\mu \neq 20$ with a p-value of 0.0164. Figure 11.27(b) represents an output screen for a directional hypothesis t-test where the alternative hypothesis is $\mu > 70$ with a p-value of 0.0593. For each test, identify the number of standard deviations the sample result deviates from the mean. Which of these output screens indicate a rejection of the null hypothesis for $\alpha = 5\%$?

FIGURE 11.27(a)

FIGURE 11.27(b)

KEY TERMS

Hypothesis Testing Procedure
    Involving a Population Mean   656
Hypothesis Testing Model   657
Sample Mean, $\bar{x}$ 655
$\mu_{\bar{x}}$: Mean of the Sampling
    Distribution of the Mean   655
$\sigma_{\bar{x}}$: Standard Error of the Mean
    (Standard Deviation of the

Sampling Distribution of the
    Mean)   662
t Distribution   661
s: Estimate of the Population
    Standard Deviation   662
$s_{\bar{x}}$: Estimate of the Standard Error
    of the Mean (Estimate of the
    Standard Deviation of the

Sampling Distribution of the
    Mean)   662
t score   664
degrees of freedom, *df*   663
critical *t* score, t_c 664
distribution of the test statistic   667
test statistic z   668
test statistic t   668

SECTION EXERCISES

Section 11.2

For questions 1–2, complete the following statements with the word: directional or nondirectional.

1. If the null hypothesis has the form: $H_o: \mu = \mu_o$, and the alternative hypothesis has the form: $H_a: \mu < \mu_o$, then this is a _____ hypothesis test.

2. If the null hypothesis has the form: $H_o: \mu = \mu_o$, and the alternative hypothesis has the form: $H_a: \mu \neq \mu_o$, then this is a _____ hypothesis test.

3. The expected results of a hypothesis test are calculated under the assumption that the null hypothesis is _____.

4. Given the null hypothesis is $H_o: \mu = \mu_o$, the standard deviation of the population is σ, and the size of the random sample selected from the population is greater than 30, then:
    a) the sampling distribution of the mean is _____.
    b) the mean of the sampling distribution of the mean is given by the formula: $\mu_{\bar{x}} =$ _____ , and
    c) the standard error of the mean is given by the formula: $\sigma_{\bar{x}} =$ _____.

5. The alternative hypothesis of a hypothesis test involving a population mean can have one of the following three forms. They are:
    a) the population mean, μ, is *greater than* the numerical value, _____. This is symbolized as: $H_a: \mu$ ____ μ_o.
    b) the population _____ , μ, is *less than* the numerical value _____. This is symbolized as: $H_a: \mu$ ____ μ_o.
    c) the _____ mean, μ, is *not equal* to the numerical value, μ_o. This is symbolized as: $H_a: \mu$ ____ μ_o.

6. The formula for the test statistic for a hypothesis test involving a population mean is:
    a) when the distribution of the test statistic is approximately normal, and the standard deviation of the population, σ, is known:
    $$z = \text{_____.}$$
    b) when the distribution of the test statistic is a *t* distribution:
    $$t = \text{_____.}$$

7. If the population is normal with $\sigma = 8$, and samples of size 16 are selected, then the standard error of the mean is:
    a) 8   **b)** 2   **c)** 0.5   **d)** 1

8. If the alternative hypothesis, H_a, is $\mu < 27$, then the hypothesis test uses a:
    a) 1TT on right
    b) 2TT
    c) 1TT on left
    d) 2TT on left

9. Which of the following could be an alternative hypothesis?
    a) $\mu \neq 17$ **b)** $\mu = 26$ **c)** $\mu = 4.3$ **d)** $\mu = 0.10$

10. The sample mean is used as the mean for the sampling distribution of the mean.
    (T/F)

11. When doing a hypothesis test about a population mean, μ, and the population standard deviation, σ, is known, then the sampling distribution of the mean is always normal, regardless of the size, n, of the random sample.
    (T/F)

For problems 12 through 19:
For each of the hypothesis testing problems, find the following:

    a) State the null and alternative hypotheses.
    b) Calculate the expected results for the hypothesis test assuming the null hypothesis is true and determine the hypothesis test model.
    c) Formulate the decision rule.
    d) Determine the statistical result and test statistic.
    e) Determine the conclusion and answer the question(s) posed in the problem, if any.

12. The mean systolic blood pressure for twenty-five year old females is given to be 124 with a population standard deviation of 12. A sociologist believes that twenty-five year old females who live in the southwestern section of the United States will have significantly lower blood pressures. To test her claim, the sociologist randomly selects 36 of these females and determines their mean systolic blood pressure to be 120. Do these sample results support the sociologist's claim at $\alpha = 5\%$?

13. A sports equipment company claims to have developed a new manufacturing process which will increase the mean breaking strength of their new tennis racquet. The present manufacturing process produces a tennis racquet with a mean breaking strength of 90 lbs. with a population standard deviation of 6 lbs. Larry K., a wealthy tennis perfectionist who is known for his intense play that usually results in a broken racquet, employs a product testing company to test the manufacturer's claim. The testing company randomly purchases sixty-four of these new racquets and tests them. If the testing company determines the mean breaking strength to be 93 lbs., can Larry K. agree with the manufacturer's claim? (use $\alpha = 1\%$)

14. An unemployment agency claims that the average age of recipients of unemployment benefits are 37 years old with a population standard deviation of 5 years. A trade union association wants to test this claim. They randomly interview 200 recipients of unemployment benefits and obtain an average age of 36 years. Using a 1% significance level, can the trade union reject the unemployment agency's claim?

15. The LIRR carries a mean average of 125,000 passengers daily with a population standard deviation of 4000. The railroad has averaged 126,000 passengers daily for the last 36 snowstorms. Does this represent a significant increase over the mean average passenger load at $\alpha = 5\%$?

16. According to the U.S. Bureau of the Census, the average age of brides marrying for the first time is 23.9 years with a population standard deviation of 4.2 years. A sociologist believes that young women are delaying marriage and marrying at a later age. The sociologist randomly samples 100 marriage records and determines the average age of the first time brides is 24.9. Is there sufficient evidence to support the sociologist's claim at $\alpha = 5\%$?

17. A Florida citrus grower claims to have devised a new method for harvesting oranges which is faster and just as efficient as the method currently used. The current method takes a mean average of 5 hours to harvest 1 acre of orange trees with a population standard deviation of 45 minutes. One hundred acres harvested by the new method averaged 4 hours and 45 minutes. The average yield for the new method was equal to that of the current method. Do the sample results support the citrus grower's claim? (Use a significance level of 1%).

18. A traffic engineer believes that the time needed to drive from the downtown area out to the suburbs has significantly decreased due to increased use of public transportation. A study done five years ago determined that it took a mean of 45 minutes for this trip with a population standard deviation of 7 minutes. Recently, the mean average time for a sample of 49 trips was 42 minutes. Does this data support the traffic engineer? Use a significance level of 5%.

19. The Fort Knox Federal Savings Bank claims that their regular passbook savings accounts have an average balance of $1236.45 with a population standard deviation of $317.68. A group of federal bank auditors believes this claim is too high. To test the bank's claim the auditors randomly selected 400 accounts and obtained a mean balance of $1217.69. Do these sample results indicate that the bank's claim was too high? (use $\alpha = 5\%$)

20. Why state the conclusion as "Fail to Reject H_o" rather than Accept H_o? In the hypothesis testing procedure, when the null hypothesis cannot be rejected we state the conclusion as "fail to reject H_o" rather than "accept H_o". This problem examines the reason why we prefer to state the conclusion as "fail to reject H_o".

Two researchers, Maria and Larry, (who often don't agree on what the null hypothesis should be) decide to perform a hypothesis test on the same population of students to determine if the population mean IQ score has increased at the 5% level of significance.

Maria states her null hypothesis as: "The population mean is 120". Larry states his null hypothesis as: "The population mean is 122". Both researchers agree that the population standard deviation is 12. Their hypothesis tests are shown side by side in the following table.

Maria's Test	Larry's Test
1. Formulate the hypotheses:	
H_o: population mean is 120	H_o: population mean is 122
$\mu = 120$	$\mu = 122$
H_a: population mean is greater than 120	H_a: population mean is greater than 122
$\mu > 120$	$\mu > 122$

2. Determine the model to test the null hypothesis, H_o.

To test their null hypotheses, Maria and Larry select a random sample of 36 students. The expected results for their respective tests are:

Sampling distribution of the mean (is approximately normal)

$\mu_{\bar{x}} = 120$

$\sigma_{\bar{x}} = 2$

Sampling distribution of the mean (is approximately normal)

$\mu_{\bar{x}} = 122$

$\sigma_{\bar{x}} = 2$

3. Formulate the decision rule.

Maria's decision rule:
Reject H₀ if the test statistic is greater than 1.65.

Larry's decision rule:
Reject H₀ if the test statistic is greater than 1.65.

4. Analyze the sample data.

Maria and Larry randomly selected 36 students and found the sample mean IQ (the statistical result) to be $\bar{x} = 123$.

The test statistic is $z = 1.5$ for Maria's test and $z = 0.5$ for Larry's test.

Using these test statistics, state:
a) The conclusion to Maria's hypothesis test.
b) The conclusion to Larry's hypothesis test.
c) Was the test statistic result statistically significant for either Maria's or Larry's hypothesis test?
d) If Maria had decided to state her conclusion as **accept H₀** rather than **fail to reject H₀**, what would she be accepting as the population mean IQ score?
e) If Larry had decided to state his conclusion as **accept H₀** rather than **fail to reject H₀**, what would he be accepting as the population mean IQ score?
f) Using the ideas of this problem, explain what is wrong with the stating the conclusion as: **accept H₀.**

Section 11.3

21. The statistic

$$s = \sqrt{\frac{\sum(x - \bar{x})^2}{n - 1}}$$

is a good _____ of the population standard deviation, σ, when the sample size is large.

22. The estimate of the standard error of the mean is symbolized as _____. The formula is _____ .

23. The distribution of the test statistic is a *t* distribution if the standard deviation of the _____ is unknown and the population from which the sample is selected is a _____ distribution.

24. The properties of a *t* distribution are:
a) The graph of a *t* distribution is _____ .
b) The *t* distribution is symmetric about the _____ _____ .
c) The percent of area to the left of a *t* score is dependent upon the degrees of _____ .

25. If samples of size 36 are selected, then the degrees of freedom for the *t* distribution is:
a) 30   **b)** 37   **c)** 6   **d)** 35

26. The formula used to determine the **df** with one sample is:
a) $df = n$
b) $df = n + 1$
c) $df = n - 1$
d) $df = s - 1$

27. The *t* distribution is used as a model for the normal distribution whenever the sample size is less than 30. (T/F)

28. Degrees of freedom is a concept used to determine critical *t* scores. (T/F)

Section 11.4

29. Use Table III to determine the critical *t* score(s) t_c, for a hypothesis test where:
a) $\alpha = 5\%$, one-tail test on the left side, and $df = 25$.
b) $\alpha = 1\%$, one-tail test on left side, and $df = 11$.
c) $\alpha = 5\%$, one-tail test on right side, and $df = 22$.
d) $\alpha = 1\%$, 1TT on right side, and $df = 17$.
e) $\alpha = 5\%$, 2TT, and $df = 43$.
f) $\alpha = 1\%$, 2TT, and $df = 56$.

30. Use the information in each of the Figures a through f to determine the critical *t* score(s), t_c, from Table III.

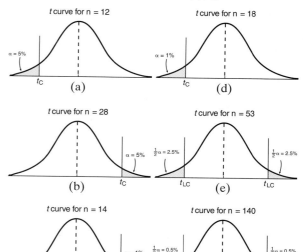

Section 11.5

For problems 31 through 40:

If the population standard deviation is unknown, assume that the population is approximately normal.

For each of the hypothesis testing problems, find the following:

a) State the null and alternative hypotheses.
b) Calculate the expected results for the hypothesis test assuming the null hypothesis is true and determine the hypothesis test model.
c) Formulate the decision rule.

d) Determine the statistical result and test statistic.

e) Determine the conclusion and answer the question(s) posed in the problem, if any.

31. A drug manufacturer specifies that their brand of cough suppressant contains a mean average of 25 milligrams of the expectorant drug DOKE for every milliliter of the suppressant. If 36 randomly selected one milliliter samples of this expectorant were found to have a mean of 25.4 mg of the expectorant drug DOKE with a standard deviation of 0.6, does this indicate that the product is not meeting the manufacturer's specifications? ($\alpha = 5\%$)

32. A certain type of oak tree has a mean growth of 14.3 inches in 4 years. A forestry biologist believes that a new variety will have a greater mean growth during this same length of time. A sample of 36 trees of this new variety are studied. If it is found that the mean growth is 15.4 inches with a sample standard deviation of 1.8 inches, can one conclude the biologist is correct? (use $\alpha = 5\%$)

33. An automobile club claims that the average time for a non-stop trip from New York City to Washington, D.C. by automobile is 4.5 hours. A disbelieving driver feels the claim is incorrect. The driver randomly questions 49 people who recently made the trip and finds that their average non-stop time was 4.3 hours with s = 0.35. Do these sample results refute the automobile club's claim at $\alpha = 1\%$?

34. A construction company specifies in their ordering of rivets that the rivets must have a mean sheer strength of 80,000 lbs. or more to be acceptable for their next contract. To test the quality of their shipment, the construction company takes a random sample of 16 rivets and finds the mean sheering strength to be 79,880 lbs. with a standard deviation of 200 lbs. Should the company accept this shipment? (Use $\alpha = 1\%$)

35. An ecologist claims that because of environmental influences, the mean life of Louisiana shellfish is 27 months. Feeling the claim is too low, a congressman decides to test the ecologist's claim at $\alpha = 5\%$. If the mean life of a random sample of 16 shellfish is 28.05 months with a standard deviation of 2.8, do the sample results indicate that the ecologist's claim is too low?

36. An advertisement for an alkaline battery claims the batteries have a mean life of 100 hours. Forty-nine batteries are tested and found to have a mean life of 97.45 hours with s = 7. Based on the sample results would you feel that a mean life of 100 hours is too high? (Use $\alpha = 1\%$)

37. A pharmaceutical company claims that their muscle relaxing tablets have a mean effective period of 4.4 hours. Researchers representing the Food and Drug Administration suspect the company's claim is too high. The researchers administer the muscle relaxing tablets to a random sample of 121 patients and find that the mean effective period is 4.2 hours with s = 1.1 hours. Do the sample results support the researcher's suspicions? (Use $\alpha = 1\%$)

38. The commerce department in a California County claims that the mean rental for a 3 room apartment is $850. A real estate company believes the commerce department's claim is not correct and randomly surveys 144 apartment dwellers and finds that their average rental is $872, with a standard deviation of $90. Do the sample data indicate that the commerce department's claim is *not* correct at $\alpha = 1\%$?

39. A pharmaceutical company manufactures a blood pressure drug which they claim will lower blood pressure an average of 20 points over a three week period. Dr. Zorba administers this drug to 36 patients for three weeks and records the following drops in their blood pressure: 22, 18, 19, 17, 24, 22, 15, 17, 21, 18, 15, 19, 24, 20, 14, 16, 19, 23, 24, 13, 18, 22, 21, 17, 24, 19, 15, 17, 21, 19, 22, 17, 19, 21, 17, 20. Do these sample data indicate that the pharmaceutical company's claim is incorrect at $\alpha = 5\%$?

40. A prominent psychologist at a New York hospital claims that a new form of psychotherapy for a certain type of mental disorder will help a patient to be ready for outpatient treatment in an average of twelve weeks. A resident psychologist decides to test this claim under the suspicion that the claim is too low. The resident psychologist uses this new form of psychotherapy on a random sample of 40 patients. The time required for these patients to reach outpatient status were (in days): 91, 88, 86, 95, 90, 93, 87, 89, 83, 91, 93, 86, 92, 91, 89, 83, 92, 88, 87, 90, 93, 87, 94, 86, 84, 92, 87, 85, 90, 88, 84, 92, 94, 86, 91, 89, 84, 89, 85, 95. Do these sample data support the claim made by the resident psychologist at $\alpha = 1\%$?

Section 11.6

For problems 41 to 58, use questions 12 to 19 of Section exercises 11.2 and 31 to 40 of Section 11.5 exercises and apply the p-value approach to hypothesis testing using the TI-83 Plus calculator. For each of these problems, use the 5 step procedure to perform a hypothesis test at **both** $\alpha = 1\%$ and $\alpha = 5\%$. Include the following within your test:

a) State the null and alternative hypotheses.

b) Calculate the expected results for the experiment assuming the null hypothesis is true and state the hypothesis test model.

c) Formulate the decision rule.

d) Identify the test statistic and its p-value.

e) State the conclusion and answer any question(s) posed in the problem for each alpha level.

f) Determine the smallest level of significance for which the null hypothesis can be rejected.

59. If the null hypothesis has the form: $H_o: \mu = \mu_o$, and the alternative hypothesis has the form: $H_a: \mu > \mu_o$, then this is a _____ hypothesis test.

60. To perform a hypothesis test involving a population mean, the distribution of the _____ is used as the hypothesis testing model.

61. The null hypothesis for a hypothesis test involving a population mean is stated as: H_o: the population mean, μ, is _____ to the numerical value, μ_o. In symbols this would be, $H_o: \mu$ ___ μ_o.

62. When performing a hypothesis test about a population mean where H_o is $\mu = 75$, the expected result $\mu_{\bar{x}} = 75$ is determined under the assumption that _____ is true.

63. When the mean of a sample, $\bar{x}$, is used to test the null hypothesis, $\mu = \mu_o$, one must use the sampling distribution of the mean and its properties. (T/F)

64. To insure that the sampling distribution of the mean can be approximated by the normal distribution, the sample size must be less than 30. (T/F)

65. When the standard deviation of the population is known then $\sigma_{\bar{x}}$ is equal to the standard deviation of the population. (T/F)

66. For a sample of size n, the degrees of freedom is equal to the sample size minus _____. In symbols, $df = $ _____.

67. The statistic, s, is a good estimate for:
   a) μ **b)** $\sigma_{\bar{x}}$ **c)** $\bar{x}$ **d)** σ

68. Whenever the population standard deviation, σ, is unknown, a good estimate of the population standard deviation is obtained from a random sample taken from the population. (T/F)

69. The *t* distribution is generally less dispersed than the normal distribution. (T/F)

70. **a)** Find the critical *t* score, t_c, for $\alpha = 5\%$, and a one-tailed test on left side for each value of n given in the following table.

n	t_c
5	
10	
50	
100	
500	

   b) From Table II: The Normal Distribution Table, find the critical z score, z_c, for $\alpha = 5\%$ and a one-tailed test on the left side.

   c) Compare the values of the critical *t* scores, t_c, to the critical z scores, z_c, as the sample size, n, increases.

For problems 71 through 78:

If the population standard deviation is unknown, assume that the population is approximately normal.

For each of the hypothesis testing problems, find the following:

   a) State the null and alternative hypotheses.
   b) Calculate the expected results for the hypothesis test assuming the null hypothesis is true and determine the hypothesis test model.
   c) Formulate the decision rule.
   d) Determine the statistical result and test statistic.
   e) Determine the conclusion and answer the question(s) posed in the problem, if any.

71. The population norms (i.e. parameters μ, and σ) for a mathematics anxiety test are known to be $\mu = 6$ and $\sigma = 1.6$. A teacher wants to determine if the students at her school will yield significantly different test results from the population norm. She administers the test to a random sample of 100 students and determines the sample mean test score to be 5.73. Can the teacher conclude that these results are different from the population norm at $\alpha = 5\%$?

72. The personnel director of a Wall Street brokerage house believes that the executives working in the "Big Apple" tend to have higher IQ's than the national executive mean IQ. The national mean IQ score for executives is 112 with a population standard deviation of 18. If a random sample of 81 "Big Apple" executives yields a mean IQ score of 116, do these sample results support the personnel director's claim at $\alpha = 1\%$?

73. A large computer corporation states that their new computer would significantly lower a university's registration time. Before investing in this new computer, the university decides to test this claim at $\alpha = 1\%$. Under the present system, the mean registration time had been 90 minutes with a population standard deviation of 20 minutes. With the new computer system, 100 students selected at random had an average registration time of 84 minutes. Should the university invest in this new computer?

74. Presently, the mean life expectancy of a rare strain of bacteria is 12 hours. A scientist claims she has developed a medium that will increase the mean life of the bacteria. The scientist tests 16 cultures of the newly treated bacteria and finds that they have a mean life of 13 hours with s = 1 hour. Do these results show that the medium is effective in increasing the bacteria's life expectancy? (Use $\alpha = 1\%$)

75. The Federal Aviation Agency (FAA) claims that on the average an air passenger's luggage weighs 35 pounds. An air carrier believes that the FAA is incorrect and randomly selects 25 passengers and determines that the average weight of the luggage is 36 pounds with a sample standard deviation of 4 pounds. Would these results indicate that the FAA's claim is incorrect? (Use $\alpha = 1\%$)

76. A new training procedure for athletes was developed and has been used during the past season. The trainer claims that this new training procedure has reduced the number of injuries to his players. Using the present training method, there were, on the average, 9 injuries per week. For a random sample of 12 weeks during the period in which the new training procedure was used, the mean number of injuries per week was only 7 with s = 2. Do the sample results support the trainer's claim at $\alpha = 5\%$?

77. A National Research Group reports that children between the ages of 6 and 10 years watch television an average of 21 hours per week. A sociologist believes that the children within her upper-middle class neighborhood watch television less than an average of 21 hours per week. She randomly selects 25 children aged 6 to 10 years from her neighborhood and determines the mean number of hours that the children watch television is 20 hours with a sample standard deviation of 3 hours. Do these sample results support the sociologist's claim at $\alpha = 5\%$?

78. A law student decides to check her professor's claim that the average time to disposition is 90 days. To test this claim, she randomly selects 15 cases of a similar type from county court records and determines the number of days to disposition for each case. The results of her sample are: 85, 97, 93, 88, 93, 92, 89, 88, 94, 87, 96, 92, 94, 89, 95. Can the law student reject her professor's claim at $\alpha = 5\%$?

WHAT DO YOU THINK?

79. Examine the two graphs shown in the figure entitled "Student Aid Falters" which represents the ten-year trend for the student-aid programs: Stafford Loans and Pell Grants.

Statistical Snapshot

Student Aid Falters

The two most popular student-aid programs aren't keeping up with soaring college tuition. The average Pell Grant declined last year to a pre-1989 level. The average Stafford Loan (formerly Guaranteed Student Loan) is climbing in miniscule steps. Here are 10-year trends:

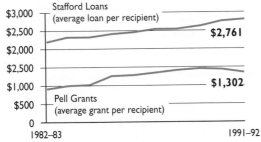

Source: The College Board

a) What parameter is represented by both graphs? Define the variable being displayed in the graphs. Is the variable discrete or continuous?

For each student-aid program, design a hypothesis test that includes:

b) A null hypothesis. Use the information contained in the graph for the '91–92 year as the status quo.

c) An alternative hypothesis. Use the direction that the line graph is heading as to your belief regarding the true value of the population parameter for this year.

d) Is the alternative hypothesis directional or nondirectional? Is this a 1TT or a 2TT? Explain.

e) Which population parameter are you assuming you know? What is the value of this parameter?

f) Which population parameter are you missing? How would you go about obtaining an estimate of this parameter?

g) State the name of the sampling distribution that will serve as the model for this test. Is the distribution of the test statistic a normal or a *t* distribution, if we assume that the distribution of student-aids is a normal distribution? Explain.

h) What is the mean of this sampling distribution? What formula would you use to estimate the standard error of the sampling distribution?

i) Which tail of the curve would the critical z or t score value of the test be placed?

j) If you decide to use a significance level of 5% for each hypothesis test, then determine the test statistic.

k) If the test statistic falls to the right of the critical z or t score value for the Stafford Loan hypothesis test, what is the conclusion to this test? Could you agree that the conclusion to this hypothesis test follows the trend shown in the graph? Explain.

l) If the p-value of the hypothesis test is 6% (or 0.06), then can you reject the null hypothesis at $\alpha = 5\%$?

Does this indicate that the Stafford Loan average is following the trend shown in the graph? Explain.
m) If the p-value of the hypothesis is 2.90% (or 0.290) and $\alpha = 2\%$, could you conclude that the Stafford Loan average is following the trend shown in the graph? Explain.

80. The snapshot entitled "Staying Longer On the Road" shown in the following figure indicates the average length of trip for the years 1989–1991.

Statistical Snapshot

Staying Longer On the Road

To cut travel costs, companies are sending employees on fewer—but longer—trips.

Source: U.S. Travel Data Center

a) Define the population.
b) Define the variable being displayed.
c) Is the variable discrete or continuous?
d) What does the graph indicate about the average length of business trips over the years shown?
e) What does the number 4.4 days indicate about the population?

Assuming you are an individual who believes that the average length number of business trips days is following the trend shown in the snapshot:
f) What is the null and alternative hypotheses for this test? Is the alternative hypothesis directional or nondirectional? Explain.
g) Which population parameter are you assuming you know? What value does this parameter have?
h) Which population parameter are you missing that you need to perform this test? How would you go about obtaining an estimate of this parameter?
i) What is the name of the sampling distribution that will serve as the model to this test? Is the test statistic distribution a normal or a t distribution, if we assume that the distribution representing the length of business trips is a normal distribution? Explain.
j) What is the mean of this sampling distribution? What formula would you use to estimate the standard error of the sampling distribution?
k) Which tail of the curve would the critical z or t score value of the test be placed?
l) If the test statistic falls to the right of the critical z or t score value, what is the conclusion to this test? Would this result indicate the average length of business trips is more or less than 4.4? Explain.
m) If the p-value of the hypothesis test is 2.47% (or 0.0247), then can you reject the null hypothesis at $\alpha = 3\%$? What would you say about the average length of business trips? Explain.
n) If the p-value of the hypothesis is 0.05% (or 0.0005) and $\alpha = 5\%$, could you conclude that the average length of business trips is more than 4.4? Explain.

PROJECTS

81. Hypothesis Testing Project
   A. Selection of a topic
   1. Select a reported fact or claim about a population mean made in a local newspaper, magazine or other source.
   2. Suggested topics:
      a) Test the claim that the average number of hours worked per week by a student is 20 hours.
      b) Test the claim that the cumulative grade point average is higher today then it was ten years ago. The cumulative grade point average ten years ago was 2.64.
      c) Test the claim that the average SAT score on the mathematics section is greater than 480.
      d) Test the claim that the average pulse rate at rest for a woman between the ages of 16 and 23 inclusive is lower than 80.

   B. Use the following procedure to test the claim selected in part A.
   1. State the claim, identify the population referred to in the statement of the claim and indicate where the claim was found.
   2. State your opinion regarding the claim (i.e., do you feel it is too high, too low, or simply don't agree with the claim) and clearly identify the population you plan to sample to support your opinion.
   3. State the null and alternative hypotheses.
   4. Develop and state a procedure for selecting a random sample from your population. Indicate the technique you are going to use to obtain your sample data.
   5. Compute the expected results, indicate the hypothesis testing model, and choose an appropriate level of significance.

6. Determine the critical z or t score value(s) and state the decision rule.
7. Calculate the statistical result, $\bar{x}$, and the test statistic.
8. Construct a hypothesis testing model and place the test statistic on the model.
9. Formulate the appropriate conclusion and interpret the conclusion with respect to your opinion (as stated in step 2).

82. Read a research article from a professional journal in a field such as: medicine, education, marketing, science, social science, etc. Write a summary of the research article that includes the following:

a) Name of article, author, and journal (include volume number and date).
b) Statement of the research problem.
c) The null and alternative hypotheses.
d) How the experiment was conducted (include the sample size and sampling technique).
e) Determine the statistical result(s), test statistic(s), and the level of significance.
f) State the conclusion(s) in terms of the null and alternative hypotheses.

ANALYZING THE DATABASE USING TECHNOLOGY

The following exercises refer to the file DATABASE listed in Appendix A. Using a technological tool, answer each exercise.

83. Use a 2TT to test the null hypothesis at $\alpha = 5\%$ and the population mean, $\mu = k$.
    a) k = 68 for the variable SHT.
    b) k = 15 for the variable WRK.
    State the null and alternative hypothesis for each variable in words and symbols. Identify the sample mean, the z or t score, p value and interpret. Is the null hypothesis rejected? State the conclusion in words with respect to the variable tested.

84. Use a 1TT to test the null hypothesis at $\alpha = 5\%$ and the population mean, $\mu = k$.

a) k = 68 for the variable SHT,
b) k = 15 for the variable WRK,
if the alternative hypothesis is *directional* with form:
a) mu < k for the variable SHT.
b) mu > k for the variable SHT.
c) mu < k for the variable WRK.
d) mu > k for the variable WRK.
State the null and alternative hypothesis for each variable in words and symbols. Identify the sample mean, the z or t score, p value and interpret. Is the null hypothesis rejected? State the conclusion in words with respect to the variable tested.

CHAPTER TESTS

85. Which of the following statements could be used for the null hypothesis, H_o?
    a) $\mu < \mu_o$ b) $\mu > \mu_o$ c) $\mu \neq \mu_o$ d) $\mu = \mu_o$

86. Which of the following could be the alternative hypothesis for a 1TT on the left?
    a) $\mu < 56$ b) $\mu > 173$ c) $\mu \neq 93$ d) $\mu = 63$

87. The hypothesis testing model for a hypothesis test involving a population mean where n = 25 and the population standard deviation, σ, is unknown, is a *t* distribution with _____ degrees of freedom.

88. Which of the following is *not* a property of the *t* distribution?
    a) Less dispersed than the normal distribution
    b) Symmetric with respect to the mean
    c) Bell-shaped
    d) Different *t* distribution for each sample size

89. When σ is unknown and the formula

$$s = \sqrt{\frac{\sum (x - \bar{x})^2}{n-1}}$$

is used as an estimate for σ, then s is said to be a good estimator.
(T/F)

90. The critical *t* score for a 1TT on the right with $\alpha = 5\%$ and $df = 17$ is:
    a) 1.74   b) 2.11   c) 2.57   d) 2.90

For the hypothesis testing problem, find the following:

a) State the null and alternative hypotheses.
b) Calculate the expected results for the hypothesis test assuming the null hypothesis is true and determine the hypothesis test model.
c) Formulate the decision rule.
d) Determine the statistical result and test statistic.
e) Determine the conclusion and answer the question(s) posed in the problem, if any.

91. An automobile manufacturer claims that their leading compact car averages 36 mpg in the city. The population standard deviation is 4 mpg for city driving. Suppose a city police department purchases 64 cars from

this auto manufacturer. If these cars were driven exclusively under city conditions and averaged 33 mpg, can one argue that the manufacturer's claim is too high at $\alpha = 5\%$?

92. A manufacturer of space vehicle components specifies that a particular part must be able to withstand a mean heat of 5,000 degrees Fahrenheit or more. To determine if the parts meet the manufacturer's specifications, a random sample of 9 parts is chosen from the supplier's shipment and found to have a mean heat resistance of 4,930 F degrees with s = 150 degrees. Should the manufacturer accept the shipment? (Use $\alpha = 5\%$)

93. A new chemical process has been developed for producing gasoline. The company claims that this new process will increase the octane rating of the gasoline. Sixteen samples of the gasoline produced with the new process are selected at random and their octane ratings were: 94, 93, 97, 92, 96, 94, 95, 91, 98, 95, 92, 91, 95, 96, 97, 93. If the mean octane using the existing process is 93, is the company's claim correct? (Use $\alpha = 5\%$)

Hypothesis Testing Involving Two Population Proportions Using Independent Samples

Contents

12.1 INTRODUCTION TO HYPOTHESIS TESTS INVOLVING A DIFFERENCE BETWEEN TWO POPULATION PROPORTIONS USING INDEPENDENT SAMPLES

In this chapter, we will present a hypothesis test involving the comparison of two population proportions to determine if the populations are statistically different. For example, a medical researcher might be interested in determining whether there is a significant difference in the proportion of individuals catching the common cold for the individuals who take large doses of vitamin C and those individuals who do not take vitamin C. Such a study would involve the comparison of two population proportions. We will now consider the procedure to conduct a hypothesis test that can be used to compare two population proportions where an independent random sample is selected from each population.

In order to conduct a hypothesis test involving two populations, we will randomly select a sample from each population. Before we can discuss the procedure to perform such a hypothesis test it is necessary to consider how each sample is selected from each population. The two samples selected can be either **independent** or **dependent** depending on the selection process.

> **DEFINITION 12.1**
> **Independent Samples.** Two samples are independent if the sample data values selected from one population are unrelated to the sample data values selected from the second population.

In this chapter we will only consider hypothesis tests where the samples selected are **independent samples.** In Chapter 10, we examined hypothesis tests involving a single population proportion. We will now discuss hypothesis tests that involve the comparison of the proportions from two populations to determine if the population proportions are statistically different. For example:

- *Is there a statistically significant difference in the proportion of individuals catching the common cold among individuals who take large doses of vitamin C and those individuals who do not take vitamin C?*

  This test involves the comparison of two population proportions: the proportion of individuals taking vitamin C who caught a common cold and the proportion of individuals not taking vitamin C who caught a common cold.

- *Is the difference between the opinion of men and women regarding their attitude towards purchasing non-designer jeans statistically significant?*

  This test involves the comparison of two population proportions: the proportion of women who will purchase non-designer jeans and the proportion of men who will purchase non-designer jeans.

- *Is there a statistically significant difference in the proportion of defective memory chips produced using a new innovative manufacturing process and the traditional manufacturing process?*

  This test involves the comparison of two population proportions: the proportion of defective memory chips produced using the new innovative manufacturing process and the proportion of defective memory chips produced using the traditional manufacturing process.

- *Is the difference between the recovery rate of patients with a certain illness who are treated with a new drug (the treatment group) and the recovery rate of patients with this same illness who are given a placebo (the control group) statistically significant ?*

  This test involves the comparison of two population proportions: the proportion of patients who recover within the treatment group using the new drug treatment and the proportion of patients who recover within the control group who take the *placebo.*

Statistical questions such as these involve the study of two populations, instead of just one population, and the comparison of the proportion from each of these two populations. The appropriate sampling distribution to perform a hypothesis test involving two population proportions is called the *Sampling Distribution of the Difference Between Two Proportions.* In Section 12.2, we will develop the concept underlying this sampling distribution.

12.2   THE SAMPLING DISTRIBUTION OF THE DIFFERENCE BETWEEN TWO PROPORTIONS

Studies involving population proportions will produce **counts** rather than measurements. For example, the question:

> *Is there a statistically significant difference in the proportion of individuals catching the common cold among individuals who take high doses of vitamin C and those individuals who do not take vitamin C?*

involves the comparison of the population of individuals taking vitamin C and the population of individuals not taking vitamin C. To determine the effectiveness of vitamin C, the researcher will **count** the number of vitamin C users who catch a cold and **count** the number of people not taking vitamin C who catch a cold. These **counts** will be used to calculate the **proportion** of individuals who caught the common cold within each group.

As mentioned in Chapter 10, the symbol **p** is used to represent the population proportion of items or individuals possessing a particular characteristic. In this chapter, however, we will need to attach subscripts 1 and 2 to the population proportion symbol p, because we need to distinguish between the proportions of two populations. For example, if we define *population 1 as the population of individuals taking vitamin C,* and *population 2 as the population of individuals not taking vitamin C,* then:

p$_1$ (read *p sub one*) = *the population proportion of individuals taking vitamin C who caught a cold.*

p$_2$ (read *p sub two*) = *the population proportion of individuals not taking vitamin C who caught a cold.*

In practice, the size of each population is either too large or infinite so that it will be impractical or impossible to determine the true proportion, p, of each population. Consequently, *an independent random sample is selected from each population and the proportion of each sample is computed.* Recall, from Chapter 10, the sample proportion, symbolized $\hat{p}$ and read *p hat,* is the ratio of the number of items or individuals in the sample that possess a particular characteristic to the sample size. That is,

$$\hat{p} = \frac{\text{number of items or individuals possessing a particular characteristic}}{\text{sample size}}$$

Thus, in the example on the effectiveness of vitamin C on the incidence of catching a cold, an independent random sample of vitamin C users is selected and the *number of individuals who caught a cold is counted.* If we let n_1 represent the size of the random sample selected while x_1 equals the number of individuals within the sample who caught a cold using vitamin C, then the sample proportion of individuals who caught a cold using vitamin C, symbolized $\hat{p}_1$ and read *p hat sub 1,* is determined using:

$$\hat{p}_1 = \frac{\text{number of individuals who caught a cold using vitamin C}}{\text{sample size}}$$

In symbols, we write:

$$\hat{p}_1 = \frac{x_1}{n_1}$$

To determine the effectiveness of vitamin C, we need to compare this sample result, $\hat{p}_1$, to a group of individuals not taking vitamin C. Therefore, another independent random sample of individuals who do not use vitamin C is selected and the number of individuals who caught a cold would be counted. Letting n_2 represent the sample size and x_2 equal the number of individuals within the sample who caught a cold not using vitamin C, then the sample proportion of individuals who caught a cold not using vitamin C, symbolized $\hat{p}_2$ and read *p hat sub 2,* is determined using:

$$\hat{p}_2 = \frac{\text{number of individuals who caught a cold not using vitamin C}}{\text{sample size}}$$

In symbols, we have:

$$\hat{p}_2 = \frac{x_2}{n_2}$$

Suppose a medical researcher decides to conduct such a study and she randomly selects 500 people for the experiment. From these 500 people, she randomly selects 250 who are given high doses of vitamin C while the other 250 people are given a placebo (that is, a fake ineffective tablet similar in appearance to the vitamin C tablet.) At the conclusion of the experiment, the researcher determines the number of individuals within each group who caught a cold. Examine the results of the study shown in Table 12.1.

Table 12.1

	Vitamin C Group	Placebo Group
Number of individuals who caught a cold	$x_1 = 104$	$x_2 = 158$
Sample Size	$n_1 = 250$	$n_2 = 250$

Using the results shown in Table 12.1, the researcher can determine the sample proportion of individuals within each group who caught a cold. These sample proportions are:

$\hat{p}_1$ = sample proportion of vitamin C users who caught a cold

$$\hat{p}_1 = \frac{x_1}{n_1} = \frac{104}{250} \approx 0.4160 \text{ (computed to 4 decimal places)},$$

while,

$\hat{p}_2$ = sample proportion of placebo users who caught a cold

$$\hat{p}_2 = \frac{x_2}{n_2} = \frac{158}{250} \approx 0.6320 \text{ (computed to 4 decimal places)}.$$

The researcher will use the *sample proportions* to decide if there is *a significant difference between the proportion of **all** individuals taking high doses of vitamin C who catch a cold and the proportion of **all** individuals not taking vitamin C who catch a cold.* To determine if there is **a significant difference between the two population proportions**, the researcher will need to compute *the difference between the two sample proportions:* $\hat{p}_1 - \hat{p}_2$. That is, the researcher will subtract the two sample proportions, $\hat{p}_1 - \hat{p}_2$, to determine if this sample difference, $\hat{p}_1 - \hat{p}_2$, is large enough to infer that the difference between the proportion of all individuals taking vitamin C and the proportion of all individuals not taking vitamin C is statistically significant. For this example, the difference between the sample proportions is:

$$\hat{p}_1 - \hat{p}_2 = 0.4160 - 0.6320 = -0.2160.$$

Consequently, the researcher must now determine if the *difference between the **sample** proportions* $\hat{p}_1 - \hat{p}_2 = -0.216$ is **large** enough to infer that there is *a significant difference between the two **population** proportions* **or** she may conclude that this *difference* between the sample proportions *is due solely to chance.*

If the researcher concludes that the difference is attributed to chance alone, then she is simply stating that it is *likely* to select an independent random sample from each of the two populations having equal proportions (i.e. $p_1 = p_2$), and obtain a difference between their sample proportions, $\hat{p}_1$ and $\hat{p}_2$ respectively. As explained in Chapter 10, when selecting random samples from a population, the values of the sample proportions can vary from sample to sample. Consequently, when selecting an independent random sample from two populations which have equal proportions (i.e. $p_1 = p_2$), their sample proportions, $\hat{p}_1$ and $\hat{p}_2$ respectively, can vary and thus exhibit a difference between the sample proportions $\hat{p}_1 - \hat{p}_2$ by chance alone.

For example, if the medical researcher were to conduct a similar study by randomly selecting another independent sample from each of these same two populations, the researcher could obtain different sample proportions, such as:

$$\hat{p}_1 = 0.5890 \text{ and } \hat{p}_2 = 0.7450,$$

which would result in the following *different* difference between the sample proportions:

$$\hat{p}_1 - \hat{p}_2 = 0.5890 - 0.7450 = -0.1560.$$

Thus the researcher needs to determine if the difference between the sample proportions, $\hat{p}_1 - \hat{p}_2$, is large enough and not just attributed to chance alone before she can conclude that the difference between the proportion of **all** individuals taking high doses of vitamin C who catch a cold and the proportion of **all** individuals not taking vitamin C who catch a cold is a statistically significant. To determine if the difference between the sample proportions, $\hat{p}_1 - \hat{p}_2$, is large enough, it is necessary to understand the characteristics of the **distribution of all possible sample differences of $\hat{p}_1 - \hat{p}_2$.** Such a distribution is called the *Sampling Distribution of the Difference Between Two Proportions. This distribution is also referred to as the Sampling Distribution of $\hat{p}_1 - \hat{p}_2$.* The researcher will need **to use the Sampling Distribution of the Difference Between Two Proportions to determine if the difference between the sample proportions** $\hat{p}_1 - \hat{p}_2 = -0.2160$ is significant (or large enough) to infer that there is a statistically significant difference between the population proportions, $\hat{p}_1 - \hat{p}_2$. *To make such a decision, the researcher must know the shape, mean, and standard deviation of the Sampling Distribution of the Difference Between Two Proportions.* These characteristics will be discussed in the next section. Before we leave this section, examine Table 12.2 which summarizes the notation which will be used in this chapter.

Table 12.2   Summary of Notation for Population and Sample Proportions

Population	Population Proportion	Sample Size	Count or number of occurrences or observations possessing a particular characteristic or number of successes	Sample Proportion
1	p_1	n_1	x_1	$\hat{p}_1 = \dfrac{x_1}{n_1}$
2	p_2	n_2	x_2	$\hat{p}_2 = \dfrac{x_2}{n_2}$

Let's consider Example 12.1, which will examine the idea and notation of a population and a sample proportion.

EXAMPLE   12.1

Craig, a psychological researcher, is trying to determine if there is a significant difference between the proportion of women and men who frequently have nightmares when taking statistics at the Big Red University. Craig randomly selected 195 women and 180 men who had taken statistics at the University to perform his study. Within his study, Craig determined that 69 of the women and 58 of the men had frequent nightmares when taking statistics at the University.

Using this information and letting the women represent population 1 and the men as population 2,

a) identify the two population proportions being compared and the symbols used to symbolize these proportions.

b) determine the sample proportion (to 4 decimal places) of students who had frequent nightmares for each population and the symbols used to symbolize these proportions.

c) calculate the difference between the sample proportions and identify the symbol to represent this difference.

Solution

a) The researcher is interested in comparing the *proportion of all University women who have frequent nightmares when taking statistics* to the *proportion of all University men who have frequent nightmares when taking statistics*. Letting the college women who took statistics at the University represent population 1, and the college men who took statistics at the University represent population 2, then:

p_1 = *the population proportion of all University women who have frequent nightmares when taking statistics*

p_2 = *the population proportion of all University men who have frequent nightmares when taking statistics*

b) The sample proportion of women who had frequent nightmares when taking statistics is symbolized by $\hat{p}_1$ and is equal to:

$$\hat{p}_1 = \frac{\text{number of women having frequent nightmares}}{\text{total number of women in the sample}} \quad ,$$

or

$$\hat{p}_1 = \frac{x_1}{n_1}$$

where:
x_1 = number of women having frequent nightmare
   = 69,
and
n_1 = total number of women in the sample
   = 195.

Thus, the sample proportion of women who had frequent nightmares when taking statistics is:

$$\hat{p}_1 = \frac{69}{195} \approx 0.3538$$

The sample proportion of men who had frequent nightmares when taking statistics is symbolized by $\hat{p}_2$ and is equal to:

$$\hat{p}_2 = \frac{\text{number of men having frequent nightmares}}{\text{total number of men in the sample}}$$

or

$$\hat{p}_2 = \frac{x_2}{n_2} ,$$

where:
x_2 = number of men having frequent nightmare
   = 58,
and
n_2 = total number of men in the sample
   = 180.

Thus, the sample proportion of men who had frequent nightmares when taking statistics is:

$$\hat{p}_1 = \frac{58}{180} \approx 0.3222$$

c)   The difference between the sample proportions is symbolized by $\hat{p}_1 - \hat{p}_2$ and is equal to:

$$\hat{p}_1 - \hat{p}_2 = 0.3538 - 0.3222$$

$$= 0.0316.$$ ———————————— ∎

We are interested in studying the relationship of the proportions of two populations, rather than just one population proportion as discussed in Chapter 10. The appropriate sampling distribution used to compare the proportions of two populations is called the *Sampling Distribution of the Difference Between Two Proportions*.

DEFINITION 12.2

The Sampling Distribution of the Difference Between Two Proportions or the Sampling Distribution of $\hat{p}_1 - \hat{p}_2$. The Sampling Distribution of $\hat{p}_1 - \hat{p}_2$ is a theoretical distribution of all the possible differences between the values of the sample proportions selected from each of the two populations.

Figure 12.1 will help you to visualize the conceptual idea behind this sampling distribution.

Notice at the top of Figure 12.1, the two populations, identified as *Population 1* and *Population 2*, are shown with their respective population proportions p_1 and p_2. Suppose an independent random sample of size n_1 is selected from population 1 and an independent random sample of size n_2 is selected from population 2. Underneath each population, the Sampling Distribution of the Proportion is shown. The theoretical Sampling Distribution of the Proportion corresponding to population 1 represents all the possible samples of size n_1 that can be selected from population 1. While the theoretical Sampling Distribution of the Proportion corresponding to population 2 represents all the possible samples of size n_2 that can be selected from population 2. As discussed in Chapter 10, each Sampling Distribution of the Proportion is approximately a normal distribution when the sample size is large. Recall, *a sample is large if both np and n(1-p) are greater than 5*. Using this rule, the theoretical Sampling Distribution of the Proportion corresponding to population 1 is approximately normal when both $n_1 p_1$ and $n_1(1-p_1)$ are greater than 5, while theoretical Sampling Distribution of the Proportion corresponding to population 2 is approximately normal when both $n_2 p_2$ and $n_2(1-p_2)$ are greater than 5.

Now, consider selecting an independent random sample and determining the sample proportion for each of these two populations. These sample proportions are symbolized as $\hat{p}_1$ and $\hat{p}_2$ for sample 1 and sample 2 respectively. Subtracting these two sample proportions, we have $\hat{p}_1 - \hat{p}_2$ **which represents the difference between the sample proportions**. *This difference will be negative if the sample proportion from population one $\hat{p}_1$ is smaller than the sample proportion from population two $\hat{p}_2$, and positive if $\hat{p}_1$ is larger than $\hat{p}_2$.* Theoretically, if we continue this process of randomly selecting an independent sample from each of the two populations and calculating the difference between the sample proportions $\hat{p}_1 - \hat{p}_2$, then the distribution of **all the possible sample differences of $\hat{p}_1 - \hat{p}_2$** represents the **Distribution of the Difference Between Two Sample Proportions** or simply the *Sampling Distribution of the Difference Between Two Proportions*. This concept is illustrated at the bottom of Figure 12.1.

Since it is impossible or impractical to construct such a Sampling Distribution of the Difference Between Two Proportions, this sampling distribution is a *theoretical probability distribution* which relates the value of each possible difference $\hat{p}_1 - \hat{p}_2$ to the probability that such a difference will occur. Since, in practice, only one sample will be randomly selected from each population, and it is impossible to construct this theoretical sampling distribution, we must rely on statisticians to provide us with the necessary theorems to completely describe the essential characteristics of this sampling distribution. These theorems will help us to determine the shape, mean and standard deviation of the Sampling Distribution of the Difference Between Two Proportions. The first theorem will discuss the

Population 1

p_1
(proportion for population 1)

The Sampling Distribution of the
Proportion for population 1

represents all the possible values
of $\hat{p}_1$ (sample proportions) selected from
population 1

Population 2

p_2
(proportion for population 2)

The Sampling Distribution of the
Proportion for population 2

represents all the possible values
of $\hat{p}_2$ (sample proportions) selected from
population 2

Sampling Distribution of the Difference Between Two Proportions
represents all the possible values of $\hat{p}_1 - \hat{p}_2$
(the difference between two sample proportions) where:
$\hat{p}_1$ = proportion of sample 1 and $\hat{p}_2$ = proportion of sample 2. That is:
all the possible differences between the sample proportions are:

$$d = \hat{p}_1 - \hat{p}_2$$

$$d_1 = \hat{p}_1 - \hat{p}_2$$
$$d_2 = \hat{p}_1 - \hat{p}_2$$
$$d_3 = \hat{p}_1 - \hat{p}_2$$
$$\vdots$$

Sampling Distribution of the Difference Between Two Proportions

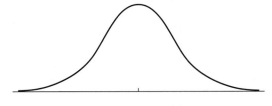

FIGURE 12.1

shape of the Sampling Distribution of $\hat{p}_1 - \hat{p}_2$, while the second theorem will provide us with formulas
to compute the mean and standard deviation of the Sampling Distribution of $\hat{p}_1 - \hat{p}_2$.

As mentioned in Chapter 10, *when sampling from one population, the Sampling Distribution of
The Proportion is approximately normal when the sample size n is large. A sample is defined to be
large when both:*

np is greater than 5
and
n(1 - p) is greater than 5.

In the case of sampling from two populations, *the Sampling Distribution of The Difference Between Two Proportions is approximately normal when the independent random sample selected from each of the two populations are both large*. Therefore, in the case of two samples, **both samples are considered to be large if the quantities n_1p_1, $n_1(1-p_1)$, n_2p_2 and $n_2(1-p_2)$ are all greater than 5.** Theorem 12.1 describes the shape of the Sampling Distribution of The Difference Between Two Proportions for large samples.

Theorem 12.1. Shape of the Sampling Distribution of The Difference Between Two Proportions For Large Samples.

If an independent random sample of size n_1 is selected from population 1 having a proportion p_1 and an independent random sample of size n_2 is selected from population 2 having a proportion p_2, then the Sampling Distribution of The Difference Between Two Proportions is approximately a normal distribution when both samples are large. (That is, when the quantities n_1p_1, $n_1(1-p_1)$, n_2p_2 and $n_2(1-p_2)$ are all greater than 5.)

Theorem 12.2 discusses the formulas to compute the mean and standard deviation of the Sampling Distribution of $\hat{p}_1 - \hat{p}_2$.

Theorem 12.2. Characteristics of the Sampling Distribution of The Difference Between Two Proportions.

Given two populations, referred to as population 1 and population 2, having proportions p_1 and p_2 respectively. If a large independent random sample of size n_1 is selected from population 1 and a second large independent random sample of size n_2 is selected from population 2, then the Sampling Distribution of The Difference Between Two Proportions has the following characteristics.

1. The **mean** of the Sampling Distribution of the Difference Between Two Proportions, denoted by $\mu_{\hat{p}_1-\hat{p}_2}$, is:

$$\mu_{\hat{p}_1-\hat{p}_2} = p_1 - p_2$$

2. The **standard deviation** of the Sampling Distribution of the Difference Between Two Proportions or commonly called the **standard error** of the difference between two proportions, denoted by $\sigma_{\hat{p}_1-\hat{p}_2}$, is:

$$\sigma_{\hat{p}_1-\hat{p}_2} = \sqrt{\frac{(p_1)(1-p_1)}{n_1} + \frac{(p_2)(1-p_2)}{n_2}}$$

■
EXAMPLE 12.2

Based upon the latest Census Bureau's information, 70% of single women who are the heads of households own a car while 82% of households headed by single men own cars. Assuming the Census Bureau's percentages represent the proportions of the indicated populations and if an independent random sample of 1800 households is selected from each population, then:

a)   define the two populations, and the proportions of these populations.
     Determine the:
b)   shape of the Sampling Distribution of $\hat{p}_1 - \hat{p}_2$
c)   mean of the Sampling Distribution of $\hat{p}_1 - \hat{p}_2$
d)   standard deviation of the Sampling Distribution of $\hat{p}_1 - \hat{p}_2$
e)   standard error of the difference between two proportions

Solution

a)   We will define the population of households headed by single women as population 1 while the population of households headed by single men will be defined as population 2. According to the Census Bureau, the proportion of single women car owners who serve as the head of a household is 70%. This percentage refers to population 1 and is denoted as $p_1 = 0.70$. While the proportion of single men car owners who head a household is 82%. This percentage refers to population 2 and is symbolized as $p_2 = 0.82$.

b)   The shape of the Sampling Distribution of $\hat{p}_1 - \hat{p}_2$ is dependent upon the size of the two samples selected. For population 1, we have a population proportion of $p_1 = 0.70$ and a sample size of $n_1 = 1800$, while for population 2, we have a population proportion of $p_2 = 0.82$ and a sample size of $n_2 = 1800$.

To determine if the two samples are large, we need to determine if:

$$n_1 p_1, \ n_1(1\text{-}p_1), \ n_2 p_2 \text{ and } n_2(1\text{-}p_2)$$
are all greater than 5.

For population 1, we have:
$n_1 p_1 = (1800)(0.70) = 1260$,
and
$n_1(1 - p_1) = (1800)(1 - 0.70) = (1800)(0.30) = 540$,
which are both greater than 5.

For population 2, we have:
$n_2 p_2 = (1800)(0.82) = 1476$,
and
$n_2(1 - p_2) = (1800)(1 - 0.82) = (1800)(0.18) = 324$,
which are also both greater than 5.

According to Theorem 12.1, since the quantities $n_1 p_1$, $n_1(1\text{-}p_1)$, $n_2 p_2$ and $n_2(1\text{-}p_2)$ are all greater than 5, then **the two samples are large** and **the Sampling Distribution of the Difference Between Two Proportions is approximately a normal distribution**.

c)   According to Theorem 12.2, the mean of the Sampling Distribution of $\hat{p}_1 - \hat{p}_2$, denoted by $\mu_{\hat{p}_1 - \hat{p}_2}$, is determined by the formula:

$$\mu_{\hat{p}_1 - \hat{p}_2} = p_1 - p_2.$$

For population 1, the proportion is $p_1 = 0.70$, while for population 2, the proportion is $p_2 = 0.82$, thus the mean of the Sampling Distribution of $\hat{p}_1 - \hat{p}_2$ is:

$$\mu_{\hat{p}_1 - \hat{p}_2} = 0.70 - 0.82$$

$$\mu_{\hat{p}_1 - \hat{p}_2} = -0.12.$$

d) Using Theorem 12.2, the **standard deviation** of the Sampling Distribution of $\hat{p}_1 - \hat{p}_2$, denoted by $\sigma_{\hat{p}_1 - \hat{p}_2}$, is computed using the formula:

$$\sigma_{\hat{p}_1 - \hat{p}_2} = \sqrt{\frac{(p_1)(1-p_1)}{n_1} + \frac{(p_2)(1-p_2)}{n_2}}.$$

For population 1, the proportion is $p_1 = 0.70$ and the sample size is $n_1 = 1800$, while for population 2, the proportion is $p_2 = 0.82$, and the sample size is $n_2 = 1800$. Substituting these values into the formula for the standard deviation, we have:

$$\sigma_{\hat{p}_1 - \hat{p}_2} = \sqrt{\frac{(p_1)(1-p_1)}{n_1} + \frac{(p_2)(1-p_2)}{n_2}}$$

$$\sigma_{\hat{p}_1 - \hat{p}_2} = \sqrt{\frac{(0.70)(1-0.70)}{1800} + \frac{(0.82)(1-0.82)}{1800}}$$

$$\sigma_{\hat{p}_1 - \hat{p}_2} = \sqrt{\frac{(0.21)}{1800} + \frac{(0.1476)}{1800}}$$

$$\sigma_{\hat{p}_1 - \hat{p}_2} = \sqrt{\frac{0.3576}{1800}}$$

$$\sigma_{\hat{p}_1 - \hat{p}_2} = \sqrt{0.000198621}$$

$$\sigma_{\hat{p}_1 - \hat{p}_2} \approx 0.0141$$

e) The standard error of the difference between two proportions is equal to the standard deviation of the Sampling Distribution of $\hat{p}_1 - \hat{p}_2$. Therefore, the standard error is:

$$\sigma_{\hat{p}_1 - \hat{p}_2} \approx 0.0141. \qquad \blacksquare$$

In most practical applications, **the true population proportions p_1 and p_2 are not known**. When the population proportions are unknown, the standard error of the difference between two proportions cannot be calculated. In these instances, a large independent sample is selected from each population and the sample proportions $\hat{p}_1$ and $\hat{p}_2$ are computed. The sample proportion $\hat{p}_1$ will serve as an **estimate** for the population proportion p_1 while the sample proportion $\hat{p}_2$ will serve as an **estimate** for the population proportion p_2. Hence, within the formula for the standard error, the sample proportion $\hat{p}_1$ replaces p_1 while the sample proportion $\hat{p}_2$ replaces p_2. Thus, the formula for the estimated value of the standard error becomes:

$$\sqrt{\frac{(\hat{p}_1)(1-\hat{p}_1)}{n_1} + \frac{(\hat{p}_2)(1-\hat{p}_2)}{n_2}}$$

This formula is called *the **estimate** of the standard error of the difference between two proportions* and is symbolized as $s_{\hat{p}_1 - \hat{p}_2}$.

**Formula for the Estimate of the Standard Error
of the Difference Between Two Proportions**

When the population proportions are not known, the formula for **the estimate of the standard error of the difference between two proportions** is used. The *estimate of the standard error,* symbolized by $s_{\hat{p}_1-\hat{p}_2}$, is:

$$s_{\hat{p}_1-\hat{p}_2} = \sqrt{\frac{(\hat{p}_1)(1-\hat{p}_1)}{n_1} + \frac{(\hat{p}_2)(1-\hat{p}_2)}{n_2}}$$

■
E X A M P L E   1 2 . 3

In an opinion poll of 750 U.S. adults, 54% of the men and 47% of the women said there would be less crime if more parents spanked their children. Assuming that there were 340 men and 410 women sampled in this poll, answer the following questions:
a) identify the two population proportions
b) state the sample proportions
c) compute the estimate of the standard error of the difference between two proportions
d) compute the estimate of the standard deviation of the Sampling Distribution of the Difference Between Two Proportions

Solution:

a) Of the two populations identified within this poll, *one proportion represents all U.S men who believe there would be less crime if more parents spanked their children,* while *the second proportion represents all U.S. women who believe there would be less crime if more parents spanked their children.*

b) If we let the sample proportion of U.S. men who believe there would be less crime if more parents spanked their children equal $\hat{p}_1$, then $\hat{p}_1 = 0.54$. If the sample proportion of U.S. women who believe there would be less crime if more parents spanked their children is $\hat{p}_2$, then $\hat{p}_2 = 0.47$.

c) Since the population proportions are not known, we must estimate the standard error of the difference between two proportions using the formula:

$$s_{\hat{p}_1-\hat{p}_2} = \sqrt{\frac{(\hat{p}_1)(1-\hat{p}_1)}{n_1} + \frac{(\hat{p}_2)(1-\hat{p}_2)}{n_2}}$$

Letting the men represent population 1, then the sample of 340 men has $\hat{p}_1 = 0.54$ and $n_1 = 340$. For the population of women, the sample of 410 women has $\hat{p}_2 = 0.47$ and $n_2 = 410$.
Substituting this sample information into the formula for $s_{\hat{p}_1-\hat{p}_2}$, we have:

$$s_{\hat{p}_1-\hat{p}_2} = \sqrt{\frac{(\hat{p}_1)(1-\hat{p}_1)}{n_1} + \frac{(\hat{p}_2)(1-\hat{p}_2)}{n_2}}$$

$$s_{\hat{p}_1-\hat{p}_2} = \sqrt{\frac{(0.54)(1-0.54)}{340} + \frac{(0.47)(1-0.47)}{410}}$$

$$s_{\hat{p}_1 - \hat{p}_2} = \sqrt{\frac{(0.54)(0.46)}{340} + \frac{(0.47)(0.53)}{410}}$$

$$s_{\hat{p}_1 - \hat{p}_2} = \sqrt{\frac{0.2484}{340} + \frac{0.2491}{410}}$$

$$s_{\hat{p}_1 - \hat{p}_2} = \sqrt{0.0007305 + 0.0006075}$$

$$s_{\hat{p}_1 - \hat{p}_2} = \sqrt{0.0013380}$$

$$s_{\hat{p}_1 - \hat{p}_2} \approx 0.0366.$$

Thus, the estimate of the standard error of the difference between two proportions is approximately 0.0366.

d)   The estimate of the standard deviation of the Sampling Distribution of the Difference Between Two Proportions is equal to the estimate of the standard error of the difference between two proportions. Thus, the estimate of the standard deviation of the sampling distribution is:

$$s_{\hat{p}_1 - \hat{p}_2} = 0.0366.$$

12.3   HYPOTHESIS TESTING INVOLVING TWO POPULATION PROPORTIONS USING LARGE SAMPLES

Within this section, we will discuss the procedure to perform a hypothesis test involving two population proportions using a large independent random sample selected from each population. This procedure involves the general 5-step procedure initially discussed in Chapter 10. To perform this hypothesis test involving two population proportions, a large independent random sample from each of the two populations is selected. The difference between the sample proportions, $\hat{p}_1 - \hat{p}_2$, is computed. If the difference between the sample proportions, $\hat{p}_1 - \hat{p}_2$, is statistically significant then we will conclude that the two population proportions are statistically different. To determine if the difference between the two sample proportions, $\hat{p}_1 - \hat{p}_2$ is large enough to indicate that the two population proportions are statistically different, we will use the Sampling Distribution of $\hat{p}_1 - \hat{p}_2$ as the hypothesis testing model.

Let's now examine the hypothesis testing procedure involving the difference between the proportions of two populations.

Hypothesis Testing Procedure Involving the Difference Between the Proportions of Two Populations for Large Samples

Step 1   Formulate the two hypotheses: H_0 and H_a.
  In most hypothesis tests involving a comparison of two population proportions, the **null hypothesis assumes that the difference between the population proportions is equal to zero**. That is, *there is no difference between the proportions of the two populations*. In such hypothesis tests, the null hypothesis, **H_0,** has the following form:

Null Hypothesis Form

H_0: There is *no difference* between the proportion of population 1, written p_1, and the proportion of population 2, written p_2.

The null hypothesis is symbolized as:

$$H_0: p_1 - p_2 = 0$$

By stating the null hypothesis, H_0, as *there is no difference between the population proportions, p_1 and p_2, we are making the assumption that p_1 equals p_2*. Consequently, only by rejecting the null hypothesis, H_0, can we conclude that there is a *statistically significant difference* between the two population proportions: p_1 and p_2. Therefore, *by rejecting H_0, we may conclude one of the three possible forms of the alternative hypothesis*:

a) The *difference* between the proportion of population 1, p_1, and the proportion of population 2, p_2, *is less than zero.*

b) The *difference* between the proportion of population 1, p_1, and the proportion of population 2, p_2, *is greater than zero.*

c) The *difference* between the proportion of population 1, p_1, and the proportion of population 2, p_2, *is not equal to zero.*

Consequently, the statement and symbolic representation for each of the three types of alternative hypothesis forms when testing the difference between two population proportions are:

Alternative Hypothesis Forms

Less Than Form	Greater Than Form	Not Equal To Form
H_a: the proportion of population 1, p_1, is *less than* the proportion of population 2, p_2.	H_a: the proportion of population 1, p_1, is *greater than* the proportion of population 2, p_2.	H_a: the proportion of of population 1, p_1, is not equal to the proportion of population 2, p_2.
This form is symbolized as:	This form is symbolized as:	This is form symbolized as:
$H_a: p_1 - p_2 < 0.$	$H_a: p_1 - p_2 > 0.$	$H_a: p_1 - p_2 \neq 0.$
That is, the *difference $p_1 - p_2$ is significantly less than zero.*	That is, the *difference $p_1 - p_2$ is significantly greater than zero.*	That is, the *difference $p_1 - p_2$ is significantly different than zero.*

Step 2   Determine the model to test the null hypothesis, H_0. Under the assumption H_0 is true, determine the expected results of the Sampling Distribution of $\hat{p}_1 - \hat{p}_2$.

Since the difference between the two sample proportions, $\hat{p}_1 - \hat{p}_2$, is used to determine if $p_1 - p_2$ is significantly different from zero we will use *the Sampling Distribution of The Difference Between Two Proportions, or **the Sampling Distribution of $\hat{p}_1 - \hat{p}_2$** as our hypothesis testing model.

To determine the **expected results** of the sampling distribution, we must identify **the shape** and calculate **the mean and standard error** of the Sampling Distribution of $\hat{p}_1 - \hat{p}_2$. For large samples, Theorem 12.1 states that *the shape of the Sampling Distribution of $\hat{p}_1 - \hat{p}_2$ is approximately a normal distribution* (i.e. the quantities $n_1\hat{p}_1$, $n_1(1-\hat{p}_1)$, $n_2\hat{p}_2$ and $n_2(1-\hat{p}_2)$ are all greater than 5).

The mean of the Sampling Distribution of $\hat{p}_1 - \hat{p}_2$ is defined by the formula: $\mu_{\hat{p}_1 - \hat{p}_2} = p_1 - p_2$, according to Theorem 12.2. Under the assumption that the null hypothesis, H_0, is true, the difference between the population proportions is zero (i.e. $p_1 - p_2 = 0$). Thus, *the mean of the Sampling Distribution, $\mu_{\hat{p}_1 - \hat{p}_2}$, of $\hat{p}_1 - \hat{p}_2$ is equal to zero*. That is, assuming H_0 is true, we have:

$$\mu_{\hat{p}_1 - \hat{p}_2} = p_1 - p_2$$

$$\mu_{\hat{p}_1 - \hat{p}_2} = 0$$

From Theorem 12.2, the *estimate of the standard error of the Sampling Distribution, $s_{\hat{p}_1 - \hat{p}_2}$, of $\hat{p}_1 - \hat{p}_2$* is given by:

$$s_{\hat{p}_1 - \hat{p}_2} = \sqrt{\frac{(\hat{p}_1)(1-\hat{p}_1)}{n_1} + \frac{(\hat{p}_2)(1-\hat{p}_2)}{n_2}}$$

Again using the assumption that the null hypothesis, H_0, is true we are assuming that there is *no difference between the population proportions p_1 and p_2, or* $\mathbf{p_1 - p_2 = 0}$. Thus, it follows that $p_1 = p_2$ when H_0 is true. Whenever we make the assumption that H_0 is true, we are assuming we have **a common population proportion value**. *p will be used to symbolize this common value of p_1 and p_2, that is:* $p_1 = p_2 = p$. Thus, *p represents the proportion of successes common to both populations.*

However, this common hypothesized population proportion p is unknown, since the population values of p_1 and p_2 are unknown. Each of these population values p_1 and p_2 must be approximated by the sample statistics $\hat{p}_1$ and $\hat{p}_2$. Consequently, we will use the sample information collected from both populations to obtain the *best estimate for the common population proportion value, p.* If we denote this *best estimate for the value of p,* by $\hat{p}$, then the formula used to compute $\hat{p}$, is determined by **pooling (i.e. combining) the sample information collected from both populations**. This *pooled formula is referred to as the pooled sample proportion and is denoted by $\hat{p}$.* The value for this pooled sample proportion can be determined by using one of the following formulas, depending upon the sample information available.

Formulas for the Pooled Sample Proportion, $\hat{p}$: The Best Estimate for the Common Population Proportion Value

$$\hat{p} = \frac{x_1 + x_2}{n_1 + n_2} \quad or \quad \hat{p} = \frac{n_1\hat{p}_1 + n_2\hat{p}_2}{n_1 + n_2}$$

where:
$\hat{p}$ is the pooled sample proportion (the best estimate for common population proportion)
$\hat{p}_1$ = sample proportion selected from population 1.
x_1 = number of successes within the sample selected from population 1.
n_1 = size of sample selected from population 1.
$\hat{p}_2$ = sample proportion selected from population 2.
x_2 = number of successes within the sample selected from population 2.
n_2 = size of sample selected from population 2.

Substituting the *pooled sample proportion result, $\hat{p}$,* into the formula for the estimated standard error of the difference between two proportions, we obtain **the pooled formula for the estimated**

standard error of the Sampling Distribution of $\hat{p}_1 - \hat{p}_2$, $s_{\hat{p}_1 - \hat{p}_2}$. Under the assumption that the null hypothesis, H_0, is true (i.e. $p_1 - p_2 = 0$), then the pooled formula for the estimated standard error of the Sampling Distribution of $\hat{p}_1 - \hat{p}_2$, denoted by $s_{\hat{p}_1 - \hat{p}_2}$, is determined by the following formula.

Pooled Formula for the Estimated Standard Error of the Sampling Distribution of $\hat{p}_1 - \hat{p}_2$, $s_{\hat{p}_1 - \hat{p}_2}$:

$$s_{\hat{p}_1 - \hat{p}_2} = \sqrt{\frac{\hat{p}(1-\hat{p})}{n_1} + \frac{\hat{p}(1-\hat{p})}{n_2}}$$

or

$$s_{\hat{p}_1 - \hat{p}_2} = \sqrt{\hat{p}(1-\hat{p})\left(\frac{1}{n_1} + \frac{1}{n_2}\right)}$$

where: $\hat{p}$ is the proportion obtained by combining both samples and is computed using one of the following formulas:

$$\hat{p} = \frac{x_1 + x_2}{n_1 + n_2} \quad or \quad \hat{p} = \frac{n_1 \hat{p}_1 + n_2}{n_1 + n_2}$$

Thus, for a large sample hypothesis test involving two population proportions, **the expected results of the Sampling Distribution of $\hat{p}_1 - \hat{p}_2$,** are summarized as follows.

The Expected Results of the Sampling Distribution of $\hat{p}_1 - \hat{p}_2$ Under the Assumption That H_0 Is True

1. *The shape of the sampling distribution is approximately a normal distribution for large samples.*
2. *The mean of the Sampling Distribution of $\hat{p}_1 - \hat{p}_2$ is equal to zero.* That is:

$$\mu_{\hat{p}_1 - \hat{p}_2} = p_1 - p_2 = 0$$

3. *The pooled formula for the estimate of the standard error of the Sampling Distribution of $\hat{p}_1 - \hat{p}_2$,*

    is:

$$s_{\hat{p}_1 - \hat{p}_2} = \sqrt{\frac{\hat{p}(1-\hat{p})}{n_1} + \frac{\hat{p}(1-\hat{p})}{n_2}}$$

or

$$s_{\hat{p}_1 - \hat{p}_2} = \sqrt{\hat{p}(1-\hat{p})\left(\frac{1}{n_1} + \frac{1}{n_2}\right)}$$

where

$$\hat{p} = \frac{x_1 + x_2}{n_1 + n_2} \quad or \quad \hat{p} = \frac{n_1 \hat{p}_1 + n_2}{n_1 + n_2}$$

The expected results are shown in Figure 12.2.

The Expected Results of the Sampling Distribution of $\hat{p}_1 - \hat{p}_2$

The Sampling Distribution of $\hat{p}_1 - \hat{p}_2$ is approximately normal for large samples.

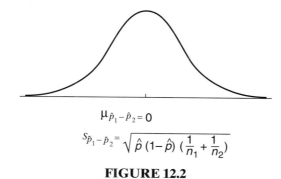

$$\mu_{\hat{p}_1 - \hat{p}_2} = 0$$

$$s_{\hat{p}_1 - \hat{p}_2} = \sqrt{\hat{p}(1-\hat{p})\left(\frac{1}{n_1} + \frac{1}{n_2}\right)}$$

FIGURE 12.2

Step 3   Formulate the decision rule.
a)   Determine the type of alternative hypothesis: *directional H_a or non-directional H_a.*
b)   Determine the type of test: *ITT or 2TT.*
c)   Identify the significance level: $\alpha = 1\%$ *or* $\alpha = 5\%$.
d)   Find the critical z score(s).
e)   Construct the appropriate hypothesis test model.
f)   State the decision rule.

Step 4   Analyze the sample data.
Randomly select a large sample from each population, and determine the proportion for each sample, denoted $\hat{p}_1$ and $\hat{p}_2$. *Calculate the z score of the difference between the two sample proportions using the formula:* $z = \dfrac{(\hat{p}_1 - \hat{p}_2) - \mu_{\hat{p}_1 - \hat{p}_2}}{s_{\hat{p}_1 - \hat{p}_2}}$. This is referred to as the test statistic.

Step 5   State the conclusion.
Compare the test statistic to the critical z score(s), z_c, of the decision rule and draw one of the following conclusions:

Conclusion (a)	or	*Conclusion (b)*
Reject H_0 and		*Fail to Reject H_0*
Accept H_a at α		*at α*

In summary, the procedure just outlined to perform a hypothesis test involving two population proportions for large samples included three refinements to the general hypothesis testing procedure developed in Chapter 9. These refinements were:

1.   The appropriate hypothesis testing model is the Sampling Distribution of the Difference Between Two Proportions or the Sampling Distribution of $\hat{p}_1 - \hat{p}_2$.
2.   Under the assumption that the null hypothesis, **H₀**, is true, the expected results of the Sampling Distribution of $\hat{p}_1 - \hat{p}_2$ are:
a)   *The shape of the sampling distribution is approximately a normal distribution for large samples.*
b)   *The mean of the Sampling Distribution of $\hat{p}_1 - \hat{p}_2$ is equal to zero.* That is:

$$\mu_{\hat{p}_1 - \hat{p}_2} = p_1 - p_2 = 0$$

c) *The pooled formula for the standard error of the Sampling Distribution of $\hat{p}_1 - \hat{p}_2$, $s_{\hat{p}_1 - \hat{p}_2}$, is:*

$$s_{\hat{p}_1 - \hat{p}_2} = \sqrt{\frac{\hat{p}(1-\hat{p})}{n_1} + \frac{\hat{p}(1-\hat{p})}{n_2}}$$

or

$$s_{\hat{p}_1 - \hat{p}_2} = \sqrt{\hat{p}(1-\hat{p})\left(\frac{1}{n_1} + \frac{1}{n_2}\right)}$$

3. The formula used to calculate the test statistic is:

$$z = \frac{(\hat{p}_1 - \hat{p}_2) - \mu_{\hat{p}_1 - \hat{p}_2}}{s_{\hat{p}_1 - \hat{p}_2}}.$$

Example 12.4 illustrates the use of the hypothesis testing procedure to perform a hypothesis test involving two population proportions.

PLEASE NOTE: FOR CHAPTER 12, ALL CALCULATIONS WILL BE ROUNDED OFF TO FOUR DECIMAL PLACES IN ALL THE EXAMPLES AND ANSWERS.

EXAMPLE 12.4

According to the Center for Disease Control and Prevention, a random survey of 1500 American men indicated that 435 smoke while a random sample of 1450 American women showed that 363 women smoke.

Perform a hypothesis test at $\alpha = 5\%$ to answer the question:

Is the proportion of U.S. men that smoke significantly greater than the proportion of U.S. women that smoke?

Solution

Step 1   Formulate the null hypothesis, H_o, and the alternative hypothesis, H_a.

If we let population 1 represent American men while population 2 represents American women, then the null hypothesis can be stated as:

H_o: There is **no difference** in the population proportion of American men who smoke and the population proportion of American women who smoke.

In symbols, we state the null hypothesis as:

H_o: $p_1 - p_2 = 0$.

Since we are trying to determine if there is a ***greater*** *proportion of American males who smoke than females who smoke* then the alternative hypothesis is *directional* and is stated using a *greater than* statement. Consequently, the alternative hypothesis can be stated as:

H_a: The population proportion of American men who smoke is greater than the population proportion of American women who smoke.

The alternative hypothesis is symbolized as:

H_a: $p_1 - p_2 > 0$.

Step 2   Determine the model to test the null hypothesis, H_o. Under the assumption H_o is true, determine the expected results of the Sampling Distribution of $\hat{p}_1 - \hat{p}_2$.

To test the null hypothesis, a large random independent sample was selected from each population and the sample results are summarized in Table 12.3.

TABLE 12.3

Population 1 represents **American men who smoke**	**Population 2 represents** **American women who smoke**
Sample information: $x_1 = 435$ $n_1 = 1500$	Sample information: $x_2 = 363$ $n_2 = 1450$

In conducting this hypothesis test, we will need to compute the difference between the two sample proportions, $\hat{p}_1 - \hat{p}_2$, to determine if this difference is *significantly greater than zero*. Consequently, we will use the **Sampling Distribution of** $\hat{p}_1 - \hat{p}_2$ as the hypothesis testing model when conducting this hypothesis test. To determine the expected results of the Sampling Distribution of $\hat{p}_1 - \hat{p}_2$, we need to use Theorems 12.1 and 12.2. Under the assumption that **H_0 is true**, we have the following expected results:

The Expected Results of the Sampling Distribution of $\hat{p}_1 - \hat{p}_2$

1. *The shape of the sampling distribution is approximately a normal distribution for large samples.*
2. *The mean of the Sampling Distribution of $\hat{p}_1 - \hat{p}_2$ is equal to zero since we are assuming that H_0 is true.*
   That is:

$$\mu_{\hat{p}_1 - \hat{p}_2} = p_1 - p_2 = 0$$

3. *To find the estimate of the standard error of the Sampling Distribution of $\hat{p}_1 - \hat{p}_2$, $s_{\hat{p}_1 - \hat{p}_2}$, we must* first compute the pooled sample proportion, $\hat{p}$. Under the assumption that H_0 is true, i.e. p_1 equals p_2, the pooled sample proportion, $\hat{p}$, is determined by **combining (i.e. pooling) the sample information collected from both populations**.

We will use the formula: $\hat{p} = \dfrac{x_1 + x_2}{n_1 + n_2}$ since we have the values $x_1 = 435$, $n_1 = 1500$, $x_2 = 363$ and n_2 = 1450. The pooled sample proportion value, $\hat{p}$, is:

$$\hat{p} = \frac{435 + 363}{1500 + 1450} = \frac{798}{2950}$$

$$\hat{p} = 0.2705 \text{ (rounded off to 4 decimal places)}$$

Substituting this pooled sample proportion result:
$\hat{p} \approx 0.2705$, the sample size for sample one: $n_1 = 1500$, and the sample size for sample two: $n_2 = 1450$ into the formula for the **pooled estimate of the standard error** of the Sampling Distribution of The Difference Between Two Proportions:

$$s_{\hat{p}_1 - \hat{p}_2} = \sqrt{\hat{p}(1 - \hat{p})\left(\frac{1}{n_1} + \frac{1}{n_2}\right)}, \text{ the \textbf{pooled estimate of the standard error} equals:}$$

$$s_{\hat{p}_1 - \hat{p}_2} = \sqrt{(0.2705)(1 - 0.2705)\left(\frac{1}{1500} + \frac{1}{1450}\right)}$$

$$s_{\hat{p}_1 - \hat{p}_2} = \sqrt{(0.2705)(0.7295)\left(\frac{1}{1500} + \frac{1}{1450}\right)}$$

$$s_{\hat{p}_1 - \hat{p}_2} = \sqrt{(0.2705)(0.7295)(0.0013562)}$$

$$s_{\hat{p}_1-\hat{p}_2} = \sqrt{0.0002676}$$

$$s_{\hat{p}_1-\hat{p}_2} \approx 0.0164 \text{ (rounded off to 4 decimal places)}$$

Thus, the **pooled estimate of the standard error** of the Sampling Distribution of The Difference Between Two Proportions is: $s_{\hat{p}_1-\hat{p}_2} \approx 0.0164$.

In summary, the Sampling Distribution of $\hat{p}_1 - \hat{p}_2$ will serve as our hypothesis testing model with the following expected results:

1. the Sampling Distribution can be approximated by the normal distribution for large samples.
2. the mean of the Sampling Distribution of $\hat{p}_1 - \hat{p}_2$ is:

$$\mu_{\hat{p}_1-\hat{p}_2} = 0$$

3. the pooled estimate of the standard error, $s_{\hat{p}_1-\hat{p}_2}$, is:

$$s_{\hat{p}_1-\hat{p}_2} \approx 0.0164$$

This hypothesis testing model is illustrated in Figure 12.3.

The Sampling Distribution of $\hat{p}_1 - \hat{p}_2$ is the hypothesis testing model and is approximately a normal distribution.

$$\mu_{\hat{p}_1-\hat{p}_2} = 0$$
$$s_{\hat{p}_1-\hat{p}_2} \approx 0.0164$$

FIGURE 12.3

Step 3   Formulate the decision rule.
  a) The alternative hypothesis is directional since we are trying to determine if the proportion of American men who smoke is *greater than* the proportion of American women who smoke.
  b) The type of hypothesis test is one-tailed on the right side.
  c) The significance level is: $\alpha = 5\%$.
  d) To find the critical score, z_c, use TABLE II. For a one-tailed test on the right side with $\alpha = 5\%$, the critical z score, z_c, is: $z_c = 1.65$.
  e) Figure 12.4 illustrates the decision rule for this hypothesis test.
  f) Thus, *the decision rule* is: **Reject H_0 if the test statistic is greater than 1.65.**

Step 4   Analyze the sample data.
  Collect the sample data and calculate the test statistic using the formula: $z = \dfrac{(\hat{p}_1 - \hat{p}_2) - \mu_{\hat{p}_1-\hat{p}_2}}{s_{\hat{p}_1-\hat{p}_2}}$.

To determine the test statistic, we must first determine the values of $\hat{p}_1$ and $\hat{p}_2$.

$$\hat{p}_1 = \frac{435}{1500} \quad \text{and} \quad \hat{p}_2 = \frac{363}{1450}$$

$$\hat{p}_1 \approx 0.29 \quad \text{and} \quad \hat{p}_2 \approx 0.2503$$

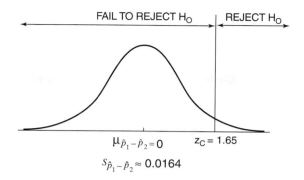

FIGURE 12.4

Thus, the difference between the sample proportions is:

$$\hat{p}_1 - \hat{p}_2 = 0.29 - 0.2503$$

$$\hat{p}_1 - \hat{p}_2 = 0.0397$$

Since $\mu_{\hat{p}_1 - \hat{p}_2} = 0$ and $s_{\hat{p}_1 - \hat{p}_2} \approx 0.0164$ the test statistic is:

$$z = \frac{0.0397 - 0}{0.0164}$$

$$z \approx 2.42.$$

Step 5   State the conclusion.
Since the test statistic, $z \approx 2.42$, is greater than the critical z score, $z_c = 1.65$, our conclusion is reject H_0 and accept H_a at $\alpha = 5\%$. Therefore, *we can conclude that the proportion of American men who smoke is significantly greater than the proportion of American women who smoke.*

In Example 12.4, we considered a directional hypothesis test. We will now consider a nondirectional hypothesis test in Example 12.5. Within this example, we will use the formula

$$\hat{p} = \frac{n_1\hat{p}_1 + n_2}{n_1 + n_2}\text{ to estimate the pooled proportion value, } \hat{p}.$$

EXAMPLE 12.5

According to a recent survey released by the National Highway Traffic and Safety Administration, 63% of women drivers use their seat belts while 60% of men drivers wear seat belts. Assume these estimates are based upon a random sample of 1150 women drivers and 1350 male drivers.
Perform a hypothesis test at $\alpha = 1\%$ to determine if there is a significant difference between the proportion of men drivers and the proportion of women drivers who use seat belts.

Solution:

Step 1   Formulate the null hypothesis, H_0, and the alternative hypothesis, H_a.
If we let population 1 be the women drivers and population 2 be the men drivers then the null hypothesis is:

H_0: *There is no difference in the population proportion of women drivers who use seat belts and the population proportion of men drivers who use seat belts.*

In symbols, we have:

H_0: $p_1 - p_2 = 0$.

Since we are interested in determining if there is a significant difference in the proportions for the two populations then the alternative hypothesis is nondirectional and is stated as:

H_a: There is a significant difference in the population proportion of women drivers who use seat belts and the population proportion of men drivers who use seat belts.

Symbolically, the alternative hypothesis is stated:

H_a: $p_1 - p_2 \neq 0$.

Step 2   Determine the model to test the null hypothesis, H_0. Under the assumption H_0 is true, determine the expected results of the Sampling Distribution of $\hat{p}_1 - \hat{p}_2$.
　　　　　To test the null hypothesis, a random sample was selected from each population and the sample results are summarized in TABLE 12.4.

TABLE 12.4

Population 1: women drivers	Population 2: men drivers
Sample information: Sample size is: $n_1 = 1150$ Proportion of women drivers wearing seat belts is: $\hat{p}_1 = 0.63$	Sample information: Sample size is: $n_2 = 1350$ Proportion of men drivers wearing seat belts is: $\hat{p}_2 = 0.60$

To determine if we can infer that $p_1 - p_2$ is significantly different from zero, we will need to decide if the difference between the two sample proportions, $\hat{p}_1 - \hat{p}_2$, is significantly different from zero. This decision will be based on our hypothesis testing model: the Sampling Distribution of Difference Between Two Proportions. Since we are working with large samples, the **expected results of the Sampling Distribution of $\hat{p}_1 - \hat{p}_2$**, are calculated using Theorems 12.1 and 12.2. Using the assumption that **H_0 is true**, the characteristics of this sampling distribution are determined using the following expected results:

The Expected Results of the Sampling Distribution of $\hat{p}_1 - \hat{p}_2$

1. *The shape of the sampling distribution is approximately a normal distribution for large samples.*
2. *Assuming that H_0 is true, the mean of the Sampling Distribution of $\hat{p}_1 - \hat{p}_2$ is equal to zero.*

　　That is: $\mu_{\hat{p}_1 - \hat{p}_2} = p_1 - p_2 = 0$.

3. *Using the assumption that H_0 is true, the pooled formula for the estimate of the standard error of the sampling distribution of $\hat{p}_1 - \hat{p}_2$, $s_{\hat{p}_1 - \hat{p}_2}$, is found using the formula:*

$$s_{\hat{p}_1 - \hat{p}_2} = \sqrt{\hat{p}(1-\hat{p})\left(\frac{1}{n_1} + \frac{1}{n_2}\right)}$$

Under the assumption that H_0 is true, i.e. p_1 equals p_2, the pooled sample proportion, $\hat{p}$, is determined by **combining (i.e. pooling) the sample information collected from both populations** using the formula:

$$\hat{p} = \frac{n_1\hat{p}_1 + n_2\hat{p}_2}{n_1 + n_2}$$

Substituting the sample information, $n_1 = 1150$, $\hat{p}_1 = 0.63$, $n_2 = 1350$, and $\hat{p}_2 = 0.60$ into the pooled sample proportion formula we obtain:

$$\hat{p} = \frac{(1150)(0.63)+(1350)(0.60)}{1150+1350}$$

$$\hat{p} = \frac{724.5+810}{2500}$$

$$\hat{p} = \frac{1534.5}{2500}$$

$$\hat{p} = 0.6138$$

Using this pooled sample proportion result, $\hat{p} = 0.6138$, the **pooled estimate of the standard error** of the Sampling Distribution of The Difference Between Two Proportions is determined using the formula:

$$s_{\hat{p}_1-\hat{p}_2} = \sqrt{\hat{p}(1-\hat{p})\left(\frac{1}{n_1}+\frac{1}{n_2}\right)}.$$

Using the information: $\hat{p} = 0.6138$, $n_1 = 1150$, and $n_2 = 1350$, the **pooled estimate of the standard error** is:

$$s_{\hat{p}_1-\hat{p}_2} = \sqrt{(0.6138)(1-0.6138)\left(\frac{1}{1150}+\frac{1}{1350}\right)}$$

$$s_{\hat{p}_1-\hat{p}_2} = \sqrt{(0.6138)(0.3862)\left(\frac{1}{1150}+\frac{1}{1350}\right)}$$

$$s_{\hat{p}_1-\hat{p}_2} \approx \sqrt{(0.6138)(0.3862)(0.0016102)}$$

$$s_{\hat{p}_1-\hat{p}_2} \approx \sqrt{(0.0003928)}$$

$$s_{\hat{p}_1-\hat{p}_2} \approx 0.0195 \text{ (rounded off to 4 decimal places)}$$

Thus, the **pooled estimate of the standard error** of the Sampling Distribution of the difference between two proportions is:

$$s_{\hat{p}_1-\hat{p}_2} \approx 0.0195.$$

In summary, the Sampling Distribution of $\hat{p}_1 - \hat{p}_2$ will serve as our hypothesis testing model with the following expected results:

1. the Sampling Distribution can be approximated by the normal distribution for large samples.
2. the mean of the Sampling Distribution of $\hat{p}_1 - \hat{p}_2$ is:

$$\mu_{\hat{p}_1-\hat{p}_2} = 0.$$

3. the pooled estimate of the standard error, $s_{\hat{p}_1-\hat{p}_2}$, is:

$$s_{\hat{p}_1-\hat{p}_2} \approx 0.0195.$$

This hypothesis testing model is illustrated in Figure 12.5.

The Sampling Distribution of $\hat{p}_1 - \hat{p}_2$ is the hypothesis testing model and is approximately a normal distribution.

$\mu_{\hat{p}_1 - \hat{p}_2} = 0$

$s_{\hat{p}_1 - \hat{p}_2} \approx 0.0195$

FIGURE 12.5

Step 3   Formulate the decision rule.
    a) The alternative hypothesis is nondirectional because we are trying to determine if there is a **significant difference** between the proportion of women drivers and the proportion of men drivers who use seat belts.
    b) The type of hypothesis test is two-tailed (2TT).
    c) The significance level is: $\alpha = 1\%$.
    d) To find two critical z scores, z_{LC} and z_{RC}, use TABLE II. From TABLE II, the critical z scores for $\alpha = 1\%$ are:

$$z_{LC} = -2.58 \text{ and } z_{RC} = 2.58$$

    e) Figure 12.6 illustrates the decision rule for this hypothesis test.

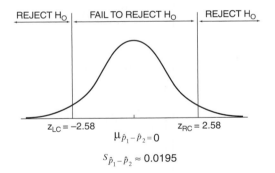

$z_{LC} = -2.58$ $z_{RC} = 2.58$

$\mu_{\hat{p}_1 - \hat{p}_2} = 0$

$s_{\hat{p}_1 - \hat{p}_2} \approx 0.0195$

FIGURE 12.6

    f) Thus, *the decision rule* is: **Reject H_0 if the test statistic is either less than –2.58 or greater than 2.58.**

Step 4   Analyze the sample data.
Collect the sample data and calculate the test statistic using the formula: $z = \dfrac{(\hat{p}_1 - \hat{p}_2) - \mu_{\hat{p}_1 - \hat{p}_2}}{s_{\hat{p}_1 - \hat{p}_2}}$.
The difference between the sample proportions is:

$$\hat{p}_1 - \hat{p}_2 = 0.63 - 0.60$$
$$\hat{p}_1 - \hat{p}_2 = 0.03.$$

Since $\mu_{\hat{p}_1 - \hat{p}_2} = 0$ and $s_{\hat{p}_1 - \hat{p}_2} \approx 0.0195$, the test statistic is:

$$z = \frac{0.03 - 0}{0.0195}$$

$$z \approx 1.54.$$

Step 5 State the conclusion.

Since the test statistic, $z \approx 1.54$, falls between the critical z scores, $z_{LC} = -2.58$ and $z_{RC} = 2.58$, our conclusion is fail to reject H_0 at $\alpha = 1\%$. Therefore, *we can conclude that there is no significant difference in the proportion of women drivers and the proportion of men drivers who wear seat belts at $\alpha = 1\%$.*

CASE STUDY 12.1

Examine the graphic entitled *'No' for Women in Combat* in Figure 12.7a. The Roper Organization surveyed 7,206 military men and women to determine their opinion of the Pentagon's policy of not assigning women to any direct combat position. Notice that results indicate that overall 57% favor the Pentagon's policy, 57% of the men are in agreement with the Pentagon's policy while only 42% of the women agree.

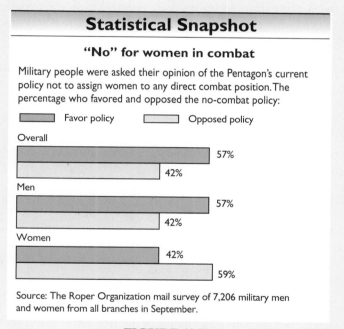

FIGURE 12.7a

a) In Figure 12.7a, is the sample data discrete or continuous? Does it represent a measurement or is it count data? Explain.

If we identify population 1 as the military men and population 2 represents the military women, then:

b) state the sample proportion of men and the sample proportion of women who favor the Pentagon's policy.

c) explain the relationship between the concept of a pooled sample proportion which was discussed in this section and the overall percentage favoring the policy reported in Figure 12.7a.

d) For this case study, assume that the number of men participating in the survey was 6,206 while the number of women polled was 1,000. Use these sample results and the sample proportion results of part (b) to compute the pooled sample proportion. How does this pooled sample result compare to the overall percentage value?

e) Using this information, perform a hypothesis test to determine if there is a significant difference in the proportion of men who favor the policy and the proportion of women who favor the policy at $\alpha = 5\%$.

12.4   HYPOTHESIS TESTING INVOLVING TWO POPULATION PROPORTIONS COMPARING TREATMENT & CONTROL GROUPS

A statistical study concerning the comparison of two groups of subjects is usually called an *experimental study* and it involves a *treatment group* and a *control group*. Usually, the subjects are randomly assigned to each group. The purpose of using a random assignment of subjects to both groups is to start the experiment with the treatment and control groups being as similar as possible with respect to all characteristics that are critical to the experiment as well as other factors which can influence the results of the experiment.

For example, if a medical researcher is interested in determining the effectiveness of aspirin in preventing heart attacks, the researcher would design an experiment by randomly assigning subjects to the treatment group who WILL be administered aspirin during the study. A second group of subjects will be randomly assigned to the control group who will NOT be administered aspirin during the study. The control group will resemble the treatment group as much as possible except they will not receive the aspirin. However, a placebo (i.e. a fake pill or an ineffective pill) is given to the subjects within the control group to insure that the subjects of the experiment aren't aware of whether they belong to the treatment or the control group. A placebo is administered to the control group as a precaution against *treatment effect*. That is, the psychological effect of the treatment group feeling better not because of the actual treatment they receive (the aspirin) but because they feel they were selected for some special treatment. In an experimental study where the subjects are unaware of whether they belong to the treatment or control group is called a *single-blind experiment*.

> ### DEFINITION 12.3
> **Single-blind experiment.** A single-blind experiment is a study in which the subjects of the experiment do not know who is receiving the treatment and who is receiving the placebo.

The treatment and control groups are compared to determine if the treatment (i.e. the aspirin) makes any difference in the subjects having a heart attack. To determine the effectiveness of the aspirin, the researcher will compare the *proportion of subjects having a heart attack* within the treatment and the control groups.

In a single-blind *experimental study,* the subjects are unaware of whether they belong to either the treatment group or the control group. However, if the researchers conducting the study are also unaware of whether the subjects belong to the treatment group or the control group, then the experiment is called a *double-blind experiment*.

> ### DEFINITION 12.4
> **Double-blind experiment.** Double-blind experiment is a study in which neither the subjects nor the researchers involved in the experiment know which group is the treatment or control group.

In an experimental study, the researcher's objective is to conduct a study where the treatment group and the control group are as similar as possible except for the treatment - i.e. the aspirin. Since all the subjects are randomly assigned to either the treatment or the control group and each subject receives a pill (the aspirin or the placebo) during the study, then the subjects of both groups are assumed to begin the experiment as similar as possible. *In essence, the only difference between the treatment and the control groups is the effect of the aspirin.* Thus, if the researcher finds a significant difference between the proportion of subjects who have a heart attack within the treatment group and the control group, then the researcher can conclude that this difference may be attributed to the aspirin (or treatment) rather than some other influence or factor.

Example 12.6 illustrates the comparison of a treatment versus a control group using a hypothesis test involving two population proportions.

EXAMPLE 12.6

According to the New England Journal of Medicine, a double-blind experiment was conducted to determine whether taking an aspirin tablet regularly helps prevent heart attacks. The medical researcher randomly assigned six thousand 40 year old males to take an aspirin while another six thousand 40 year old males were given a placebo. Perform a hypothesis test to determine if the following sample results indicate that taking aspirin will significantly lower the incidence of having a heart attack at $\alpha = 1\%$.

After 6 years, 78 of the males within the treatment group while 112 males in the control group suffered heart attacks.

Solution

Step 1   Formulate the null hypothesis, H_0, and the alternative hypothesis, H_a.

If we let population 1 represent the 40 year old males taking an aspirin daily while population 2 represents the 40 year old males taking a placebo daily, then the null hypothesis can be stated as:

H_0: There is **no difference** in the proportion of heart attacks between the population of 40 year old men who take an aspirin daily and the population of 40 year old men who take a placebo daily.

In symbols, we state the null hypothesis as:

$H_0: p_1 - p_2 = 0.$

Since we are trying to determine if the men taking the aspirin will have a *lower proportion of heart attacks* then the alternative hypothesis is *directional* and is stated using a *less than* statement. Consequently, the alternative hypothesis can be stated as:

H_a: The population proportion of heart attacks for 40 year old men taking an aspirin daily is less than the population proportion of heart attacks for 40 year old men taking a placebo daily.

The alternative hypothesis is symbolized as:

H_a: $p_1 - p_2 < 0.$

Step 2   Determine the model to test the null hypothesis, H_0. Under the assumption H_0 is true, determine the expected results of the Sampling Distribution of $\hat{p}_1 - \hat{p}_2$.

To test the null hypothesis, the medical researcher selected a large random independent sample from each population and the sample results are summarized in TABLE 12.5.

TABLE 12.5

Population 1 represents **40 year old men taking aspirin**	**Population 2 represents** **40 year men taking a placebo**
Sample information: $x_1 = \quad 78$ $n_1 = 6{,}000$	Sample information: $x_2 = \quad 112$ $n_2 = 6{,}000$

To conduct this hypothesis test, we will need to compute the difference between the two sample proportions, $\hat{p}_1 - \hat{p}_2$, to determine if this difference is *significantly less than zero*. Consequently, we will use the **Sampling Distribution of $\hat{p}_1 - \hat{p}_2$ as the hypothesis testing model when conducting this hypothesis test.** To determine the expected results of the Sampling Distribution of $\hat{p}_1 - \hat{p}_2$, we need to use Theorems 12.1 and 12.2. Under the assumption that H_0 **is true**, we expect the following results:

The Expected Results of the Sampling Distribution of $\hat{p}_1 - \hat{p}_2$

1. *The shape of the sampling distribution is approximately a normal distribution for large samples.*
2. *The mean of the Sampling Distribution of $\hat{p}_1 - \hat{p}_2$ is equal to zero since we are assuming that H_0 is true.*

$$\mu_{\hat{p}_1 - \hat{p}_2} = p_1 - p_2 = 0.$$

3. *The estimate of the standard error of the sampling distribution of $\hat{p}_1 - \hat{p}_2$, $s_{\hat{p}_1 - \hat{p}_2}$, is found using the pooled formula:*

$$s_{\hat{p}_1 - \hat{p}_2} = \sqrt{\hat{p}(1-\hat{p})\left(\frac{1}{n_1} + \frac{1}{n_2}\right)}$$

Using the assumption that H_0 is true, i.e. p_1 equals p_2, the pooled sample proportion, $\hat{p}$, is determined by **combining (i.e. pooling) the sample information collected from both populations** and calculated using the formula: $\hat{p} = \dfrac{x_1 + x_2}{n_1 + n_2}$.

Using the sample information, $x_1 = 78$, $n_1 = 6000$, $x_2 = 112$ and $n_2 = 6000$, the pooled sample proportion value, $\hat{p}$, is:

$$\hat{p} = \frac{78 + 112}{6000 + 6000} = \frac{190}{12000}$$

$$\hat{p} \approx 0.0158 \text{ (rounded off to 4 decimal places)}$$

The pooled estimate of the standard error of the Sampling Distribution of The Difference Between Two Proportions is determined using the formula:

$$s_{\hat{p}_1 - \hat{p}_2} = \sqrt{\hat{p}(1-\hat{p})\left(\frac{1}{n_1} + \frac{1}{n_2}\right)}$$

Using the information: $\hat{p} \approx 0.0158$, $n_1 = 6000$, and $n_2 = 6000$, the pooled estimate of the standard error is:

$$s_{\hat{p}_1 - \hat{p}_2} = \sqrt{(0.0158)(1-0.0158)\left(\frac{1}{6000} + \frac{1}{6000}\right)}$$

$$s_{\hat{p}_1 - \hat{p}_2} = \sqrt{(0.0158)(0.9842)\left(\frac{1}{6000} + \frac{1}{6000}\right)}$$

$$s_{\hat{p}_1 - \hat{p}_2} = \sqrt{(0.0158)(0.9842)(0.0003333)}$$

$$s_{\hat{p}_1 - \hat{p}_2} = \sqrt{(0.0000051)}$$

$$s_{\hat{p}_1 - \hat{p}_2} \approx 0.0023 \text{ (rounded off to 4 decimal places)}$$

Thus, the pooled estimate of the standard error of the Sampling Distribution of The Difference Between Two Proportions is:

$$s_{\hat{p}_1 - \hat{p}_2} \approx 0.0023$$

In summary, the Sampling Distribution of $\hat{p}_1 - \hat{p}_2$ will serve as our hypothesis testing model with the following expected results:

1. the Sampling Distribution can be approximated by the normal distribution for large samples.
2. the mean of the Sampling Distribution of $\hat{p}_1 - \hat{p}_2$ is:

$$\mu_{\hat{p}_1 - \hat{p}_2} = 0.$$

3. the pooled estimate of the standard error, $s_{\hat{p}_1 - \hat{p}_2}$, is:

$$s_{\hat{p}_1 - \hat{p}_2} \approx 0.0023$$

This hypothesis testing model is illustrated in Figure 12.7b.

The Sampling Distribution of $\hat{p}_1 - \hat{p}_2$ is the hypothesis testing model and is approximately a normal distribution.

$$\mu_{\hat{p}_1 - \hat{p}_2} = 0$$
$$s_{\hat{p}_1 - \hat{p}_2} \approx 0.0023$$

FIGURE 12.7b

Step 3 Formulate the decision rule.
  a) The alternative hypothesis is directional since we are trying to determine if the proportion of 40 year old men taking aspirin have a *lower* heart attack rate than the proportion of 40 year old men taking a placebo.
  b) The type of hypothesis test is one-tailed on the left side.
  c) The significance level is: $\alpha = 1\%$.
  d) To find the critical score, z_c, use TABLE II.
     For a one-tailed test on the left side with $\alpha = 1\%$, the critical z score, z_c, is: $z_c = -2.33$.
  e) Figure 12.8 illustrates the decision rule for this hypothesis test.

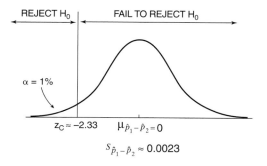

REJECT H_0 FAIL TO REJECT H_0

$\alpha = 1\%$

$z_c \approx -2.33$ $\mu_{\hat{p}_1 - \hat{p}_2} = 0$

$$s_{\hat{p}_1 - \hat{p}_2} \approx 0.0023$$

FIGURE 12.8

f) Thus, *the decision rule* is: **reject H_0 if the test statistic is less than −2.33.**

Step 4   Analyze the sample data.
Collect the sample data and calculate the test statistic using the formula: $z = \dfrac{(\hat{p}_1 - \hat{p}_2) - \mu_{\hat{p}_1 - \hat{p}_2}}{s_{\hat{p}_1 - \hat{p}_2}}$.
We must first determine the values of $\hat{p}_1$ and $\hat{p}_2$.

$$\hat{p}_1 = \frac{78}{6000} \quad \text{and} \quad \hat{p}_2 = \frac{112}{6000}$$

$$\hat{p}_1 \approx 0.0130 \quad \text{and} \quad \hat{p}_2 = 0.0187.$$

Thus, the difference between the sample proportions is:

$$\hat{p}_1 - \hat{p}_2 = 0.0130 - 0.0187$$
$$\hat{p}_1 - \hat{p}_2 = -0.0057$$

Since $\mu_{\hat{p}_1 - \hat{p}_2} = 0$ and $s_{\hat{p}_1 - \hat{p}_2} \approx 0.0023$, the test statistic is:

$$z = \frac{-0.0057 - 0}{0.0023}$$

$$z \approx -2.48$$

Step 5   State the conclusion.
Since the test statistic, $z \approx -2.48$, is less than the critical z score, $z_c = -2.33$, our conclusion is reject H_0 and accept H_a at $\alpha = 1\%$. Therefore, *we can conclude that the proportion of 40 year old men taking an aspirin daily who have heart attacks is significantly less than the proportion of 40 year old men who don't take aspirin.*

CASE STUDY 12.2

The data in Table 12.6 represents the findings from the aspirin component of a Physicians Health Study which appeared in the January, 1988 issue of The New England Journal of Medicine. The Physicians Health Study was a randomized, double-blind, placebo-controlled trial testing two hypotheses. One hypothesis was formulated to determine whether 325 mg of aspirin taken every other day reduces mortality from cardiovascular disease. Another hypothesis was formulated to determine the benefits of aspirin on the fatality of strokes.

Table 12.6   Data on the Randomized Aspirin Component of the Study regarding myocardial infarction and stroke

END POINT	ASPIRIN	PLACEBO
MYOCARDIAL INFARCTION		
Fatal	5	18
Nonfatal	99	171
Total	104	189
STROKE		
Fatal	6	2
Nonfatal	74	68
Total	80	70

The study involved male physicians aged 40 to 84 years of age residing in the United States at the beginning of the study in 1982. The selection of the physicians for the study was based on many factors. Many

CASE STUDY 12.2 (continued)

physicians were not selected for the study because of their previous history of myocardial infarction or stroke, or their current use of aspirin. Those physicians with liver or renal disease, gout, or peptic ulcer were also excluded. After the physicians were finally selected for the study, there was a trial run for 18 weeks. During this trial period, all the participants were given calendar packs containing active aspirin and the placebo. At the end of the trial, physicians were excluded from the study if they had changed their minds or demonstrated inadequate compliance with taking their medication. The physicians selected for the actual study were randomly selected to one of two groups: those assigned to the active aspirin group and those assigned to the aspirin placebo. Every six months, the physicians were sent a supply of monthly calendar packs with white tablets which were either aspirins or placebos. An independent group called the Data Monitoring Board met twice a year to review the accumulated data and to monitor the progress of the study. The Board recommended to terminate the randomized aspirin component of the study based upon the data shown in Table 12.6.

If we define the physicians taking aspirin as population 1 and the physicians taking the placebo as population 2, then:

a) determine the sample proportion of physicians taking aspirin who had a fatal myocardial infarction and the sample proportion of physicians taking the placebo who had a fatal myocardial infarction.

b) determine the sample proportion of physicians taking aspirin who had a fatal stroke and the sample proportion of physicians taking the placebo who had a fatal stroke.

c) Why do you believe many physicians were excluded from the study because of their personal medical history or their use of aspirin?

d) Why do you think a trial run of the study was conducted?

e) Explain why you think that the placebo was a white tablet?

f) What was the purpose of randomly assigning the physicians to the aspirin or the placebo group?

g) How did the trial run help to make this a better study?

h) Explain what you believe to be the meaning of was a randomized, double-blind, placebo-controlled trial study?

i) Which group would you call the treatment group and which group would you identify as the control group? Explain.

j) What do you believe is the purpose of the Data Monitoring Board?

k) Conduct a hypothesis test to determine if aspirin taken every other day reduces mortality from cardiovascular disease at $\alpha = 1\%$.

l) Conduct a hypothesis test to determine if aspirin taken every other day reduces mortality from strokes at $\alpha = 1\%$.

m) Based on the results of your hypothesis test, would you conclude that aspirin helps to prevent cardiovascular disease?

n) Based upon your analysis, would it be advisable to have the general population take aspirin to prevent cardiovascular disease? If not, to whom would you advise to take aspirin for the prevention of myocardial infarction? Explain.

o) Why do you think the monitoring board decided to terminate the study earlier than had been scheduled and release the results in a preliminary report through the New England Journal of Medicine?

p) Based on your analysis of the data, do you think that the board was correct in terminating the study?

12.5 p-VALUE APPROACH TO HYPOTHESIS TESTING INVOLVING TWO POPULATION PROPORTIONS USING THE TI-83 PLUS CALCULATOR

The p-value approach will require refinements in steps 3, 4 and 5 of the hypothesis testing procedure. In step 3, the decision rule will be stated as: Reject the H_0 if the p-value of the test statistic is less than α. In step 4, the p-value will be determined using the TI-83 Plus calculator. While in step 5, the conclusion of the hypothesis test is determined by comparing the p-value to the level of significance, α.

Let's reexamine the hypothesis test shown in Example 12.6 using a p-value approach with the aid of the TI-83 Plus Calculator.

EXAMPLE 12.7

According to the New England Journal of Medicine, a double-blind experiment was conducted to determine whether taking an aspirin tablet regularly helps prevent heart attacks. The medical researcher randomly assigned six thousand 40 year old males to take an aspirin while another six thousand 40 year old males were given a placebo. Perform a hypothesis test to determine if the following sample results indicate that taking aspirin will significantly lower the incidence of having a heart attack at $\alpha = 1\%$.

After 6 years, 78 of the males within the treatment group while 112 males in the control group suffered heart attacks.

Solution

Step 1 Formulate the null hypothesis, H_0, and the alternative hypothesis, H_a.

If we let population 1 represent the 40 year old males taking an aspirin daily while population 2 represents the 40 year old males taking a placebo daily, then the null hypothesis can be stated as:

H_0: *There is **no difference** in the proportion of heart attacks between the population of 40 year old men who take an aspirin daily and the population of 40 year old men who take a placebo daily.*

In symbols, we state the null hypothesis as:

H_0: $p_1 - p_2 = 0$.

Since we are trying to determine if the men taking the aspirin will have a *lower proportion of heart attacks* then the alternative hypothesis is *directional* and is stated using a *less than* statement. Consequently, the alternative hypothesis can be stated as:

H_a: *The population proportion of heart attacks for 40 year old men taking an aspirin daily is less than the population proportion of heart attacks for 40 year old men taking a placebo daily.*

The alternative hypothesis is symbolized as:

H_a: $p_1 - p_2 < 0$.

Step 2 Determine the model to test the null hypothesis, H_0. Under the assumption H_0 is true, determine the expected results of the Sampling Distribution of $\hat{p}_1 - \hat{p}_2$.

To test the null hypothesis, the medical researcher selected a large random independent sample from each population and the sample results are summarized in Table 12.6.

TABLE 12.6

Population 1 represents 40 year old men taking aspirin	Population 2 represents 40 year old men taking a placebo
Sample information: $x_1 = 78$ $n_1 = 6,000$	Sample information: $x_2 = 112$ $n_2 = 6,000$

To conduct this hypothesis test, we will need to compute the difference between the two sample proportions, $\hat{p}_1 - \hat{p}_2$, to determine if this difference is *significantly less than zero*.

Consequently, we will use the **Sampling Distribution of $\hat{p}_1 - \hat{p}_2$** as the hypothesis testing model when conducting this hypothesis test. To determine the **expected results of the Sampling Distribution of $\hat{p}_1 - \hat{p}_2$**, we need to use Theorems 12.1 and 12.2. Under the assumption that H_0 **is true**, we expect the following results:

The Expected Results of the Sampling Distribution of $\hat{p}_1 - \hat{p}_2$

1. *The shape of the sampling distribution is approximately a normal distribution for large samples.*
2. *The mean of the Sampling Distribution of $\hat{p}_1 - \hat{p}_2$ is equal to zero since we are assuming that H_0 is true.*
   That is:

$$\mu_{\hat{p}_1 - \hat{p}_2} = p_1 - p_2 = 0$$

3. *The estimate of the standard error of the sampling distribution of $\hat{p}_1 - \hat{p}_2$, $s_{\hat{p}_1 - \hat{p}_2}$, is found using the pooled formula:*

$$s_{\hat{p}_1 - \hat{p}_2} = \sqrt{\hat{P}(1 - \hat{P})\left(\frac{1}{n_1} + \frac{1}{n_2}\right)}$$

Using the assumption that H_0 is true, i.e. p_1 equals p_2, the pooled sample proportion, $\hat{p}$, is determined by **combining (i.e. pooling) the sample information collected from both populations** and calculated using the formula:

$$\hat{p} = \frac{x_1 + x_2}{n_1 + n_2}$$

Using the sample information, $x_1 = 78$, $n_1 = 6000$, $x_2 = 112$ and $n_2 = 6000$, the pooled sample proportion value, $\hat{p}$, is:

$$\hat{p} = \frac{78 + 112}{6000 + 6000} = \frac{190}{12000}$$

$$\hat{p} \approx 0.0158 \text{ (rounded off to 4 decimal places)}$$

The pooled estimate of the standard error of the Sampling Distribution of The Difference Between Two Proportions is determined using the formula:

$$s_{\hat{p}_1 - \hat{p}_2} = \sqrt{\hat{P}(1 - \hat{P})\left(\frac{1}{n_1} + \frac{1}{n_2}\right)}.$$

Using the information: $\hat{p} \approx 0.0158$, $n_1 = 6000$, and $n_2 = 6000$, the pooled estimate of the standard error is:

$$s_{\hat{p}_1 - \hat{p}_2} = \sqrt{(0.0158)(1 - 0.0158)\left(\frac{1}{6000} + \frac{1}{6000}\right)}$$

$$s_{\hat{p}_1 - \hat{p}_2} = \sqrt{(0.0158)(0.9842)\left(\frac{1}{6000} + \frac{1}{6000}\right)}$$

$$s_{\hat{p}_1 - \hat{p}_2} = \sqrt{(0.0158)(0.9842)(0.0003333)}$$

$$s_{\hat{p}_1 - \hat{p}_2} = \sqrt{(0.0000051)}$$

$$s_{\hat{p}_1 - \hat{p}_2} \approx 0.0023 \text{ (rounded off to 4 decimal places)}$$

Thus, the pooled estimate of the standard error of the Sampling Distribution of The Difference Between Two Proportions is: $s_{\hat{p}_1 - \hat{p}_2} \approx 0.0023$.

In summary, the Sampling Distribution of $\hat{p}_1 - \hat{p}_2$ will serve as our hypothesis testing model with the following expected results:

1. the Sampling Distribution can be approximated by the normal distribution for large samples.
2. the mean of the Sampling Distribution of $\hat{p}_1 - \hat{p}_2$ is:

$$\mu_{\hat{p}_1 - \hat{p}_2} = 0$$

3. the pooled estimate of the standard error, $s_{\hat{p}_1 - \hat{p}_2}$, is:

$$s_{\hat{p}_1 - \hat{p}_2} \approx 0.0023$$

This hypothesis testing model is illustrated in Figure 12.9.

The Sampling Distribution of $\hat{p}_1 - \hat{p}_2$ is the hypothesis testing model and is approximately a normal distribution.

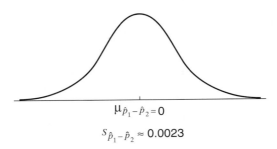

$$\mu_{\hat{p}_1 - \hat{p}_2} = 0$$

$$s_{\hat{p}_1 - \hat{p}_2} \approx 0.0023$$

FIGURE 12.9

Step 3   Formulate the decision rule.
   a)   The alternative hypothesis is directional since we are trying to determine if the proportion of 40 year old men taking aspirin have a *lower* heart attack rate than the proportion of 40 year old men taking a placebo.
   b)   The type of hypothesis test is one-tailed on the left side.
   d)   The significance level is: $\alpha = 1\%$.
   d)   Figure 12.10 illustrates the decision rule for this hypothesis test.

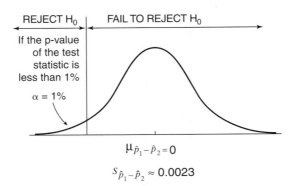

REJECT H_0 FAIL TO REJECT H_0

If the p-value of the test statistic is less than 1%

$\alpha = 1\%$

$$\mu_{\hat{p}_1 - \hat{p}_2} = 0$$

$$s_{\hat{p}_1 - \hat{p}_2} \approx 0.0023$$

FIGURE 12.10

e) Thus, *the decision rule* is: **reject H_0 if the p-value of the test statistic is less than $\alpha = 1\%$.**

Step 4 Analyze the sample data.

Determine the p-value of the test statistic by entering the sample data into the TI-83 Plus calculator. The TI-83 Plus output screen is shown in Figure 12.11.

FIGURE 12.11

From the output screen, the p-value of the test statistic $z \approx -2.49$ is 0.0065. Using this p-value we can position the test statistic on the hypothesis testing model shown in Figure 12.12.

FIGURE 12.12

Step 5 State the conclusion.

Since the p-value (0.0065) of the test statistic is less than $\alpha = 1\%$, our conclusion is reject H_0 and accept H_a at a p-value of 0.0065. Therefore, *we can conclude that the proportion of 40 year old men taking an aspirin daily who have heart attacks is significantly less than the proportion of 40 year old men who don't take aspirin.*

12.6   TWO POPULATION HYPOTHESIS TESTING SUMMARIES USING INDEPENDENT SAMPLES

The following outline is a summary of the 5-step hypothesis testing procedure for a hypothesis test involving two population proportions for large independent samples using the test statistic.

Test Statistic Approach to Hypothesis Tests Involving Two Population Proportions for Large Independent Samples

---

STEP 1. Formulate the hypotheses, H_0 and H_a.
Null Hypothesis, H_0: $p_1 - p_2 = 0$
Alternative Hypothesis, H_a: *has one of the following three forms:*

  H_a: $p_1 - p_2 < 0$ or
  H_a: $p_1 - p_2 > 0$ or
  H_a: $p_1 - p_2 \neq 0$

STEP 2. Determine the model to test the null hypothesis, H_0. Under the assumption H_0 is true, the expected results of the Sampling Distribution of $\hat{p}_1 - \hat{p}_2$

are:

(1) *The shape of the sampling distribution is approximately a normal distribution for large samples.*
(2) *The mean of the Sampling Distribution of $\hat{p}_1 - \hat{p}_2$ is equal to zero.* That is:

$$\mu_{\hat{p}_1 - \hat{p}_2} = p_1 - p_2 = 0$$

(3) *The pooled formula for the estimate of the standard error of the Sampling Distribution of $\hat{p}_1 - \hat{p}_2$, symbolized* $s_{\hat{p}_1 - \hat{p}_2}$*, is:*

$$s_{\hat{p}_1 - \hat{p}_2} = \sqrt{\hat{p}(1-\hat{p})\left(\frac{1}{n_1} + \frac{1}{n_2}\right)}$$

where $\hat{p}$ represents the pooled sample proportion and is computed by one of the following formulas:

$$\hat{p} = \frac{x_1 + x_2}{n_1 + n_2} \quad or \quad \hat{p} = \frac{n_1\hat{p}_1 + n_2\hat{p}_2}{n_1 + n_2}$$

STEP 3. Formulate the decision rule.
(a) *alternative hypothesis, H_a: directional or non-directional.*
(b) *type of test: 1TT or 2TT.*
(c) *significance level: $\alpha = 1\%$ or $\alpha = 5\%$.*
(d) *find critical z scores using Table II.*
(e) *construct the hypothesis testing model.*
(f) *state the decision rule.*

STEP 4. Analyze the sample data.
Calculate the test statistic using the formula:

$$z = \frac{(\hat{p}_1 - \hat{p}_2) - \mu_{\hat{p}_1 - \hat{p}_2}}{s_{\hat{p}_1 - \hat{p}_2}}$$

STEP 5. State the conclusion.
Compare the test statistic to the critical z score(s), z_c, of the decision rule and either:

Reject H_0 and Accept H_a at α

or

Fail to Reject H_0 at α

TABLE 12.7 contains a condensed version of the hypothesis test involving two population proportions for large samples.

TABLE 12.7 SUMMARY OF HYPOTHESIS TESTS INVOLVING TWO POPULATION PROPORTIONS FOR LARGE INDEPENDENT SAMPLES

FORM OF THE NULL HYPOTHESIS	CONDITIONS OF TEST	TEST STATISTIC FORMULA	SAMPLING DISTRIBUTION IS A:
$p_1 - p_2 = 0$	*the two samples are large, if:* $n_1 p_1, n_1(1-p_1), n_2 p_2$ *&* $n_2(1-p_2)$ *are all greater than 5.*	$z = \dfrac{(\hat{p}_1 - \hat{p}_2) - \mu_{\hat{p}_1 - \hat{p}_2}}{s_{\hat{p}_1 - \hat{p}_2}}$ where: $s_{\hat{p}_1 - \hat{p}_2} = \sqrt{\hat{p}(1-\hat{p})\left(\dfrac{1}{n_1} + \dfrac{1}{n_2}\right)}$ and $\hat{p} = \dfrac{x_1 + x_2}{n_1 + n_2}$ or $\hat{p} = \dfrac{n_1 \hat{p}_1 + n_2 \hat{p}_2}{n_1 + n_2}$	Normal Distribution

The following outline is a summary of the 5-step hypothesis testing procedure for a hypothesis test involving two population proportions for large independent samples using p-values.

---

p-Value Approach to Hypothesis Tests Involving Two Population Proportions for Large Independent Samples Using the TI-83 Plus Calculator

STEP 1. Formulate the hypotheses, H_0 and H_a.
Null Hypothesis, H_0: $p_1 - p_2 = 0$
Alternative Hypothesis, H_a: *has one of the following three forms:*

    H_a: $p_1 - p_2 < 0$ or
    H_a: $p_1 - p_2 > 0$ or
    H_a: $p_1 - p_2 \neq 0$

STEP 2. Determine the model to test the null hypothesis, H_0. Under the assumption H_0 is true, the expected results of the Sampling Distribution of $\hat{p}_1 - \hat{p}_2$ are:

(1) *The shape of the sampling distribution is approximately a normal distribution for large samples.*

(2) *The mean of the Sampling Distribution of $\hat{p}_1 - \hat{p}_2$ is equal to zero. That is:*

$$\mu_{\hat{p}_1 - \hat{p}_2} = p_1 - p_2 = 0$$

(3) *The pooled formula for the estimate of the standard error of the Sampling Distribution of $\hat{p}_1 - \hat{p}_2$, symbolized $s_{\hat{p}_1 - \hat{p}_2}$, is:*

$$s_{\hat{p}_1 - \hat{p}_2} = \sqrt{\hat{p}(1-\hat{p})\left(\frac{1}{n_1} + \frac{1}{n_2}\right)}$$

where $\hat{p}$ represents the pooled sample proportion and is computed by one of the following formulas:

(continued)

p-Value Approach to Hypothesis Tests Involving Two Population Proportions for Large Independent Samples Using the TI-83 Plus Calculator (continued)

$$\hat{p} = \frac{x_1 + x_2}{n_1 + n_2} \quad or \quad \hat{p} = \frac{n_1\hat{p}_1 + n_2\hat{p}_2}{n_1 + n_2}$$

STEP 3. Formulate the decision rule.

(a) alternative hypothesis, H_a: directional or non-directional.

(b) type of test: ITT or 2TT.

(c) significance level: $\alpha = 1\%$ or $\alpha = 5\%$.

(d) construct the hypothesis testing model.

(e) state the decision rule as: Reject the H_0 if the p-value of the test statistic is less than α.

STEP 4. Analyze the sample data.

Enter the necessary sample data into the TI-83 Plus calculator to determine the p-value of the test statistic.

STEP 5. State the conclusion.

Compare the p-value of the test statistic to the decision rule and either:

Reject H_0 and Accept H_a at α

or

Fail to Reject H_0 at α

12.7   USING TECHNOLOGY

For the information in Table 12.8, the MINITAB output to test the hypothesis that the proportion of "A"'s given in a statistics class is significantly greater than the number of "A"'s given in a computer class at $\alpha = 5\%$ is shown in Figure 12.13.

TABLE 12.8

Course	Number of Students	Number of "A" Grades
STATISTICS	350	170
Computer Class	220	83

TWO SAMPLE T FOR C1 VS C2

	N	MEAN	STDEV	SE MEAN
C1	350	0.486	0.501	0.027
C2	220	0.377	0.486	0.033

95 PCT CI FOR MU C1 – MU C2: (0.025, 0.192)

TTEST MU C1 = MU C2 (VS GT): T= 2.55 P=0.0056 DF= 568

POOLED STDEV = 0.495

FIGURE 12.13

Can you identify the p-value? Does this p-value indicate a rejection of the null hypothesis? Do the sample results support the claim that there are significantly more "A's" given in the statistics class than in the computer class? Can you identify the estimate of the standard error for the sampling distribution?

Can you identify the proportion of the number of "A" grades given in the statistics course? Can you identify the proportion of the number of "A" grades given in the computer course?

Similarly, using the TI-83 Plus calculator to perform the same hypothesis test produces the output screen shown in Figures 12.14(a) and 12.14(b).

```
2-PropZTest
 P1>P2
 z=2.536814136
 P=.0055933384
 p̂1=.4857142857
 p̂2=.3772727273
↓p̂=.4438596491
■
```

```
2-PropZTest
 P1>P2
↑p̂1=.4857142857
 p̂2=.3772727273
 p̂=.4438596491
 n1=350
 n2=220
■
```

FIGURE 12.14(a)   **FIGURE 12.14(b)**

For the TI-83 Plus output, identity the test statistic, p-value and pooled standard deviation. Does the p-value indicate a rejection of the null hypothesis at 1%? Notice that the pooled standard deviations are different in the MINITAB and TI-83 Plus outputs. Compare the test statistics of the MINITAB and the TI-83 Plus outputs and give an explanation as to why you believe the pooled standard deviations are different for the respective output screens.

KEY TERMS

Independent Samples   693
Count data   694
Population proportion,   694
Sample proportion, $\hat{p}$ 695
The Sampling Distribution of the Difference Between Two Proportions or the Sampling Distribution of $\hat{p}_1 - \hat{p}_2$ 699
Difference between sample proportions, $\hat{p}_1 - \hat{p}_2$ 696
Theoretical probability distribution 699

Mean of the Sampling Distribution of the Difference Between Two Proportions, $\mu_{\hat{p}_1 - \hat{p}_2}$ 701
Standard deviation of the Sampling Distribution of the Difference Between Two Proportions or Standard error of the difference between two proportions, $\sigma_{\hat{p}_1 - \hat{p}_2}$ 701
Estimate of the standard error of the difference between two proportions, $s_{\hat{p}_1 - \hat{p}_2}$ 703

Common hypothesized population proportion, p   707
Pooled sample proportion, $\hat{p}$ 707
Pooled estimate of the standard error of the Sampling Distribution of $\hat{p}_1 - \hat{p}_2$, $s_{\hat{p}_1 - \hat{p}_2}$ 708
Treatment group   718
Control group   718
Placebo   718
Treatment effect   718
Single-blind experiment   718
Double-blind experiment   718
Test statistic   712

Sections 12.1–12.2

1. Studies consisting of population means involve measurements while studies dealing with population proportions will produce _____.

2. The symbol used to represent the population proportion of items or individuals possessing a particular characteristic is _____.

3. When dealing with two populations, the symbol used to represent the population proportion for population 2 is _____.

4. A sample proportion is symbolized by _____ and read _____ _____.

5. The symbol p_1 represents _____.
   The symbol n_1 represents _____.
   The symbol x_1 represents _____.

6. The sampling distribution used to compare the proportions of two populations is called the _____.

7. The symbol used to represent the difference between the sample proportions is _____.

8. In the case of sampling from two populations, the Sampling Distribution of The Difference Between Two Proportions is approximately normal when the independent random sample selected from each of the two populations are both _____. Therefore, in the case of two samples, both samples are considered to be large if the quantities _____, _____, _____, and _____ are all greater than 5.

9. The mean of the Sampling Distribution of the Difference Between Two Proportions, denoted by $\mu_{\hat{p}_1-\hat{p}_2}$, is equal to _____.

10. The standard deviation of the Sampling Distribution of the Difference Between Two Proportions or commonly called the standard error of the differences between two proportions, denoted by $\sigma_{\hat{p}_1-\hat{p}_2}$, is equal to _____.

11. For large samples, the shape of the Sampling Distribution of $\hat{p}_1 - \hat{p}_2$ is approximately a _____ _____.

12. According to Theorem 12.2, the mean of the Sampling Distribution of $\hat{p}_1 - \hat{p}_2$ is determined by the formula:
    _____ = _____. Under the assumption that the null hypothesis, H_0, is true, then $\mu_{\hat{p}_1-\hat{p}_2} =$ _____.

13. The estimate of the standard error of the Sampling Distribution, $s_{\hat{p}_1-\hat{p}_2}$, of $\hat{p}_1 - \hat{p}_2$ is determined by the formula: _____ = _____.

14. If the sample data values selected from one population are unrelated to the sample data values selected from the second population, then the two sample are _____.

15. The survey information within the following table represents the number of men and women aged 18 and over who never eat breakfast. Use the table information to determine the sample proportion of men and women aged 18 and over who never eat breakfast.

| | Groups | |
	Men 18 years and over	Women 18 years and over
Sample Size	$n_1 = 1450$	$n_2 = 1500$
Number of individuals who don't eat breakfast	$x_1 = 389$	$x_2 = 327$

16. According to a recent survey of 760 men aged 25 - 34 and 790 women aged 25-34 produced the following results: 26.3% of the men live alone while 12% of the women live alone. Determine:
    a) the sample proportion of men aged 25-34 who do not live alone
    b) the sample proportion of women aged 25-34 who do not live alone
    c) the number of men within the survey who indicated that they lived alone
    d) the number of women within the survey who indicated that they lived alone
    e) the number of men within the survey who indicated that they do not live alone
    f) the number of women within the survey who indicated that they do not live alone

17. Identify the notation and state the formula for:
    a) the mean of the Sampling Distribution of the Difference Between Two Proportions.
    b) the standard deviation of the Sampling Distribution of the Difference Between Two Proportions.
    c) the standard error of the difference between two proportions.
    d) the estimate of the standard error of the difference between two proportions

18. Based upon the latest Reality Poll, 16% of home owners have an annual maintenance expenditure of between $1000-$2000, while 38% of condo owners have an annual maintenance expenditure of between $1000-$2000. Assuming these percentages represent the proportions of the indicated populations and if an independent random sample of 900 owners is selected from each population, then:
    a) define the two populations, and the proportions of these populations.
    Determine the:
    b) shape of the Sampling Distribution of $\hat{p}_1 - \hat{p}_2$
    c) mean of the Sampling Distribution of $\hat{p}_1 - \hat{p}_2$
    d) standard deviation of the Sampling Distribution of $\hat{p}_1 - \hat{p}_2$
    e) standard error of the difference between two proportions

19. **a)** Identify the notation and formula used to compute the estimate of the standard error of the difference between two proportions.
   b) State the conditions of when this estimate of the standard error can be applied.
   c) Identify the notation and formula used to compute the estimate of the standard deviation of the Sampling Distribution of the Difference Between Two Proportions.

20. Using the following sample values:

$$\hat{p}_1 = 0.38 \text{ and } n_1 = 270$$
$$\hat{p}_2 = 0.46 \text{ and } n_2 = 350.$$

compute:
   a) the estimate of the standard error of the difference between two proportions
   b) the estimate of the standard deviation of the Sampling Distribution of the Difference Between Two Proportions.

21. Using the following sample values:

$$x_1 = 360 \text{ and } n_1 = 1500$$
$$x_2 = 388 \text{ and } n_2 = 1250$$

compute:
   a) the proportions for each of the two samples.
   b) the estimate of the standard error of the difference between two proportions
   c) the estimate of the standard deviation of the Sampling Distribution of the Difference Between Two Proportions.

22. In a PC magazine for dummies, a poll of 1500 readers indicated that 78% of men and 83% of the women said they preferred at most one technical article on computer hardware in each monthly issue. Assuming that there were 970 men and 530 women sampled in this poll, answer the following questions:
   a) identify the two population proportions
   b) identify each sample proportion
   c) state the value of each sample proportion
   d) compute the estimate of the standard error of the difference between two proportions
   e) compute the estimate of the standard deviation of the Sampling Distribution of the Difference Between Two Proportions.

23. According to the Nielsen Media Research, the share of the T.V. viewing audience of the Networks: CBS, ABC and NBC was 61% for 2001. The share of the T.V. viewing audience of the Networks was 70% in 2000. If the Nielsen Media Research surveyed 1500 households in 2000 and 2000 households in 2001 then answer the following questions:
   a) identify the two population proportions
   b) identify each sample proportion
   c) compute the value of each sample proportion
   d) compute the estimate of the standard error of the difference between two proportions
   e) compute the estimate of the standard deviation of

the Sampling Distribution of the Difference Between Two Proportions.

24. The Center for Disease Control and Prevention reported that low-income groups exercise less. In particular, CDC stated that 55.4% of people with incomes between $25,000 to $50,000 don't exercise often or not at all, while 48.3% of people with incomes over $50,000 don't exercise often or not at all. If the CDC survey was based on 1350 people with incomes between $25,000 to $50,000 and 1025 people with incomes over $50,000, then:
   a) identify the two population proportions
   b) identify each sample proportion
   c) compute the value of each sample proportion
   d) compute the estimate of the standard error of the difference between two proportions
   e) compute the estimate of the standard deviation of the Sampling Distribution of the Difference Between Two Proportions.

25. According to a study by the Better Sleep Council which appeared in the August 8, 1994 issue of *USA Today,* nearly one-third of people say their job has been affected by a lack of sleep. Of those people who were surveyed, 26% of the men and 13% of the women admit to dozing off at their workplace. If this study involved 975 men and 895 women, then:
   a) identify the two population proportions
   b) identify each sample proportion
   c) compute the value of each sample proportion
   d) compute the estimate of the standard error of the difference between two proportions
   e) compute the estimate of the standard deviation of the Sampling Distribution of the Difference Between Two Proportions.

26. The U.S. Census Bureau reported that fewer children live with both parents in 2000 compared to 1990. The following table represents the Census Bureau's results:

Percentage of children who live with both parents

Race	1990	2000
Black	59%	36%
White[1]	90%	79%

[1]Non-Hispanic

Source: U.S. Census Bureau

If the Census Bureau's figures are based on a survey of 2150 white households and 1875 black households then:
   a) identify the two population proportions for each year.
   b) identify each sample proportion for each year.
   c) compute the value of each sample proportion
   d) compute the estimate of the standard error of the difference between two proportions for each year

e) compute the estimate of the standard deviation of the Sampling Distribution of the Difference Between Two Proportions for each year.

27. The problems in this chapter require the selection of two samples from:
a) the same population
b) two different populations
c) either the same or different populations.

28. In practice, it is extremely easy to compute the proportion of a population.
(T/F)

29. The Sampling Distribution of the Differences Between Sample Proportions is used to determine if the difference between the sample proportions, $\hat{p}_1 - \hat{p}_2$, is significant to infer that there is a statistically significant difference between the population proportions, $\hat{p}_1 - \hat{p}_2$.
(T/F)

30. The estimate of the standard deviation of the Sampling Distribution of the Difference Between Two Proportions, $s_{\hat{p}_1 - \hat{p}_2}$ can be obtained using:

$$s_{\hat{p}_1 - \hat{p}_2} = \sqrt{\hat{p}(1-\hat{p})\left(\frac{1}{n_1} + \frac{1}{n_2}\right)}$$

only when we assume $p_1 = p_2$.
(T/F)

31. One way to insure that $n_1 p_1$, $n_2 p_2$, $n_1(1-p_1)$ and $n_2(1-p_2)$ are all greater than 5 is to choose the sample sizes that are large enough.
(T/F)

32. A study was conducted to determine if the effectiveness of two vaccines in the prevention of a new flu strain. The results of the study are shown in the following table.

| | Vaccines | |
	Vaccine A	Vaccine B
Number of individuals who didn't catch the flu	$x_1 = 432$	$x_2 = 270$
Sample Size	$n_1 = 650$	$n_2 = 580$

Use the information in the previous table to determine the sample proportion of individuals receiving:
a) vaccine A
a) vaccine B
c) vaccine A who caught the flu.
d) vaccine B who caught the flu.

33. Last year, a random sample of 978 people making dinner reservations, 392 people requested the nonsmoking section. Recently, a random sample 1014 people showed that 729 people prefer the nonsmoking section when making dinner reservations. Using this information, determine the sample proportion of:
a) people who preferred the nonsmoking section last year.

b) people who preferred the nonsmoking section this year.
c) people who did not prefer the nonsmoking section last year.
d) people who did not prefer the nonsmoking section this year.

34. A current newspaper article reported that 73% of women drivers and 87% of men drivers pump their own gas. If this survey was based upon a random sample of 1005 male drivers and a random sample of 1100 female drivers, then determine:
a) the sample proportion of male drivers who do not pump their own gas
b) the sample proportion of women drivers who do not pump their own gas
c) the number of men drivers within the survey who indicated that they pump their own gas
d) the number of women drivers within the survey who indicated that they pump their own gas
e) the number of men within the survey who indicated that they do not pump their own gas
f) the number of women within the survey who indicated that they do not pump their own gas

35. Using the following information:

$$p_1 = 0.73, n_1 = 1230, \text{ and } x_1 = 901$$
$$p_2 = 0.62, n_2 = 1570, \text{ and } x_2 = 989$$

determine:
a) the proportion of the sample selected from population 1
b) the proportion of the sample selected from population 2
c) if the samples are considered large
d) the difference between the sample proportions: $\hat{p}_1 - \hat{p}_2$
e) the shape of the Sampling Distribution of $\hat{p}_1 - \hat{p}_2$
f) mean of the Sampling Distribution of $\hat{p}_1 - \hat{p}_2$
g) standard deviation of the Sampling Distribution of $\hat{p}_1 - \hat{p}_2$
h) standard error of the difference between two proportions

36. According to a survey of business travelers conducted by Hawthorn Suites during March and April of 1994, 73% of the women travelers said they determine their favorite hotel because of location and convenience while only 59% of the men travelers selected their favorite hotel for the same reason. If this business traveler survey was based on 1500 business women travelers and 1200 business men travelers then answer the following questions:
a) identify the two population proportions
b) identify each sample proportion
c) compute the value of each sample proportion
d) compute the estimate of the standard error of the Difference Between Two Proportions
e) compute the estimate of the standard deviation of

the Sampling Distribution of the Difference Between Two Proportions.

37. According to the Bruskin/Goldring Research Poll, 30% of the people in the 25-34 age group and 37% of the people in the 65 and over age group say Richard Nixon, who resigned the presidency 20 years ago, will be remembered as a great president. If 1050 people in the 25-34 age group and 1325 people in the 65 and over age group were polled, then answer the following questions:
  a) identify the two population proportions
  b) identify each sample proportion
  c) compute the value of each sample proportion
  d) compute the estimate of the standard error of the difference between two proportions
  e) compute the estimate of the standard deviation of the Sampling Distribution of the Difference Between Two Proportions.

Section 12.3

38. The common population proportion value is symbolized by ____. The best estimate for this common population proportion value $\hat{p}$, is determined by ____ the sample information collected from both populations.

39. The formula for the pooled sample proportion, $\hat{p}$, is determined by using one of the following formulas:

$$\hat{p} = \underline{\quad} \text{ or } \hat{p} = \underline{\quad}.$$

40. The pooled formula for the estimated standard error of the sampling distribution of $\hat{p}_1 - \hat{p}_2$, $s_{\hat{p}_1 - \hat{p}_2}$, is:

$$s_{\hat{p}_1 - \hat{p}_2} = \underline{\qquad\qquad}$$

41. To perform a hypothesis test involving two population proportions, the Sampling Distribution of the Difference Between ____ ____ is used as the hypothesis testing model.

42. The notation $\hat{p}_1 - \hat{p}_2$ represents the difference between the ____ ____, where $\hat{p}_1$ represents the ____ of sample 1 and $\hat{p}_2$ represents the ____ of sample 2.

43. The null hypothesis of a hypothesis test involving two population proportions, p_1 and p_2, is stated as: There is ____ difference between the ____ of population 1 and the ____ of population 2. In symbols, H_0 is written as: ____ = 0.

44. The alternative hypothesis of a hypothesis test involving two population proportions, p_1 and p_2, has one of three possible forms. They are:
  a) The proportion of population 1 is greater than the ____. In symbols, H_a is written as H_a: $p_1 - p_2$ ____ 0.
  b) The ____ of population 1 is less than the proportion of ____. In symbols, H_a is written as H_a: $p_1 - p_2$ ____ 0.
  c) The proportion of ____ 1 is not equal to the ____ of population ____. In symbols, H_a is written as: H_a: $p_1 - p_2$ ____ 0

45. The formula for the critical z score, z_c, for a hypothesis test involving two population proportion is: $z_c =$ ____.

46. To determine the conclusion of a hypothesis test involving two population proportions, the test statistic, denoted ____, is compared to the critical z score(s), z_c.

47. The pooled sample proportion value, $\hat{p}$, is used when:
  a) computing $\mu_{\hat{p}_1 - \hat{p}_2}$
  b) stating H_0
  c) computing $s_{\hat{p}_1 - \hat{p}_2}$
  d) stating H_a

48. When computing the critical z score(s), z_c, a value from which distribution is utilized?
  a) normal distribution
  b) binomial distribution
  b) t distribution
  d) skewed distribution

49. If 40 out of 100 men and 50 out of 150 women agreed with the proposal, then what is the pooled sample proportion value, $\hat{p}$?
  a) 0.40 (b) 0.60 (c) 0.365 (d) 0.36

50. If the pooled sample value is $\hat{p} = 0.40$, $n_1 = 200$ and $n_2 = 150$, then $s_{\hat{p}_1 - \hat{p}_2}$ equals:
  a) 0.003 (b) 0.002 (c) 0.053 (d) 529

51. If the critical z score is 1.65 and the test statistic is: z = 1.96, then the conclusion for a 1TT on the right is:
  a) Reject H_0 and Accept H_a
  b) Fail to reject H_0
  c) Accept H_0
  d) Reject H_a

52. The form of the null hypothesis, H_0, for testing the difference between two population proportions is:
  a) H_0: $p_1 - p_2 = 0$
  b) H_0: $p_1 - p_2 < 0$
  c) H_0: $p_1 - p_2 > 0$
  d) H_0: $p_1 - p_2 \neq 0$

53. The standard error of the difference between the two proportions is the standard deviation of the Sampling Distribution of the Difference Between Two Proportions.
  (T/F)

54. The null hypothesis for tests that compare the proportions from two populations is usually expressed as $p_1 - p_2 = 0$, where p_1 represents the proportion of population 1 and p_2 represents the proportion of population 2.
  (T/F)

55. If the difference between the sample proportions $\hat{p}_1 - \hat{p}_2$ is different from zero, then we can conclude that there is a statistically significant difference between p_1 and p_2.
  (T/F)

56. If p_1 and p_2 are unknown, then one cannot perform a hypothesis test for the difference between two proportions.
  (T/F)

57. $\hat{p}$, the proportion obtained by combining results from both samples is based upon the assumption that n_1 and n_2 are equal.
(T/F)

58. If the test statistic is $z = 0$, then the null hypothesis is correct.
(T/F)

59. When doing a hypothesis test for a comparison of population proportions, it is very important to choose random samples.
(T/F)

60. Under the assumption that the null hypothesis, H_0, is true, what is the value of the mean of the Sampling Distribution of $\hat{p}_1 - \hat{p}_2$?

61. State the pooled formulas for the best estimate for the common population proportion value, p. What is the name of each of these formulas?

62. The following information concerning hypothesis tests for two proportions. For each

    (i)   define the two population proportions.

    (ii) state the null and alternative hypotheses.

    (iii) identify the type of test: 1TT or 2TT.

a) A researcher would like to determine if married women are more apt to express anger than unmarried women.

b) The Naturalizer Company would like to determine if there is a significantly smaller percentage of males compared to females that believe wearing miniskirts is inappropriate office attire for women.

c) The National Association of Home Builders is interested in determining if the percentage of new homes with garages is large enough for two or more cars in 2000 is different compared to new homes in 1990.

d) A pharmaceutical company is preparing to do a study to investigate whether the proportion of college educated mothers who breast feed their babies in the hospital is higher than non-college educated mothers.

e) The Motion Picture Association of America would like to study whether the percentage of the U. S. population that attends the movies every week has decreased in 2001 compared to 1991.

f) The American Medical Association is interested in determining whether the percentage of physicians with managed care contracts increased significantly in 2000 compared to 1995.

g) A researcher would like to determine if men drivers are more apt to nod off while driving than women drivers.

h) A medical study is being conducted to determine if more infants under private health insurance will receive well-baby care than infants under publically funded Medicaid.

i) A radio station survey is being conducted to determine if there is a difference in the proportion of men from the proportion of women who will want to sing along while listening to country music on the radio or stereo.

j) The American Medical Association would like to determine if the proportion of black male physicians is significantly less than the proportion of white male physicians.

k) The League of Women Voters would like to determine if a greater proportion of females over males believes that women politicians will do a better job while serving in Congress.

l) The U.S. Department of Education is conducting a study to determine if the proportion of people in poverty is significantly greater for people at the least literate level as opposed to the people at the most literate level.

m) A pharmaceutical company is interested in studying if the proportion of patients taking their new allergy medication will suffer significantly less drowsiness than the patients who receive a placebo tablet.

n) Psychology Today is interested in determining whether there is a difference in the percentage of males who elect to have plastic surgery from the percentage of females who elect to have plastic surgery.

o) A cable company would like to study whether the percentage of the U. S. population that has cable connected to their homes has significanlty increased in 2001 as compared to 1994.

63. State the pooled formula for $s_{\hat{p}_1 - \hat{p}_2}$, the estimated standard error of the Sampling Distribution of $\hat{p}_1 - \hat{p}_2$.

64. Compute the pooled sample proportion, $\hat{p}$, for the sample information in parts (a) to (h):
    a) $x_1 = 540$, $n_1 = 1175$, $x_2 = 415$ and $n_2 = 950$
    b) $x_1 = 663$, $n_1 = 850$, $x_2 = 537$ and $n_2 = 1060$
    c) $n_1 = 1050$, $\hat{p}_1 = 0.46$, $n_2 = 1170$, and $\hat{p}_2 = 0.58$
    d) $n_1 = 750$, $\hat{p}_1 = 0.74$, $n_2 = 675$, and $\hat{p}_2 = 0.69$
    e) $x_1 = 930$, $n_1 = 1260$, $x_2 = 685$ and $n_2 = 1075$
    f) $x_1 = 786$, $n_1 = 1150$, $x_2 = 846$ and $n_2 = 1390$
    g) $n_1 = 1510$, $\hat{p}_1 = 0.86$, $n_2 = 1425$, and $\hat{p}_2 = 0.79$
    h) $n_1 = 870$, $\hat{p}_1 = 0.37$, $n_2 = 990$, and $\hat{p}_2 = 0.45$

65. (a) to (h): For each part in question 64, use the sample information to determine the pooled estimate of the standard error of the Sampling Distribution of The Difference Between Two Proportions.

For the problems 66-87, use the 5 step procedure to perform a hypothesis test. Include the following within your test:

    a) state the null and alternative hypotheses.

    b) calculate the expected results for the experiment assuming the null hypothesis is true and state the hypothesis test model.

    c) formulate the decision rule.

    d) compute the test statistic

    e) state the conclusion and answer any question(s) posed in the problem.

66. According to a Psychology Today survey, 29% of females like to take chances while 35% of males prefer to take chances. Assume these estimates are based upon a random sample of 750 females and 730 males. Perform a hypothesis test at $\alpha = 1\%$ to determine if there is a significant difference between the proportion of females and the proportion of males who like to take chances.

67. A survey conducted by the Institute for Social Research stated that 19% of high school seniors smoked daily in 1999. In 1994, the Institute reported that 17% of the high school seniors smoked daily. If each of these estimates were based on a random sample of 1250 high school seniors, then perform a hypothesis test at $\alpha = 5\%$ to determine if the percentage of high school seniors who smoke daily significantly increased during this period.

68. According to a survey by Opinion Research Corporation, 38% of 1050 smokers and 61% of 1125 non-smokers said that they strongly agree that smoking should be banned in all public places. Perform a hypothesis test at $\alpha = 1\%$ to determine if the proportion of non-smokers who strongly agree that smoking should be banned in all public places is significantly greater than that of smokers.

69. According to a survey conducted by USA Today, 19% of males said they sleep in the nude while 12% of the females said they sleep in the nude.

Assume these estimates are based upon a random sample of 850 males and 780 females. Perform a hypothesis test at $\alpha = 5\%$ to determine if there is a significant difference between the proportion of males and the proportion of females who like to sleep in the nude.

70. The U.S. Census Bureau reports that the high school dropout rates for black children fell from 11% in 1970 to 5% in 2000. Perform a hypothesis test at $\alpha = 5\%$ to determine if the difference between the proportion of black children who have dropped out of high school has significantly decrease in 2000 from 1970. Assume these estimates are based on a random sample of 1270 black children in 1970 and 1350 black children in 2000.

71. The Regional Financial Associates reports that the unemployment rate in 1994 for the New England States was 6.4% while the unemployment rate for the Middle Atlantic States was 7.2%. Perform a hypothesis test at $\alpha = 1\%$ to determine if there is a significant difference between the unemployment rate for the New England States and the unemployment rate for the Middle Atlantic States. Assume these estimates are based on a random sample of 1050 New Englanders and 1175 Middle Atlantic adults.

72. According to the National Football League (NFL), the two-point after touchdown conversion was successful during its first year. A comparison of the run versus the pass on two-point conversions resulted in the following data:

TYPE OF TWO-POINT CONVERSION	ATTEMPTS	SUCCESS
PASSING	126	71
RUNNING	108	55

Using the information contained within the previous table, perform a hypothesis test at $\alpha = 0.05$ to determine if there is a significant difference in the success rate of the two-point conversion between passing for the two-pointer and running for the two-pointer.

73. A poll of women aged 18-59 years conducted by New Woman determined that 71% of the women in the Northwest say they are attractive without makeup while only 57% of the women in the Midwest say they are attractive without makeup. Perform a hypothesis test at $\alpha = 0.05$ to determine if the proportion of Northwest women who say they are attractive without makeup is significantly greater than the proportion of Midwest women who say they are attractive without makeup. Assume these estimates are based on a random sample of 1070 Northwest women and 1180 Midwest women.

74. The results of a poll conducted by Prevention magazine compared the diets of children in 2000 to 1995. According to the 2000 poll, 50% of parents are trying to convince their children to avoid eating too much fat while in 1995, 64% of parents tried to help their children to avoid fats. Perform a hypothesis test at $\alpha = 0.05$ to determine if the proportion of parents who are trying to help their children eat less fat has significantly decreased from 1995. Assume these estimates are based on a random sample of 424 parents in 2000 and 575 parents in 1995.

75. The National Highway Traffic Safety Administration has released the results of a recent survey which indicate that people who wear seat belts are more likely to survive and be uninjured in car crashes than people not wearing seat belts. According to their survey, 21.1% of people not wearing seat belts are uninjuried in passenger car crashes compared to 58.8% of people wearing a seat belt. Perform a hypothesis test at $\alpha = 0.01$ to determine if the proportion of people wearing seat belts who are uninjured in passenger car crashes is significantly greater than the proportion of people not wearing seat belts. Assume these estimates are based on a random sample of 1025 passenger car crashes where the passengers wore seat belts and a random sample of 1185 passenger car crashes involving passengers who didn't wear seat belts.

76. The Opinion Research Corporation released a study stating that 83% of non-smokers strongly believe that nicotine is an addictive substance while only 79% of smokers believe that nicotine is an addictive substance.

Perform a hypothesis test at $\alpha = 0.05$ to determine if the proportion of smokers is significantly less than the proportion of non-smokers who strongly believe that nicotine is an addictive substance. Assume these estimates are based on a random sample of 990 smokers and a random sample of 1040 non-smokers.

77. According to the US Census Bureau, the percentage of households having one or more computers in 2000 has increased significantly from 1998. Use the following sample data to perform a hypothesis test to test the Census Bureau's claim at $\alpha = 5\%$. A 1998 survey of 1180 households found that 543 had at least one computer while a 2000 survey of 1320 households found that 673 had at least one computer.

78. According to the American Journal of Sports Medicine, the following table represents the frequency of knee injuries for grass and AstroTurf for the National Football League from 1980–1989.

	MCL Sprains[1]	ACL Sprains[2]	Other	Total number of Injuries
AstroTurf	395	59	123	577
Natural Grass	342	55	107	504
Total number of Injuries	737	114	230	1081

[1]Medical Collateral Knee; [2]Anterior Cruciate Knee Ligament

Using the table information, perform a hypothesis test to determine:

i) if there is a significant greater proportion of MCL Sprains on AstroTurf than Natural Grass at $\alpha = 0.05$.

ii) if there is a significant greater proportion of ACL Sprains on AstroTurf than Natural Grass at $\alpha = 0.05$.

iii) if there is a significant greater proportion of total injuries on AstroTurf than Natural Grass at $\alpha = 0.05$.

79. The following table contains the number and percentage of home-team victories and the number of visiting-team victories for the sports basketball, baseball, hockey, and football for a sample of games during the 1990-1991 professional sports seasons. This information appeared in the article entitled Predicting Professional Sports Game Outcomes from Intermediate Game Scores in the 1992 Chance magazine, issue number 3-4, volume 5.

Sport	n	Home Wins	Visitor Wins	% Home Wins
Basketball	198	127	71	64.1%
Baseball	100	53	47	53.0%
Hockey	93	50	43	53.8%
Football	99	57	42	57.6%

Using the table information, perform a hypothesis test to determine:

i) if there is a significant greater proportion of home-team victories verses visiting-team victories for basketball at $\alpha = 5\%$.

ii) if there is a significant greater proportion of home-team victories verses visiting-team victories for baseball at $\alpha = 0.05$.

iii) if there is a significant greater proportion of home-team victories verses visiting-team victories for hockey at $\alpha = 5\%$.

iv) if there is a significant greater proportion of home-team victories verses visiting-team victories for football at $\alpha = 0.05$.

v) if there is a significant greater proportion of home-team victories verses visiting-team victories across all sports at $\alpha = 5\%$.

80. Researchers at the University of Singapore believe that diet is a critical factor in coronary heart disease in men. To test this claim, a sample of case histories of men was randomly chosen from society A where the main protein component of their diet is red meat. A second sample of case histories of men was randomly chosen from society B where the main protein component of their diet is fish. Researchers found that of 200 case histories from society A, 26 have experienced some form of coronary heart disease and of 200 case histories from society B, 14 have experienced some form of coronary heart disease. Do these results indicate that the researchers belief is correct at $\alpha = 1\%$?

81. A consumer advocate wants to determine if the proportion of Maymark dishwashers that need repairs within the first five years of use is less than the proportion of dishwashers made by Whirlsteam that need repairs within the first five years of use. To test this claim she samples 150 Maymark dishwashers that are at least five years old and finds that 17 needed repairs during their first five years of use. A sample of 190 Whirlsteam dishwashers that are at least five years old had 32 that needed repairs during their first five years of us. Do these results indicate that the proportion of Maymark dishwashers that need repair is significantly lower than the proportion of Whirlsteam dishwashers that need repair at $\alpha = 0.01$?

82. The placement officer at a small private college wants to determine if the proportion of graduates from the State University system who have jobs in their chosen field within six months of graduating is significantly different from the proportion for graduates of private colleges in the state. She randomly surveys 450 graduates of the State University system and 300 graduates of private colleges in the state. The results of the survey are summarized below:

State University Graduates	Private College Graduates
$x_1 = 265$	$x_2 = 185$
$n_1 = 450$	$n_2 = 300$

Do these sample results indicate a significant difference in the two proportions at $\alpha = 0.05$?

83. A health expert believes that women are more aware of being overweight than men. In a random sample of 250 women and 250 men who have been classified as overweight, only 175 women and 165 men were aware of their overweight condition. Do these sample results confirm the health experts belief at $\alpha = 1\%$?

84. A researcher wishes to determine if there is a significant difference in the proportion of men and women who approve of mothers working when their children are less than five years old. Two random samples of men and women are independently drawn. On the basis of the sample data below, can the researcher show that there is a significant difference in the men's and women's attitude toward working mothers at $\alpha = 5\%$?

Group	Sample Size	Number who approve of working mothers
MEN	300	120
WOMEN	200	90

85. A quality control computer engineer would like to determine if a new manufacturing process will significantly reduce the proportion of defective computer chips. In a random sample of 400 computer chips manufactured using the new process, 31 were defective while in a random sample of 400 computer chips manufactured using the present process, 47 were defective.

Based upon the sample data, can the quality control engineer state the new manufacturing process is significantly better than the present process at $\alpha = 0.05$?

86. A medical researcher is studying the effects of two alternative drugs for the treatment of high blood pressure. Drug A has no apparent side-effect whereas Drug B sometimes has a side-effect of mild headaches. The medical researcher is willing to recommend the use of Drug B if the proportion of people cured is significantly higher than the proportion of people cured using Drug A. The medical researcher used the drugs experimentally on two random samples of people suffering from high blood pressure. Drug A was administered to a group of 100 patients while Drug B was administered to a group of 105 patients. At the end of the experimental period, 62 of those treated with Drug A were classified as "cured" while 69 of those treated with Drug B were also classified as "cured". Can the medical researcher recommend the use of Drug B over Drug A at the 0.01 level of significance?

87. A 1999 Lou Harris Poll stated that 53% of Americans said they were "very concerned" about their privacy. A similar poll in 1991 reported 48% of Americans said they were "very concerned" about their privacy. Conduct a hypothesis test at $\alpha = 0.05$ to determine if there is a significant difference in the proportion of Americans who were very concerned about their privacy for the years 1999 and 1991. The sample size for the 1999 poll was 1500 while the sample size for the 1991 poll was 1450.

Section 12.4

88. Statistical studies concerning the comparison of two groups of subjects usually consists of an experiment involving a _____ and _____.

89. An ineffective pill administered to the control group is called a _____.

90. An experiment where the subjects of the experiment do not know who is receiving the treatment and who is receiving the placebo is called a ____-____ _____.

91. An experiment where neither the subjects nor the researchers involved in the experiment know which group of subjects is the treatment or the control group is called a ____-____ _____.

92. Hypotheses tests that involve the comparison of the proportions from two populations use the Sampling Distribution of the Difference Between Two Proportions as the hypothesis testing model. (T/F)

93. Explain the difference between a treatment and control group.

94. What is a placebo?

95. What is meant by a treatment effect?

96. Define:
a) a single-blind experiment.
b) a double-blind experiment.

For each of the following studies stated in problems 97 to 98, define:

a) the treatment group
b) the control group
c) the null and alternative hypotheses.

97. The results of a study conducted at Thomas Jefferson University indicated that a cancer vaccine treatment made from a patient's own tumor cells was administered to a group of patients who were operated on for malignant melanoma while another group of patients received the standard treatment of surgery and a placebo vaccine. The results of the study showed that the group receiving the cancer vaccine and the surgery had a greater percentage of patients remaining disease free after three years.

98. The consumer report publication, Health Letter, reported the following research to determine whether acupuncture significantly relieves pain. In one acupuncture study, a group of randomly selected people suffering from back pain and headache received genuine acupuncture while a similar group of people also suffering from back pain and headache received a "sham" acupuncture in which needles were placed at non-acupuncture points.

For problems 99-102, use the 5 step procedure to perform a hypothesis test. Include the following within your test:

a) state the null and alternative hypotheses.

b) calculate the expected results for the experiment assuming the null hypothesis is true and state the hypothesis test model.

c) formulate the decision rule.

d) compute the test statistic

e) state the conclusion and answer any question(s) posed in the problem.

99. A study in the New England Journal of Medicine reported that an experimental drug significantly reduces life-threatening blockages after the artery-opening procedure angioplasty one year later. In the study, for a group of 150 patients who received angioplasty and the drug CentoRx 125 patients didn't have life-threatening blockages after the angioplasty procedure. While the second group of 75 patients who received the artery-opening procedure and was administered a fake ineffective pill 50 patients didn't have life-threatening blockages after the angioplasty procedure.

Can one conclude that the experimental drug significantly reduces life-threatening blockages after the artery-opening procedure angioplasty at $\alpha = 1\%$?

100. A study conducted by Brigham and Women's Hospital reported that regular aspirin use substantially decreases the risk of colon cancer. For a group of 250 subjects who were administered two or more aspirins a week during the study 20 contracted colon cancer while a second group of 225 subjects who were administered a fake pill similar in appearance to an aspirin 32 contracted colon cancer. Can one conclude that regular use of aspirin can significantly reduce the risk of colon cancer $\alpha = 1\%$?

101. Findings released by the North American Association for the Study of Obesity showed that a cream treated with an asthma drug may melt away fat. The group of 265 women in the study applied the cream five days a week for six weeks to one thigh, while a placebo cream was applied to the other thigh. At the end of the study, the researchers measured each thigh to determine the proportion of women who lost at least an average of half an inch. Perform a hypothesis test using the data in the following table to determine if the proportion of thighs which lost an average of half an inch of fat is significantly greater for the thighs administered the treated cream than for thighs treated with the placebo cream at $\alpha = 0.01$.

THIGH APPLIED WITH THE	NUMBER OF THIGHS MEASURING AN AVERAGE OF HALF AN INCH LESS
TREATED CREAM	169
PLACEBO CREAM	96

102. Harvard researchers conducted a study on 456 elderly women to determine if cranberry juice can help women avoid bladder infections. Half the women were randomly assigned to the group who was administered one cup of cranberry juice while the remaining women were given a berry-free imitation liquid similar in appearance to cranberry juice. After eight weeks, the results of the survey showed that 15% of the women consuming the cranberry juice had bladder infections while 28% of the berry-free group contracted bladder infections. Perform a hypothesis test at $\alpha = 0.01$ to determine if the women on the cranberry juice suffered a significantly less proportion of bladder infections.

For problems 103–108: The information within the following table contains the result of a double-blind clinical study which was conducted to compare a group of subjects who were administered a seasonal allergy drug called Hismanal and a group of subjects who were administered a sugar pill. For problems 13 to 18, perform a hypothesis test using the 5-step procedure outline within the text to determine at $\alpha = 0.01$ if there is a significant difference in the proportion of patients receiving Hismanal and the proportion of patients receiving the sugar pill with respect to the following adverse events:

103. headache

104. fatigue

105. weight increase

106. dry mouth

107. nervousness

108. drowsiness.

Percent of Patients Reporting in Controlled Clinical Studies*

ADVERSE EVENT	HISMANAL (n = 1630)	Placebo (n = 1109)
Central Nervous System		
Drowsiness	7.1	6.4
Headache	6.7	9.2
Fatigue	4.2	1.6
Appetite Increase	3.9	1.4
Weight Increase	3.6	0.7
Nervousness	2.1	1.2
Dizzy	2.0	1.8
Gastrointestinal System		
Nausea	2.5	2.9
Diarrhea	1.8	2.0
Abdominal Pain	1.4	1.2
Eye, Ear, Nose, and Throat		
Mouth Dry	5.2	3.8
Pharyngitis	1.7	2.3
Conjunctivitis	1.2	1.2
Other		
Arthralgia	1.2	1.6

*Duration of treatment in Controlled Studies ranged from 7 to 182 days

109. Within the advertisement for Hismanal the ad states that Hismanal causes no more drowsiness than a placebo. Do you support this statement? Explain.

110. Within the advertisement for Hismanal the ad states that Hismanal causes no more dry mouth or nervousness than with a sugar pill. Do you support this statement? Explain.

Section 12.5

For problems 111–136, refer to problems 66 to 87 in section exercises 12.3 and problems 99 to 102 in section exercises 12.4, and use the p-value approach to hypothesis testing using the TI-83 Plus calculator. For each of these problems,

use the 5 step procedure to perform a hypothesis test at **both** $\alpha = 1\%$ and $\alpha = 5\%$. Include the following within your test:

a) state the null and alternative hypotheses.
b) calculate the expected results for the experiment assuming the null hypothesis is true and state the hypothesis test model.
c) formulate the decision rule.
d) identify the test statistic and its p-value.
e) state the conclusion and answer any question(s) posed in the problem for each alpha level.
f) determine the smallest level of significance for which the null hypothesis can be rejected.

> ### CHAPTER REVIEW:

137. When the sample size is large, the Sampling Distribution of the Proportion is approximately a _____ distribution. A sample is large if both _____ and _____ are greater than 5.

138. Studies involving population means deal with measurements while studies involving population proportions produce _____.

139. Identify what each of the following symbols represent:
a) n_1 **d)** $\hat{p}_2$
b) n_2 **e)** p_1
c) $\hat{p}_1$ **f)** p_2

140. The name of the Sampling Distribution which is used to determine if the difference between the sample proportions, $\hat{p}_1 - \hat{p}_2$, is large enough to conclude that the difference between the population proportions, $\hat{p}_1 - \hat{p}_2$, is statistically significant is: _____.

141. The mean of the Sampling Distribution of the Difference Between Two Proportions, denoted by $\mu_{\hat{p}_1 - \hat{p}_2}$,
a) $\mu_{\hat{p}_1 - \hat{p}_2} = 0$
b) $\mu_{\hat{p}_1 - \hat{p}_2} = p_1 + p_2$
c) $\mu_{\hat{p}_1 - \hat{p}_2} = p_1 - p_2$

142. To determine if the distribution of difference between sample proportions can be approximated by a normal distribution, both $n_1 p_1$ and $n_2 p_2$ must be greater than 5. (T/F)

143. A random sample of 625 male drivers showed that 376 wear seatbelts, while a random sample of 758 female drivers revealed that 492 wear seatbelts. Using this information, determine the sample proportion of:
a) men drivers who wear seatbelts
b) women drivers who wear seatbelts
c) men drivers who do not wear seatbelts
d) women drivers who do not wear seatbelts

144. Define:
a) the Sampling Distribution of the Difference Between Two Proportions.

b) the conditions under which the Sampling Distribution of the Proportion can be approximated by a normal distribution.
c) the conditions under which the Sampling Distribution of The Difference Between Two Proportions can be approximated by a normal distribution.

145. Using the following information:

$$p_1 = 0.56, n_1 = 1860, \text{ and } x_1 = 1172$$
$$p_2 = 0.82, n_2 = 1945, \text{ and } x_2 = 1537$$

determine:
a) the proportion of the sample selected from population 1
b) the proportion of the sample selected from population 2
c) if the samples are considered large
d) the difference between the sample proportions: $\hat{p}_1 - \hat{p}_2$
e) the shape of the Sampling Distribution of $\hat{p}_1 - \hat{p}_2$
f) mean of the Sampling Distribution of $\hat{p}_1 - \hat{p}_2$
g) standard deviation of the Sampling Distribution of $\hat{p}_1 - \hat{p}_2$
h) standard error of the difference between two proportions

146. A marketing research agency conducted a survey to determine the spending plans for the forthcoming holiday season of the consumers in the Green Acres Shopping Mall on Long Island. Out of 1952 people surveyed, 650 responded that they planned to spend less than last year's holiday season. According to a similar survey in 2000, 809 of the 1924 consumers surveyed indicated that they planned to spend less during the upcoming holiday season. Using this information:
a) identify the two population proportions
b) identify each sample proportion
c) compute the value of each sample proportion
d) compute the estimate of the standard error of the difference between two proportions

e) compute the estimate of the standard deviation of the Sampling Distribution of the Difference Between Two Proportions.

147. A survey by Simmons Research for Interep Radio Store reported on the level of education and the percentage of sports watchers or listeners. According to the survey, 33% of college graduates listen to sports on the radio while 27% of college graduates watch sports on TV. If the Simmons Research polled 830 college graduates who listen to the radio and 910 college graduates who watch TV, then:

a) identify the two population proportions
b) identify each sample proportion
c) compute the value of each sample proportion
d) compute the estimate of the standard error of the difference between two proportions
e) compute the estimate of the standard deviation of the Sampling Distribution of the Difference Between Two Proportions.

148. For a hypothesis test involving two population proportions, p_1 and p_2, state, in words and in symbols, the general form of the:
a) null hypothesis
b) alternative hypothesis

149. Which of the following would not be suitable as an alternative hypothesis:
a) $p_1 - p_2 < 0$
b) $p_1 - p_2 > 0$
c) $p_1 - p_2 \neq 0$
d) $p_1 - p_2 = 0$

150. For large samples, state the expected results of the Sampling Distribution of $\hat{p}_1 - \hat{p}_2$. That is, identify the shape and give the formulas needed to calculate the mean and the estimate of the standard error of the Sampling Distribution of $\hat{p}_1 - \hat{p}_2$.

151. When performing a hypothesis test involving two population proportions, the expected result $\mu_{\hat{p}_1 - \hat{p}_2} = p_1 - p_2 = 0$ is determined under the assumption that _____ is true.

152. Give the notation and formulas for the pooled sample proportion, and state under what conditions you would use these formulas.

153. Using the assumption that H_0 is _____, p_1 ___ p_2 and then we can pool the two samples together to obtain the pooled estimate of the standard error formula, $s_{\hat{p}_1 - \hat{p}_2}$, is:

$$s_{\hat{p}_1 - \hat{p}_2} = \sqrt{(\quad)(\quad)(\frac{1}{n_1} + \frac{1}{n_2})}$$

154. The following information concerning hypothesis tests for two proportions. For each
(i) define the two population proportions.
(ii) state the null and alternative hypotheses.
(iii) identify the type of test: 1TT or 2TT.

a) American Express is interested in determining if the percentage of no-shows for dinner reservations is greater on the weekend.
b) Psychology Today is interested in determining whether there is a difference in the percentage of males who pray and the percentage of females who pray.

155. Compute the pooled sample proportion, $\hat{p}$, for the sample information in parts (a) to (b):
a) $x_1 = 450, n_1 = 975, x_2 = 615$ and $n_2 = 1050$
b) $n_1 = 1250, \hat{p}_1 = 0.76, n_2 = 1370$, and $\hat{p}_2 = 0.85$

156. a) to **b)**: For each part in question 155, use the sample information to determine the pooled estimate of the standard error of the Sampling Distribution of The Difference Between Two Proportions.

For problems 157–161, use the 5 step procedure to perform a hypothesis test. Include the following within your test:

a) state the null and alternative hypotheses.
b) calculate the expected results for the experiment assuming the null hypothesis is true and state the hypothesis test model.
c) formulate the decision rule.
d) compute the test statistic
e) state the conclusion and answer any question(s) posed in the problem.

157. According to a survey conducted by International Mass Retail Association, 85% of the people surveyed in 2004 said that U.S.-made goods have improved in the last few years. In 2000, a similar survey reported that 67% of the people said that U.S.-made goods have improved in the last few years. Assuming 1260 people were surveyed in 2004 while 1500 people were surveyed in 2000, then perform a hypothesis test to determine if there was a significantly greater proportion of people in 2004 who said that U.S.-made goods have improved in the last few years at $\alpha = 1\%$.

158. According to a League of Women Voters survey, 63% of males said that people have very little influence on government while 52% females said that people have very little influence on government. If there were 1050 women and 1275 males in the survey, perform a hypothesis test to determine if there is a significantly different proportion of males than females who believe that people have very little influence on government at $\alpha = 0.01$.

159. An educational researcher believes that students from small classes (i.e. class size less than 35) receive more A's and B's as compared to students from large classes (i.e. class size at least 35). To test this claim he randomly samples students from large and small classes and finds that of 400 students from small classes 150 received A's and B's, whereas 75 of the 350 students from large classes received A's and B's. Do these results support the researcher's claim at $\alpha = 5\%$?

160. A sociologist in the bay area believes that the proportion of residents of condominiums who are under 40 is lower outside the metropolitan areas than the proportion of residents of condominiums who are under 40 who live inside the metropolitan area. To test this claim he randomly surveys each population. The survey results are summarized below:

Inside Metropolitan Area	Outside Metropolitan Area
$x_1 = 40$	$x_2 = 15$
$n_1 = 120$	$n_2 = 90$

Do these results confirm the sociologist's belief at $\alpha = 1\%$?

161. According to research conducted by Brigham and Women's Hospital, two groups of women were studied to determine if the rate of heart attack was significantly different among those who took the vitamin E supplement versus the women who didn't take any vitamin E supplements. One group of 375 women who took vitamin E supplements of 100 or more units a day, while a second group of 425 women who didn't take any vitamin E supplements. The number of heart attacks for the women who took the vitamin E supplement was 15 while 32 of the women who didn't take the vitamin E supplement had heart attacks.

Do these sample results indicate there is a significant difference in the number of heart attacks among women who take vitamin E supplements versus women who do not take any vitamin E supplements at $\alpha = 5\%$?

WHAT DO YOU THINK?

162. What Do You Think?

Read the following article which appeared in the June 15, 1993 USA TODAY issue.

The placebo effect: Gauging the mind's role in healing

Long ignored and disparaged, the so-called placebo effect may finally be getting the respect it deserves. A new study out today in the Annals of Internal Medicine underlines the power the placebo effect - a person's expectation about the outcome of an illness or therapy and suggests that the success of many therapies may really spring from our own minds, experts say.

"The placebo effect is greatly under appreciated," says Dr. David Sobel, co-author of the *Healing Brain,* (Simon & Schuster). "When we treat patients with various drugs or procedures, we often forget that a sizable portion of the improvement nay not be due to therapy but to the positive expectations of the patient." The new study examined the effectiveness of increasingly popular mental techniques used for lowering high blood pressure. It found that the techniques—

medication, biofeedback and relaxation—were a little better than doing nothing, but no better than sham or placebo techniques. The finding may be bad news for people who paid a lot of money to lower blood pressure with the methods. But it also demonstrates that everyone has a natural ability to help themselves, and all that's needed is something to believe in. "I would say placebo, which reflects patient expectations, is very powerful medicine indeed," says Dr. Thomas L. Delbanco, Beth Israel Hospital, Boston, who helped conduct the study. "What we've shown, which is very important, is that the cognitive therapies have a small impact when you compare them to sham therapy, or placebo, then you find no difference at all. So, it is possible that the meditation and relaxation response basically reflects the placebo effect."

Pharmaceutical companies, academic researchers and the Food and Drug Administration are well aware of the placebo effect. New drugs and many other therapies approved in the USA, including those for cancer and heart disease, must be compared to a placebo. Carefully conducted studies show placebos alleviate symptoms in 10% to 70% of people, depending on their condition. On average, if you take 100 people with certain illnesses and give them a sugar pill, about a third would be expected to improve. If the new drug is better than the placebo, then it's considered effective. But, even though placebos work, doctors tend to view the effect as a nuisance, says Dr. Margaret Caudill, Mind/Body Medical Institute of New England Deaconess Hospital and Harvard Medical School, Boston. "Placebo is the X factor and we have to account for it because it keeps appearing," Caudill says. "But we often say, 'The effect is not real or meaningful, it's just placebo.' I say if it works, who cares."

Parents know the power of placebo and practice it every time they make a child's scrape feel better by kissing it. We might take offense if doctors took the same approach, but they could learn a few lessons. The first thing a parent does is show concern, compassion and thoughtfulness. And in their authority as a parent, they inspire confidence in the child when they tell them a kiss will stop the pain.

Sobel says studies show that doctors spend less than 18 seconds listening to a patient talk about 'where it hurts' before interrupting. And when treatment is prescribed, the emphasis is usually on technology or drugs.

"Some of the most powerful prescriptions are those filled in the natural pharmacy of the brain," says Sobel, who teaches doctors to use the placebo effect by improving the doctor-patient relationship and communication better with their patient's expectation that they will feel better after having seen the doctor.

Until the explosion of medical technology in the 20th century, placebo power was, by necessity, the foundation of medicine for thousands of years. And to maximize its benefit, many cultures mastered the use of symbols and rituals to trigger the response.

"The placebo effect is the triggering of our intrinsic healing mechanisms. You can do it with a pill, a surgical scalpel or headdress," Sobel says. "No treatment is immune to the effect of the positive expectation and this is why medicine has been so successful despite treatments throughout history which themselves were ineffective or harmful."

And even modern medicine makes use of symbols to exploit the placebo effect, the experts say.

In the U.S., we give magical powers to the doctor's white lab coat, the stethoscope and the laboratory test. Other cultures may use a wooden mask, a headdress and a rattle.

"We don't like to think that we use primitive symbols, but the lab coat and stethoscope definitely are," Caudill says. "Patients demand certain stereotypes."

Delbanco agrees: "Magic has always played an enormously important role in virtually every type of society. While we pride ourselves on our scientific foundations, there's no doubt in my mind that medicine will always be mixture of art and science. Part of that art is magic."

A small number of doctors are beginning to appreciate the placebo phenomenon as a tool for everyday medical practice, Sobel says.

By understanding its potential as well as its limitations, it should be possible to harness the power of placebo and boost the effectiveness of any medical therapy or procedure.

"Making the maximum use of placebo power in the modern doctor's office may mean displaying these symbols, or whatever is relevant, to particular types of patients," Delbanco says. "Some may prefer blue jeans to a lab coat."

Taking time to learn about a patient's particular belief system also may be a critical element and key part of communication.

Says Sobel: "A placebo is not a good substitute for an effective antibiotic or a life-saving surgery. But words can be scalpels. They can cut and damage, and when used effectively, they can also heal."

  a) Summarize the article and explain what is meant by the "placebo effect."

  b) Pharmaceutical companies purposely use certain colors for different type pills. For example, pills used for depression are usually small yellow pills, sedative pills are blue, and stimulants are red or pink pills. Using the ideas discussed within the article, explain why you think the pharmaceutical companies might purposely use these different color pills for the indicated ailments?

  c) For each of the following excerpts from different studies:

    —identify the treatment and placebo groups within the first two studies.

    —discuss what you think contributed to the unusual results in the studies.

  (i)   In the late 1950's, surgeons were using a new operation to relieve chest pain by making an incision in the patient's chest and tieing off the mammary artery. In the 1960's, Dr. E. Grey Diamond of the University of Kansas Medical Center who was suspicious of the benefit of this procedure decided to do a study to test the procedure. Dr. Diamond divided a group of patients into two small groups. One group received the actual surgery while the other group had sham surgery, that is, an incision was made on their chest but the artery was left intact. Both groups had identical results.

  (ii) Studies on the use of beta blockers have shown that these drugs can reduce the risk of heart attack in certain patients. In 1990, Dr. R. Horowitz published in Lancet the following results on beta blocker studies. Dr. Horowitz indicated that the patients who failed to take the beta blockers had a 2.6 times higher incidence of death than the patients who regularly took their medication. He also noted there was a higher death rate among the patients who failed to take the fake pill than the patients who took the fake pill regularly.

  (iii) In an article in a 1950 issue of the Journal of Clinical Investigation Dr. Sobel reported that a group of doctors were having difficultly treating a pregnant woman who was suffering from severe nausea and vomiting. As a last resort, the doctors gave her syrup of ipecac and told her it was a powerful new drug that would help her. Although ipecac is actually used to induce vomiting in people who have swallowed poison, the pregnant woman's nausea and vomiting stopped 20 minutes after taking the syrup of ipecac.

  d) With respect to the discussed ideas in the previous article, the unusual results mentioned in the previous studies and the concepts discussed in this chapter, what factors would you consider if you were conducting an experiment which involved a treatment and a control group?

163. What Do You Think?

A study entitled Personality Characteristics of Nightmare Sufferers appeared in the July, 1971 issue of The Journal of Nervous and Mental Disease contained in Table 12.9.

Table 12.9

Groups	Frequent		Sometimes		Seldom		Never	
	N	%	N	%	N	%	N	%
Males	14	9	41	25	38	24	67	42
Females	12	6	48	25	48	25	84	44
Total	26	7	89	25	86	25	151	43

Table 12.9 reports the percentages of nightmares in the 352 subjects of the study. In this study, a nightmare was operationally defined as a frightening dream that awakens the dreamer. The categories of the nightmares were defined as follows:

    frequent — *at least once a week;*
    sometimes — *at least once a month;*
    seldom — *at least once a year;*
    never — *it never happens.*

a) How many males participated in this study? How many females participated in this study?

b) Determine the sample proportion of the males that have experienced a nightmare and the sample proportion of females that have experienced a nightmare.

c) What percentage of the participants have experienced a nightmare? How does this result compare to the results you found in part (b)? Explain the relationship between a pooled sample proportion which was discussed in this chapter and this overall percentage of participants who experienced a nightmare.

d) Conduct a hypothesis test at $\alpha = 0.05$ to determine if the proportion of males who have experienced a nightmare is significantly different from the proportion of males who have never experienced a nightmare. Does your conclusion indicate that there is a significant difference? Explain.

e) Conduct a hypothesis test at $\alpha = 0.05$ to determine if the proportion of females who have experienced a nightmare is significantly greater than the proportion of males who have experienced a nightmare. Does your conclusion indicate that the females experience a significant greater proportion of nightmares than males? Explain.

164. What Do You Think?

In the April 25, 1994 issue of Newsweek magazine, an advertisement for the prescription nasal allergy medicine called Seldane-D appeared. In the ad, Seldane-D is advertised as a allergy medicine that "lets you stay alert as it relieves sneezing, runny nose, and itchy watery eyes plus stuffed-up nose." Within the advertisement, a brief summary regarding double-blind, parallel, controlled studies was included. Table 12.10 presents the percent of patients within the study who reported some general adverse reactions to the drugs or placebo administered to the patients of the study.

Table 12.10 Frequently (>1%) Reported Adverse Events for Seldane-D in Double-blind, Parallel, Controlled Clinical Trials*

| ADVERSE EVENT | Percent of Patients Reporting | | |
	SELDANE-D (n = 374)	Pseudo-ephedrine (n = 287)	Placebo (n = 193)
Central Nervous System			
Insomnia	25.9	26.8	6.2
Headache	17.4	17.1	22.3
Drowsiness/ Sedation	7.2	4.9	11.4
Nervousness	6.7	8.4	1.6
Anorexia	3.7	3.8	0.0
Fatigue	2.1	1.4	2.1
Restlessness	2.1	1.0	0.0
Irritability	1.1	0.0	1.0
Disorientation	1.1	0.0	0.5
Increased Energy	1.1	0.0	0.0
Hyperkinesia	1.1	1.0	0.0
Autonomic			
Dry Mouth/ Nose/Throat	21.7	21.3	11.4
Blurring of Vision	1.1	0.3	0.5
Gastrointestinal			
Nausea	4.5	6.6	5.2
Skin			
Rash	1.1	0.0	0.0
Cardiovascular			
Palpitations	2.4	3.8	0.5
Allergy Symptoms			
Sore Throat	1.9	1.7	1.0
Cough	1.6	0.3	1.0
Other			
Infection, Upper Respiratory	1.3	2.4	0.5
Taste Alternations	1.1	1.0	1.0

*SELDANE-D B.I.D., pseudoephedrine 120 mg B.I.D.

a) In the previous table, the words "double-blind and controlled clinical studies" are mentioned. Explain what you think these terms indicate to you about the study?

b) Examining the previous table, why do you think that Seldane-D was compared to a placebo in the clinical studies?

c) Pseudoephedrine is a decongestant in Seldane-D as well as in many over the counter allergy medicines. Why do you think that Seldane-D was compared to pseudoephedrine in the cinical studies?

d) Examining Table 12.10, what do you observe about the reported percentages for all three groups? In particular, which two groups seem to have similar percentage values? What might you contribute to the fact that these two groups have such similar results?

The advertisement for Seldane-D reported:

"In medical studies with hundreds of patients, there was no significant difference in drowsiness between those who took Seldane-D and those who took a sugar pill."

e) Which of the groups in Table 12.10 are they comparing when making this statement?

f) What are the reported percentages for drowsiness for these two groups?

If you were to use the information in Table 12.10 to conduct a hypothesis test to determine *if there is a significant difference in drowsiness between those who took Seldane-D and those who took a sugar pill at $\alpha = 0.01$:*

g) identify the two populations.

h) Which of these two groups would you identify as the treatment group and which group would represent the control group? Explain.

i) identify the two sample sizes.

j) identify the type of data that is collected and whether the data represents a measurement or a count. Explain.

k) state the null and alternative hypotheses for this test.

l) identify the sampling distribution used to conduct this test.

m) state the expected results for the sampling distribution. What assumption is needed determine these expected results?

n) state the value of the pooled estimate of the standard error of the sampling distribution. What assumption was made to determine its value?

o) using the sample data pertaining to this test in Table 12.10 determine your conclusion. Can you state that *there is a significant difference in drowsiness between those who took Seldane-D and those who took a sugar pill at α = 0.01?* .

If you were to use the information in Table 12.10 to conduct a hypothesis test to determine *if there is a significant difference in insomnia between those who took Seldane-D and those who took a sugar pill at α = 0.01*:

p) identify the two populations.

q) Which of these two groups would you identify as the treatment group and which group would represent the control group? Explain.

r) identify the two sample sizes.

s) identify the type of data that is collected and whether the data represents a measurement or a count. Explain.

t) state the null and alternative hypotheses for this test.

u) identify the sampling distribution used to conduct this test.

v) state the expected results for the sampling distribution. What assumption is needed to determine these expected results?

w) state the value of the pooled estimate of the standard error of the sampling distribution. What assumption was made to determine its value?

x) using the sample data pertaining to this test in Table 12.10 determine your conclusion. Can you state that *there is a significant difference in insomnia between those who took Seldane-D and those who took a sugar pill at α = 0.01?* .

165. **What Do You Think?**

Table 12.11 appeared in the December 16, 1993 issue of the New England Journal of Medicine and involved a study on whether moderate alcohol intake exerts a protective effect against coronary heart disease. Table 12.11 compared the characteristics of the case patients and control patients prior to the study. These characteristics are referred to as the base-line characteristics.

Table 12.11   BASE-LINE CHARACTERISTICS OF CASE PATIENTS AND CONTROLS

CHARACTERISTIC	CASE PATIENTS (N = 340)	CONTROLS (N = 340)	P VALUE
AGE (YR)	57.7 ± 9.6	57.7 ± 9.7	0.953
MALE SEX (%)	78.2	78.2	1.000
HIGH BLOOD PRESSURE (%)	34.7	25.1	0.008
BODY-MASS INDEX	25.9 ± 3.9	25.6 ± 4.0	0.402
HISTORY OF DIABETES (%)	13.5	7.6	0.018
FAMILY HISTORY OF PREMATURE MYOCARDIAL INFARCTION (%)	22.1	15.3	0.030
TYPE A PERSONALITY (%)	58.8		
PHYSICAL-ACTIVITY INDEX	43.5	49.4	0.017
≥ 2500 KCAL/WK (%)		55.0	0.004
CIGARETTE SMOKING (%)			<0.001
NEVER	25.4		
FORMER	31.6	31.6	
CURRENT	43.1	40.7	
TOTAL CALORIES/DAY	2482 ± 927	27.7	0.050
CALORIES AS SATURATED FAT (%)	13.1 ± 3.4	2354 ± 773	<0.001

a) Why do you believe that these base-line characteristics of the case patients and the controls are computed prior to the study?

b) In a treatment group versus a control group study, what is assumed about the characteristics of these groups prior to the treatment?

c) With regards to the high blood pressure characteristic, what can you say about the difference between the case patients and the controls?

d) With regards to the history of diabetes characteristic, what can you say about the difference between the case patients and the controls?

e) With regards to the type A personality characteristic, what can you say about the difference between the case patients and the controls?

f) With regards to the history of myocardial infarction characteristic, what can you say about the difference between the case patients and the controls?

PROJECTS

166. Hypothesis Testing Project

  A. Selection of a topic.

    1. Select a reported fact or claim about two population proportions made in a local newspaper, magazine or other source.

    2. Suggested topics:

      a) More men smoke than women! Test the claim that the proportion of men who smoke is higher than the proportion of women who smoke.

      b) More men vote than women! Test the claim that the proportion of men who vote is higher than the proportion of women who vote.

      c) Women get better grades! Test the claim that the proportion of women whose G.P.A. is higher than 3.3 is greater than the proportion of men with a G.P.A. higher than 3.3.

      d) According to the Mars Company, each package of M&M's should contain 30% brown, 20% yellow, 20% red, and 10% each of green, orange and blue. Test the claim that the proportion of brown M&M's is significantly greater than the proportion of red M&M's.

  B. Use the following procedure to test the claim selected in Part A.

    1. State the claim, and identify the populations referred to in the statement of claim, also indicate the source.

    2. State your opinion regarding the claim (True or False) and clearly identify the populations you plan to sample to support your opinion.

    3. State the null and alternative hypotheses.

    4. Develop and state a procedure for the selection of a random sample from each population. Indicate the technique you are going to use to obtain your sample data.

    5. Perform the experiment and compute the following:

      a) $\mu_{\hat{p}_1 - \hat{p}_2}$

      b) p (pooled value for p)

      c) $s_{\hat{p}_1 - \hat{p}_2}$

      d) Critical z score(s)

    6. State the Decision Rule.

    7. Calculate the test statistic: z

    8. Construct a hypothesis testing model and place the test statistic on the model

    9. Formulate the appropriate conclusion and interpret the conclusion with respect to your opinion (as stated in STEP 2).

167. Read a research article from a professional journal in a field such as medicine, education, marketing, science, social science, etc. Write a summary of the research article that includes the following:

  a) Name of article, author, and journal (include volume number and date).

  b) Statement of research problem.

  c) The null and alternative hypotheses.

  d) How the experiment was conducted (give the sample sizes and how the sampling was done.

  e) Determine the test statistic statistic, p-value and the level of significance.

  f) State the conclusion in terms of the null and alternative hypotheses.

ANALYZING THE DATABASE USING TECHNOLOGY

The following exercises refer to file DATABASE listed in Appendix A. Using a technological tool, answer each exercise.

168. For the variables: SEX and AST.
a) Conduct a hypothesis test to determine if there is a difference between males and females regarding the question—"Do you believe in Astrology?"
b) State the null and alternative hypotheses.
c) Is the null hypothesis rejected? Why? What is the p-value.

169. For the variable names: SEX and HND.
a) Conduct a hypothesis test to determine if there is a difference between males and females regarding the proportion of *left handedness* for each gender.
b) State the null and alternative hypotheses.
c) Is the null hypothesis rejected? Why? What is the p-value.
d) Conduct a hypothesis test that compares *the proportion of right handedness* for each gender.

 CHAPTER TESTS:

170. Write the notation used to represent each of the following:
a) a population proportion
b) the proportion for population 2
c) a sample proportion
d) the proportion for a sample selected from population 1
e) the size of a sample
f) the sample size for a sample selected from population 2
g) the difference between two sample proportions
h) the number of occurrences or observations possessing a particular characteristic within a sample
i) the formula for the proportion of a sample selected from population 1

171. Using the following information:

$$p_1 = 0.48, n_1 = 970, \text{ and } x_1 = 470$$

$$p_2 = 0.56, n_2 = 1060, \text{ and } x_2 = 670$$

determine:
a) the proportion of the sample selected from population 1
b) the proportion of the sample selected from population 2
c) if the samples are considered large
d) the difference between the sample proportions: $\hat{p}_1 - \hat{p}_2$
e) the shape of the Sampling Distribution of $\hat{p}_1 - \hat{p}_2$
f) mean of the Sampling Distribution of $\hat{p}_1 - \hat{p}_2$
g) standard deviation of the Sampling Distribution of $\hat{p}_1 - \hat{p}_2$
h) standard error of the Difference Between Two Proportions

172. According to a poll conducted by a national health magazine, 295 of 1200 male readers and 694 of the 1275 female readers surveyed were on a diet at the time of its poll. Using this information:

a) identify the two population proportions.
b) identify each sample proportion.
c) identify each sample size.
d) determine if the two samples are considered large.
e) compute the value of each sample proportion.
f) compute the estimate of the standard error of the difference between two proportions.
g) compute the estimate of the standard deviation of the Sampling Distribution of the Difference Between Two Proportions.

173. The Sampling Distribution of the Difference Between Two Proportions has the following characteristics:
a) the mean of the Sampling Distribution of the Difference Between Two Proportions, denoted _____, is determined by the formula:

$$\mu_{\hat{p}_1 - \hat{p}_2} = \text{_____} - \text{_____},$$

where p_1 represents the _____ proportion of _____ 1 and p_2 represents the _____ proportion of _____ 2.

b) The formula for the estimate of the standard deviation of the Sampling Distribution of the Difference Between Two Proportions, denoted by _____, is given by the formula:

$$s_{\hat{p}_1 - \hat{p}_2} = \text{_____}$$

c) The Sampling Distribution of the Difference Between Two Proportions is approximately normal when:

n_1 _____, $n_1(1\text{-}p_1)$, n_2 _____ and n_2 _____ are all greater than _____.

174. One correct formula for the pooled sample proportion, $\hat{p}$, is:

(a) $\dfrac{\hat{p}_1 + \hat{p}_2}{2}$ (b) $\dfrac{x_1 + x_2}{n_1 + n_2}$ (c) $\dfrac{\hat{p}_1 + \hat{p}_2}{x_1 + x_2}$ (d) $\dfrac{\hat{p}_1 + \hat{p}_2}{n_1 + n_2}$

175. In a random sample of size 200, $x_1 = 120$ and in another independent random sample of size 300, $x_2 = 140$, then the "pooled" formula for $s_{\hat{p}_1 - \hat{p}_2}$ is approximately equal to .

176. The pooled sample proportion formulas are: $\hat{p} = $ ____ or ____.

177. The following information concerning hypothesis tests for two proportions. For each
    (i) define the two population proportions.
    (ii) state the null and alternative hypotheses.
    (iii) identify the type of test: 1TT or 2TT.
    a) The League of Women Voters would like to determine if a greater proportion of females than males believe that people can have at least some influence on government.
    b) The American Association for Marriage and Family Therapy wants to conduct a study to determine whether the percentage of divorce is smaller for couples who don't live together before marriage than for those who do live together before marriage.

178. According to a CNN/Gallup phone poll on ownership of guns within the USA, it was reported that 59% of gun owners said that stricter gun laws would eventually lead to a total ban while 50% of the non-gun owners believe that stricter gun laws would eventually lead to total ban.

Using the 5 step procedure perform a hypothesis test at $\alpha = 1\%$ to answer the question:

Can we conclude from the sample data that the proportion of non-gun owners who believe that stricter gun laws will eventually lead to total ban on guns is significantly less than the proportion of gun owners who believe this statement to be true?

Assume that the pollsters interviewed 1025 gun owners and 1215 non-gun owners.

For each of the following problems, use the 5 step procedure to perform a hypothesis test. Include the following within your test:

    a) state the null and alternative hypotheses.
    b) calculate the expected results for the experiment assuming the null hypothesis is true and state the hypothesis test model.
    c) formulate the decision rule.
    d) compute the test statistic
    e) state the conclusion and answer any question(s) posed in the problem.

179. According to the Department of Transportation (DOT), a significantly greater proportion of Southwest airline flights arrived on time as compared to on time flights for Alaska airlines. Perform a hypothesis test at $\alpha = 5\%$, if 84% of a sample 1250 flights for Southwest airlines arrived on time and 80.9% of a sample size of 1175 flights for Alaska airlines arrived on time. Do you agree with the DOT's claim?

180. In a double blind clinical study of 725 subjects, a prescription medication for seasonal allergy called Hismanal was administered to a group of 400 subjects while a second group of 325 subjects received a sugar pill for their allergies. The number of subjects suffering from drowsiness while taking Hismanal was 120 while the number of subjects who reported drowsiness taking the sugar pill was 75. Based on the sample data, can one conclude that there was a significant difference in the proportion of drowsiness for the subjects on Hismanal and the sugar pill at $\alpha = 1\%$?

Hypothesis Test Involving Two Population Means Using Independent Samples

Contents

13.1   INTRODUCTION

In Chapter 11, we discussed hypothesis tests involving one population mean. In this chapter we will study hypothesis tests that involve the comparison of two population means where an independent random sample is selected from each population to determine if the population means are statistically different.

For example:

- Is there a difference in the mean physical fitness scores of third grade girls and boys? This involves the comparison of two populations: the population of physical fitness scores for the girls and the population of physical fitness scores for the boys.
- Will Goodday automobile tires give better average mileage wear than Goodpoor tires? (Neither company owns a blimp!) The mileage data for Goodday tires would comprise one of the populations and the mileage data for the Goodpoor tires would comprise the other population.
- Does a toothpaste that contains fluoride significantly lower the mean number of cavities as compared to the toothpaste without fluoride? One population represents those people that used the toothpaste with fluoride and the other population represents those people that used the tooth paste without fluoride.

To answer these questions about whether there is a significant difference between the means of two independent populations, we have to select a random sample from each population, calculate the mean of each sample and determine the difference between the sample means. We would then have to test whether the **difference between the two sample means** is significant enough to conclude that the two population means are different. To help us perform this test, we need to examine the **sampling distribution of the difference between two means.**

13.2   THE SAMPLING DISTRIBUTION OF THE DIFFERENCE BETWEEN TWO MEANS

To perform a hypothesis test involving two population means, an **independent random sample**[1] from each population will be selected and compared to determine whether **the difference** between the two sample means is significantly different. This is illustrated in Figure 13.1.

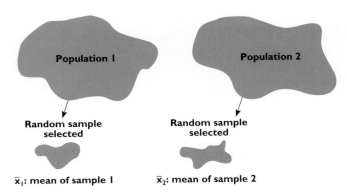

FIGURE 13.1

To determine if the difference between the sample means, denoted by $d = \bar{x}_1 - \bar{x}_2$, is statistically significant, we must compare this difference to a distribution formed by calculating the difference between the means of all possible random sample pairs, where the first random sample with size n_1 for the pair is selected from an infinite population 1 and the second random sample with size n_2 of the pair is selected from an infinite population 2. This sampling distribution is referred to as the **sampling distribution of the difference between two means** or the **sampling distribution of $\bar{x}_1 - \bar{x}_2$**. This is illustrated in Figure 13.2.

The distribution of the differences between the means of all possible independent random sample pairs form the sampling distribution of the difference between two means.

Let's now examine Theorem 13.1 which explains the properties of the sampling distribution of the differences between two means where the population standard deviations are known and the sample sizes are greater than 30.

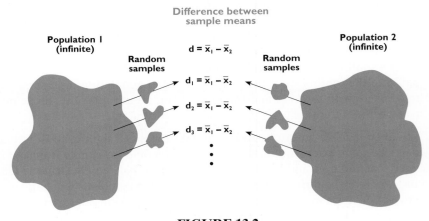

FIGURE 13.2

---

[1]By independent random samples, we mean that the selection of one random sample has no influence upon the selection of the other random sample. See chapter 12 for definition of independent samples.

Theorem 13.1   Characteristics of the Sampling Distribution of The Difference Between Two Means with Population Standard Deviations Known

---

Given two populations, referred to as population 1 and population 2, with means μ_1 and μ_2 respectively and standard deviations σ_1, and σ_2, respectively. If all possible independent random samples of size n_1 and n_2 (where **both sample sizes are greater than 30**) are selected from population 1 and population 2 respectively, the mean of all these pairs of samples are determined, and the differences between the pairs of sample means $(\bar{x}_1 - \bar{x}_2)$ are computed, then the sampling distribution of the difference between two means is formed and has the following characteristics.

1. The **mean of the sampling distribution of the difference between two means**, denoted by $\mu_{\bar{x}_1 - \bar{x}_2}$, is:

$$\mu_{\bar{x}_1 - \bar{x}_2} = \mu_1 - \mu_2$$

2. The **standard deviation** of the sampling distribution of the difference between two means, denoted by $\sigma_{\bar{x}_1 - \bar{x}_2}$, is:

$$\sigma_{\bar{x}_1 - \bar{x}_2} = \sqrt{\frac{\sigma_1^2}{n_1} + \frac{\sigma_2^2}{n_2}}$$

This standard deviation is also referred to as **the standard error of the difference between two means**.

3. The sampling distribution of the difference between two means is **approximately normal**.

In most instances the standard deviations of the two populations are ***unknown***. Thus, the **estimates** of the two population standard deviations, s_1 and s_2 respectively, are used to approximate the two population standard deviations, σ_1 and σ_2 respectively, and the Central Limit Theorem may not apply. That is, the sampling distribution of the difference between two means may not be approximated by a normal distribution. However, if the two populations are approximately normal with equal standard deviations, and the sample standard deviations are used to estimate the population standard deviations, then the distribution of the test statistic can be approximated by a *t* distribution. This result and the characteristics of the sampling distribution of the difference between two means with population standard deviations unknown is stated in Theorem 13.2.

Theorem 13.2   Characteristics of the Sampling Distribution of the Difference Between Two Means with Population Standard Deviations Unknown

---

Given two approximately normal populations, referred to as population 1 and population 2, with means μ_1 and μ_2 and approximately equal standard deviations σ_1 and σ_2 respectively. If all possible independent random samples (i.e. the selection of one random sample has no influence upon the selection of the other random sample) of size n_1 and n_2 are selected from

---

Theorem 13.2   Characteristics of the Sampling Distribution of the Difference Between Two Means with Population Standard Deviations Unknown (continued)

population 1 and population 2 respectively, the means of all these pairs of samples are determined, and the differences between the pairs of sample means $(\bar{x}_1 - \bar{x}_2)$ are computed, then the sampling distribution of the difference between two means has the following characteristics:

1. The mean of the sampling distribution of the difference between two means, denoted by $\mu_{\bar{x}_1 - \bar{x}_2}$, is:

$$\mu_{\bar{x}_1 - \bar{x}_2} = \mu_1 - \mu_2$$

2. The standard error of the difference between two means cannot be determined since the population standard deviations, σ_1 and σ_2, are unknown. However, since the two sample standard deviations, s_1 and s_2, provide good estimates of the population standard deviations, σ_1 and σ_2, we can combine the sample standard deviations to obtain **an estimate of the standard error of the difference between two means**. The process of combining the two independent sample results to provide an estimate of this standard error is referred to as **pooling**. The formula to calculate this pooled estimate for the standard error, written $s_{\bar{x}_1 - \bar{x}_2}$, is:

$$s_{\bar{x}_1 - \bar{x}_2} = \sqrt{\frac{(n_1 - 1)s_1^2 + (n_2 - 1)s_2^2}{n_1 + n_2 - 2} \cdot \left(\frac{1}{n_1} + \frac{1}{n_2}\right)}$$

where:

s_1 is the estimate of the standard deviation of population 1.
n_1 is the sample size for the sample selected from population 1.
s_2 is the estimate of the standard deviation of population 2.
n_2 is the sample size for the sample selected from population 2.

3. The distribution of the test statistic t defined as:

$$t = \frac{(\bar{x}_1 - \bar{x}_2) - \mu_{\bar{x}_1 - \bar{x}_2}}{s_{\bar{x}_1 - \bar{x}_2}}$$

is approximated by a t distribution with degrees of freedom given by: $df = n_1 + n_2 - 2$.

13.3   HYPOTHESIS TESTING INVOLVING TWO POPULATION MEANS AND UNKNOWN POPULATION STANDARD DEVIATIONS

Applying the general five step hypothesis testing procedure discussed in Chapter 9 to hypotheses involving **two population means**, where the population standard deviations are **unknown**, we will develop a hypothesis testing procedure that will allow us to determine if there is a significant difference between the means of two independent population. This type of hypothesis test is often referred to as a **two sample t test**.

Two Sample t Test

Step 1   Formulate the two hypotheses, H_o and H_a.
Null Hypothesis, H_o:
The **Null Hypothesis, H_o**, in testing the difference between two population means has the following form:

Null Hypothesis Form

H_o: There is **no difference** between the mean of population 1, written μ_1, and the mean of population 2, written μ_2.
This is symbolized as:

$$H_o: \mu_1 - \mu_2 = 0$$

By stating H_o as there is no difference between the population means, μ_1 and μ_2, we are making the assumption that μ_1 **equals** μ_2. Consequently, only by **rejecting the null hypothesis**, H_o, can we conclude that there is a *statistically significant difference* between μ_1 and μ_2. Therefore, by rejecting H_o, we can conclude that the alternative hypothesis is true.

Alternative Hypothesis, H_a
The **Alternative Hypothesis, H_a**, in testing the difference between two population means, has one of the following three forms:

Form (a): Less Than Form for H_a

H_a: the mean of population 1, written μ_1, is **less than** the mean of population 2, written μ_2.
This can also be stated as: **the difference $(\mu_1 - \mu_2)$ is significantly less than zero.**
This is symbolized as:

$$H_a: \mu_1 - \mu_2 < 0$$

Form (b): Greater Than Form for H_a

H_a: the mean of population 1, written μ_1, is **greater than** the mean of population 2, written μ_2.
This can also be stated as: **the difference $(\mu_1 - \mu_2)$ is significantly greater than zero.**

This is symbolized as:

$$H_a: \mu_1 - \mu_2 > 0$$

Form (c): Not Equal Form for H_a

H_a: the mean of population 1, written μ_1, is **not equal to** the mean of population 2, written μ_2.
This can also be stated as: **difference $(\mu_1 - \mu_2)$ is significantly different from zero.**
This is symbolized as:

$$H_a: \mu_1 - \mu_2 \neq 0$$

Step 2 Determine the model to test the null hypothesis, H_o. Under the assumption H_o is true, calculate the expected results.

Since we are testing the hypothesis that the **difference between two population means $(\mu_1 - \mu_2)$** is significantly different from zero by **using the difference between two sample means, $\bar{x}_1 - \bar{x}_2$**, then we will use the **sampling distribution of the difference between two means as the hypothesis test model.**

Using Theorem 13.2, and under the assumption H_o is true (that is: $\mu_1 - \mu_2 = 0$ is true), then:

the expected results for a two sample *t* test are:

a) The test statistic hypothesis testing model is approximately a *t* Distribution with degrees of freedom:

$$df = n_1 + n_2 - 2$$

b) The mean of the sampling distribution of the difference between two means is given by the formula:

$$\mu_{\bar{x}_1 - \bar{x}_2} = \mu_1 - \mu_2$$

Under the assumption H_o is true (i.e. $\mu_1 - \mu_2 = 0$ is true), then we can state that:

$$\mu_{\bar{x}_1 - \bar{x}_2} = 0$$

c) The estimate of the standard error of the of the difference between two means, written $s_{\bar{x}_1 - \bar{x}_2}$, is given by the formula:

$$s_{\bar{x}_1 - \bar{x}_2} = \sqrt{\frac{(n_1 - 1)s_1^2 + (n_2 - 1)s_2^2}{n_1 + n_2 - 2} \cdot \left(\frac{1}{n_1} + \frac{1}{n_2}\right)}$$

Step 3   Formulate the decision rule.
   a) Determine the type of alternative hypothesis: directional or non-directional.
   b) Determine the type of test: 1TT or 2TT.
   c) Identify the significance level: $\alpha = 1\%$ or $\alpha = 5\%$.
   d) Find the critical t score(s).
   e) Construct the hypothesis test model.
   f) State the decision rule.

Step 4   Analyze the sample data.
   Randomly select an independent sample from each population and calculate the mean of each sample, denoted $\bar{x}_1$ and $\bar{x}_2$. **Determine the difference between the two sample means, the statistical result, using the formula: $d = \bar{x}_1 - \bar{x}_2$.** Calculate the t score of the difference between the two sample means using the formula:

$$t = \frac{(\bar{x}_1 - \bar{x}_2)}{s_{\bar{x}_1 - \bar{x}_2}}$$

This is referred to as the **test statistic**.

Step 5   State the conclusion.
   Compare the test statistic, t, to the critical t score(s), t_c, of the decision rule and draw one of the following conclusions:

(a)		(b)
Reject H_o and	or	Fail to reject H_o
Accept H_a at α		at α

In summary, the procedure just used outlined to perform a **two sample *t* test**, there were three refinements to the general hypothesis testing procedure developed in Chapter 9. They were:

1. The test statistic hypothesis testing model is a *t* distribution, with df $= n_1 + n_2 - 2$.
2. The properties of the sampling distribution of the difference between two means are used to calculate the expected values.

3. The formula to calculate the test statistic t is:

$$t = \frac{(\bar{x}_1 - \bar{x}_2)}{s_{\bar{x}_1 - \bar{x}_2}}$$

Example 13.1 illustrates the use of a two sample *t* test to perform a hypothesis test involving two population means.

EXAMPLE 13.1

A computer programming aptitude test was given to 50 men and 60 women. The women's sample mean test score was 84 with s = 7, while the men's mean test score was 82 with s = 5. Can one conclude that there is a significant difference between the mean test scores for the population of men and the population of women on this test? (Use a = 1%)

Solution

Step 1   Formulate the hypotheses.

If we let population 1 represent the men's computer aptitude scores and population 2 represent the women's computer aptitude scores then the null hypotheses is:

Since we are trying to show that there is a significant difference between the population mean test scores of the men and women we state the null hypothesis in such a way that by *rejecting* H_o we can conclude that there *is* a difference between the population means. Therefore, we will always state the null hypothesis as "there is no difference between the mean of population 1 and the mean of population 2." This is symbolized as: $\mu_1 - \mu_2 = 0$.

H_o: There is **no difference** between the population means of the computer programming aptitude test scores for men and women.

In symbols, H_o: $\mu_1 - \mu_2 = 0$

We are trying to show that there is a difference between the population mean for the men's and women's aptitude test scores. Thus, the alternative hypothesis is non-directional and is stated as:

H_a: The difference between the population mean computer aptitude test scores for the men and women **is significantly different** from *zero*.

This is symbolized as: H_a: $\mu_1 - \mu_2 \neq 0$

Step 2   Determine the model to test the null hypothesis, H_o.

To test the null hypothesis an independent random sample is selected from each population. The sample results are summarized in Table 13.1.

TABLE 13.1

Random Sample Selected from Population 1 (Men)	Random Sample Selected from Population 2 (Women)
$\bar{x}_1 = 82$	$\bar{x}_2 = 84$
$s_1 = 5$	$s_2 = 7$
$n_1 = 50$	$n_2 = 60$

Since the difference between the two sample means, $\bar{x}_1 - \bar{x}_2$, will be used to determine if $(\mu_1 - \mu_2)$ is **significantly different** from **zero, the expected results** are:

a) The test statistic is approximated by a t distribution with degrees of freedom:

$$df = n_1 + n_2 - 2 = 108.$$

b) The mean of the sampling distribution of the difference between two means is:

$$\mu_{\bar{x}_1 - \bar{x}_2} = \mu_1 - \mu_2$$
$$= 0$$

c) The estimate of the standard error of the of the difference between two means formula is:

$$s_{\bar{x}_1 - \bar{x}_2} = \sqrt{\frac{(n_1 - 1)s_1^2 + (n_2 - 1)s_2^2}{n_1 + n_2 - 2} \cdot \left(\frac{1}{n_1} + \frac{1}{n_2}\right)}$$

Substituting $s_1=5$, $n_1=50$, $s_2=7$ and $n_2=60$ into the formula for $s_{\bar{x}_1 - \bar{x}_2}$, we have:

$$s_{\bar{x}_1 - \bar{x}_2} = \sqrt{\frac{(n_1 - 1)s_1^2 + (n_2 - 1)s_2^2}{n_1 + n_2 - 2} \cdot \left(\frac{1}{n_1} + \frac{1}{n_2}\right)}$$

$$= \sqrt{\frac{(50 - 1)5^2 + (60 - 1)7^2}{50 + 60 - 2} \left(\frac{1}{50} + \frac{1}{60}\right)}$$

$$= \sqrt{\frac{(49)25 + (59)49}{108} \left(\frac{1}{50} + \frac{1}{60}\right)}$$

$$\approx \sqrt{(38.11111)(0.03666)}$$

$$s_{\bar{x}_1 - \bar{x}_2} \approx 1.18$$

Figure 13.3 illustrates the hypothesis testing model.

distribution of the test statistic
(is a t Distribution with $df = 108$)

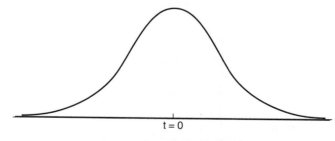

t = 0

FIGURE 13.3

Step 3 Formulate the decision rule.

a) The alternative hypothesis is non-directional since we are trying to show that there is a significant difference between the population mean scores of the men and women.

b) The type of hypothesis test is two-tailed (2TT).

c) The significance level is: $\alpha = 1\%$.

d) To determine the critical t scores t_{LC} and t_{RC}, for a two-tailed test with $\alpha = 1\%$ and $df = 108$ use Table III.

From TABLE III, the critical *t* scores are:

$$t_{LC} = -2.63 \qquad \text{and} \qquad t_{RC} = 2.63$$

e) Figure 13.4(a) illustrates the decision rule for this hypothesis test.

FIGURE 13.4(a)

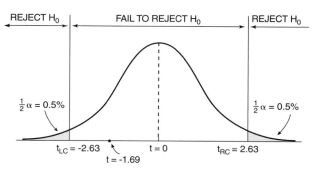

FIGURE 13.4(b)

The decision rule is:

f) Reject H_o if the test statistic t is either less than $t_{LC} = -2.63$ or more than $t_{RC} = 2.63$.

Step 4   Analyze the sample data.
Calculate the test statistic *t* using

$$t = \frac{(\bar{x}_1 - \bar{x}_2)}{s_{\bar{x}_1 - \bar{x}_2}}$$

The difference between the two sample means, $\bar{x}_1 - \bar{x}_2$, is:

$$\bar{x}_1 - \bar{x}_2 = 82 - 84$$
$$= -2$$

Since $s_{\bar{x}_1 - \bar{x}_2} = 1.18$, the test statistic *t* is:

$$t = \frac{(\bar{x}_1 - \bar{x}_2)}{s_{\bar{x}_1 - \bar{x}_2}}$$

$$t = \frac{-2}{1.18}$$

$$t \approx -1.69$$

Step 5   State the conclusion.
Using Figure 13.4(b), since the test statistic t = −1.69 falls between the critical t scores −2.63 and 2.63, we fail to reject H_o at $\alpha = 1\%$. Therefore, we conclude that the difference in the population mean aptitude test scores for men and women is **not statistically significant** at $\alpha = 1\%$.

E X A M P L E   1 3 . 2

A sociologist claims that women in the South marry at a younger age than women in the North. An independent random sample of 40 recently married southern women had a mean age of 21 years with s = 2 years. An independent random sample of 40 recently married northern women had a mean age of 23.5 years with s = 3 years. Do these sample results support the sociologist's claim at $\alpha = 5\%$?

Solution

Step 1   Formulate the hypotheses.

If we let population 1 represent the ages of the southern brides and population 2 represent the ages of the northern brides then the null hypothesis is:

H_o: there is **no difference** in the population mean age of southern and northern brides.

In symbols we have, $H_o: \mu_1 - \mu_2 = 0$.

H_a: the population mean age for southern brides is **less than** the population mean age of northern brides.

In symbols we have, $H_a: \mu_1 - \mu_2 < 0$.

Step 2   Determine the model to test the null hypothesis, H_o.

To test the null hypothesis, an independent random sample is selected from each population and the sample results are summarized in Table 13.2.

TABLE 13.2   Summary of the Data for the Random Samples Selected from Each Population

Population 1 (South)	Population 2 (North)
$\bar{x}_1 = 21$	$\bar{x} = 23.5$
$s_1 = 2$	$s_2 = 3$
$n_1 = 40$	$n_2 = 40$

Since the differences between the two sample means, $\bar{x}_1 - \bar{x}_2$, will be used to determine if $(\mu_1 - \mu_2)$ is significantly less than zero, the expected results are:

a) The test statistic is approximated by a t distribution with $df = 78$.

b) The mean of the sampling distribution of the difference between two means is:

$$\mu_{\bar{x}_1 - \bar{x}_2} = \mu_1 - \mu_2$$
$$= 0$$

c) The estimate of the standard error of the difference between two means is:

$$s_{\bar{x}_1 - \bar{x}_2} = \sqrt{\frac{(n_1 - 1)s_1^2 + (n_2 - 1)s_2^2}{n_1 + n_2 - 2} \cdot \left(\frac{1}{n_1} + \frac{1}{n_2}\right)}$$

Substituting $s_1 = 2$, $n_1 = 40$, $s_2 = 3$ and $n_2 = 40$ into $s_{\bar{x}_1 - \bar{x}_2}$, we have:

$$s_{\bar{x}_1 - \bar{x}_2} = \sqrt{\frac{(n_1 - 1)s_1^2 + (n_2 - 1)s_2^2}{n_1 + n_2 - 2} \cdot \left(\frac{1}{n_1} + \frac{1}{n_2}\right)}$$

$$= \sqrt{\frac{(40 - 1)2^2 + (40 - 1)3^2}{40 + 40 - 2} \left(\frac{1}{40} + \frac{1}{40}\right)}$$

$$= \sqrt{\frac{(39)4 + (39)9}{78} \left(\frac{1}{40} + \frac{1}{40}\right)}$$

$$\approx \sqrt{(6.5)(0.05)}$$

$$s_{\bar{x}_1 - \bar{x}_2} \approx 0.57$$

Figure 13.5 illustrates the hypothesis testing model.

distribution of the test statistic
(is a *t* Distribution with *df* = 78)

$t = 0$

FIGURE 13.5

Step 3   Formulate the decision rule.
  a) The alternative hypothesis is directional since we are trying to show that the population mean age of southern brides is significantly less than the population mean age of northern brides.
  b) The type of hypothesis test is one-tailed (i.e. 1TT) on the **left side** since we are trying to show that $(\mu_1 - \mu_2)$ is **less than** zero.
  c) The significance level is: $\alpha = 5\%$.
  d) For a one-tailed test on the left side with $\alpha = 5\%$ and $df = 78$ the critical t score, t_c, using Table III is $t_c = -1.66$.
  e) Figure 13.6(a) illustrates the decision rule for this hypotheses test.

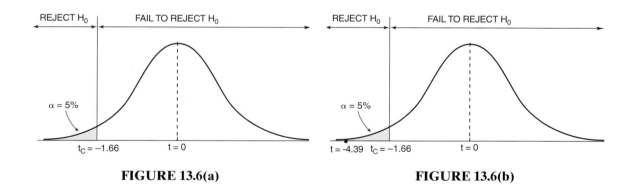

| REJECT H₀ | FAIL TO REJECT H₀ | | REJECT H₀ | FAIL TO REJECT H₀ |

$\alpha = 5\%$ $\alpha = 5\%$

$t_c = -1.66$ $t = 0$ $t = -4.39$ $t_c = -1.66$ $t = 0$

FIGURE 13.6(a)   **FIGURE 13.6(b)**

The decision rule is:
  f) Reject H_o if the test statistic t is less than $t_c = -1.66$.

Step 4   Analyze the sample data.
Calculate the test statistic t where:

$$\bar{x}_1 - \bar{x}_2 = 21 - 23.5 = -2.5 \text{ and } s_{\bar{x}_1 - \bar{x}_2} \approx 0.57$$

The test statistic is $t = \dfrac{-2.5}{0.57} \approx -4.39$.

Step 5   State the conclusion.

Examine Figure 13.6(b). The test statistic t = –4.39 is *less than* the critical t score –1.66 we *reject* H_o *and* accept H_a at $\alpha = 5\%$. Therefore, we can agree with the sociologist's claim that women in the south marry at a younger mean age than women in the north. _____ ∎

13.4   HYPOTHESIS TESTS COMPARING TREATMENT AND CONTROL GROUPS

Frequently, an experimenter wants to compare two populations or groups where one group receives a treatment called the **treatment group**, while a second group called the **control group** does not receive the treatment. Ideally, the members of both groups are similar in every way except that the members of the control group are not given the treatment.

For example, a new medication is tested to determine if it is effective. A random sample of the population called the treatment group is selected and given this new medication. Another random sample of the population called the control group is selected and does not receive the medication. However, the control group is given a placebo, that is, a pill which looks like the real medication but does not contain the medication. This is done to guard against the psychological effect of the treatment group feeling better not because of the new medication but because they were picked for the special treatment. This type of experimental design is called a **single-blind study**, because the *subjects* do **not** know who is receiving the *real* medication. Sometimes it has been shown that studies have been affected by the *doctors* who are administering the medication, since *they* know who is and who is not receiving the placebo. Consequently, it becomes necessary to conduct a study where *both* the subjects and doctors are *not* aware of who is receiving the medication and who is receiving the placebo. This type of experimental design is called a **double-blind study**.

Example 13.3 illustrates the comparison of treatment verses control groups using a two sample *t* test.

EXAMPLE 13.3

A pharmaceutical company has developed a diet pill called, Effective Anti-Hunger Tablet (E.A.T.), which the company believes will significantly reduce an individual's weight at the end of one week. To support their claim, the company selects 30 overweight individuals and randomly divides them into two independent groups: a **treatment** group of 15 subjects who are administered the diet pill E.A.T. and a *control* group of 15 subjects who are given a *placebo* tablet (i.e. **a pill that has *no effect* on weight**).

After one week, the treatment group had a sample mean weight loss of $\bar{x} = 7.1$ lbs. with s = 3.6 lbs. while the control group had a sample mean weight loss of $\bar{x} = 4.2$ lbs. with s = 2.3 lbs.

Can the company conclude that their diet pill E.A.T. will significantly reduce an individual's weight within one week at $\alpha = 5\%$?

Remark: In this study the administration of the diet pill E.A.T. to the treatment group is the only difference between the two groups. Therefore, if we can show a significant difference between the treatment and control groups then this *difference can be attributed only to the treatment (the diet pill).*

Solution

Step 1   Formulate the hypotheses.

If we let population 1 represent the treatment group and population 2 represent the control group then the null hypothesis is:

H_o: there is **no difference** in the population mean weight loss for the treatment group and the control group.

In symbols we have, H_o: $\mu_1 - \mu_2 = 0$

H_a: the population mean weight loss for the treatment group is **greater than** the population mean weight loss for the control group.

In symbols we have, H_a: $\mu_1 - \mu_2 > 0$.

Step 2 Determine the model to test the null hypothesis, H_o.

To test the null hypothesis the company selects 30 overweight individuals and randomly divides them into two independent groups and the sample results are summarized in Table 13.3.

TABLE 13.3   Summary of the Data for the Random Samples Selected from Each Population

Population 1 (Treatment)	Population 2 (Control)
$\bar{x}_1 = 7.1$	$\bar{x}_2 = 4.2$
$s_1 = 3.6$	$s_2 = 2.3$
$n_1 = 15$	$n_2 = 15$

Since the differences between the two sample means, $\bar{x}_1 - \bar{x}_2$, will be used to determine if $(\mu_1 - \mu_2)$ is significantly greater than zero, the expected results are:

a) The test statistic is approximated by a t distribution with $df = 28$.

b) The mean of the sampling distribution of the difference between two means is:

$$\mu_{\bar{x}_1 - \bar{x}_2} = \mu_1 - \mu_2$$
$$= 0$$

c) The estimate of the standard error of the of the difference between two means is:

$$s_{\bar{x}_1 - \bar{x}_2} = \sqrt{\frac{(n_1 - 1)s_1^2 + (n_2 - 1)s_2^2}{n_1 + n_2 - 2} \cdot \left(\frac{1}{n_1} + \frac{1}{n_2}\right)}$$

Substituting $s_1 = 3.6$, $n_1 = 15$, $s_2 = 2.3$ and $n_2 = 15$ into $s_{\bar{x}_1 - \bar{x}_2}$, we have:

$$s_{\bar{x}_1 - \bar{x}_2} = \sqrt{\frac{(15 - 1)(3.6)^2 + (15 - 1)(2.3)^2}{15 + 15 - 2} \left(\frac{1}{15} + \frac{1}{15}\right)}$$

$$= \sqrt{\frac{181.44 + 74.06}{28}(0.13)}$$

$$\approx \sqrt{(9.1250)(0.1333)}$$

$$s_{\bar{x}_1 - \bar{x}_2} \approx 1.10$$

Figure 13.7 illustrates the hypothesis testing model.

Step 3 Formulate the decision rule.

a) The alternative hypothesis is **directional** since we are trying to show that the population mean weight loss for the treatment group is **significantly greater** than the population mean weight loss for the control group.

b) The type of hypothesis test is one-tailed (1TT) on the **right side** since we are trying to show that $(\mu_1 - \mu_2)$ is **greater than** zero.

distribution of the test statistic
(is a t Distribution with *df* = 28)

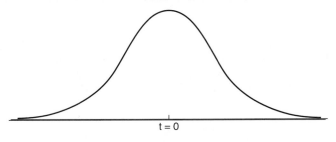

t = 0

FIGURE 13.7

c) The significance level is: $\alpha = 5\%$.
d) For a one-tailed test on the right with $\alpha = 5\%$ and $df = 28$, the critical *t* score, t_c, using Table III is $t_c = 1.70$.
e) Figure 13.8(a) illustrates the decision rule for this hypothesis test.

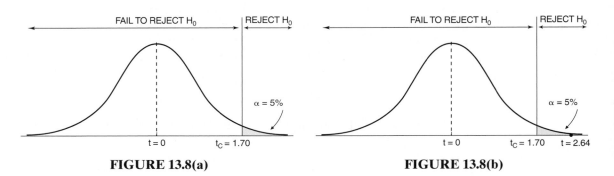

FIGURE 13.8(a)   **FIGURE 13.8(b)**

The decision rule is:
f) Reject H_o if the test statistic t is greater than $t_c = 1.70$.

Step 4 Analyze the sample data.
Calculate the test statistic t where

$$\bar{x}_1 - \bar{x}_2 = 7.1 - 4.2 = 2.9 \text{ and } s_{\bar{x}_1 - \bar{x}_2} \approx 1.10$$

The test statistic t is: $t = \dfrac{2.9}{1.10} \approx 2.64$.

Step 5 State the conclusion.
Using Figure 13.8(b), since the test statistic t ≈ 2.64, is greater than the critical t score $t_c = 1.70$, *reject* H_o and *accept* H_a at $\alpha = 5\%$.
Therefore, the company can conclude that their diet pill (E.A.T.) will **significantly reduce** an individual's weight at the end of one week at $\alpha = 5\%$.

CASE STUDY 13.1   Academic Differences

A research article entitled "Differences in Extracurricular Activity Participation, Achievement, And Attitudes Toward School Between Ninth-grade Students Attending Junior High School And Those Attending Senior High School" appeared in *Adolescence*. The following table represents a comparison of the Mean Number of Total Extracurricular Activities Participated, Overall GPA, and Mean Attitude Toward Self and School for Ninth Graders in Junior High (n = 771) and Senior High Settings (n = 825).

Groups	Mean	Standard Deviation	t value
Extracurricular Activities			
Ninth Graders in JHS	2.68	2.30	6.20*
Ninth Graders in SHS			
Overall GPA			
Ninth Graders in JHS	2.59	0.89	6.91
Ninth Graders in SHS	2.24	1.11	
Attitude Toward Self and School			
Ninth Graders in JHS	77.87	8.07	0.60
Ninth Graders in SHS	78.12	8.48	

*p < 0.01

Let's define population 1 as: Ninth Graders in Junior High School (JHS) and population 2 is defined as: Ninth Graders in Senior High School (SHS).

a) If you are trying to show that there is a significant difference in the mean number of extracurricular activities for these two populations, then state the null hypothesis and alternative hypothesis for this two-sample t test.

b) If you want to show that there is a significant difference in the mean overall GPA for these two populations, then state the null and alternative hypotheses for this two-sample t test.

c) If you would like to show that there is a significant difference in the mean attitude toward self and school for these two populations, then state the null and alternative hypotheses for this two-sample t test.

d) What is the mean of the sampling distribution which serves as a model for this test? Is the test statistic distribution a normal or a t distribution? Explain.

e) For the Extracurricular Activities Study, which group had the greater variability? For the Overall GPA Study, which group had the less variability? For the Attitude Study, which group had the greater variability? Do these measures of variability represent a parameter or a statistic? Explain.

f) Was there a significant difference between the populations with respect to the mean number of extracurricular activities? Explain.

g) If the significance level for the extracurricular activities had been 0.5%, would the null hypothesis be rejected? Explain.

h) Was there a significant difference between the populations with respect to the mean overall GPA? Was the null hypothesis rejected? Explain.

i) Would the null hypothesis have been rejected for the overall GPA study if $\alpha = 1\%$? Explain.

j) Was there a significant difference between the populations with respect to the mean attitude? Was the null hypothesis rejected? Explain.

k) Would the null hypothesis have been rejected for the attitude study if $\alpha = 2\%$? Explain.

CASE STUDY 13.2   Potency of the Placebo Effect

In Figure 13.9 is an article entitled *Study says 'placebo effect' is potent* appeared in the Orange County Register, a California newspaper, on July 1, 1993.

Study says 'placebo effect' is potent

Health: Research shows people with certain diseases
get better 70 percent of the time with dummy treatment.

By Lee Siegel
The Associated Press

LOS ANGELES—People with certain diseases get better 70 percent of the time even when they receive dummy treatments, according to a study that suggests the "placebo effect" can be a powerful healer.

"Even if a treatment is not effective, large numbers of people will feel they've been helped if both the therapist and the patient believe in its effectiveness." said Alan H. Roberts, principal author of the study, being published Thursday in Clinical Psychology Review.

The research is "consistent with what we knew, but documents it better than before," said William Jarvis, a preventive medicine professor at Loma Linda University and president of the National Council Against Health Fraud.

The findings suggest doctors as well as patients may be too quick to use experimental treatments that seem promising but ultimately prove ineffective, said Roberts, chief psychologist at Scripps Clinic and Research Foundation in La Jolla.

He said the research also indicates people seek unconventional, unproven therapies because they often seem to be helped by them, but that they would do even better with scientifically proven treatments.

That would allow them to benefit from both real medicine and the "placebo effect"—the improvement patients get from inert drugs or ineffective treatments purely because of belief the treatments will work, he said.

Roberts and colleagues at San Diego State University and the University of Michigan, Ann Arbor, analyzed dozens of old studies on five treatments that were medically accepted in the 1960s or 1970s but later found ineffective.

The treatments were glomectomy, an asthma-relief surgery; briefly freezing the stomach lining in an attempt to treat peptic ulcers; and three drugs applied to herpes simplex sores.

Of the 6,931 patients treated in the old studies, the outcome was excellent for 40 percent, good for 30 percent and poor for only 30 percent.

That shows "a lot of healing from medicine—and probably from psychotherapy—is the result of what are generally called placebo effects," Roberts said.

The most frequently cited research on the subject has been a 1955 study that found the placebo effect accounted for one-third of the improvement in people who got better after being given either a medicine or a placebo for a variety of ailments, Roberts said.

FIGURE 13.9

Read the article and comment on the following questions.
a) What does the term 'dummy treatment' mean to you? Is there another name for this?
b) What does the author mean by the statement: "the 'placebo effect' can be a powerful healer"?
c) What does the "placebo effect" mean? Give examples from the article to illustrate this effect.
d) How did the researchers come to the conclusion of a placebo effect? What did they use to support their claim?

Summary of the Hypothesis Tests Involving Two Population Means

The following outline is a summary of the 5 step hypothesis testing procedure for a hypothesis test involving two population means.

Hypothesis Testing Involving Two Population Means

Step 1   Formulate the two hypotheses, H_o and H_a.

Null Hypothesis, H_o: $\mu_1 - \mu_2 = 0$

Alternative Hypothesis, H_a: has one of the following three forms:

$$H_a: \mu_1 - \mu_2 < 0 \quad \text{or} \quad H_a: \mu_1 - \mu_2 > 0 \quad \text{or} \quad H_a: \mu_1 - \mu_2 \neq 0$$

Step 2   Determine the model to test the null hypothesis, H_o.

Under the assumption H_o is true, the expected results are:

a) The distribution of the test statistic is either:

   (i) a normal distribution, if the standard deviations of both populations are known and both sample sizes are greater than 30,

   or (ii) is a t distribution with degrees of freedom: $df = n_1 + n_2 - 2$, if the standard deviations of both populations are unknown.

b) The mean of the sampling distribution of the difference between two means is given by the formula: $\mu_{\bar{x}_1 - \bar{x}_2} = \mu_1 - \mu_2 = 0$ (since H_o is true: i.e. $\mu_1 - \mu_2 = 0$)

c) For a normal distribution: the standard error of the difference between two means, denoted by $\sigma_{\bar{x}_1 - \bar{x}_2}$, is:

$$\sigma_{\bar{x}_1 - \bar{x}_2} = \sqrt{\frac{\sigma_1^2}{n_1} + \frac{\sigma_2^2}{n_2}}$$

or for a t distribution: the estimate of the standard error of the difference between two means, written $s_{\bar{x}_1 - \bar{x}_2}$, is given by the formula:

$$s_{\bar{x}_1 - \bar{x}_2} = \sqrt{\frac{(n_1 - 1)s_1^2 + (n_2 - 1)s_2^2}{n_1 + n_2 - 2} \cdot \left(\frac{1}{n_1} + \frac{1}{n_2}\right)}$$

Step 3   Formulate the decision rule.

a) Alternative hypothesis: directional or nondirectional.

b) Type of test: 1TT or 2TT.

c) Significance level: $\alpha = 1\%$ or $\alpha = 5\%$.

d) Critical score:

for a normal distribution: z_c is found in Table II

for a t distribution: t_c is found in Table III where $df = n_1 + n_2 - 2$

e) Construct the hypothesis testing model.

f) State the decision rule.

Step 4   Analyze the sample data.

a) Compute the difference between the two sample means: $\bar{x}_1 - \bar{x}_2$.

(continues)

Summary of the Hypothesis
Tests Involving Two Population Means (continued)

b) For a normal distribution: test statistic: $z = \dfrac{\bar{x}_1 - \bar{x}_2}{\sigma_{\bar{x}_1 - \bar{x}_2}}$

   For a t distribtion: test statistic: $t = \dfrac{\bar{x}_1 - \bar{x}_2}{s_{\bar{x}_1 - \bar{x}_2}}$

Step 5   State the conclusion.
Compare the test statistic to the critical score of the decision rule and state the conclusion: either: (a) Reject H_o and Accept H_a at α or (b) Fail to Reject H_o at α

Table 13.4 contains a condensed version of the hypothesis tests involving two population means.

TABLE 13.4   Summary of Hypothesis Tests Involving Two Population Means

Form of the Null Hypothesis	Conditions of Test	Test Statistic Formula	Distribution of the test statistic is a:
$\mu_1 - \mu_2 = 0$	KNOWN: σ_1 and σ_2 and n_1 and n_2 are both greater than 30	$z = \dfrac{\bar{x}_1 - \bar{x}_2}{\sigma_{\bar{x}_1 - \bar{x}_2}}$ where: $\sigma_{\bar{x}_1 - \bar{x}_2} = \sqrt{\dfrac{\sigma_1^2}{n_1} + \dfrac{\sigma_2^2}{n_2}}$	Normal Distribution
$\mu_1 - \mu_2 = 0$	UNKNOWN: σ_1 and σ_2 and $\sigma_1 \approx \sigma_2$	$t = \dfrac{\bar{x}_1 - \bar{x}_2}{s_{\bar{x}_1 - \bar{x}_2}}$ where: $s_{\bar{x}_1 - \bar{x}_2} = \sqrt{\dfrac{(n_1 - 1)s_1^2 + (n_2 - 1)s_2^2}{n_1 + n_2 - 2} \cdot \left(\dfrac{1}{n_1} + \dfrac{1}{n_2}\right)}$	t Distribution where: $df = n_1 + n_2 - 2$

13.5   p-VALUE APPROACH TO HYPOTHESIS TESTING INVOLVING TWO POPULATION MEANS USING THE TI-83PLUS CALCULATOR

The p-value approach will require refinements in steps 3, 4 and 5 of the hypothesis testing procedure. In step 3, the decision will be stated as: Reject the H_O if the p-value of the test statistic is less than α. In step 4, the p-value will be determined using the TI-83 Plus calculator. While in step 5, the conclusion of the hypothesis test is determined by comparing the p-value to the level of significance, α.

Let's reexamine the hypothesis test shown in Example 13.3 using a p-value approach with the aid of the TI-83 Plus Calculator.

EXAMPLE 13.4

A pharmaceutical company has developed a diet pill called, Effective Anti-Hunger Tablet (E.A.T.), which the company believes will significantly reduce and individual's weight at the end of one week. To support their claim, the company selects 30 overweight individuals and randomly divides them into independent groups: a **treatment** group of 15 subjects who are administered the diet pill E.A.T. and a **control** group of 15 subjects who are given a **placebo** tablet (i.e. **a pill that has** *no effect* **on weight**).

After one week, the treatment group had a sample mean weight loss of $\bar{x} = 7.1$ lbs. with s = 3.6 lbs. while the control group had a sample mean weight loss of $\bar{x} = 4.2$ lbs. with s = 2.3 lbs.

a) Use the 5 step hypothesis testing procedure to answer the question: can the company conclude that their diet pill E.A.T. will significantly reduce an individual's weight within one week at $\alpha = 5\%$?

b) Can we conclude that their diet pill E.A.T. will significantly reduce an individual's weight within one week at $\alpha = 1\%$?

c) What is the smallest α level that can be used to accept the pharmaceutical company's claim?

Remark: In this study the administration of the diet pill E.A.T. to the treatment group is the only difference between the two groups. Therefore, if we can show a significant difference between the treatment and control groups then this *difference can be attributed only to the treatment (the diet pill).*

Solution

part (a):

Step 1   Formulate the hypotheses.

If we let the population 1 represent the treatment group and population 2 represent the control group then the null hypothesis is:

H_0: there is **no difference** in the population mean weight loss for the treatment group and the control group.

In symbols we have, $H_0: \mu_1 - \mu_2 = 0$

H_a: the population mean weight loss for the treatment group is **greater than** the population mean weight loss for the control group.

In symbols we have $H_a: \mu_1 - \mu_2 > 0$.

Step 2   Determine the model to test the null hypothesis, H_0.

To test the null hypothesis the company selects 30 overweight individuals and randomly divides them into two independent groups and the sample results are summarized in Table 13.5.

Table 13.5   Summary of the Data for the Random Samples Selected from Each Population

Population 1 (Treatment)	Population 2 (Control)
$\bar{x}_1 = 7.1$	$\bar{x}_2 = 4.2$
$s_1 = 3.6$	$s_2 = 2.3$
$n_1 = 15$	$n_2 = 15$

Since the differences between the two sample means, $\bar{x}_1 - \bar{x}_2$, will be used to determine if $(\mu_1 - \mu_2)$ is significantly greater than zero, **the expected results** are:

a) The distribution of the test statistic is approximated by a t distribution with $df = 28$.
b) The mean of the Sampling Distribution of the Difference Between Two Means is:

$$\mu_{\bar{x}_1 - \bar{x}_2} = \mu_1 - \mu_2 = 0$$

c) The estimate of the standard error of the difference between two means is:

$$s_{\bar{x}_1 - \bar{x}_2} = \sqrt{\frac{(n_1 - 1)s_1^2 + (n_2 - 1)s_2^2}{n_1 + n_2 - 2} \cdot \left(\frac{1}{n_1} + \frac{1}{n_2}\right)}$$

Substituting $s_1 = 3.6$, $n_1 = 15$, $s_2 = 2.3$ and $n_2 = 15$ into $s_{\bar{x}_1 - \bar{x}_2}$, we have:

$$s_{\bar{x}_1 - \bar{x}_2} = \sqrt{\frac{(15 - 1)(3.6)^2 + (15 - 1)(2.3)^2}{15 + 15 - 2} \left(\frac{1}{15} + \frac{1}{15}\right)}$$

$$= \sqrt{\frac{181.44 + 74.06}{28}(0.13)}$$

$$\approx \sqrt{(9.1250)(0.1333)}$$

$$s_{\bar{x}_1 - \bar{x}_2} \approx 1.10$$

Figure 13.10 illustrates hypothesis testing model.

distribution of the test statistic
(is a t Distribution with $df = 28$)

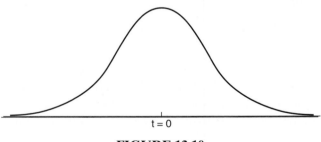

$t = 0$

FIGURE 13.10

Step 3 Formulate the decision rule.
     a) the alternative hypothesis is **directional** since we are trying to show that the population mean weight loss for the treatment group is **significantly greater** than the population mean weight loss for the control group.
     b) the type of hypothesis test is one-tailed (1TT) on the **right side** since we are trying to show that $(\mu_1 - \mu_2)$ is **greater than** zero.
     c) the significance level is: $\alpha = 5\%$.
     d) Figure 13.11 illustrates the decision rule for this hypothesis test.
     The decision rule is:
     e) Reject H_0 if the p-value of the test statistic t is less than $\alpha = 5\%$.

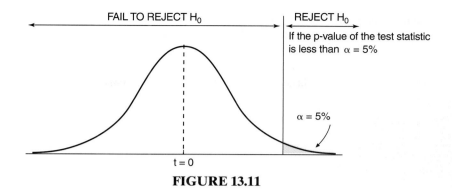

FIGURE 13.11

Step 4 Analyze the sample data.

Determine the p-value of the test statistic by entering the sample data into the TI-83 Plus calculator. The output screen of the TI-83 Plus calculator is shown in Figures 13.12(a) and 13.12(b).

FIGURE 13.12(a)   **FIGURE 13.12(b)**

From the output screen the p-value of the test statistic $t \approx 2.63$ is approximately 0.0069. Using the p-value we can position the test statistic on the hypothesis testing model shown in Figure 13.13.

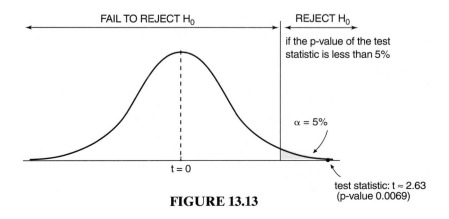

FIGURE 13.13

Step 5   State the conclusion.

Since the p-value (0.0069) of the test statistic t is less than $\alpha = 5\%$ *reject* H_O and *accept* H_a at a p-value of 0.0069. Therefore, the company can conclude that their diet pill (E.A.T.) will **significantly reduce** an individual's weight at the end of one week at $\alpha = 5\%$.

part (b):   Since the p-value of 0.0069 is still less than $\alpha = 1\%$, we can accept the pharmaceutical company's claim as shown in Figure 13.14.

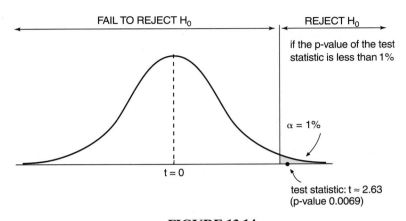

FIGURE 13.14

part (c):   The smallest α level that can be used to accept the pharmaceutical company's claim is equal to the p-value, 0.0069.

The following outline is a summary of the 5 step hypothesis testing procedure for a hypothesis test involving two population means using p-values.

Summary of the p-value Approach to Hypothesis Testing Involving Two Population Means Using the TI-83 Plus Calculator

---

Step 1   Formulate the two hypotheses, H_o and H_a.

Null Hypothesis, $H_o: \mu_1 - \mu_2 = 0$

Alternative Hypothesis, H_a: has one of the following three forms:

$$H_o: \mu_1 - \mu_2 < 0 \quad \text{or} \quad H_o: \mu_1 - \mu_2 > 0 \quad \text{or} \quad H_o: \mu_1 - \mu_2 \neq 0$$

Step 2   Determine the model to test the null hypothesis, H_o.

Under the assumption H_o is true, the expected results are:

a) The distribution of the test statistic is either:

(i) a normal distribution, if the standard deviations of both populations are known and both sample sizes are greater than 30,

or (ii) is a t distribution with degrees of freedom: $df = n_1 + n_2 - 2$, if the standard deviations of both populations are unknown.

(continues)

Summary of the Hypothesis
Tests Involving Two Population Means (continued)

b) The mean of the sampling distribution of the difference between two means is given by the formula: $\mu_{\bar{x}_1-\bar{x}_2} = \mu_1 - \mu_2 = 0$ (since H_o is true: i.e. $\mu_1 - \mu_2 = 0$)

c) For a normal distribution: the standard error of the difference between two means, denoted by $\sigma_{\bar{x}_1-\bar{x}_2}$, is:

$$\sigma_{\bar{x}_1-\bar{x}_2} = \sqrt{\frac{\sigma_1^2}{n_1} + \frac{\sigma_2^2}{n_2}}$$

or for a t distribution: the **estimate of the standard error** of the difference between two means, written $s_{\bar{x}_1-\bar{x}_2}$, is given by the formula:

$$s_{\bar{x}_1-\bar{x}_2} = \sqrt{\frac{(n_1-1)s_1^2 + (n_2-1)s_2^2}{n_1+n_2-2} \cdot \left(\frac{1}{n_1} + \frac{1}{n_2}\right)}$$

Step 3   Formulate the decision rule.
a) Alternative hypothesis: directional or nondirectional.
b) Type of test: 1TT or 2TT.
c) Significance level: $\alpha = 1\%$ or $\alpha = 5\%$.
d) Construct the hypothesis testing model.
e) State the decision rule as: Reject H_o if the p-value of the test statistic is less than α.

Step 4   Analyze the sample data.
Enter the necessary sample data into the TI-83 Plus calculator to determine the p-value of the test statistic.

Step 5   Determine the conclusion.
Compare the p-value of the test statistic to the decision rule and either:
(a) Reject H_o and Accept H_a at α or (b) Fail to Reject H_o at α

13.6   USING TECHNOLOGY

In this chapter, we studied hypothesis testing involving two population means. This is commonly referred to as a two sample t test. MINITAB and the TI–83 Plus calculator can perform this test easily.

A nondirectional hypothesis test was conducted using sample data values identified by lists C1 and C2. This test assumes that the population standard deviations were equal. The MINITAB output is shown in Figure 13.15.

MINITAB OUTPUT

TWOSAMPLE T FOR C1 VS C2

	N	MEAN	STDEV	SE MEAN
C1	36	105.4	13.8	2.3
C2	36	95.6	17.0	2.8

95 PCT CI FOR MU C1 – MU C2: (2.5, 17.1)

TTEST MU C1 = MU C2 (VS NE): T = 2.68 P = 0.0093 DF = 70

POOLED STDEV = 15.5

FIGURE 13.15

The MINITAB output reports the summary sample statistics, the null and alternative hypotheses, the t score, degrees of freedom and the p-value. Examine the output and find the p-value. You should see that it is contained on the line

TTEST MU C1 = MU C2 (VS NE): T= 2.68 P = 0.0093 DF = 70

Notice that the p-value for this test is p-value=0.0093 and the t score is T=2.68.

How is the p-value interpreted in terms of the significance of the statistical result? Does this p-value indicate that the null hypothesis is rejected at $\alpha = 1\%$? Why?

You should also notice that the line indicates that the test is a 2TT from the portion of the statement

TTEST MU C1 = MU C2 (VS NE)

Finally, the line indicates that for this hypothesis test involving two population means, the degrees of freedom, DF = 70.

The output contains other information. For example, the statement

POOLED STDEV = 15.5

indicates that the pooled estimate of the standard deviations of the samples is used and calculated. The output also shows summary statistics about each of the samples used.

	N	MEAN	STDEV	SE MEAN
C1	36	105.4	13.8	2.3
C2	36	95.6	17.0	2.8

How many data values were in random sample C1? What was the sample standard deviation for the random sample contained in C2? What is the standard error of the mean for the random sample contained in C2? How was it calculated?

There is one last item included on the output.

95 PCT CI FOR MU C1 – MU C2: (2.5, 17.1)

This line has to do with estimating the mean of the differences between two populations. This concept was presented in Chapter 8.

A directional (greater than) hypothesis test was conducted using sample data values identified by lists C1 and C2. This test assumed that the population standard deviations were equal. The MINITAB output is shown in Figure 13.16.

MINITAB OUTPUT

TWOSAMPLE T FOR C1 VS C2

	N	MEAN	STDEV	SE MEAN
C1	36	100.5	16.6	2.8
C2	33	97.3	17.8	3.0

95 PCT CI FOR MU C1 – MU C2: (–4.9, 11.3)

TTEST MU C1 = MU C2 (VS GT): T = 0.79 P = 0.22 DF = 67

POOLED STDEV = 17.2

FIGURE 13.16

For this MINITAB output:

Identify the p-value. What is the statistical result? How is the significance of the p-value interpreted? Is the null hypothesis rejected at $\alpha = 5\%$? Why? Where in the MINITAB output does it indicate a 1TT greater than hypothesis test? How was DF calculated?

A TI–83 Plus calculator output for a nondirectional hypothesis test is displayed in Figures 13.17(a) and 13.17(b). This test assumes that the population standard deviations were equal.

FIGURE 13.17(a)   **FIGURE 13.17(b)**

Two output screens are necessary to display the hypothesis test results. The output screens display the type of test, form of the alternative hypothesis, and the summary statistics. Examine the output and identify the t score, p-value, degrees of freedom, sample means and standard deviations, pooled standard deviation and the sample sizes.

Can you compute the standard error for this test? Are you able to reject the null hypothesis at $\alpha = 5\%$ or 1%? Explain.

KEY TERMS

Difference between the sample means   751

Sampling Distribution of the Difference Between Two Means   752

Independent Random Samples   752

$\mu_{\bar{x}_1 - \bar{x}_2}$, Mean of the Sampling Distribution of the Difference Between Two Means   753

$\sigma_{\bar{x}_1 - \bar{x}_2}$, the Standard Error of the Difference Between Two Means   753

$s_{\bar{x}_1 - \bar{x}_2}$, Estimate of the Standard Error of the Difference Between Two Means   754

Two Sample t Test   754

Single-Blind Study   762

Double-Blind Study   762

Treatment Group   762

Control Group   762

Placebo   762

Test statistic   756

P-value   768

SECTION EXERCISES

Section 13.2

1. To perform a hypothesis test involving two population means, the distribution of the _____ _____ is used as the hypothesis testing model.

2. The notation $\bar{x}_1 - \bar{x}_2$ represents the difference between the _____ _____, where: $\bar{x}_1$ represents the _____ of sample 1 and $\bar{x}_2$ represents the _____ of sample 2.

3. The sampling distribution of the difference between two means has the following characteristics:
   a) The mean of the sampling distribution of the difference between two means, denoted _____, is determined by the formula: $\mu_{\bar{x}_1 - \bar{x}_2} = $ _____ – _____, where: μ_1 represents the mean of _____ one and μ_2 represents the mean of _____ two.
   b) The formula for the estimate of the standard error of the of the difference between two means, denoted $s_{\bar{x}_1 - \bar{x}_2}$, is dependent upon the sample standard deviations and the sample sizes. The formula for $s_{\bar{x}_1 - \bar{x}_2}$ is_____.
   c) Under Theorem 13.2, the distribution of the test statistic is approximated by a _____ distribution with df, degrees of freedom, given by the formula: $df = $ _____.

4. If $n_1 = 35$, $n_2 = 40$, $\sigma_1 = 4$ and $\sigma_2 = 6$, then $\sigma_{\bar{x}_1 - \bar{x}_2} = $ _____.

Section 13.3

5. The null hypothesis of a hypothesis test involving two population means, μ_1 and μ_2, is stated as: There is _____ difference between the _____ of population 1 and the _____ of population 2. In symbols, H_o is written as: _____ $= 0$.

6. The alternative hypothesis of a hypothesis test involving two population means, μ_1, and μ_2, has one of three possible forms. They are:
   a) The mean of population 1 is greater than the _____. In symbols, this H_a is written: _____.
   b) The _____ of population 1 is less than the mean of _____. In symbols, this H_a is written: _____.

c) The mean of _____ 1 is not equal to the _____ of population _____. In symbols, this H_a is written: _____.

7. The null hypothesis used in most comparisons involving two population means is based upon the assumption that mean of population 1 equals the mean of population 2. (T/F)

8. The formula for the test statistic t, for a hypothesis test involving two population means, is:

   $t = $ _____.

   Under the assumption H_o is true, $\mu_{\bar{x}_1 - \bar{x}_2} = $ _____, and thus, the formula for the test statistic is reduced to:
   $t = $ _____.

9. To determine the conclusion of a hypothesis test involving two population means, the _____ _____ is compared to the critical score(s).

10. The formula for the degrees of freedom of a t Distribution for testing the difference between two population means using two independent samples is:
    a) $df = n - 1$ b) $df = n_1 + n_2 - 2$ c) $df = n_1 - n_2$

11. When performing a two-tailed hypothesis test, if the test statistic t falls between the two critical values, t_{LC} and t_{RC}, then the conclusion is:
    a) Reject H_o
    b) Reject H_a
    c) Fail to Reject H_o
    d) Accept H_a

12. To determine if the difference between the sample means is significantly different from zero the test statistic t is compared to a critical t score, t_c, that is determined by:

$$t = \frac{\bar{x}_1 - \bar{x}_2}{s_{\bar{x}_1 - \bar{x}_2}}$$

   (T/F)

13. If the difference between the sample means, $\bar{x}_1 - \bar{x}_2$, is different from zero then there is a significant difference between the sample means.
    (T/F)

For each of the problems 14 to 20:

a) Define population 1 and population 2.

b) Formulate the null and alternative hypotheses.

c) Calculate the expected results for the hypothesis test assuming the null hypothesis is true and determine the hypothesis test model.

d) Formulate the decision rule.

e) Determine the test statistic.

f) Determine the conclusion and answer the question(s) posed in the problem, if any.

14. A psychologist who needs two groups of students for a learning experiment decides to select a random sample 100 female college students and 81 male college students. Before the experiment, the psychologist administers an IQ test to both groups to determine if there is a significant difference in their mean IQ scores. The population standard deviation for this IQ test is known to be 12. If the sample mean IQ score of the 100 female students is 116.9 and the sample mean IQ score of the 81 male students is 120.8, can the psychologist conclude that there is a significant difference in the mean IQ score of both groups at $\alpha = 1\%$? (Use Theorem 13.1 and the hypothesis testing procedure)

15. A light bulb manufacturer has developed a new light bulb which the manufacturer claims has a greater mean life than that of their leading competitor. The mean life for an independent random sample of 50 of the manufacturer's bulbs is 2,500 hours with s = 100 hours. The mean life for an independent random sample of 50 of their competitor's bulbs is 2,450 hours with s = 90. Do these sample results support the manufacturer's claim at $\alpha = 5\%$?

16. Members of the student government at Valley College in Sacramento believe that female students receive significantly lower final grades in the liberal arts math course than male students. From an independent random sample of 100 female students it was found that the mean final grade was 78 with a standard deviation of 10. From an independent random sample of 100 male students the mean final grade was 80 with a standard deviation of 6. Do these sample results support the student government's claim at $\alpha = 5\%$?

17. The personnel director of a large computer company has been hiring word processing students from community colleges and from secretarial schools. The director would like to determine if there is a significant difference in the mean typing speed of these graduates. Each graduate was administered a typing test and the sample results are summarized in the following table:

Community College Graduates	Secretarial School Graduates
$\bar{x}_1 = 65$ words per minute	$\bar{x}_2 = 61$ words per minute
$s_1 = 12$	$s_2 = 15$
$n_1 = 40$	$n_2 = 36$

Can the personnel director conclude that there is significant difference in the mean typing speed of the Community College graduates and the secretarial school graduates at $\alpha = 5\%$?

18. A farmer believes that his special fertilizer will significantly increase his tomato crop yield. To test his belief, he randomly divides 200 acres into two groups. In Group I, he administers his special fertilizer. In Group II, he administers the usual tomato fertilizer. The table below summarizes the tomato yields for this experiment.

	Group I	Group II
Number of acres, n	100	100
sample average bushels per acre, $\bar{x}$	830	805
sample standard deviation, s	40	36

Do these sample results support the farmers claim at $\alpha = 1\%$?

19. A sociologist claims that marriage lowers the cumulative average of graduate students. If the cumulative average of 16 randomly selected married graduate students was 3.35 with a standard deviation of 0.3 and the cumulative average of 9 unmarried graduate students was 3.56 with a standard deviation of 0.5, do you agree with the sociologist's claim at $\alpha = 1\%$?

20. A statistics instructor wants to determine if the addition of statistics projects integrated into his statistics classes will result in significantly better performance by the students on the final exam. In one of his statistics classes, he integrates the statistics projects with his regular lessons. In another statistics class he does not integrate the projects. The results in the following table summarize the results of his experiment.

Statistic Class (with projects)	Statistic Class (without projects)
$n_1 = 25$	$n_2 = 22$
$\bar{x}_1 = 82$	$\bar{x}_2 = 79$
$s_1 = 8$	$s_2 = 10$

Based upon these sample results, can the instructor conclude that the addition of statistics projects significantly increases student performance on the final exam at $\alpha = 5\%$?

Section 13.4

21. To study whether a new pill will significantly reduce the blood pressure of patients, forty patients are randomly selected and divided randomly into two equal sized groups, A and B. Group A is administered the new blood pressure pill, while Group B is administered a placebo. Then, the control group is Group _____, while the treatment group is Group _____.

For each of the problems 22 to 23:

a) Define population 1 and population 2.

b) Formulate the null and alternative hypotheses.

c) Calculate the expected results for the hypothesis test assuming the null hypothesis is true and determine the hypothesis test model.
d) Formulate the decision rule.
e) Determine the test statistic.
f) Determine the conclusion and answer the question(s) posed in the problem, if any.

22. A school nutritionist believes that her special diet given along with a rigorous training routine will significantly increase stamina. She randomly selects 30 students and divides them into two equal independent groups. Group I, called the treatment group, is put on the special diet and the rigorous training routine. Group II, called the control group, is just given the rigorous training routine with no special diet. After six months the increase in stamina level of all subjects is measured. The results are given in the following table.

Treatment Group	Control Group
$n_1 = 15$	$n_2 = 15$
$\bar{x}_1 = 26$	$\bar{x}_2 = 18$
$s_1 = 4$	$s_2 = 10$

Do these sample results support the nutritionist's belief at $\alpha = 5\%$?

23. A medical researcher wants to study whether a diet deficient in Vitamin E affects the mean amount of Vitamin A stored in mice. She randomly selects two samples of fifteen mice each. Group I called the control group is feed a normal diet while the second group called the treatment group is fed a diet deficient in vitamin E. She collected the following data:

Control Group I.U. of Vitamin A	Treatment Group I.U. of Vitamin A
3850	3300
3700	3250
3650	2900
3500	2700
3450	2000
3450	2550
3900	2400
3700	2600
2900	2300
3400	2450
3200	1900
3150	2100
3850	2500
3000	2350
2800	2800

Can the researcher conclude that the mean amount of Vitamin A for mice on the deficient diet is less than the mean amount of Vitamin A for mice on a normal diet at $\alpha = 1\%$?

Section 13.5

For problems 24–32, use questions 14 to 20 of Section 13.3 exercises and 22 & 23 of section 13.4 exercises and apply the p-value approach to hypothesis testing using the TI-83 Plus calculator. For each of these problems, use the 5 step procedure to perform a hypothesis test at **both** $\alpha = 1\%$ and $\alpha = 5\%$. Include the following within your test:

a) state the null and alternative hypotheses.
b) calculate the expected results for the experiment assuming the null hypothesis is true and state the hypothesis test model.
c) formulate the decision rule.
d) identify the test statistic and its p-value.
e) state the conclusion and answer any question(s) posed in the problem for each alpha level.
f) determine the smallest level of significance for which the null hypothesis can be rejected.

33. For a 1TT on the right side, as the test statistic increases the p-value also increases. (T/F)

>>> **CHAPTER REVIEW**

34. Symbolically, the difference between two sample means is expressed as:
a) $\bar{x}_1 - \bar{x}_2$
b) $\mu_1 - \mu_2$
c) $\mu_{\bar{x}_1 - \bar{x}_2}$
d) $p_1 - p_2$

35. The formula for the mean of the sampling distribution of the difference between two means is:
a) $\mu_{\bar{x}_1 - \bar{x}_2} = \mu_1 + \mu_2$
b) $\mu_{\bar{x}_1 - \bar{x}_2} = \mu_1 - \mu_2$
c) $\mu_{\bar{x}_1 - \bar{x}_2} = \bar{x}_1 - \bar{x}_2$
d) $\mu_{\bar{x}_1 - \bar{x}_2} > 0$

36. The formula

$$\sigma_{\bar{x}_1 - \bar{x}_2} = \sqrt{\frac{\sigma_1^2}{n_1} + \frac{\sigma_2^2}{n_2}}$$

can be used only if:
a) Both population standard deviations are known
b) Both population standard deviations are unknown
c) Both s_1 and s_2 are known

37. If $n_1 = 25$, $n_2 = 50$, $s_1 = 3$ and $s_2 = 5$, then $s_{\bar{x}_1 - \bar{x}_2} =$ _____.

38. The sampling distribution of the difference between two means is formed by finding the differences be-

tween all possible independent sample means of the form $\bar{x}_1 - \bar{x}_2$, where $\bar{x}_1$ represents the mean of an independent random sample selected from population 1 and $\bar{x}_2$ represents the mean of an independent random sample selected from population 2.
(T/F)

39. The mean of the sampling distribution of the difference between two means is computed by the formula: $\bar{x}_1 - \bar{x}_2$.
(T/F)

40. The standard error of the difference between two means is estimated by the formula: $s_{\bar{x}_1 - \bar{x}_2} = s_1 - s_2$.
(T/F)

41. When performing a hypothesis test involving two population means, the expected result $\mu_{\bar{x}_1 - \bar{x}_2} = 0$ is determined under the assumption that _____ is true.

42. When using the t distribution with $n_1 = 16$ and $n_2 = 20$ to approximate the sampling distribution of the difference between two means, the degrees of freedom for the t distribution is _____.

43. The null hypothesis, H_o, for testing the difference between two population means can be represented as:
a) H_o: $\mu_1 = 0$
b) H_o: $\mu_1 = \mu_2$
c) H_o: $\mu_1 - \mu_2 > 0$
d) H_o: $\mu_1 - \mu_2 = 0$

44. When the experimenter shows no significant difference between the sample means, then the mean of population 1 is said to equal the mean of population 2.
(T/F)

45. Only by rejecting H_o can you conclude that there is a difference between the population means.
(T/F)

46. The treatment group is frequently compared to the:
a) Control group
b) Null group
c) Test group
d) Pseudo group

For each of the problems 47 to 52:
a) Define population 1 and population 2.
b) Formulate the null and alternative hypotheses.
c) Calculate the expected results for the hypothesis test assuming the null hypothesis is true and determine the hypothesis test model.
d) Formulate the decision rule.
e) Determine the test statistic.
f) Determine the conclusion and answer the question(s) posed in the problem, if any.

47. An educational researcher wants to determine if the mean score of urban sixth grade students is significantly greater than the mean score of rural sixth grade students on a standardized reading comprehension test. From past experience, the population standard deviation of the scores on this standardized test is 10. If a random sample of 64 urban students had a mean test score of 78.4, and a random sample of 36 rural students had a mean test score of 73.9, can the educational researcher conclude that the urban sixth grade students performed significantly better on the standardized test at $\alpha = 5\%$? (Use Theorem 13.1 and the hypothesis testing procedure)

48. A new insecticide was developed by a chemical company. The company claims that the new insecticide has a more effective life than their present insecticide. An independent random sample of 40 cans of the new insecticide had a mean effective life of 45 minutes with a standard deviation of 8 minutes.
An independent random sample of 50 cans of the present insecticide had a mean effective life of 42 minutes with a standard deviation of 6 minutes. Do these sample results support the manufacturer's claim, at $\alpha = 1\%$?

49. A New York sportswriter claims the American League pitchers have lower earned run averages than National League pitchers. If 20 randomly selected American League pitchers have a mean E.R.A. of 2.50 with s = 0.15 while 16 randomly selected National League pitchers have a mean E.R.A. of 2.6 with s = 0.25. Is the New York sportswriter's claim justified at $\alpha = 1\%$?

50. An insurance company claims that male drivers under age 25 have more accidents per year than male drivers 25 years of age or older. An independent sample of size 40 is randomly selected from each age group. The mean number of accidents per year for the male drivers under age 25 was found to be 1.2 with a standard deviation of 0.1 while the mean number of accidents per year for the drivers 25 years of age or older was found to be 0.94 with a standard deviation of 0.2. Do you believe the claim of the company is correct at $\alpha = 5\%$?

51. An educational researcher wants to determine whether the Scholastic Aptitude Test (SAT) scores of students attending an Ivy League College is significantly different than the SAT scores of students attending a Military Academy. A independent random sample is chosen from each population and the SAT scores for the verbal, the mathematics and the combined sections are summarized in the following table.

Verbal SAT's		Mathematics SAT's		Combined SAT's	
Ivy	Military	Ivy	Military	Ivy	Military
$\bar{x} = 680$	$\bar{x} = 640$	$\bar{x} = 675$	$\bar{x} = 710$	$\bar{x} = 1355$	$\bar{x} = 1350$
s = 50	s = 60	s = 70	s = 50	s = 86	s = 78
n = 50	n = 50	n = 50	n = 50	n = 50	n = 50

Using this sample data, can the educational researcher conclude that the:

(I) Population mean verbal score is higher for the Ivy League students at $\alpha = 5\%$?

(II) Population mean math score is higher for the military academy students at $\alpha = 5\%$?

(III) Population mean score of the combined SAT scores is significantly different from the Ivy League and military academy students at $\alpha = 5\%$?

52. A botanist wants to test whether the new product "Miraculous Growth" would significantly increase the number of flowers per plant over an eight week period. Two trays of 12 plants were prepared. Tray I received the "Miraculous Growth" during the test period while Tray II served as the **control group**. The plants were grown in a controlled environment for this eight week period. At the end of this period, the number of flowers per plant were recorded. The results are summarized in the following table:

Tray I (treatment group)		Tray II (control group)	
14	17	12	9
16	19	10	10
20	20	13	15
19	18	14	12
16	17	15	13
15	16	12	14

Can the botanist conclude that the plants treated with "Miraculous Growth" had greater number of flowers per plant than the plants in the control group at $\alpha = 5\%$?

>>> **WHAT DO YOU THINK?**

---

53. A research article entitled "Japanese And American Tendencies To Argue" appeared in *Psychological Reports* on June, 1990. The article discussed argumentativeness as a personality trait composed of the tendencies to approach and avoid arguments. The authors defined people with approach tendencies as being predisposed to advocate positions on controversial issues and attack conflicting positions argue while people with avoidance tendencies try to keep arguments from happening.

The purpose of the study was to compare the argumentativeness in Japan and the United States using an argumentativeness scale called Infante-Rancer which measures the approach and avoidance tendencies as well as the respondents' arguementativeness.

The study involved 168 Japanese subjects representing three Tokyo Universities and 153 Americans attending West Virginia University. The authors indicated that there was no significant difference between the Japanese and Americans in age, proportion of men and women, and years of education. The following table represents the analysis of the study.

Tendency	Culture	Mean	Standard Deviation	t value	p
Approach	Japanese	29.00	6.54		
	American	33.00	6.65	5.19	<0.01
Avoidance	Japanese	27.00			
	American	26.00	ns		
Argumen-	Japanese	2.00	9.70		
tativeness	American	7.00	11.10	3.66	<0.01

a) Define the two populations within the study. By examining the *t* value can you determine which culture has been defined as population 1? Explain.

b) What variables are being measured? How are they being measured?

c) What is the difference between people who have an approach tendency and people with an avoidance tendency?

d) If a larger mean score indicates a greater inclination to have that tendency, then how might you interpret the mean scores for each of these cultures on the approach tendency?

e) If the null hypothesis for the approach tendency aspect of the study is stated as: there is no significant difference between the mean scores of the Japanese and American subjects on the approach tendencies, then state the alternative hypothesis for a nondirectional test.

f) Can we accept this alternative hypothesis at a 1% level of significance? Explain.

g) Does the *t* test analysis indicate that there is a significant or nonsignificant difference between the Japanese and the Americans with respect to approach tendencies? Explain.

h) Which statement agrees with the conclusion of the results of the approach tendency? The Japanese are more inclined to argue or the Americans are more inclined to argue? Explain.

i) State the null and alternative hypotheses for the study pertaining to the avoidance tendency?

j) Can we reject the null hypothesis at a 1% level of significance? Explain.

k) Does the t test analysis indicate that there is a significant or nonsignificant difference between the Japanese and the Americans with respect to avoidance tendencies? Explain.

l) State the null and alternative hypotheses for the study pertaining to the arguementativeness tendency?

m) Can we reject the null hypothesis at a 5% level of significance? Explain.

n) Does the *t* test analysis indicate that there is a significant or nonsignificant difference between the

Means, Standard Deviations, and t Ratios For Subscale Scores On Leadership Skills Inventory and Factors (Sten Scores) of High School Personality Questionnaire For Boys and Girls in Leadership Studies Program.

Variable	All Subjects		Boys		Girls		t^*
	M	SD	M	SD	M	SD	
1. Fundamentals of Leadership	50.04	11.09	49.61	12.02	50.37	10.40	−.33
2. Written Communication Skills	55.27	7.98	53.66	6.88	56.45	8.60	−1.77
3. Speech Communication Skills	53.21	9.48	52.19	9.30	54.01	9.64	−.93
4. Values Clarification	52.96	6.78	51.35	6.08	54.24	7.09	−2.10*
5. Decision-making Skills	54.10	7.48	53.09	7.43	54.92	7.50	−1.18
6. Group Dynamic Skills	53.58	7.53	51.97	6.72	54.86	7.97	−1.88
7. Problem-solving Skills	55.08	9.17	54.11	10.38	55.84	8.10	−.91
8. Personal Development Skills	54.55	6.39	53.26	6.51	55.58	6.16	−1.78
9. Planning Skills	55.94	7.20	54.90	7.55	56.77	6.88	−1.26
10. A Warmth	5.98	1.93	5.88	2.34	6.07	1.56	−.48
11. B Intelligence	6.52	1.85	6.40	1.72	6.62	1.95	−.57
12. C Emotional Stability	6.26	1.82	5.81	1.89	6.62	1.71	−2.20*
13. D Excitability	5.69	1.89	5.85	2.07	5.56	1.74	.74
14. E Dominance	5.89	2.16	5.33	1.85	6.34	2.30	−2.30*
15. F Cheerfulness	5.41	2.10	5.54	2.23	5.30	2.00	.56
16. G Conformity	6.35	1.89	6.38	1.88	6.34	1.91	.11
17. H Boldness	6.07	2.16	5.95	2.23	6.17	2.11	−.49
18. I Sensitivity	6.45	2.21	6.45	2.10	6.45	2.31	.00
19. J Withdrawal	5.90	1.95	5.59	1.93	6.15	1.94	−1.38
20. O Apprehension	4.26	2.14	4.40	2.16	4.15	2.13	.57
21. Q_2 Self-sufficiency	5.36	1.95	5.00	1.87	5.66	1.99	−1.65
22. Q_3 Self-discipline	6.11	1.86	5.88	1.86	6.30	1.86	−1.09
23. Q_4 Tension	5.15	1.90	5.28	2.06	5.05	1.78	.58
24. Extraversion	6.90	1.60	7.11	1.70	6.74	1.51	1.09
25. Anxiety	4.71	1.86	5.13	1.85	4.38	1.83	1.97
26. Tough Poise	5.13	2.19	5.09	2.20	5.16	2.20	−.16
27. Independence	6.30	1.93	5.71	1.60	6.77	2.06	−2.71*
28. Delinquency	6.49	2.04	6.22	1.84	6.70	2.17	−1.15
29. Accident Proneness	4.55	1.91	4.73	1.73	4.41	2.05	.81
30. Creativity	6.75	1.98	6.77	1.99	6.82	1.99	−.36
31. Leadership Potential	6.52	1.98	6.74	2.09	6.34	1.89	.95
32. School Achievement	6.51	2.10	6.25	1.95	6.70	2.20	−1.08
33. Vocational Growth	6.62	2.26	6.22	2.21	6.93	2.28	−1.52
34. Vocational Success	5.91	2.20	5.91	2.15	5.91	2.27	−.02

*$p = .05$.

FIGURE 13.18

Japanese and the Americans with respect to argumentativeness tendencies? Explain.

o) Indicate whether you agree or disagree with the following statements as they pertain to the results of this study.

(1) the Japanese are more nonargumentative.

(2) Americans feel that arguing offers intellectual challenges and is exciting.

(3) Japanese view arguments positively.

(4) Americans value group harmony and shun controversy.

54. A research study explored the relationship between the personality characteristics and concepts and skills necessary for leadership development in students. The study involved 53 girls and 42 boys attending a Leadership Studies Program for one week on a university campus. Figure 13.18 presents the means and standard deviations for the girls and boys on the Leadership Skills Inventory subscale scores and for each of the High School Personality Questionnaire factors along with the t values of the comparison of the mean scores. The purpose of administering these instruments was to assess the strengths and weaknesses of the students' leadership concepts and skills.

a) Define the two populations within the study. By examining the *t* value can you determine which group has been defined as population 1? Explain.

b) What variables are being measured? How are they being measured?

c) On which of the variables are the results of the *t* test significant?

d) Would these results be significant at $\alpha = 1\%$? Explain.

e) State the null and alternative hypotheses for each of these significant *t* tests if the alternative hypothesis was a nondirectional hypothesis.

f) What is the name and mean of the sampling distribution that serves as the model for this test?

g) Did the boys or girls score significantly higher on the Dominance Factor?

h) Who scored significantly higher on the Independence Factor?

i) For the Dominance and Independence Factor, was the null hypothesis rejected at $\alpha = 5\%$? at $\alpha = 1\%$? Explain.

j) For the Fundamentals of Leadership Skill, was the null hypothesis rejected at $\alpha = 5\%$? at $\alpha = 1\%$? Explain.

k) Does the t test analysis indicate that there is a significant or nonsignificant difference between the girls and boys with respect to Speech Communication Skills at $\alpha = 5\%$? Explain.

l) Does the t test analysis indicate that there is a significant or nonsignificant difference between the girls and boys with respect to Values Clarification at $\alpha = 5\%$? at $\alpha = 1\%$? Explain.

55. The following excerpt is from a recent research article from the *New England Journal of Medicine* regarding a study concerning the effects of oat bran on cholesterol. Read this excerpt and answer the following questions.

A Harvard study from the *New England Journal of Medicine* found no significant difference on cholesterol levels between people who ate oat bran and those that ate a placebo supplement, which consisted of just plain flour. In both cases, the levels decreased slightly, mainly because the volunteers ate grains instead of fatty foods. In the study, 20 healthy people from the staff of Brigham and Women's Hospital in Boston were put for six weeks on an oat bran high-fiber diet, two weeks on their normal diets, and then six weeks on a diet high in white flour, which is low in fiber. The study was double-blinded.

a) Define the two groups contained within the study.

b) State the purpose of the study, and a null and an alternative hypothesis for this study.

c) What was the result of the study? Was the null hypothesis rejected? Explain.

d) What does "placebo supplement" mean?

e) What is the purpose of giving a group a placebo? How does this help to conduct the study?

f) Explain what is meant by the statement: "the study was double-blinded"?

g) Comment on the following statement about this study: "twenty volunteers are too few to be meaningful and that the participants had cholesterol levels of 186, which is less than the 235 cutoff point set by the American Heart Association for serious concern about heart disease."

h) Comment on the following statement about this study: "Because the cholesterol levels dropped slightly, but equally, regardless of whether the volunteers ate high- or low fiber foods, the oat bran hype is clearly overblown. This is a classic case of where the oat bran industry has run ahead of science."

PROJECTS

56. Hypothesis Testing Project:

   A. Selection of a topic.

   1. Select a reported fact or claim involving two population means made in a local newspaper, magazine or other source.

   2. Suggested topics:

      a) Compare the cumulative averages of males and females at your school and test the hypothesis that there is no significant difference between their cumulative averages.

      b) Compare the mean number of traffic violations incurred during the past 3 years for drivers under 25 against the average for drivers over 25 to determine if a significant difference exists between these averages.

   c) Compare the average pulse rate of football players and cheerleaders at your school and test the hypothesis that there is no significant difference between their average pulse rates.

   d) Compare the average number of part-time hours worked by freshmen and sophomores at your school to determine if there is a significant difference between these averages.

   B. Use the following procedure to test the claim selected in Part A.

   1. State the claim, identify the two populations referred to in the statement of the claim, and indicate where the claim was found.

   2. State your opinion regarding the claim of the two population means, μ_1 and μ_2 (i.e. $\mu_1 > \mu_2$, $\mu_1 < \mu_2$ or $\mu_1 \neq \mu_2$).

3. State the null and alternative hypotheses.

4. Develop and state a procedure for selecting an independent random sample from each population. Indicate the technique you are going to use to obtain your sample data.

5. Compute the expected results, indicate the hypothesis testing model, and choose an appropriate level of significance.

6. Calculate the critical score(s) and state the decision rule.

7. Calculate the test statistic.

8. Construct a hypothesis testing model and place the test statistic on the model.

9. Formulate the appropriate conclusion and interpret the conclusion with respect to your opinion (as stated in Step 2).

57. Read a research article from a professional journal in a field such as medicine, education, marketing, science, social science, etc. Write a summary of the research article that includes the following:

a) Name of article, author, and journal (include volume number and date).

b) Statement of the research problem.

c) The null and alternative hypotheses.

d) How the study was conducted (give the definition of the treatment group, treatment used and the sample size; give the definition of the control group and the sample size. Were placebos used? If so, what were they?)

e) Determine the test statistic and the level of significance.

f) State the conclusion in terms of the null and alternative hypotheses.

ANALYZING THE DATABASE USING TECHNOLOGY

The following exercises refer to the file DATABASE listed in Appendix A. Using a technological tool, answer each exercise.

58. For the variable names:

a) AVE

b) SEX

Test the hypothesis that the mean high school average of females is not equal to the mean high school average of males.

State the null and alternative hypotheses for this test. Identify the sample statistics, the t score, p value and interpret. Is the null hypothesis rejected? State the conclusion in words with respect to the variable tested.

59. For the variable names:

a) GFT

b) SEX

Test the hypothesis that the mean amount of dollars spent on a gift by males is more than the mean amount of dollars spent on a gift by females.

State the null and alternative hypotheses for this test. Identify the sample statistics, the t score, p value and interpret. Is the null hypothesis rejected? State the conclusion in words with respect to the variable tested.

CHAPTER TESTS

60. The distribution used to approximate the sampling distribution of the differences between two means, when the population standard deviations are unknown, is the:

a) Binomial distribution

b) t distribution

c) Normal distribution

61. If the sample sizes, n_1 and n_2, are increased and the sample standard deviations, s_1 and s_2, remain the same then the value of $s_{\bar{x}_1-\bar{x}_2}$ will:

a) Increase

b) Remain the same

c) Decrease

62. If the test statistic t is beyond the critical t score, then the conclusion is:

a) Reject H_o

b) Reject H_a

c) Fail to Reject H_o

d) Accept H_a

63. If the conclusion of a hypothesis test involving two population means is that there is no significant difference between the population means then the experimenter has failed to reject H_o.

(T/F)

64. If the test statistic of the difference between the sample means, $\bar{x}_1 - \bar{x}_2$, does not fall beyond t_c then the null hypothesis, H_o, is assumed true.

(T/F)

For each of the problems 65 to 67:

a) Define population 1 and population 2.

b) Formulate the null and alternative hypotheses.

c) Calculate the expected results for the hypothesis test assuming the null hypothesis is true and determine the hypothesis test model.

d) Formulate the decision rule.

e) Determine the test statistic.

f) State the conclusion and answer the question(s) posed in the problem, if any.

65. A psychologist administered a perception test to two randomly selected groups. The first group of 10 subjects were asked to estimate the length of an object dangling from a rod at a distance of 20 feet. These subjects had both eyes open while observing the object. The second group of 12 subjects estimated the length of the object with one eye covered. The results are summarized in the following table.

Group I (using both eyes)	Group II (one eye covered)
$n_1 = 10$	$n_2 = 12$
$\bar{x}_1 = 12.5$ inches	$\bar{x}_2 = 14.25$ inches
$s_1 = 1.25$ inches	$s_2 = 2.5$ inches

Can the psychologist (with both eyes open) conclude that there is a significant difference in the perception of the two groups at $\alpha = 1\%$?

66. The Affirmative Action Officer of a city newspaper decides to determine if the recently hired male journalists earn a greater mean salary than the recently hired female journalists. The Affirmative Action Officer randomly selected independent samples of 16 recently hired male and 16 recently hired female journalists. If the male journalists had a mean salary of $40,750 per year with a standard deviation of $700 and the female journalists had a mean salary of $39,650 per year with a standard deviation of $1200, can the Affirmative Action Officer of the city newspaper conclude there is a significant difference in their population mean salaries at $\alpha = 5\%$?

67. A new toothpaste containing an anti-cavity substance DPT claims to significantly reduce cavities in children. To test this claim, researchers from a dental school randomly select two groups of children. To one group, called the treatment group, the children are given the toothpaste containing DPT. To the other group, called the control group, the children are given the toothpaste *without* DPT. After one year the mean number of cavities for each group is determined. The results for each group are summarized in the following table:

Treatment Group	Control Group
$n_1 = 64$	$n_2 = 100$
$\bar{x}_1 = 3$	$\bar{x}_2 = 3.2$
$s_1 = 0.4$	$s_2 = 0.6$

Do these sample results indicate that DPT significantly reduces cavities at $\alpha = 1\%$?

CHAPTER 14

Chi-Square

Contents

14.1   INTRODUCTION

A population can be divided many ways. For example, it can be divided according to gender, age group, type of personality, religion, marital status, annual income, political affiliation, or education. Divisions such as these are usually referred to as classifications or factors of the population.

In this chapter, we will present a technique that determines whether two classifications of a population are **independent** (i.e., the classifications are not related) or **dependent** (i.e., the classifications are related). For example,

- are annual income and education level dependent? If the classifications of annual income and education level are **dependent**, then one might *expect* to find individuals with a low education level to have a low annual income, and, those with a high education level to have a high annual income. On the other hand, if the classifications are **independent**, then knowledge of one's education level is *not* indicative of that individual's annual income level.
- are movie preference and an individual's gender dependent? If the classifications of movie preference and gender are **dependent** then a relationship between the classifications might be that females generally prefer romance type movies and males generally prefer adventure type movies. Whereas, if the classifications are **independent** then knowing one's gender would *not* give you a clue to their movie preference.
- are male personality types and incidence of heart attack dependent? If the classifications of age and incidence of heart attack are **dependent** then we might expect to find type A personality more susceptible to heart attack then type B personality. If the classifications are **independent** then one's personality type would have no relation to the incidence of heart attack.

All of these examples involve the analysis of **qualitative** data to determine if there is a statistically significant relationship between the population classifications. That is, are the classifications dependent?

A statistical technique used to investigate whether the classifications of a population are related is the **chi-square test of independence**. To apply the chi-square test, a random sample is selected from the population and the sample data is separated into the different categories for each classification of the population. The **frequency** (or number) of responses falling into the distinct categories for each classification are recorded in a table. These sample results are called *observed frequencies*.

Table 14.1 illustrates the observed frequencies for a random sample of 200 co-eds selected from a mid-western university. The sample is classified by gender and movie preference. This table is referred to as a **contingency table**.

DEFINITION 14.1

A **contingency table** is an arrangement of sample count data into a two-way classification.

TABLE 14.1   Contingency Table

Gender	Romance	Comedy	Drama	Adventure	Mystery	Row Total
			Movie Preference			
Male	a 10	b 20	c 5	d 40	e 15	90
Female	f 50	g 25	h 5	i 15	j 15	110
Column Total	60	45	10	55	30	200

A contingency table with the row classification (i.e., the Gender classification) separated into two categories and the column classification (i.e., the Movie Preference classification) separated into five categories. A contingency table with 2 row classifications and 5 column classifications is referred to as a *2 by 5 contingency table.*

In general, an *r by c contingency table* is a table where the row classification has been separated into **r** rows and the column classification has been separated into **c** columns.

Each individual box in the table is referred to as a **cell**. The number within each cell is the **observed cell frequency**. For example, in cell d of Table 14.1 the observed cell frequency is 40. That is, the number of males within this sample that prefer adventure movies is 40. Similarly, in cell f the observed frequency is 50 which represents the number of females within the sample that prefer a romantic movie.

To determine whether the two classifications, gender and movie preference, are related we will compare the observed frequencies of the random sample to the frequencies we would expect if there is no relationship between the classifications gender and movie preference. If the differences between the **observed** and these **expected frequencies** are *small,* then we will conclude that the two classifications are not related or independent. If the differences between the observed and expected frequencies are *large,* then we will conclude that the two classifications are related or dependent. The statistic used to determine whether the differences between the observed and expected frequencies for all the cells of the contingency table are **large** or **small** is known as **Pearson's chi-square statistic, denoted by** X^2 (where X is the capital Greek letter Chi, pronounced kye which rhymes with hi). Pearson's chi-square statistic is also referred to as the **test statistic**.

The Definition Formula For Computing Pearson's Chi-Square Test Statistic, (X^2)

Pearson's Chi-Square Test Statistic $= \sum_{all\ cells} \dfrac{(Observed - Expected)^2}{Expected}$

This formula is symbolized as:

$$X^2 = \sum_{all\ cells} \dfrac{(O - E)^2}{E}$$

where: O = Observed Cell Frequency
E = Expected Cell Frequency

If the classifications are *truly independent*, then this would be indicated by a situation where each expected cell frequency, symbolized by E, is *close* or *equal* to its corresponding observed cell frequency, symbolized by O. Consequently, in the case of independence, the numerical value of X^2 would be *small* or *zero*.

When the observed and expected frequencies are the same (i.e., there are *no differences* between the observed and expected frequencies), the value of X^2 is zero. Whereas, *any difference* between the observed and expected frequencies will result in a positive value for X^2. As the differences between the observed and expected frequencies get larger, the value of X^2 will increase.

It then follows that a *large* value of X^2 would tend to indicate a **significant** relationship exists between the two classifications. Thus, we need to determine how *large* a value of X^2 would indicate that the two classifications are dependent. To determine when a value of Pearson's chi-square statistic is considered to be large, we need to examine a distribution that consists of all the possible values of the chi-square statistic. This distribution is called the sampling distribution of Pearson's chi-square statistic. The sampling distribution of Pearson's chi-square statistic is approximated by the **chi-square distribution**, denoted as χ^2 **distribution** (where χ is the lowercase Greek letter chi, pronounced kye and rhymes with hi). Let us now examine the properties of the **chi-square, χ^2, distribution**.

14.2 PROPERTIES OF THE CHI-SQUARE DISTRIBUTION

Figure 14.1 illustrates a typical chi-square distribution.

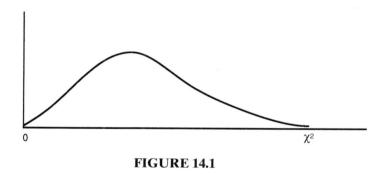

FIGURE 14.1

Properties of the Chi-Square Distribution

1. The value of χ^2 is always non-negative; it is zero or positively valued.
2. The graph of a chi-square distribution is *not symmetric*, it is *skewed* to the right and extends infinitely to the right of zero.
3. There is a family of chi-square distributions similar to the family of *t* distributions as illustrated in Figure 14.2. Each chi-square distribution is dependent upon the number of degrees of freedom, *df*, determined by the formula:

$$df = (r - 1)(c - 1),$$

where: r   represents the number of row classifications within the contingency table, and
        c   represents the number of column classifications within the contingency table.

As the number of degrees of freedom, *df*, increases, the shape of the chi-square distribution approaches the shape of the normal distribution.

Various Chi-Square Distributions

FIGURE 14.2

14.3   CHI-SQUARE HYPOTHESIS TEST OF INDEPENDENCE

Let's apply the general five step hypothesis testing procedure to test the independence of two population classifications. This hypothesis testing procedure is called the *Chi-Square Test of Independence.*

Step 1   Formulate the two Hypotheses, H_o and H_a.
These hypotheses have the following form:
Null Hypothesis Form

H_o: The two population classifications are **independent**.

This means that the population classifications are *not* related.
Alternative Hypothesis Form

H_a: The two population classifications are **dependent**.

This means that the population classifications *are* related.

By stating the null hypothesis as "the two population classifications are independent" we are making the assumption that there is *no relationship* between the classifications. Consequently, by *rejecting* the null hypothesis we can conclude that the two population classifications are *dependent*. This infers that there is a relationship between the two population classifications.

Step 2   Determine the model to test the null hypothesis, H_o.
The chi-square distirbution with $df = (r–1)(c–1)$ is the hypothesis testing model (see Figure 14.2). Under the assumption that *H_o is true*, calculate the expected cell frequencies. To calculate the expected frequency for a particular cell, we multiply its row total (RT) by its column total (CT) and divide this product by the sample size (n).

Expected Frequency Cell Formula

The expected frequency formula for a particular cell is:

$$\text{expected cell frequency} = \frac{(RT)(CT)}{n}$$

where:

RT   is the row total for the cell
CT   is the column total for the cell
n   is the sample size

Step 3   Formulate the decision rule.

All chi-square tests of independence will be one-tailed tests on the right, since a significant Pearson's X^2 statistic will always be a large positive number.

To determine the critical chi-square value necessary to formulate the decision rule, we perform the following steps:

Procedure to Formulate the Decision Rule

a) Identify the significance level, $\alpha = 1\%$ or $\alpha = 5\%$.
b) Calculate the degrees of freedom, df, using:
   $df =$ (number of rows minus one)(number of columns minus one)
   In symbols, $df = (r-1)(c-1)$.
c) Determine the **critical χ^2 value, denoted χ_α^2**, using Table IV: Critical Values for the Chi-Square Distribution, χ_α^2, found in Appendix D: Statistical Tables, and draw a chi-square distribution model with the χ_α^2 value appropriately placed on the curve. This hypothesis testing model is illustrated in Figure 14.3.
d) State the decision rule.
   The decision rule is: reject H_o if X^2 test statistic is greater than χ_α^2.

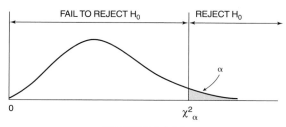

FIGURE 14.3

Step 4   Analyze the sample data.

Calculate Pearson's X^2 test statistic.

There are two equivalent formulas, the definition formula and the computational formula, that are used to calculate Pearson's X^2 statistic. Let's examine each of these two formulas for the X^2 statistic.

Pearson's Chi-Square Test Statistic Formulas

The definition formula for Pearson's chi-square test statistic is:

$$X^2 = \sum_{all\ cells} \frac{(O-E)^2}{E}$$

The computational formula for Pearson's chi-square test statistic is:

$$X^2 = \sum_{all\ cells} \left(\frac{O^2}{E}\right) - n$$

where: O   represents the observed frequency of a particular cell,
         E   represents the expected frequency for the same cell,
         n   represents the sample size.

Step 5   State the conclusion.

Compare the value of Pearson's chi-square test statistic, X^2, to the critical value of chi-square, χ_α^2, and choose the appropriate conclusion.

If the value of the X^2 test statistic is greater than the critical value of chi-square, χ_α^2, then the conclusion is:

Reject H_o and Accept H_a at α and we would conclude that there is a significant relationship between the two population classifications. This means that the two population classifications are dependent.

Similarly, if the value of the X^2 test statistic is less than or equal to the critical value of chi-square, χ_α^2, then the conclusion is:

Fail to Reject H_o at α and we would conclude that there is no significant relationship between the two population classifications. This means that the two population classifications are independent.

In summary, we have:

Conclusions for the Chi-Square Test of Independence

(a)
If $X^2 > \chi_\alpha^2$, then:
Reject H_o
and
Accept H_a at α

(b)
If $X^2 \leq \chi_\alpha^2$, then:
Fail to Reject H_o
at α

These conclusions are illustrated in Figure 14.4.

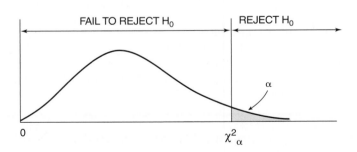

FIGURE 14.4

EXAMPLE 14.1

A study was conducted at the 1% level of significance to determine if there is a relationship between gender and one's view on capital punishment. A random sample of 100 adults was selected and asked their opinion on the question:

"Do you believe that the death penalty should be given to those convicted of first degree murder?"

The sample results which represent the observed frequencies are summarized in Table 14.2.

TABLE 14.2 Table of Observed Frequencies

Gender	View on Capital Punishment			
	Favor	Against	Undecided	Row Totals
Male	[a] 20	[b] 25	[c] 15	60
Female	[d] 10	[e] 25	[f] 5	40
Column Totals	30	50	20	100

Based on these sample results can we conclude that there is a relationship between gender and one's view on capital punishment at $\alpha = 1\%$?

Solution

Step 1   Formulate the two hypotheses, H_o and H_a.

H_o: The population classifications gender and one's view on capital punishment are **independent.**

H_a: The population classifications gender and one's view on capital punishment are **dependent.**

Step 2   Determine the model to test the null hypothesis, H_o.
The hypothesis testing model is a chi-square distribution with degrees of freedom:
$df = (r - 1)(c - 1)$.

For this contingency table the row classification of **gender** has a row value of 2; the column classification of **view on capital punishment** has a column value of 3.

$$df = (2 - 1)(3 - 1)$$
$$df = 2$$

Thus, this 2 by 3 contingency table has **two degrees of freedom**.

Chi-Square Distribution with $df = 2$

0

FIGURE 14.5

Thus, the chi-square distribution with $df = 2$ is the hypothesis testing model shown in Figure 14.5. Table 14.2 is a contingency table of the observed frequencies. *To test H_o, the expected frequencies for each cell must be computed.* To compute these expected frequencies, we assume H_o is true. That is, we assume that the classifications of gender and one's view on capital punishment are independent. This means that since 30 of the 100 people sampled favor capital punishment then we would expect 30% of the 60 males to favor capital punishment. Similarly, we would also expect 30% of the 40 females to favor capital punishment. Therefore, the expected number of males favoring capital punishment is

$$\frac{(30)}{(100)}(60) = 18$$

and the expected number of females favoring capital punishment is

$$\frac{(30)}{(100)}(40) = 12$$

Table 14.3 represents the *expected frequencies* for each of the cells a through f. Notice that the value in cell (a) in Table 14.3 is 18. This cell value represents the number of males that are *expected* to favor capital punishment. Also the value in cell (d) in Table 14.3 is 12. This cell value represents the number of females that are expected to favor capital punishment.

Each of the remaining cell values are obtained based upon the assumption that there is no relationship between gender and one's view on capital punishment. The expected frequency for a particular cell may be calculated by multiplying its row total by its column total and then dividing the product by the sample size. Therefore, the value in cell (a), the expected frequency for cell (a), could have been obtained by the formula:

$$\begin{aligned} \text{expected frequency for cell a} \; &= \; \frac{\left(\begin{array}{c}\text{row total}\\ \text{for cell a}\end{array}\right)\left(\begin{array}{c}\text{column total}\\ \text{for cell a}\end{array}\right)}{\text{sample size}} \\[2mm] &= \; \frac{(60)(30)}{100} \\[2mm] &= \; 18 \end{aligned}$$

Therefore, each of the remaining expected cell values can be obtained using the formula:

$$\text{expected frequency for a cell} \; = \; \frac{\left(\begin{array}{c}\text{row total}\\ \text{for the cell}\end{array}\right)\left(\begin{array}{c}\text{column total}\\ \text{for the cell}\end{array}\right)}{\text{sample size}}$$

TABLE 14.3   Table of Expected Frequencies
View on Capital Punishment

Gender	View on Capital Punishment			
	Favor	Against	Undecided	Row Totals
Male	[a] 18	[b] 30	[c] 12	60
Female	[d] 12	[e] 20	[f] 8	40
Column Totals	30	50	20	100

The observed and expected frequencies are conveniently summarized in Table 14.4. In each cell, the expected frequency is shown in the upper right corner and the observed cell frequency is in the center of the cell.

TABLE 14.4   Table of Observed and Expected Frequencies
View on Capital Punishment

Gender	View on Capital Punishment			
	Favor	Against	Undecided	Row Totals
Male	[a] 20^{18}	[b] 25^{30}	[c] 15^{12}	60
Female	[d] 10^{12}	[e] 25^{20}	[f] 5^{8}	40
Column Totals	30	50	20	100

Step 3   Formulate the decision rule.

     a) The significance level is $\alpha = 1\%$.

     b) The degrees of freedom is:

$$df = 2$$

Thus, this 2 by 3 contingency table has *two degrees of freedom*.

     c) The critical value, χ^2_α, is found in Table IV. For $\alpha = 1\%$ and $df = 2$,

$$\chi^2_\alpha = 9.21$$

The hypothesis testing model is a chi-square distribution with $df = 2$ and $\chi^2_\alpha = 9.21$.

     d) The decision rule is : reject H_o if X^2 test statistic is greater than 9.21. This is illustrated in Figure 14.6.

Step 4   Analyze the sample data.

Calculate the X^2 test statistic. For this example we will use the definition formula to calculate Pearson's chi-square test statistic. The definition formula is:

$$X^2 = \sum_{all\ cells} \frac{(O - E)^2}{E}$$

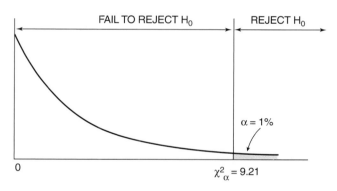

FIGURE 14.6

Table 14.5 has been constructed to aid in the computation of this formula. The observed and expected cell frequency values were obtained from Table 14.4.

TABLE 14.5

Cell	Observed Frequency (O)	Expected Frequency (E)	(O – E)	(O – E)²	$\frac{(O-E)^2}{E}$
a	20	18	2	4	0.22
b	25	30	–5	25	0.83
c	15	12	3	9	0.75
d	10	12	–2	4	0.33
e	25	20	5	25	1.25
f	5	8	–3	9	1.13

$$\sum_{all\ cells} \frac{(O - E)^2}{E} = 4.51$$

To determine the X^2 test statistic sum the values in the last column labelled:

$$\frac{(O-E)^2}{E}.$$

Thus, the test statistic is:

$$X^2 = 4.51$$

Pearson's X^2 test statistic could have been calculated using the computational formula:

$$X^2 = \sum_{all\ cells} \frac{O^2}{E} - n$$

We will illustrate the use of the computational formula in Example 14.2.

Step 5   State the conclusion.
Since X^2 test statistic value of 4.51 is less than χ_α^2 value of 9.21 we *fail to reject the null hypothesis at* $\alpha = 1\%$. Thus, there is no statistically significant relationship between gender and one's view on capital punishment. (i.e., the two classifications are independent). This is illustrated in Figure 14.7.

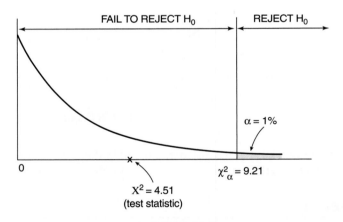

FIGURE 14.7

EXAMPLE 14.2

A study was conducted to determine if there is a significant relationship between the frequency of times meat is served as a main meal per month for individuals living in eastern, central, and western United States.

A questionnaire was administered to a random sample of 300 families and the results are summarized in Table 14.6.

Do these sample results indicate that there is a significant relationship between the frequency of meat served as a main meal per month and geographic living area at $\alpha = 5\%$?

TABLE 14.6 **Table of Observed Frequencies**

Living Area	Frequency of Meat as Main Meal Per Month			
	Less Than 11	11 to 20	More Than 20	Row Totals
Eastern US	[a] 46	[b] 36	[c] 20	102
Central US	[d] 40	[e] 40	[f] 26	106
Western US	[g] 16	[h] 38	[i] 38	92
Column Totals	102	114	84	300

Solution

Step 1 Formulate the two hypotheses, H_o and H_a.

H_o: The population classifications frequency of meat served as a main meal per month and geographic living area are independent.

H_a: The population classifications frequency of meat served as a main meal per month and geographic living area are dependent.

Step 2 Determine the model to test the null hypothesis, H_o.
The hypothesis testing model is a chi-square distribution with degrees of freedom: $df = (r-1)(c-1)$. The degrees of freedom for a 3 by 3 contingency table is:

$$df = (3-1)(3-1)$$
$$df = 4$$

Thus, this 3 by 3 contingency table has **four degrees of freedom**.
The chi-square distribution with $df = 4$ is the hypothesis testing model as shown in Figure 14.8.

chi-square distribution with $df = 4$

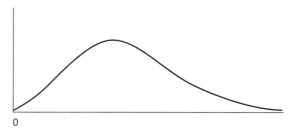

0

FIGURE 14.8

The results of the sample are summarized in Table 14.6. To calculate the chi-square statistic, an expected frequency table representing the expected frequency for each cell must be developed. The expected frequency table is based upon the assumption that the null hypothesis is true. Each of the cell entries is found by the formula:

$$\text{expected frequency for a cell} = \frac{\left(\begin{array}{c}\text{row total} \\ \text{for the cell}\end{array}\right)\left(\begin{array}{c}\text{column total} \\ \text{for the cell}\end{array}\right)}{\text{sample size}}$$

The expected and observed cell frequencies are summarized in Table 14.7.

TABLE 14.7   Table of Observed and Expected Frequencies

Living Area	Frequency of Meat as Main Meal Per Month			
	Less Than 11	11 to 20	More Than 20	Row Totals
Eastern US	a 46 34.68	b 36 38.76	c 20 28.56	102
Central US	d 40 36.04	e 40 40.28	f 26 29.68	106
Western US	g 16 31.28	h 38 34.96	i 38 25.76	92
Column Totals	102	114	84	300

Step 3 Formulate the decision rule.
   a) The significance level is $\alpha = 5\%$.
   b) The degrees of freedom, df, is:

$$df = 4$$

   c) Using Table IV, the critical χ_α^2 value for $\alpha = 5\%$ and $df = 4$ is:

$$\chi_\alpha^2 = 9.49$$

The hypothesis testing model is a chi-square distribution with $df = 4$ and $\chi_\alpha^2 = 9.49$.
   d) The decision rule is: reject H_o if X^2 test statistic is greater than 9.49.
      Figure 14.9 illustrates the decision rule for this hypothesis test.

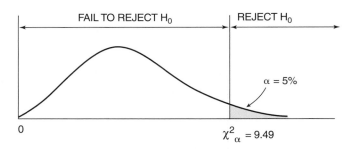

FIGURE 14.9

Step 4 Analyze the sample data.
Calculate X^2 test statistic.
For this example we will use the computational formula for Pearson's chi-square test statistic.

$$X^2 = \sum_{all\ cells} \left(\frac{O^2}{E} \right) - n$$

Table 14.8 has been constructed to aid in the computation of this formula.

TABLE 14.8

Cell	O	O^2	E	$\dfrac{O^2}{E}$
a	46	2116	34.68	61.01
b	36	1296	38.76	33.44
c	20	400	28.56	14.01
d	40	1600	36.04	44.40
e	40	1600	40.28	39.72
f	26	676	29.68	22.78
g	16	256	31.28	8.18
h	38	1444	34.96	41.30
i	38	1444	25.76	56.06

$$n = 300 \qquad \sum_{all\ cells} \frac{(O^2)}{E} = 320.90$$

To compute X^2 test statistic using the computational formula:

$$X^2 = \sum_{all\ cells} \frac{(O^2)}{E} - n$$

1) Sum the values in the last column labelled

$$\frac{(O^2)}{E}$$

in Table 14.8. Thus,

$$\sum_{all\ cells} \frac{(O^2)}{E} = 320.90$$

2) The sample size, n, is 300. Therefore,

$$X^2 = \sum_{all\ cells} \frac{(O^2)}{E} - n$$

$$= 320.90 - 300$$

$$X^2 = 20.90$$

Step 5   State the Conclusion.

Since X^2 test statistic value of 20.90 is greater than the χ^2_α value of 9.49, we reject H_o and accept H_a at $\alpha = 5\%$. These results are illustrated in Figure 14.10.

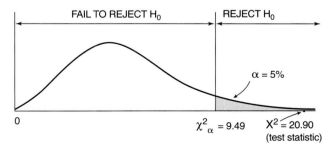

FIGURE 14.10

Thus, there is a **statistically significant** relationship between the frequency of times meat is served as a main meal and one's geographic living location at $\alpha = 5\%$. ▪

CASE STUDY 14.1   Music for the Ages

Examine the snapshot entitled "Music for the ages" in Figure 14.11, which presents the percentage of tapes, CDs and records for the indicated age groups.

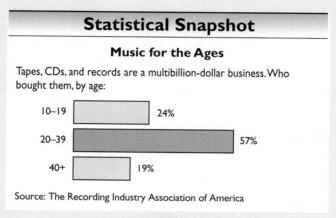

FIGURE 14.11

a) Identify the population classifications presented within Figure 14.11.

b) If you were to perform a hypothesis test to determine if there is a relationship between the population classifications, how would the null hypothesis be stated?

c) How would the alternative hypothesis be stated?

d) When the null hypothesis is assumed to be true, what does that indicate about the relationship between the two population classifications?

e) How many age categories are presented within the snapshot? If for each age category, we classify the people as either purchasing or not purchasing music, then what would be the size of the contingency table for this type of chi-square test?

f) Assuming 2,000 people were randomly selected for the information contained within the snapshot, where 800 people were aged 10–19 years, 1000 were 20–39 and 200 were 40 or older, then determine the number of people that would fall within the categories of the contingency table.

g) What are these values within the contingency table called?

h) Determine the expected frequencies for this hypothesis test.

i) What is the number of degrees of freedom for this test?

j) Determine the critical value for the 5% and 1% level of significance.

k) State a decision rule for each level of significance.

l) Calculate Pearson's Chi-Square test statistic.

m) What is the conclusion for this test, if $\alpha = 5\%$? Can the null hypothesis be rejected at $\alpha = 5\%$? Can you conclude that the two population classifications are independent?

n) Is there a statistically significant relationship between the population classifications at $\alpha = 1\%$? Can the null hypothesis be rejected at $\alpha = 1\%$? Can you conclude that the two population classifications are dependent?

o) Can you conclude that the p-value of this hypothesis test is less than 5%? Explain.

p) Can you conclude that the p-value of this hypothesis test is less than 1%? Explain.

Summary of The Chi-Square Hypothesis Test of Independence

The following outline is a summary of the 5 step hypothesis testing procedure for The Chi-Square Test of Independence.

Step 1   Formulate the two hypotheses, H_o and H_a.

H_o: The two population classifications are independent.

H_a: The two population classifications are dependent.

Step 2   Determine the model to test the null hypothesis, H_o.
The chi-square distribution with the $df = (r–1)(c–1)$ is the hypothesis testing model. Under the assumption that H_o *is true*, calculate the expected cell frequencies using the formula:

$$\text{expected cell frequency} = \frac{(RT)(CT)}{n}$$

Step 3   Formulate the decision rule.
All chi-square tests of independence will be one-tailed tests on the right, since a significant Pearson's X^2 test statistic will always be a large positive number. To determine the critical chi-square value, perform the following steps:
a) Identify the significance level, $\alpha = 1\%$ or $\alpha = 5\%$.
b) Calculate the degrees of freedom: $df = (r-1)(c-1)$.
c) Determine the critical χ^2 value, denoted χ^2_α, using Table IV: Critical Values for the Chi-Square Distribution, χ^2_α, found in Appendix D: Statistical Tables, and draw a chi-square distribution model with the χ^2_α value appropriately placed on the curve.
d) State the decision rule.
The decision rule is: reject H_o if X^2 test statistic is greater than χ^2_α.

Step 4   Analyze the sample data.
Calculate Pearson's X^2 test statistic, using either of the following formulas:

$$X^2 = \sum_{all\ cells} \frac{(O - E)^2}{E} \qquad or \qquad X^2 = \sum_{all\ cells} \frac{(O^2)}{E} - n$$

Step 5   State the conclusion.
Compare the value of Pearson's chi-square test statistic, X^2, to the critical value of chi-square, χ^2_α, and either:
a) Reject H_o and Accept H_a at α, if X^2 is greater than the critical value of chi-square, χ^2_α.
or
b) Fail to Reject H_o at α, if X^2 is less than or equal to the critical value of chi-square, χ^2_α.

14.4   ASSUMPTIONS UNDERLYING THE CHI-SQUARE TEST

When using the χ^2 distribution to perform a hypothesis test, several conditions must be satisfied. These conditions are referred to as the **assumptions underlying the chi-square test.** Let's now discuss these assumptions.

Assumptions Underlying the Chi-Square Test

- Each of the observations must be **independent of all other observations**.
- Each observation must be **classified into one and only one cell**. Care must be exercised to avoid designing classifications that allow an observation to fall into more than one cell.
- Perhaps the most important condition necessary to perform a χ^2 test is that the sample size, n, be sufficiently large. To be sufficiently large means that the **smallest expected cell frequency is at least five**.

14.5   TEST OF GOODNESS-OF-FIT

Another important application of the chi-square distribution is the determination of how well sample data fits a particular theoretical probability model. This type of Chi-Square Test is referred to as a **Goodness-of-Fit Test**.

The Goodness-of-Fit Test is used to determine whether a particular population can be described by a known theoretical distribution model. Throughout the text, we have always assumed that the distribution we were working will fit a particular theoretical distribution. For example, in several chapters, we assumed that certain distributions were normal. Using the Goodness-of-Fit Test, we can use the chi-square distribution to determine whether a particular distribution is approximately normal by comparing a random sample of data selected from the distribution to a theoretical normal distribution.

The chi-square test statistic is used to compare the sample data to the theoretical distribution model, like a normal distribution, to see if the model provides a "good fit" for the data. This type of statistical test is called a Goodness-of-Fit Test. The procedure to perform a Goodness-of-Fit Test involves the same five step hypothesis testing procedure that we've used in the preceding chapters with a few modifications. Example 14.3 outlines the procedure for a Goodness-of-Fit Test.

EXAMPLE 14.3

A market researcher wants to determine if the color of a clients' packaging material is an important factor when a consumer is selecting their product. To answer this question the researcher selects 800 consumers at random and gives them four different colored packages of the same product. However, the consumers are told that the four packages have different chemical properties and that the different color wrappers are to be used only for identification. Six weeks later each person in the sample is asked to complete an order form indicating which one of the four packages they preferred. To insure that the consumer selects the color they truly prefer, each consumer will be sent a free months supply of the product of their choice. The results of this survey are given in Table 14.9.

TABLE 14.9   Survey Results

Color of Wrapper	Pink	Blue	Brown	Grey
Number of consumers selecting wrapper	250	300	100	150

Remark: In this example the market researcher is trying to determine if the consumer prefers a particular colored package. If color is **not** a factor in the consumer's selection then we would expect an **equal** number of consumers choosing each color package. Whenever a statistician expects an equal number of observations in each category, the theoretical distribution model is called the **uniform distribution**. The Goodness-of-Fit test can now be used to determine if the observed data in Table 14.9 fits the theoretical uniform distribution.

Solution

We will modify the five step hypothesis testing procedure used to perform a chi-square test of independence to outline the Goodness-of-Fit test.

Step 1 Formulate the two hypotheses H_o and H_a.
In a Goodness-of-Fit test, the **null hypothesis** is stated as:

Null Hypothesis Form

H_o: the sample data fits a particular distribution

In this example we are trying to determine if there is an equal preference for each color. Therefore, the null hypothesis, H_o, is stated:

H_o: The sample data fits a uniform distribution.

In a *Goodness-of-Fit* test, the **alternative hypothesis** is stated as:

Alternative Hypothesis Form

H_a: the sample data does *not* fit the particular distribution

---

If color is a significant factor in consumer selection of this product then the alternative hypothesis, H_a, is:

H_a: The sample data does not fit a uniform distribution.

Step 2 Determine the model to test the null hypothesis, H_o
The chi-square distribution with $df = k-1$ is the hypothesis testing model.
In this example the sample data is only classified by color. This is referred to as a single classification case. **In a Goodness-of-Fit test, the degrees of freedom are dependent upon the number of categories within a single classification case.**

The degrees of freedom, *df*, for a single classification case

$$df = k - 1$$
where: k equals the number of categories within the single classification.

Since there are four categories of color, then k = 4.

$$\text{Thus, } df = 4 - 1$$
$$df = 3$$

Thus, the chi-square distribution with $df = 3$ is the hypothesis testing model as shown in Figure 14.12.

chi-square distribution with *df* = 3

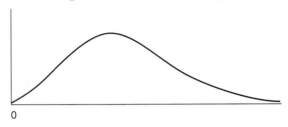

FIGURE 14.12

To calculate the expected frequency for each cell, we assume the null hypothesis to be true. Thus **if we assume that the sample data fits a uniform distribution, then all the expected frequencies would be equal**. Thus, the expected frequency for each cell of the four cells is 200, since 800 consumers responded to the survey. The observed and expected frequencies are summarized in Table 14.10.

TABLE 14.10   Observed and Expected Frequencies

Color of Wrapper	Pink	Blue	Brown	Grey	Total
Number of consumers selecting wrapper	a 250 200	b 300 200	c 100 200	d 150 200	800

Step 3 Formulate the decision rule.
   a) In this example we will use a significance level $\alpha = 1\%$.
   b) In this example the sample data is only classified by color.

Since there are four categories of color, then k = 4.

$$\text{Thus, } df = 3$$

   c) The critical χ^2 value for this test can be found in Table IV where $\alpha = 1\%$ and $df = 3$. The critical χ^2 value is:

$$X_\alpha^2 = 11.34$$

   d) The decision rule is: reject H_o if Pearson's X^2 test statistic is greater than 11.34. The hypothesis testing model is illustrated in Figure 14.13.

Step 4 Analyze the sample data.
Calculate the X^2 test statistic using the definition formula:

$$X^2 = \sum_{all\ cells} \frac{(O - E)^2}{E}$$

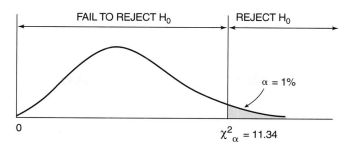

FIGURE 14.13

Table 14.11 is used for the computation of the X^2 test statistic.

TABLE 14.11

Cell	Observed Frequency (O)	Expected Frequency (E)	(O – E)	$(O - E)^2$	$\dfrac{(O - E)^2}{E}$
a	250	200	50	2500	12.50
b	300	200	100	10000	50.00
c	100	200	–100	10000	50.00
d	150	200	–50	2500	12.50
					$X^2 = 125.00$

Step 5 State the conclusion.

Since the X^2 test statistic of 125.00 is greater than χ^2_α value of 11.34, we reject H_o and accept H_a at $\alpha = 1\%$. **Thus the sample data does not fit a uniform distribution.** This conclusion is illustrated in Figure 14.14.

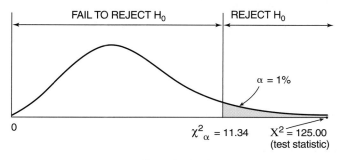

FIGURE 14.14

Thus, color is a significant factor in consumer selection of this product.

EXAMPLE 14.4

Table 14.12 indicates the proportion of viewers per network that watched the six o'clock news last year.

TABLE 14.12   Percent of Viewers

Network	Percent of Viewers
ABC	30
CBS	25
NBC	30
Independent	15

This year a random sample of 400 viewers was conducted to determine if the number of viewers watching the six o'clock news on each of the networks has significantly changed from last years results. The results of the sample data is listed in Table 14.13.

TABLE 14.13   Sample of Viewers

Network	Number of Viewers
ABC	110
CBS	95
NBC	130
Independent	65

Based on the results of this sample data can we conclude that this year's viewing audience has significantly changed from last year's? Use $\alpha = 5\%$.

Solution

The Goodness-of-Fit Test will be used to test whether this year's sample data fits last year's viewing distribution.

Step 1   Formulate the two hypotheses H_o and H_a.

H_o: The sample data fits last year's viewing distribution.

H_a: The sample data does not fit last year's viewing distribution.

Step 2   Determine the model to test the null hypothesis, H_o.

Thus, the chi-square distribution with $df = 3$ is the hypothesis testing model as shown in Figure 14.15.

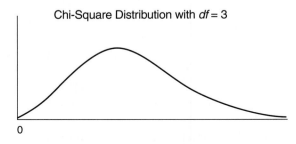

Chi-Square Distribution with $df = 3$

0

FIGURE 14.15

In this example the sample data is only classified by network. The degrees of freedom, *df*, for a single classification case is $df = k - 1$, where k is the number of categories within the single classification.

Since there are four networks, then k = 4.

$$\text{Thus, } df = 4 - 1$$
$$df = 3$$

To calculate the expected frequency for each cell, we assume the null hypothesis to be true. Thus if we assume that the sample data fits last year's viewing distribution, then the expected frequencies are calculated from last year's viewing audience. For example, 30 percent of last year's viewing audience watched the six o'clock news on the ABC network. Thus, for this year's sample of 400 viewers, we would expect that 30 percent of the viewers to have watched the six o'clock news on ABC network. Therefore we would expect 120 viewers to watch ABC's six o'clock news. The expected and the observed frequencies are summarized in Table 14.14.

TABLE 14.14   Observed and Expected Frequencies

Network	ABC	CBS	NBC	Independent	Total
Number of Viewers	[a] 110 ^{120}	[b] 95 ^{100}	[c] 130 ^{120}	[d] 65 ^{60}	400

Step 3   Formulate the decision rule.
  a) The significance level is $\alpha = 5\%$.
  b) In this example the sample data is only classified by network. Since there are four networks, then k = 4.

$$\text{Thus, } df = 3$$

  c) The critical χ^2 value for this test can be found in Table IV where $\alpha = 5\%$ and $df = 3$. The critical χ^2 value is:

$$\chi_\alpha^2 = 7.82$$

  d) The decision rule is: reject H_o if the X^2 test statistic is greater than 7.82. The hypothesis testing model is illustrated in Figure 14.16.

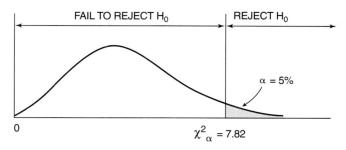

FIGURE 14.16

Step 4   Analyze the sample data.
Calculate the X^2 test statistic using the definition formula:

$$X^2 = \sum_{all\ cells} \frac{(O-E)^2}{E}$$

Table 14.15 is used for the computation of the X^2 statistic.

TABLE 14.15

Cell	Observed Frequency (O)	Expected Frequency (E)	(O – E)	(O – E)²	$\frac{(O - E)^2}{E}$
a	110	120	–10	100	0.83
b	95	100	–5	25	0.25
c	130	120	10	100	0.83
d	65	60	5	25	0.25
					$X^2 = 2.16$

Step 5   State the conclusion..

Since the X^2 test statistic (2.16) is less than χ_α^2 (7.82) we fail to reject H_o at $\alpha = 5\%$. This conclusion is illustrated in Figure 14.17.

FIGURE 14.17

Thus, we can conclude that this year's viewing distribution has not significantly changed from last year's.

A research article entitled "The Rekurring Kase Of The Special K" examined whether the letter K occurs with more frequency as the initial letter in top brand names than it does as a first letter in our language in general. This study appeared in the October/November 1990 issue of the *Journal of Advertising Research*. One aspect of this research was to examine the eight most frequently occurring initial letters were: C, S, A, B, M, P, D and T in top name brands to determine if they occur more frequently as the initial letter in top brand names than they appear as a first letter in our language in general.

These eight most frequently occurring letters were selected by the researchers from a composite list of unduplicated top brand names. From this list, only unique names were selected. Using only unique names eliminated overrepresentation of certain letters. The expected frequency for each of these letters were based on *Webster's Ninth New Collegiate Dictionary* (1987) model. The result of this chi-square test is shown in Figure 14.18. The letter K does not appear on this list since it was not among the most frequent occurring initial letters.

The second aspect of this research was to determine what happens to the analysis when the letter K is added to this list. This aspect of the hypothesis test will be examined in the: What Do You Think? question set of the exercise section at the end of this chapter.

CASE STUDY 14.2 Special K (continued)

Chi-Square Analysis of Most Frequently Occurring Initial Letters of Top Brand Names

Initial letter	Observed frequency	Expected* frequency	Cumulative percent	
			Observed	Expected
C	51	52.4	9.43	9.68
S	46	67.3	17.93	22.12
A	42	32.2	25.69	28.08
B	42	29.2	33.45	33.47
M	40	29.5	40.84	38.92
P	40	47.5	48.23	47.70
D	30	28.2	53.78	52.91
T	29	32.0	59.14	58.83

$$X^2 = 20.677 \quad df = 7 \quad p < .005$$

* Based on Webster's Ninth New Collegiate Dictionary (1987), distribution of words beginning with each letter.

FIGURE 14.18

a) Define the population for this test.

b) What variable is being examined within this test?

c) Is this variable numeric or categorical? Explain

d) What type of chi-square test is being illustrated in this research?

e) What distribution serves as the theoretical distribution?

f) What serves as the sample data for this test?

g) What would serve as the null hypothesis for this test?

h) What would serve as the alternative hypothesis?

i) What assumption was used to calculate the expected frequencies within the table? Which hypothesis does this assumption represent?

j) How many classifications are there for this test? State the classification(s) for this test. What does each category within a classification represent for this test?

k) What formula was used to calculate the number of degrees of freedom for this test? What were the degrees of freedom for this test?

l) What is the value of $\dfrac{(O-E)^2}{E}$ for each initial letter of the information contained within the table of Figure 14.18, where O is the Observed frequency and E is the Expected frequency? What does the sum of the values of $\dfrac{(O-E)^2}{E}$ represent?

m) What are the critical chi-square values for this test at $\alpha = 5\%$ and $\alpha = 1\%$?

n) What is the conclusion of this hypothesis test for each of these significance levels? Can you reject the null hypothesis for any of these significance levels? Explain.

o) What is the conclusion to this test for a significance level of 0.75%? What information did you use to answer this question? Explain.

p) What is the smallest level of significance that you can use to obtain a significant result?

q) State the conclusion to the chi-square test shown in Figure 14.18.

r) Was the chi-square result significant for the hypothesis test shown in Figure 14.18? Explain.

14.6   p-VALUE APPROACH TO CHI-SQUARE HYPOTHESIS TEST OF INDEPENDENCE USING THE TI-83 PLUS CALCULATOR

The p-value approach will require refinements in steps 3, 4 and 5 of the hypothesis testing procedure. In step 3, the decision rule will be stated as: Reject the H_o if the p-value of the X^2 test statistic is less than α. In step 4, the p-value will be determined using the TI-83 Plus calculator. While in step 5, the conclusion of the hypothesis test is determined by comparing the p-value to the level of significance, α.

Let's reexamine the hypothesis test shown in Example 14.2 using a p-value approach with the aid of the TI-83 Plus calculator.

■
EXAMPLE 14.5

A study was conducted to determine if there is a significant relationship between the frequency of times meat is served as a main meal per month for individuals living in eastern, central, and western United States.

A questionnaire was administered to a random sample of 300 families and the results are summarized in Table 14.16.

Table 14.16   Frequency of Meat as Main Meal Per Month

Living Area	Less Than 11	11 to 20	More Than 20	Row Totals
Eastern US	a 46	b 36	c 20	102
Central US	d 40	e 40	f 26	106
Western US	g 16	h 38	i 38	92
Column Totals	102	114	84	300

a) Do these sample results indicate that there is a significant relationship between the frequency of meat served as a main meal per month and geographic living are at $\alpha = 5\%$?

b) Can we conclude that there is a significant relationship between the frequency of meat served as a main meal per month and geographic living area at $\alpha = 1\%$?

c) What is the smallest α level that can be used to show a significant relationship between the frequency of times meat is served as a main meal per month for individuals living in eastern, central, and western United States?

Solution

part (a):

Step 1   Formulate the two hypothesis, H_o and H_a.

H_o: The population classifications frequency of meat served as a main meal per month and geographic living area are independent.

H_a The population classifications frequency of meat served as a main meal per month and geographic living area are dependent.

Step 2   Determine the model to test the null hypothesis, H_o.

The hypothesis testing model is a chi-square distribution with $df = (r - 1)(c - 1)$. Since $r = 3$ and $c = 3$, then df = 4. The chi-square distribution with df = 4 is the hypothesis testing model as shown in Figure 14.19.

Chi-Square Distribution with *df* = 4

0

FIGURE 14.19

To determine the expected results on the TI-83 Plus calculator, we will use the MATRIX function of the calculator. The expected results of this test are shown as MATRIX (B) of the TI-83 Plus output screen in Figure 14.20.

FIGURE 14.20

The expected and observed cell frequencies are summarized in Table 14.17.

Table 14.17 Frequency of Meat as Main Meal Per Month

Living Area	Less Than 11		11 to 20		More Than 20		Row Totals
Eastern US	a 46	34.68	b 36	38.76	c 20	28.56	102
Central US	d 40	36.04	e 40	40.28	f 26	29.68	106
Western US	g 16	31.28	h 38	34.96	i 38	25.76	92
Column Totals	102		114		84		300

Step 3 Formulate the decision rule.
 a) The significance level is $\alpha = 5\%$.
 b) The decision rule is: reject H_o if the p-value of the X^2 test statistic is less than $\alpha = 5\%$. Figure 14.21 illustrates the decision rule for this hypothesis test.

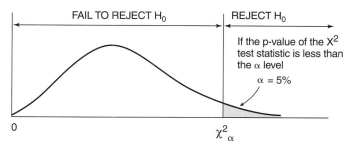

FAIL TO REJECT H₀   REJECT H₀

If the p-value of the X^2 test statistic is less than the α level

$\alpha = 5\%$

0

χ^2_{α}

FIGURE 14.21

Step 4   Analyze the sample data.

Enter the sample data into the TI-83 Plus using the Matrix function and determine the p-value of the X^2 test statistic using the Chi-Square test. The TI-83 Plus output screen is shown in Figure 14.22

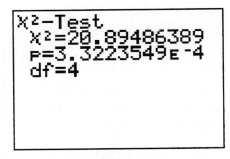

```
X²-Test
 X²=20.89486389
 P=3.3223549E-4
 df=4
```

FIGURE 14.22

Notice from the output screen, the p-value of the test statistic ($X^2 \approx 20.89$) is 3.22 E-4.

Step 5   State the Conclusion.

Since the p-value of this X^2 test statistic is less than $\alpha = 5\%$, we reject H_o and accept H_a at a p-value of 0.000322. These results are illustrated in Figure 14.23.

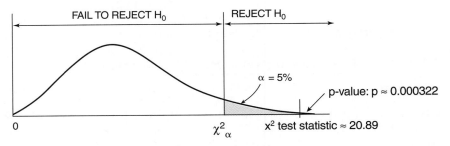

FIGURE 14.23

part (b):   Since the p-value of 0.000322 is less than $\alpha = 1\%$, we can conclude that there is a significant relationship between the frequency of meat is served as a main meal per month and geographic living area at $\alpha = 1\%$. This is shown in Figure 14.24.

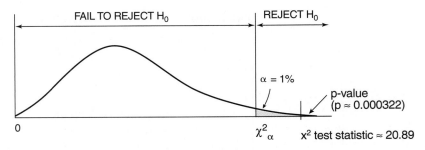

FIGURE 14.24

part (c):   The smallest α level that can be used to show a significant relationship between the frequency of times meat is served as a main meal per month for individuals living in eastern, central, and western United States is equal to the p-value, 0.000322. _____ ∎

Summary of the p-value Approach to the Chi-Square Hypothesis Test of Independence Using the TI-83 Plus Calculator

The following outline is a summary of the 5 step hypothesis testing procedure for the p-value approach to the Chi-Square Test of Independence Using the TI-83 Plus Calculator

Step 1.   *Formulate the two Hypothesis, H_o and H_a.*

H_o: The two population classifications are independent.

H_a: The two population classifications are dependent.

Step 2.   *Determine the model to test the null hypothesis, H_o.*
   a) Construct the chi-square distribution with $df = (r - 1)(c - 1)$ that serves as the hypothesis testing model.
   b) Using H_o *is true* and the Matrix function of the TI-83 Plus calculator, determine the expected cell frequencies.

Step 3.   *Formulate the decision rule.*
   a) Identify the significance level, $\alpha = 1\%$ or $\alpha = 5\%$.
   b) State the decision rule.
   The decision rule is: reject H_o if the p-value of the X^2 test statistic is less than α.

Step 4.   *Analyze the sample data.*
   Enter the sample data into the TI-83 Plus using the Matrix function and determine the p-value of the X^2 test statistic using the χ^2 – test.

Step 5.   *State the conclusion.*
   Compare the p-value of the X^2 test statistic to the significance level α and either:
   a) Reject H_o and Accept H_a at the computed p-value, if the p-value of the X^2 test statistic is less than α.
   b) Fail to Reject H_o at the computed p-value, if the p-value of the X^2 test statistic is not less than α.

14.7   USING TECHNOLOGY

In this chapter we examined the chi-square statistic as a technique to analyze categorical data. Two hypothesis tests were discussed:
   1. Chi-Square Test of Independence,
   2. Test of Goodness-of-Fit.
Let's use MINITAB to perform these tests.

In Example 14.2, a contingency table was given that summarized the results for a random sample of 300 families that were administered a questionnaire to explore the relationship between the frequency of times meat is served as a main meal per month and a family's living area. The table for this example is repeated here.

TABLE 14.18   Table of Observed Frequencies

Living Area	Frequency of Meat as Main Meal Per Month			Row Totals
	Less Than 11	11 to 20	More Than 20	
Eastern US	a 46	b 36	c 20	102
Central US	d 40	e 40	f 26	106
Western US	g 16	h 38	i 38	92
Column Totals	102	114	84	300

Do these sample results indicate that there is a significant relationship between frequency of meat served as a main meal per month and geographic living area? The answer to this question was explored within Example 14.2 using the chi-square test of independence.

The MINITAB output for the expected and observed results is shown in Figure 14.25. The expected counts are printed below observed counts.

MINITAB OUTPUT

C1	C2	C3	Total	
1	46	36	20	102
34.68	38.76	28.56		
2	40	40	26	106
36.04	40.28	29.68		
3	16	38	38	92
31.28	34.96	25.76		
Total	102	114	84	300

ChiSq = 3.695 + 0.197 + 2.566 +
        0.435 + 0.002 + 0.456 +
        7.464 + 0.264 + 5.816 = 20.895

df = 4

FIGURE 14.25

If you examine the output you will notice that **both** the observed and the expected cell values are contained within the contingency table. Compare this output to the contingency table in Table 14.16. Notice that the value of X^2 is given and is 20.895 along with the degrees of freedom, df = 4.

Although the p-value is not included on the output, MINITAB can calculate the p-value for the output to be 0.000299990. Thus the p-value for the X^2 test statistic is 0.00029990. Is the test statistic significant? What is the maximum allowable significance level?

Using the sample data from Table 14.19, the TI–83 Plus calculator output screen in Figure 14.26 displays the expected frequencies of the chi-square test of independence. Notice that the expected frequencies are displayed in a 3x3 Matrix.

FIGURE 14.26

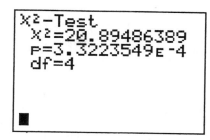

FIGURE 14.27

Figure 14.27 shows the results of the chi-square test of independence. The output displays Pearson's Chi-Square test statistic, the p-value and degrees of freedom.

SECTION EXERCISES

Section 14.1

1. A population can be classified by gender, age, religion, marital status, etc. These divisions are called _____.

2. The sample data falling into each of the cells of the population classifications are called the _____ frequencies.

3. A 4 x 3 contingency table has _____ rows and _____ columns.

4. Pearson's Chi-Square test statistic is computed by comparing the observed frequencies to the _____ frequencies of each cell within the contingency table.

5. How many degrees of freedom does a 3 by 4 contingency table have?
   a) 3   **b)** 12   **c)** 6   **d)** 4

6. Chi-Square tests of independence involve the analysis of quantitative continuous data.
   (T/F)

Section 14.2

7. The value of the Chi-Square test statistic is always _____.

8. There are a family of Chi-Square distributions where each chi-square distribution is dependent upon the number of _____ .The formula to calculate *df* is given by: $df = $ _____.

9. The shape of the chi-square distribution is similar to the shape of the normal distribution.
   (T/F)

Section 14.3

10. A statistical technique used to investigate whether the classifications of a population are related is the Chi-Square Test of _____.

11. **a)** The definition formula for computing Pearson's Chi-Square test statistic is: $X^2 = $ _____

b) The computational formula for computing Pearson's Chi-Square test statistic is: $X^2 = $ _____

12. In a Chi-Square test of Independence, the null hypothesis is stated as: the two population classifications are _____. The alternative hypothesis is stated as: the two population classifications are _____.

13. In a Chi-Square test of Independence, the expected frequency for a particular cell is calculated by multiplying its row _____ by its _____ total and dividing this product by the _____.

14. In formulating the conclusion of a Chi-Square test of Independence when:
   a) The value of the X^2 test statistic is less than or equal to the critical value of chi-square, χ^2_α, then the conclusion is _____.
   b) The value of the X^2 test statistic is greater than the critical value of chi-square, χ^2_α, then the conclusion is

   _____.

15. What is the critical value for a χ^2 test of independence for a 2 by 5 contingency table using $\alpha = 1\%$?
   a) 13.28   **b)** 11.07   **c)** 5.99   **d)** 9.49

16. In a χ^2 test for independence the null hypothesis is always
   a) The distribution is normal
   b) The population classifications are independent
   c) The population classifications are dependent
   d) The distribution is uniform

17. The expected frequency for a particular cell is calculated by multiplying its row total by its column total and dividing by
   a) The degrees of freedom
   b) The critical χ^2
   c) The sample size
   d) Number of classifications

18. If the value of the X^2 test statistic is greater than the critical value of chi-square, χ^2_α, then the conclusion is to reject H_o and accept H_a at α.
   (T/F)

19. If the conclusion is that the classifications are independent then the Pearson's chi-square test statistic, X^2, is greater than the χ^2_α.
   (T/F)

Problems 20–28 use the chi-square test of independence.

For all of these problems :
   a) Formulate the hypotheses.
   b) State the decision rule.
   c) Calculate Pearson's chi-square test statistic.
   d) Determine the conclusion, and answer the question(s) posed in the problem, if any.

20. A study was undertaken to determine whether or not membership in campus fraternity groups is related to grades. A random sample of 100 students was selected and the results are summarized in the following table:

Fraternity Group	Grade Point Average(GPA)			Row Totals
	Less Than 2.00	From 2.00 to 3.00	Greater Than 3.00	
Member	[a] 16	[b] 17	[c] 7	40
Non-member	[d] 9	[e] 28	[f] 23	60
Column Totals	25	45	30	100

Based on these sample results can we conclude that there is a relationship between membership in a campus fraternity group and GPA at $\alpha = 1\%$?

21. A study was conducted to determine if a relationship exists between gender and movie preference. Two hundred students were questioned regarding their movie preference. The results of the survey are listed in the following table:

Gender	Movie Preference					Row Totals
	Romance	Comedy	Drama	Adventure	Mystery	
Male	[a] 10	[b] 20	[c] 5	[d] 40	[e] 15	90
Female	[f] 50	[g] 25	[h] 5	[i] 15	[j] 15	110
Column Totals	60	45	10	55	30	200

Based on the sample data can we conclude that gender is related to movie preference at $\alpha = 5\%$?

22. A consumer research agency was asked to determine if the consumer preference in packaging material was independent of marital status. Three different types of packaging material (clear, white and dark plastic) were tested. The research agency randomly selected and interviewed 500 individuals to determine their packaging preference. These results are summarized in the following table:

Marital Status	Plastic Packaging Material			Row Totals
	Clear	White	Dark	
Married	[a] 200	[b] 75	[c] 25	300
Not-Married	[d] 50	[e] 75	[f] 75	200
Column Totals	250	150	100	500

Do these sample data indicate that marital status and preference in packaging material are independent at $\alpha = 1\%$?

23. In an experiment designed to compare the effectiveness of different brands of pain relievers, a group of 225 individuals who complained of chronic pain were randomly assigned to three daily treatments: three tablets of Brand A (prescription drug), three tablets of Brand B(non-prescription drug), or three placebos.

   After the experiment, each subject was questioned to determine the effectiveness of their treatment. Their responses are classified in the following table.

Result of Treatment	Drug Treatment			
	Brand A	Brand B	Placebo	Row Totals
Relief from Pain	[a] 17	[b] 15	[c] 13	45
Some Relief from Pain	[d] 33	[e] 34	[f] 38	105
No Relief from Pain	[g] 25	[h] 26	[i] 24	75
Column Totals	75	75	75	225

Based upon these sample results can one conclude that drug treatment and relief from pain are independent at $\alpha = 5\%$?

24. A Nassau County study was conducted to determine the relationship between a person's educational level and their selection to serve on a grand jury. A random sample of 240 people were interviewed for grand jury service and the selection results were classified with respect to the person's educational level. These results are summarized in the following table.

Educational Level	Grand Jury		
	Selected	Not Selected	Row Totals
Elementary	[a] 30	[b] 20	50
Secondary	[c] 63	[d] 47	110
Some College	[e] 15	[f] 31	46
College Degree	[g] 12	[h] 22	34
Column Totals	120	120	240

Do the results of the study indicate at $\alpha = 1\%$ that a person's selection to serve on the grand jury is dependent on educational level?

25. Prof. H. Elp Me-John, a mathematics counselor, is interested in the relationship between math anxiety and the successful completion of the introductory college math course. A random sample of 300 college students enrolled in the introductory college math course were given a test to measure their anxiety level on the first day of the course. The results of the anxiety test and their final grade in the math course are given in the following table.

Grade	Anxiety Level		
	Low	Medium	High
Passed	[a] 59	[b] 32	[c] 29
Failed or Withdrew	[d] 31	[e] 58	[f] 91

Based upon the sample data, can you conclude that anxiety level and successful completion of the math course are independent at $\alpha = 1\%$?

26. A sociologist is researching the question: "Is there a relationship between the level of education and job satisfaction?" For a random sample of 270 workers she determines each individual's education level and level of job satisfaction. The results are recorded in the following table:

Education Level	Job Satisfaction Level		
	Low	Medium	High
College	[a] 20	[b] 70	[c] 30
High School	[d] 15	[e] 60	[f] 25
Grade School	[g] 15	[h] 25	[i] 10

Perform a chi-square test of independence to determine if educational level and job satisfaction are dependent at $\alpha = 5\%$.

27. A record company conducted a random survey of 500 people to determine if there was a relationship between a person's age and their favorite music category. The results of their survey are summarized in the following table.

Music Category	Age				
	Under 20 years	20 to 29	30 to 39	40 to 49	Over 49
Rock	[a] 45	[b] 32	[c] 29	[d] 14	[e] 10
Jazz	[f] 5	[g] 7	[h] 18	[i] 19	[j] 21
Country	[k] 7	[l] 11	[m] 22	[n] 15	[o] 15
Classical	[p] 5	[q] 8	[r] 11	[s] 24	[t] 32
Contemporary	[u] 23	[v] 35	[w] 34	[x] 33	[y] 25

Based on the survey results, can the record company conclude that a person's age and their favorite music category are dependent at $\alpha = 5\%$?

28. Tom the Greek, a serious basketball handicapper, wants to determine if an NBA team's winning home record is independent of their division. He uses the results of last season's NBA games (given on next page) as his random sample and records the following information.
a) Using this information, complete the following contingency table.

Home Record	NBA Division			
	Atlantic	Central	Midwest	Pacific
Wins	[a]	[b]	[c]	[d]
Losses	[e]	[f]	[g]	[h]

b) Based upon the sample data, can Tom conclude that a team's winning home record is independent of their NBA division at $\alpha = 1\%$?

Sample Information for question #28.

Division	Home Record	
Atlantic	Wins	Losses
Team #1	35	6
Team #2	30	11
Team #3	32	9
Team #4	30	11
Team #5	17	24
Team #6	12	29

Division	Home Record	
Central	Wins	Losses
Team #1	37	4
Team #2	37	4
Team #3	33	8
Team #4	31	10
Team #5	30	11
Team #6	20	21

Division	Home Record	
Midwest	Wins	Losses
Team #1	34	7
Team #2	31	10
Team #3	35	6
Team #4	24	17
Team #5	18	23
Team #6	12	29

Division	Home Record	
Pacific	Wins	Losses
Team #1	35	6
Team #2	35	6
Team #3	31	10
Team #4	29	12
Team #5	28	13
Team #6	21	20
Team #7	17	24

Section 14.4

29. The assumptions underlying the Chi-Square test of Independence are:
a) Each of the observations must be _____ of all the other observations.
b) Each observation must be classified into one and only one _____.
c) The sample size must be sufficiently large so that the smallest expected cell frequency is at least _____.

30. When doing an χ^2 test what must be true about the sample size?
a) At least 50
b) No more than 300
c) Large enough so that the smallest expected cell frequency is at least 5
d) Large enough so that each cell in the expected frequency is at least 30

Section 14.5

31. The Goodness-of-Fit Chi-Square Test is used to determine if the sample data fits a particular _____ distribution model.

32. In a Goodness-of-Fit Test, the null hypothesis is stated as the _____ data fits a particular theoretical distribution model.

33. In a Goodness-of-Fit Test, the degrees of freedom of a single classification case with k categories is: $df =$ _____.

34. The test of Goodness-of-Fit refers to a type of chi-square test that can be used to determine how well sample data fits the normal distribution. (T/F)

35. A Goodness-of-Fit test is used to determine if sample data fits a uniform distribution. The conclusion is to reject H_o and accept H_a at α. This conclusion means that the sample data does not fit a uniform distribution. (T/F)

Problems 36–40 use the test of Goodness-of-Fit. For all of the problems :
a) Formulate the hypotheses.
b) State the decision rule.
c) Calculate Pearson's chi-square test statistic.
d) Determine the conclusion, and answer the question(s) posed in the problem, if any.

36. A marketing research agency conducted a random survey to determine the opinions of prospective customers for a new product. The results of the survey were:

Opinion	Number
outstanding	97
excellent	98
good	88
fair	67
not interested	70

If the opinions are uniformly distributed among the five categories then the marketing agency will not recommend the manufacturer to mass produce the new product. Test the null hypothesis that the sample data (opinions of the customers) fits a uniform distribution at $\alpha = 5\%$. Should the marketing agency recommend mass production of the new product to the manufacturer?

37. A market researcher wants to determine if the shape of a client's packaging material is an important factor in a consumer's selection of the product. The researcher randomly selects 2000 consumers and gives each of them five differently shaped packages of the same product. One month later each consumer is asked to indicate a preference for one of the shaped packages. The results of the survey are given in the table below.

Number of Consumers Selecting Package	Shape of Package				
	#1	#2	#3	#4	#5
	430	450	385	365	370

Use a Goodness-of-Fit Test to test the null hypothesis that sample data fits a uniform distribution at $\alpha = 1\%$. Can you conclude that the sample data indicates a preference for packaging shape?

38. According to recently published census figures the socio-economic stratification for a small northeast town is: 20% upper, 50% middle and 30% lower. One hundred and fifty residents of this town are supposedly chosen at random. To check this the sample data is sorted and summarized to be:

Socio-Economic Stratification	Number of Residents
Lower	37
Middle	86
Upper	27

Should we conclude that the sample was not randomly selected from the town using $\alpha = 1\%$?

39. The quality control engineer of a parts manufacturing company wants to determine if more defective parts are produced on a particular day of the six day work week. A random sample of the production records indicate the following data:

Day of the Week	Number of Defective Parts
Monday	26
Tuesday	15
Wednesday	24
Thursday	27
Friday	12
Saturday	16

The engineer states the null hypothesis as: the sample data (number of rejected parts) fits a uniform distribution. Perform a Goodness-of-Fit Test at $\alpha = 5\%$ and determine if the engineer can conclude that the production of defective parts is not evenly distributed throughout the workweek.

40. The Pit Boss at the Mirage casino can't believe her eyes when she notices that a particular pair of dice rarely rolls certain numbers. She decides to test if the dice are "loaded." She tosses the dice 1080 times and records the sum for each toss. The data for her experiment is listed below:

Sum of the Pair of Dice	Number of Times
2	24
3	70
4	77
5	128
6	156
7	156
8	148
9	136
10	111
11	48
12	26

Can the Pit Boss conclude that the dice are indeed "loaded" using $\alpha = 5\%$?

The following problem outlines a Goodness-of-Fit Test to determine if the sample data fits a normal distribution.

41. It has been claimed that the number of hours worked per week by a full-time college student is normally distributed. To test this claim a random sample of 600 full-time college students were selected. It was determined that the sample data had a mean number of hours worked per week per student of 21.7 hrs with s = 6.7 hrs. Six intervals were used to summarize the data and the sample results are given in the following table.

Interval Boundaries	Frequency
Below 12.32	31
12.32–17.01	96
17.01–21.70	173
21.70–26.39	147
26.39–31.08	112
Above 31.08	41

Complete the following steps which outline a Goodness-of-Fit Test to test the null hypothesis that the number of hours worked per week by a full-time student is normally distributed at $\alpha = 5\%$.

Step 1. Formulate the two hypotheses H_0 and H_a.
  H_0
  H_a

Step 2. Determine the model to test the null hypothesis, H_0.

To calculate the expected frequency for each interval we assume the null hypothesis to be true, that is, we assume a normal distribution with $\mu \approx$ sample mean = 21.70 and $\sigma \approx s = 6.70$.

The expected frequencies for each of the interval boundaries are calculated by:

  1) converting each boundary into a z score.
  2) obtaining the corresponding probabilities for the z scores from Table II:

3) calculating each expected frequency using these probabilities and the sample size.

Complete the following table using this procedure.

Interval Boundaries	z score	Expected Probability	Frequency
Below 12.32	−1.40	0.0808	48.48
12.32 – 17.01			
17.01 – 21.70			
21.70 – 26.39			
26.39 – 31.08			
Above 31.08			

Step 3. Formulate the decision rule.

1) In this example we will use a significance level $\alpha =$ _____ .

2) The degrees of freedom, df, for a single classification case is $df = k - 1$, where k is the number of categories within the single classification. However, since the mean and standard deviation were estimated then the degrees of freedom must be reduced by one for each estimated parameter used.

Thus, $df = k - 3$

$df =$ _____

3) The critical chi-square value for this test can be found in Table IV where $\alpha = 5\%$ and $df = 3$. The critical chi-square value is:

$\chi_\alpha^2 =$ _____

4) The decision rule is: _____ .

Step 4.   Calculate Pearson's chi-square test statistic.

$X^2 =$ _____

Step 5.   State the conclusion.

State whether the number of hours worked per week by a full-time student fits a normal distribution.

Section 14.6

For problems 42–50, use questions 20 to 28 of Section 13.2 exercises and apply the p-value approach to hypotheses testing using the TI-83 Plus calculator. For each of these problems, use the 5 step procedure to perform a hypothesis test at **both** $\alpha = 1\%$ and $\alpha = 5\%$. Include the following within your test:

a) state the null and alternative hypotheses.

b) formulate the chi-square decision rule.

c) identify the test statistic and its p-value.

d) state the conclusion and answer any question(s) posed in the problem for each alpha level.

e) determine the smallest level of significance for which the null hypothesis can be rejected.

CHAPTER REVIEW

51. If the test statistic is a very large positive number, then the probability is small that the null hypothesis will be rejected.
(T/F)

52. An arrangement of sample count data into a two-way classification is called a _____ table.

53. Each individual box in the contingency table is referred to as a _____ .

54. The graph of a Chi-Square distribution is not symmetric, but it is skewed to the _____ .

55. In a Chi-Square Test of Independence the sample data represents qualitative or _____ data.

56. For a sample of 200, what is the expected frequency for a cell whose row total is 70 and its column total is 30?
a) 10.5   **b)** 21   **c)** 105   **d)** 2100

57. All chi-square tests of independence are one-tailed tests on the right.
(T/F)

58. If the value of Pearson's chi-square test statistic is 6.79 and $\chi_\alpha^2 = 9.49$, what is the conclusion of this test?
a) Reject H_o and accept H_a
b) Fail to reject H_o
c) Reject H_o and reject H_a
d) Fail to reject H_a

59. If the test statistic X^2 is less than the critical χ_α^2, then the conclusion is: Fail to reject the null hypothesis at α.
(T/F)

60. What type of test is used to determine if the sample data conforms to a theoretical distribution model?
a) Sample mean hypothesis test
b) Goodness-of-fit test
c) Chi-square test of independence
d) A normal distribution test

61. A Goodness-of-Fit Test is used to determine if sample data fits a uniform distribution. The conclusion is fail to reject H_o at α. This means that the data fits a normal distribution.
(T/F)

Problems 62–65 use the chi-square test of independence. For each problem:
a) Formulate the hypotheses.
b) State the decision rule.
c) Calculate Pearson's chi-square test statistic.
d) Determine the conclusion, and answer the question(s) posed in the problem, if any.

62. A study was conducted to determine if gender is related to the number of compact discs (CDs) purchased per year. A random sample of 200 CD buyers were interviewed and their responses are recorded in the following table:

| Gender | Number of Compact Discs Purchased Per Year | | | |
	0 – 20	21 – 40	41 and Higher	Row Totals
Male	a 40	b 50	c 30	120
Female	d 20	e 50	f 10	80
Column Totals	60	100	40	200

Based on the sample data can we conclude that gender is related to the number of CDs purchased per year at $\alpha = 5\%$?

63. A financial investment broker believes the Dow Jones Average is related to the prime interest rate. She studies the Dow Jones Average and the prime interest rate for a three year period. Her results are summarized in the following table.

| Prime Rate | Dow Jones Average | | | |
	Increase	Decrease	No Change	Row Totals
Increase	a 17	b 15	c 13	45
Decrease	d 33	e 34	f 38	105
No Change	g 25	h 26	i 24	75
Column Totals	75	75	75	225

Do the results of the study indicate the Dow Jones Average and the Prime Interest Rate are dependent at $\alpha = 1\%$?

64. Columbia Casa advertising would like to determine if gender is related to the number of DVD's purchased per year. A random sample of 300 people were interviewed and their responses are summarized in the following table.

| Gender | Number of DVD's Purchased Per Year | | |
	0–20	21–40	Above 40
Male	a 50	b 55	c 35
Female	d 40	e 70	f 50

Based on the sample data can the advertising firm conclude that the number of DVD's purchased per year is based upon gender? (Use $\alpha = 5\%$).

65. A study was conducted on a random sample of 500 married couples to determine if there is a significant rela-

tionship between the frequency of times per year a married couple goes to the movies and their educational background. The results of the study are shown below:

| Frequency of Movie Attendance Per Year | Educational Background (Highest Level Achieved) | | | |
	Neither Went To College	Each Has Some College	Only One Grad College	Both Grad College
0–6	a 55	b 20	c 35	d 17
6–12	e 65	f 30	g 30	h 8
Above 12	i 55	j 75	k 45	l 65

Do these sample results indicate at $\alpha = 5\%$ that there is a significant relationship between frequency of times married couples go to the movies and their educational background?

Problems 66–67 use the test of Goodness-of-Fit. For each problem:

a) Formulate the hypotheses.

b) State the decision rule.

c) Calculate Pearson's chi-square test statistic.

d) Determine the conclusion, and answer the question(s) posed in the problem, if any.

66. "Let it Ride" Jack decides to test the fairness of a die. He rolls it 120 times with the results shown in the following table:

Number Rolled	Frequency
1	24
2	18
3	27
4	17
5	16
6	18

Use a Goodness-of-Fit Test to determine if the die is fair at $\alpha = 5\%$.

67. The student government at Fernworth College has been told that the student population consists of 58% female and 42% male. A random sample of 400 students consists of 54% female and 46% male. Are the sample data consistent with the population proportions at $\alpha = 5\%$?

WHAT DO YOU THINK?

68. Examine the snapshot entitled "Would You Date a Co-worker" in the Figure 14.28.

a) If you wanted to determine if there was a relationship between the sex of a worker and the response to the question: Would you date a co-worker, then identify the population classifications presented within the snapshot.

b) If you were to perform a hypothesis test to determine if there is a relationship between the population classifications, how would the null hypothesis be stated?

c) How would the alternative hypothesis be stated?

d) When the null hypothesis is assumed to be true, what does that indicate about the relationship between the two population classifications?

Statistical Snapshot

Would You Date a Co-worker?

Source: Gallup Organization poll of 679 employed adults

FIGURE 14.28

e) If we classify the response to the question as either: **yes**, **no** and **undecided**, then what would be the size of the contingency table for this type of chi-square test?

f) What is the sample size for this information contained within the snapshot? If three hundred of the sample were women, then determine the number of people that would fall within each category of the contingency table.

g) What are these values within the contingency table called?

h) Determine the expected frequencies for this hypothesis test.

i) What is the number of degrees of freedom for this test?

j) Determine the critical value for the 5% and 1% level of significance.

k) State a decision rule for each level of significance.

l) Calculate Pearson's Chi-Square test statistic.

m) What is the conclusion for this test, if $\alpha = 5\%$? Can the null hypothesis be rejected at $\alpha = 5\%$? Can you conclude that the two population classifications are independent?

n) Is there a statistically significant relationship between the sex of a worker and the response to the question: *Would you date a co-worker* at $\alpha = 1\%$? Can the null hypothesis be rejected at $\alpha = 1\%$? Can you conclude that the two population classifications are dependent?

o) Can you conclude that the p-value of this hypothesis test is less than 5%? Explain.

p) Can you conclude that the p-value of this hypothesis test is less than 1%? Explain.

69. A research article entitled "Research On Attitudes Of Professionals Toward Advertising: A Methodological Caveat" appeared in June/July 1990 issue of the *Journal of Advertising Research*. One aspect of this article investigates the sampling frames actually used to represent the professional population to determine if they represent the population under study. This research stresses the importance of selecting a sampling frame which is a valid representation of the population under study since the authors believe that researchers may be making inaccurate predictions from surveys in which they have relied on an inappropriate sampling frame. The authors of the study state the choice of a sampling frame leaves one important question unanswered: Are all members of a profession (which depicts the population) equally represented in the various sampling frames? Given that professional association membership lists are commonly used in studies of professionals, the researchers decided to compare the responses of members and non-members of a professional state association. Since using a sampling frame for a study which omitted the non-members of a professional association might raise serious doubts about the results of the study. In their study, the researchers selected a random sample of 600 dentists from a list of currently licensed Oregon dentists provided by the Oregon Board of Dentistry. This sampling frame was used to be certain that all Oregon dentists in practice during the study had the opportunity of being selected for the study. To allow a thorough comparison of the members and non-members of the professional association, questions were designed to span the range of issues that were typically addressed in surveys of professional providers—their values, attitudes, behaviors, and demographic characteristics. The questionnaire used in the study contained the items listed in Figure 14.29.

QUESTIONS USED TO MEASURE VALUES, ATTITUDES, BEHAVIORS AND DEMOGRAPHIC TRAITS

Values

V1. I am satisfied with dentistry as a career.
V2. I encourage young people to consider dentistry as a career.
V3. The government should guarantee the availability of dental service to all Americans.

Attitudes

A1. Advertising my services would be beneficial to me personally.
A2. The advertising of fees would adversely affect the public image of dentists.
A3. Dentists should be allowed to advertise without restrictions.

Behaviors

B1. What was the average number of patients that you had per day in 1987?
B2. Number of weekdays taken as vacation.
B3. How frequently do you attend religious services?

Demographic

D1. Net Income.
D2. Gross Income
D3. Gender
D4. Age
D5. Self-Employed
D5. Practice Type

FIGURE 14.29

Values and attitudes were measured using five-point Likert-type scales, while behavior questions used ordinal categories except for 'days on vacation' which was ratio scaled. The income question used a six-point ordinal scale; practice type was a three category nominal measure, gender and "employee" were (nominal) dichotomous measures, and age was actual (ratio-scaled).

The results of the comparisons are shown in Figure 14.30. You should notice that chi-square tests were used for the comparison between the members and the non-members for each of the measures listed in the following table with the exception of "age" and "days of vacation" for which a *t*-test was performed.

TESTS OF DIFFERENCES BETWEEN THOSE INCLUDED FROM TYPICAL SAMPLING FRAMES Professional Organization Members versus Non-Members				
Question	Statistic[c]	p ≤	df	N[*]
V1	$\chi^2 = 10.92$	.05	4	414
V2	$\chi^2 = 13.90$	.01	4	414
V3	$\chi^2 = 6.16$	.18	4	412
A1	$\chi^2 = 9.80$	.05	4	408
A2	$\chi^2 = 11.58$	.05	4	411
A3	$\chi^2 = 3.88$	.42	4	411
B1	$\chi^2 = 21.71$	.001	5	411
B2	$t = -3.17$	.002	192	402
B3	$\chi^2 = 6.09$	.10	3	406
D1	$\chi^2 = 24.49$	.001	5	393
D2	$\chi^2 = 40.01$	.001	5	384
D3	$\chi^2 = 1.65$	.19	1	410
D4	$t = -2.77$	.01	397	399
D5	$\chi^2 = 30.90$	.001	1	413
D6	$\chi^2 = 66.15$	.001	2	413

[c]A significant statistic is evidence that the groups are different.
[*]Variations in numbers reflect non-response to a question.

FIGURE 14.30

a) What are the null and alternative hypotheses for the chi-square test shown for question V1? Was the result of this test significant at $\alpha = 5\%$? at $\alpha = 1\%$? What is the degrees of freedom for this test? How did they arrive at this value?

b) What are the null and alternative hypotheses for the chi-square test shown for question V3? Can the null hypothesis be rejected at $\alpha = 5\%$? at $\alpha = 1\%$? What is the degrees of freedom for this test? What is the smallest level of significance that would result in the rejection of the null hypothesis?

c) Which chi-square test shown for Attitudes A1, A2, and A3 would not lead to the rejection of the null hypothesis at $\alpha = 10\%$? Explain.

d) What are the null and alternative hypotheses for the chi-square test shown for question B1? Can the alternative hypothesis be accepted at $\alpha = 5\%$? at $\alpha = 1\%$? What is the degrees of freedom for this test? What is the smallest level of significance that would result in the rejection of the null hypothesis?

e) Why wasn't a chi-square test used to perform a hypothesis test to detect a difference between members and non-members with regard to the number of weekdays taken as vacation?

f) What are the null and alternative hypotheses for the chi-square test shown for question D1? Can the null hypothesis be rejected at $\alpha = 5\%$? at $\alpha = 1\%$? What is the degrees of freedom for this test? What is the smallest level of significance that would result in the rejection of the null hypothesis? What is the degrees of freedom for this test? Based on this number of degrees of freedom, what can you conclude regarding the number of categories for net income? Explain.

g) Why wasn't a chi-square test used to perform a hypothesis test to detect a difference between members and non-members with regard to the age? What type of test was used to detect this difference? What is the degrees of freedom for test? How was this determined? Explain. Was this difference significant at $\alpha = 5\%$? at $\alpha = 1\%$? What is the smallest level of significance that would result in the rejection of the null hypothesis for this test?

h) For which of these chi-square tests would the null hypothesis test be rejected at a 0.5% level of significance?

i) For which questions, was there no significant difference between the members and non-members of the professional association?

j) Can you conclude that there is a significant difference between the members and non-members with regard to private practice at $\alpha = 1\%$? Explain.

k) Can you conclude that self-employment and membership in the professional association are independent at $\alpha = 1\%$? Explain.

l) Can you conclude that advertising without restrictions and membership in the professional association are dependent at $\alpha = 5\%$? Explain.

m) Based on the test results, can you conclude that the dentists who are members of the professional association are significantly different from the non-members? Explain.

70. A research article entitled "The Rekurring Kase Of the Special K" studied whether the letter K occurs with more frequency as the initial letter in top brand names than it does as a first letter in our language in general which appeared in the October/November 1990 issue of the *Journal of Advertising Research*. The first aspect of this research examined the eight most frequently occurring initial letters: **C, S, A, B, M, P, D** and **T** in top name brands to determine if they occur more frequently as the initial letter in top brand names than

they appear as a first letter in our language in general. The results of this study were examined in Case Study 14.2. The second aspect of this research was to determine what happens to the analysis when the letter K was added to the list. This aspect of the test will be discussed within this question. Figure 14.31 shows the results of a chi-square test with the letter K added to the previous list of the eight most frequently occurring initial letters. The expected frequency for each of these letters were based on *Webster's Ninth New Collegiate Dictionary* (1987) model.

Chi-Square Analysis of Most Frequently Occurring Initial Letters Plus the Letter K

Initial letter	Observed frequency	Expected* frequency	Cumulative percent Observed	Cumulative percent Expected
C	51	52.4	9.43	9.68
S	46	67.3	17.93	22.12
A	42	32.2	25.69	28.08
B	42	29.2	33.45	33.47
M	40	29.5	40.84	38.92
P	40	47.5	48.23	47.70
D	30	28.2	53.78	52.91
T	29	32.0	59.14	58.83
K	16	4.6	62.10	59.68

$$X^2 = 48.927 \quad df = 8 \quad p < .001$$

* Based on Webster's Ninth New Collegiate Dictionary (1987), distribution of words beginning with each letter.

FIGURE 14.31

a) Read Case Study 14.2, and discuss the objective of the hypothesis test along with the results of the chi-square analysis.
b) Define the population for this test.
c) What variable is being examined within this test?
d) Is this variable numeric or categorical? Explain.
e) What type of chi-square test is being illustrated in this research?
f) What distribution serves as the theoretical distribution?
g) What serves as the sample data for this test?

h) What would serve as the null hypothesis for this test?
i) What would serve as the alternative hypothesis?
j) What assumption was used to calculate the expected frequencies within the table? Which hypothesis does this assumption represent?
k) How many classifications are there for this test? State the classification(s) for this test. What does each category within a classification represent for this test?
l) What formula was used to calculate the number of degrees of freedom for this test? What were the degrees of freedom for this test? Why is the degrees of freedom for this test different from the degrees of freedom for the test in Case Study 14.2?
m) What is the value of $\frac{(O-E)^2}{E}$ for each initial letter of the information contained within the table of Figure 14.14, where O is the Observed frequency and E is the Expected frequency? What does the sum of the values of $\frac{(O-E)^2}{E}$ represent?
n) What are the critical chi-square values for this test at $\alpha = 5\%$ and $\alpha = 1\%$?
o) What is the conclusion of this hypothesis test for each of these significance levels? Can you reject the null hypothesis for any of these significance levels? Explain.
p) What is the conclusion to this test for a significance level of 0.30%? What information did you use to answer this question? Explain.
q) What is the smallest level of significance that you can use to obtain a significant result?
r) State the conclusion to the chi-square test shown in Figure 14.18.
s) Was the result of the chi-square significant for the hypothesis test shown in Figure 14.18? Explain.
t) What happened to the value of the chi-square test statistic when the letter K was added to the initial list of eight most frequently occurring letters? What do you think this result indicates about the letter K?
u) What letter do you think occurred significantly more often as an initial letter on the brand-name list than it did for words in the dictionary? Explain your reasoning in answering this question.

PROJECTS

71. Chi-Square Test of Independence Hypothesis Testing Project.
  A. Selection of a topic
    1. Select an article from a local newspaper, magazine or other source that can be used to perform a chi-square test of independence.

2. Suggested topics:
  a) Test the claim that there is a relationship between student views on course requirements for their major and the major area of concentration.
  b) Test the claim that there is a relationship between gender and student views on capital punishment.

B. Use the following procedure to test the claim selected in part A.

   1. Identify the classifications of the population referred to in the statement of the claim and indicate where the claim was found.

   2. State the null and alternative hypotheses.

   3. Develop and state a procedure for selecting a random sample from your population. Indicate the technique you are going to use to obtain your sample data.

   4. Indicate the hypothesis testing model, and choose an appropriate level of significance.

   5. Collect the data and summarize the observed frequencies in a contingency table.

   6. Find the degrees of freedom and determine the appropriate critical chi-square value.

   7. Calculate the expected frequencies and determine Pearson's chi-square test statistic.

   8. Construct a chi-square distribution model and place Pearson's chi-square test statistic on the model.

   9. Formulate the appropriate conclusion and interpret the conclusion with respect to your opinion (as stated in step 2).

72. Read a research article from a professional journal in a field such as: medicine, education, marketing, science, social science, etc that illustrates the use of the chi-square test of independence. Write a summary of the research article that includes the following:

   a) Name of article, author, and journal (include volume number and date).

   b) Statement of the research problem.

   c) The null and alternative hypotheses.

   d) How the experiment was conducted. (include the sample size and sampling technique)

   e) Determine the contingency table, the level of significance, the value of Pearson's chi-square test statistic and the critical chi-square value.

   f) State the conclusion(s) in terms of the null and alternative hypotheses.

73. Get hold of a pair of dice from any board game. Do an experiment by tossing the dice 1000 times and record the number of times each sum appears. Compare the experimental results to the results that one would expect if the dice were fair. Use $\alpha = 5\%$.

ANALYZING THE DATABASE USING TECHNOLOGY.

The following exercises refer to the file DATABASE listed in Appendix A. Using a technological tool, answer each exercise.

74. For the variables Hair color and Eye color:

   a) construct a table for the variables HR and EYE.

   b) calculate Pearson's chi-square test statistic along with the expected and the observed frequencies in each cell.

   c) test the significance at $\alpha = 5\%$.

   d) interpret the results in terms of the variables Hair color and Eye color.

75. For the variables SEX and MAJ.

   a) construct a table for the variables SEX and MAJ.

   b) calculate Pearson's chi-square test statistic along with the expected and the observed frequencies in each cell.

   c) test the significance at $\alpha = 5\%$.

   d) interpret the results in terms of the variables SEX and MAJ.

CHAPTER TEST

76. Chi-square tests of independence involve the analysis of qualitative data.
(T/F)

77. The graph of a chi-square distribution is not symmetric, but it is skewed left.
(T/F)

78. If the conclusion is to reject H_o and accept H_a at α, then the chi-square test of independence has indicated that the population classifications are independent.
(T/F)

79. In designing a contingency table, care must be taken so that each observation falls into

   a) At least one cell

   b) No more than two cells

   c) Only one cell

   d) None of these choices

80. What are the degrees of freedom for a Goodness-of-Fit Test with a single classification of six categories?

   a) 4   **b)** 5   **c)** 6   **d)** 3

81. The test of Goodness-of-Fit refers to a type of chi-square test that can be used to determine how well sample data fits a chi-square distribution.
(T/F)

Problems 82–83 use the chi-square test of independence.
For each problem:

   a) Formulate the hypotheses.

   b) State the decision rule.

c) Calculate Pearson's chi-square test statistic.

d) Determine the conclusion, and answer the question(s) posed in the problem, if any.

82. A quality control engineer wants to compare the production process of parts manufactured by three different companies. The engineer randomly samples a total of 270 parts from the three companies and summarizes the results in the following table.

Part Quality	Different Companies			
	Company A	Company B	Company C	Row Totals
Defective	[a] 15	[b] 10	[c] 10	35
Non-Defective	[d] 70	[e] 80	[f] 85	235
Column Totals	85	90	95	270

Based upon the results of the sample, can the quality control engineer conclude that part quality and manufacturer are independent at $\alpha = 5\%$?

83. A statistics instructor decides to investigate the relationship between a student's grade in the course and class attendance. The instructor randomly samples the records of 120 students and the results are listed in the following table.

Number of Absences	Grade in Course		
	F–D+	C–B	B+ – A
0 – 1	[a] 10	[b] 18	[c] 12
2 – 5	[d] 25	[e] 17	[f] 8
above 5	[g] 20	[h] 5	[i] 5

Perform a chi-square test of independence to determine if a student's grade in the statistics course and class attendance are dependent at $\alpha = 1\%$?

84. Use the test of Goodness-of-Fit.

a) Formulate the hypotheses.

b) State the decision rule.

c) Calculate Pearson's chi-square test statistic.

d) Determine the conclusion, and answer the question posed in the problem, if any.

A mathematics professor has analyzed the results of her statistics final exam for the past few years. She has determined that the grade distribution for her final exam is:

Grade	Percent of Students Receiving
A	10%
B	15%
C	40%
D	25%
F	10%

This year the professor administers the exam to 200 students. The number of students receiving the letter grades A, B, C, D, and F are 24, 20, 89, 40, and 27 respectively. Use the Goodness-of-Fit Test to determine if this year's final exam results fit her previous grade distribution at $\alpha = 5\%$.

CHAPTER 15

Linear Correlation and Regression Analysis

Contents

15.1   INTRODUCTION

Most of us have examined a chart in a doctor's office or health magazine that relates height to weight. Imagine the following scenario in a *doctor's examination room* as illustrated in Figure 15.1.

FIGURE 15.1

The patient a rather plump individual about 5 feet 2 inches, is standing on a doctor's scale, facing the doctor. The doctor, dressed in a white examination jacket, is facing the patient.

DOCTOR: "Now let's see . . . you weigh about 160 lbs. How tall are you?"
PATIENT: "Six feet."
DOCTOR: "You are not anywhere near six feet tall!"
PATIENT: "But Doctor, then I would be too short for my weight!"

The above scenario illustrates the two major concepts that are presented in this chapter. The first concept is known as correlation analysis. In this chapter, we will discuss correlation as a technique that measures the strength (or the degree) of the relationship between two continuous variables. For example, in this scenario, the height and weight of an individual represent the two variables.
Since we are familiar with the notion that there is a strong relationship between the height and weight of an individual, then using the statistical concept of correlation, we could measure the strength of this relationship. We will examine how to determine this measure in a later section.

Remember the chart you use to estimate your "ideal" weight given your respective height? Such charts have been developed using a statistical technique known as regression. Essentially, regression is a statistical technique that produces a model of the relationship (correlation) between the two variables.

The height/weight chart discussed in the previous scenario was generated by a regression formula. This chart represents the model for the relationship between height and weight of an individual. When there is a strong correlation between two variables, such as height and weight, then the regression analysis can be applied to produce a formula (or rule) to model the relationship between the two variables. In this chapter, we will examine two important concepts in elementary statistics: **linear correlation** and **linear regression.**

15.2   THE SCATTER DIAGRAM

As illustrated in Section 15.1, there are times when we are interested in determining whether a relationship exists between two variables. In Chapter 14, we examined whether or not a relationship exists between two classifications where each classification represented a categorical variable. Now, we will examine the relationship between two continuous variables.

To help us begin our examination of the relationship between two variables, let's consider studying the relationship between a female's height and weight for female students attending Bermuda Community College. We will randomly select a sample of 12 female students from a statistics class at this community college and measure each female's height and weight. Thus, *two* measurements are recorded for *each* female student. These two measurements represent the value of each of the two variables, height and weight, for each female student.

If we label the height as the x variable and the weight as the y variable, then for each female student we will have a pair of numbers. The sample data representing the pair of numbers for the twelve female students has been recorded and summarized in Table 15.1.

These pair of numbers can also be written in the following form: **(x,y)**, which is called an **ordered pair** since the value of the x variable is always written first within the parentheses.

For example, the ordered pair for female student number 1 is written: (62, 123), where the first number, 62, within the parentheses represents the height of student number 1 and the second number, 123, within the parentheses represents the weight of student number 1.

Using the sample information contained in Table 15.1, we can begin to analyze the relationship between a female's height and weight by constructing a graph of these ordered pairs. This type of graph is called a **scatter diagram**.

DEFINITION 15.1
A **scatter diagram** is a graph representing the ordered pairs of data on a set of axes.

Table 15.1

Female Student Number	Height (inches) x	Weight (lbs) y
1	62	123
2	58	102
3	64	110
4	69	137
5	61	145
6	70	132
7	59	108
8	60	112
9	63	124
10	72	155
11	71	170
12	68	140

To construct a scatter diagram, we begin by drawing two lines, a horizontal and a vertical line, to represent the two axes. The horizontal line is called the x axis and represents the x values, in this case the heights of the female students. Thus, the x axis is labeled heights.

While, the vertical line is called the y axis and represents the y values, in this case the weights of the female students. Thus, the y axis is labeled weights. This is illustrated in Figure 15.2.

FIGURE 15.2

We use a dot to represent each ordered pair of measurements. The dot is placed directly above the female's height and directly to the right of the female's weight. Thus, for the first female student with a height of 62 inches and a weight of 123 pounds, a dot is placed above 62 on the axis labeled height and to the right of 123 on the axis labeled weight. This dot represents the height and weight of female student number 1. This same procedure is used to plot all the ordered pairs of the sample data of Table 15.1 and Figure 15.3 illustrates the scatter diagram for this sample data.

Visual examination of a scatter diagram can help to determine whether there is an apparent relationship or correlation between the two variables and, if one does exist, to determine the type of correlation that exists. For example, it appears that a relationship does exist between a female's height and her weight as we examine the scatter diagram in Figure 15.3.

FIGURE 15.3

Let's examine the type of relationship that we notice in Figure 15.3. The scatter diagram of Figure 15.3 seems to show that as a female's height, represented by the x values, increases then her weight, represented by the y values, also increases. This type of correlation is called a **positive correlation**.

DEFINITION 15.2
A **positive correlation** between two variables, x and y, occurs when high measurements for the x variable tend to be associated with high measurements for the y variable and low measurements for the x variable tend to be associated with low measurements for the y variable.

You will also notice that the dots in the scatter diagram tend to follow a straight-line path. This is type of correlation is called a **linear correlation**. This can be better visualized by drawing a straight line through the scatter diagram of Figure 15.3, and noticing that the points *tend* to lie very close to the line. This is illustrated in Figure 15.4.

FIGURE 15.4

Now, we can state that there is a positive linear correlation between the two variables, height and weight.

Another type of correlation that can exist between two variables is a **negative correlation**.

DEFINITION 15.3

A **negative correlation** between two variables, x and y, occurs when high measurements for the x variable tend to be associated with low measurements for the y variable and low measurements for the x variable tend to be associated with high measurements for the y variable.

Let's examine this idea of negative correlation using the scatter diagram in Figure 15.5. Notice in Figure 15.5, as the values of the x variable increases, the value of the y variable tend to decrease. The two variables tend to vary in opposite directions. Thus, the relationship between the two variables is a negative correlation.

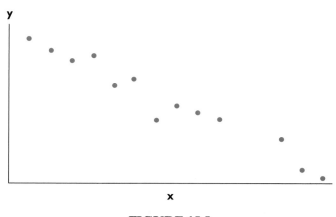

FIGURE 15.5

It is possible that when examining the relationship between two variables, you may notice that there is no linear relationship between the two variables. This is referred to as **no linear correlation**.

DEFINITION 15.4

No linear correlation means there is no linear relationship between the two variables. That is, high and low measurements for the two variables are not associated in any predictable straight line pattern.

Figure 15.6 illustrates a scatter diagram that shows no linear correlation.

Remark: We will only examine linear (or straight line) correlations in this chapter. Although, it is possible that two variables can be related to each other in a curvilinear relationship, this type of correlation is beyond the scope of this textbook. An example of a curvilinear relationship is illustrated by the scatter diagram in Figure 15.7

Let's construct a few scatter diagrams and determine the type of correlation that may exist.

FIGURE 15.6

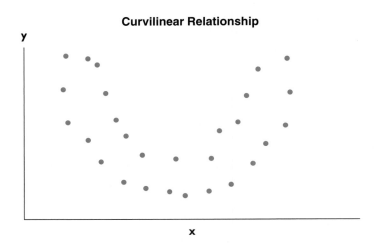

FIGURE 15.7

E X A M P L E   1 5 . 1

Using the sample data in Table 15.2, construct a scatter diagram and indicate the type of correlation, if any exists.

TABLE 15.2

x	1	2	3	5	8
y	4	5	5	6	9

Solution

To construct a scatter diagram, perform the following steps:

Step I   Draw a horizontal axis and label it as the x axis. Now draw a vertical axis and label it as the y axis.

Step 2   Plot each ordered pair (x,y) of the sample data from Table 15.2 in the appropriate position on the set of axes. Figure 15.8 represents the scatter diagram for the sample data of Table 15.2.

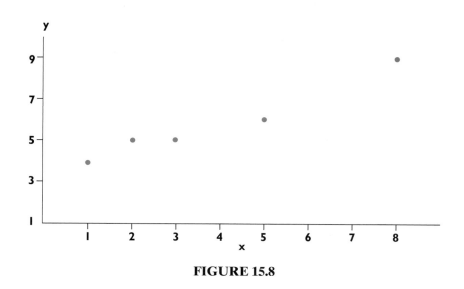

FIGURE 15.8

To determine the type of correlation that may exist, we must examine the pattern that is shown by the sample data pairs in Figure 15.8. As you examine the scatter diagram from left to right, you will notice the pattern of the points are going in an upward direction. That is, as the x values *increase*, the y values also *increase*. Thus, the scatter diagram indicates a pattern that corresponds to a *positive* correlation.

EXAMPLE   15.2

Using the sample data in Table 15.3, construct a scatter diagram and indicate the type of correlation, if any exist.

TABLE 15.3

x	2	3	5	6	8	10
y	11	9	8	6	6	3

Solution

Step 1   Draw a horizontal axis and label it as the x axis. Now draw a vertical axis and label it as the y axis.

Step 2   Plot each ordered pair (x,y) of the sample data from Table 15.3 in the appropriate position on the set of axes. Figure 15.9 represents the scatter diagram for the sample data of Table 15.3.

To determine the type of correlation that may exist, we must examine the pattern that is shown by the sample data pairs in Figure 15.9. As you examine the scatter diagram from left to right, you will notice the pattern of the points are going in a downward direction. That is, as the x variable ***increases***,

FIGURE 15.9

the y variable *decreases*. This scatter diagram indicates a *negative correlation* for the sample data listed in Table 15.3.

E X A M P L E   1 5 . 3

Using the sample data in Table 15.4, construct a scatter diagram and indicate the type of correlation, if any exist.

TABLE 15.4

x	3	4	5	7	5	3	6	7	8	6
y	1	3	2	5	5	4	4	2	1	3

Solution

Step 1   Draw a horizontal axis and label it as the x axis. Now draw a vertical axis and label it as the y axis.

Step 2   Plot each ordered pair (x,y) of the sample data from Table 15.4 in the appropriate position on the set of axes. Figure 15.10 represents the scatter diagram for the sample data of Table 15.4.

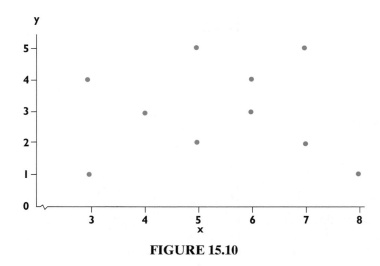

FIGURE 15.10

To determine the type of correlation that may exist, we must examine the pattern that is shown by the sample data pairs in Figure 15.10 As you examine the scatter diagram from left to right, you will notice that there is no definite pattern for the points. This scatter diagram indicates that we have ***no linear correlation*** for the sample data listed in Table 15.4.

15.3   THE COEFFICIENT OF LINEAR CORRELATION

When a scatter diagram seems to indicate that there is a linear correlation between two variables, our next step is to determine the strength of the relationship that exist between the two variables. By a **linear correlation,** we mean how closely the points of a scatter diagram closely approximates a straight-line pattern.

The closer the points of a scatter diagram approximate a straight-line pattern, the stronger the linear correlation between the two variables. The **strength** of a linear correlation between the two variables can be numerically measured by **Pearson's correlation coefficient, r**.

DEFINITION 15.5

Pearson's Correlation Coefficient, r, measures the strength of a linear relationship between two variables for a sample. This **sample correlation coefficient**, r, is calculated by the following formula:

$$r = \frac{n\Sigma(xy) - (\Sigma x)(\Sigma y)}{\sqrt{n(\Sigma x^2) - (\Sigma x)^2}\,\sqrt{n(\Sigma y^2) - (\Sigma y)^2}}$$

where: **r**   is the **sample correlation coefficient**
          x   represents the data values for the **first variable**.
          y   represents the data values for the **second variable**.
          n   represents the **number of pairs of data values**

The sample correlation coefficient, r, will always be a numerical value between −1 and +1. That is,

$$-1 \le r \le +1$$

Let's interpret what the different values of r mean before we examine how to calculate the sample correlation coefficient.

Interpreting the Values of r

A value of **r = +1 represents the strongest positive linear correlation** possible and it indicates a perfect positive linear correlation. This means that all the points of the scatter diagram will lie on a straight line which is sloping upward from left to right.

A value of **r = −1 represents the strongest negative linear correlation** possible and it indicates a perfect negative linear correlation. This means that all the points of the scatter diagram will lie on a straight line which is sloping downward from left to right.

A value of **r = 0 represents no linear correlation** between the two variables.

The closer the value of the correlation coefficient, r, is to –1 or to +1 the stronger the linear relationship between the two variables. For example, if we say that height, represented by variable one, is strongly correlated to weight, represented by variable two, then we would expect the numerical value of r to be either close to –1 or close to +1. However, a value of r close to zero indicates a weak linear relationship between the two variables.

Let's examine how to use the sample correlation coefficient formula to calculate the strength of the linear correlation for the sample data in Example 15.4.

EXAMPLE 15.4

Using the sample data in Table 15.5, calculate the sample correlation coefficient, r.

TABLE 15.5

x	1	2	3	5	8
y	4	5	5	6	9

Solution

To use the sample correlation coefficient formula:

$$r = \frac{n\Sigma(xy) - (\Sigma x)(\Sigma y)}{\sqrt{n(\Sigma x^2) - (\Sigma x)^2} \sqrt{n(\Sigma y^2) - (\Sigma y)^2}}$$

to calculate r, we need to determine the values for n, $\Sigma(xy)$, Σx, Σx^2, Σy and Σy^2. To obtain the sums needed to calculate r, we will construct a table that has a column for each of the variables: **x, y , x^2, y^2** and **xy**. This is the first step in calculating r.

Step 1   Construct a table that lists the quantities: x, y, x^2, y^2 and xy.
Now, perform the calculation for each of these variables and list the result in the appropriate column. These results are listed in Table 15.6.

TABLE 15.6

x	y	x^2	y^2	xy
1	4	1	16	4
2	5	4	25	10
3	5	9	25	15
5	6	25	36	30
8	9	64	81	72

Step 2   Using the information in Table 15.6, calculate $\Sigma(xy)$, Σx, Σx^2, Σy and Σy^2.
Adding the values within each column, we obtain the following results:

$\Sigma x = 19$ $\Sigma y = 29$ $\Sigma x^2 = 103$ $\Sigma y^2 = 183$ $\Sigma(xy) = 131$

Remembering that n is the **number of pairs of x and y values** and since there are five pairs of x and y values, then **n** equals 5.

Step 3   Substitute the calculated values of n, $\Sigma(xy)$, Σx, Σx^2, Σy and Σy^2 into the formula and calculate r.

$$r = \frac{5(131) - (19)(29)}{\sqrt{5(103) - (19)^2}\,\sqrt{5(183) - (29)^2}}$$

$$r = \frac{655 - 551}{\sqrt{515 - 361}\,\sqrt{915 - 841}}$$

$$r = \frac{104}{\sqrt{154}\,\sqrt{74}}$$

$$r \approx \frac{104}{106.73}$$

$$r \approx 0.97$$

Thus, the sample correlation coefficient for the sample data is: $r = 0.97$. ■

You should notice that the sign associated with an $r = 0.97$ is *positive*. Whenever the sign associated with a correlation coefficient is positive, this indicates that there is a positive linear correlation between the two variables. Similarly, whenever the sign associated with a correlation coefficient is *negative*, the linear correlation between the two variables is *negative*.

EXAMPLE 15.5

Using the sample data in Table 15.7, calculate the sample correlation coefficient, r.

TABLE 15.7

x	2	3	5	6	8	10
y	11	9	8	6	6	3

Solution

Step 1   Construct a table that lists the variables: x, y, x^2, y^2 and xy.
Now, perform the calculation for each of these variables and list the result in the appropriate column. These results are listed in Table 15.8.

TABLE 15.8

x	y	x^2	y^2	xy
2	11	4	121	22
3	9	9	81	27
5	8	25	64	40
6	6	36	36	36
8	6	64	36	48
10	3	100	9	30

Step 2   Using the information in Table 15.8 calculate n, $\Sigma(xy), \Sigma x, \Sigma x^2, \Sigma y$ and Σy^2.
Adding the values within each column, we obtain the following results:

$n = 6$ $\Sigma x = 34$ $\Sigma y = 43$ $\Sigma x^2 = 238$ $\Sigma y^2 = 347$ $\Sigma(xy) = 203$

Step 3   Substitute the calculated values of n, $\Sigma(xy), \Sigma x, \Sigma x^2, \Sigma y$ and Σy^2 into the formula and calculate r.

$$r = \frac{n\Sigma(xy) - (\Sigma x)(\Sigma y)}{\sqrt{n(\Sigma x^2) - (\Sigma x)^2}\sqrt{n(\Sigma y^2) - (\Sigma y)^2}}$$

$$r = \frac{6(203) - (34)(43)}{\sqrt{6(238) - (34)^2}\sqrt{6(347) - (43)^2}}$$

$$r = \frac{1218 - 1462}{\sqrt{1428 - 1156}\sqrt{2082 - 1849}}$$

$$r = \frac{-244}{\sqrt{272}\sqrt{233}}$$

$$r \approx \frac{-244}{251.76}$$

$$r \approx -0.97$$

Thus, the sample correlation coefficient is: $r = -0.97$.

**Procedure to Calculate the
Sample Correlation Coefficient, r**

Step 1   Construct a table that contains the variables:
x, y, x^2, y^2 and xy. Perform the calculation for each of these quantities and list the result in the appropriate column of the table.

Step 2   Using the information in the table, calculate:
$n, \Sigma(xy), \Sigma x, \Sigma x^2, \Sigma y$ and Σy^2.

Step 3   Substitute the calculated values of $n, \Sigma(xy), \Sigma x, \Sigma x^2, \Sigma y$ and Σy^2 into the formula and calculate r.
To calculate r, use the sample correlation coefficient formula:

$$r = \frac{n\Sigma(xy) - (\Sigma x)(\Sigma y)}{\sqrt{n(\Sigma x^2) - (\Sigma x)^2}\sqrt{n(\Sigma y^2) - (\Sigma y)^2}}$$

When the sample correlation coefficient is greater than zero, that is: $r > 0$, then there is a positive linear correlation between the two variables.

When the sample correlation coefficient is less than zero, that is: $r < 0$, then there is a negative linear correlation between the two variables.

15.4   MORE ON THE RELATIONSHIP BETWEEN THE CORRELATION COEFFICIENT AND THE SCATTER DIAGRAM

We have previously stated that the correlation coefficient, r, measures the strength of a linear relationship between two variables. Furthermore, we have indicated that $-1 \le r \le +1$. Carefully examine Figures 15.11(a), 15.11(b) and 15.11(c).

The scatter diagrams illustrated in Figures 15.11(a) or 15.11(b), have correlation coefficients equal to +1 and –1 respectively. In each case such a value of r would mean that a **perfect linear rela-**

FIGURE 15.11

tionship exists between the x and y variables. If the value of r is +1, then all the points of the scatter diagram would lie on a line that is sloping upward from left to right as illustrated in Figure 15.11(a) and the relationship between the variables would be referred to as a **perfect positive linear relationship.**

If the value of r is −1, then all the points of the scatter diagram would lie on a line that is sloping downward from left to right as illustrated in Figure 15.11(b) and the relationship between the variables would be referred to as a **perfect negative linear relationship.**

On the other hand if r = 0, then the scatter diagram would indicate no linear correlation as illustrated in Figure 15.11(c). Such a scatter diagram would suggest **no linear** relationship exists between the variables x and y.

In practice, Pearson correlation coefficient values of r that are +1, or −1, or 0 rarely occur. In the next section we will consider one way to interpret the correlation coefficient specifically for values other than +1, −1, and 0.

15.5 TESTING THE SIGNIFICANCE OF THE CORRELATION COEFFICIENT

There are many practical situations where it is necessary to determine whether a *significant* correlation exists between two variables. For example:

- Is there a significant correlation between High School average and success in college? or,
- Is there a significant correlation between the number of hours of television a five year old watches per week and their IQ score? or,
- Is there a significant correlation between a person's age and their blood pressure? or,
- Is there a significant correlation between a company's advertising expenditures and their sales for one of their new products?

To help us answer these questions, we would need to determine the population correlation coefficient for the two variables. The population correlation coefficient is symbolized by the lower case Greek letter rho: ρ, pronounced as row. However, it is impractical to collect the entire population data for the two variables, consequently, we would use a random sample to help us estimate the population correlation coefficient, ρ. We use the sample correlation coefficient, r, to calculate the correlation coefficient for the sample data. The correlation coefficient, r, for the sample is used as an estimate of the **population correlation coefficient, ρ.**

After we calculate the correlation coefficient, r, for the sample, we need to determine if this sample value of r indicates that the unknown population correlation coefficient, ρ, is a significant correlation. That is, the value of the population correlation coefficient, ρ, **is significantly different from a correlation of zero (i.e. no linear correlation).**

In this section, we will **examine how to test the correlation coefficient for statistical significance**. The statistical procedure needed to perform this test involves a modification of the general five step hypothesis testing procedure that was developed in Chapter 9. Let's develop this procedure to test the significance of a population correlation coefficient.

Procedure to Test the Significance of the Correlation Coefficient

This test is based upon the assumption that both variables x and y are normally distributed.

Step 1   Formulate the two hypotheses, H_o and H_a.
Null Hypothesis:
In general, the null hypothesis for testing the significance of the population correlation coefficient has the following form.

Null Hypothesis Form

H_o: The population correlation coefficient is equal to zero. That is, there is no linear correlation between the two variables.
Thus, the null hypothesis is symbolized as:

$$H_o: \rho = 0$$

Alternative Hypothesis:
Since the alternative hypothesis, H_a, can be stated as the population correlation coefficient is either: *greater than*, *less than*, or *not equal to zero*, then the alternative hypothesis can have one of three forms:

Form (a): Positive or Greater Than Form For H_a

H_a: The population correlation coefficient, ρ, is claimed to be greater than zero. That is, there is a positive linear correlation between the two variables. This is symbolized as:

$$H_a: \rho > 0$$

Form (b): Negative or Less Than Form For H_a

H_a: The population correlation coefficient, ρ, is claimed to be less than zero. That is, there is a negative linear correlation between the two variables. This is symbolized as:

$$H_a: \rho < 0$$

Form (c): Not Equal Form For H_a

H_a: The population correlation coefficient, ρ, is claimed to be not equal to zero. That is, there is a significant linear correlation between the two variables. This is symbolized as:

$$H_a: \rho \neq 0$$

Step 2 Determine the model to test the null hypothesis, H_o.

An important consideration to the design is the assumption that the variables x and y are both normally distributed. Under the assumption the null hypothesis is true, that is: $\rho = 0$, the distribution of r values is symmetric about r = 0 and is referred to as **the sampling distribution of the correlation coefficients.** This distribution will be used as the **model for the hypothesis test**. Figure 15.12 illustrates different sampling distributions of the correlation coefficients for various choices of n *pairs* of data.

Hypothesis Testing Model
the sampling distribution of the correlation coefficients
when $\rho = 0$

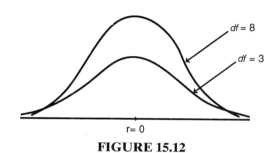

FIGURE 15.12

Step 3 Formulate the decision rule.

The decision rule is based on the following information.

a) Determine the type of alternative hypothesis (i.e., is the alternative hypothesis directional or nondirectional?)

b) Determine the type of hypothesis test (i.e., is the test 1TT or 2TT?)

c) Identify the significance level (i.e., is $\alpha = 1\%$ or $\alpha = 5\%$?)

d) Calculate the critical r value(s), r_α, using Table V: Critical Values of the Correlation Coefficient, r_α, found in Appendix D: Statistical Tables.

Table V contains the Critical Values of the Correlation Coefficient, r_α. To determine the appropriate critical r value, denoted as r_α, from Table V for the decision rule, we need to determine the degrees of freedom for testing the correlation coefficient.

Degrees of freedom, *df*.

The degrees of freedom, df, for testing the correlation coefficient is calculated by subtracting two from the number of pairs of sample data, n. Thus, the formula for *df* is: $df = n - 2$

e) Construct the appropriate hypothesis testing model.

Figure 15.13 illustrates the appropriate sampling distribution of the correlation coeffi-

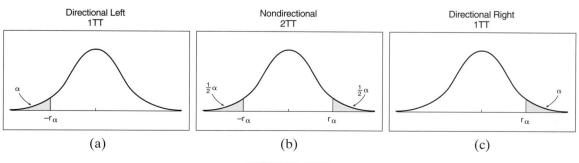

FIGURE 15.13

cients that are used as the hypothesis testing model. Notice that the actual model chosen is dependent upon the form of the alternative hypothesis.

Step 4   Analyze the sample data.
Randomly select the necessary data from the population to calculate the sample correlation coefficient, r, for the sample data. This r value is called the **test statistic**. To calculate the sample correlation coefficient, r, use the formula:

$$r = \frac{n\Sigma(xy) - (\Sigma x)(\Sigma y)}{\sqrt{n(\Sigma x^2) - (\Sigma x)^2}\sqrt{n(\Sigma y^2) - (\Sigma y)^2}}$$

Step 5   State the conclusion.
Compare the **test statistic, (i.e., the sample correlation coefficient r)** to the **critical r value, r_α,** of the decision rule and draw one of the following conclusions:

a)
Reject Ho and
Accept H_a at α

b)
Fail to reject Ho
at α

In summary, the general procedure used to perform a hypothesis test about a population correlation coefficient, ρ, is similar to the general hypothesis testing procedure developed in Chapter 9. However, there were some refinements to this general procedure. They were:

- The variables x and y are each normally distributed and the sampling distribution of the correlation coefficients which is symmetric about r = 0 when ρ = 0 is used as the appropriate hypothesis testing model.
- The test statistic is calculated by using the sample correlation coefficient, r, for the sample data.
- The critical value, r_α, for the decision rule is found in Table V using degrees of freedom, df, calculated by the formula: $df = n - 2$, the α value and the form of the alternative hypothesis..

Example 15.6 illustrates the use of this hypothesis testing procedure to test the significance of a correlation coefficient.

EXAMPLE 15.6

A Parents' Association in a Mission Viejo, California school district interviewed and collected data from a random sample of twenty parents whose children attend the elementary school. The data indicated the number of hours per week that each child watches television and the number of hours spent doing homework. The Association believes there is a negative correlation between the number of hours per week a child watches television and the number of hours per week the child spends doing homework. The sample correlation coefficient, r, was calculated to be –0.52. Test the hypothesis that there is a negative linear relationship between the number of hours a child watches television and spends doing homework. Use α = 5%.

Solution

Step 1   Formulate the hypotheses.
Null Hypothesis:

H_o: The population correlation coefficient of the number of hours a child watches TV and spends doing homework is zero.

This is symbolized as: H_o: $\rho = 0$.
A population correlation coefficient of zero is interpreted to mean that there is no linear relationship between the number of hours per week a child watches television and the number of hours per week the child spends doing homework.

Alternative Hypothesis:

Since the association believes that there is a negative linear correlation between the number of hours per week a child watches television and the number of hours per week the child spends doing homework, then they are trying to show that the population correlation coefficient is *less than* zero.

H_a: The population correlation coefficient of the number of hours a child watches TV and spends doing homework is *less than* zero.

This is symbolized as: H_a: $\rho < 0$.

Step 2   Determine the model to test the null hypothesis, H_o.

To test the null hypothesis, the association randomly selected 20 parents whose children attend the elementary school and determines the number of hours per week each child watched television and the number of hours per week each child dedicated to homework. To test the null hypothesis the sampling distribution of the correlation coefficients is used as the hypothesis testing model and both variables are assumed to be normally distributed.

Assuming the null hypothesis is true, i.e. $\rho = 0$, the distribution of r values is symmetric about r = 0 and serves as the hypothesis testing model. This is illustrated in Figure 15.14.

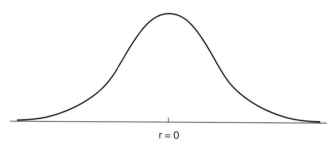

Hypothesis Testing Model
the sampling distribution of the correlation coefficients
when $\rho = 0$

r = 0

FIGURE 15.14

Step 3   Formulate the decision rule.
a)   The alternative hypothesis is directional, since the association is trying to show that ρ is less than zero.
b)   The type of hypothesis test is one-tailed on the left side.
c)   The significance level is: $\alpha = 5\%$.
d)   To determine the critical r value, r_α, we need to compute the degrees of freedom, *df*, using:

$$df = n - 2.$$

For n = 20, we have: df = 20 – 2 = 18. Thus, the critical r value, r_α , for a 1TT on the left with *df* = 18 is found in Table V. From Table V, the critical value is: $r_\alpha = -0.38$.
e)   Thus, the decision rule is: *Reject H_o*, if the test statistic, r, is *less than* –0.38.
Figure 15.15 illustrates the decision rule for this hypothesis test.

Step 4   Analyze the sample data.
The Parents' Association calculated the *test statistic* using the sample correlation coefficient formula. The test statistic is:

$$r = -0.52.$$

Hypothesis Testing Model
the sampling distribution of the correlation coefficients
when $\rho = 0$

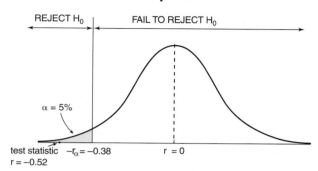

FIGURE 15.15

Step 5   State the conclusion.

Since the test statistic, r = –0.52, is *less than* the critical value, r_α = –0.38, then the conclusion is *Reject H_o* and *Accept H_a* at α = 5%. Therefore, the Parents' Association found that there is a significant negative linear correlation between the number of hours per week a child watches television and the number of hours per week the child spends doing homework at α = 5%.

EXAMPLE 15.7

A personnel director for ECHO publishing, Inc. believes that there is a significant correlation between the distance (in miles) an employee travels to work and the number of minutes per month the employee is late. Data from a random sampling of 10 employees obtained a sample correlation coefficient of: r = 0.65. Test the significance of the population correlation coefficient at α = 1%.

Solution

Step 1   Formulate the hypotheses.
Null Hypothesis:

H_o:The population correlation coefficient of the number of miles traveled to work and number of late minutes per month is zero.

This is symbolized as: H_o: $\rho = 0$.

Alternative Hypothesis:

Since the personnel director did not indicate a direction as to his belief about the relationship between the number of miles an employee travels to work and the number of minutes per month the employee is late, the alternative hypothesis in *nondirectional*.

Therefore, the alternative hypothesis is:

H_a: The population correlation coefficient of the number of miles traveled to work and number of late minutes per month is *not equal* to zero.

This is symbolized as: H_a: $\rho \neq 0$.

Step 2   Determine the model to test the null hypothesis, H_o.
The personnel director will randomly select 10 employees and determine the number of miles each employee travels to work and the number of minutes per month the employee is late. The sampling distribution of the correlation coefficients is used as the hypothesis testing model and both variables are assumed to be normally distributed. Under the assumption

that the null hypothesis is true, i.e. $\rho = 0$, the distribution of values is symmetric about $r = 0$ and serves as the hypothesis testing model. This is illustrated in Figure 15.16.

Hypothesis Testing Model
the sampling distribution of the correlation coefficients
when $\rho = 0$

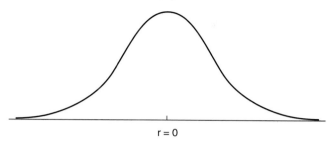

r = 0

FIGURE 15.16

Step 3 Formulate the decision rule.
    a) The alternative hypothesis is nondirectional, since the director is trying to show that ρ is not equal to zero.
    b) The type of hypothesis test is *two-tailed*.
    c) The significance level is: $\alpha = 1\%$.
    d) To determine the critical r values, r_α, we need to compute the degrees of freedom, df, using $df = n - 2$.
    For n = 10, we have: df = 10 − 2 = 8. Thus, the critical r value, r_α, for a 2TT with $df = 8$ and $\alpha = 1\%$ is found in Table V. From Table V, the critical r values are: $r_\alpha = \pm 0.76$.
    e) Thus, the decision rule is to Reject H_o, if the test statistic, r, is either: less than the critical r value, $r_\alpha = -0.76$ or r is greater than the critical value, $r_\alpha = 0.76$. Figure 15.17 illustrates the appropriate hypothesis testing model.

Hypothesis Testing Model
the sampling distribution of the correlation coefficients
when $\rho = 0$

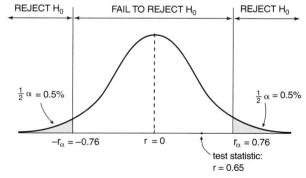

REJECT H_0 FAIL TO REJECT H_0 REJECT H_0

$\frac{1}{2}\alpha = 0.5\%$ $\frac{1}{2}\alpha = 0.5\%$

$-r_\alpha = -0.76$ r = 0 $r_\alpha = 0.76$
test statistic:
r = 0.65

FIGURE 15.17

Step 4 Analyze the sample data.
    For this study, ten employees were surveyed. The sample correlation coefficient, r, was calculated to be 0.65. Thus, the test statistic is: r = 0.65.

Step 5 State the conclusion.

Since the test statistic, r = 0.65, is neither less than the critical value of $r_\alpha = -0.76$ nor greater than the critical value of $r_\alpha = 0.76$, then the personnel director *fails to reject H_o at $\alpha = 1\%$.* Thus, the linear correlation between the number of miles travelled to work and the number of minutes late per month is *not statistically significant at $\alpha = 1\%$.* ∎

15.6   THE COEFFICIENT OF DETERMINATION

An important statistic measure that can be calculated from the correlation coefficient, r, is called the **Coefficient of Determination**. This statistical measure is used to explain the degree of influence that one variable called the independent variable, usually denoted by x, has on the other variable called the dependent variable, usually denoted by y.

> **DEFINITION 15.6**
>
> The **coefficient of determination** measures the proportion of the variance of the dependent variable **y** that can be accounted for by the variance of the independent variable **x**. It is calculated by squaring the correlation coefficient, r.
>
> Thus, we can write:
>
> $$\text{Coefficient of Determination} = r^2$$

EXAMPLE 15.8

In Example 15.6, it was shown that a significant linear correlation, r = −0.52, was found between the number of hours per week a child watches television (the independent variable) and the number of hours per week the child spends doing homework (the dependent variable). Using this information, then:

a) Calculate the coefficient of determination, r^2.
b) Interpret the meaning of r^2.

Solution

a) To calculate the coefficient of determination, the correlation coefficient, r, must be determined. Since r was found to be −0.52, the coefficient of determination is found by squaring r. Thus, the coefficient of determination is:

$$r^2 = (-0.52)^2$$
$$r^2 = 0.27$$

b) To convert the coefficient of determination to a percent multiply r^2 by 100%. Thus, in percent form, the coefficient of determination is 27%. This means that 27% of the variance in the number of hours per week a child spends doing homework (the dependent variable) can be accounted for by the variance in the number of hours per week the child watches television (the independent variable). ∎

The coefficient of determination can also be used to suggest the existence of other reasons for the variation one variable due to the variation in the other. Looking back at the previous example, one may conclude that the variation in the hours a child spends doing homework that cannot be accounted for, (i.e., 100% − 27% = 73%) may be attributed to a number of reasons. For example, a child may not be assigned homework on a regular basis. Or, the child is inconsistent in doing homework regularly. Since the coefficient of determination is 27%, we may conclude that there is significant amount of variance in the number of hours per week the child spends doing homework that is **not explained**. Thus, **73% reflects this unexplained amount.**

CASE STUDY 15.1   Dropping Out or Missing School

The research article entitled "Dropping Out And Absenteeism in High School" appeared in *Psychological Reports* in the June 1990 issue. The study investigated the relationships among dropping out, absenteeism days of school year, and size of school enrollment. The data were collected from the records of a North Central Kansas High School District. The table in Figure 15.18 represents the Pearson correlations for the variables.

Pearson Correlations For Variables

	1	2	3	4	5	6	7
1. Days of school in the year							
2. Enrollment	.80*						
3. Total days students absent less semester test days	.81*	.92*					
4. Number of students dropping out	.53†	.74*	.48†				
5. Percentage of dropouts							
6. Total number of graduating seniors	.07	.72*	.66*	.29			
7. Total number of seniors not graduating	−.74†	−.15	−.37	−.18		.09	

*p<.01.   †p<.05.

FIGURE 15.18

a) Identify the different variables that were investigated within the study.

b) If a scatter diagram were constructed for the variables enrollment and total number of seniors not graduating, what would you expect the general pattern to look like?

c) If a scatter diagram were constructed for the variables enrollment and total days students absent less semester test days, what would you expect the general pattern to look like?

d) As enrollment increases, what would you expect would happen to the value of the variable number of students dropping out?

e) Interpret the meaning of 0.80 within the second row and first column of the table? What variables are being compared? Is this a positive or negative relationship between the variables? Explain. Is this a significant relationship at $\alpha = 5\%$? at $\alpha = 1\%$? Explain.

f) Interpret the meaning of 0.07 within the sixth row and first column? What variables are being compared? Is this a positive or negative relationship between the variables? Explain. Is this a significant result at 5%? at $\alpha = 1\%$? Explain.

g) What happens to the value of the variables on enrollment, days of school of the school year, and absences as the value of the variable on the number of students dropping out increases? Are these relationships positive or negative?

h) Can the null hypothesis be rejected for the variables number of students dropping out and days of the school year at $\alpha = 5\%$? at $\alpha = 1\%$? Explain. What is the smallest level of significance that would cause the rejection of the null hypothesis? Explain.

i) What is proportion of the variance in enrollment that can be accounted for by the variance in the number of students dropping out? What formula is used to determine this proportion, and what is this statistical measure called?

j) What is proportion of the variance in total number of seniors not graduating that can be accounted for by the variance in the days of school in the year?

15.7   LINEAR REGRESSION ANALYSIS

Once a significant linear correlation has been established between two variables, a **linear model** can be developed that is used to predict a value for the dependent variable, usually denoted as the y variable, given a value for the independent variable, usually denoted as the x variable.

For example, if a significant linear correlation has been established between a father's height (the independent variable) and his son's height (the dependent variable), then it would be useful to develop a linear model that could reasonably *predict* the son's height *given* his father's height. This linear model could be used to predict a son's height simply by using the father's height.

You are probably aware that many colleges and universities successfully use a student's standardized test result as a main criteria for acceptance into the school. The schools are able to predict success with a high degree of confidence because research studies have established that there is a high correlation between the standardized test results and success at the college, as measured by the student's first year grade point average (GPA). To accomplish this, a model is statistically developed that can be used to predict a student's first year GPA from his/her standardized test scores.

These examples show how statistical modeling can be applied to the relationship between two variables. This type of modeling involves regression analysis. Regression analysis enables us to develop models so we can make these types of predictions. Linear regression analysis provides us with a linear model or equation that can be used to predict the value of the y or dependent variable given the value of the x or independent variable. The value of y that is predicted by this model is usually not the exact value, however it is a "close" estimate of the actual y value. To determine the linear model that will generate a "close" estimate of the actual y value, we obtain the line that "best fits" all the sample points of the scatter diagram. In regression analysis, the technique used to obtain this best fitting line is called the **method of least squares**. Essentially, this technique selects as the "best fitting" line the line which minimizes the sum of the squared distances between the predicted y values and the actual or observed y values. This idea is illustrated in Figure 15.19.

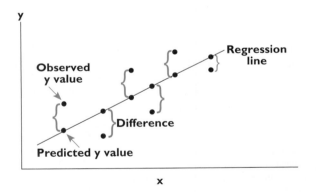

FIGURE 15.19

The best fitting line is called the **regression line**. It is used to predict the dependent variable (y) based upon the value of the independent variable (x). Let's examine how to obtain the regression line by examining the regression line formula.

Regression Line Formula

$$y' = a + bx$$

where: y' is the **predicted value of y, the dependent variable**, given the value of x, the **independent variable**.

and

a and **b** **are the regression coefficients** obtained by the formulas:

$$b = \frac{n\Sigma(xy) - \Sigma x \Sigma y}{n(\Sigma x^2) - (\Sigma x)^2}$$

$$a = \frac{\Sigma y - b\Sigma x}{n}$$

Example 15.9 illustrates how to calculate the regression line.

EXAMPLE 15.9

A psychologist has established that there is a significant negative correlation between the number of sunny days per year for a given region and the number of adult suicides in that region. The data pairs listed in Table 15.9 represent the random sample used by the psychologist.

TABLE 15.9

Region Number	Number of Sunny Days per Year	Number of Suicides per Year
1	250	28
2	330	10
3	210	34
4	342	08
5	265	30
6	227	41
7	280	19
8	278	21
9	321	14
10	338	09

Use the sample data listed in Table 15.9 to develop a regression line to predict the number of suicides per year given the number of sunny days per year.

Solution

Step 1   Choose the independent and dependent variables.
To find the regression line, y' = a + bx, we must first choose the dependent variable (y). The dependent variable is the variable you want to predict. Thus, the *number of suicides per*

year is the dependent variable. Therefore, the independent variable (x), is the *number of sunny days per year*. This choice of the variable names will produce a regression line model that will *predict* the number of suicides per year, y', *given* the number of sunny days, x.

Step 2   Calculate the regression constants, a and b.

Of the two regression constants, b **must** be computed **first**, since the calculated value of b is *used* in the formula to calculate a.

To calculate b, use the formula:

$$b = \frac{n\Sigma(xy) - \Sigma x \Sigma y}{n(\Sigma x^2) - (\Sigma x)^2}$$

Since the calculation of b requires Σx, Σy, Σx^2, Σxy and n, use Table 15.10 to help organize the calculations.

TABLE 15.10

x	y	xy	x^2
250	28	7,000	62,500
330	10	3,300	108,900
210	34	7,140	44,100
342	08	2,736	116,964
265	30	7,950	70,225
227	41	9,307	51,529
280	19	5,320	78,400
278	21	5,838	77,284
321	14	4,494	103,041
338	09	3,042	114,244

From Table 15.10, we obtain the following sums:

$$\Sigma x = 2,841 \qquad \Sigma y = 214 \qquad \Sigma x^2 = 827,187 \qquad \Sigma xy = 56,127$$

Since there are 10 pairs of sample data, n = 10.

To calculate the regression coefficient b, substitute the above values into the formula for b:

$$b = \frac{n\Sigma(xy) - \Sigma x \Sigma y}{n(\Sigma x^2) - (\Sigma x)^2}$$

$$b = \frac{10(56127) - (2841)(214)}{10(827187) - 2841^2}$$

$$b = \frac{561,270 - 607,974}{8,271,870 - 8,071,281}$$

$$b = \frac{-46,704}{200,589}$$

$$b \approx -0.2328$$

To calculate regression coefficient a, use the formula:

$$a = \frac{\Sigma y - b\Sigma x}{n}$$

$$a = \frac{214 - (-0.2328)(2,841)}{10}$$

$$a = \frac{214 + 661.38}{10}$$

$$a = \frac{875.38}{10}$$

$$a \approx 87.54$$

Step 3   Substitute the values of a and b into the equation for the regression line:

$$y' = a + bx$$

$$y' = 87.54 + (-0.2328)x$$

$$y' = 87.54 - 0.2328x$$

Let's summarize the procedure to calculate the regression line: **y' = a + bx.**

Procedure to Determine the Regression Line

Step 1   Choose the independent and dependent variables.
The dependent variable is the variable you are going to predict.

Step 2   Calculate the regression coefficients, a and b.
Calculate b first. Use the formula:

$$b = \frac{n\Sigma(xy) - \Sigma x\Sigma y}{n(\Sigma x^2) - (\Sigma x)^2}$$

Calculate a. Use the formula:

$$a = \frac{\Sigma y - b\Sigma x}{n}$$

Step 3   Substitute the values of a and b into the equation for the regression line:

y' = a + bx

EXAMPLE 15.10

In Example 15.9 we found the regression line to be y' = 87.54 − 0.2328x. This formula represents a *linear* model of the *best fitting line* for the sample data in Table 15.9. Use this regression line model to predict the number of suicides in a year where the number of sunny days is: a) 200 b) 300 c) 0.

Solution

Since we want to predict the number of suicides per year, this represents the dependent variable y. Thus, the number of sunny days per year represents the independent variable x. The regression line equation,

$$y' = 87.54 - 0.2328x,$$

is a model to predict the number of suicides per year (y) given the number of sunny days per year (x).

a)   If x = 200 then

$$y' = 87.54 - 0.2328(200)$$

$$y' = 40.98 \text{ suicides per year.}$$

Thus, the predicted number of suicides per year for a region with 200 sunny days per year is 40.98.

b)   If x = 300 then

$$y' = 87.54 - 0.2328(300)$$

$$y' = 17.70 \text{ suicides per year}$$

Thus, the predicted number of suicides per year for a region with 300 sunny days per year is 17.70.

c)   If x = 0 then

$$y' = 87.54 - 0.2328(0)$$

$$y' = 87.54 \text{ suicides per year}$$

Thus, the predicted number of suicides per year for a region with zero sunny days per year is 87.54.

■

EXAMPLE 15.11

Use the regression line equation and the sample data pairs from Example 15.9 to graph, on the *same* axes, the scatter diagram of the sample data and the regression line. The regression line model equation from Example 15.9 is:

$$y' = 87.54 - 0.2328x$$

and the sample data is listed in Table 15.11.

TABLE 15.11

Region Number	Number of Sunny Days Per year	Number of Suicides per Year
1	250	28
2	330	10
3	210	34
4	342	08
5	265	30
6	227	41
7	280	19
8	278	21
9	321	14
10	338	09

Solution

The scatter diagram for these data pairs, where the independent variable x represents the number of sunny days per year and the dependent variable y represents the number of suicides per year, is shown in Figure 15.20. The regression line has also been drawn on the axes. Notice that the regression line has the property that it **"best fits"** the data.

FIGURE 15.20

The research article entitled "Suicide Rates, Handgun Control Laws, and Sociodemographic Variables" appeared in *Psychological Reports* of the June 1990 issue. One aspect of the study examined the relationships between suicide rates, and sex, age, percent black, percent metropolitan population, population density, and rates of population change (increase or decrease), divorce, crime, and unemployment. The Pearson correlation coefficient obtained among suicide rates, handgun control laws (identified as Attribute I: Restrictions on the seller of handguns and Attribute II: Restrictions on the buyer of handguns), and all sociodemographic variables are presented in the table of Figure 15.21.

Pearson Correlations (N = 51)

Variable	1	2	3	4	5	6
1. Suicide rate, 1985						
2. Percent male, 1980	.55‡					
3. Percent ages 35-64, 1986	−.29*	−.35†				
4. Percent black, 1985	−.42†	−.52‡	.23			
5. Percent metropolitan, 1985	−.31*	−.35†	.54‡	.32*		
6. Percent per square mile, 1985	−.37†	−.42†	.21	.67‡	.32*	
7. Percent population change, 1980-1985	.52‡	.63‡	−.17	−.14	.03	−.15
8. Divorce rate, 1985	.69‡	.41†	−.05	−.12	−.08	−.11
9. Crime rate, 1985	.19	.02	.19	.26	.60‡	.34*
10. Unemployment rate, 1985	.15	.08	−.20	.22	−.18	.04
11. Restrictions on seller (Attribute I), 1987	−.45‡	−.25	.45‡	−.02	.48‡	−.07
12. Restrictions on buyer (Attribute II), 1987	−.54‡	−.30*	.30*	.37†	.35†	.44‡
M	12.80	48.90	31.80	10.80	64.10	351.30
SD	3.20	1.10	1.90	12.50	22.50	1386.40

	7	8	9	10	11	12
8. Divorce rate, 1985	.58‡					
9. Crime rate, 1985	.51‡	.32*				
10. Unemployment rate, 1985	−.01	.22	.03			
11. Restrictions on seller (Attribute I), 1987	−.40†	−.35†	−.06	−.09		
12. Restrictions on buyer (Attribute II), 1987	−.31*	−.29*	.18	−.03	.21	
M	6.00	5.20	48.20	7.10	1.30	0.50
SD	5.70	1.80	13.60	1.90	1.20	0.90

*p<.05.   †p<.01.   ‡p < .001.

FIGURE 15.21

CASE STUDY 15.2   Sociodemographic Variables (continued)

a) Examine the table in Figure 15.21 and identify all the variables examined within this study.

b) What type of relationship exists between the suicide rate and the restrictions of the seller? Is this a significant relationship at $\alpha = 5\%$? at $\alpha = 1\%$? Can one conclude from this relationship that high suicide rates had significantly less stringent handgun control laws? Explain. What proportion of the variance in the suicide rate that can be accounted for by the variance in the restrictions of the seller? What formula is used to determine this proportion, and what is this statistical measure called?

c) What type of relationship exists between the suicide rate and the percent of males? Is this a significant relationship at $\alpha = 5\%$? at $\alpha = 1\%$? What proportion of the variance in the suicide rate that can be accounted for by the variance in the percent of males? What formula is used to determine this proportion, and what is this statistical measure called?

d) If a scatter diagram were constructed for the variables suicide rate and divorce rate, what would you expect the general pattern to look like?

e) As suicide rates increase, what would you expect would to happen to the variable persons per square mile?

f) As crime rates increase, what would you expect would to happen to the variable persons per square mile?

g) With what variables would suicide rates be significantly correlated? Complete the following statements:

high suicide rates had significantly _____ percent of blacks.
high suicide rates had significantly _____ divorce rates.
high crime rates had significantly _____ persons per square mile.
For each of the other variables, write a similar statement.

h) Can the null hypothesis be rejected for the variables suicide rate and percentage of persons in the 35- to 64 age group at $\alpha = 5\%$? at $\alpha = 1\%$? Explain. What is the smallest level of significance that would cause the rejection of the null hypothesis? Explain.

Summary of Hypothesis Testing Procedure to Test the Significance of a Correlation Coefficient

---

The following outline is a summary of the 5 step hypothesis testing procedure for the test of a correlation coefficient.

Step 1   Formulate the two hypotheses, H_o and H_a.
Null Hypothesis: $H_o: \rho = 0$
Alternative Hypothesis, H_a: can have one of following three forms:

$$H_a: \rho > 0 \text{ or } H_a: \rho < 0 \text{ or } H_a: \rho \neq 0$$

Step 2   Determine the model to test the null hypothesis, H_o.
Under the assumption the null hypothesis is true, that is: $\rho = 0$, the distribution of r values is symmetric about r=0 and is referred to as the:

sampling distribution of the correlation coefficients.

This is the hypothesis testing model.

Summary of Hypothesis Testing Procedure to
Test the Significance of a Correlation Coefficient (continued)

Step 3   Formulate the decision rule.
a) alternative hypothesis: directional or nondirectional
b) type of test: 1TT or 2TT
c) significance level: $\alpha = 1\%$ or $\alpha = 5\%$
d) determine the critical r value, r_α, using Table V.
using degrees of freedom: $df = n - 2$
e) draw diagram.
f) state the decision rule.

Step 4   Analyze the sample data.
Calculate the sample correlation coefficient, r. This is the test statistic.

Step 5   State the conclusion.
Compare the test statistic, (i.e., the sample correlation coefficient r) to the critical r value, r_α, and state the conclusion:

either: a)   Reject H_o and Accept H_a at α
or   b)   Fail to reject H_o at α

15.8   ASSUMPTIONS FOR LINEAR REGRESSION ANALYSIS

Beside the assumption of a **linear relationship** between the two variables **x** and **y**, the following three assumptions must be satisfied in order to apply the linear regression model.

For each value of x under consideration, there exists a population of y values and they must conform to the following conditions:

- these y populations must have a normal distribution.
- the means of all these populations must lie on a straight line called the population regression line.
- the standard deviation of all the y populations must be equal.

Furthermore, when selecting a value for the independent variable x, this x value must be within the range of the sample x data.

Some Cautions Regarding the Interpretation of Correlation Results

There are some common mistakes that people make when they interpret correlation results. To help you avoid these pitfalls, we will discuss two cautions regarding the use of correlation.

Caution #1:
Don't Overlook the Possibility of a Non-Linear Relationship

The correlation coefficient, r, only measures the **linear** relationship between two variables. It is possible for two variables to have a linear correlation near zero, and, yet they could have a significant non-linear relationship. Be careful not to interpret a non-significant linear correlation as meaning there doesn't exist any relationship between the variables.

Caution #2:
Correlation Doesn't Indicate a Cause-And-Effect Relationship

You must be careful not to interpret a significant linear relationship between two variables to imply there exists a ***cause-and-effect*** relationship. Simply because two variables are correlated does not guarantee a cause-and-effect relationship. Two seemingly non-correlated variables may often be highly correlated.

For example, the number of storks nesting in various European towns in the early 1900's and the number of human babies born in the same towns during this period had a very high correlation. However, we can't conclude that an increase in the number of storks will cause an increase in the number of babies.

Therefore, a significant linear correlation between two variables should not be interpreted to mean that a change in one variable *causes* a change in the other variable, but rather only that changes in one variable are associated with or accompanied by changes in the other variable.

15.9 p-VALUE APPROACH TO TESTING THE SIGNIFICANCE OF THE CORRELATION COEFFICIENT USING THE TI-83PLUS CALCULATOR

The p-value approach will require refinements in steps 3, 4 and 5 of the hypothesis testing procedure. In step 3, the decision rule will be stated as: Reject the H_0 if the p-value of the test statistic, r, is less than α. In step 4, the p-value will be determined using the TI-83 Plus calculator. While in step 5, the conclusion of the hypothesis test is determined by comparing the p-value to the level of significance, α.

Let's reexamine the hypothesis test shown in Example 15.7 using a p-value approach with the aid of the TI-83 Plus Calculator.

EXAMPLE 15.12

A personal director of ECHO publishing, Inc. believes that there is a significant correlation between the distance (in miles) an employee travels to work and the number of minutes per month the employee is late. The sample data from a random sampling of 10 employees is shown in Table 15.12.

Table 15.12

miles traveled to work:	5	10	15	20	25	30	35	40	45	50
minutes late per month:	3	6	6	5	2	4	7	7	12	8

Perform a hypothesis test at $\alpha = 1\%$ to determine if there is a significant correlation between the distance an employee travels to work and the number of minutes late per month.

Solution

Step 1 Formulate the hypotheses.

Null Hypothesis:

H_o: **The population correlation coefficient of the number of miles traveled to work and the number of minutes late per month is zero.**

This is symbolized as: H_o: $\rho = 0$.

Alternative Hypothesis:

Since the personnel director did not indicate a direction as to his belief about the relationship between the number of miles an employee travels to work and the number of minutes per month the employee is late, the alternative hypothesis in *nondirectional*.

Therefore, the alternative hypothesis is:

H_a: The population correlation coefficient of the number of miles traveled to work and the number of minutes late per month is *not equal* to zero.

This is symbolized as: H_a: $\rho \neq 0$.

Step 2   Determine the model to test the null hypothesis, H_0.

The personnel director will randomly select 10 employees and determine the number of miles each employee travels to work and the number of minutes per month the employee is late. The sampling distribution of correlation coefficients is used as the hypothesis testing model and both variables are assumed to be normally distributed. Under the assumption that the null hypothesis is true, i.e. $\rho = 0$, the distribution of r values is symmetric about $r = 0$ and serves as the hypothesis testing model. This is illustrated in Figure 15.22.

Hypothesis Testing Model
the sampling distribution of the correlation coefficients
when $\rho = 0$

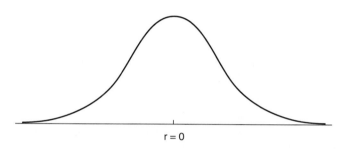

r = 0

FIGURE 15.22

Step 3   Formulate the decision rule.
   a) The alternative hypothesis is nondirectional, since the director is trying to show that ρ is not equal to zero.
   b) The type of hypothesis test is two-tailed.
   c) The significance level is: $\alpha = 1\%$.
   d) The decision rule is: Reject H_0 if the p-value of the test statistic, r, is less than $\alpha = 1\%$. Figure 15.23 illustrates the decision rule.

Hypothesis Testing Model
the sampling distribution of the correlation coefficients
when $\rho = 0$

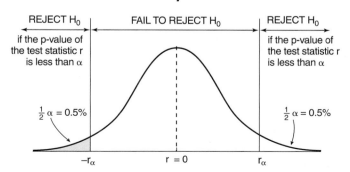

REJECT H_0 FAIL TO REJECT H_0 REJECT H_0

if the p-value of the test statistic r is less than α if the p-value of the test statistic r is less than α

$\frac{1}{2}\alpha = 0.5\%$ $\frac{1}{2}\alpha = 0.5\%$

$-r_\alpha$ r = 0 r_α

FIGURE 15.23

Step 4   Analyze the sample data.

Enter the sample data of Table 15.12 into the TI-83 Plus calculator and use LinRegTTest to determine the p-value of the test statistic, r. The TI-83 Plus output screen in shown in Figures 15.24(a) and 15.24(b).

```
LinRegTTest
  y=a+bx
  B≠0 and ρ≠0
  t=2.411214111
  p=.0424277434
  df=8
 ↓a=2.666666667
```

```
LinRegTTest
  y=a+bx
  B≠0 and ρ≠0
 ↑b=.1212121212
  s=2.283007055
  r²=.4208754209
  r=.6487491201
```

FIGURE 15.24(a)   **FIGURE 15.24(b)**

Notice from the output screen, the **p-value** of the test statistic ($r \approx 0.65$) is approximately 0.0424.

Step 5   Determine the conclusion.

Since the p-value (0.0424) of the test statistic is greater then $\alpha = 1\%$, the personnel director *fails to reject H_o at $\alpha = 1\%$*. This is illustrated in Figure 15.25. Thus, the linear correlation between the number of miles traveled to work and the number of minutes late per month is *not statistically significant at $\alpha = 1\%$*.

Notice for a 2TT, the position of the test statistic ($r \approx 0.65$) was determined by taking half of the p-value, i.e. ½(0.0424) = 0.0212, as illustrated is Figure 15.25.

Hypothesis Testing Model
the sampling distribution of the correlation coefficients
when $\rho = 0$

FIGURE 15.25

The following outline is a summary of the 5 step hypothesis testing procedure for the p-value approach to test the significance of a correlation coefficient using the TI-83 Plus calculator.

Summary of p-Value Approach To the Hypothesis Testing Procedure To Test the Significance of a Correlation Coefficient Using the TI-83 Plus Calculator

Step 1   Formulate the two hypotheses, H_o and H_a.
Null Hypothesis: H_o: $\rho = 0$
Alternative Hypothesis, H_a: can have one of following three forms:

$$\textbf{H}_\textbf{a}\textbf{:}\ \rho > 0 \text{ or } \textbf{H}_\textbf{a}\textbf{:}\ \rho < 0 \text{ or } \textbf{H}_\textbf{a}\textbf{:}\ \rho \neq 0$$

Step 2   Determine the model to test the null hypothesis, H_o.
Under the assumption the null hypothesis is true, that is: $\rho = 0$, the distribution of r values is symmetric about r=0 and is referred to as the:

sampling distribution of the correlation coefficients.

Step 3   Formulate the decision rule.
a) alternative hypothesis: directional or nondirectional
b) type of test: 1TT or 2TT
c) significance level: $\alpha = 1\%$ or $\alpha = 5\%$
d) state the decision rule as Reject H_o if the p-value of the test statistic, r, is less than α.

Step 4   Analyze the sample data.
Enter the sample data into the TI-83 Plus calculator and use LinRegTTest to determine the p-value of the test statistic, r.

Step 5   State the conclusion.
Compare the p-value of the test statistic, (i.e., the sample correlation coefficient r) to α and state the conclusion as either:
  a) Reject H_o and Accept H_a at the computed p-value, if the p-value of the test statistic r is less than α

or
  b) Fail to reject H_o at the computed p-value, if the p-value of the test statistic r is not less than α

15.10   USING TECHNOLOGY

Table 15.1 listed the heights and respective weights for a sample of 12 female students. The MINITAB output for Table 15.1 is shown in Figure 15.26.

MINITAB OUTPUT

ROW	HT(IN)	WT(LB)
1	62	123
2	58	102
3	64	110

FIGURE 15.26 (continues)

4	69	137
5	61	145
6	70	132
7	59	108
8	60	112
9	63	124
10	72	155
11	71	170
12	68	140

Correlation of HT(IN) and WT(LB) = 0.789

FIGURE 15.26 (continued)

Using MINITAB, the scatter diagram for these variables is displayed in Figure 15.27.

FIGURE 15.27

The MINITAB output for the regression equation for these variables is displayed in Figure 15.28.

```
The regression equation is
WT(LB) = - 81.1 + 3.26 HT(IN)

Predictor        Coef        Stdev      t-ratio          p
Constant       -81.12        52.14        -1.56      0.151
HT(IN)         3.2580       0.8031         4.06      0.002

s = 13.30      R-sq = 62.2%      R-sq(adj) = 58.4%
```

FIGURE 15.28 (continues)

```
Analysis of Variance

SOURCE         DF            SS           MS         F          p
Regression      1        2911.0       2911.0     16.46      0.002
Error          10        1768.7        176.9
Total          11        4679.7


Unusual Observations
  Obs.   HT(IN)      WT(LB)        Fit Stdev.Fit  Residual   St.Resid
    5      61.0      145.00     117.62      4.88     27.38       2.21R

R denotes an obs. with a large st. resid.
```

FIGURE 15.28 (continued)

As you can see there is a lot of output generated by MINITAB. Let's consider the output as blocks of information. The first line of the output gives the regression equation. Next you'll see information on the regression equation as well as the variables used. In the last block of the output there is listed information about potential outliers. Can you find where the coefficients a and b, that are used in the regression equation, are listed? Of course the regression equation is one place to look. Can you find those values for a and b anywhere else?

Notice that the p-value of 0.002 is given for the line labelled 'HT'. This indicates that the correlation between HT and WT has a p-value of 0.002. Would you consider HT and WT to be significantly correlated?

Using the sample data from Table 15.1, the TI–83 Plus calculator output screens are shown in Figure 15.29. Figure 15.29a displays the regression coefficients a & b for the regression line $y' = a + bx$, coefficient of determination, r^2, and the sample correlation coefficient, r. Figure 15.29b shows a scatter diagram of the sample data while Figure 15.29c plots the regression line ($y' = -81.12 + 3.26x$) on the scatter diagram.

(a)

(b)

(c)

FIGURE 15.29

>>>>   **SECTION EXERCISES**

Many exercises require calculations that are long and tedious. Therefore, we recommend that you use a calculator or a computer with statistical application software to help you perform these calculations.

Section 15.2

1. In correlational analysis, the two variables are _____ .
2. A pair of numbers that is written in the following form: (x,y) is called an _____ pair since the value of the x variable is always written _____ within the parentheses.
3. A graph representing the ordered pairs of sample data on a set of axes is called a _____ _____.
4. A _____ correlation is a correlation between two variables, x and y, that occurs when high measurements on the x variable tend to be associated with high measurements on the y variable and low measurements on the x variable tend to be associated with low measurements on the y variable.
5. If the points in the scatter diagram tend to follow a straight-line path, then this is type of correlation is called a _____ .
6. A _____ correlation means there is no linear relationship between the two variables. That is, high and low measurements on the two variables are _____ associated in any predictable way.
7. Which type of correlation is indicated by a scatter diagram whose points appear to be randomly placed in no particular pattern?
    a) Positive
    b) None
    c) Negative
8. A linear correlation between the two variables is a line drawn between the variables.
    (T/F)
9. Scatter diagrams are graphs that indicate the degree of variation between x and y.
    (T/F)
10. For each of the following two variables, state whether you would expect a positive, negative or no linear correlation.
    a) An individual's IQ score and annual salary
    b) An individual's age and blood pressure
    c) The number of days a student misses class and final grade
    d) A mother's birthday and her daughter's birthday
    e) An individual's driving speed above 55 mpg and gasoline mileage
    f) An individual's annual income and education level
    g) Average daily temperature during the summer months and the number of air conditioners sold during these months

h) An adult's shoe size and IQ score
i) Amount of fertilizer applied to tomato plants and the number of tomatoes per plant

11. In each of the following scatter diagrams, if a linear correlation exists between the two variables, then state whether the type of linear correlation is positive or negative. If no linear correlation exists, then state none.

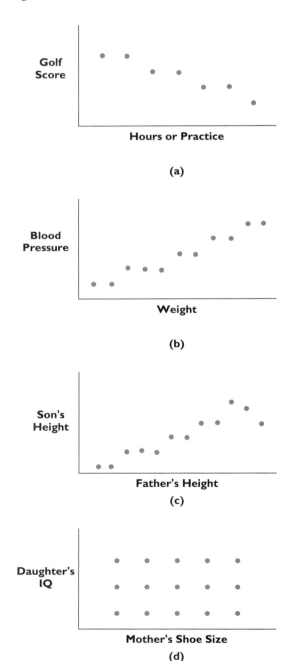

(a)

(b)

(c)

(d)

Sections 15.3–15.4

12. The closer the points of a scatter diagram approximate a straight-line pattern, the _____ the linear correlation between the two variables.

13. The strength of the linear correlation between the two variables of a sample can be numerically measured by _____ .

15. Pearson's correlation coefficient, r, will always be a numerical value between _____ and _____ .

15. A value of r = +1 represents the _____ positive correlation possible and it indicates a _____ positive linear correlation. This means that all the points of the scatter diagram will lie on a straight line which is sloping _____ from left to right.

16. A value of r = 0 represents no _____ correlation between the two variables.

17. The closer the value of the correlation coefficient, r, is to _____ or to _____ the stronger the linear relationship between the two variables. However, a value of r close to zero indicates a _____ linear relationship between the two variables.

18. To calculate the sample correlation coefficient, we use the formula r = _____ .

19. The linear correlation between two variables, x and y, is a number between −1 and +1. (T/F)

20. A linear correlation that is close to zero can be interpreted to mean that no relationship exists between the variables, x and y. (T/F)

21. When the coefficient of determination is zero, this means that there is a perfect linear correlation between the x and y variables. (T/F)

22. For the following scatter diagrams:
a) Identify those that you believe represent a linear relationship between x and y.
b) For those that you have identified as representing a linear relationship between x and y, determine which are positive relationships and which are negative.

(i)

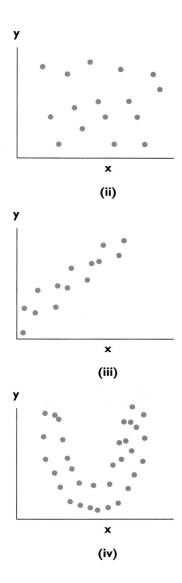

(ii)

(iii)

(iv)

23. Explain the difference between the following pair of r values.
a) r = 0.55 and r = 0.87
b) r = −0.60 and r = 0.60
c) r = 0.05 and r = 0.95

24. Using the sample correlation coefficient formula, calculate the value of r for each of the following data pairs.

a) x	y	b) x	y	c) x	y
2	4	5	11	4	9
3	7	7	8	5	11
4	8	9	1	6	13
5	11	10	6	7	15
6	11	16	2	8	17

d)	x	y	e)	x	y	f)	x	y
	2	3		11	12		72	222
	2	5		16	9		62	145
	3	5		15	9		58	125
	6	6		21	5		68	165
	7	9		23	4		68	172
	4	3		16	8		63	135
	1	4		26	4		61	120
	5	8		29	3		73	185
	3	6		34	1		75	210
	9	10		28	5		66	158

Section 15.5

25. The population correlation coefficient is symbolized by the lower case Greek letter ____, pronounced as row.

26. We use the sample correlation coefficient, r, to calculate the correlation coefficient for the _____ data. The correlation coefficient, r, for the sample is used as _____ of the population correlation coefficient, ρ.

27. **a)** The null hypothesis for testing the significance of the population correlation coefficient is stated as: the population correlation coefficient is equal to _____. That is, there is _____ linear correlation between the two variables. This is symbolized as: $H_o: \rho = $ _____.
b) The alternative hypothesis can be stated in one of the following three forms:
form a: The population correlation coefficient, ρ, is claimed to be greater than zero. That is, there is a _____ linear correlation between the two variables. This is symbolized as: $H_a: \rho$ _____ 0.
form b: The population correlation coefficient, ρ, is claimed to be less than zero. That is, there is a _____ linear correlation between the two variables. This is symbolized as: $H_a: \rho$ _____ 0
form c: The population correlation coefficient, ρ, is claimed to be not equal to zero. That is, there is a _____ linear correlation between the two variables. This is symbolized as: $H_a: \rho$ _____ 0.

28. The test of the significance of the correlation coefficient is based upon the assumption that both variables x and y are _____ distributed. This test uses as its hypothesis testing model: the sampling distribution of the _____ _____.

29. The critical value of the correlation coefficient is denoted as _____ . To determine this critical r value, you need to calculate the degrees of freedom for the test using the formula: $df = $ _____ .

30. The coefficient of determination measures the proportion of the variance of the _____ variable that can be accounted for by the variance of the _____ variable. To calculate the coefficient of determination, you need to square the value of _____.

31. Negative correlations are usually not significant. (T/F)

32. In a to f, there is a list of sample information, Pearson's correlation coefficient, type of test, and alpha level. Use this information and Table V to determine r_α, and to test if r is significant.
a) $n = 15, r = 0.60, 2TT, \alpha = 1\%$
b) $n = 25, r = -0.60, 1TT, \alpha = 1\%$
c) $n = 30, r = 0.60, 1TT, \alpha = 1\%$
d) $df = 10, r = 0.42, 2TT, \alpha = 5\%$
e) $df = 20, r = -0.42, 1TT, \alpha = 5\%$
f) $df = 28, r = 0.42, 1TT, \alpha = 5\%$

Section 15.6

33. If r=0.8, then the coefficient of determination is?
a) 0.88   **b)** 0.64   **c)** 1.6   **d)** 0.40

34. The coefficient of determination, r^2, measures the proportion of variance of:
a) The independent variable which can be accounted for by dependent variable.
b) The dependent variable which can be accounted for by the independent variable.
c) Neither of these

35. Audrey, an anthropologist, has made a study of the linear relationship between the leg length and total height of prehistoric animals. Using a random sample of 17 prehistoric animal fossils, she obtained a correlation coefficient of 0.48.
a) Can Audrey conclude that there is a positive correlation between the length and total height of prehistoric animals at $\alpha = 5\%$?
b) What percent of variability in total height can be accounted for by the variability in the leg length of the prehistoric animals?

Section 15.7

36. In linear regression analysis, the technique used to obtain the best fitting line is called the method of _____ _____. The best fitting line is called the _____ line.

37. The regression line formula is given by: _____ . To calculate the regression coefficients a and b, we use the following formulas: b = _____ and a = _____ .
The regression line is used to predict the _____ variable given the value of the _____ variable.

In problems requiring the testing of the significance of the correlation coefficient, assume that both the independent and dependent variables are normally distributed.

38. Craig, a marketing executive for a microbrewery company, wants to determine if there is a positive linear relationship between advertising expenditures and sales for their new lite beer product, Less Ale. He randomly samples data for the past 7 sales years and records the sample data in the following table, where advertising expenditure is measured in thousands and the beer sales in millions of dollars.

Year	Expenditure (thousand $)	Sales (million $)
1996	35	38
1997	47	35
1998	65	42
1999	92	50
2000	55	40
2001	25	35
2002	82	48

a) Construct a scatter diagram.
b) Calculate the sample correlation coefficient, r.
c) Determine if r is significant at $\alpha = 1\%$.
If r is significant at $\alpha = 1\%$, then do parts d,e,f.
d) Find r^2 and interpret its meaning.
e) Determine the regression equation, y'.
f) Using the regression equation, predict the beer sales for the advertising budget expenditure of $50,000.

39. Don, the grounds keeper, at the Sunview Golf course wants to know if there is a positive linear relationship between the density of seed spread on a newly land-scaped fairway and the density of new grass six months later. The following data pairs represent some sample plantings made by Don.

Seed Density (lbs/400ft^2)	Grass Density (seedlings/ft^2)
1.0	170
2.0	200
3.0	240
4.0	300
5.0	310
6.0	290
7.0	290

a) Construct a scatter diagram.
b) Calculate the sample correlation coefficient, r.
c) Determine if r is significant at $\alpha = 5\%$.
If r is significant at $\alpha = 5\%$, then do parts d,e,f.
d) Find r^2 and interpret its meaning.
e) Determine the regression equation, y'.
f) Using the regression equation, predict the grass density given that grass seed was applied at rate of 3.5 (lbs/400ft^2).

40. The scientists at the Micro Biology Laboratory in Woods Hale, Ma. want to determine if there is a linear relationship between the amount of rainfall in May and the number of mosquitoes. For each of the selected years, a random sample of data pairs have been collected and are listed in the table that follows:

Year	Amount of Rainfall in Inches	Mosquito Population Index
2002	5.3	7.3
2001	2.7	2.3
2000	3.9	2.7
1999	2.4	1.2
1998	5.7	5.2
1997	3.5	2.6

a) Construct a scatter diagram.
b) Calculate the sample correlation coefficient, r.
c) Determine if r is significant at $\alpha = 1\%$.
If r is significant at $\alpha = 1\%$, then do parts d,e,f.
d) Find r^2 and interpret its meaning.
e) Determine the regression equation, y'.
f) Using the regression equation, predict the mosquito population index if we have 3.1 inches of rain in May.

41. Grace, the personnel director at Weight Lookers International, believes there is a negative linear relationship between the number of sick days taken per year by an employee and the percent of annual salary increase the employee receives. A random sample of 20 employees yielded the following data pairs.

Number of Sick Days per Year	% of Annual Salary Increase
4	12
16	8
11	8
14	7
6	14
20	0
9	10
12	9
13	7
1	14
0	12
17	2
18	2
7	13
9	10
15	7
15	8
13	9
10	8
5	12

a) Construct a scatter diagram.
b) Calculate the sample correlation coefficient, r.
c) Determine if r is significant at $\alpha = 5\%$.
If r is significant at $\alpha = 5\%$, then do parts d,e,f.
d) Find r^2 and interpret its meaning.

e) Determine the regression equation, y'.

f) Using the regression equation, predict an employee's annual percentage of salary increase if over a given year the employee was out sick eight times.

42. Professor DePorto believes there is a positive linear relationship between Midterm examination grades and Final examination grades for students taking his introduction to statistics course. A random sample of 26 students who have taken both exams produced the following data pairs.

Midterm Exam Grade	Final Exam Grade
39	17
28	42
32	30
35	24
30	15
42	39
34	16
36	15
22	19
33	32
22	39
38	20
29	25
50	42
16	36
41	37
43	35
44	40
39	21
30	44

Midterm Exam Grade	Final Exam Grade
24	11
16	17
29	19
33	15
44	29
39	35

a) Construct a scatter diagram.

b) Calculate the sample correlation coefficient, r.

c) Test the significant of r at $\alpha = 5\%$.
If r is significant at $\alpha = 5\%$, the do parts d,e,f.

d) Find r^2 and interpret its meaning.

e) Determine the regression equation, y'.

f) Linda received a 24 on her Midterm exam. Use the regression equation and predict Linda's Final exam grade.

Section 15.8

For problems 43–47, use questions 38 to 42 of Section 15.7 exercises and apply the p-value approach to hypothesis testing using the TI-83 Plus calculator. For each of these problems, use the 5 step procedure to perform a hypothesis test at **both** $\alpha = 1\%$ and $\alpha = 5\%$. Include the following within your test:

a) state the null and alternative hypotheses.

b) calculate the expected results for the experiment assuming the null hypothesis is true and state the hypothesis test model.

c) formulate the decision rule.

d) identify the test statistic and its p-value.

e) state the conclusion and answer any question(s) posed in the problem for each alpha level.

f) determine the smallest level of significance for which the null hypothesis can be rejected.

CHAPTER REVIEW

48. For a 1TT on the left side, as the value of the test statistic decreases, then the p-value increases. (T/F)

49. A _____ linear correlation is a correlation between two variables, x and y, that occurs when high measurements on the x variable tend to be associated with low measurements on the y variable and low measurements on the x variable tend to be associated with high measurements on the y variable.

50. If y increases as x decreases this indicates that x and y are correlated:
a) Positively
b) Not at all
c) Negatively

51. A value of r = –1 represents the _____ negative linear correlation possible and it indicates a _____

negative linear correlation. This means that all the points of the scatter diagram will lie on a straight line which is sloping _____ from left to right.

52. For each of the following two variables, state whether you would expect a positive, negative or no linear correlation.
a) Number of hours practicing golf and golf score
b) A husband's age and his wife's age
c) Number of hours practicing bowling and bowling score
d) Amount of alcohol consumed and reaction time
e) Mother's birth weight and her child's birth weight
f) A person's age and number of days of sick-leave
g) A person's age and life insurance premium
h) High school average and college grade-point average

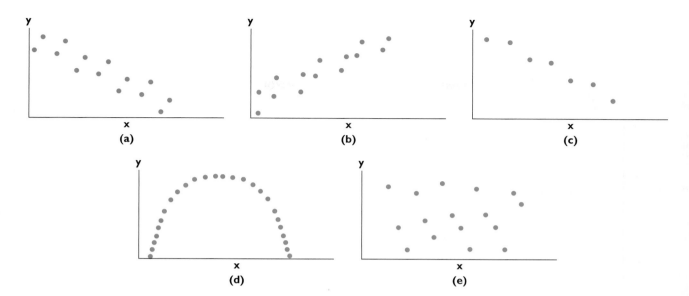

(a)   **(b)**   **(c)**

(d)   **(e)**

i) Amount of grams of fat consumed daily and cholesterol level

53. When the sample correlation coefficient is greater than zero, that is: r > 0, then there is a _____ linear correlation between the two variables. When the sample correlation coefficient is less than zero, that is: r < 0, then there is a _____ linear correlation between the two variables.

54. A negative value of r indicates:
a) No linear relationship
b) A weak linear relationship
c) A positive linear relationship
d) A negative linear relationship

55. For each of the scatter diagrams above, choose the statement that best describes the type of relationship that exists between the two variables.
1) strong linear correlation.
2) moderate or weak linear correlation.
3) no linear correlation.

56. Rank the following values of Pearson's correlation coefficient, r, from the strongest to weakest linear association.

$-0.95, 0.05, +1.00, 0.69, -0.69, 0, 0.50$

57. When testing the significance of the correlation coefficient, r, the null hypothesis, H_o, is always symbolized as:
a) $\rho > 0$
b) $\rho < 0$
c) $\rho = 0$
d) $\rho \neq 0$

58. When the test statistic, r, is significant, then the coefficient of determination is greater than 50%.
(T/F)

59. In a to f, there is a list of sample information, Pearson's correlation coefficient, type of test, and alpha level. For each part, use the information and Table V to determine r_α, and to test if r is significant.
a) $n = 18, r = 0.35, H_a: \rho \neq 0, \alpha = 1\%$
b) $n = 28, r = +0.47, H_a: \rho > 0, \alpha = 1\%$
c) $n = 30, r = -0.46, H_a: \rho < 0, \alpha = 1\%$
d) $df = 19, r = 0.58, H_a: \rho \neq 0, \alpha = 5\%$
e) $df = 25, r = -0.34, H_a: \rho < 0, \alpha = 5\%$
f) $df = 13, r = 0.40, H_a: \rho > 0, \alpha = 5\%$

60. A coefficient of determination of 0.5, means that there is a 50% chance that a linear relationship exists between variables x and y.
(T/F)

61. Linear regression can be used to predict a value for the dependent variable from a value of the independent variable.
(T/F)

62. A linear regression model produces a line that best fits the data pairs from a sample.
(T/F)

63. Matthew, a medical researcher, wants to determine if a positive linear relationship exists between the number of pounds a male is overweight and his blood pressure. He randomly selects a sample of 10 males and records the number of pounds that the individual is over his "ideal" weight according to a medical weight chart and his systolic blood pressure. Matthew's sample data is listed in the following table.

Male Subject	Number of Lbs Above Ideal Weight	Systolic Blood Pressure
1	12	150
2	8	142
3	20	165
4	17	152

Male Subject	Number of Lbs Above Ideal Weight	Systolic Blood Pressure
5	14	147
6	23	158
7	6	135
8	4	128
9	15	135
10	19	153

a) Construct a scatter diagram.
b) Calculate the sample correlation coefficient, r.
c) Determine if r is significant at $\alpha = 1\%$.
If r is significant at $\alpha = 1\%$, then do parts d,e,f.
d) Find r^2 and interpret its meaning.
e) Determine the regression equation, y'.
f) Using the regression equation, predict a male's systolic blood pressure if the individual is 10 pounds over his ideal weight.

64. A sports statistician wants to test whether there is a negative linear correlation between practice hours and golf score for the golf players who belong to the Arnie Palmer Country Club. She randomly selected ten golf players and determined the number of hours they practiced per week and their golf score on the Country Club Golf Course during the annual tournament. The sample results were:

Golf Score : 92 83 85 87 91 95 80 84 90 88
Practice Hrs.: 10 15 17 20   9 11 26 18 13 22

a) Construct a scatter diagram.
b) Calculate the sample correlation coefficient, r.
c) Determine if r is significant at $\alpha = 1\%$.
If r is significant at $\alpha = 1\%$, then do parts d,e,f.
d) Find r^2 and interpret its meaning.
e) Determine the regression equation, y'.
f) Using the regression equation, predict the golf score for a golfer who practices 17 hours per week.

WHAT DO YOU THINK?

65. Examine the following table which represents the correlations between the SAT (Scholastic Aptitude Test) scores and the GRE (Graduate Record Examination) scores for 22,923 subjects of a study entitled "The Differential Impact Of Curriculum On Aptitude Test Scores" which appeared in the *Journal of Educational Measurement* in 1990.

The population of interest for the study consisted of examinees who took the SAT and also the GRE General Test at the normal times in their academic careers, with the typical number of years intervening.

Intercorrelations Between SAT and GRE Scores for the Total Study Sample
n = 22,923

	SAT Verbal	SAT Mathe- matical	GRE Verbal	GRE Quanti- tative	GRE Analyt- ical	Mean	Standard Deviation
SAT Verbal	1.000	.628	.858	.547	.637	518.8	104.7
SAT Mathematical	.628	1.000	.598	.862	.734	556.0	110.2
GRE Verbal	.858	.598	1.000	.560	.649	510.1	107.7
GRE Quantitative	.547	.862	.560	1.000	.730	573.4	125.6
GRE Analytical	.637	.734	.649	.730	1.000	579.7	117.6

The SAT is a test administered by the College Board to college-bound high school students. The results are used by college undergraduate admission departments in making decisions regarding high school applicants. While the Graduate Record Examination (GRE), a College Board administered exam, is taken by college students preparing to apply for admission to graduate schools. The purpose of the study was to determine the correlation between the SAT and GRE scores of students who took these exams the normal times during their academic careers with the typical number of years between exams.

a) What type of correlation exists between the SAT Verbal and the GRE Verbal? Interpret this relationship? That is, in general, what would you expect to happen to the value of the GRE Verbal scores as the scores on the SAT Verbal increases? If a scatter diagram were constructed for the variables SAT Verbal and the GRE Verbal, what would you expect the general pattern to look like?

b) What proportion of the variance in the SAT Verbal scores can be accounted for by the variance in the GRE Verbal scores? What formula is used to determine this proportion, and what is this statistical measure called?

c) What does a value of 1.000 indicate about the relationship between SAT Verbal and SAT Verbal? What type of a relationship is this called?

d) For the SAT Verbal Column, what row variable, other than the SAT Verbal, has the strongest relationship with the SAT Verbal? Explain. Why do you believe might cause this to happen?

e) For the SAT Mathematical Column, what row variable, other than the SAT Mathematical, has the strongest relationship with the SAT Mathematical? Explain. What do you think might lead to this strong relationship?

f) What proportion of the variance in the SAT Mathematical scores can be accounted for by the variance in the GRE Analytical? What proportion of the variance in the SAT Mathematical scores can be accounted for by the variance in the GRE Quantitative? Explain what the difference in these two results mean?

g) The authors of the study state: "the correlations between SAT Verbal and GRE Verbal and between the SAT Mathematical and GRE Quantitative, both of which are 0.86, indicating that the linear relationship between SAT and GRE scores explains almost three fourths of the variance in GRE Verbal and GRE Quantitative scores taken four years later." Explain the meaning of this statement and how do you think the authors arrived at this three fourths value? What is an equivalent percentage value for this three fourths figure? What do the authors mean by "linear relationship"? Explain.

h) For the GRE Analytical Column, what row variable has the weakest relationship with the GRE Analytical? Explain. What do you think might lead to this weak relationship?

i) In words, describe the type of relationship and the strength of the relationship between the variables GRE Quantitative and SAT Mathematical.

j) Interpret the information that the mean and standard deviation indicate about the SAT and GRE test results. Which distribution of test scores has the greatest variability?

k) If the distribution of each of these test scores is approximately normal, then what is the median and modal test score for each test?

l) If the distribution of each of these test scores is approximately normal, then what percent of the SAT Mathematical scores are within 110.2 points of 556? within 220.4 points of 556? within 330.6 points of 556?

m) As the scores of the SAT Mathematical increase, what would you expect would happen to the scores on the variable GRE Quantitative? Explain.

---

66. A research article from the *Journal of Social and Behavior Personality* entitled "Effort and reward in college: A replication of some puzzling findings" presented the following intercorrelations table. The table represents the correlations between the overall grade point average (GPA) and predictor variables for students in three sections of an Introduction to Sociology class taught by the researcher.

Intercorrelations (r) among GPA and Predictor Variables for Three Sections of Introduction to Sociology

	(1)	(2)	(3)	(4)	(5)	(6)	(7)	(8)
GPA (1)	-	.45***	.65***	.72***	.70***	.00	.30**	−.39**
HSGPA (2)		-	.52***	.32***	.37***	.06	.16	−.01
SYNGRADE (3)			-	.86***	.81***	.02	.29*	−.50***
FINAL (4)				-	.83***	−.11	.31*	−.51***
EXAM1 (5)					-	−.13	.26*	−.37**
STUDYDAY (6)						-	.17	−.01
STUDYEND (7)							-	.00
ABSENCES (8)								-

*Abbreviations:
GPA = reported overall college Grade Point Average
HSGPA = reported High School Grade Point Average
SYNGRADE = semester grade in Sociology course
FINAL = score in comprehensive Final in Sociology
EXAM1 = score in first exam in Sociology
STUDYDAY = estimated average number of hours studied during weekdays
STUDYEND = estimated average number of hours studied on weekends
ABSENCES = actual number of absences in the Sociology course
Correlations involving SYNGRADE are based on $N = 58$; correlations involving FINAL on $N = 55$. All other correlations based on $N = 60$.
 * .05 level of significance; ** .01 level of significance; ** .001 level of significance.

Use this table to answer the following questions.

a) Which variable has the greatest significant correlation with the GPA variable? the smallest correlation? Interpret these results.

b) In words, describe the type and strength of the relationship between the variables number of absences in the Sociology course and semester grade in the course.

c) If a student has missed a large number of classes, then what might you predict about this student's performance on the comprehensive final exam in Sociology? Explain. What did you use to make this prediction?

d) If you performed a hypothesis test to determine if there exists a positive linear relationship between the grade on the first exam and the grade on the final exam at a significance level of 1%, then could you conclude that there existed a significant positive linear correlation? Explain.

e) If you performed a hypothesis test to determine if there exists a negative linear relationship between the grade on the first exam and the number of absences in the course at a significance level of 1%, then could you conclude that there existed a significant negative linear correlation? Explain.

f) If you performed a hypothesis test to determine if there exists a negative linear relationship between the grade point average and the number of absences in the course at a significance level of 5%, then can you reject the null hypothesis for this test? Explain.

g) Which variable is not a significant predictor of the other variables? How might you interpret this result?

h) If the p-value for the hypothesis test to determine if there exists a positive linear relationship between the grade on the first exam and grade point average is 0.020, then could you conclude that there existed a significant positive linear correlation? Explain.

i) If the p-value for the hypothesis test to determine if there exists a positive linear relationship between the semester grade for the Sociology course and grade point average is 0.002, then could you reject the null hypothesis for this test? Explain.

j) What proportion of the variance in the GPA can be accounted for by the variance in the scores on the comprehensive Sociology? What formula is used to determine this proportion, and what is this statistical measure called?

k) If a scatter diagram were constructed for the variables GPA and Absences, what would you expect the general pattern to look like? Explain.

l) If a scatter diagram were constructed for the variables GPA and EXAM1, what would you expect the general pattern to look like? Explain.

m) As GPA increases, what would you expect would to happen to the variable FINAL? Explain.

67. The following are excerpts from different studies.

1. In a study of 748 pregnant women, maternal birth weight was significantly related to baby's birth weight. The lower the maternal birth weight, the lower the baby's birth weight.

2. The College Board which administers the SAT's stated that there is a correlation between family income and test performance with low-income students not doing as well on the SAT's as students from high-income families.

3. A research finding indicated that tall children under age 8 tend to do better on intelligence tests than short children.

4. The results of a study support the notion that a child's drive is related to the age of the father. The higher the scores of a student, the younger the father. Older fathers were defined as those over age 30 at the time of their offspring's birth.

5. A researcher cites that time spent on homework is positively related to achievement.

a) For each excerpt state the variables within the study. Identify which variable is the independent and dependent variable.

b) Indicate the type of relationship that exists between the two variables.

c) If a scatter diagram were constructed for each of the variables, what would you expect the general pattern to look like? Explain.

PROJECTS

68. Randomly collect the heights to the nearest inch (x) and the weights to the nearest pound (y) of 20 students at your school.

a) Construct a scatter diagram.

b) Find r for your random sample.

c) What type of linear correlation, if any, do you observe?

d) Test $H_o: \rho = 0$, against $H_a: \rho > 0$ at $\alpha = 5\%$.

e) If the test is significant at $\alpha = 5\%$, determine the regression line model and plot it on your scatter diagram.

f) Estimate the weight of a student if his height is 74 inches.

g) Determine the percent of variance in weight that is accounted for by the variance in height.

69. Randomly select 25 students at your school and ask them the following questions:

I. How many hours per week do you work?

II. What is your most recent cumulative average?

With the data you obtain do the following: (let x represent the number of hours the student works per week)

a) Construct a scatter diagram.

b) Find r for your random sample.

c) What type of linear correlation, if any, do you observe?

d) Test $H_o: \rho = 0$, against $H_a: \rho \neq 0$ at $\alpha = 5\%$.

e) If the test is significant at $\alpha = 5\%$, determine the regression line model and plot it on your scatter diagram.

f) Estimate the cumulative average of a student who works 35 hours per week.

g) Determine the percent of variance in cumulative hours that is accounted for by the variance in hours worked.

70. Select two variables that you believe are related and randomly sample the selected population. Using your sample data follow the procedures set forth in projects 68 and 69 above.

>>>>>>>> **ANALYZING THE DATABASE USING TECHNOLOGY**

The following exercises refer to the file DATABASE listed in Appendix A. Using a technological tool, answer each exercise.

71. **a)** For the variables: AVE and GPA, identify the independent and the dependent variable.

b) Plot a scatter diagram for the variables AVE and GPA.

c) Calculate the correlation between AVE and GPA. Determine the strength of the correlation between the two variables. Identify the p-value and determine if the correlation coefficient is significant at $\alpha = 5\%$.

d) Determine the regression equation.

e) Calculate and interpret r^2.

72. For the variable names: SHT and PHT, identify the independent and the dependent variable.

b) Plot a scatter diagram for the variables SHT and PHT.

c) Calculate the correlation between SHT and PHT. Determine the strength of the correlation between the two variables. Identify the p-value and determine if the correlation coefficient is significant at $\alpha = 5\%$.

d) Determine the regression equation.

e) Calculate and interpret r^2.

>>>>>>>> **CHAPTER TEST**

73. Which type of linear correlation is indicated by a scatter diagram whose points are generally lower as you move from left to right?

a) Positive

b) None

c) Negative

74. If y increases as x increases this indicates that x and y are correlated:

a) Positively

b) Not at all

c) Negatively

75. If x and y are perfectly linearly correlated then r must equal:

a) 1

b) −1

c) 0

d) 1 or −1

76. A positive value of r indicates:

a) No linear relationship

b) A weak linear relationship

c) A positive linear relationship

d) A negative linear relationship

77. When the coefficient of determination is one, this means that there is a perfect positive linear correlation between the x and y variables.

(T/F)

78. When testing the significance of r the degrees of freedom is given by:

a) n   **b)** n − 2   **c)** n − 1   **d)** 2n

79. When testing the significance of the correlation coefficient, if there are ten pairs of data, $\alpha = 5\%$ and it's a 1TT, the $r_\alpha =$ _____.

a) 0.54   **b)** 0.83   **c)** 0.62   **d)** 0.71

80. MaryRose, a nutritionist, has conducted a study to determine the linear relationship between oat bran consumption and cholesterol level.

a) If MaryRose obtains a correlation coefficient of −0.56 from a random sample of 24 people, can she conclude that there is a negative linear correlation between the amount of oat bran consumed and cholesterol level at $\alpha = 1\%$?

b) What percent of the variability in cholesterol level can be accounted for by the variability in the amount of oat bran consumed?

81. I.M.Smart, a statistics nerd, wants to investigate if there is a positive linear relationship between the number of hours a student studies for a statistics exam and the student's test grade. He randomly samples 12 students that are taking statistics at a community college and records the sample data in the following table.

Student	Hours Studying for Exam	Test Grade
1	10	80
2	8	60
3	12	78
4	20	90
5	7	65
6	4	60
7	9	70
8	15	85
9	11	75
10	6	70
11	2	45
12	1	50

a) Construct a scatter diagram.
b) Calculate the sample correlation coefficient, r.
c) Determine if r is significant at $\alpha = 1\%$.
If r is significant at $\alpha = 1\%$, then do parts d,e,f.
d) Find r^2 and interpret its meaning.
e) Determine the regression equation, y'.
f) Using the regression equation, predict a student's statistics grade if the student spent 14 hours studying for the exam.

The F-Distribution and an Introduction to Analysis of Variance (ANOVA)

Contents

16.1 INTRODUCTION

We have studied various hypothesis testing procedures. Some of these procedures involved population proportions, while others involved population means. You should be aware that each application of an hypothesis testing procedure requires a specific model distribution whose *critical values* are obtained from a table listed in Appendix D. For example, when a hypothesis test involved two population means where the population standard deviations were unknown, the specific model distribution was called the sampling distribution of the difference between two means. Critical values for the distribution of the test statistic for this model were found using the *t* distribution table listed in Appendix D.

In this chapter we will present a new distribution called the *F-Distribution*. This distribution will be used to answer questions about variability or variance. Let's consider the following two examples. As you read through each example you will notice each one raises a different question. However, both questions will be answered by using the **same** distribution, that is, by using the F-Distribution.

■ EXAMPLE 16.1

In traveling to work Paulette likes to drive different routes on different days. One day she might drive through the side streets and back roads and the next day, she would ride on the highway. A sample of her travel times, measured in minutes, appears in Table 16.1.

TABLE 16.1   Paulette's Travel Times to Work During a Two Week Time Period

Back Roads	Highway
10	12
12	13
14	14
16	15
18	16
$\bar{x} = 14$	$\bar{x} = 14$
$s^2 = 8$	$s^2 = 2$

Notice that **both** *mean values are the same but the sample variances are* **different** (Remember that variance is a measure of variability and that the positive square root of the variance is the standard deviation). For these data, the variance for highway driving is **smaller** than the variance for back road driving. Can Paulette infer from these sample results that the population variances have a similar relationship?

To answer this question an *F-Test* can be used. However to use an F-Test, a distribution called the F-Distribution must be explored.

EXAMPLE 16.2

Jim is interested in buying a highly rated computer. He checks a PC magazine and selects three manufacturers. From these manufacturers he draws a sample of computers rated by the magazine. Table 16.2 displays the samples with their respective means and variances.

TABLE 16.2   Ratings of Computers From a PC Magazine

Computers	Compost	Dovell	ACE Power
	29.2	33.6	24.4
	21.4	44.4	42.0
	47.1	25.2	25.2
	34.0	33.6	34.9
	37.1	46.4	52.9
$\bar{x}$	33.76	36.64	35.88
s^2	90.63	76.21	143.52

Jim would like to determine which manufacturer has a **significantly** higher mean rating. Notice that this question is similar to those posed when using an hypothesis testing procedure like a t-test. However the t-test was only used with hypotheses involving one population mean or at most two population means. In this instance we are comparing three population means. To answer this question we would use a procedure called *Analysis of Variance* or to use the acronym, *ANOVA*. As in Example 16.1 the ANOVA procedure also makes use of the F-Distribution. Thus, in order for us to answer the questions posed in Examples 16.1 and 16.2, we must first explore the F-Distribution.

16.2   F-DISTRIBUTION

When we studied the differences of two population means we used the t-test for independent samples and assumed the means were calculated from data randomly selected from two distinct approximately normal populations. We also assumed that **the populations had equal variances** and consequently equal standard deviations. However, at the time we did not have the tools to test the assumption of equal population variances. The F-Distribution and its corresponding F-Test, can be used to test if two population variances are equal. Let us first consider the F-Distribution.

> **DEFINITION 16.1**
>
> **F-Distribution.** The F-Distribution is a family of distributions composed of the ratio of the variances for samples drawn from two distinct normal populations with equal variances. This is illustrated in Figure 16.1.

To form an F-Distribution, we theoretically select independent random samples from two normal populations having equal variances, one from population one and one from population two. For each

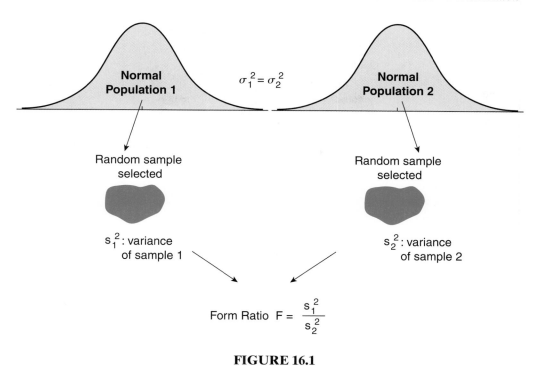

FIGURE 16.1

random sample, the sample variance is computed. The ratio (fraction) of each pair of sample variances is formed. Each ratio is called an F-ratio.

Formula to Compute an F-ratio, Denoted by F

$$F = \frac{s_1^2}{s_2^2}$$

where s_1^2 represents a sample variance for a random sample of size n_1 selected from population one,

and

      s_2^2 represents a sample variance for a random sample of size n_2 selected from population two.

If this process is continued for all possible random sample pairs the resulting distribution of ratios is called an F-Distribution. This is shown in Figure 16.2.

To illustrate the creation of the F-Distribution further consider Table 16.3. The three samples displayed in Table 16.3 were randomly selected from two populations, identified as population one and population two, having equal population variances of 2.87 . Within Table 16.3, the sample variances of each sample are given along with the corresponding F-ratio

$$F = \frac{s_1^2}{s_2^2} \quad .$$

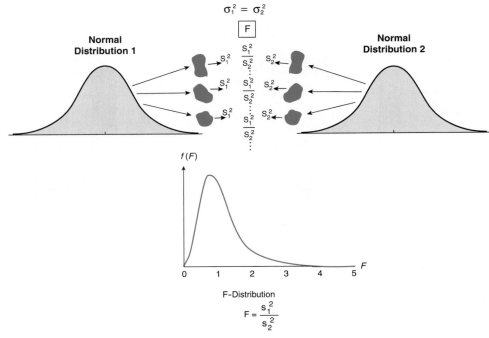

FIGURE 16.2

The three F-ratios represent just three possible F-statistics that might appear in a F-Distribution. Although the random samples in this illustration each contain ten data values, in general the random samples need not contain ten data values, nor do they need to be of equal size.

TABLE 16.3   SAMPLES DRAWN FROM TWO POPULATIONS WITH EQUAL VARIANCES: $\sigma_1^2 = \sigma_2^2$

	Population 1 $\sigma_1^2 = 2.87$	Population 2 $\sigma_2^2 = 2.87$
1st Sample	7	14
n = 10	8	16
	5	10
	1	11
	4	17
	7	11
	6	17
	8	12
	8	11
	3	15
Sample Variances	$s_1^2 = 5.76$	$s_2^2 = 7.38$
F-ratio	$F = \dfrac{s_1^2}{s_2^2} = \dfrac{5.76}{7.38} \approx 0.78$	
2nd Sample	8	13
n = 10	3	15
	1	15
	3	10
	5	16

TABLE 16.3   (*continued*)

	Population 1 $\sigma_1^2 = 2.87$	Population 2 $\sigma_2^2 = 2.87$
	7	19
	4	16
	9	16
	2	19
	5	10

Sample Variances $\qquad\qquad s_1^2 = 6.90 \qquad\qquad\qquad s_2^2 = 9.88$

F-ratio $\qquad\qquad\qquad F = \dfrac{s_1^2}{s_2^2} \quad = \quad \dfrac{6.90}{9.88} \quad \approx \quad 0.70$

3rd Sample n=10	4	19
	3	14
	0	13
	9	13
	3	16
	4	16
	2	13
	4	18
	9	10
	8	11

Sample Variances $\qquad\qquad s_1^2 = 9.38 \qquad\qquad\qquad s_2^2 = 8.46$

F-ratio $\qquad\qquad\qquad F = \dfrac{s_1^2}{s_2^2} \quad = \quad \dfrac{9.38}{8.46} \quad \approx \quad 1.11$

By examining the F-ratios in Table 16.3 you should notice that each are positive and *close to the value one.* In fact, all F-ratios are non-negative since they are composed of variances which are always non-negative. **In this illustration the F-ratios of the sample variances were near one because the population variances were equal.** In fact, the ratio of the population variances is equal to one. Since the sample variances are approximations of the population variances the ratio of the sample variances should also be near one. Thus, if a sampling distribution of all possible F-ratios of sample variances where the population variances are equal were constructed, we might expect the mean value of the F-ratios to be 1.

Let's examine the possible values of the F-ratios if the population variances are not equal. In Table 16.4 the samples displayed are drawn from two populations with *unequal* population variances. Notice that population 1 has a variance of 32.94 while the second population has a variance of 8.24.

TABLE 16.4   SAMPLES DRAWN FROM POPULATIONS WITH UNEQUAL POPULATION VARIANCES $\sigma_1^2 \neq \sigma_2^2$

	Population 1 $\sigma_1^2 = 32.94$	Population 2 $\sigma_2^2 = 8.24$
1st Sample n=10	8	7
	12	8
	0	5
	2	1
	14	4
	2	7
	14	6
	4	8

(*continues*)

TABLE 16.4   (continued)

	Population 1 $\sigma_1^2 = 32.94$	Population 2 $\sigma_2^2 = 8.24$
n=10	2	8
	10	3
Sample Variances	$s_1^2 = 29.16$	$s_2^2 = 5.76$
F-ratio	$F = \dfrac{s_1^2}{s_2^2} \quad = \quad \dfrac{29.16}{5.76} \quad \approx \quad 6.06$	
2nd Sample	6	8
n = 10	10	3
	10	1
	0	3
	12	5
	18	7
	12	4
	12	9
	18	2
	0	5
Sample Variances	$s_1^2 = 39.51$	$s_2^2 = 6.90$
F-ratio	$F = \dfrac{s_1^2}{s_2^2} \quad = \quad \dfrac{39.51}{6.90} \quad \approx \quad 5.73$	
3rd Sample	18	4
n = 10	8	3
	6	0
	6	9
	12	3
	12	4
	6	2
	16	4
	0	9
	2	8
Sample Variances	$s_1^2 = 33.83$	$s_2^2 = 9.38$
F-ratio	$F = \dfrac{s_1^2}{s_2^2} \quad = \quad \dfrac{33.83}{9.38} \quad \approx \quad 3.61$	

By examining the F-ratios in Table 16.4 you should notice that they are all larger than one and in fact, they are larger than any F-ratio in Table 16.3. Since the variance of population 1 is larger than the variance of population 2, the ratio of the population variances is:

$\sigma_1^2 / \sigma_2^2 = 32.94/8.24 = 4$, which is greater than one.

Since the sample variances approximate their respective population variances, we would expect the F-ratios of the sample variances in Table 16.4 to be approximately 4.

Now let us consider the effects of *sample size on the value of the sample variances.* When we use relatively small sample sizes we are not selecting many data values from the population. Thus extreme data values selected within a small sample can cause their sample variances to vary greatly. However, if we selected larger sample sizes extreme data values would not affect the sample variances as much, and, thus the sample variances would vary less. Consequently, the F-ratios attained from smaller sample sizes would vary more than those F-ratios computed from larger sample sizes. **Hence the shape of the resulting F-Distribution would change relative to the *sizes* of the samples drawn.** Thus the F-Distribution *is a family of curves,* similar to the concept of family of curves for the *t*-distribution or the chi-square distribution. As you recall with the *t*-distribution we used the degrees of freedom associated with the sample size to determine the appropriate critical *t* value(s). In a similar way, to determine the appropriate F-Distribution curve, the degrees of freedom, *df*, for *each* sample is used. The degrees of freedom associated with the sample sizes are placed in parenthesis (***df for sample variance one in the numerator, df for sample variance two in the denominator***). This is written as $F(dfs^2_1, dfs^2_2)$. The first number in the parenthesis represents the degrees of freedom for sample variance one of the **numerator.** It is calculated using $df = n_1 - 1$. The **second** number in the parenthesis represents the degrees of freedom for the sample variance used in the **denominator** of the F-ratio. The degrees of freedom for this sample is $df = n_2 - 1$. Figure 16.3 displays the F-Distribution curve for different size samples.

The F-Distribution Family of Curves for Different Degrees of Freedom, *df*

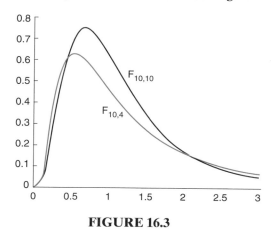

FIGURE 16.3

The family of F-Distribution curves is based on two basic assumptions.

Assumptions of the F-Distribution

1. The two populations from which the samples are drawn must be independent.
2. The two populations from which the samples are selected are normally distributed and have equal variances.

The first assumption implies that the data values in one population must not depend in any way on the data values in the second population. The second assumption indicates that the two populations must be normal distributions. This last assumption is **critical** to the F-Distribution. If the original populations are not normal other statistical models would have to be used instead of the F-Distribution. Let's examine the main characteristics of a F-Distribution.

Characteristics of the F-Distribution

1. The F-Distribution is composed of statistics called F-ratios formed from the sample variances calculated from two independent and random samples selected from two normal populations having equal variances. Each F-statistic is determined by the formula:

(continues)

Characteristics of the F-Distribution (*continued*)

$$F - statistic = \frac{s_1^2}{s_2^2}$$

where s_1^2 represents a sample variance for a random sample of size n_1 selected from population one,

and s_2^2 represents a sample variance for a random sample of size n_2 selected from population two.

2. The F-Distribution is a family of curves dependent upon the degrees of freedom values of the sample variances associated with an F-ratio. Each pair of degrees of freedom for the F-Distribution is determined by the degrees of freedom of the variance in the numerator and the degrees of freedom of the variance in the denominator.

3. The F-Distribution is skewed to the right. As the degrees of freedom increases, the F-Distribution approaches the shape of a normal distribution.

4. The peak or modal value of the F-Distribution is about 1. Thus, values *far* from 1 in either direction provide evidence *against* a hypothesis of equal population standard deviations.

The F-Distribution is a probability distribution. Therefore, the probability that a given F-statistic will be above a certain critical F-value can be computed. Statisticians have constructed tables representing critical F-values. In Appendix D: Table VII you will find such a table. Table VII is called *Critical Values of the F-Distribution*. The critical values of the F-Distribution table is set up to give values of F which must be **exceeded** at a given level of significance, α, **to provide the evidence that the population standard deviations are not equal.** To determine the critical F-value, denoted $F_\alpha(dfs_1^2, dfs_2^2)$, you must calculate the degrees of freedom for the sample variance (dfs_1^2) of the numerator and degrees of freedom of the sample variance of the denominator (dfs_2^2) for the F-statistic.

Let's discuss how to use **Appendix D: Table VII Critical Values of the F-Distribution** to find a critical F-value.

EXAMPLE 16.3

Find the critical F-value if $dfs_1^2 = 8$, $dfs_2^2 = 10$ and $\alpha = 0.05$.

Solution

A portion of Table VII Critical Values of the F-Distribution found in Appendix D is shown in Table 16.5. You should notice that to use the F-Distribution table you must identify the degrees of freedom for the numerator, the degrees of freedom for the denominator and the level of significance.

TABLE 16.5   Critical Values of F-Distribution F_α (dfs_1^2, dfs_2^2)

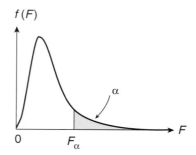

TABLE 16.5   *(continued)*

s_2^2 \\ s_1^2	Numerator Degrees of Freedom								
	1	2	3	4	5	6	7	8	9
1	161.4	199.5	215.7	224.6	230.2	234.0	236.8	**238.9**	240.5
2	18.51	19.00	19.16	19.25	19.30	19.33	19.35	**19.37**	19.38
3	10.13	9.55	9.28	9.12	9.01	8.94	8.89	**8.85**	8.81
4	7.71	6.94	6.59	6.39	6.26	6.16	6.09	**6.04**	6.00
5	6.61	5.79	5.41	5.19	5.05	4.95	4.88	**4.82**	4.77
6	5.99	5.14	4.76	4.53	4.39	4.28	4.21	**4.15**	4.10
7	5.59	4.74	4.35	4.12	3.97	3.87	3.79	**3.73**	3.68
8	5.32	4.46	4.07	3.84	3.69	3.58	3.50	**3.44**	3.39
9	5.12	4.26	3.86	3.63	3.48	3.37	3.29	**3.23**	3.18
10	**4.96**	**4.10**	**3.71**	**3.48**	**3.33**	**3.22**	**3.14**	3.07	3.02
11	4.84	3.98	3.59	3.36	3.20	3.09	3.01	2.95	2.90
12	4.75	3.89	3.49	3.26	3.11	3.00	2.91	2.85	2.80
13	4.67	3.81	3.41	3.18	3.03	2.92	2.83	2.77	2.71

(left axis label: **Denominator Degrees of Freedom**)

Since the $dfs_1^2 = 8$ represents the degrees of freedom for the numerator, $dfs_2^2 = 10$ represents the degrees of freedom for the denominator, and the level of significance, $\alpha = 0.05$, the critical F-value, $F_\alpha(dfs_1^2, dfs_2^2)$, expressed as $F_{0.05}(8,10)$ has a table value of 3.07. This is highlighted in Table 16.5 and is denoted as

$$F_{0.05}(8,10) = 3.07$$

16.3   TESTING VARIANCES: THE F-TEST

In the previous section, we discussed the F-Distribution and mentioned one of its uses is to test for the equality of variances from two independent and **normal** populations having equal variances. Now we will present the procedure to perform this test for equality.

In the chapter introduction we proposed the following example:

In traveling to work Paulette likes to drive different routes on different days. One day she might drive through the side streets and back roads and the next day, she would ride on the highway. A sample of her travel times, measured in minutes, are shown in Table 16.6.

TABLE 16.6   **Paulette's Travel Times to Work During a Two Week Time Period**

Back Roads	Highway
10	12
12	13
14	14
16	15
18	16
$\bar{x} = 14$	$\bar{x} = 14$
$s^2 = 8$	$s^2 = 2$

Can we conclude that there is a significant difference in the population variances for the given sample results?

To answer this question we can *compare* the sample variances by forming a ratio of the **larger** sample variance to the **smaller** sample variance. This ratio is called an F-statistic and is expressed as:

$$\textbf{F-Statistic} = \frac{Larger\ Variance}{Smaller\ Variance} = \frac{8}{2} = 4$$

Since the larger sample variance has been substituted in the numerator of the F ratio we would expect the F-statistic value to be greater than one. The question is whether this F-statistic is *significantly* greater than one. If we can conclude that the F-statistic is significantly greater than one then we can infer that the population variances from which the samples were randomly selected are *different*. The question to be answered lends itself to an analysis for which our *five step hypothesis testing procedure* can be applied. The hypothesis testing procedure summarized below explains how the procedure can be applied to this problem. This application is called the *F-Test*.

F-Test: Hypothesis Testing Procedure to Test if Population Variances are Different

Step 1   *Formulate the two hypotheses, H_0 and H_a.*
The Null Hypothesis, H_0, in testing the difference between two population variances has the following form:

Null Hypothesis Form

H_0: *The variance of population 1, written σ_1^2, and the variance of population 2, written σ_2^2 are equal.*

In symbols:

$$\textbf{H}_0\textbf{:}\ \sigma_1^2 = \sigma_2^2$$

The Alternative Hypothesis, H_a, for the F-test has the following form:

Alternative Hypothesis Form

H_a: *The variance of population 1, written σ_1^2, and the variance of population 2, written σ_2^2, are **not** equal.*

This is symbolized:

$$\textbf{H}_a\textbf{:}\ \sigma_1^2 \neq \sigma_2^2$$

Step 2   *Determine the model to test the null hypothesis, H_0.*
The appropriate sampling distribution is the F-Distribution. Assuming the null hypothesis of equality of population variances is true, the F-ratio equals one.

Step 3   *Formulate the Decision Rule.*
Since the form of the alternative hypothesis is nondirectional, to test the calculated F-statistic we would need an F-Distribution Table that contains two critical F-values, a left and right critical value. This is illustrated in Figure 16.4.

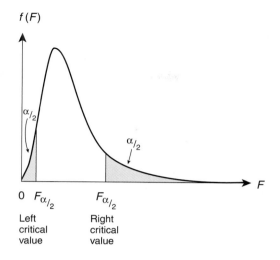

FIGURE 16.4

We can simplify the F-Distribution table by calculating the F-statistic, also known as the *test statistic,* by always placing the **larger sample variance in the numerator.** *This procedure will insure that the F-test statistic is always greater than or equal to one. Consequently we will only need the right hand side of the F-Distribution which contains the critical F-value. This is shown in Figure 16.5.*

Thus the computed F-test statistic will be significant when its value is **greater** than the critical F-value. Thus, if the computed F-test statistic is greater than the critical F-value, $F_{\alpha/2}$ of Table VII, we will **reject** the null hypothesis, H_0, and accept the alternative hypothesis, H_a.

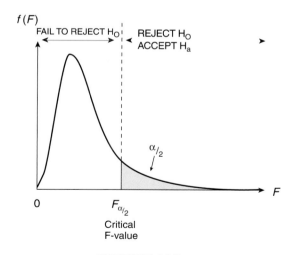

FIGURE 16.5

In order to complete the analysis, an alpha level, α, must be chosen. But since we have eliminated the need for critical F-values less than one, to use the F-Distribution Table VII in Appendix D, look up the critical F-value using the chosen alpha level divided by 2.

For this example, $\alpha = 0.05$, thus $\alpha/2 = 0.05/2$ or 0.025. To determine if the F-statistic is significantly greater than one, we use the F-Table located in Appendix D: Table VII. Remember to use the F-Table we must first find the degrees of freedom for the two sample variances. Table 16.7 contains a summary of the sample variances, the sample sizes and the corresponding degrees of freedom for the sample data values given in Table 16.6.

TABLE 16.7   Summary Table to compute the F-statistic

	Numerator of F-Statistic *Larger s²*	Denominator of F-Statistic *Smaller s²*
Sample variance, s²	8	2
Sample size, n	5	5
Degrees of freedom, *df = n – 1*	4	4

Thus we are using a F-Distribution with (4,4) degrees of freedom where $\alpha/2 = 0.025$. Therefore, the critical F-value from Table VII is:

$$F_{\alpha/2}(dfs_1{}^2, dfs_2{}^2) = F_{0.025}(4,4) = 9.60.$$

The decision rule is: Reject H_o, if the F-statistic is greater than 9.60.

Step 4   *Analyze the sample data.*
Calculate the **F-Statistic** using the test statistic formula:

$$F = \frac{\text{larger } s^2}{\text{smaller } s^2}$$

The F-Statistic is also referred to as the **test statistic.**
Using sample variances in Table 16.7, the calculated F-Statistic is

$$F = \frac{8}{2}$$

$$F = 4$$

Step 5   *State the conclusion.*
In Figure 16.6 the calculated F-statistic (F = 4) and the critical F-value (9.60) are indicated on the graph. Since the test statistic is **not** greater than the critical F-value, we fail to reject the null hypothesis, H_0. Thus, although there is a difference in the sample variances, the difference is not statistically significant at an alpha level of 0.05.

Therefore, Paulette can be assured, based on the results of this hypothesis test, the two routes to work are approximately equal in their variability of travel times. _____ ■

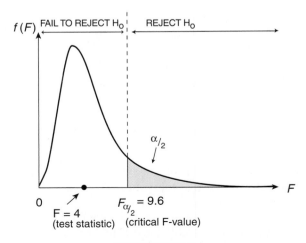

FIGURE 16.6

Let's now summarize the F-Test used to test the equality of two population variances.

A Summary of the F-Test:
A hypothesis test to compare variances from two NORMAL populations

---

Step 1   Formulate the two hypotheses, H_0 and H_a.

H_0: The variance of population 1, written σ_1^2, and the variance of population 2, written σ_2^2 are equal.

$$H_0: \sigma_1^2 = \sigma_2^2$$

H_a: The variance of population 1, written σ_1^2, and the variance of population 2, written σ_2^2 are **not** equal.

$$H_a: \sigma_1^2 \neq \sigma_2^2$$

Step 2   Determine the model to test the null hypothesis, H_0.
The appropriate sampling distribution is the F-Distribution. Assuming the null hypothesis of equality of population variances is true, the F-ratio equals one.

Step 3   Formulate the Decision Rule.
a) Choose a significance level, α, and divide by 2: $\alpha/2$.
b) Determine the degrees of freedom for the larger sample variance, and the degrees of freedom for the smaller sample variance. Look up in Appendix D: Table VII, the critical F-value using the notation:

$$F_{\alpha/2}(dfs_1^2, dfs_2^2)$$

where s_1^2 represents the **larger** sample variance for a random sample of size n_1 selected from population one,

and s_2^2 represents the **smaller** sample variance for a random sample of size n_2 selected from population two.
c) State the decision rule.

Step 4   Analyze the sample data.
Calculate the F-statistic using the test statistic formula:

$$F = \frac{larger\ s^2}{smaller\ s^2}$$

Step 5   State the conclusion.
If the test statistic, F, is greater than the critical F-value, symbolized $F_{\alpha/2}$ (dfs_1^2, dfs_2^2), then the population variances are significantly different at the significance level, α. Otherwise, the population variances are not significantly different at the level of significance, α. This is shown in Figure 16.7.

EXAMPLE 16.4

(a)   Compute an F-statistic for the following sample variances.

$$s_1^2 = 14 \qquad s_2^2 = 4$$
$$n_1 = 10 \qquad n_2 = 11$$

(b)   Conduct an F-Test for the equality of the population variances using $\alpha = 0.10$.

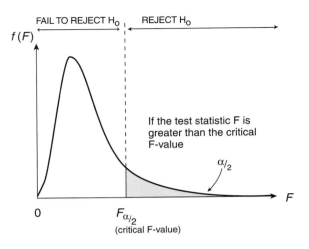

FIGURE 16.7

Solution

(a) To compute an F-statistic use the test statistic formula

$$F = \frac{larger\ s^2}{smaller\ s^2}$$

Since the larger of the two sample variances is $s_1^2 = 14$, and the smaller is $s_2^2 = 4$, then the F- statistic is

$$F = \frac{14}{4} = 3.5$$

(b) To conduct a hypothesis test for the equality of the population variances, we will follow the F-Test procedure.

Step 1 *Formulate the two hypotheses, H_0 and H_a.*
H_0: The population variances are equal.
This is symbolized as:

$$H_o{:}\sigma_1^2 = \sigma_2^2$$

and
H_a: The population variances are not equal.
This is symbolized as:

$$H_a{:}\sigma_1^2 \neq {}_2^2$$

Step 2 *Determine the model to test the null hypothesis, H_0.*
Since the sample size of the larger sample variance is $n_1 = 10$ and the sample size of the smaller sample variance is $n_2 = 11$ the F-Distribution with degrees of freedom $df = (9,10)$ will be used as the hypothesis testing model. The F-Distribution model is shown in Figure 16.8.

Step 3 *Formulate the Decision Rule.*
a) This F-Test is to be conducted using an $\alpha = 0.10$ therefore, $\alpha/2 = 0.1/2 = 0.05$.
b) The degrees of freedom for the larger sample variance is $dfs_1^2 = 10 - 1 = 9$, and for the smaller sample variance is $dfs_2^2 = 11 - 1 = 10$.

FAIL TO REJECT H$_0$ REJECT H$_0$

$F_{\alpha/2} = 3.02$
(critical F-value) $F = 3.5$ (test statistic)

FIGURE 16.8

Using Table VII, the critical F-value is

$$F_{\alpha/2}(dfs_1{}^2, dfs_2{}^2) = F_{0.05}(9,10)$$

$$F_{0.05}(9,10) = 3.02$$

c) The decision rule is: Reject H$_0$ if the test statistic F is greater than 3.02.

Step 4 *Analyze the sample data.*
The test statistic is, F = 3.5. (see part a.)

Step 5 *State the conclusion.*
Since the test statistic, F = 3.5, is greater than the critical F-value, $F_{0.05}(9,10) = 3.02$, reject the null hypothesis and accept the alternative hypothesis. Thus, the population variances are significantly different at $\alpha = 0.10$.

16.4 TYPES OF VARIANCES

In this chapter, we have discussed the concept of variance. In the previous two sections, population and sample variances were revisited and an application to inferential statistics was presented. That is, sample variances were used to make inferences about population variances. Let us now consider variance in a different manner.

The hypothesis testing procedure is used to analyze an experiment that is designed and conducted around a test of a null hypothesis. The experiment is set up so that by rejecting the null hypothesis at a given significance level, an alternative hypothesis is accepted. Various applications to population parameters have been explored. For example, we have tested hypotheses about one or two population proportions. And, we have tested hypotheses about one or two population means.

This section is concerned with a hypothesis testing procedure designed to compare **more than two** population means. Its application is used to analyze many problems. For example, let's consider the following problems:

1. Which of the life saving *procedures* will produce the longest life expectancy in someone who is deathly ill with the xyz virus: *drug therapy, a surgical procedure,* or *laser therapy*?
2. Which *method* of instruction will increase the achievement levels of students: *directed method, undirected method* or a *combination of both?*

In each of these problems there is a need to find the best alternative among those given. Many times the "best" (i.e. best method or procedure) is measured by using the mean, such as mean life expectancy, or mean achievement level.

As we have seen in the other hypothesis testing procedures, besides a comparison of means we also must account for the differences in variability. We have done this by examining standard deviations as a measure of variability. In the application to compare many population means we will use variance as a measure of variability.

Let's examine the problem about the effect of various medical procedures on life expectancy. The variable being measured is the length of life. Each individual (subject) in the experiment will live a number of years. Besides being able to calculate a *mean* lifetime, a *variation* of lifetime among the **total** participants in the experiment can be calculated. Also, **within** each treatment, not every person will live the same number of years. Thus there is a mean lifetime as well as variability in length of life when considering those people within each medical treatment. Finally, if we look at the mean number of years people live under one medical treatment in comparison to people within each of the other medical treatments, we will notice differences in those mean times as well as the variability **between** the means of each treatment group.

This first example illustrates the different ways means and variability can be examined when performing an experiment. What are the causes for the differences in variability and how we can explain them is a major objective of the **analysis of variance**. The analysis of the variability has been used extensively in many research scenarios. First there is the variability *within each of the treatment* procedures: drug therapy, surgical procedures and laser therapy. Everyone given the *same* treatment will *not* live the same number of years. This variance is referred to as **Within Group Variance.** Second, there is variability in length of life *among all the participants regardless* of which treatment procedure they were given. This variance is referred to as **Total Variance.** Finally, there is variability *between* the mean length of life among *the three treatment groups*. This variability is referred to as **Between Group Variance.**

> **DEFINITION 16.2**
> **Within Group Variance.** The variance due to the differences among the individual data values within each group is called Within Group Variance.

This concept of within group variance is examined in Table 16.8.

TABLE 16.8   No Within Group Variance

Groups:	I	II	III
	30	45	60
	30	45	60
	30	45	60
	30	45	60
	30	45	60
Means:	30	45	60

Examining Table 16.8, you will notice that there is **no Within Group Variance** since every data value within each group is the same. However, there is variation among the groups since the means are different. This variation among the groups is called **Between Group Variance.**

DEFINITION 16.3

Between Group Variance. The variance due to the differences among the groups or the differences among the sample means is called Between Group Variance.

The concept of between group variance is examined in Table 16.9.

TABLE 16.9   No Between Group Variance

Groups:	I	I	III
	32	25	30
	40	35	43
	48	45	49
	50	55	47
	55	65	56
Means:	45	45	45

Examining Table 16.9, you will notice that there is **no Between Group Variance** since the mean of each group is the *same.* However, there *is* variation *within* each group since the data values within each group are *not* the same.

In the second example regarding *method of instruction* and *achievement* we would notice the **same** breakdown of variances. The students who receive only one method of instruction or treatment will still have some variability in their achievement scores. This variance is the **Within Group Variance.** Since within group variance is oftentimes due to *individual differences* among subjects that is not explainable, the **Within Group Variance** is also called **error variance**.

There will be variability in achievement scores regardless of how the students are assigned into their treatment subgroups. This variance is the **Total Variance.**

Finally there will be differences in the variability of the mean achievement scores of the groups, that is, there will be differences in the variability of the mean achievement scores of those students given the **Within Group Variance** directed method versus those given the non-directed method versus those given the combined method. This variance is the **Between Group Variance.** In most experiments the experimenter is interested in the effects of different methods of treatment or the effects of different methods of instruction. Thus, the **Between Group Variance is also referred to as Experimental or Treatment Variance.**

This breakdown of variance into Within Group Variance, Total Variance and Between Group Variance can be discussed in terms of the population variance or the sample variances. When the population variance is broken down by the three variances then the following relationship holds:

Total Variance = Between Group Variance + Within Group Variance

Pictorially we can represent the relationship with the following circle (see Figure 16.9). The total circle is the total population variance. The two subdivisions are the Between Group Variance and the Within Group Variance.

To illustrate the relationship in Figure 16.9 assume we have a **total population** of 15 students and their scores on an achievement test. The 15 students were subdivided into three groups, called treatment 1, treatment 2, and treatment 3. The achievement scores of the students, the means and standard deviations of the scores within each treatment group are displayed in Table 16.10.

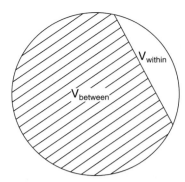

Variance Total = Variance between + Variance within
Vtotal = Vbetween + Vwithin

FIGURE 16.9

TABLE 16.10   Achievement Scores of a Population of 15 Students Subdivided into Three Groups

	Treatment 1	Treatment 2	Treatment 3
	10	28	10
	20	29	29
	30	30	30
	40	31	31
	50	32	50
Population means μ	30	30	30
Population variances **Within** each treatment σ^2	200	2	160.4

You should notice that the means for each treatment is the same, whereas each of the population variances are different. You could interpret this to indicate that although three different treatments have been administered, the effects due to the treatments were equal. However since the variability in each treatment group is different you could attribute this effect to the differences among individual subjects. Let's examine the different types of variability that are displayed in the example.

Given the population variances within each group the *average within variance* can be found by **pooling** the three population variances. Pooling the three population variances is accomplished by summing the three population variances within each treatment and dividing by three:

$$\text{Sum of the population variances} = 200 + 2 + 160.4 = 362.4$$

Dividing by the sum by three

$$362.4/3 = 120.8$$

yields

$$\text{Within Variance} = 120.8$$

Thus, the Within Group variance, or simply the variance due to differences among the individuals is 120.8

We can compute the *Between Group Variance* by using the population variance formula with the values of the group means: 30, 30, and 30. Since there is no variability between the group means, the Between Group Variance is zero.

$$\text{Between Group Variance} = 0$$

Thus, the Between Group Variance, or simply the variance due to the treatment (i.e. the experiment) is 0.

Finally to compute the *Total Variance* regardless of how the students are grouped we use the population variance formula for all 15 achievement scores. Performing that task we find the

$$\text{Total Variance to be } 120.8$$

(To get a greater appreciation of this result, it might be helpful to actually calculate the Total Variance of the data in Table 16.10.)

Thus,

	Between Variance	+	Within Variance	=	Total Variance
	0	+	120.8	=	120.8

In the above example the **means of the treatment were all equal** and thus the Total Variance was determined **solely** by the Within Variance. You might ask:

Can the same relationship be demonstrated when the means are *not equal,* and, as a result, the Between Group Variance would *not* be equal to zero? Let's examine this question in Example 16.5.

EXAMPLE 16.5

Consider the data in Table 16.11.

TABLE 16.11   Achievement Scores of a Population of 21 Students Subdivided into Three Groups

	Treatment 1	Treatment 2	Treatment 3
	10	17	24
	11	18	25
	12	19	26
	13	20	27
	14	21	28
	15	22	29
	16	23	30
Population means			
μ	13	20	27
Population variances **Within** each treatment			
σ^2	4	4	4

a)   Using the within group variance for each group calculate the pooled Within Variance.
b)   Compute the Between Group Variance using the population variance formula on the group means.
c)   Calculate the Total Group Variance for all 21 data values in Table 16.11.
d)   Verify the relationship

$$\text{Between Variance} + \text{Within Variance} = \text{Total Variance}$$

Solution

a) Given the Within Variances for each group the pooled Within Variance can be found by summing the three variances and dividing by three:

$$4 + 4 + 4 = 12$$

$$12/3 = 4$$

Within Variance = 4

b) To compute the Between Group Variance we use the population variance formula for the values of the group means : 13, 20, 27.
First, the mean of the group means is

$$\mu = \frac{\Sigma X}{N} = \frac{13 + 20 + 27}{3} = 20$$

Second, compute the population variance using the formula:

$$\sigma^2 = \frac{\Sigma(X - \mu)^2}{N} \quad ,$$

to obtain the Between Group Variance.
Table 16.12 summarizes the relevant data necessary for the calculation of the Between Group Variance.

TABLE 16.12   Between Group Variance

	X	$X - \mu$	$(X - \mu)^2$
	13	−7	49
	20	0	0
	27	7	49
Σ	60	0	98

Substituting $\Sigma (X - \mu)^2 = 98$ and N = 3 into the formula for the population variance

$$\sigma^2 = \frac{\Sigma(X - \mu)^2}{N}$$

$$\sigma^2 = \frac{98}{3}$$

$$\sigma^2 \approx 32.67$$

Thus, the Between Group Variance ≈ 32.67.

c) Finally to compute the Total Variance regardless of how the students are grouped we use the population variance formula for all 21 achievement scores. Performing this task we find the

Total Group Variance = 36.67

Table 16.13 summarizes the relevant data necessary for the calculation of the Total Group Variance. For these data the Total Group Mean = 20.

TABLE 16.13 Total Group Variance
All Achievement Scores for a Population of 21 Students

X	$X - \mu$	$(X - \mu)^2$
10	−10	100
11	−9	81
12	−8	64
13	−7	49
14	−6	36
15	−5	25
16	−4	16
17	−3	9
18	−2	4
19	−1	1
20	0	0
21	1	1
22	2	4
23	3	9
24	4	16
25	5	25
26	6	36
27	7	49
28	8	64
29	9	81
30	10	100
Σ 420	0	9170

Substituting $\Sigma(X - \mu) = 9170$ and N = 21 into the formula for the population variance

$$\sigma^2 = \frac{\Sigma(X - \mu)^2}{N}$$

$$\sigma^2 = \frac{9170}{21}$$

$$\sigma^2 = 36.67$$

d) Since the values of the Between Variance, Within Variance and Total Variance have been computed, the relationship

Between Variance + Within Variance = Total Variance
32.67   +   4   =   36.67

is verified.

Most of the time when performing statistical experiments we do not have the population data values available. That is, we only have sample data to use. And, as a result, we are unable to use population parameters, such as μ and σ. Thus, statistics are computed using other formulas, and the values obtained by these statistics are used for inferential conclusions about the parameters.

As you recall, the sample variances are *estimates* of the population variance. The relationship

$$\text{Between Variance} + \text{Within Variance} = \text{Total Variance}$$

does not hold for **sample variances.**

A formula that can be used in the calculation of the sample variance is

$$s^2 = \frac{\Sigma(X - \overline{X})^2}{n - 1}$$

The expression

$$SS = \Sigma(X - \overline{X})^2$$

is referred to as the **Sums of Squares**. The degrees of freedom, *df*, associated with the sample is $n - 1$. Thus the sample variance

$$s^2 = \frac{\Sigma(X - \overline{X})^2}{n - 1}$$

can be rewritten as:

$$s^2 = \frac{Sums\ of\ squares}{degrees\ of\ freedom}$$

or simply,

$$s^2 = \frac{SS}{df}$$

It turns out that when we *only consider* the Sums of Squares, SS, then the relationship

Sums of Squares Between Treatments	+	Sums of Squares Within Treatments	=	Sums of Squares Total Subjects

will hold all the time. This relationship can also be denoted as,

$$SS_{(between\ treatments)} + SS_{(within\ treatments)} = SS_{(total)}.$$

16.5   ONE-WAY ANALYSIS OF VARIANCE

A statistical procedure that accounts for differences between treatment effects by studying variability as measured by variance is called *Analysis of Variance.*

In this section an Analysis of Variance procedure for one-way ANOVA, will be presented.

DEFINITION 16.4

ANOVA. ANOVA is a statistical procedure that involves the analysis of one or more independent variables called factors with two or more levels for each factor. When only one independent variable is used in the ANOVA it is called *one-way* ANOVA.

The ANOVA procedure compares variances under the *assumption* that the variance due to experimental manipulation or treatment is the same. This implies that all sample means in an experiment must be equal or, at best, differences between the sample means are not significant. Thus, the differences are simply due to chance (i.e. error) variance. Since the F-Distribution compares two estimates of population variances, we will use the ANOVA procedure to find estimates of the population variance. In fact, the *within group* variance and the *between group* variance that was discussed in Section 16.3 are the two estimates of the population variance that the analysis of variance procedure uses and compares via an F-ratio.

A basic fundamental question that ANOVA explores concerns variability is:

Basic Fundamental Question:

Is the variation among individual sample means due purely to chance or are these differences due to different experimental conditions?

Let's consider the following example.

A market researcher decides to test market a new coffee product using a random sample of 15 supermarkets. Besides the quality of the coffee product, the predominant color used in the packaging design is a major concern. Three colors are chosen to be used as the predominant color. They are Gold, Silver, and Blue as shown in Figure 16.10.

FIGURE 16.10

Of the total of 15 stores, five are randomly chosen to carry the coffee packaged in Gold, five are randomly chosen to carry the coffee packaged in Silver, and five are randomly chosen to carry the coffee packaged in Blue.

After one month of sales the following results were found and summarized in Table 16.14. The results lists the number of units sold (i.e. the independent variable) from each supermarket, along with the mean number of units sold, and the corresponding sample variance s^2, (i.e. the population variance estimates).

TABLE 16.14   Units of Coffee Product Sold After 1 month
N= 15 stores participating

	Gold package	Silver package	Blue package	
	7	19	8	
	15	12	12	
	20	21	19	
	18	23	11	
	19	15	16	
sample mean, $\bar{x}$	15.8	18	13.2	overall <u>mean</u> = 15.67
sample variance, s^2	27.7	20	18.7	

The basic question that the market researcher would like answered is whether the *variation* among the individual sample means for the number of units sold is due purely to chance or are these differences due mainly to packaging color?

The ANOVA technique *compares variances* under the *assumption* that the variance among all levels, that is packaging colors, are the same. Let's modify our hypothesis testing procedure and perform an analysis of variance to determine if the market researcher can indeed show a statistical difference in sales due to packaging differences.

Based on the hypothesis testing procedure:

Step 1   *Formulate the two hypotheses, H_0 and H_a.*

In ANOVA, all population means are assumed equal. For this example, we will assume the color of packaging used to sell the coffee is *not* related to coffee product sales. The null hypothesis can also be stated as: there is no difference in the population mean number of units sold for the coffee product packaged in Gold, Silver or Blue.

Symbolically, if μ_G = the population mean number of units of the coffee product sold when packaged in Gold, μ_S = the population mean number of units of the coffee product sold when packaged in Silver, and μ_B = the population mean number of units of the coffee product sold when packaged in Blue, then the null hypothesis, H_0, is expressed

$$H_0: \mu_G = \mu_S = \mu_B$$

whereas, the alternative hypothesis, H_a, is expressed

$$H_a: \text{all three means are } not \text{ equal.}$$

The alternative hypothesis implies that there is at least one population mean that is different from the other population means. That is, the population mean number of units sold for at least one of the packaging coloring techniques is different from one of the others.

In general the null and alternative hypothesis forms for this type of ANOVA test are:

Null Hypothesis Form

H_0: There is no difference between the population means.

In the case where there are only three population means we write H_0 as:

$$H_0: \mu_1 = \mu_2 = \mu_3$$

The general alternative hypothesis form is:

H_a: There is a difference between the population means.

or, in this case,

H_a: all three population means are not equal.

Step 2 *Determine the model to test the null hypothesis, H_0.*
The appropriate sampling distribution is the F-Distribution based on the null hypothesis of equality of population means and variances. To use the ANOVA technique, the following assumptions **must be true.**
(a) Each sample is selected from a population that is approximately normally distributed.
(b) Each sample is selected from a population that has the same population variance, σ^2.
(c) When samples are drawn from different populations the samples must be random and independent.
     In the example we are examining, to use ANOVA, we are assuming that for the three package coloring techniques the population of data values for each technique is approximately normally distributed. Second, we are assuming that the population of data values for each packaging technique has the same variance, σ^2. Third, for each sample used in the procedure, the samples are independent and were randomly selected from each population.

Step 3 *Formulate the Decision Rule.*
     To do the one-way ANOVA test, the right hand side of the F-Distribution is always used. This is illustrated in Figure 16.11. The critical F-value, $F_\alpha(df$ between, df within) is determined from Appendix D:Table VII, by using α, df between and df within. These three values are indicated in the experimental design for the problem and are generated using the sample data. Specifically,
(a) the *df associated with the numerator and denominator* for the F-value are found using the degrees of freedom associated with the sample variances. These two estimates are called the *between group* variance and the *within group* variance.
     For the *df* associated with the numerator we use the *df* for the between group variance.
     df(between) = k-1,
                    where k is the number of levels of the factor.
     For the *df* associated with the denominator, use the *df* for the within group variance.
     df(within) = N − k, where N is the total number of data for all samples and k is the number of levels of the factor.
(b) the level of significance, α.
(c) State the decision rule.

ANOVA: HYPOTHESIS TESTING MODEL

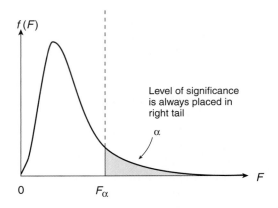

FIGURE 16.11

Thus when the ANOVA test is applied, a *computed* test statistic F will be significant if its value is **greater** than the *critical* F-value, F_α. When this occurs we will **reject** the null hypothesis. This is shown in Figure 16.12.

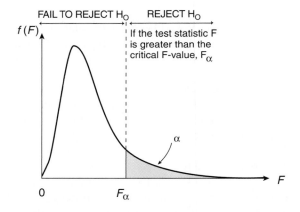

FIGURE 16.12

In this example, let us choose $\alpha = 0.05$. To determine the critical F-value, $F\alpha(df$ between, df within), the degrees of freedom for the between group variance and the degrees of freedom for the within group variance must be obtained.

The degrees of freedom for the between group variance, *df(between groups),* is determined by the **number of levels, k,** of the factor being compared minus 1. In this example, the 3 different packaging colors represent the 3 levels of the factor: packaging colors. Thus k = 3 and the:

$$df(between\ groups) = k - 1$$
$$= 3 - 1$$

$$df(between\ groups) = 2$$

The *df(between groups)* is often referred to as *df(between treatments).* Thus, we can say,

$$df(between\ treatments) = k - 1 = 2$$

The degrees of freedom for the within group variance, *df(within groups)* is determined by the **total** number of sample data, N, minus the number of levels of the factor being compared, k. In this example, we have fifteen data values representing our total number of sample data, so N = 15, and we are comparing these data values by separating them into three packaging techniques, therefore, k = 3, thus the

$$df(within\ groups) = N - k$$
$$= 15 - 3$$
$$df(within\ groups) = 12$$

The Critical F-value, $F_\alpha(df$ between, df within$) = F_{.05}(2,12)$ is determined from Appendix D:Table VII. Using the Table VII,

$$F_{.05}(2,12) = 3.89$$

Therefore, the decision rule is: if the test statistic F is **greater** than the *critical* F-value, $F_{.05}(2,12)=3.89$, we reject H_0. This decision rule is illustrated in Figure 16.13.

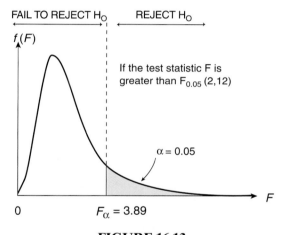

FIGURE 16.13

Step 4   *Analyze the sample data.*

The ANOVA test requires the calculation of a test statistic F by forming a ratio of the variance due to treatment (also called the *between* group variance) **to** the variance within each group (called the *within* sample variance). This test statistic F is computed by the formula:

$$F = \frac{treatment\ sample\ variance}{within\ sample\ variance}$$

Let's calculate the test statistic F for the data in Table 16.14. We have reprinted the data values of Table 16.14 and represent these data in Table 16.15.

TABLE 16.15   Units of Coffee Product Sold After 1 month
N= 15 stores participating

	Gold package	Silver package	Blue package	
	7	19	8	
	15	12	12	
	20	21	19	
	18	23	11	
	19	15	16	
sample mean, $\bar{x}$	15.8	18	13.2	overall mean = 15.67
sample variance, s^2	27.7	20	18.7	

To calculate the ANOVA test statistic F, a *special ANOVA Table* which is shown in Table 16.16 has been used to summarize the Analysis of Variance results.

TABLE 16.16   ANOVA TABLE

Source of Variation	Sum of Squares SS	Degrees of Freedom df	Mean Square MS	Calculated F-statistic
Between (Treatment)				
Within				
Total				

Notice that the **sources of variation** have been *partitioned* into three distinct cells called Between, Within and Total. Recall that in Section 16.3 we observed that the **sums of squares** of variation due to the Between, Within and Total variation were related as follows:

Sum of Squares Between Treatments	+	Sum of Squares Within Treatments	=	Sum of Squares Total Subjects

or

$$SS_{(between\ treatments)} + SS_{(within\ treatments)} = SS_{(total)}$$

The second column of the ANOVA Table is labelled Sum of Squares, denoted SS. To determine the values needed to help complete the column for Sum of Squares in the ANOVA table, formulas are needed for each of the sum of squares. These formulas are:

$$SS_{(total)} = \Sigma X^2 - \frac{(\Sigma X)^2}{N}$$

$$SS_{(between\ treatments)} = \left(\frac{(\Sigma T_1)^2}{n_1} + \frac{(\Sigma T_2)^2}{n_2} + ... + \frac{(\Sigma T_i)^2}{n_i} \right) - \frac{(\Sigma X)^2}{N}$$

$$SS_{(within\ treatment)} = \Sigma X^2 - \left(\frac{(\Sigma T_1)^2}{n_1} + \frac{(\Sigma T_2)^2}{n_2} + ... + \frac{(\Sigma T_i)^2}{n_i} \right)$$

where X = a data value
n_1 = the size of sample 1
n_2 = the size of sample 2
n_i = the size of sample i

N = the total number of data values

T_1 = the data values of sample 1
T_2 = the data values of sample 2
T_i = the data values of sample i

Let's compute the various Sums of Squares for the market research problem using the data of Table 16.17.

Step 1 Compute $SS_{(total)} = \Sigma X^2 - \frac{(\Sigma X)^2}{N}$

To compute $SS_{(total)}$ you must:
(a) calculate ΣX^2, the sum of the squared data values for **all** the data of Table 16.17. This is,

$$\Sigma X^2 = (7)^2 + (15)^2 + (20)^2 + (18)^2 + ... + (11)^2 + (16)^2 = 4005$$

(b) calculate $(\Sigma X)^2$, the sum of all the data values squared. This is,

$$(\Sigma X)^2 = [\,7 + 15 + 20 + ... + 11 + 16\,]^2 = (235)^2$$

(c) divide $(\Sigma X)^2$ by N, that is, compute $\frac{(\Sigma X)^2}{N}$.

$$\frac{(\Sigma X)^2}{N} = \frac{(235)^2}{15}$$

Therefore,

$$SS_{(total)} = 4005 - \frac{(235)^2}{15}$$
$$= 4005 - 3681.67$$
$$SS_{(total)} = 323.33$$

Step 2 *Compute* $SS_{(between\ treatments)} = \left(\frac{(\Sigma T_1)^2}{n_1} + \frac{(\Sigma T_2)^2}{n_2} + \frac{(\Sigma T_3)^2}{n_3} \right) - \frac{(\Sigma X)^2}{N}$

(a) To compute $SS_{(between\ treatments)}$ the

$$\frac{(\Sigma T)^2}{n}$$

needs to be calculated for each **level** of treatment.

Thus, for the gold packaging,

$$\frac{(\Sigma T)^2}{n} = \frac{(7 + 15 + 20 + 18 + 19)^2}{5} = \frac{(79)^2}{5}$$

For the Silver packaging,

$$\frac{(\Sigma T)^2}{n} = \frac{(19 + 12 + 21 + 23 + 15)^2}{5} = \frac{(90)^2}{5}$$

And, for the Blue packaging,

$$\frac{(\Sigma T)^2}{n} = \frac{(8 + 12 + 19 + 11 + 16)^2}{5} = \frac{(66)^2}{5}$$

Since

$$\frac{(\Sigma X)^2}{N}$$

was computed in Step one, where the value of

$$\frac{(\Sigma X)^2}{N}$$

was found to be

$$\frac{(235)^2}{15} \approx 3681.67$$

Therefore,

$$SS_{\text{(between treatments)}} = \frac{(79)^2}{5} + \frac{(90)^2}{5} + \frac{(66)^2}{5} - \frac{235^2}{15}$$
$$= 3739.4 - 3681.67$$

$$SS_{\text{(between treatments)}} = 57.73$$

Step 3   Compute

$$SS_{\text{(within treatment)}} = \Sigma X^2 - \left(\frac{(\Sigma T_1)^2}{n_1} + \frac{(\Sigma T_2)^2}{n_2} + \frac{(\Sigma T_3)^2}{n_3} \right)$$

Since both ΣX^2 and

$$\left(\frac{(\Sigma T_1)^2}{n_1} + \frac{(\Sigma T_2)^2}{n_2} + \frac{(\Sigma T_3)^2}{n_3} \right)$$

have been computed in Steps one and two respectively, we have

$$SS_{\text{(within treatment)}} = 4005 - \frac{(79)^2}{5} + \frac{(90)^2}{5} + \frac{(66)^2}{5}$$
$$= 4005 - 3739.4$$

$$SS_{\text{(within treatment)}} = 265.6$$

You should notice that the relationship

$$SS_{(between\ treatments)} + SS_{(within\ treatments)} = SS_{(total)}$$

holds for the calculated SS values

$$57.73 + 265.6 = 323.33.$$

When doing ANOVA calculations it is **helpful to remember the relationship for the Sum of Squares:**

$$SS_{(between\ treatments)} + SS_{(within\ treatments)} = SS_{(total)}$$

because knowing any two of the calculations will yield the third.

Thus, the Sum of Squares column in the ANOVA table can be filled in as shown in Table 16.17.

TABLE 16.17   ANOVA TABLE

Source of Variation	Sum of Squares SS	Degrees of Freedom df	Mean Square MS	Calculated F-statistic
Between	57.73			
Within	265.6			
Total	323.33			

The third column of the ANOVA Table represents the *Degrees of Freedom, df,* for each Sum of Squares. The Degrees of Freedom of each Sum of Squares is computed by the formulas:

$df_{(Between)} = k - 1,$

where k = the number of levels of factors (or treatments).

$df_{(within)} = N - k,$

where N = total number of data values,

and   k = the number of treatment levels.

$df_{(Total)} = N - 1$

where N = total number of data values.

For the color packaging data of Table 16.15 we have a total of 15 data values (N = 15) and 3 levels (k = 3) of treatment (i.e. package design), thus,

$df_{(Between)} = k - 1,$
$= 3 - 1$
$= 2$

$df_{(within)} = N - k,$
$= 15 - 3$
$= 12$

$df_{(Total)} = N - 1$
$= 15 - 1$
$= 14$

Notice that $df_{(Between)}$ + $df_{(within)}$ = $df_{(Total)}$

2   +   12   =   14.

This is always true!

In Table 16.18, the Degrees of Freedom column in the ANOVA table has been completed.

TABLE 16.18   ANOVA TABLE

Source of Variation	Sum of Squares SS	Degrees of Freedom df	Mean Square MS	Calculated F-statistic
Between	57.73	**2**		
Within	265.6	**12**		
Total	323.33	**14**		

The fourth column of the ANOVA table represents the Mean Square, (denoted MS), which can be determined by the formulas:

$$MS_{(between)} = \frac{SS_{bet}}{df_{bet}}$$

$$MS_{(within)} = \frac{SS_{within}}{df_{within}}$$

To calculate the Mean Square for each sum of square, you need only to use the ANOVA table since the values needed for each calculation is contained within the table. Using Table 16.18, we have:

$$MS_{(between)} = \frac{SS_{bet}}{df_{bet}}$$

$$MS_{(between)} = \frac{57.73}{2}$$

$$MS_{(between)} = 28.87$$

and

$$MS_{(within)} = \frac{SS_{within}}{df_{within}}$$

$$MS_{(within)} = \frac{265.6}{12}$$

$$MS_{(within)} = 22.13$$

Substituting these values into the ANOVA Table, produces Table 16.19.

TABLE 16.19   ANOVA TABLE

Source of Variation	Sum of Squares SS	Degrees of Freedom df	Mean Square MS	Calculated F-statistic
Between	57.73	2	**28.87**	
Within	265.6	12	**22.13**	
Total	323.33	14		

Mean Square is an alternative way of referring to the estimates of the population variances. Recall that a sample variance was computed using the formula:

$$\text{sample variance} = \frac{\Sigma(X - \overline{X})^2}{n-1} = \frac{Sum\ of\ Squares}{degrees\ of\ freedom} = \frac{SS}{df}$$

In ANOVA, the terminology, Mean Square (or MS) is used to represent the term variance. Thus, in ANOVA,

Mean Square = Variance

In general, the Mean Square is computed using the formula

$$MS = \frac{SS}{df} = \text{sample variance}$$

The

$$\text{Between sample variance} = \frac{SS_{between}}{df} = MS_{Between}$$

and

$$\text{Within sample variance} = \frac{SS_{within}}{df} = MS_{Within}$$

Thus, once they are calculated, the test statistic F can be determined. Therefore, the **test statistic** is computed by the formula:

$$F = \frac{MS_{bet}}{MS_{within}}$$
$$F = \frac{28.87}{22.13}$$
$$F \approx 1.30$$

Therefore the test statistic for the data representing the three different coffee packaging colors is F= 1.30.

Step 4 *State the conclusion.*

The test statistic (F=1.30) and the critical F-value, $F_{0.05}(2,12) = 3.89$, is indicated in Figure 16.14. Since the test statistic is not greater than the critical F-value, then our conclusion is that we fail to reject H_0. Thus, although there is a difference between the sample means, the difference is not statistically significant at an alpha level of 0.05.

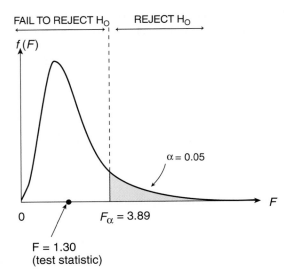

FIGURE 16.14

In practice, when conducting an ANOVA procedure **two** summary tables are needed. The first lists the raw data along with the appropriate statistics ultimately needed for the calculation of the test statistic F. Table 16.20 includes the appropriate sums, sums of squares, k, n, and N needed for the ANOVA procedure. These are highlighted in Table 16.20.

TABLE 16.20   Units of Coffee Product Sold After 1 month
N= 15 stores participating

	Gold package	Silver package	Blue package	
	7	19	8	
	15	12	12	
	20	21	19	
	18	23	11	
	19	15	16	
sample mean, $\bar{x}$	15.8	18	13.2	overall mean = 15.67
sample variance, s^2	27.7	20	18.7	
$\sum T$	**79**	**90**	**66**	
n	**5**	**5**	**5**	
k (levels) = 3				$\sum X = 235$ $\sum X^2 = 4005$ N = 15 data values

The second table that is necessary to compute the test statistic F is called **the ANOVA Table.** The ANOVA Table is pictured in Table 16.21.

TABLE 16.21   The ANOVA TABLE

Source of Variation	Sum of Squares SS	Degrees of Freedom df	Mean Square MS	Calculated test statistic F
Between				
Within				
Total				

Table 16.22 lists the Formulas necessary to complete the ANOVA Table. As you can see, the highlighted statistics of Table 16.20 are needed in the formulas for **sums of squares** and **degrees of freedom** shown in Table 16.22.

TABLE 16.22   ANOVA FORMULAS

Formulas for Sums of Squares

$$SS_{(total)} = \Sigma X^2 - \frac{(\Sigma X)^2}{N}$$

$$SS_{(between\ treatments)} = \left(\frac{(\Sigma T_1)^2}{n_1} + \frac{(\Sigma T_2)^2}{n_2} + ... + \frac{(\Sigma T_i)^2}{n_i} - \frac{(\Sigma X)^2}{N} \right)$$

$$SS_{(within\ treatment)} = \Sigma X^2 - \left(\frac{(\Sigma T_1)^2}{n_1} + \frac{(\Sigma T_2)^2}{n_2} + ... + \frac{(\Sigma T_i)^2}{n_i} \right)$$

where X = a data value
n_1 = the size of sample 1
n_2 = the size of sample 2
n_i = the size of sample i

N = the total number of data values

T_1 = the data values of sample 1
T_2 = the data values of sample 2
T_i = the data values of sample i

Formulas for Degrees of Freedom

$df_{(between)} = k - 1,$
where k = the number of treatment levels.
$df_{(within)} = N - k,$
where N = total number of data values,
and   k = the number of treatment levels.
$df_{(total)} = N - 1$
where N = total number of data values.

TABLE 16.22   ANOVA FORMULAS (continued)

Formulas for Mean Square

$$MS_{(between)} = \frac{SS_{bet}}{df_{bet}}$$

$$MS_{(within)} = \frac{SS_{within}}{df_{within}}$$

Calculated test statistic F

$$F = \frac{MS_{bet}}{MS_{within}}$$

Therefore, to conduct an Analysis of Variance application, the five step hypothesis testing procedure that we have used throughout the text can be **modified** to include the two summary tables. The hypothesis testing procedure for ANOVA is summarized below.

ANOVA
Hypothesis Testing Procedure

Step 1   *Formulate the two hypotheses, H_0 and Ha.*
In general the null and alternative hypothesis forms in this type of ANOVA test are:

Null Hypothesis Form

H_0: There is no difference between the population means.
In the case where there are only three population means we have:

$$H_0: \mu_1 = \mu_2 = \mu_3$$

Alternative Hypothesis Form

H_a: There is a difference between the population means.
or
In the case of three population means:
H_a: all three population means are not equal.

Step 2   *Determine the model to test the null hypothesis, H_0.*
The appropriate sampling distribution is the F-Distribution based on the null hypothesis of equality of population means and variances. To use the ANOVA technique, the following assumptions **must be true.**

Assumptions for ANOVA

(a) Each sample is selected from a normal population.
(b) Each sample is selected from a population that has the same population variance, σ^2.
(c) When samples are drawn from different populations the samples must be random and independent.

Step 3 *Formulate the Decision Rule.*

In performing the ANOVA test, the right hand side of the F-Distribution is always used as shown in Figure 16.15. The critical F-value, $F_\alpha(df$ between, df within) is determined from Appendix D:Table VII, by using α, df between and df within. The α value is determined by the researcher. The df between is computed by the number of levels of the factor (treatment), k, minus 1. And, the df within by the number of data values in the experiment, N, minus k.

Specifically,

(a) the *df associated with the numerator and denominator* for the critical F-value are found using the degrees of freedom associated with the two estimates of population variance from the sample data. These two estimates are called the *between group* variance and the *within group* variance.

For the *df* associated with the numerator we use the *df* for the between group variance.
df(between) = k − 1,
where k is the number of levels of the factor.

For the *df* associated with the denominator, use the *df* for the within group variance.
df(within) = N − k, where N is the total number of data for all samples and k is the number of levels of the factor.

(b) the level of significance, α , is assumed or given by the researcher.

(c) State the Decision Rule. The Decision Rule is shown in Figure 16.15.

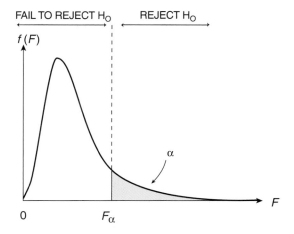

FIGURE 16.15

Thus when the ANOVA test is applied, a test statistic F will be shown to be significant if its value is **greater** than the *critical* F-value. When this occurs we **reject** the null hypothesis. This is shown in Figure 16.16.

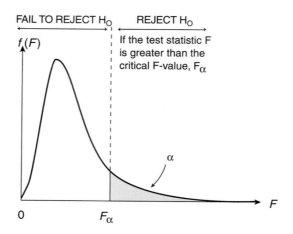

FIGURE 16.16

Step 4   *Analyze the sample data.*

The ANOVA test requires the calculation of a test statistic F by comparing the variance due to treatment, (or the *between* group variance) **to** the variance within each group, (or the *within* sample variance). This test statistic F is expressed as:

$$F = \frac{MS_{between}}{MS_{within}}$$

Using the sample data complete the following list of calculations:

ΣT **for each level of sample data.**
n   **for each level of sample data.**
ΣX **= Sum of ALL the data values using all the samples.**
ΣX^2 **= Sum of ALL the Squared data values using all the samples.**
N   **= Total number of data values using all the samples.**
k   **= Number of Treatment Levels.**

Formulas for Sums of Squares

$$SS_{(total)} = \Sigma X^2 - \frac{(\Sigma X)^2}{N}$$

$$SS_{(between\ treatments)} = \left(\frac{(\Sigma T_1)^2}{n_1} + \frac{(\Sigma T_2)^2}{n_2} + ... + \frac{(\Sigma T_i)^2}{n_i} - \frac{(\Sigma X)^2}{N} \right)$$

$$SS_{(within\ treatment)} = \Sigma X^2 - \left(\frac{(\Sigma T_1)^2}{n_1} + \frac{(\Sigma T_2)^2}{n_2} + ... + \frac{(\Sigma T_i)^2}{n_i} \right)$$

where X = a data value
n_1 = the size of sample 1
n_2 = the size of sample 2
n_i = the size of sample i

N = the total number of data values

T_1 = the data values of sample 1
T_2 = the data values of sample 2
T_i = the data values of sample i

Formulas for Degrees of Freedom

$df_{(Between)} = k - 1$,
  where k = the number of treatment levels.
$df_{(within)} = N - k$,
  where N = total number of data values,
  and k = the number of treatment levels.
$df_{(Total)} = N - 1$
  where N = total number of data values.

Formulas for Mean Square

$$MS_{(between)} = \frac{SS_{bet}}{df_{bet}}$$

$$MS_{(within)} = \frac{SS_{within}}{df_{within}}$$

Calculated test statistic F

$$F = \frac{MS_{bet}}{MS_{within}}$$

Substitute the calculated values into the ANOVA TABLE shown in Table 16.23.

TABLE 16.23   ANOVA TABLE

Source of Variation	Sum of Squares SS	Degrees of Freedom df	Mean Square MS	Calculated F-statistic
Between				
Within				
Total				

Step 5   *State the conclusion.*
    Figure 16.17 is used to model the possible conclusions.

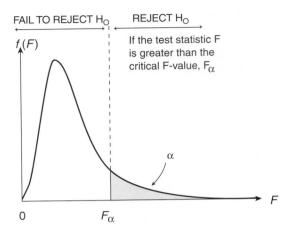

FIGURE 16.17

CASE STUDY 16.1

The 1994 baseball season began with Ray Lankford of the St. Louis Cardinals hitting a home run. During the 1994 baseball season, the month of April produced more runs a game since 1930 and more homers per game than ever before. This led to the speculation that the 1994 baseballs were "juiced" or "livelier". Independent tests were conducted on a sample of '94 baseballs to determine if the balls were livelier which would account for the 1994's offensive firepower. One test conducted on the baseballs was to determine the average bounce of the balls when they were heated, cold or regular. Figure 16.18 presents the results of the test.

FIGURE 16.18

a) What was the average bounce for the heated baseballs? for the cold baseballs? for the regular baseballs?

b) What is the independent variable? Name the different levels of the variable.

c) Interpret the within group variance and between group variance for this test.

d) Does the temperature of the ball seem to have an effect on the average bounce?

e) What additional information would you need to determine whether the temperature of the ball plays a significant role in the distance the ball will travel or bounce?

f) If you were to conduct an ANOVA test to determine whether there was a significant difference in the distance the balls bounced, then what assumptions would be made regarding the sample of balls selected for the experiment and the population from which the balls were selected?

Let's consider an ANOVA where the samples are **not** of equal size n.

EXAMPLE 16.6

A medical researcher is interested in the comparison of the effectiveness of four different exercise programs for infants. The researcher randomly selects 23 infants, and randomly assigns them to four treatment groups. After administering to each treatment group, one of the four exercise programs, she measures the age at which each infant first walks without support. Table 16.24 lists the relevant data values.

TABLE 16.24   Age at which infant first walks without support (in months)

Treatment Group	A	B	C	D
	9.50	11.25	11.75	13.25
	9.25	10.50	12.50	11.50
	9.75	9.75	9.50	12.25
	10.00	9.50	11.50	13.25
	12.75	11.75	13.50	11.50
	9.50	10.25	13.25	

Do these data indicate that an exercise treatment program is related to the number of months an infant will walk without support at $\alpha = 0.05$?

Solution

Step 1   *Formulate the two hypotheses, H_0 and H_a.*

H_0: There is no difference between the population means for infants to walk without support.

$$H_0: \mu_A = \mu_B = \mu_C = \mu_D$$

H_a: Not all four population means are equal.

Step 2   *Determine the model to test the null hypothesis, H_0.*

The appropriate sampling distribution is the F-Distribution.

Step 3   *Formulate the Decision Rule.*

To perform the ANOVA test, the right hand side of the F-Distribution is always used as shown in Figure 16.19. The critical F-value, $F_\alpha(df$ between, df within) is determined from

Appendix D: Table VII, by using α, df between and df within.

For this problem, $\alpha = 0.05$. Since there are four levels of treatment, $k = 4$ and:

$$df\text{(between)} = k - 1,$$
$$df\text{(between)} = 3$$

Since there are 23 data values, $N = 23$. Thus:

$$df\text{(within)} = N - k$$
$$df\text{(within)} = 23 - 4$$
$$df\text{(within)} = 19$$

Using $df\text{(between)} = 3$, $df\text{(within)} = 19$, and Appendix D: Table VII, the critical F-value is $F_{0.05}(3,19) = 3.13$.

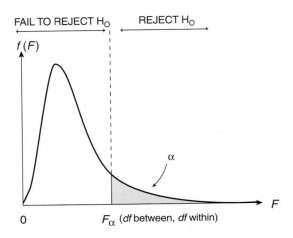

FIGURE 16.19

In this ANOVA test the **decision rule** is: *if the test statistic F is **greater** than the critical F-value, $F_{0.05}(3,19) = 3.13$, **reject** the null hypothesis.* This decision rule is illustrated in Figure 16.20.

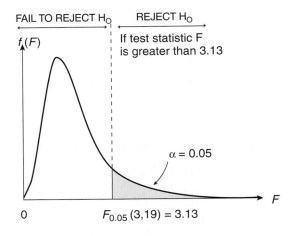

FIGURE 16.20

Step 4 *Analyze the sample data.*

The ANOVA test requires the calculation of the test statistic F by comparing the variance due to treatment, (or the *between* group variance) **to** the variance within each group, (or the *within* sample variance). This test statistic F is expressed as

$$F = \frac{MS_{between}}{MS_{within}}$$

Using the sample data complete the following list of calculations:

ΣT for each level of sample data.

n for each level of sample data.

ΣX = Sum of ALL the data values using all the samples.

ΣX^2 = Sum of ALL the Squared data values using all the samples .

N = Total number of data values using all the samples.

k = Number of Treatment Levels.

Table 16.25 contains all the data values of Example 16.6 along with the necessary calculations required to determine the sums of squares expressions.

TABLE 16.25   Age, in months, at which infant first walks without support

Treatment Group	A	B	C	D
	9.50	11.25	11.75	13.25
	9.25	10.50	12.50	11.50
	9.75	9.75	9.50	12.25
	10.00	9.50	11.50	13.25
	12.75	11.75	13.50	11.50
	9.50	10.25	13.25	
ΣT	**60.75**	**63**	**72**	**61.75**
n	**6**	**6**	**6**	**5**

$\Sigma X = \mathbf{257.5}$
$\Sigma X^2 = \mathbf{2929.25}$
N = **23** data values
k = **4** levels

Using the calculated values listed in Table 16.25 we can apply the formulas for the Sums of Squares, degrees of freedom, Means Square and the calculated test statistic F.

Calculations for Sums of Squares

$$SS_{(total)} = \Sigma X^2 - \frac{(\Sigma X)^2}{N} = 2929.25 - \frac{(257.5)^2}{23}$$

$$SS_{(total)} = 46.37$$

$$SS_{(between\ treatments)} = \left(\frac{(\Sigma T_1)^2}{n_1} + \frac{(\Sigma T_2)^2}{n_2} + ... + \frac{(\Sigma T_i)^2}{n_i} \right) - \frac{(\Sigma X)^2}{N}$$

since there are four treatments we have,

$$= \left(\frac{(60.75)^2}{6} + \frac{(63)^2}{6} + \frac{(72)^2}{6} + \frac{(61.75)^2}{5} \right) - \frac{(257.5)^2}{23}$$

$$= 2903.21 - 2882.88$$

$$SS_{(between\ treatments)} = 20.33$$

$$SS_{(within\ treatment)} = \Sigma X^2 - \left(\frac{(\Sigma T_1)^2}{n_1} + \frac{(\Sigma T_2)^2}{n_2} + \dots + \frac{(\Sigma T_i)^2}{n_i} \right)$$

$$= 2929.25 - 2903.21$$

$$SS_{(within\ treatment)} = 26.04$$

Calculations for Degrees of Freedom

$df_{(between)} = k - 1,$ where k = the number of treatment levels.
$df_{(between)} = 4 - 1$

$df_{(between)} = 3$

$df_{(within)} = N - k,$ where N = total number of data values,
                            and k = the number of treatment levels.

$df_{(within)} = 23 - 4$
$df_{(within)} = 19$

$df_{(total)} = N - 1,$ where N = total number of data values.
$df_{(total)} = 23 - 1$
$df_{(total)} = 19$

Calculations for Mean Square

$$MS_{(between)} = \frac{SS_{bet}}{df_{bet}} = \frac{20.33}{3}$$

$$MS_{(between)} = 6.78$$

$$MS_{(within)} = \frac{SS_{within}}{df_{within}} = \frac{26.04}{19}$$

$$MS_{(within)} = 4.95$$

Calculated test statistic F

$$F = \frac{MS_{bet}}{MS_{within}}$$

$$F = \frac{6.78}{1.37}$$

$$F = 4.95$$

Substitute the calculated values into the ANOVA TABLE shown in Table 16.26.

TABLE 16.26   ANOVA TABLE

Source of Variation	Sum of Squares SS	Degrees of Freedom df	Mean Square MS	Calculated test statistic F
Between	20.33	3	6.78	4.95
Within	26.04	19	1.37	
Total	46.37	22		

Step 5   *State the conclusion.*

The calculated test statistic F is 4.95, and the critical F-value, $F_{0.05}(3,19) = 3.13$. Since the test statistic F is **greater than** the critical F-value, the **null hypothesis is rejected.** This is illustrated in Figure 16.21. Thus, the alternative hypothesis is **accepted** at $\alpha = 0.05$. Therefore, the population means are **not** all equal. This implies that at least one of the exercise treatment programs affects the initial month that an infant will begin to walk without support.

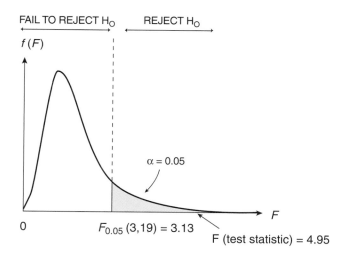

FIGURE 16.21

A study entitled Teacher Job Satisfaction and Teacher Job Stress: School Size, Age and Teaching Experience appeared in *Education* (volume 112 issue number 2). The purpose of this study was to determine the effect that school size, age and teaching experience has on job satisfaction and job stress.

The subjects selected for the study were 229 North Florida and South Georgia urban secondary school physical education teachers. Two instruments were used to measure the job satisfaction and job related stress of the teachers. A high score on the Job Satisfaction Scale indicates a high level of job satisfaction while a high score on the Job-Related Stress Scale indicates a high level of job stress. Some of the results of this study are shown in Table 16.27 to Table 16.29.

(continued)

Table 16.27   Differences in Job Stress Scores by School Size

Size of School	Number of Subjects	Mean Scores	Standard Deviation	F-statistic	Probability level
500–1000	45	34.87	12.21	5.33	0.00*
1001–1500	69	37.80	12.51		
1501–2000	60	44.01	15.02		
2001+	55	44.35	14.24		
Total	229	40.29			

* Exceeds the 0.05 alpha level

Table 16.28   Differences in Job Satisfaction Scores by Age Group

Size of School	Number of Subjects	Mean Scores	Standard Deviation	F-statistic	Probability level
30 or less	52	46.50	11.13	0.82	0.48
31–45	88	45.77	13.35		
46–60	66	43.40	12.24		
61+	23	47.22	16.72		
Total	229	44.39			

Table 16.29   Differences in Job Stress Scores by Age Group

Size of School	Number of Subjects	Mean Scores	Standard Deviation	F-statistic	Probability level
30 or less	52	42.38	13.74	0.010	0.99
31–45	88	42.62	14.17		
46–60	66	42.50	16.09		
61+	23	43.00	11.82		
Total	229	42.57			

For Table 16.27:

a) identify the independent variable. State the different levels of this variable.

b) compare the mean job stress score for a school of size 500–1000 to the mean job stress score for a school size of 2001+. Interpret the meaning of a each mean score.

c) Within which group are the job stress scores more variable? less variable? How would you interpret each of these results?

d) What would you compare to determine the between group variance?

e) What are the degrees of freedom for the within groups and the degrees of freedom for the between groups?

f) As the size of the school increases, what appears to happen to the job stress scores?

g) Explain the meaning of the probability level for the given F-statistic.

h) Based upon the results of Table 16.27, can you conclude that the largest schools are significantly more stressful? Explain.

For Table 16.28:

a) identify the independent variable. State the different levels of this variable.

b) compare the mean job satisfaction score for teachers aged 61+ to the mean job satisfaction score for teachers aged 46–60. Interpret the meaning of each mean score.

c) Within which group are the job satisfaction scores more variable? less variable? How would you interpret each of these results?

d) What would you compare to determine the between group variance?

e) Explain the meaning of the probability level for the given F-statistic.

f) What are the degrees of freedom for the within groups and the degrees of freedom for the between groups?

(continued)

g) Based upon the results of Table 16.28, can you conclude that the age of teachers is a significant factor in their job satisfaction? Explain.

h) Identify the age group that had the lowest job satisfaction and the age group with the highest job satisfaction. Can you conclude at an alpha level of 0.01 that this difference is significant?

For Table 16.29:

a) identify the independent variable. State the different levels of this variable.

b) compare the mean job stress score for teachers aged 30 or less to the mean job stress score for teachers aged 61+. Interpret the meaning of each mean score.

c) Within which group are the job stress scores more variable? less variable? How would you interpret each of these results?

d) What would you compare to determine the between group variance?

e) Explain the meaning of the probability level for the given F-statistic.

f) What are the degrees of freedom for the within groups and the degrees of freedom for the between groups?

g) Based upon the results of Table 16.29, can you conclude that the age of teachers is a significant factor in their job stress? Explain.

h) Identify the age group that had the lowest job stress and the age group with the highest job stress. Can you conclude at an alpha level of 0.05 that this difference is significant?

Case Study 16.3

The study entitled Factors In Children's Attitudes Toward Pets which appeared in the journal *Psychological Reports,* 1990, issue 66, investigated the parental attitudes, family size, structure, and presence or absence of household pets as influences on children's attitudes toward pets. The researchers, Kidd & Kidd, believe that attachment to pet animals begin as early as 18 months. Since a child-pet attachment begins at such an early age, Kidd and Kidd decided to investigate the factors which may influence feelings and attitudes toward pets. The researchers administered a Parent Questionnaire to the parents of the 700 children who were the subjects of the study. These subjects were composed of 339 boys and 361 girls between the ages of 6 months and 18 years: 150 boys and 150 girls from two-parent pet-owning homes, 43 boys and 55 girls from one-parent owning homes, 97 boys and 105 girls from two-parent, nonpet-owning homes, and 49 boys and 51 girls from one-parent, nonpet-owning homes.

The Parent Questionnaire were scored for the children's Activities with Pets and Interest in Pet's scales whether or not the family owned a pet. They were scored for a child's Responsibility for Pet Care scale only if the family owned a pet or indicated that the child actually helped with responsible care for a neighbor's or a friend's pet. One aspect of the study was to determine whether the age of the child significantly influenced the scores on each of the three scales. The researchers believed that involvement in activities with and interest in pets were good measures of attachment to pets, who showed more interest in them, and who took more responsibility for them also were reported as having a greater affection for their pets than children who were scored lower on these scales. A higher score on each of these scales is interpreted as displaying more activities with the pets, showing more interest in the pets and more responsibility with the pets. The results of the nonpet-owning children on the three scales are given in Table 16.30. The results of the pet-owning children on the three scales are discussed in the What Do You Think Exercises at the end of the chapter.

Table 16.30 Mean and Standard Deviations For Nonpet-Owning Children On Three Scales

	n	Mean	Std Dev
Activities Scale			
Ages			
0–5	110	15.26	7.10
Grade School	122	18.64	9.38
High School	70	18.11	10.16

(continued)

Table 16.30 (continued)

	n	Mean	Std Dev
Interest Scale			
Ages			
0–5	110	9.92	7.80
Grade School	122	12.89	9.19
High School	70	9.03	7.96

Table 16.31 One-Way Analysis of Variance of Activities With Pets, Interest In Pets: Scores of Children Without Household Pets By Age Groups

Source of Variance	SS	df	MS	F
Activities With Pets				
SS Between Age Groups	622.75	2	311.38	4.54[*]
SS Within Groups	20505.89	299	68.58	
Interest In Pets				
SS Between Age Groups	725.42	2	362.71	4.66[*]
SS Within Groups	23250.09	299	77.76	

*p<0.05

Using the information on the Activities Scale in Table 16.30 and Table 16.31:

   a) Identify the independent variable. State the different levels of this variable.
   b) Which age group should the greatest activity with pets? the smallest activity with pets?
   c) Which age group had the greatest variability in the activities scale with pets? the smallest variability?
   d) Which age group had the greatest mean score on the Activities scale? the smallest mean score?
   e) Determine the difference between the mean scores of part d? Do you think this difference is significant? If it is significant, state the alpha level and explain how you came to this conclusion.
   f) What are the degrees of freedom for the within groups and the degrees of freedom for the between age groups?
   g) Determine the Sums of Square due to Factor variance. Determine the Sums of Square due to Error variance.
   h) Explain what the MS = 311.38 indicates about the between age groups for the activities scale.
   i) Explain what the MS = 68.58 indicates about the within groups for the activities scale.
   j) Identify the Mean Square population variance estimate for the variance Between the groups.
   k) Identify the Mean Square population variance estimate for the variance within the groups.
   l) Based upon the results of Table 16.30, can you conclude that the age of a child is a significant factor in heir activities with pets at an alpha level of 0.10? at an alpha level of 0.01? Explain.

Using the information on the Interest Scale in Table 16.30 and Table 16.31:

   m) Identify the independent variable. State the different levels of this variable.
   n) Which age group should the greatest interest with pets? the smallest interest with pets?
   o) Which age group had the greatest variability in the interest scale with pets? the smallest variability?
   p) Which age group had the greatest mean score on the Interest scale? the smallest mean score?
   q) Determine the difference between the mean scores of part p? Do you think this difference is significant? If it is significant, state the alpha level and explain how you came to this conclusion.
   r) What are the degrees of freedom for the within groups and the degrees of freedom for the between age groups?

(continued)

s) Determine the Sums of Square due to Factor variance. Determine the Sums of Square due to Error variance.

t) Explain what the MS = 362.71 indicates about the between age groups for the interest scale.

u) Explain what the MS = 77.76 indicates about the within groups for the interest scale.

v) Identify the Mean Square population variance estimate for the variance Between the groups.

w) Identify the Mean Square population variance estimate for the variance within the groups.

x) Based upon the results of Table 16.31, can you conclude that the age of a child is a significant factor in their interest with pets at an alpha level of 0.10? at an alpha level of 0.01? Explain.

16.6   A BRIEF LOOK AT TWO-WAY ANOVA

Single factor or one-way ANOVA examines populations that have been classified with one categorical variable or factor. When populations have been classified using two categorical variables or two factors, each with its own levels, the ANOVA model is called *Two-Way ANOVA*.

Consider an experiment designed to study the effects of diet and aerobic exercise on blood pressure. In such an experiment, each of the categorical variables (factors) could have its own levels. For example, the categorical variable diet could be classified into three fat-content levels, such as low, medium or high. The other categorical variable aerobic exercise could be classified into the levels of low, normal or high aerobic activities. Table 16.32 diagrams the way the categories and levels are examined for the experiment.

TABLE 16.32   Diet (Fat Content)

	Low	Medium	High
EXERCISE			
Low	LL	LM	LH
Normal	NL	NM	NH
High	HL	HM	HH

In this two way design there are **nine** combinations of experimental treatment conditions. Using the first letter of each category level we have:

LL or Low-Low to be a combination where a subject is placed in a low aerobic exercise program and a low fat diet.

NL or Normal-Low to be a combination where a subject is placed in a normal aerobic exercise program and a low fat diet.

HL or High-Low to be a combination where a subject is placed in a high aerobic exercise program and a low fat diet.

These combinations of treatment conditions continue to HH, where HH indicates a high aerobic exercise program and a high fat diet.

All levels of exercise are combined with **all levels of diet.** The efficiency and control obtained in combining and analyzing the treatment conditions in this design are major advantages for using the two-way design.

Further development for a two-way design are beyond the scope of this text. However, many of the key concepts in the two-way design are similar to those of the one-way ANOVA.

16.7   USING TECHNOLOGY

The application of using MINITAB to perform an ANOVA is very useful. The many formulas involved for the development of the ANOVA table inspires you to enlist the aid of a computer to carry out these calculations. Let's relist in Table 16.33 the data values originally listed in Table 16.14 and show how the MINITAB command **AOVONEWAY** is used to perform the one-way analysis of variance.

TABLE 16.33   Units of Coffee Product Sold
After 1 month
N = 15 stores participating

Gold package	Silver package	Blue package
7	19	8
15	12	12
20	21	19
18	23	11
19	15	16

After these data are entered into a MINITAB work sheet, the MINITAB command **AOVONEWAY** completes all the necessary calculations for ANOVA to produce the ANOVA table along with the summary statistics for each level of treatment.

The MINITAB **output** is:

```
ANALYSIS OF-VARIANCE
SOURCE          DF-   SS       MS      F-      p
FACTOR          2     57.7     28.9    1.30    0.307
ERROR           12    265.6    22.1
TOTAL           14    323.3
                                        INDIVIDUAL 95 PCT CI'S FOR MEAN
                                        BASED ON POOLED STDEV
LEVEL           N     MEAN    STDEV   -------------+-------------+-------------+--------------
GOLD            5     15.800   5.263                (----------------*----------------)
SILVER          5     18.000   4.472                      (----------------*----------------)
BLUE            5     13.200   4.324    (----------------*----------------)
                                        -------------+-------------+-------------+--------------
POOLED STDEV =        4.705                       12.0          16.0          20.0
```

You should notice the ANOVA table lists the calculated test statistic F *along* with the *p-value* for this statistic. What does the p-value = 0.307 mean regarding the null hypothesis? Is your answer consistent to the results developed in Section 16.4?

Furthermore by examining the output, listed under the SOURCE column in the ANOVA table are the words 'FACTOR' and 'ERROR' respectively. The word 'FACTOR' refers to the variance due to TREATMENT, that is, the BETWEEN variance. The word 'ERROR' refers to the variance due to error WITHIN the treatments, that is, the WITHIN variance.

Also listed on the output are summary statistics for the levels of treatment, as well as, *95% confidence levels* for each of these levels of treatment.

The TI-83 Plus has an ANOVA statistical function for doing one-way ANOVA problems. The data representing age at which an infant first walks without support (in months) in Example 16.6 has been used to illustrate how the TI-83 Plus displays the ANOVA tables.

The data pertaining to the four groups A, B, C, and D were entered into Lists L1, L2, L3, and L4 respectively. Entering the command ANOVA(L1,L2,L3,L4) found in STAT>TESTS>F:ANOVA generated the following One-way ANOVA table shown in Figures 16.22 and 16.23.

FIGURE 16.22

FIGURE 16.23

Compare the statistical computations appearing in the One-way ANOVA table computed using the TI-83 Plus to the statistical results shown in Table 16.26 of Example 16.6. Notice the test statistic F computed by the TI-83 Plus is 4.94 while the computed test statistic F appearing in Table 16.26 is 4.95. What do you think attributed to this discrepancy? Notice that the TI-83 Plus uses the statistical terms Factor and Error. What statistical terms within Table 16.26 refer to the terms Factor and Error? Explain. The TI-83 Plus also displays the value of the pooled standard deviation, Sxp, as 1.17.

KEY TERMS

F-Distribution   872
F-Test   879
Test statistic   882
Test statistic F   882
Critical F-Value   878
Analysis of Variance, ANOVA   886

One-way ANOVA   892
Between Variance   887
Within Variance   886
Total Variance   886
Treatment Variance   887
Error Variance   887

Experimental Variance   887
Pooling Variance   888
Sums of Squares, SS   898
Mean Square, MS   903
ANOVA Table   901
Two-Way ANOVA   919

SECTION EXERCISES

Sections 16.1–16.2

1. ANOVA is an acronym for _____.

2. The F-Distribution is a family of distributions composed of the value of the variances for samples drawn from two distinct _____ populations with equal _____.

3. The symbol used to represent the variance of a sample selected from population 2 is _____.

4. The formula to compute the test statistic F is given by: F= _____.

5. If $s_1^2 = 12.93$ and $s_2^2 = 8.47$, then F= _____.

6. The shape of the F-Distribution is _____. However, as the degrees of freedom increases, the shape approaches a _____.

7. The peak or modal value of the F-Distribution is approximately _____.

8. In the expression $F_{0.01}(10, 20)$, the quantity 0.01 represents the _____, the value 10 represents the _____, while the value 20 represents _____.

9. From Table VII, the value of $F_{0.01}(10, 20)$ is _____.

10. If a test statistic F is around one, then the population variances are approximately equal.
(T/F)

11. Unlike standard deviations, the test statistics F are sometimes negative.
(T/F)

12. There is a different F-Distribution for each set of degrees of freedom associated with the numerator and denominator of the test statistic F.
(T/F)

Use **Table VII: Critical Values of the F-Distribution in Appendix D** to answer questions 13 – 17.

13. Find the critical F-value if $df_{numerator} = 8$, $df_{denominator} = 9$ and $\alpha = 0.01$.

14. Find the critical F-value if $dfs_1^2 = 24$, $dfs_2^2 = 22$ and $\alpha = 0.01$.

15. Find the critical F-value, $F_\alpha(dfs_1^2, dfs_2^2)$, expressed as $F_{0.01}(13,20)$.

16. Find the critical F-value, $F_{0.10}(35,45)$.

17. Place the critical F-values on the following F-Distribution graph.
(a) $F_{0.10}(30,40)$
(b) $F_{0.05}(30,40)$
(c) $F_{0.025}(30,40)$
(d) $F_{0.01}(30,40)$

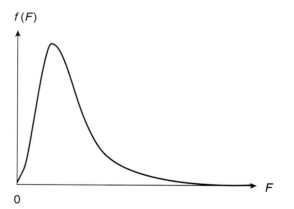

f (F)

0   F

Section 16.3

18. In an F-test, the null hypothesis: the variance of population 1 and the variance of population 2 are equal is symbolized as _____.

The alternative hypothesis: the variance of population 1, and the variance of population 2 are **not** equal is symbolized as _____.

19. In an F-test, the test statistic is computed using the formula: $F =$ _____.

20. In an F-test, if the test statistic, F, is greater than the critical F-value, symbolized $F\alpha/2(dfs_1^2, dfs_2^2)$, then the population variances are _____ _____ at the significance level, α.

21. To perform an F-test, which represents the null hypothesis?
(a) $H_0: \sigma_1^2 = \sigma_2^2$ (b) $H_0: \sigma_1 = \sigma_2$ (c) $H_0: \mu_1 = \mu_2$
(d) $H_0: p_1 = p_2$

For questions 22 to 26:

If $F_{0.025}(12,20)$, is the critical F-value for an F-Test, then which number represents:

22. the degrees of freedom for the larger variance?
(a) 21   (b) 12   (c) 20   (d) 13

23. the degrees of freedom for the smaller variance?
(a) 21   (b) 12   (c) 20   (d) 13

24. the sample size for the larger variance?
(a) 21   (b) 12   (c) 20   (d) 13

25. the sample size for the smaller variance?
(a) 21   (b) 12   (c) 20   (d) 13

26. the value for the critical F-statistic?
(a) 2.68   (b) 2.28   (c) 3.07   (d) 2.54

27. The F-test is a hypothesis testing procedure to determine if sample variances are different.
(T/F)

28. (a) Compute the test statistic F for the following sample variances.
$s_1^2 = 10$ $s_2^2 = 6$
$n_1 = 22$ $n_2 = 25$
(b) Conduct an F-Test for the equality of the population variances using an $\alpha = 0.05$.

29. (a) Compute the test statistic F for the following sample variances.
$s_1^2 = 6.25$ $s_2^2 = 9.85$
$n_1 = 50$ $n_2 = 50$
(b) Conduct an F-Test for the equality of the population variances using an $\alpha = 0.10$.

30. (a) Compute the test statistic F for the following sample variances.
$s_1^2 = 18$ $s_2^2 = 16$
$n_1 = 12$ $n_2 = 15$
(b) Conduct an F-Test for the equality of the population variances using an $\alpha = 0.05$.

31. (a) Compute the test statistic F for the following sample variances.
$s_1^2 = 49$ $s_2^2 = 18$
$n_1 = 21$ $n_2 = 22$
(b) Conduct an F-Test for the equality of the population variances using an $\alpha = 0.05$.

32. (a) Compute the test statistic F for the following sample variances.
$s_1^2 = 4.25$ $s_2^2 = 9.45$
$n_1 = 40$ $n_2 = 40$
(b) Conduct an F-Test for the equality of the population variances using an $\alpha = 0.10$.

33. (a) Compute the test statistic F for the following sample variances.

$s_1^2 = 1.6 \qquad s_2^2 = 3.8$
$n_1 = 100 \qquad n_2 = 100$

(b) Conduct an F-Test for the equality of the population variances using an $\alpha = 0.10$.

34. (a) Compute the test statistic F for the following samples.

sample 1	sample 2
2.4	5.6
7.8	6.7
8.9	5.9
5.8	8.05
6.7	8.93
8.8	7.34

(b) Conduct an F-Test for the equality of the population variances using an $\alpha = 0.05$.

35. (a) Compute the test statistic F for the following samples.

sample 1	sample 2
112	111
146	137
134	88
156	109
126	98
114	122
	149
	159

(b) Conduct an F-Test for the equality of the population variances using an $\alpha = 0.02$.

36. (a) Compute the test statistic F for the following samples.

sample 1	sample 2
3	11
7	13
9	8
23	10
5	9
18	12
	14
	15

(b) Conduct an F-Test for the equality of the population variances using an $\alpha = 0.02$.

37. Kathleen, an educational psychologist, is interested in the academic achievement of third graders enrolled in a special computer assisted problem solving program. Prior to the beginning of the school year, the total group of third graders and the total group of teachers are randomly assigned to two treatment groups within their school. Treatment Group 1 contains third graders not enrolled in the special computer assisted problem solving program, whereas, Treatment Group 2 contains students that are enrolled in the special computer assisted problem solving program. Kathleen would like to pool the sample variances but first she must perform an F-Test. Using the data within the table determine if Kathleen could pool the sample variances. ($\alpha = 0.10$).

Treatment Group	Mean Achievement	Variance	Sample Size
Group 1	74.6	75.9	31
Group 2	115.8	38.4	41

38. Good neighbor Dave runs a limousine service from Hempstead, New York to JFK airport. Dave is considering one of two routes. The first is via Sunrise Highway and the other is the Southern State Parkway. Dave decided to conduct a study of both routes and compares and finds that the mean times for the routes are very similar, but there is more variation in the Sunrise Highway route, since it contains more stoplights than the Southern State Parkway route. But the Parkway route is somewhat longer in miles. The statistics recorded by Dave for his study are listed in the following table. Use the F-test to determine if there really is a difference in the variation of the two routes at $\alpha = 0.05$.

Route	Mean Time(MIN)	Variance	Sample Size
Sunrise Highway	25	169	8
Southern State Pkwy	28	25	8

39. A medical researcher decides to perform an experiment comparing the effects of calcium and a placebo on the blood pressure of males between the ages of 40 and 55. The researcher wants to use a two sample t test where a pooled standard deviation is to be calculated. Since the procedure requires equal population standard deviations, an F-Test is called upon to determine if the population standard deviations are equal. The experimental data produce two standard deviations. The larger of the two is s = 8.45 from 10 observations, while the smaller is s = 6.14 using 11 observations. Do these results support the use of the two sample t test with a pooled standard deviation? (use $\alpha = 0.02$)

16.4 Section Exercises

40. The variability in the differences among the individual data values of each group is called _____.

41. The variability in the differences among the sample means is called _____.

42. In an experiment, if all the subjects were grouped into one overall sample, the variability in the differences among all the subjects is called _____.

43. Another name for error variance is _____.

44. The relationship of the three variances: within, between and total is: _____ variance equals _____ variance + _____ variance.

45. The symbol SS is an abbreviation for _____ and is computed using the expression _____.

46. If the $SS_{(within\ treatments)} = 140$, and the value of $SS_{(total)} = 190$ then $SS_{(between\ treatments)}$ is:
(a) 50 (b) 140 (c) 330 (d) not enough information

47. If the $SS_{\text{(between treatments)}} = 33$, and the value of $SS_{\text{(total)}}$ =117 then $SS_{\text{(within treatments)}}$ is:
(a) 33   (b) 84   (c) 150   (d) not enough information

48. Between Group Variance is often referred to as Experimental Variance.
(T/F)

49. If the variance due to treatment is zero, then the Within Group Variance must equal the Total Variance.
(T/F)

50. Consider the following information about three different populations:

	Population one	Population two	Population three
Population means μ	23	23	23
Population variances Within each treatment σ^2	4	4	4

(a) Identity the population variance within each group.
(b) Find the average within group variance.
(c) Calculate the between group variance.
(d) Determine the total group variance.
(e) Is the Total group variance due solely to the Within group variance? Explain.

51. Consider the following information about three different populations:

	Population one	Population two	Population three
Population means μ	100	150	200
Population variances Within each treatment σ^2	4	4	4

(a) Identity the population variance within each group.
(b) Find the average within group variance.
(c) Calculate the between group variance.
(d) Determine the total group variance.
(e) Is the Total group variance due solely to the Within group variance? Explain.

52. Consider the following information about three different populations:

	Population one	Population two	Population three
Population means μ	350	400	450
Population variances Within each treatment σ^2	100	100	100

(a) Identity the population variance within each group.
(b) Find the average within group variance.
(c) Calculate the between group variance.
(d) Determine the total group variance.
(e) Is the total group variance due solely to the within group variance? Explain.

53. Data Values of a Population of 21 Students Subdivided into Three Groups

Treatment 1	Treatment 2	Treatment 3
10	24	38
12	26	40
14	28	42
16	30	44
18	32	46
20	34	48
22	36	50

Population means μ	16	30	44
Population variances Within each treatment σ^2	16	16	16

(a) Calculate $SS_{\text{(within treatments)}}$ ·
(b) Calculate $SS_{\text{(between treatments)}}$·
(c) Calculate $SS_{\text{(total)}}$.
(d) Is the relationship
$SS_{\text{(between treatments)}} + SS_{\text{(within treatments)}} = SS_{\text{(total)}}$
True?
(e) Identity the population variance within each group.
(f) Find the average within group variance.
(g) Calculate the between group variance.
(h) Determine the total group variance.
(i) Is the Total group variance due solely to the Within group variance? Explain.

54. Data Values of a Population of 15 Students Subdivided into Three Groups

Treatment 1	Treatment 2	Treatment 3
23	34	45
26	37	48
28	39	50
35	46	57
39	50	61

Population means μ	30.2	41.2	52.2
Population variances Within each treatment σ^2	34.96	34.96	34.96

(a) Calculate $SS_{\text{(within treatments)}}$ ·
(b) Calculate $SS_{\text{(between treatments)}}$·
(c) Calculate $SS_{\text{(total)}}$.
(d) Is the relationship
$SS_{\text{(between treatments)}} + SS_{\text{(within treatments)}} = SS_{\text{(total)}}$
True?
(e) Identity the population variance within each group.
(f) Find the average within group variance.
(g) Calculate the between group variance.
(h) Determine the total group variance.
(i) Is the Total group variance due solely to the Within group variance? Explain.

55. Data Values of a Population of 15 Scores Subdivided into Three Groups

	Treatment 1	Treatment 2	Treatment 3
	115	121	112
	118	124	115
	121	127	118
	124	130	121
	127	133	124
Population means			
μ	121	127	118
Population variances			
Within each treatment			
σ^2	18	18	18

(a) Calculate $SS_{(within\ treatments)}$.

(b) Calculate $SS_{(between\ treatments)}$.

(c) Calculate $SS_{(total)}$.

(d) Is the relationship
$SS_{(between\ treatments)} + SS_{(within\ treatments)} = SS_{(total)}$
True? Verify your results.

(e) Identity the population variance within each group.

(f) Find the average within group variance.

(g) Calculate the between group variance.

(h) Determine the total group variance.

(i) Is the total group variance due solely to the within group variance? Explain.

Section 16.5

56. In this section we have presented the one-way analysis of variance procedure. Why is the procedure called "one way"?

57. What are the assumptions necessary to use the one-way ANOVA procedure?

58. Which distribution is used to test the calculated results?

59. One-way ANOVA involves the analysis of one independent variable with two or more treatment levels. (T/F)

60. To use one-way ANOVA, how may independent variables are compared?
(a) 1   (b) 2   (c) at least 2
(d) not enough information

61. The ANOVA procedure uses the normal distribution as the model distribution to determine differences between experimental conditions. (T/F)

62. The ANOVA procedure assumes that the variation between the sample means is zero. (T/F)

63. The test statistic F is found by dividing the within group variance by the between group variance. (T/F)

64. The ANOVA technique compares variances under the assumption that the variance among all levels is the same. (T/F)

65. In ANOVA, as the value of between group variance increases, the value of the test statistic F will _____. As the value of the within group variance increases, the value of the test statistic F will _____.

66. The formula for the degrees of freedom for the between group variance is: df(between groups) = k – 1, where k represents _____. The formula for df(between treatments) = _____.

67. The formula for the degrees of freedom for the within group variance is: df(within groups) = N – k, where k represents _____ and N is _____.

68. If a sample one contains 15 data values, and sample two contains 18 data values, then the degrees of freedom for the F-value is
(a) $df = 33$
(b) $df = 31$
(c) $df = (15,18)$
(d) $df = (14,17)$

69. In the ANOVA Hypothesis Test, the null hypothesis is stated as: the _____ means are _____.
The alternative hypothesis states that there is at least _____ mean of the _____ which is _____.

70. In the ANOVA Hypothesis Test, assuming the null hypothesis is true, then we would expect the value of the test statistic F to be around the value _____.

71. Which null hypothesis is used for the ANOVA procedure?
(a) all sample means are the same.
(b) not all sample means are equal.
(c) all population variances are equal.
(d) all population means are equal.

72. If $\alpha = 0.05$, the $df_{between\ groups}$ is 4 and $df_{within\ groups}$ is 26, then the critical F-value is:
(a) 5.77   (b) 3.78   (c) 2.74   (d) 2.17

73. If the critical F-value is greater than the test statistic (i.e. the calculated F-statistic) then what is the appropriate conclusion.
(a) fail to reject H_0
(b) reject H_0
(c) reject H_a
(d) not enough information

74. In the ANOVA hypothesis test, if the critical F-value is $F_{0.01}(7,22)$, then the df(within groups) is _____ and the df(between treatments) = _____.

75. In the ANOVA hypothesis test, if the calculated test statistic F is greater than the critical F-value, then the decision is to _____.

76. The formula to compute the $SS_{(total)}$ is:
$SS_{(total)} =$ _____ + _____.

77. The formula to compute the $SS_{(between\ treatments)}$ for four levels of a factor is: $SS_{(between\ treatments)} =$ _____ - _____.

78. The formula to compute the $SS_{(within\ treatments)}$ for four levels of a factor is: $SS_{(within\ treatments)} =$ _____ - _____.

79. Identify what each of the following notations represent:
$n_4 =$ _____
$N =$ _____
$T_3 =$ _____

80. If $\Sigma T_1 = 3, \Sigma T_2 = 6, \Sigma T_3 = 12, \Sigma T_4 = 15, N = 12, \Sigma X^2 = 154, n_1 = n_2 = n_3 = n_4 = 3$ then:

$\Sigma X =$ ____,

$SS_{(total)} =$ _____,

$SS_{(between\ treatments)} =$ _____

$SS_{(within\ treatments)} =$ _____

$k =$ _____

$df_{(between)} =$ _____

$df_{(within)} =$ _____

$df_{(total)} =$ _____

$MS_{(between)} =$ _____

$MS_{(within)} =$ _____

Calculated test statistic F = _____

Critical F-value = _____

81. If the $SS_{(total)} = 87$ and the $SS_{(between\ treatments)} = 53$, then the $SS_{(within\ treatments)} =$ _____.

If the $df_{(between)} = 4$, and $df_{(total)} = 40$, then $df_{(within)} =$ _____.

The $MS_{(between)} =$ _____, $MS_{(within)} =$ _____ and the calculated F-statistic = _____.

82. Use the information within the following table:

Treatment #1	Treatment #2	Treatment #3	Treatment #4	Treatment #5
n = 7	n = 6	n = 7	n = 8	n = 7
$\Sigma T_1 = 182$	$\Sigma T_2 = 162$	$\Sigma T_3 = 182$	$\Sigma T_4 = 224$	$\Sigma T_5 = 175$
$\Sigma T_1^2 = 4754$	$\Sigma T_2^2 = 4396$	$\Sigma T_3^2 = 4764$	$\Sigma T_4^2 = 6294$	$\Sigma T_5^2 = 4407$

to determine the quantities:

a) $\Sigma X^2 =$ _____

b) $(\Sigma X)^2 =$ _____

c) N= _____

d) $SS_{(total)} =$ _____

e) $SS_{(between\ treatments)} =$ _____

f) $SS_{(within\ treatments)} =$ _____

g) $df_{(between)} =$ _____

h) $df_{(total)} =$ _____

i) $df_{(within)} =$ _____

j) $MS_{(between)} =$ _____

k) $MS_{(within)} =$ _____

l) calculated test statistic F = _____

Use the F-Distribution Table located in Appendix D: Table VII to answer questions 83 – 91.

83. Find the critical F-value

if $df_{numerator = 10}, df_{denominator} = 10$ and _ = 0.05.

84. Find the critical F-value

if $df_{numerator} = 18, df_{denominator} = 19$ and $\alpha = 0.01$.

85. Find the critical F-value

if $dfs^2_1 = 17, dfs^2_2 = 15$ and $\alpha = 0.05$.

86. Find the critical F-value

if $dfs_1^2 = 22, dfs_2^2 = 24$ and $\alpha = 0.01$.

87. Find the critical F-value,

$F_\alpha(dfs_1^2, dfs_2^2)$, expressed as $F_{0.05}(19,20)$.

88. Find the critical F-value,

$F_\alpha(dfs_1^2, dfs_2^2)$, expressed as $F_{0.01}(23,20)$.

89. Find the critical F-value, $F_{0.025}(15,15)$.

90. Find the critical F-value, $F_{0.10}(25,35)$.

91. Place the critical F-values on the graph.

(a) $F_{0.10}(20,20)$

(b) $F_{0.05}(20,20)$

(c) $F_{0.025}(20,20)$

(d) $F_{0.01}(20,20)$

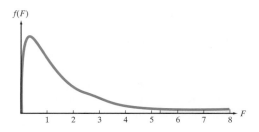

92. Examine the ANOVA table. Notice that you are given information about Sums of Squares for the Between group variance and the Within group variance along with their respective degrees of freedom.

(a) Complete the table.

(b) Determine if the calculated test statistic F is significant at $\alpha = 0.05$.

Source of Variation	Sum of Squares SS	Degrees of Freedom df	Mean Square MS	Calculated test statistic F
Between	15.51	3		
Within	27.43	16		
Total				

93. Examine the ANOVA table. Notice that you are given information about Sums of Squares for the Between group variance and the Within group variance along with their respective degrees of freedom.

(a) Complete the table.

(b) Determine if the calculated test statistic F is significant at $\alpha = 0.01$.

Source of Variation	Sum of Squares SS	Degrees of Freedom df	Mean Square MS	Calculated test statistic F
Between	39.2	1		
Within	392.6	18		
Total				

94. Examine the ANOVA table. Notice that you are given information about Sums of Squares for the Between group variance and the Within group variance along with their respective degrees of freedom.
(a) Complete the table.
(b) Determine if the calculated test statistic F is significant at $\alpha = 0.01$.

Source of Variation	Sum of Squares SS	Degrees of Freedom df	Mean Square MS	Calculated test statistic F
Between	14.79	3		
Within	43.84	21		
Total				

95. Fill in the missing values, a through e in the following ANOVA table. Determine the critical F-value $F_{0.05}(df \text{ between}, df \text{ within})$. Is the result statistically significant?

The ANOVA TABLE

Source of Variation	Sum of Squares SS	Degrees of Freedom df	Mean Square MS	Calculated test statistic F
Between	456	2	c	e
Within	140	b	d	
Total	a	11		

96. Fill in the missing values, a through e in the following ANOVA table. Determine the critical $F_{0.01}(df \text{ between}, df \text{ within})$. Is the result statistically significant?

The ANOVA TABLE

Source of Variation	Sum of Squares SS	Degrees of Freedom df	Mean Square MS	Calculated test statistic F
Between	896	b	c	e
Within	a	18	d	
Total	1931	21		

97. For the following sample data. Test the hypothesis that the means are equal at the 0.05 significance level.

Treatment one	Treatment two	Treatment Three
6	3	4
8	2	5
9	1	4
9	2	5

a) State the null and alternative hypotheses.
b) Identify the model distribution.
c) Determine the decision rule.
d) Compute all Sum of Squares and Degrees of Freedom.
e) Complete an ANOVA Table.
f) State the conclusion regarding the null hypothesis.

98. For the following sample data. Test the hypothesis that the means are equal at the 0.05 significance level.

Treatment 1	Treatment 2	Treatment 3	Treatment 4
13	14	19	13
11	12	13	15
15	10	17	17
13	11		

a) State the null and alternative hypotheses.
b) Identify the model distribution.
c) Determine the decision rule.
d) Compute all Sum of Squares and Degrees of Freedom.
e) Complete an ANOVA Table.
f) State the conclusion regarding the null hypothesis.

99. A study to compare the playing weights of female athletes in the sports of basketball, track and soccer produced a Mean Square for treatment of 239.5 and a Mean Square Within of 45.3.
(a) State the null and alternative hypotheses of interest.
(b) Calculate the test statistic F for this test.
(c) If the study used 10 females per sport do the results indicate a significant result at $\alpha = 0.01$?.

100. The human resource manager of Bigco Corporation is investigating employee down time on the job. Four types of employees were examined. Of the four types of employees random samples of 20 were chosen. A Mean Square Between the groups was calculated to be 151.4 and a Mean Square Within the groups produced a value of 73.8.
(a) State the null and alternative hypotheses of interest.
(b) Calculate the test statistic F for this test.
(c) Do the results indicate a significant result at $\alpha = 0.05$?

101. A medical technician wants to compare the water holding properties of three different brands of diapers. The technician devises a test that measures the maximum amount of fluid that each diaper can hold. The following results (in fluid ounces) were obtained:

Brand 1	Brand 2	Brand 3
5.6	6.1	4.5
5.8	6.0	5.5
5.1	5.9	4.9
6.1	6.2	4.8
5.7	5.8	5.2

Use the one-way ANOVA procedure to determine whether the differences among the means of each sample is significant at $\alpha = 0.05$.

102. To study the effectiveness of four kinds of packaging, a processor of yogurt foods obtained the following data on the numbers of sales for five different weeks.

Packaging Type(number of Sales per week in hundreds of units)

one	*two*	*three*	*four*
6.0	5.5	5.5	7.1
5.2	6.6	5.6	6.5
5.6	6.8	7.0	6.0
5.2	5.7	5.8	5.9
6.5	5.5	5.6	6.2

Use the one-way ANOVA procedure to determine whether the differences among the means of each sample is significant at $\alpha = 0.01$.

103. The ages and the mercury levels of 12 Loons inspected in a Lake in Southern Maine are listed in the following table.

Mercury Levels (ppm)

Young of the year	Yearlings	Two years or older
0.54	0.65	1.02
0.59	0.82	0.83
0.57	0.83	0.78
0.44	0.77	0.95

Using the 1% significance level, use the five step hypothesis testing procedure to test the null hypothesis that the mean mercury level for the Loons are all equal.

104. The police commissioner of the City of Oz has four districts. She wants to determine if there is a difference in the mean number of traffic tickets served in the four districts. The following data reflects the number of tickets served for a random sample of five business days.

Can the police commissioner conclude there is a significant difference with $\alpha = 0.05$ in the mean number of tickets served?

Number of Tickets served

District 1	*District 2*	*District 3*	*District 4*
23	31	22	26
25	23	24	27
24	28	25	28
25	29	23	25
24	28	22	30

CHAPTER REVIEW

105. If $s_1^2 = 14.78$ and $s_2^2 = 7.93$, then F = _____.

106. An F-curve is dependent upon the degrees of freedom of the sample _____.

107. The F-Distribution is a family of distributions composed of the value of the standard deviations for samples drawn from two distinct populations. (T/F)

108. If a test statistic F is much greater than one, then the population variances are approximately equal. (T/F)

109. Which is **not** a characteristic of an F-Distribution?

(a) Each sample used in the test statistic F is independent.

(b) The populations for each sample is assumed to be normally distributed.

(c) The F-Distribution is assumed to be approximately normally distributed.

(d) The modal value of the F-Distribution is assumed to be 1.

Use **Table VII: Critical Values of the F-Distribution in Appendix D** to answer questions 110–113.

110. Find the critical F-value if $df_{numerator} = 15$, $df_{denominator} = 20$ and $\alpha = 0.05$.

111. Find the critical F-value if $dfs_1^2 = 7$, $dfs_2^2 = 10$ and $\alpha = 0.05$.

112. Find the critical F-value, $F\alpha(dfs_1^2, dfs_2^2)$, expressed as $F_{0.05}(20,19)$.

113. Find the critical F-value, $F_{0.025}(15,17)$.

FOR QUESTIONS 114 to 118:

If $F_{0.01}(9,25)$, is the critical F-value for an F-Test, then which number represents:

114. the degrees of freedom for the larger variance?
(a) 9   (b) 12   (c) 25   (d) 1

115. the degrees of freedom for the smaller variance?
(a) 9   (b) 12   (c) 25   (d) 1

116. the sample size for the larger variance?
(a) 10   (b) 34   (c) 26   (d) 35

117. the sample size for the smaller variance?
(a) 10   (b) 34   (c) 26   (d) 35

118. the value for the critical F-value?
(a) 4.73   (b) 3.22   (c) 2.28   (d) 1.89

119. (a) Compute the test statistic F for the following sample variances.

$$s_1^2 = 2.9 \qquad s_2^2 = 1.08$$
$$n_1 = 19 \qquad n_2 = 22$$

(b) Conduct an F-Test for the equality of the population variances using an $\alpha = 0.05$.

120. (a) Compute the test statistic F for the following sample variances.

$$s_1^2 = 136 \qquad s_2^2 = 398$$
$$n_1 = 100 \qquad n_2 = 100$$

(b) Conduct an F-Test for the equality of the population variances using an $\alpha = 0.10$.

121. (a) Compute the test statistic F for the following samples.

sample 1	sample 2
4	5
7	3
6	4
3	8
6	8
8	12

(b) Conduct an F-Test for the equality of the population variances using an $\alpha = 0.05$.

122. Mark of East Bluff Glass replaces car windshields. During the past year Mark has rejected an average of 9 windshield replacement glass per month with a variance of 2. For the same period, Lori who also replaces windshields, has rejected an average of 8.5 windshield replacement glass per month with a variance of 1.5. At the 0.05 significance level, can we conclude that there is more variation in the number of rejects per day attributed to Mark?

123. Experimental or Treatment Variance is also referred to as _____.

124. Using the expressions SS and df, the formula for the sample variance is: $s^2 = $ _____.

125. Using the following expressions: $SS_{(between\ treatments)}$, $SS_{(total)}$ and $SS_{(within\ treatments)}$, write a relationship that is always true. _____ = _____ + _____.

126. If $SS_{(between\ treatments)} = 14$, the $SS_{(within\ treatments)} = 160$, then the value of $SS_{(total)}$ is:
(a) 146   (b) 160   (c) 174
(d) not enough information

127. Consider the following information about three different populations:

	Population one	Population two	Population three
Population means			
μ	100	100	100
Population variances			
Within each treatment			
σ^2	25	25	25

(a) Identity the population variance within each group.
(b) Find the average within group variance.
(c) Calculate the between group variance.
(d) Determine the total group variance.
(e) Is the total group variance due solely to the within group variance? Explain.

128. Consider the following information about three different populations:

	Population one	Population two	Population three
Population means			
μ	200	250	300
Population variances			
Within each treatment			
σ^2	7	7	7

(a) Identity the population variance within each group.
(b) Find the average within group variance.
(c) Calculate the between group variance.
(d) Determine the total group variance.
(e) Is the Total group variance due solely to the Within group variance? Explain.

129. Data Values of a Population of 21 Students Subdivided into Three Groups

Treatment 1	Treatment 2	Treatment 3
20	34	48
22	36	50
24	38	52
26	40	54
28	42	56
30	44	58
32	46	60

Population means			
μ	26	40	54
Population variances			
Within each treatment			
σ^2	16	16	16

(a) Calculate $SS_{(within\ treatments)}$.
(b) Calculate $SS_{(between\ treatments)}$.
(c) Calculate $SS_{(total)}$.
(d) Is the relationship
$$SS_{(between\ treatments)} + SS_{(within\ treatments)} = SS_{(total)}$$
True?
(e) Identity the population variance within each group.
(f) Find the average within group variance.
(g) Calculate the between group variance.
(h) Determine the total group variance.
(i) Is the Total group variance due solely to the Within group variance? Explain.

130. Data Values of a Population of 12 scores Subdivided into Three Groups

	Treatment 1	Treatment 2	Treatment 3
	70	74	78
	74	78	82
	78	82	86
	82	86	90
Population means			
μ	76	80	84
Population variances			
Within each treatment			
σ^2	20	20	20

(a) Calculate $SS_{(within\ treatments)}$.
(b) Calculate $SS_{(between\ treatments)}$.
(c) Calculate $SS_{(total)}$.
(d) Is the relationship
$$SS_{(between\ treatments)} + SS_{(within\ treatments)} = SS_{(total)}$$
True? Verify your answer.
(e) Identity the population variance within each group.
(f) Find the average within group variance.
(g) Calculate the between group variance.
(h) Determine the total group variance.
(i) Is the total group variance due solely to the within group variance? Explain.

131. Identify what each of the following notations represent:
$n_6 = $ _____
$N = $ _____
$T_5 = $ _____

132. If $\Sigma T_1 = 6, \Sigma T_2 = 18, \Sigma T_3 = 24, \Sigma T_4 = 30, N = 12, \Sigma X^2 = 612, n_1 = n_2 = n_3 = n_4 = 3$ then:
$\Sigma X = $ _____,
$SS_{(total)} = $ _____,
$SS_{(between\ treatments)} = $ _____
$SS_{(within\ treatments)} = $ _____
$k = $ _____
$df_{(between)} = $ _____
$df_{(within)} = $ _____
$df_{(total)} = $ _____
$MS_{(between)} = $ _____
$MS_{(within)} = $ _____
Calculated test statistic F = _____
Critical F-statistic = _____

133. Examine the ANOVA table. Notice that you are given information about Sums of Squares for the Between group variance and the Within group variance along with their respective degrees of freedom.
(a) Complete the table.
(b) Determine if the calculated test statistic F is significant at $\alpha = 0.05$.

Source of Variation	Sum of Squares SS	Degrees of Freedom df	Mean Square MS	Calculated test statistic F
Between	150.51	4e		
Within	87.43	26		
Total				

134. Debbie wants to compare the effectiveness of three methods of teaching word processing. Method 1 is a traditional lecturing technique without instructor accessing a computer. Method 2 is in a laboratory setting with instructor using a computer to illustrate techniques. Method 3 uses no traditional lecturing but rather individual paced learning material with instructor giving individual attention to students having special difficulty. Of the many students taught by one of the three methods the following random samples representing achievement test scores in word processing were obtained:

Method 1	Method 2	Method 3
69	70	88
73	75	78
63	74	84
67	77	82

Use the one-way ANOVA procedure to determine whether the differences among the means of each sample is significant at $\alpha = 0.01$.

135. The following table lists the hourly salaries of certain randomly selected college students working part time representing colleges from the Northeast, Midwest and Southwest portions of the United States.

Northeast	Midwest	Southwest
7.80	6.90	7.60
8.65	7.10	6.90
7.75	6.40	7.85
9.40	6.90	8.10
8.80	6.75	6.85

Using the $\alpha = 0.05$ significance level, use the five step hypothesis testing procedure to test the null hypothesis that the mean hourly wage for colleges students working part time employment from colleges in the Northeast, Midwest and Southwest portions of the United States are all equal.

>>> **WHAT DO YOU THINK?**

136. In Case Study 16.2, we discussed the effect of school size and age of teachers on job satisfaction and job stress for the study entitled Teacher Job Satisfaction and Teacher Job Stress: School Size, Age and Teaching Experience. The subjects selected for the study were 229 North Florida and South Georgia urban secondary school physical education teachers. Two instruments were used to measure the job satisfaction and job re- lated stress of the teachers. A high score on the Job Sat- isfaction Scale indicates a high level of job satisfaction while a high score on the Job-Related Stress Scale indi- cates a high level of job stress. The following tables pre- sent the results of this study which examined the relationship of number of years of teaching with re- spect to job satisfaction and job stress.

Table A
Differences in Job Satisfaction Scores by Number of Years of Teaching Experience

Years of Teaching	Number of Subjects	Mean Scores	Standard Deviation	F-statistic	Probability level
1–5	36	44.42	10.71	0.65	0.63
6–10	62	46.77	11.95		
11–15	66	44.21	14.35		
16–20	36	44.30	13.78		
21+	29	47.65	13.02		
Total	229	45.39			

Table B
Differences in Job Stress Scores by Number of Years of Teaching Experience

Years of Teaching	Number of Subjects	Mean Scores	Standard Deviation	F-statistic	Probability level
1–5	36	42.65	13.62	0.18	0.95
6–10	62	42.90	15.07		
11–15	66	42.33	14.46		
16–20	36	41.13	13.78		
21+	29	44.06	14.99		
Total	229	42.57			

For Table A:

a) identify the independent variable. State the differ- ent levels of this variable.

b) compare the mean job satisfaction score for teach- ers with 11–15 years of teaching experience to the mean job satisfaction score for teachers with 21+ years of teaching experience. Interpret the meaning of each mean score.

c) Within which group are the job satisfaction scores more variable? less variable? How would you inter- pret each of these results?

d) What would you compare to determine the between group variance?

e) Explain the meaning of the probability level for the given F-statistic.

f) What are the degrees of freedom for the within groups and the degrees of freedom for the between groups?

g) Based upon the results of Table A, can you conclude that the number of years of teaching experience is a significant factor in their job satisfaction? Explain.

h) Identify the number of years of teaching experience group that had the lowest job satisfaction and the number of years of teaching experience group with the highest job satisfaction. Can you conclude at an alpha level of 0.10 that this difference is significant?

For Table B:

i) identify the independent variable. State the differ- ent levels of this variable.

j) compare the mean job stress score for teachers with 11–15 years of teaching experience to the mean job stress score for teachers with 21+ years of teaching experience. Interpret the meaning of each mean score.

k) Within which group are the job stress scores more variable? less variable? How would you interpret each of these results?

l) What would you compare to determine the between group variance?

m) Explain the meaning of the probability level for the given F-statistic.

n) What are the degrees of freedom for the within groups and the degrees of freedom for the between groups?

o) Based upon the results of Table B, can you conclude that the number of years of teaching experience is a significant factor in their job stress? Explain.

p) Identify the number of years of teaching experience group that had the lowest job stress and the number of years of teaching experience group with the highest job stress. Can you conclude at an alpha level of 0.10 that this difference is significant?

137. The study entitled Factors In Children's Attitudes Toward Pets which appeared in the journal *Psychological Reports,* 1990, issue 66, investigated the parental attitudes, family size, structure, and presence or absence of household pets as influences on children's attitudes toward pets. The researchers, Kidd & Kidd, believe that attachment to pet animals begin as early as 18 months. Since a child-pet attachment begins at such an early age, Kidd and Kidd decided to investigate the factors which may influence feelings and attitudes toward pets. The researchers administered a Parent Questionnaire to the parents of the 700 children who were the subjects of the study. These subjects were composed of 339 boys and 361 girls between the ages of 6 months and 18 years: 150 boys and 150 girls from two-parent pet-owning homes, 43 boys and 55 girls from one-parent owning homes, 97 boys and 105 girls from two-parent, nonpet-owning homes, and 49 boys and 51 girls from one-parent, nonpet-owning homes.

The Parent Questionnaire were scored for the children's Activities with Pets and Interest in Pet's scales whether or not the family owned a pet. They were scored for a child's Responsibility for Pet Care scale only if the family owned a pet or indicated that the child actually helped with responsible care for a neighbor's or a friend's pet. One aspect of the study was to determine whether the age of the child significantly influenced the scores on each of the three scales. The researchers believed that involvement in activities with and interest in pets were good measures of attachment to pets, who showed more interest in them, and who took more responsibility for them also were reported as having a greater affection for their pets than children who were scored lower on these scales. A higher score on each of these scales is interpreted as displaying more activities with the pets, showing more interest in the pets and more responsibility with the pets. The results of the pet-owning children on the three scales is given in Table C. The results of the nonpet-owning children on the three scales were discussed in Case Study 16.3.

Table C

Mean and Standard Deviations For Pet-Owning Children On Three Scales

	n	Mean	Std Dev
Activities Scale			
Ages			
0–5	120	27.12	6.32
Grade School	141	34.26	8.62
High School	137	35.12	7.98
Interest Scale			
Ages			
0–5	120	19.35	6.40
Grade School	141	24.28	7.71
High School	137	22.63	7.63
Responsibility Scale			
Ages			
0–5	120	2.32	2.17
Grade School	141	6.04	4.04
High School	137	4.48	3.79

Table D

One-Way Analysis of Variance of Activities With Pets, Interest In Pets, and Responsibility For Care of Pets: Scores of Children With Household Pets By Age Groups

Source of Variance	SS	df	MS	F
Activities With Pets				
SS Between Age Groups	140.61	2	70.31	3.34*
SS Within Groups	8314.75	395	21.05	
Interest In Pets				
SS Between Age Groups	88.02	1	86.02	4.53*
SS Within Groups	7702.46	396	19.45	
Responsibility For Care				
SS Between Age Groups	891.52	2	445.76	36.78[†]
SS Within Groups	4786.92	395	12.12	

*$p0.05.$ [†]$p\ 0.0005.$

Using the information on the Activities Scale in Table C and Table D:

a) Identify the independent variable. State the different levels of this variable.

b) Which age group should the greatest activity with pets? the smallest activity with pets?

c) Which age group had the greatest variability in the activities scale with pets? the smallest variability?

d) Which age group had the greatest mean score on the Activities scale? the smallest mean score?

e) Determine the difference between the mean scores of part d? Do you think this difference is significant? If it is significant, state the alpha level and explain how you came to this conclusion.

f) What are the degrees of freedom for the within groups and the degrees of freedom for the between age groups?

g) Determine the Sums of Square due to Factor variance. Determine the Sums of Square due to Error variance.

h) Explain what the MS = 70.31 indicates about the between age groups for the activities scale.

i) Explain what the MS = 21.05 indicates about the within groups for the activities scale.

j) Identify the Mean Square population variance estimate for the variance Between the groups.

k) Identify the Mean Square population variance estimate for the variance within the groups.

l) Based upon the results of Table D, can you conclude that the age of a child is a significant factor in their activities with pets at an alpha level of 0.01? at an alpha level of 0.10? Explain.

Using the information on the Interest Scale in Table C and Table D:

m) Identify the independent variable. State the different levels of this variable.

n) Which age group should the greatest interest with pets? the smallest interest with pets?

o) Which age group had the greatest variability in the interest scale with pets? the smallest variability?

p) Which age group had the greatest mean score on the Interest scale? the smallest mean score?

q) Determine the difference between the mean scores of part p? Do you think this difference is significant? If it is significant, state the alpha level and explain how you came to this conclusion.

r) What are the degrees of freedom for the within groups and the degrees of freedom for the between age groups?

s) Determine the Sums of Square due to Factor variance. Determine the Sums of Square due to Error variance.

t) Explain what the MS = 86.02 indicates about the between age groups for the interest scale.

u) Explain what the MS = 19.45 indicates about the within groups for the interest scale.

v) Identify the Mean Square population variance estimate for the variance Between the groups.

w) Identify the Mean Square population variance estimate for the variance within the groups.

x) Based upon the results of Table D, can you conclude that the age of a child is a significant factor in their interest with pets at an alpha level of 0.01? at an alpha level of 0.10? Explain.

Using the information on the Responsibility Scale in Table C and Table D:

y) Identify the independent variable. State the different levels of this variable.

z) Which age group should the highest responsibility with pets? the lowest responsibility with pets?

aa) Which age group had the greatest variability in the Responsibility Scale with pets? the smallest variability?

bb) Which age group had the greatest mean score on the Responsibility Scale? the smallest mean score?

cc) Determine the difference between the mean scores of part bb? Do you think this difference is significant? If it is significant, state the alpha level and explain how you came to this conclusion.

dd) What are the degrees of freedom for the within groups and the degrees of freedom for the between age groups?

ee) Determine the Sums of Square due to Factor variance. Determine the Sums of Square due to Error variance.

ff) Explain what the MS = 445.76 indicates about the between age groups for the Responsibility Scale.

gg) Explain what the MS = 12.12 indicates about the within groups for the Responsibility Scale.

hh) Identify the Mean Square population variance estimate for the variance Between the groups.

ii) Identify the Mean Square population variance estimate for the variance within the groups.

jj) Based upon the results of Table D, can you conclude that the age of a child is a significant factor in their Responsibility with pets at an alpha level of 0.0001? at an alpha level of 0.01? Explain.

From the results of the previous tables, comment on the following statements.

kk) Why would you think that preschool children would have low activities scores? Comment.

Can we conclude that the Activities scores of preschool children are significantly lower than those of older children? What do you think?

ll) Why would you think that preschool children would have low interest scores? Comment.

Can we conclude that the Interest scores of preschool children are significantly lower than those of older children? What do you think?

mm) Why would you think that the grade school children would have a higher responsibility scores that either the high school or the preschool children? Comment.

Can we conclude that the Responsibility scores of grade school children were significantly higher than those of high school and preschool children? What do you think?

138. Analysis of variance is often used as a statistical procedure in research scenarios in both the natural and social science arenas.
   a) Choose a professional journal from an area of interest and examine the statistical methods used in the analysis of the data to determine if an ANOVA model is employed.
   b) Read the research article and list the hypotheses that have been tested.
   c) Determine if significant results have been found. List these results with their corresponding p-value.
   d) Identify the statistical terms used in the article that are not familiar.

139. a) Develop a questionnaire to determine a student's class, (e.g. freshman, sophomore, junior, senior) and the number of hours the student dedicates to study.
   b) Randomly sample 100 students and administer the questionnaire.
   c) Use the one-way ANOVA procedure outlined in this chapter to test the hypothesis that the mean number of hours dedicated to study by each type student is equal at $\alpha = 0.05$.

140. a) Using a technological tool, input the following data.

C1	C2	C3	C4
82	71	70	65
65	70	65	62
73	64	72	72
71	65	63	64
84	79	59	65
62	68	77	60
67	77	73	68
78	83	65	65
79	78	63	59
79	63	69	72
81	71	71	69
76	72	68	64

   b) Produce an ANOVA Table for this data.
   Identify
   c) the Sums of Square due to Factor variance.
   d) the Sums of Square due to Between group variance.
   e) the Sums of Square due to Error variance.
   f) the Sums of Square due to Within group variance.
   g) the degrees freedom for each sums of square.
   h) the Mean Square population variance estimate for the variance Between the groups.

   i) the Mean Square population variance estimate for the variance within the groups.
   j) the calculated test statistic F.
   k) the p-value for the test statistic F.
   l) Are the group means significantly different if $\alpha = 0.05$?
   m) Are the group means significantly different if $\alpha = 0.01$?

141. A researcher wishes to determine if three different diets result in different average weight losses. Subjects with similar weight problems are chosen for the study and randomly assigned one of the diets. The weight loss (in pounds) after one month are recorded and indicated as follows.

Diet A	Diet B	Diet C
3	24	21
15	12	24
16	10	9
7	11	15
13	5	19
	12	40
		12
		27

   a) Input this data into a technological tool.
   b) Produce an ANOVA Table for this data.
   Identify
   c) the Sums of Square due to Factor variance.
   d) the Sums of Square due to Between group variance.
   e) the Sums of Square due to Error variance.
   f) the Sums of Square due to Within group variance.
   g) the degrees freedom for each sums of square.
   h) the Mean Square population variance estimate for the variance Between the groups.
   i) the Mean Square population variance estimate for the variance within the groups.
   j) the calculated test statistic F.
   k) the p-value for the test statistic F.
   l) Are the group means significantly different if $\alpha = 0.05$?
   m) Are the group means significantly different if $\alpha = 0.01$?

142. Use a technological tool, enter the data for those problems in this chapter. Compare the output generated by the technological tool to the results obtained by pencil and paper calculation.

ANALYZING THE DATABASE USING TECHNOLOGY

The following exercises refer to the file DATABASE listed in Appendix A.

143. Using TECHNOLOGY,
a) on the data values for variable GPA and MAJ perform a one-way ANOVA to determine if there is a significant difference in the mean GPA for the indicated student majors at $\alpha = 0.05$.
b) Identify the independent and dependent variable.
c) What is the calculated test statistic F?
d) Identify the p-value for the test statistic.
e) Is the F-statistic significant?
f) Interpret the results in terms of the null and alternative hypotheses.

144. Using TECHNOLOGY,
a) on the data values for variable GFT and EYE to perform a one-way ANOVA to determine if there is a significant difference in the mean GFT for the indicated student eye color at $\alpha = 0.05$.
b) Identify the independent and dependent variable.
c) What is the calculated test statistic F?
d) Identify the p-value for the test statistic.
e) Is the F-statistic significant?
f) Interpret the results in terms of the null and alternative hypotheses.

145. Using TECHNOLOGY,
a) on the data values for variable AM and HR to perform a one-way ANOVA to determine if there is a significant difference in the mean AM for the indicated hair colors at $\alpha = 0.05$.
b) Identify the independent and dependent variable.
c) What is the calculated test statistic F?
d) Identify the p-value for the test statistic.
e) Is the F-statistic significant?
f) Interpret the results in terms of the null and alternative hypotheses.

146. Using TECHNOLOGY,
a) on the data values for variable STY and MAJ to perform a one-way ANOVA to determine if there is a significant difference in the mean STY for the indicated student majors at $\alpha = 0.05$.
b) Identify the independent and dependent variable.
c) What is the calculated test statistic F?
d) Identify the p-value for the test statistic.
e) Is the F-statistic significant?
f) Interpret the results in terms of the null and alternative hypotheses.

CHAPTER TEST

147. The F-Distribution is a symmetric and approximately bell shaped distribution. (T/F)

148. If $s_1^2 = 15.76$ and $s_2^2 = 13.85$, then F= _____.

149. When given population variances it is always true that Between Variance + Within Variance = Total Variance. (T/F)

150. Error Variance is often due to the individual differences for subjects within the treatment groups. (T/F)

151. Find the critical F-value if $dfs_1^2 = 22$, $dfs_2^2 = 24$ and $\alpha = 0.01$.

152. (a) Compute the test statistic F for the following sample variances.

$$s_1^2 = 44 \qquad s_2^2 = 58$$
$$n_1 = 33 \qquad n_2 = 28$$

(b) Conduct the test statistic F for the equality of the population variances using an $\alpha = 0.05$.

153. Harmony Music Associates is interested in the radio listening habits of men and women between the ages of 18 and 25. They found that although the mean number of minutes per day was similar for both men and women, the variances were not. Forty men and 48 women were sampled and the relevant statistics for the study is listed in the following table. Use the F-test to determine if there is statistical difference in the variation of the radio listening habits of men and women. (Use $\alpha = 0.10$).

Sex	Mean Time (MIN/day)	Variance	Sample Size
Men	98	23	8
Women	93	15	8

154. At the beginning of this chapter, Example 16.2 explored a problem that can be analyzed using the ANOVA procedure developed in this section. The example has been reprinted in this exercise. Apply ANOVA to answer the question posed by Jim.

Jim is interested in buying a highly rated computer. He checks a PC magazine and selects three manufacturers. From these manufacturers he draws a sample of computers rated by the magazine. Table 16.30 displays the samples with their respective means and variances.

Table 16.30
Ratings of Computers from a PC Magazine

Computers	*Compost*	*Dovell*	*ACE Power*
	29.2	33.6	24.4
	21.4	44.4	42.0
	47.1	25.2	25.2
	34.0	33.6	34.9
	37.1	46.4	52.9
$\bar{x}$	33.76	36.64	35.88
s^2	90.63	76.21	143.52

Perform a hypothesis test at $\alpha = 0.01$ to determine which manufacturer has a significantly higher rating.

CHAPTER 17

Nonparametric Statistics

Contents

17.1 INTRODUCTION

So far we have explored many elementary concepts of statistics. We studied descriptive statistics through the concepts of graphing, central tendency and variability. We introduced the concepts of probability and theoretical distributions such as the normal, binomial, t and F. The role of hypothesis testing and estimation as a branch of inferential statistics has been extensively examined. Linear correlation and regression was explored to measure the strength of the relationship between two variables and how such a relationship can be modelled.

Many of these statistical models were based on certain basic assumptions about the populations from which sample data was collected. Some of these assumptions were:

1. the random samples are selected from a *normal population.*
2. the population variances are *equal.*

Inferential statistics which are based on assumptions such as the shape of the population is normal or the population variances are equal are called ***Parametric Statistics.*** However, there are situations when it is **not** possible to assume that a population is normal or approximately normal or the population variances are approximately equal. Inferential statistics that make no assumptions about the shape of the population or the parameters of a population are referred to as ***Nonparametric Statistics.***

> **DEFINITION 17.1**
> **Nonparametric Statistics.** Statistical tests that require few, if any, assumptions about the population from which sample data is collected.

There are many statistical tests that are classified as nonparametric. In fact we have already studied one such nonparametric test namely the *Chi-Square Test of Independence.* The Chi-Square Test of Independence is used to determine whether or not two distinct population classifications are independent or dependent. This test does not involve any population parameters. Such a test is a nonparametric test. The main objective of this chapter is to make you aware of the existence of nonparametric statistics and some nonparametric tests. Nonparametric tests will have the same basic characteristic, that is, they will be statistical tests that do not require assumptions about the underlying population shapes or form. These statistical tests are also called *distribution-free* tests.

> **DEFINITION 17.2**
> **Distribution-free Tests.** Statistical tests that can be applied to many types of data regardless of the shape of the underlying population.

Nonparametric tests have many advantages over parametric tests. Let's examine some of these advantages.

The Advantages of Nonparametric Tests

(1) *Nonparametric tests are easy to apply.* Usually only ranking, counting, adding and subtraction of the data values are needed.
(2) *Nonparametric tests are quick to apply for small samples.*
(3) *Nonparametric tests can be applied to many applications.* Usually few, if any, assumptions are necessary for the applications.
(4) *Nonparametric tests can be applied to data as long as the data values can be at least ranked.*

On the other hand, there are some drawbacks to their application. Some of the disadvantages of the nonparametric tests are:

The Disadvantages of Nonparametric Tests

(1) *Nonparametric tests are less powerful than a similar parametric test.* This means that the ability of a nonparametric test to detect a significant difference compared to its counterpart parametric test is not as efficient.
(2) *Nonparametric tests do not use all the information contained in the sample data.*
(3) *Nonparametric tests are difficult to use for large samples.*

Statisticians agree that if you are fairly sure that your data comes from a normal population, use the appropriate parametric test. This notwithstanding, in this chapter we will study three nonparametric statistical tests. They are:

The Sign Test for Medians
The Mann Whitney Rank Sum Test
The Kruskal-Wallis Test

17.2   THE SIGN TEST FOR MEDIANS

One of the easiest nonparametric test, the **SIGN test for Medians** is the nonparametric counterpart to the **t test** about a population mean. Let's examine a situation where the Sign test can be applied.

Suppose the snack bar owner at a university claims that students drink, on the "average", four cups of coffee per day. A representative of the student government believe's that the owner's claim is too high. The representative randomly samples twenty students to determine the number of cups of coffee per day each student consumes. The results of the sample are as follows:

number of cups of coffee consumed each day

2 3 6 1 2 4 8 1 0 2
3 1 0 4 2 7 5 2 1 4

The student government representative decides to perform a hypothesis test using the sample data.

The student government representative is testing the hypothesis that students drink, on the "average", four cups of coffee per day. Thus, the null hypothesis is:

$$H_o: \text{students drink four cups of coffee per day.}$$

Since the student government representative believes the claim is *too high* the alternative hypothesis is:

$$H_a: \text{students drink less than four cups of coffee per day.}$$

To test the null hypothesis, the student representative randomly interviews 20 students.

Usually, when performing a hypothesis test, an appropriate distribution hypothesis testing model is chosen. The model is typically based on the *assumption that the population from which the sample data is drawn is **approximately normal**.* **But this is NOT the case here. In fact, the distribution of coffee consumption is known to be skewed. This violates an assumption that is required for parametric tests.**

If you were to construct a Stem-and-Leaf display as shown in Figure 17.1 for the sample data, you would notice a sample that is skewed right.

Stem-and-Leaf Display

	0	00
	1	0000
number	2	00000
of	3	00
cups of	4	0000 skewed right
coffee per	5	
day	6	0
	7	0
	8	0

FIGURE 17.1

Computing the measures of Central Tendency for the sample data, the mean is 2.85, the median is 2 and the mode is 2 cups of coffee per day. Nonparametric tests are used *whenever the population from the which the data is sampled is not approximately normally distributed.* In this example we suspect from the examination of the stem-and-leaf display in Figure 17.1 that the distribution of coffee consumption is not normally distributed.

The Stem-and-Leaf display introduced in Chapter 2 is an exploratory data analysis technique that enables the experimenter to learn about a distribution. The Stem-and-Leaf display for the sample data in Figure 17.1 is skewed and the sample size, n = 20, is relatively small. In a skewed distribution, the mean may not be appropriate as a measure of central tendency. [Why?] For a skewed distribution the median is usually the measure of central tendency that best indicates the "typical value or average". Recall that the median is the value above which half or 50% of the data values lie and below which the other half or 50% lie.

To conduct an hypothesis test about the median, **the number of values above the median and the number of values below the median are counted. If a data value is equal to the median value, then the data value is omitted from the analysis.**

Thus, the claim made by the snack bar owner is a claim about a population *median*. The student government representative believes that the median value of 4 is too high. If we assume that the null hypothesis is correct, (i.e. H_o: median = 4) then the number of sample values above the median of 4, and the number of sample values below the median of 4 must be equal. [WHY?] The sample data indicates that there are 3 data values above the median and 13 data values less than the median. Since four data values are the same as the median, they are omitted from the analysis. *The first calculation in conducting the SIGN test about a Median is to determine the number of data values above the median value and the number of data values below the median value.* Table 17.1 illustrates the tabulation of the sample data values used in the SIGN Test. Notice that a "+" sign is listed next to a sample data value that is more than the median, while a "-" sign is listed next to a sample data value that is less than the median. The data values which are equal to the median have a "0" listed next to them. These data values are omitted from further analysis.

TABLE 17.1   number of cups of coffee consumed each day

2	–	3	–
3	–	1	–
6	+	0	–
1	–	4	0
2	–	2	–
4	0	7	+
8	+	4	0
1	–	2	–
0	–	1	–
2	–	4	0

Thus, by counting the number of "+" signs and the number of "–" signs we see that there are 3 data values greater than the hypothesized median of 4 and 13 data values less than the hypothesized median of 4. The question we need to answer is: *"Do these sample results indicate enough evidence to reject the null hypothesis that the median number of cups of coffee is 4?"* Or could this *difference or imbalance* be due to sampling error?

If the null hypothesis about the median were true, then we would expect half the students drink less than 4 cups of coffee each day and half the students drink more than 4 cups of coffee each day. Thus, the probability that the number of cups of coffee consumed per day by a university student is less than the median would be 0.5 and, similarly, the probability that the number of cups of coffee consumed per day is greater than the median would also be 0.5.

To determine if the sample results indicate enough evidence to reject the null hypothesis, we must calculate the probability that for a sample of 16 coffee consumers, 3 students drink less than four cups per day. The sign test for medians satisfies the conditions of a binomial probability experiment. These conditions are:

1. there are *n identical trials,* n = 16.
2. there are *only two possible and independent* results: a "+" sign or a "–" sign.

3. the *probability for either a "+" sign or a "–" sign is ½* since the median is the middle value and we are assuming that half of the values are above the median and half the values are below the median.

Using this information, this probability question can be analyzed as a binomial probability experiment with a probability of success of p = 0.5, the number of identical trials is n = 16 and the outcome, O, is 3. Furthermore, for a binomial distribution where both np and n(1 – p) are greater than 5, the normal distribution can be used to approximate the binomial distribution. For this sample of n = 16 and p = 0.5, we have

$$np = (16)(0.5) = 8$$
and
$$n(1\text{-}p) = (16)(0.5) = 8$$

are both greater than five.

Thus, the normal distribution can be used to approximate the binomial distribution. To apply this approximation, we must compute the binomial mean, μ_s, and the binomial standard deviation, σ_s. For n = 16 and p = 0.5, the binomial mean and standard deviation are:

$$\mu_s = np$$
$$= (16)(0.5) = 8$$

and

$$\sigma_s = \sqrt{np(1-p)}$$
$$= \sqrt{(16)(0.5)(0.5)}$$
$$\sigma_s = 2$$

When using the normal distribution to approximate binomial probability, the continuity correction must be applied. Therefore, to calculate the probability that **3 students or less** will drink more than 4 cups of coffee per day, you need to find the area under the normal curve to the left of 3.5 (i.e. the continuity correction factor). To determine this area, calculate the z-score for 3.5 and use TABLE II to find the area to the left of the z-score. This is illustrated in Figure 17.2.

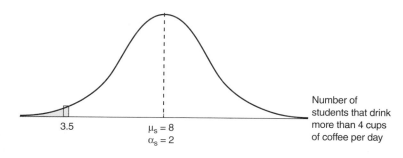

FIGURE 17.2

Using the z-score formula,

$$z = \frac{x - \mu_s}{\sigma_s} \text{ with } \mu_s = 8,\ \sigma_s = 2 \text{ and } x = 3.5$$

$$z = \frac{3.5 - 8}{2}$$

$$z \approx -2.25$$

Using TABLE II the portion of area to the left of $z = -2.25$ is 0.0122. Therefore, for a sample of sixteen students the probability of 3 students or less will drink 4 cups of coffee per day is 0.0122.

Remember, that this probability is based on the assumption that the median number of cups of coffee consumed per day is 4. Since the probability of this occurrence is so small (i.e. 0.0122) you might conclude that either the random sample was highly unusual or that the *null hypothesis of 4 cups per day* is **not likely.**

The student government representative decided that this unusual random sample was unlikely to occur just by chance and concluded the snack bar owner's claim was incorrect!

The above explanation is called the sign test for MEDIANS. It is a hypothesis testing procedure about a median. The sign test procedure will be developed. Within this procedure we will assume that the normal distribution can be used to approximate the binomial distribution.

The SIGN TEST for MEDIANS

Step 1   Formulate the two hypotheses, H_o and H_a.
         Null Hypothesis:
         In general, the null hypothesis for the sign test for a median has the following form.

Null Hypothesis Form:

H_o: *The population median is claimed to be equal to a numerical value which will be symbolized as:* M_o.

The null hypothesis can be symbolized as:

$$H_o: \text{ population median} = M_o$$

Alternative Hypothesis:
Since the alternative hypothesis, H_a, can be stated as either *greater than, less than,* or *not equal* to the hypothesized median value, M_o, then the alternative hypothesis can have one of three forms.

Forms of the Alternative Hypothesis

GREATER THAN FORM FOR H_a

H_a: *The population median is claimed to be **greater than** the hypothesized median value,* M_o.

This is symbolized as:

$$H_a: \text{ population median} > M_o$$

LESS THAN FORM FOR H_a

H_a: *The population median is claimed to be **less than** the hypothesized median value,* M_o.

This is symbolized as:

$$H_a: \text{ population median} < M_o$$

NOT EQUAL FORM FOR H$_a$

H_a: *The population median is claimed to be **not equal** to the hypothesized median value, M$_o$.*

This is symbolized as:

H$_a$: population median $\neq$ M$_o$

Step 2 **Determine the model to test the null hypothesis, H$_o$.**

Under the assumption that H$_o$ is true, a binomial distribution is used as the hypothesis testing model. For this distribution, the usable sample size, n, is equal to the number of negative (–) signs, denoted as n(– signs), plus the number of plus (+) signs, symbolized as n(+ signs). Thus: n = n(– signs) + n(+ signs).

Remember the number of sample data values *not* equal to the median value represents the usable sample size, n. While the probability of a success is p = 0.5 since we are assuming there is a 1/2 chance that a data value within the sample is either below the median (assigned a "–" sign) or above the median (assigned a "+" sign). If both np and n(1 – p) are greater than five, the normal approximation to the binomial distribution can be used as the model distribution. When using the normal distribution to approximate the binomial distribution, the mean and standard deviation of the binomial distribution must be computed. The formulas to determine the binomial mean and standard deviation are:

$$\mu_s = np$$

and

$$\sigma_s = \sqrt{np(1-p)}$$

Step 3 **Formulate the Decision Rule.**

a) Determine the type of alternative hypothesis: directional or nondirectional.
b) Determine type of test: 1TT or 2TT.
c) Identify the significance level: $\alpha = 0.01$ or $\alpha = 0.05$.
d) Construct a normal distribution (used to approximate the binomial distribution) as the hypothesis testing model.
e) Determine the critical z-score(s) using the following chart.

Critical z-scores

For significance level of $\alpha = 0.05$:
For a 2TT: $z_{LC} = -1.96$ and $z_{RC} = +1.96$.
For a 1TT test on left side: $z_c = -1.65$
For a 1TT test on right side: $z_c = +1.65$

For significance level of $\alpha = 0.01$:
For a 2TT: $z_{LC} = -2.58$ and $z_{RC} = +2.58$.
For a 1TT test on left side: $z_c = -2.33$
For a 1TT test on right side: $z_c = +2.33$

f) Using the critical z-score(s), state the decision rule.

Step 4 **Analyze the sample data.**
Using the necessary sample data, tabulate the number of data values that are either less than the median or are greater than the median. This statistical result will be denoted by O. (**For a nondirectional alternative 2TT, use the number of the less frequent sign when computing the statistical result O.**) Calculate the z-score for the statistical result, O. This is referred to as the **test statistic.** Remember, when using the normal approximation to the binomial distribution, a continuity correction factor of 1/2 is either subtracted or added to the statistical result, O. If the statistical result O, is less than n/2, then the test statistic is:

$$z = \frac{(O + \frac{1}{2}) - \mu_s}{\sigma_s}$$

If the statistical result O, is greater than n/2, then the test statistic is:

$$z = \frac{(O - \frac{1}{2}) - \mu_s}{\sigma_s}$$

Step 5 **Determine the Conclusion.**
Compare the test statistic to the critical z-score and either:

a) **Reject H$_o$ and accept H$_a$ at α,**
   OR
b) **Fail to reject H$_o$ at α.**

Example 17.1 will illustrate the hypothesis testing procedure for the SIGN TEST for MEDIANS.

EXAMPLE 17.1

The corporate division of Mountain Records believes that the median number of compact disk purchases per customer visit is 3. The sales manager at one of the local stores does not believe this claim to be correct. She decides to use the Sign Test for Medians and conducts an experiment by randomly keeping track of the number of compact disk purchases of 14 customers. For the fourteen customers she finds that seven purchased more than 3 compact disks, five purchased less than 3 compact disks, and two purchased 3 compact disks. Test the sales manager's claim using an $\alpha = 5\%$.

Solution

Step 1 **Formulate the two hypotheses, H$_o$ and H$_a$.**
The null hypothesis has the general form:

H$_o$: The population median is claimed to be equal to a numerical value M$_o$.

For this example the corporate division of Mountain Records believes that the median number of compact disk purchases per customer visit is 3. The null hypothesis is:

H$_o$: The population median number of compact disk purchases per customer visit is 3.

The null hypothesis can be symbolized as:

H₀: population median = 3

Since the sales manager believes the claim by the corporate division is **not correct**, then the alternative hypothesis, H_a, is a not equal statement and is nondirectional. Thus, the alternative hypothesis is:

H_a: The population median number of compact disk purchases per customer visit is not 3.

This alternative hypothesis is symbolized as:

H_a: population median ≠ 3

Step 2 **Determine the model to test the null hypothesis, H₀.**
Under the assumption that H_0 is true, a binomial distribution is used as the hypothesis testing model.

For the 14 customers, the sales manager determined the following information:

less than 3 CDs:	5 customers
3 CDs (the hypothesized median):	2 customers
more than 3 CDs:	7 customers

Converting the data to plus (+) signs, negative (–) signs and a zero (0), using the following rule: assign a negative (–) sign to each customer below the hypothesized value of the median, a plus (+) sign to the customers above the hypothesized value of the median, and a zero (0) to the customers who purchased exactly the same number of CDs equal to the hypothesized median value, we have:

5 negative (–) signs
7 plus (+) signs
2 zeros (0).

Since the sign test only uses negative and plus signs, the 2 zeros are discarded from the test. Consequently, the usable sample size, n, is: n = 14 – 2 = 12.

The number of negative (–) signs, symbolized as n(–), is n(–) = 5, while the number of plus (+) signs, symbolized as n(+), is n(+) = 7. Thus the usable sample size, n, is equal to the number of negative (–) signs plus the number of plus (+) signs. That is:

$$n = n(-) + n(+)$$
$$= 5 + 7$$
$$n = 12$$

Since the number of data values *not* equal to the median value is n = 12, and p = 0.5, then

$$np = (0.5)(12) = 6$$
and
$$n(1-p) = (0.5)(12) = 6$$

are both greater than five. Thus, the normal approximation to the binomial distribution can be used as the hypothesis testing model. Using the normal distribution to approximate the binomial distribution, we must compute the mean and standard deviation of the binomial distribution by the formulas:

$$\mu_s = np$$

and

$$\sigma_s = \sqrt{np(1-p)}$$

For p = 0.5 and n = 12:

$$\mu_s = np = (12)(0.5) = 6$$

and

$$\sigma_s = \sqrt{np(1-p)}$$
$$= \sqrt{(12)(0.5)(0.5)}$$
$$\sigma_s = \sqrt{3} \approx 1.73.$$

Step 3   Formulate the Decision Rule.

For this hypothesis test:
a) the type of alternative hypothesis is nondirectional.
b) the type of test is 2TT.
c) the significance level is $\alpha = 5\%$.
d) The hypothesis testing model is the normal distribution.
e) For a 2TT and a significance level of $\alpha = 5\%$, the critical z-score(s) are $z_{LC} = -1.96$ and $z_{RC} = +1.96$.
f) The decision rule is:

Reject the null hypothesis, H_o, if the test statistic is either less than -1.96 or greater than 1.96. The decision rule is illustrated in Figure 17.3.

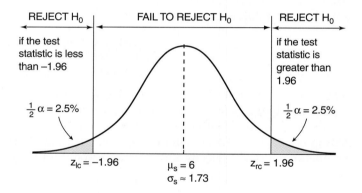

FIGURE 17.3

Step 4   Analyze the sample data.

Using the five customers who purchased *less than* the hypothesized median number of 3 compact disks as the statistical result, this statistical result is expressed as O = 5. To determine the test statistic z, we will use a continuity correction value of 5.5 since we are interested in the area under the normal curve that corresponds to 5 or less customers. Using the z score formula, $\mu_s = 6$ and $\sigma_s = 1.73$, the z-score of 5.5 is:

$$z = \frac{(O + \frac{1}{2}) - \mu_s}{\sigma_s}$$

$$z = \frac{5.5 - 6}{1.73}$$

$$z \approx -0.29$$

$z \approx -0.29$ is the test statistic.

Step 5 **Determine the Conclusion.**
Since the test statistic z = –0.29 is not less than –1.96 or greater than 1.96 as stated in the decision rule, we fail to reject H$_o$ at α = 5%. Therefore, the sales manager **cannot** conclude that the corporate division of Mountain Records is incorrect in their claim that the median number of compact disks purchased by a customer is 3.

17.3   THE MANN-WHITNEY RANK-SUM TEST

As the Sign Test for Medians is comparable to the one sample t-test, the Mann-Whitney rank-sum test is the nonparametric alternative to the two-sample t test. *This test is designed to determine whether two independent samples came from the same population.* However, when samples are selected from two populations that are essentially the same, the test can be used to investigate if there is a difference between one specific characteristic of each population. For example, the test can be used to determine if the medians or means of two populations are the same. Besides being called the Mann-Whitney Rank-Sum test, the test is also referred to as the Wilcoxon Rank-Sum test as well as the Mann-Whitney-Wilcoxon U test.

To use the Mann-Whitney Rank-Sum test on two independent samples, the samples are combined into one larger sample and the data are ranked accordingly. The null hypothesis is that each sample comes from the same population, or, if there are two populations, they are the same. *If the null hypothesis is true, then the ranks would essentially be evenly distributed between the samples.* If the ranks are evenly distributed between the samples then the *sum* of the ranks for each sample would be the *same.*

On the other hand *if the alternative hypothesis is true, that is, that the samples come from different distributions, then the ranks would not be evenly distributed between the samples. That is, one of the samples would contain more of one type of rank. For example, one sample may contain more lower ranks.* In this case, the sum of the ranks for each sample *would not be the same.*

To determine if the difference in the sum of the ranks is statistically significant, we can use the standard normal distribution for the hypothesis testing model provided each sample contains at least ten observations. When the normal distribution can be applied, the test statistic, z, is computed using the formula:

$$z = \frac{W - \dfrac{n_1(n_1 + n_2 + 1)}{2}}{\sqrt{\dfrac{n_1 n_2 (n_1 + n_2 + 1)}{12}}}$$

where:

n_1 = the number of data values in sample one.
n_2 = the number of data values in sample two.
W = the **sum** of the **ranks** from **sample one.**

Let's examine a problem that can be analyzed using the Mann-Whitney Rank-Sum test.

Mr. Barry, the current registrar at a college has noticed that the number of withdrawals per class has increased for day students verses evening students. A random sample of 10 classes were chosen from all day classes while a random sample of 10 classes where selected from all the evening classes. The number of withdrawals per class was tabulated and are summarized in Table 17.2.

TABLE 17.2   Number of Withdrawals per class

Day Classes	Evening Classes
8	6
6	7
10	3
7	5
8	6
11	4
9	4
8	7
11	4
8	9

Can Mr. Barry conclude that there are significantly more withdrawals in the day verses the evening? (Use $\alpha = 5\%$).

In order to conclude this Mr. Barry would test the null hypothesis, H_0: the population number of day class withdrawals and the population number of evening class withdrawals are the same, and use the Mann-Whitney Rank-Sum test to determine if the null hypothesis can be rejected.

To reject H_0 would imply an acceptance of the alternative hypothesis, H_a: there is a significantly greater number of withdrawals from the day classes than from the evening classes.

To use the Mann-Whitney Rank-Sum test we must first combine the data of the two samples (sample one being the withdrawals in the day and sample two being the withdrawals in the evening) into **one** sample and **ASSIGN a rank** to each data value. Table 17.3 list the original data along with an assigned ranking that combines **all** the data values as if they belonged to **one** sample. The letter D is indicated for those data values from the day classes and E for those data values from the evening classes. Notice that if data values are equal, the *assigned* rank is the **mean** of the ranks they occupy. For example, data value 4 occupies the ranks 2, 3, and 4. The mean of the possible ranks 2,3 and 4 is 3. The rank of data value 5 is assigned 5 since it **alone** occupies the fifth rank.

TABLE 17.3   Number of Withdrawals per class along with RANKing

Number of Withdrawals	Class	Possible Rank	Assigned Rank
3	E	1	1
4	E	2 ⎤mean	3
4	E	3	3
4	E	4 ⎦is 3	3
5	E	5	5
6	D	6 ⎤mean	7
6	E	7	7
6	E	8 ⎦is 7	7
7	D	9 ⎤mean	10
7	E	10	10
7	E	11 ⎦is 10	10
8	D	12 ⎤mean	13.5
8	D	13	13.5
8	D	14	13.5
8	D	15 ⎦is 13.5	13.5

Number of Withdrawals	Class	Possible Rank		Assigned Rank
9	D	16 ⎤mean		16.5
9	E	17 ⎦is 16.5		16.5
10	D	18		18
11	D	19 ⎤mean		19.5
11	D	20 ⎦is 19.5		19.5

To compute the test statistic, use the z formula for The Mann-Whitney Test:

$$z = \frac{W - \frac{n_1(n_1 + n_2 + 1)}{2}}{\sqrt{\frac{n_1 n_2(n_1 + n_2 + 1)}{12}}}$$

Since n_1 is the number of data values in sample one (i.e. day classes), then, $n_1 = 10$. Similarly n_2 is the number of data values in sample two (i.e., evening classes), thus, $n_2 = 10$. To compute W which represents the **sum** of the **ranks** from **sample one,** it is helpful to list the **assigned ranks** for the day classes separately. Table 17.4 lists the data values for the number of day class withdrawals along with their assigned ranks.

TABLE 17.4

Day Class Data Values	Assigned Ranks
8	13.5
6	7
10	18
7	10
8	13.5
11	19.5
9	16.5
8	13.5
11	19.5
8	13.5

Thus, W, the sum of the assigned ranks for sample one is:

$$13.5 + 7 + 18 + 10 + 13.5 + 19.5 + 16.5 + 13.5 + 19.5 + 13.5 = 144.5$$

W = 144.5

Therefore, substituting the values of $n_1 = 10$, $n_2 = 10$ and W = 144.5 into the z statistic formula for the Mann-Whitney Test we have:

$$z = \frac{W - \dfrac{n_1(n_1 + n_2 + 1)}{2}}{\sqrt{\dfrac{n_1 n_2 (n_1 + n_2 + 1)}{12}}}$$

$$z = \frac{144.5 - \dfrac{(10)(10 + 10 + 1)}{2}}{\sqrt{\dfrac{(10)(10)(10 + 10 + 1)}{12}}}$$

$$z = \frac{144.5 - \dfrac{(10)(21)}{2}}{\sqrt{\dfrac{(10)(10)(21)}{12}}}$$

$$z = \frac{144.5 - 105}{\sqrt{175}}$$

$$z \approx 2.99$$

$z \approx 2.99$ is the test statistic.

For a 1TT on the right, the critical z score at $\alpha = 5\%$ is 1.65. This is illustrated in Figure 17.4.

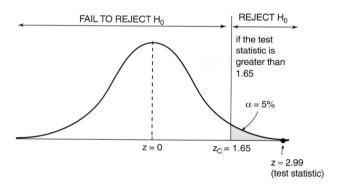

FIGURE 17.4

Since the test statistic $z \approx 2.99$ is greater than the critical z score 1.65, Mr. Barry can reject H_o and accept H_a at $\alpha = 0.05$. Therefore, the number of day class withdrawals is significantly greater than the number of evening class withdrawals.

Let's modify the hypothesis testing procedure to accommodate the Mann-Whitney Test. Remember the test can be used as an alternative to the two sample t test whenever the assumption about the normality of the populations or the assumption regarding the population variances being equal are not made. For our application of this test we will assume that the number of data values for each sample is at least ten. However, although we will not deal here with samples that are smaller than ten, there are statistical tables available that will enable you to perform the Mann-Whitney Test for these smaller samples.

The Mann-Whitney Test For Samples of Size of at least 10

Step 1   *Formulate the two hypotheses, H_o and H_a.*
       Null Hypothesis:
       In general, the null hypothesis for the Mann-Whitney Test has the following form.

Null Hypothesis Form:

H_o: *The two populations are the same*

Alternative Hypothesis: The alternative hypothesis for the Mann-Whitney Test is stated as:

Alternative Hypothesis Form:

H_a: *The two populations are NOT the same*

The alternative hypothesis, H_a, could be that the population means, medians, or shapes are different.

Step 2   **Determine the model to test the null hypothesis, H_o.**

Under the assumption that H_o is true, when each sample contains at least ten data values, the *standard normal distribution* can be used as the hypothesis testing model. This is illustrated in Figure 17.5.

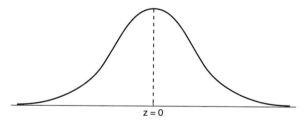

FIGURE 17.5

Step 3   **Formulate the Decision Rule.**

a) Determine the type of alternative hypothesis: directional or nondirectional.
b) Determine type of test: 1TT or 2TT.
c) Identify the significance level: $\alpha = 0.01$ or $\alpha = 0.05$.
d) Construct a standard normal distribution as the hypothesis testing model.
e) Determine the critical z-score(s) using the following chart.

Critical z-scores

For significance level of $\alpha = 0.05$:
For a 2TT: $z_{LC} = -1.96$ and $z_{RC} = +1.96$.
For a 1TT test on left side: $z_c = -1.65$
For a 1TT test on right side: $z_c = +1.65$

For significance level of $\alpha = 0.01$:
For a 2TT: $z_{LC} = -2.58$ and $z_{RC} = +2.58$.
For a 1TT test on left side: $z_c = -2.33$
For a 1TT test on right side: $z_c = +2.33$

    f) Using the critical z-score(s), state the decision rule.

Step 4 **Analyze the sample data.**
    a) Collect the necessary sample data from each population and combine the data into one sample. Assign a rank to each data value. For data values that are equal, the rank assigned is the **mean** of the ranks they occupy.
    b) Calculate W, the sum of the assigned ranks from the first sample. The value of W represents the statistical result.
    c) Calculate the test statistic using the formula:

$$z = \frac{W - \dfrac{n_1(n_1 + n_2 + 1)}{2}}{\sqrt{\dfrac{n_1 n_2 (n_1 + n_2 + 1)}{12}}}$$

where:

n_1 = the number of data values in sample one.
n_2 = the number of data values in sample two.
W = the **sum** of the **ranks** from **sample one.**
z = test statistic

Step 5 **Determine the Conclusion.**
    Compare the Mann-Whitney z statistic, test statistic, to the critical z-score and either:

    a) Reject H$_o$ and accept H$_a$ at α,

    OR

    b) Fail to reject H$_o$ at α.

Example 17.2 will illustrate the hypothesis testing procedure for the Mann-Whitney Test.

EXAMPLE 17.2

The number of trains arriving at least 5 minutes late on Route A and Route B (two major commuter routes) were determined for randomly selected days in the month of December. The number of late arrivals for each of the selected days are listed in Table 17.5.

TABLE 17.5

Route A	Route B
5	18
34	23
11	19
12	32
19	8
24	25
28	22
17	16
24	14
31	10
29	

Use the Mann-Whitney Test at an $\alpha = 5\%$ to determine if there is a significant difference between the average number of late arrivals.

Solution

Step 1 **Formulate the two hypotheses, H_o and H_a.**

H_o: The population average number of late arrivals for trains using Route A and Route B are the same during the month of December.

H_a: The population average number of late arrivals for trains using Route A and Route B are NOT the same during the month of December.

Step 2 **Determine the model to test the null hypothesis, H_o.**

Under the assumption that H_o is true, when each sample contains at least ten data values, the *standard normal distribution* can be used as the hypothesis testing model. This is illustrated in Figure 17.6.

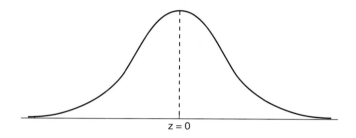

$z = 0$

FIGURE 17.6

Step 3 **Formulate the Decision Rule.**

For this hypothesis test:

a) the type of alternative hypothesis, H_a, is nondirectional.

b) the type of test is 2TT.

c) the significance level is $\alpha = 0.05$.

d) The hypothesis testing model is the normal distribution.

d) For a 2TT and a significance level of $\alpha = 0.05$, the critical z-score(s) are $z_{LC} = -1.96$ and $z_{RC} = +1.96$.

f) The decision rule is: Reject H_o, if the Mann Whitney z statistic, test statistic, is either less than -1.96 or greater than 1.96. The decision rule is illustrated in Figure 17.7.

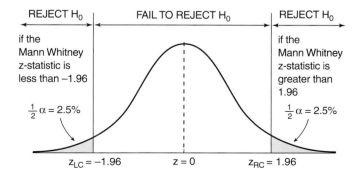

REJECT H_0 FAIL TO REJECT H_0 REJECT H_0

if the Mann Whitney z-statistic is less than -1.96

if the Mann Whitney z-statistic is greater than 1.96

$\frac{1}{2}\alpha = 2.5\%$ $\frac{1}{2}\alpha = 2.5\%$

$z_{LC} = -1.96$ $z = 0$ $z_{RC} = 1.96$

FIGURE 17.7

Step 4   **Analyze the sample data.**

a) Table 17.6 lists the sorted data values for the number of trains that were at least five minutes late along with their assigned ranks.

TABLE 17.6

Number of Late Trains	Route	Possible Rank		Assigned Rank
5	A	1		1
8	B	2		2
10	B	3		3
11	A	4		4
12	A	5		5
14	B	6		6
16	B	7		7
17	A	8		8
18	B	9	mean is	9
19	A	10		10.5
19	B	11	10.5	10.5
22	B	12		12
23	B	13	mean is	13
24	A	14		14.5
24	A	15	14.5	15.5
25	B	16		16
28	A	17		17
29	A	18		18
31	A	19		19
32	B	20		20
34	A	21		21

For Route A (sample 1) the Assigned Ranks are listed in Table 17.7.

TABLE 17.7

Route A Data Values	Assigned Ranks
5	1
34	21
11	4
12	5
19	10.5
24	14.5
28	17
17	8
24	14.5
31	19
29	18
34	21

b) W, the statistical result, is the sum of the assigned ranks for sample one is:

$$1 + 21 + 4 + 5 + 10.5 + 14.5 + 17 + 8 + 14.5 + 19 + 18 + 21 = 153.5$$

c) Substituting the values of $n_1 = 12$, $n_2 = 11$ and $W = 153.5$ into the test statistic formula z for the Mann-Whitney Test we have:

$$z = \frac{W - \dfrac{n_1(n_1 + n_2 + 1)}{2}}{\sqrt{\dfrac{n_1 n_2 (n_1 + n_2 + 1)}{12}}}$$

$$z = \frac{153.5 - \dfrac{(12)(12 + 11 + 1)}{2}}{\sqrt{\dfrac{(12)(11)(12 + 11 + 1)}{12}}}$$

$$z = \frac{153.5 - \dfrac{(12)(24)}{2}}{\sqrt{\dfrac{(12)(11)(24)}{12}}}$$

$$z = \frac{153.5 - 144}{\sqrt{16.25}}$$

$$z \approx 0.59$$

$z \approx 0.59$ is the test statistic.

Step 5   Determine the Conclusion.

Since the Mann-Whitney test z statistic, $z = 0.59$, falls between the critical z scores, we fail to reject the null hypothesis, H_o, at $\alpha = 5\%$. Therefore, although there is a difference for the average number of trains arriving late for Route A verses Route B, the difference is not statistically significant at $\alpha = 5\%$. The result is illustrated in Figure 17.8.

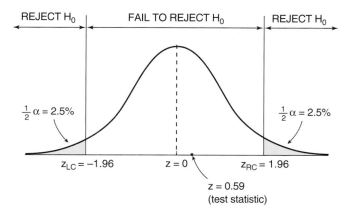

FIGURE 17.8

17.4 THE KRUSKAL-WALLIS H TEST

In the previous section the Mann-Whitney test was used to test whether or not two populations were the same. Recall that the Mann-Whitney test was the nonparametric counterpart to the two-sample *t* test studied in Chapter 13. A nonparametric test that is analogous to the Analysis of Variance test (ANOVA) covered in Chapter 16 is called the *Kruskal-Wallis H Test*. It is also referred to as simply the H test. Essentially, the Kruskal-Wallis tests whether three or more populations are the same.

The null hypothesis, H_o, for this test is that the populations are the same. While the alternative hypothesis, H_a, is that the populations are not the same. That is there are differences among the populations, in particular the populations may have different means or medians.

If each sample has at least five observations the sampling distribution of the data can be approximated by a Chi-Square, X^2, distribution. The test statistic for a Kruskal-Wallis test, denoted by H, is computed using the formula:

$$H = \frac{12}{N(N+1)} \left[\frac{(\sum R_1)^2}{n_1} + \frac{(\sum R_2)^2}{n_2} + \ldots + \frac{(\sum R_k)^2}{n_k} \right] - 3(N+1)$$

where $\sum R_1, \sum R_2, \ldots, \sum R_k$ are the sum of the ranks for samples $1, 2, \ldots, k$.

$n_1, n_2, \ldots, n_k$ are the sizes of samples $1, 2, \ldots, k$.

and N is the combined number of data values for all samples (i.e. $N = n_1 + n_2 + \ldots + n_k$)

After the Kruskal-Wallis test statistic, H, is computed its value is compared to a *critical value* approximated by using Table IV: the critical values for the Chi-Square Distributions in Appendix D. To determine the critical value for either $\alpha = 5\%$ or 1%, use k-1 degrees of freedom, where k represents the number of distinct random samples.

Let's apply the Kruskal-Wallis H test to a selection process problem for a college admissions officer.

For example, suppose the admissions officer at a prestigious university is interested in attempting to determine if there are differences between students transferring from three community colleges that are within one hundred miles of each other. Part of the selection process that the university uses for entrance is to administer an achievement test to prospective entrants. Table 17.8 contains the achievement test scores for recent prospective entrants from the three community colleges.

TABLE 17.8   Achievement Scores: Students from Three Community Colleges

1 NCC	2 WCC	3 TCC
30	65	55
75	25	65
65	35	85
90	20	95
95	45	75
85	40	80
85		75

If the administrator were able to assume that the population of achievement scores are normally distributed with their respective population variances equal, then a nonparametric test would not be necessary. [What test would the administrator use?] Since these assumptions cannot be made, the administrator decides to use the Kruskal-Wallis H test.

To apply the test, the three samples of achievement scores are combined into one group and are ranked as though they were scores from one population. (This is based on the assumption that the null hypothesis for the test is true.) The sorted scores and ranks are listed in Table 17.9.

TABLE 17.9   The combined Samples of Achievement Scores from three community colleges Sorted and Ranked based on the null hypothesis, H_0.

scores	sample	sorted scores	rank
30	1	20	1.0
75	1	25	2.0
65	1	30	3.0
90	1	35	4.0
95	1	40	5.0
85	1	45	6.0
85	1	55	7.0
65	2	65	9.0
25	2	65	9.0
35	2	65	9.0
20	2	75	12.0
45	2	75	12.0
40	2	75	12.0
55	3	80	14.0
65	3	85	16.0
85	3	85	16.0
95	3	85	16.0
75	3	90	18.0
80	3	95	19.5
75	3	95	19.5

In Table 17.9, notice the second column is *labelled* **sample** to identify the sample the ranked score belongs. For example, the score, 30, in the first row is from sample 1, NCC. Since it is the third lowest ranked score it has a rank of 3. Whereas, 65, the first score from sample 2, has a rank of 9, as well as the second score, 65, from sample 3.

Table 17.10 lists the individual scores, their ranks, the sum of their ranks, and the sample size, n, for each sample. The three samples have been separated as they were initially collected, with the overall rank shown alongside each data value.

TABLE 17.10   Students from Three Community Colleges Scores, Ranks and Sum of Ranks

NCC		WCC		TCC	
Score	Ranks from Sample 1	Score	Ranks from Sample 2	Score	Ranks from Sample 3
30	3	65	9	55	7
75	12	25	2	65	9
65	9	35	4	85	16
90	18	20	1	95	19.5
95	19.5	45	6	75	12
85	16	40	5	80	14
85	16			75	12
	$\Sigma R_1 = 93.5$		$\Sigma R_2 = 27$		$\Sigma R_3 = 89.5$
	$n_1 = 7$		$n_2 = 6$		$n_3 = 7$

To determine H, the Kruskal-Wallis H test statistic, we use the formula:

$$H = \frac{12}{N(N+1)} \left[\frac{(\Sigma R_1)^2}{n_1} + \frac{(\Sigma R_2)^2}{n_2} + \cdots + \frac{(\Sigma R_k)^2}{n_k} \right] - 3(N+1)$$

Since N is the combined number of observations for all the samples, N = 7 + 6 + 7 = 20. Substituting N and the values from Table 17.10 in the formula H, we get:

$$H = \frac{12}{20(20+1)} \left[\frac{(93.5)^2}{7} + \frac{(27)^2}{6} + + \frac{(89.5)^2}{7} \right] - 3(20+1)$$

$$H = (0.029)\,[2514.714] - 63$$

$$H \approx 9.93 \text{ is the test statistic.}$$

To determine if the Kruskal-Wallis H test statistic, H = 9.93, is significant, compare H to the critical chi-square value χ_{α}^2 found in TABLE IV of Appendix D. For an $\alpha = 1\%$ and $df = k-1 = 3-1 = 2$, the critical value, χ_{α}^2, is 9.21. Since the test statistic H = 9.93 is greater than the critical value $\chi_{\alpha}^2 = 9.21$, the null hypothesis, H_o, is *rejected at an* $\alpha = 1\%$ and the alternative hypothesis, H_a, is accepted. Thus, we can conclude that there is a significant difference between the achievement scores of the prospective entrants from the three community colleges.

Figure 17.9 illustrates the results of the hypothesis test.

Chi-Square Distribution with *df* = 2

FIGURE 17.9

Let's now summarize the hypothesis testing procedure for the Kruskal-Wallis H test.

The Kruskal-Wallis H Test

Step 1. Formulate the two hypotheses, H_0 and H_a.
Null Hypothesis:
In general, the null hypothesis for the Kruskal-Wallis H Test has the following form.

Null Hypothesis Form:

H_0: *The two populations are the same*

Alternative Hypothesis: The alternative hypothesis for the Kruskal-Wallis H Test is stated as:

Alternative Hypothesis Form:

H_a: *The two populations are NOT the same*

When it is assumed that certain characteristics of the distributions are the same the alternative hypothesis could be that the population means, medians, or shapes are different.

Step 2   **Determine the model to test the null hypothesis, H_o.**
Under the assumption that H_o is true, and when each sample contains at least five data values, a *Chi-Square Distribution* with df = k-1 degrees of freedom, where k represents the number of distinct samples, can be used as the hypothesis testing model. Figure 17.10 displays a typical chi-square distribution.

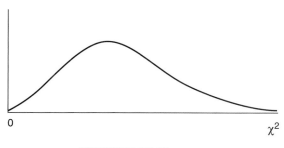

0 χ^2

FIGURE 17.10

Step 3   **Formulate the Decision Rule.**
a) Identify the significance level, $\alpha = 1\%$ or $\alpha = 5\%$.
b) Find the critical chi-square value, χ_α^2, in TABLE IV: Critical Values for the Chi-Square Distribution, in Appendix D: Statistical Tables.
c) Construct a Chi Square Distribution with k − 1 degrees of freedom as the hypothesis testing model with the critical chi-square value χ_α^2 appropriately placed on the curve.
d) The decision rule is: if the Kruskal-Wallis H test statistic is larger than the critical chi-square value, χ_α^2, then reject H_o and accept H_a.

Step 4   **Analyze the sample data.**
a) Collect the necessary sample data from each population and combine the data into one sample. **Assign a rank** to each data value. For data values that are equal, the rank assigned is the **mean** of the ranks they occupy.
b) Calculate the Kruskal-Wallis H test statistic using the formula:

$$H = \frac{12}{N(N+1)}\left[\frac{(\Sigma R_1)^2}{n_1} + \frac{(\Sigma R_2)^2}{n_2} + \ldots + \frac{(\Sigma R_k)^2}{n_k}\right] - 3(N+1)$$

where $\Sigma R_1, \Sigma R_2, \ldots, \Sigma R_k$ are the sum of the ranks
for samples $1, 2, \ldots, k$.

$n_1, n_2, \ldots n_k$, are the sizes of samples $1, 2, \ldots, k$.

and N is the combined number of data values for all samples

Step 5   Determine the Conclusion.
Compare the Kruskal-Wallis H test statistic to the critical chi-square value χ_α^2 and either:

a) **Reject H$_o$ and accept H$_a$ at α,**

OR

b) **Fail to reject H$_o$ at α.**

Example 17.3 will illustrate a Kruskal-Wallis H hypothesis test procedure.

■
EXAMPLE 17.2

Allison, a health and fitness coordinator, at a local racquet and fitness club wants to experiment with three different fitness routines for women over 35 years old. Since no experience exits regarding the three routines, she is unwilling to make any assumptions about the shape of the distribution of pulse rate recovery times. Use the Kruskal-Wallis H test to test if the participants in the fitness routines have different pulse rate recovery times after the fitness routines are given for a specified length of time. Use $\alpha = 5\%$. Table 17.11 represents the pulse rate recovery times for each participant along with their respective fitness routine type.

TABLE 17.11

| Pulse rate recovery times in minutes | | |
Routine A	Routine B	Routine C
3.2	7.5	3.5
2.1	3.8	4.2
4.4	5.6	5.5
8.3	6.4	8.4
5.7	4.8	6.1
	6.2	6.3

Solution

Step 1   Formulate the two hypotheses, H$_o$ and H$_a$.
The null hypothesis is:

H$_o$: The populations of pulse rate recovery times are the same.

The alternative hypothesis is:

H$_a$: The populations of pulse rate recovery times are not the same.

Step 2   Determine the model to test the null hypothesis, H$_o$.
Since each of the three samples contain at least five data values, the Chi-Square Distribution will be used as the hypothesis testing model. For this Chi-Square Distribution, the degrees of freedom are determined by the formula: $df = k-1$. Since there are $k = 3$ distinct samples, then $df = 3-1 = 2$. Figure 17.11 shows the Chi-Square Distribution with 2 degrees of freedom.

Chi-Square Distribution with $df = 2$

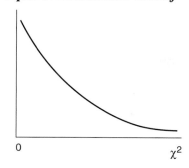

FIGURE 17.11

Step 3 **Formulate the Decision Rule.**

a) The significance level is: $\alpha = 5\%$.

b) Using TABLE IV: Critical Values for the Chi-Square Distribution, in Appendix D, the critical chi-square, χ_α^2, for $df = 2$ and $\alpha = 5\%$ is: $\chi_\alpha^2 = 5.99$.

c) The Chi-Square Distribution with 2 degrees of freedom and $\alpha = 5\%$ serves as the hypothesis testing model and is shown in Figure 17.12 with the critical chi-square value $\chi_\alpha^2 = 5.99$.

d) The decision rule is: if the Kruskal-Wallis H test statistic is larger than the critical chi-square value χ_α^2 of 5.99, then reject H_o and accept H_a. The decision rule is illustrated in Figure 17.12.

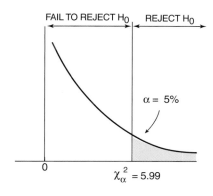

FIGURE 17.12

Step 4 **Analyze the sample data.**

a) The sample data from Table 17.11, have been combined, labelled and sorted along with their assigned ranks. The results are indicated in Table 17.12.

Table 17.13 lists the score, the ranks, the sum of the ranks, and the sample size, n, from each sample. The samples have been separated as they were initially collected, but this time the overall ranks are alongside each of the initial data values.

b) To determine H, the Kruskal-Wallis H test statistic, use the formula:

$$H = \frac{12}{N(N+1)}\left[\frac{(\Sigma R_1)^2}{n_1} + \frac{(\Sigma R_2)^2}{n_2} + \ldots + \frac{(\Sigma R_k)^2}{n_k}\right] - 3(N+1)$$

TABLE 17.12   The combined Samples of Pulse Rate Recovery Times from three Fitness Routines Sorted and Ranked based on the null hypothesis, H_o.

rates	sample	sorted rates	rank
3.2	1	2.1	1
2.1	1	3.2	2
4.4	1	3.5	3
8.3	1	3.8	4
5.7	1	4.2	5
7.5	2	4.4	6
3.8	2	4.8	7
5.6	2	5.5	8
6.4	2	5.6	9
4.8	2	5.7	10
6.2	2	6.1	11
4.2	3	6.2	12
5.5	3	6.3	13
8.4	3	6.4	14
6.1	3	7.5	15
3.5	3	8.3	16
6.3	3	8.4	17

TABLE 17.13   Pulse Rate Recovery Times for Each Fitness Routine Rates, Ranks and Sum of Ranks

Routine A		Routine B		Routine C	
Rate	Ranks from Sample 1	Rate	Ranks from Sample 2	Rate	Ranks from Sample 3
3.2	2	7.5	15	3.5	3
2.1	1	3.8	4	4.2	5
4.4	6	5.6	9	5.5	8
8.3	16	6.4	14	8.4	17
5.7	10	4.8	7	6.1	11
		6.2	12	6.3	13
	$\Sigma R_1 = 35$		$\Sigma R_2 = 61$		$\Sigma R_3 = 57$
	$n_1 = 5$		$n_2 = 6$		$n_3 = 6$

Since N is the combined number of observations for all the samples, N = 19. Substituting N and the values from Table 17.13 in the test statistic formula H, we get:

$$H = \frac{12}{17(17+1)}\left[\frac{(35)^2}{5} + \frac{(61)^2}{6} + \frac{(57)^2}{6}\right] - 3(17+1)$$

$$H = (0.039)[1406.667] - 54$$
$$H \approx 0.86 \text{ is the test statistic.}$$

Step 5   Determine the Conclusion.

Comparing the Kruskal-Wallis H test statistic to the critical chi-square value χ_α^2, you will find that test statistic H = 0.86 is less than the critical chi-square value, $\chi_\alpha^2 = 5.99$. Consequently, we fail to reject the null hypothesis, H_o, at $\alpha = 5\%$. This is illustrated in Figure 17.13.

FIGURE 17.13

Thus, although there are differences between the samples, the differences are not statistically significant. Therefore, Allison cannot conclude that the different fitness routines for women over the age of 35 will yield different population recovery pulse rate times. ∎

Case Study 17.1

The following information is based on the 1990 U.S. Census Bureau survey data. The data represents housing costs (rent or mortgage plus taxes and utilities) for some randomly selected Nassau County communities on Long Island, New York.

1990 monthly

Community	*housing cost*	*Community*	*housing cost*
Baldwin	$809	Levittown	$846
Bellmore	$950	Long Beach	$714
Carle Place	$680	Lynbrook	$727
East Meadow	$732	Malverne	$785
E. Rockaway	$799	Massapequa	$876
Elmont	$692	Merrick	$998
Garden City	$1,027	Oceanside	$847
Glen Cove	$661	Rockville Centre	$708
Great Neck	$801	Roosevelt	$894
Hempstead	$694	Uniondale	$835
Hewlett	$835	Wantagh	$909
Lawrence	$1,207	Westbury	$822

The Census Bureau states that the monthly median housing cost for Nassau County for 1990 is $801. Using this value, and the sign test for medians:
a) what sign would be assigned to the community of Elmont?
b) what sign would be assigned to the community of Merrick?
c) what sign would be assigned to the community of Great Neck?
d) what is the n(– signs)? n(+ signs)? usable sample size (n)?
e) if you are interested in determining whether the Census Bureau's statement about the median housing cost is reasonable, how would you state the alternative hypothesis?
f) how would you state the null hypothesis?
g) would it be acceptable to use the normal approximation to the binomial distribution?
h) what is the mean of the binomial distribution? the standard deviation?
i) what are the critical z score(s) for a significance level of $\alpha = 0.05$?
j) what is your statistical result? Explain why you chose this value for the statistical result?
k) can you reject the null hypothesis at $\alpha = 0.05$?
l) do you find the Census Bureau's statement about the median housing cost for all Nassau County Communities reasonable? Explain.

Case Study 17.2

The article "Senior Nursing Students' and Professional Nurses' Perceptions of Effective Caring Behaviors: A Comparative Study" which appeared in the *Journal of Nursing Education* (volume 30, 1991) compared the ranks of a group of 30 senior baccalaureate students to 30 professional nurses on 50 behavioral items. Both groups of nurses were given 50 cards containing behavioral items which were ordered in six subscales of caring. These subscales of caring were:

1   *Accessible - 6 items*
2)   *Explains and facilitates - 6 items*
3)   *Comforts—9 items*
4)   *Anticipates—5 items*
5)   *Trusting relationship—16 items*
6)   *Monitors and follows through—8 items*

All the nurses were given 50 cards containing these caring behavioral items and were instructed to sort the cards from most important to not important. The Mann-Whitney test was used to determine if there was a significant difference in the ranks of the caring behaviors of the nursing students and the professional nurses. Table 17.14 contains the sum of the ranks for the nursing students and the professional nurses on each of the six subscales of caring.

Table 17.14

Subscales	Nursing Group	Student Group	z*	p
Accessibility	906.0	924.0	−0.12	0.89
Explains	874.5	955.5	−0.59	0.54
Anticipates	903.5	926.5	−0.16	0.86
Comforts	820.5	1009.5	−1.39	0.16
Monitors	903.0	927.0	−0.17	0.86
Trusts	1041.5	788.5	1.86	0.06

* The Mann-Whitney test requires finding a z-value if one of the groups is greater than 20.
   a)   Describe the type of data used in this study.
   b)   Identify each population within this study.
   c)   The behavioral items in each subscale were rated from one for most important to N for the least important nursing care behavior. Using this information, determine which group rated the items on each subscale as more important.
   d)   For the accessibility subscale, state the null and alternative hypotheses for the Mann-Whitney test. At the 0.10 significance level, can the null hypothesis be rejected?
   c)   For the trusts subscale, state the null and alternative hypotheses for the Mann-Whitney test. At the 0.10 significance level, can the null hypothesis be rejected?
   d)   For what p-value can the null hypothesis be rejected on the trust subscale?
   e)   For what p-value can the null hypothesis be rejected on the comforts subscale?
   f)   For the Anticipates subscale, which group was identified as population one on the Mann-Whitney test? Explain.
   g)   Was there a significant difference at $\alpha = 0.20$ in the way that the professional nurses ranked those items in the comforts subscales than the student nurses? If it is significant, then which group ranked the items higher? Explain.
   h)   Is there a significant difference between the way the professional nurses and the student nurses perceive nursing care behavior?

17.5   USING TECHNOLOGY

In this chapter we have studied three nonparametric tests. Let's apply the appropriate MINITAB commands to illustrate the ease in which each of the nonparametric tests can be performed using MINITAB.

Section 17.2 explored the use of the SIGN test for medians to test the hypothesis that students drink, on the average, four cups of coffee per day. This hypothesis test was performed using the data listed in Table 17.15.

TABLE 17.15

number of cups of coffee consumed each day

2	3	6	1	2	4	8	1	0	2
3	1	0	4	2	7	5	2	1	4

For this test, the MINITAB output is:

```
SIGN TEST OF MEDIAN = 4.000 VERSUS  L.T.  4.000
             N      BELOW        EQUAL      ABOVE    P-VALUE    MEDIAN
coffee      20       13            4          3      0.0106     2.000
```

Notice, that the p-value is less than $\alpha = 0.05$. Therefore, the null hypothesis is rejected and the alternative hypothesis is accepted.

The Mann-Whitney Rank-Sum Test was examined in Section 17.3. The test was demonstrated using the data listed in Table 17.16.

TABLE 17.16   Number of Withdrawals per class

Day Classes	Evening Classes
8	6
6	7
10	11
7	5
8	6
3	4
9	4
8	7
11	4
8	

The MINITAB output for this test is:

Mann-Whitney Confidence Interval and Test
day   N = 10   Median =   8.000
eve   N = 9   Median =   6.000
Point estimate for ETA1-ETA2 is   2.000
95.5 pct c.i. for ETA1-ETA2 is (0.000,3.999)
W = 123.5
Test of ETA1 = ETA2 vs. ETA1 g.t. ETA2 is significant at 0.0302
The test is significant at 0.0289 (adjusted for ties)

Notice the value of the test statistic W. How does this compare to the calculation of W in Section 17.3? Can you determine the p-value for W? Is W significant?

Using MINITAB for the sample information in Example 17.3 shown in Table 17.17, we can perform the Kruskal-Wallis test.

TABLE 17.17   Pulse rate recovery times in minutes

Routine A	Routine B	Routine C
3.2	7.5	3.5
2.1	3.8	4.2
4.4	5.6	5.5
8.3	6.4	8.4
5.7	4.8	6.1
	6.2	6.3

The MINITAB output for the Kruskal-Wallis test is:

LEVEL	NOBS	MEDIAN	AVE. RANK	Z VALUE
1	5	4.40	6.8	–0.96
2	5	5.600	9.2	0.40
3	6	5.800	9.3	0.54
OVERALL	16		8.5	

H = 0.93   d.f. = 2   p = 0.628

By examining the output for the Kruskal-Wallis H test statistic, the value of H = 0.93. The calculation of H in the solution to Example 17.3 was 0.86. This difference in the values of H was due to *round-off* errors. Can you identify the p-value for the H statistic? Is the H statistic significant? Explain.

KEY TERMS

Parametric Statistics   937
Nonparametric Statistics   937
Distribution Free Tests   938
n (– signs)   940
n (+ signs)   940

Sign Test for Medians   939
Mann-Whitney Rank Sum Test   947
Critical z scores   943
Usable sample size, n   943
Kruskal-Wallis H Test   956

Population Median, μ_o 942
Test statistic z   944

EXERCISES

17.1 Section Exercises

1. Inferential statistics which are based on assumptions such as the shape of the population is normal or the population variances are equal are called _____ statistics.

2. Inferential statistics that make no assumptions about the shape of the population or the parameters of a population are referred to as _____ statistics.

3. Nonparametric tests that do not require assumptions about the underlying population shape are also called _____ tests.

4. If you are not sure that your sample data comes from a normal population, you should
    a) use a parametric test
    b) use a nonparametric test
    c) increase your sample size
    d) use the normal distribution
    e) redesign your experiment

5. Nonparametric statistics are used when the population parameters are not known.
    (T/F)

6. You should use a nonparametric test whenever it is known that the distribution from which you are sampling is highly skewed.
    (T/F)

17.2 Section Exercises

7. a) Define Nonparametric Statistics.
    b) Why do statisticians frequently call nonparametric tests, distribution free tests?

8. What are some of the advantages of using nonparametric tests over parametric tests?

9. The sign test for medians requires the use of the binomial distribution where the probability of a success is p = ____.

10. In the sign test for medians, the data value is assigned a "+" if the data value is _____ the median, while a data value equal to the median is assigned a ____ and a data value below the median is assigned a ____.

11. The formulas for the binomial mean and standard deviation are:
    $\mu_s =$ ____ and $\sigma_s =$ ____.

12. The null hypothesis for the sign test for a median is a statement about the _____ median.

13. In the sign test for a median, the usable sample size, denoted n, is equal to the number of _____ signs, plus the number of _____.

14. In the sign test for a median, if the $\alpha = 0.01$ and a 1TT on the right side, the critical z score is: _____. While a 1TT on the left side and $\alpha = 0.05$ has a critical z score of _____.

15. In the sign test for medians, if there are 18 values below the hypothesized median, 4 equal to the hypothesized median and 17 values above the hypothesized median then the usable sample size is:
    a) n = 39
    b) n = 18
    c) n = 17
    d) n = 35
    e) none of these

16. Consider the following sample of 20 measurements.
    18, 21, 8, 19, 22, 7, 5, 23, 11, 6
    23, 11, 19, 9, 25, 11, 22, 29, 24, 29
    Use these data to conduct a Sign Test for Medians using the following hypotheses (use $\alpha = 0.05$):
    a) H_0: M = 12 versus H_a: M > 12
    b) H_0: M = 12 versus H_a: M ≠ 12
    c) H_0: M = 22 versus H_a: M < 22
    d) H_0: M = 22 versus H_a: M ≠ 22

17) Perform a sign test for medians using the following data where the median = 26 against the claim that the median does not equal 26. Use an 0.05 level of significance.
    30, 106, 44, 217, 19, 94, 21, 92, 22, 109, 11, 7, 90,
    55, 29, 44, 64, 4, 53, 59, 55, 89, 17, 19, 21, 294,
    26, 14, 15, 31, 18, 99, 6, 32, 12, 17, 10, 26, 65, 17,
    42, 50, 106, 102, 18, 74, 49, 14, 44, 40, 91, 94, 21,
    49, 17, 22, 42, 8, 52, 106, 100, 80, 42, 49, 35, 64,
    80, 30.
    a) Determine the sample size.
    b) How many data values are less than the hypothesized median?
    c) How many data values equal the hypothesized median?
    d) How many data values are greater than the hypothesized median?
    e) What is the median sample value?

f) Is the hypothesized median value rejected?

g) What is the p-value for the median sample value?

18. Perform a sign test for medians using the following data where the median = 10.6 against the claim that the median is greater than 10.6. Use an 0.05 level of significance.

11.6, 8.8, 10.4, 10.8, 11.2, 10.9, 10.4, 10.8, 10.1, 10.8, 10.2, 10.9, 10.5, 10.9, 11.5, 10.8, 10.9, 10.9.

a) Determine the sample size.

b) How many data values are less than the hypothesized median?

c) How many data values equal the hypothesized median?

d) How many data values are greater than the hypothesized median?

e) What is the median sample value?

f) Is the hypothesized median value rejected?

g) What is the p-value for the median sample value?

19. A manufacturer of Stereo VCR players has established that the median time to failure for its VCR's is 8340 hours of use. A sample 30 VCR players from the manufacturer's leading competitor is obtained. Each VCR player is tested until failure. For the sample of 30 VCR players, the 30 failure times ranged from 2 hours until 11,740 hours. Of the 30 failure times 20 was less than the 8340 hours. Do these results support the claim that the median failure time of the competitor differs from 8340 hours? Use $\alpha = 0.05$.

20. The following data represent the waiting time to play tennis at Salisbury Tennis Club on a typical Saturday morning.

Time (in minutes)

3, 6, 7, 6, 4, 8, 6, 20, 8, 6, 1, 10, 7, 11.

The club's manager claims that the median waiting time is 8 minutes. Aaron, the club's principal owner, believes that the claim is too low. Use the Sign Test for Medians to test Aaron's claim against the club manager's claim using a 0.05 level of significance.

21. Most nutritionists believe that a healthy diet contains no more than 30% of its total calories from fat. Dr. John believes that the claim is too high and determines the amount of calories from fat in diets of 16 healthy men that are on a 2000 calorie diet per day. The results of the sample are as follows:

Calories (from fat)

590, 450, 720, 600, 450, 320, 550, 490, 700, 800, 200, 445, 600, 590, 480, 730

Do these results support Dr. John's claim at 0.05 level of significance?

22. The median hourly wage for the population of students between the ages of 18 and 21 is $8 per hour. Professor DePorto believes that the median hourly for students at his college is not equal to $8 per hour. To test his claim a sample of students in this age group was selected and the results are listed below:

Hourly Wages:

10.50, 7.40, 10.75, 9.05, 9.25, 7.00, 12.65, 6.05, 8.05, 10.90, 8.80, 5.85, 14.35, 10.10, 13.70, 12.15, 12.10, 5.55, 12.10, 8.10, 9.15, 10.05, 9.45, 5.85, 9.80

Using a 0.05 level of significance can Professor DePorto support his claim?

17.3 Section Exercises

23. State the assumptions for using the Mann-Whitney Rank Sum Test.

24. The null hypothesis of the Mann-Whitney Rank Sum test is

H_0: The two populations are the same.

State three different alternative hypotheses that may be tested.

25. The nonparametric alternative hypothesis test to the two-sample t test which determines whether two independent samples came from the same population is called the _____.

26. In the Mann-Whitney rank-sum test, the test statistic, z, is computed using the formula: $z =$ ____ where $n_1 =$ ____, $n_2 =$ ____ and $W =$ ____.

27. In the Mann-Whitney rank-sum test, all the data values combined into one group and are ranked. If four data values are equal then their rank is determined by finding the ____ of the ranks of the four data values.

28. In the Mann-Whitney Test, if the $\alpha = 0.01$ and a 1TT on the left side, the critical z score is: _____. While a 1TT on the right side and $\alpha = 0.05$ has a critical z score of _____.

29. In the Mann-Whitney Test, the statistical result is equal to the value of ____.

30. The Mann-Whitney test
a) combines all the data values into one sample
b) ranks the data values of the combined samples
c) assumes the data values come from a normal distribution
d) is also referred to as the Wilcoxon rank-sum test
e) all of the above
f) none of the above
g) does only a and b
h) does only a, b, and c
i) does only a, b, and d

31. If the data values of two combined samples are:

20, 20, 21, 22, 22, 25, 27, 30, 31, 31, 33, 35

then the rank assigned to 22 in the Mann-Whitney test is:
a) 4 for the both values of 22
b) 4 for the first value of 22 and 5 for the second one
c) 4.5 for both values of 22
d) 4 but only one value of 22 is kept
e) 0 since there is a tie in the rankings

32. The Wilcoxon Rank-Sum Test is also referred to as the Mann-Whitney Rank Sum Test.
(T/F)

33. If it is known that the shapes of two populations are the same, then the Mann-Whitney Rank-Sum Test can be used to determine if the population means are different. (T/F)

34. Apply the Mann-Whitney Rank Sum Test to determine if the samples come from different distributions. Use a 0.05 level of significance.

Sample 1	Sample 2
85	57
67	80
56	73
61	61
76	75
64	86
54	64
65	72
	79

a) Identify the sample size of each sample.
b) What is the median for each sample?
c) Identify W.
d) Is W significant?
e) What is the p-value for W?

35. Apply the Mann-Whitney Rank Sum Test to determine if the median of distribution 1 is less than the median of distribution 2. Use a 0.05 level of significance.

Sample 1	Sample 2
28	26
16	42
42	65
29	38
31	29
22	32
50	59
42	42
23	27
25	41
	46
	18

a) Identify the sample size of each sample.
b) What is the median for each sample?
c) Identify W.
d) Is W significant?
e) What is the p-value for W?

36. The following collections of test scores have been randomly sampled from two distinct groups of students taking a reading placement exam.

Group 1	Group 2
78	86
29	65
74	78
66	80
82	65
65	95
66	88
84	94
73	75
55	89

a) Combine the two groups into one and assign a ranking of the data values.
b) Using the assigned ranking of the data values for the combined group, list the data values of group 1 and their respective assigned ranks.
c) Using the formula for the Mann-Whitney test, calculate the test statistic z.
d) If the Dean of Students believed that the reading placement exam scores are higher for group 2 as compared to group 1, perform a hypothesis test comparing the placement exam scores for the two groups. Use $\alpha = 0.01$.

37. Suppose you want to compare two treatments of physical therapy of the lower back. You wish to determine whether treatment A and treatment B are not the same by using the Mann-Whitney test.
a) State the null and alternative hypotheses you would test.
b) Suppose you were able to obtain for the following independent random samples measures as to the effectiveness of each treatment.

Treatment A: 45, 47, 25, 32, 54, 24, 18, 19, 42, 33
Treatment B: 23, 42, 31, 29, 24, 24, 19, 18, 17, 21

c) Using the formula for the Mann-Whitney test, calculate the test statistic z.
d) Do these data indicate that there is a difference in treatments at $\alpha = 0.05$?

38. Use the Mann-Whitney test to compare the number of sick days taken per year by male and female employees of a certain company. Use the 0.05 level of significance. The following data represents two randomly selected samples of the number of sick days taken for employees of the company.

Males: 11, 2, 4, 4, 4, 8, 3, 7, 8, 4
Females: 2, 4, 1, 6, 5, 3, 2, 3, 8, 4

39. The following data represents the result from a preference test of 100 individuals in a taste test involving Cokey versus Pipsi diet soft drink.

preference results:
Cokey 45   Pipsi 55

If H_0 is: There is no difference in preference of one product exists over the other (i.e. p = 0.50). and If H_a is: There is a difference in preference for one product over the other (i.e. p ≠ 0.50). Do the sample data indicate a significant difference in preference of one product over the other at $\alpha = 0.05$?

40. Ron's Japanese restaurant has noted an increase in the number of no-shows for dinner reservations when the reservations are made by a male caller than when made by a female caller. For the past 10 Saturdays the number of no-show reservations when the call was made by a male caller versus a female caller has been recorded.

Number of No-Shows for Dinner

male caller	female caller
11	13
15	14
10	10
18	9
11	10
12	8
10	11
14	12
20	15
11	7

At the 0.05 level of significance can Ron conclude that there are more no-shows for dinner when the caller is male versus when the caller is female?

41. Rich, the research director for a micro brewery, wants to know if there is a difference in the distribution of the number of liters consumed by men in the 22 to 35 age category for their Big Foot versus their Little Foot premium beer. A careful record of the total number of liters consumed by these men was collected over an eight day period. The results are as follows:

total number of liters consumed

Big Foot: 252, 263, 279, 273, 271, 265, 257, 280

Little Foot: 262, 242, 256, 260, 258, 243, 239, 265

Can Rich conclude that there is a difference between the two distributions? (use $\alpha = 0.05$)

42. Two groups are randomly selected. One group is to be given an experimental drug that is to enhance learning, the other a placebo. The time in minutes necessary to learn a specific task is recorded for each subject. The results are as follows:

Experimental Group: 41, 36, 42, 39, 36, 48, 49, 48, 52

Placebo Group: 61, 48, 55, 49, 70, 63, 74, 82

Does the drug enhance learning? Use a 0.05 level of significance.

17.4 Section Exercises:

43. When using the Kruskal-Wallis H test state a typical null and alternative hypotheses.

44. If you able to apply either the Kruskal-Wallis H test or ANOVA in an experiment, which is more desirable? Why?

45. A nonparametric test that is analogous to the Analysis of Variance test (ANOVA) is called the _____.

46. In the Kruskal-Wallis H Test, the null hypothesis, H_o, is: the populations are _____ . While the alternative hypothesis, H_a, is stated as the populations are _____.

47. The test statistic, for a Kruskal-Wallis H test is denoted by _____ and computed using the formula _____.

48. In the Kruskal-Wallis H test, the critical chi-square value, χ^2_α, is dependent upon the significance level, α,

and the formula for the degrees of freedom $df =$ _____ where the number of distinct samples is denoted by _____.

49. The decision rule of the Kruskal-Wallis H test is: reject H_o and accept H_a if the _____ is larger than the _____.

50. The quantity ΣR_2 represents the sum of the _____ for sample _____, while n_3 equals the size of sample _____ and N equals the combined number of data values for _____ samples.

51. The Kruskal-Wallis H Test is a nonparametric statistic that is used to test whether populations are approximately normally distributed. (T/F)

52. The binomial approximation by the normal distribution is used to calculate the H statistic. (T/F)

53. The Kruskal-Wallis H test is use to test whether three or more populations are the same. (T/F)

54. Use the Kruskal-Wallis H test statistic to compute the value of H for each of the following samples:

a)
X	Y	C
93	84	88
86	81	66
90	78	71
73	83	75
86	60	68
96	71	
79		

b)
A	B	C	D
8.3	9.8	13.2	11.4
10.1	13.2	7.3	10.8
10.3	11.1	8.1	9.0
13.8	7.6	9.5	12.1
14.1	13.4	11.4	8.9
7.8	12.6	8.6	11.1
12.8	7.9		

55. For the following data, use the the Kruskal-Wallis H Test to determine if the test statistic H is significant.

sample 1	sample 2	sample 3
30	68	56
75	25	77
65	35	64
90	22	84
98	43	96
95	36	71
88		79

a) Apply the Kruskal-Wallis H Test.
b) Identify the value of H.
c) Identify the df for the test.
d) Is H significant at 0.05? at 0.01?
e) If H is significant write the conclusion in terms of the null and alternative hypotheses.
f) What is the p-value for H?

56. The following are the final examination scores of samples of students who are taught statistics by three different methods:

Method A: traditional lecture with no emphasis on the use of technology, Method B: traditional lecture with emphasis on the use of technology with no laboratory requirement, and Method C: traditional lecture with an emphasis on the use of technology with a laboratory requirement.

Method A: 88, 66, 71, 75, 68

Method B: 84, 81, 78, 83, 60, 71, 80

Method C: 95, 88, 91, 75, 88, 97

Use the Kruskal-Wallis H test to test the null hypothesis that the three populations are the same against the alternative hypothesis that they are not the same. Use $\alpha = 0.05$.

57. Samples of annual income in thousands of dollars for police officers of patrolmen rank representing three major metropolitan cities are listed below. Use the Kruskal-Wallis H test to determine if the data indicate significant differences in annual income among the police officers representing the three cities at $\alpha = 0.05$.

NYC	LA	Boston
46	38	34
56	46	38
42	41	43
44	58	39
53	48	44

58. The following are the number of hours worked per week for a part-time job for students majoring in either Liberal Arts, Science or Business.

Liberal Arts: 23, 18, 35, 42, 22, 38

Science: 14, 9, 11, 25, 16

Business: 19, 22, 32, 39, 25, 48

Use the H test at a 0.05 level of significance to test the null hypothesis that there is no difference in the number of hours worked per week for a part-time job for the students majoring in Liberal Arts, Science or Business.

59. The number of patients treated in the emergency room of three area hospitals during the holiday week of July 4 are as follows:

Mercy Hospital: 157, 160, 178, 109, 99, 78, 77

Nassau Hospital: 180, 178, 190, 120, 102, 88, 90

Helpme Hospital: 140, 160, 128, 111, 98, 67, 40

Using an 0.01 level of significance, test the null hypothesis that the number of patients treated at the hospitals is the same.

CHAPTER REVIEW

60. Which one is *not* a nonparametric test?
a) Sign Test
b) Chi-Square
c) Mann Whitney
d) Kruskal-Wallis
e) none of these

61. What are some of the disadvantages of using nonparametric tests over parametric tests?

62. The normal distribution can be used to approximate the binomial distribution if the quantities _____ and _____ are both greater than 5.

63. The sign test for median
a) stipulates how to assign each data value a "+", a "−" or a "0".
b) uses the binomial distribution
c) assumes equal variances
d) assumes the data values come from a normal distribution
e) does all of the above
f) none of the above
g) does a and b
h) does a, b, and c
i) does a, b, and d

64. For the Mann-Whitney Test, the null hypothesis is stated as:

H_o: The two populations are _____ _____. While the alternative hypothesis is written as: H_a: The two populations are _____

65. When using the Mann-Whitney Rank Sum Test the normal distribution can be used as a model for the test if
a) each sample contains at least 5 data values
b) at least 80% of the samples contain 5 data values
c) each sample contains at least 10 data values
d both np and n(1 − p) are greater than 5
e) at least 80% of the samples contain 10 data values

66. When using the Mann-Whitney Rank Sum Test, the null hypothesis is based on the assumption that for each sample the sum of the ranks are equal. (T/F)

67. Identify the conditions to use the Kruskal-Wallis H test.

68. In the Kruskal-Wallis H test, the value of the test statistic is compared to the critical _____ to determine if the populations are the same.

69. To reject the null hypothesis in a Kruskal-Wallis H Test means that
a) H is larger than W
b) W is significant at $\alpha = 0.05$
c) H is larger than $\alpha = 0.05$
d) the populations from which the samples were drawn are not the same
e) W is greater than the critical χ_α^2 value at $\alpha = 0.05$

70. The Kruskal-Wallis H test
a) uses the chi-square distribution
b) uses the binomial distribution
c) is also called the H test

d) is similar to the counterpart parametric ANOVA test
e) combines all the data values into one group
f) assumes the data values come from a normal distribution
g) all of the above
h) none of the above
i) does only a and b
j) does only a, b, and c
k) does only a, b, and d
l) does only a, c, and d
m) does only a, c, d, and e
n) does only b, c, d, e, and f

71. A medical researcher believes that the effects of a particular drug therapy will begin to appear approximately 12 days after regular use of the drug begins. The researcher randomly selects 20 patients that will be administered the drug therapy. The patients begin to report drug related effects for the following number of days after the drug therapy was administered: 10, 14, 13, 18, 11, 12, 9, 13, 17, 12, 16, 15, 9, 16, 17, 15 , 18, 19, 11 and 14 days.

Use the Sign Test for Medians to test the null hypothesis that the population median number of days that the effects of the drug will begin to appear is 12 days against the claim that it is more than 12 days. Use $\alpha = 0.05$.

72. Big Joe's Pizza Palace believes families order more pies with toppings than without toppings. A sample of 20 orders are collected where the number of pies containing toppings versus without toppings is compared. The results are listed as follows:

number of pies ordered

with topping	*without topping*
3	2
4	1
3	4
2	1
1	3
5	2
3	1
2	3
1	2
2	1

At the 0.05 level of significance, can Joe conclude that more pies are order with toppings than without toppings?

73. A young new automobile driver suspects that the annual median cost for automobile insurance in his geographic region is approximately $2000. His parents believe that the annual cost is greater than $2000. He samples 14 insurance companies and finds the following insurance quotes for automobile insurance in his region:

$2,350 $1920 $1936 $2008 $1995 $2300 $2100
$2,550 $2320 $2036 $2108 $1945 $2000 $2040

Use the Sign Test for Medians to test the null hypothesis that the population median cost for automobile insurance is $2000 against the claim that it is more than $2000. Use $\alpha = 0.05$.

74. Bobby's music store has three mall locations. For the last ten weeks, Bobby has kept track of the number of customers who make a purchase of at least $100. The sample of those data are represented below. Use the Kruskal-Wallis H test to determine if there is a significant difference in the number of purchases of at least $100 for the three locations?

New York Mall: 98 63 100 84 78 87 98 94 90 99
Huntington Mall: 84 101 124 60 90 95 93 88 92 74
New Jersey Mall: 88 97 57 106 87 91 86 100 76 90

75. Two independent groups of nursing students have been instructed on the proper techniques of administering an upper arm injection. Group I was instructed using a preprogrammed video instruction tape while Group II was instructed by a traditional instructional lecture technique. The following data represents the number of minutes needed by each group's members to learn the procedure.

time to learn procedure in minutes

Group I   71 82 51 33 45 46 52 63 48 77
Group II 28 44 32 19 22 61 23 34 42 47

Use the Mann-Whitney Test to determine if the population mean time for learning the procedure is different between the groups. (Use $\alpha = 0.01$).

76. Use the Kruskal-Wallis H test to compare the probability distributions of three populations. The following three random samples were selected from each of the populations.

Pop I: 36, 58, 67, 61, 84, 72, 47
Pop II: 26, 20, 29, 43, 36, 44, 35
Pop III: 74, 103, 93, 78, 82, 76

Determine if there is a significant difference in the probability distributions for the three populations at $\alpha = 0.01$?

77. The human resource manager at a large municipality is interested in conducting a sexual awareness seminar to its employees. Before scheduling the seminar sessions, the manager is interested in finding out whether different groups of workers within the company are equally knowledgeable about sexual awareness. The manager randomly samples individuals from each group of company workers and administer's a test to each worker to determine if there are significant differences between the groups. The results of the tests are in the following table. Use these data and conduct a Kruskal-Wallis H test at $\alpha = 0.01$ to determine if the distributions of the sexual awareness scores for each group are equal.

Group 1	*Group 2*	*Group 3*	*Group 4*
42	71	43	29
51	74	58	45
50	69	46	49
61	80	50	56
68	81	38	52
38	75		46

78. The following information is based on the 1990 U.S. Census Bureau survey data. The data represents age of housing for some randomly selected Nassau County communities on Long Island, New York.

Community	age of housing (years)
Baldwin	47.3
Bellmore	35.7
Carle Place	39.5
East Meadow	35.9
E. Rockaway	42.6
Elmont	39.9
Garden City	42.5
Glen Cove	35.8
Great Neck	42.5
Hempstead	37.6
Hewlett	41.4
Lawrence	42.7

Community	age of housing (yrs)
Levittown	41.2
Long Beach	35.0
Lynbrook	49.0
Malverne	48.0
Massapequa	35.3
Merrick	35.7
Oceanside	35.9
Rockville Centre	48.8
Roosevelt	37.4
Uniondale	39.6
Wantagh	36.4
Westbury	38.5

The Census Bureau states that the median age of housing (years) for Nassau County in 1990 was 37.6. Using this value, and the sign test for medians:

a) what sign would be assigned to the community of Elmont?

b) what sign would be assigned to the community of Merrick?

c) what sign would be assigned to the community of Hempstead?

d) what is the n(– signs)? n(+ signs)? usable sample size (n)?

e) if you are interested in determining whether the Census Bureau's statement about the median age is reasonable, how would you state the alternative hypothesis?

f) how would you state the null hypothesis?

g) would it be acceptable to use the normal approximation to the binomial distribution?

h) what is the mean of the binomial distribution? the standard deviation?

i) what are the critical z score(s) for a significance level of $\alpha = 0.05$?

j) what is your statistical result? Explain why you chose this value for the statistical result?

k) can you reject the null hypothesis at $\alpha = 0.05$?

l) do you find the Census Bureau's statement about the median age for all Nassau County Communities reasonable? Explain.

79. In the Journal of Personality and Social Psychology (volume 54, 1988), a study entitled "*The Dark Side of Self- and Social Perception: Black Uniforms and Aggression in Professional Sports*" was conducted to determine if the color of a football team's uniform within the National Football League (NFL) has a significant effect on a person's perception of the team's behavior. Twenty-five subjects were selected to rate the uniforms of all the 28 teams in the NFL on several scales from one to seven. The researchers were interested in determining if there was a perception between black uniforms and aggressive behavior. Five of the 28 NFL teams have uniforms which are considered to be black. These teams are: Chicago Bears, Cincinnati Bengals, New Orleans Saints, Pittsburgh Steelers and the Los Angeles Raiders. Table 17.18 represents the average malevolence ratings on three semantic differential scales: nice/mean, timid/aggressive, and good/bad. Notice the top five teams within Table 17.18 all wear a uniform considered to be black.

Table 17.18

Football Team	Rating
Los Angeles Raiders	5.10
Pittsburgh Steelers	5.00
Cincinnati Bengals	4.97
New Orleans Saints	4.83
Chicago Bears	4.68
Kansas City Chiefs	4.58
Washington Redskins	4.40

St. Louis Cardinals	4.27
New York Jets	4.12
Los Angeles Rams	4.10
Cleveland Browns	4.05
San Diego Chargers	4.05
Green Bay Packers	4.00
Philadelphia Eagles	3.97
Minnesota Vikings	3.90
Atlanta Falcons	3.87
San Francisco 49ers	3.83
Indianapolis Colts	3.83
Seattle Seahawks	3.82
Denver Broncos	3.80
Tampa Bay Buccaneers	3.77
New England Patriots	3.60
Buffalo Bills	3.53
Detroit Lions	3.38
New York Giants	3.27
Dallas Cowboys	3.15
Houston Oilers	2.88
Miami Dolphins	2.80

a) How would you interpret a higher malevolence rating? a lower malevolence rating?

b) Separate the 28 NFL teams into two groups: the teams who wear black uniforms and the teams not identified as wearing black uniforms. If you wanted to perform a large-sample Mann-Whitney test to determine whether teams wearing black uniforms are perceived as being more aggressive, mean or bad, then state a null and alternative hypothesis for such a test.

c) Identify the data type for this test.

d) If the null hypothesis is true, then how would you expect the ranks to be distributed within each of the two groups? Does this appear to be true for the information contained in Table 17.18?

e) What rank would you assign the Cleveland Browns? the San Francisco 49ers?

f) What is the value of W for this Mann-Whitney test?

g) Can you conclude at $\alpha = 0.05$ that malevolence rating of the NFL teams that wear black uniforms is significantly higher? Can you conclude the same conclusion at $\alpha = 0.01$? Explain. What do you think has contributed to this conclusion?

80. The following article entitled *Order of the Draft Drawing* which appeared in the New York Times shows the order in which birth dates were selected during the 1969 draft lottery. On December 1, 1969 the lottery was held in the Selective Service headquarters in Washington, D.C. to determine the draft status of all 19 year-old males for the Vietnam Conflict. The 366 possible birth dates were inserted within a small capsule. The capsules were placed in a stationary drum beginning with January, then February and so on until all the birth dates of December were placed in the drum last. The first capsule drawn would have the highest draft priority, and so on. Table 17.19 shows the actual order in which the 366 days were selected.

Theoretically, if the capsules were adequately mixed, then the resulting draft order should have been random with respect to each month. That is, if the lottery were fair then we would expect a birth date in December should have the same chance of being selected early in the draft as a birth date for any other month, such as January. Examine the list of birth dates within the Table 17.19 which represents the actual order of the 1969 draft drawing.

a) If the lottery was random, then how would you expect the assigned ranks to be distributed within each month?

b) If you wanted to conduct a Kruskal-Wallis test, then how would you state the null hypothesis? the alternative hypothesis?

c) How many groups would you have within this test? What does each group represent? In the Kruskal-Wallis test, what would the values of k and N represent for this test?

d) What would the value of the test statistic H for this Kruskal-Wallis test?

e) Is this value of the H statistic significant at $\alpha = 0.01$? at $\alpha = 0.0001$?

f) Do you think the 1969 Draft Lottery was fair? Explain your answer. What do you think might have contributed to this result?

g) If you were going to conduct a draft lottery how would you conduct the draft to insure that the lottery would be fair?

TABLE 17.19

Order of the Draft Drawing

Special to The New York Times
WASHINGTON, Dec. 1—Following is the order in which birth dates were drawn tonight in the draft lottery.

#	Date	#	Date	#	Date	#	Date	#	Date	#	Date	#	Date	#	Date
1	Sept. 14	48	Aug. 8	95	Dec. 24	142	Aug. 12	189	Feb. 17	236	Feb. 24	283	Oct. 8	325	Jan. 10
2	April 24	49	Sept. 3	96	Dec. 16	143	Nov. 17	190	July 18	237	Oct. 11	284	July 10	326	May 22
3	Dec. 30	50	July 7	97	Nov. 8	144	Feb. 2	191	April 29	238	Jan. 14	285	Feb. 29	327	July 6
4	Feb. 14	51	Nov. 7	98	July 17	145	Aug. 4	192	Oct. 20	239	Mar. 28	286	Aug. 25	328	Dec. 2
5	Oct. 18	52	Jan. 25	99	Nov. 29	146	Nov. 18	193	July 31	240	Dec. 19	287	July 30	329	Jan. 11
6	Sept. 6	53	Dec. 22	100	Dec. 31	147	Apr. 7	194	Jun. 9	241	Oct.19	288	Oct. 17	330	May 1
7	Oct. 26	54	Aug. 5	101	Jan. 5	148	Apr. 16	195	Sept. 24	242	Sept. 12	289	July 27	331	July 14
8	Sept. 7	55	May 16	102	Aug. 15	149	Sept. 25	196	Oct. 24	243	Oct. 21	290	Feb. 22	332	Mar. 18
9	Nov. 22	56	Dec. 5	103	May 30	150	Feb. 11	197	May 9	244	Oct. 3	291	Aug. 21	333	Aug. 30
10	Dec. 6	57	Feb. 23	104	June 19	151	Sept. 29	198	Aug. 14	245	Aug. 26	292	Feb. 18	334	Mar. 21
11	Aug. 31	58	Jan. 19	105	Dec. 8	152	Feb. 13	199	Jan. 3	246	Sept. 18	293	Mar. 5	335	June 9
12	Dec. 7	59	Jan. 24	106	Aug. 9	153	July 22	200	Mar. 19	247	June 22	294	Oct. 14	336	April 19
13	July 8	60	June 21	107	Nov. 16	154	Aug. 17	201	Oct. 23	248	July 11	295	May 13	337	Jan. 22
14	April 11	61	Aug. 29	108	March 1	155	May 6	202	Oct. 4	249	June 1	296	May 27	338	Feb. 9
15	July 12	62	April 21	109	June 23	156	Nov. 21	203	Nov. 19	250	May 21	297	Feb. 3	339	Aug. 22
16	Dec. 29	63	Sept. 20	110	June 6	157	Dec. 3	204	Sept. 21	251	Jan. 3	298	May 2	340	April 26
17	Jan. 15	64	June 27	111	Aug. 1	158	Sept. 11	205	Feb. 27	252	April 23	299	Feb. 28	341	June 18
18	Sept. 26	65	May 10	112	May 17	159	Jan. 2	206	June 10	253	April 6	300	Mar. 12	342	Oct. 9
19	Nov. 1	66	Nov. 12	113	Sept. 15	160	Sept. 22	207	Sept. 16	254	Oct. 16	301	June 3	343	Mar. 25
20	June 4	67	July 25	114	Aug. 6	161	Sept. 2	208	April 30	255	Sept 17	302	Feb. 20	344	Aug. 26
21	Aug. 10	68	Feb. 12	115	July 3	162	Dec. 23	209	June 30	256	Mar. 23	303	July 26	345	April 20
22	June 26	69	June 13	116	Aug. 23	163	Dec. 13	210	Feb. 4	257	Sept. 28	304	Dec. 17	346	April 12
23	July 24	70	Dec. 21	117	Oct. 22	164	Jan. 30	211	Jan. 31	258	Mar. 24	305	Jan. 1	347	Feb. 6
24	Oct. 5	71	Sept. 10	118	Jan. 23	165	Dec. 4	212	Feb. 16	259	Mar. 13	306	Jan. 7	348	Nov. 3
25	Feb. 19	72	Oct. 12	119	Sept. 23	166	Mar. 16	213	Mar. 8	260	April 17	307	Aug. 13	349	Jan. 29
26	Dec. 14	73	June 17	120	July 16	167	Aug. 28	214	Feb. 5	261	Aug. 3	308	May 28	350	July 2
27	July 21	74	April 27	121	Jan. 16	168	Aug. 7	215	Jan. 4	262	April 28	309	Nov. 26	351	April 25
28	June 5	75	May 19	122	Mar. 7	169	Mar. 15	216	Feb. 10	263	Sept. 9	310	Nov. 5	352	Aug. 27
29	Mar. 2	76	Nov. 6	123	Dec. 28	170	Mar. 26	217	Mar. 30	264	Oct. 27	311	Aug. 19	353	June 29
30	Mar. 21	77	Jan. 28	124	April 13	171	Oct. 15	218	April 10	265	Mar. 22	312	April 8	354	Mar. 14
31	May 24	78	Dec. 27	125	Oct. 2	172	July 23	219	April 9	266	Nov. 4	313	May 11	355	Jan. 27
32	April 1	79	Oct. 31	126	Nov. 13	173	Dec. 26	220	Oct. 10	267	Mar. 3	314	Dec. 12	356	June 14
33	Mar. 17	80	Nov. 9	127	Nov. 14	174	Nov. 30	221	Jan. 12	268	Mar. 27	315	Sept. 30	357	May 26
34	Nov. 2	81	April 4	128	Dec. 18	175	Sept. 13	222	Jan. 25	269	April 5	316	April 22	358	June 24
35	May 7	82	Sept. 5	129	Dec. 1	176	Oct. 25	223	Mar. 25	270	July 29	317	Mar. 9	359	Oct. 1
36	Aug. 24	83	April 3	130	May 15	177	Sept. 19	224	Jan. 6	271	April 2	318	Jan. 13	360	June 20
37	May 31	84	Dec. 23	131	Nov. 15	178	May 14	225	Sept. 1	272	June 12	319	May 23	361	May 25
38	Oct. 30	85	June 7	132	Nov. 25	179	Feb. 25	226	May 29	273	April 15	320	Dec. 18	362	Mar. 29
39	Dec. 11	86	Feb. 1	133	May 12	180	June 13	227	July 19	274	June 16	321	May 8	363	Feb. 21
40	May 3	87	Oct. 6	134	June 11	181	Feb. 8	228	June 2	275	Mar. 4	322	July 15	364	May 5
41	Dec. 10	88	July 28	135	Dec. 20	182	Nov. 23	229	Oct. 29	276	May 4	323	Mar. 10	365	Feb. 26
42	July 13	89	Feb. 18	136	Mar. 11	183	May 20	230	Nov. 24	277	July 9	324	Aug. 11	366	June 8
43	Dec. 9	90	April 18	137	June 25	184	Sept. 3	231	April 14	278	May 13				
44	Aug. 16	91	Feb. 7	138	Oct. 13	185	Nov. 20	232	Sept. 4	279	July 4				
45	Aug. 2	92	Jan. 26	139	Mar. 6	186	Jan. 21	233	Sept. 27	280	Jan. 20				
46	Nov. 11	93	July 1	140	Jan. 18	187	July 20	234	Oct. 7	281	Nov. 28				
47	Nov. 27	94	Oct. 28	141	Aug. 18	188	July 5	235	Jan. 17	282	Nov. 10				

Following is the order of the alphabet to be applied to the first letter of last names in determining the order of call for inductees with the same birth dates: J, G, D, X, N, O, Z, T, W, P, Q, Y, U, C, F, I, K, H, S, L, M, A, R, E, B, V

PROJECTS:

81. Find examples of the uses of nonparametric statistics in a professional journal.
   a) Identify the type of test that is demonstrated.
   b) Do the authors give a rationale for the use of the statistics? Explain.

82. a) Identify five quantitative variables that you are able to measure.

   b) For each variable randomly sample 250 data values.
   c) For each sample construct a Stem-and-Leaf display.
   d) Do the sample results indicate that the populations from which the data were sampled suggest the use of nonparametric statistics? Explain.

ANALYZING THE DATABASE USING TECHNOLOGY

The following exercises refer to the file DATABASE listed in Appendix A. Using a technological tool, answer each exercise.

83. a) Construct a STEM-and-LEAF Display and a BOX PLOT for the variables: GFT and PH
   b) Describe the shape of each variable.
   c) Explain why it is reasonable to perform a nonparametric test on each variable.
   d) For the variable GFT test that the population median amount spent on a gift is not equal to 100 dollars. Use $\alpha = 0.05$.
   e) For the variable PH test that the population median number of hours spent on the phone per week is less than 5. Use $\alpha = 0.05$.

84. a) For the variable GFT, use the Mann-Whitney test to determine if there is a difference in the spending habits of males versus females. Use $\alpha = 0.05$.
   b) By examining the output, determine
   1. the sample size for each group.
   2. W
   3. the p-value.

85. a) For the variable PH, use the Mann-Whitney test to determine if there is a difference in the spending habits of males versus females. Use $\alpha = 0.05$.

   b) By examining the output, determine
   1. the sample size for each group.
   2. W
   3. the p-value.

86. a) For the variable WRK, use the Kruskal-Wallis H test to determine if there is a difference in the number of hours worked for the variable academic area of concentration (MAJ). Use $\alpha = 0.05$.
   b) By examining the output, determine
   1. the sample size for each major.
   2. H
   3. *df*
   4. the p-value.

87. a) For the variable GPA, use the Kruskal-Wallis H test to determine if there is a difference in the number of hours worked for the variable academic area of concentration (MAJ). Use $\alpha = 0.05$.
   b) By examining the output, determine
   1. the sample size for each major.
   2. H
   3. *df*
   4. the p-value.

CHAPTER TEST

88. Which assumptions are necessary to use a parametric test?

   I.   The distributions from which the samples are selected are not symmetric.
   II. The population variances must be equal.
   III. The populations are normally distributed.

   a) I only
   b) II only
   c) III only
   d) I and II
   e) II and III

89. The nonparametric counterpart test to the t-test about a population mean is called the _____.

90. The sign test for medians is analogous to the one sample t test.
   (T/F)

91. The Kruskal-Wallis H test is the nonparametric counterpart to the Analysis of Variance test.
   (T/F)

92. Everett Evergreen of Evergreen Entertainment hypothesized that the population median price a couple will spend on a wedding band is $4400. His partner

Francis, believes that the claim is too high. They decide to randomly sample twenty recent wedding band contracts. The following data represent the result of the sample:

contract amount is dollars: 3850, 6000, 3600, 3900, 4200, 4700, 3900, 4100, 4400, 3750, 4200, 4500, 4600, 5500, 3800, 4200, 4800, 5200, 3900, 4000

Use the Sign Test for Medians to test Francis's claim against Everett's claim using a 0.01 level of significance.

93. The following collections of times have been randomly sampled from two distinct groups of runners performing in the 440m relay. Group 1 represents runners who have trained while under a specific high carbohydrate diet while Group 2 represents those runners who have trained using a balanced diet. The track coach believes that the runners that have been using the high carbohydrate diet will perform better in the next track meet.

Times in Seconds

Group 1	*Group 2*
54.2	64.1
53.8	55.6
54.9	58.1
60.1	53.4
63.4	55.6
51.9	53.2
56.4	58.4
54.2	64.1
53.7	52.2
55.6	55.6

60.5

a) Combine the two groups into one and assign a ranking of the data values.

b) Using the assigned ranking of the data values for the combined group, list the data values of group 1 and their respective assigned ranks.

c) Using the formula for the Mann-Whitney test, calculate the test statistic z.

d) State a null and alternative hypothesis to test the coach's belief.

e) Do these data support the track coach's claim at $\alpha = 0.05$?

94. Frozen Yogurt may contain different amounts of calories for a 3 oz serving. The data in the table below show the calorie content from samples of three different brands of frozen yogurt. Test for significant differences in the calorie content of these three frozen yogurts. Are there significant differences at the 0.01 level of significance?

Yummy Frozen Yogurt: 105, 110, 102, 106, 104
Creamy Frozen Yogurt: 109, 115, 107, 109, 118
Dreamy Frozen Yogurt: 100, 104, 108, 112, 108

CHAPTER I

1. Raw

3. Descriptive; Inferential

5. Population

7. Statistic

9. Descriptive

11. **a)** Working women in San Francisco, CA
  b) 250 working women
  c) Average annual Salary

13. b

15. b

17. false

19. true

21. **a)** Freshman from the fall, '92 to spring, '93 at 2 yr and 4 yr colleges
  b) The students were paid stipends to participate in the study.
  c) They measured their abilities in reading comprehension, mathematics, critical thinking and composite achievement. They controlled for pre-college ability by selecting students that were most similar in their pre-academic preparation.

d) Among the results of the study, 2 yr college freshman had higher gains in mathematics & composite achievement while 4 yr freshman had higher gains in reading comprehension and critical thinking.

23. Inferential

25. census

27. population; sample

29. N

31. statistic

33. d

35. equal chance

37. true

39. strata

41. clusters; population

43. a) not random b) random

45. answers vary—discuss with your instructor

47. 6327; 5998; 5110; 1514; 5868; 1355; 0989; 0830; 0104; 2003

49. 2487; 8467; 1898; 0402; 3469; 0784; 6202; 7791; 1277; 8596; 3891; 7965; 3610; 0010; 8314

51. Pictograph

53a

53b

55. Discuss this with your instructor.

57. Sample

59. Parameter

61. a) Sample;   **b)** Population;   **c)** Statistic

63. a

65. a

67. true

69. true

71. a) (i) **inferential statistics** is the process of using sample information to draw inferences or conclusions about the population.

    (ii) **sampling** is the process of selecting a portion, or sample, of the entire population

    (iii) **census** is a survey that includes every item or individual within the population.

    (iv) **destructive testing**—when it is necessary to destroy an item to test it.

    (v) **population** is the entire group that has been identified for study.

    (vi) **sample** is the portion of the population selected for study.

    (vii) **parameter** is a number that describes a characteristic of the population.

    (viii) **statistic** is a number that describes a characteristic of a sample.

    (ix) **sample size** is the number of data values within the sample.

    (x) **population size** is the number of data values within a finite population.

b) A sample is selected because a census is impossible, and the cost of a census is too prohibitive, less time to select a sample and the results of a sample are more accurate than taking a census.

c) (i) population mean = μ
    (ii) sample mean = $\bar{x}$
    (iii) population standard deviation = σ
    (iv) sample standard deviation = s
    (v) population size = N
    (vi) sample size = n

73. true

75. true

77. a) Use the three distinct income brackets: low, middle and high to represent the strata.

b) a sample from each strata is selected corresponding to the proportion of people within each income bracket. The three samples are combined to represent the total sample selected.

79. a) yes, since each of the students has an equal chance of being selected.

b) no because she is only selecting students attending morning classes.

c) all the students attending the morning European History classes.

81. no; only people interested in gun control will participate

83. answers vary—discuss with instructor

85. 1514; 1355; 989; 830; 104; 2003; 845; 2836; 991; 1976; 4010; 2664; 1570; 4627; 4479; 4557; 2162; 1699; 1338; 2278

87. 14,877; 10,924; 2,771; 5,697; 2,865; 4,237; 8,710; 4,284; 1,181; 4,230; 9,205

89a.   **89b.**

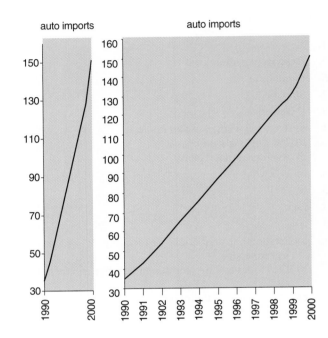

91. Both are examples of inferential statistics.

I. Why we don't "just do it":
population: assume USA population
sample size: n = 2000
conclusion: answers vary

II. When pets get "people food"
population: pet owners
sample size: n = 1,049
conclusion: answers vary

93. Some of the problems are:

1. A bias sample is used by the manufacturer in their claims.

2. False or misleading conclusions drawn from the sample.

3. Small samples are used in the claims.

95. a) Women and men voters

b) Graphic conveys there have been more women voters during the indicated years.

c) There is a Presidential election every four years. The 2000 election year was a Presidential election year.

d) There are more voters during the Presidential election years.
In 1998, 40 million men voters were expected according to the pattern of men voters.

In 1998, 44 million women voters were expected according to the pattern of women voters.

e) 1992

f) Yes

CHAPTER 2

1. variable

3. categorical; numerical

5. numerical; data

7. continuous

9. true

11. **a)** sex, status & frat: categorical; age, ht, wt, havg & gpa: numerical & continuous.

 b) sex = male; status = sophomore; age = 20; height = 71"; weight = 145 lbs; fraternity = member, Havg = 86; gpa = 2.86.

13. distribution

15. 34; 6

17. stem

19. a

21. **a)**

```
1 | 9 9
2 | 4 6 8 9 9
3 | 0 1 2 2 3 4 4 5 7 7 9
4 | 1 1 4 6 6 9 9
5 | 0 1 2 2 4 6 9
6 | 1 3 3 6
7 | 3 4 6
8 | 4
```

 b) skewed to the right   **c)** 30's   **d)** 25–39 years

23. **a)**

```
        9 8 7 5 5 | 10 | 9
  9 9 8 7 5 4 3 3 2 | 11 | 3 7
  8 7 6 5 5 3 1 0 0 | 12 | 4 6 6 7 8
              0 1 | 13 | 5 5 6 6 7 7 8 8 8 9
                    | 14 | 2 3 5 7 8 8 9
```

 b) yes

 c) experimental: symmetric bell-shaped; control: skewed to the left

25. classes; frequency

27. significant

29. midpoint

31. percent; 100; 100%

33. sum; greater than

35. b

37. b

39. true

41.

classes	freq	class marks	class boundaries	relative percentages
20–22	2	21	19.5–22.5	3.33%
23–25	5	24	22.5–25.5	8.33%
26–28	15	27	25.5–28.5	25%
29–31	20	30	28.5–31.5	33.33%
32–34	13	33	31.5–34.5	21.67%
35–37	4	36	34.5–37.5	6.67%
38–40	1	39	37.5–40.5	1.67%

 i) yes;   **ii)** no   **iii)** no   **iv)** no

43. **a)** age & continuous

 b)

classes	freq	class boundaries	class marks	relative percentages
18–28	39	17.5–28.5	23	32.5%
29–39	25	28.5–39.5	34	20.83%
40–50	19	39.5–50.5	45	15.83%
51–61	17	50.5–61.5	56	14.17%
62–72	20	61.5–72.5	67	16.67%

45. discrete; categorical

47. vertical; horizontal

49. omission

51. marks; continuous

53. false

55. **a)** day of the week is categorical;

 b)

 c) monday: 10.32%; tuesday: 5.81%; wednesday: 11.77%; thursday: 7.41%; friday: 35.32%; saturday: 23.55%; sunday: 5.81%

 d)

 e) the bar graphs are essentially the same.

57. a) class width = 5

b) Married:

classes:	class marks	freq	relative %
30–34	32	299	15.86%
35–39	37	247	13.10%
40–44	42	286	15.17%
45–49	47	286	15.17%
50–54	52	247	13.10%
55–59	57	260	13.79%
60–64	62	260	13.79%

Unmarried:

classes:	class marks	freq	relative %
30–34	32	481	16.52%
35–39	37	429	14.73%
40–44	42	455	15.63%
45–49	47	468	16.67%
50–54	52	325	11.16%
55–59	57	429	14.73%
60–64	62	325	11.16%

c)

d)

e) answers vary; frequency polygon using percentages
f) married

59.

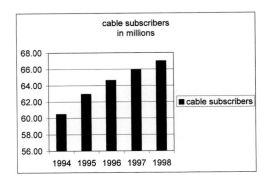

61. pictograph
63. center; decreasing
65. right; low; high
67. same
69. one; opposite
71. d
73. a
75. c
77. d
79. a) numerical; continuous
   b) numerical; continuous
   c) categorical
   d) numerical; discrete
81. a)

1	0
2	
3	0 2 5 7 8 9
4	2 5 5 5 7 8 8 8 9 9
5	0 0 3 5 8
6	1 2 4
7	0 0 1 2 2 2 2 2 3 4 5 5 5 5 5 7 7 7 9 9 9 9
8	0
9	5
10	
11	
12	0

b) bimodal
c) yes; there are two outliers: 10 and 120 minutes.
d) 66%
e) ²⁄₅₀ or 4%

83. **a)**

	smoking		non-smoking
4 1	3	
	4	
12 12 9 9 7 5 4 3 3 2 2	5	9 11 11 13 15
9 9 8 8 8 6 6 6 6 5 5 2 2 1 1	6	5 6 6 6 8 8 9 10 12 14 14 14
8 8 7 6 6 5 5 5 4 4 3 2 2 0	7	0 1 1 2 3 3 5 6 6 8 9 9 10 11 12 14 15
3 3 2 2 0 0	8	1 2 4 4 5 6 8 9
3 2 1	9	0 3 3 4 8
	10	1 5
	11	2

b) skewed;

c) yes

85. **a)** yes **b)** no **c)** yes **d)** no **e)** no

87. **a)** & **b)**

classes (preference)	frequency	relative frequency	relative percentage
SIPEPS	20	0.40	40%
COAKS	24	0.48	48%
NEITHER	6	0.12	12%

c)

Pie Chart
Preference for Soft Drink

89. **a)**

Classes (Indices)	Frequency	class boundaries	class marks
30–37	6	29.5–37.5	33.5
38–45	16	37.5–45.5	41.5
46–53	18	45.5–53.5	49.5
54–61	31	53.5–61.5	57.5
62–69	14	61.5–69.5	65.5
70–77	10	69.5–77.5	73.5
78–85	5	77.5–85.5	81.5

b)

Histogram
Pollution Indices

c)

Frequency Polygon
Pollution

91. **a)** Income is numerical & treated as continuous.

b)

classes	freq	class boundaries	class marks	relative%
15–29	8	14.5–29.5	22	16%
30–44	14	29.5–44.5	37	28%
45–59	11	44.5–59.5	52	22%
60–74	17	59.5–74.5	67	34%

c)

classes	cumm. freq
less than 15	0
less than 30	8
less than 45	22
less than 60	33
less than 75	50

d) 66%

e) 84%

f) no

g) specific data values are lost; no

93. **a)**

Classes (IQ Scores)	class boundaries	Boys Rel. Freq.	Girls Rel. Freq.	Third Graders Rel. Freq.
60– 79	59.5– 79.5	11.43%	2.5%	6.67%
80– 99	79.5– 99.5	38.57%	43.75%	41.33%
100–119	99.5–119.5	32.86%	18.75%	25.33%
120–139	119.5–139.5	14.29%	31.25%	23.33%
140–159	139.5–159.5	2.86%	3.75%	3.33%

b)

Histogram
Third Grade Boys

d)

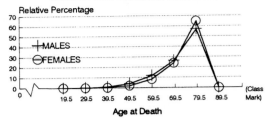

Frequency Polygon
Deaths From Cardiovascular Disease

97. a)

classes (age)	freq.	class marks	class boundaries	relative frequency
18–22	27	20	17.5–22.5	0.13
23–27	54	25	22.5–27.5	0.26
28–32	55	30	27.5–32.5	0.26
33–37	31	35	32.5–37.5	0.15
38–42	21	40	37.5–42.5	0.10
43–47	10	45	42.5–47.5	0.05
48–52	7	50	47.5–52.5	0.03
53–57	3	55	52.5–57.5	0.01
58–62	2	60	57.5–62.5	0.01

b) shape: skewed to the right

Histogram
Third Grade Girls

Frequency Polygon
Age When Starting a Business

Histogram
Third Grade Students

c)

classes	cumulative frequency
less than 18	0
less than 23	27
less than 28	81
less than 33	136
less than 38	167
less than 43	188
less than 48	198
less than 53	205
less than 58	208
less than 63	210

c) 1) 53.75%
  2) 50.01%
  3) 51.99%
  4) 93.33%
  5) 6.67%

95. a) class width = 10
  b)

class mark	class boundaries	relative percentage for males	relative percentage for females
29.5	24.5–34.5	0.11%	0.08%
39.5	34.5–44.5	0.94%	0.42%
49.5	44.5–54.5	4.05%	2.08%
59.5	54.5–64.5	11.63%	8.27%
69.5	64.5–74.5	26.31%	24.22%
79.5	74.5–84.5	56.96%	64.94%

c) males: sum of rel. percents = 100%; females: sum of rel. percents = 100.01%

d)

classes	cumulative frequency
18 or more	210
23 or more	183
28 or more	129
33 or more	74

38 or more	43
43 or more	22
48 or more	12
53 or more	5
58 or more	2
63 or more	0

e)

Ogive
Age When Starting a Business

f) 65%   **g)** 10%   **h)** 52%

99.

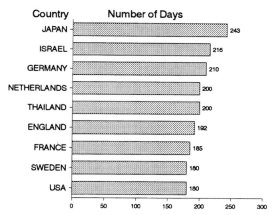

Horizontal Bar Graph
Length of School Year

101. a)

Classes	Cumulative Frequency
Less Than 0.5	0
Less Than 1.0	26
Less Than 1.5	74
Less Than 2.0	134
Less Than 2.5	200
Less Than 3.0	273
Less Than 3.5	358
Less Than 4.0	458
Less Than 4.5	500

b)

Ogive
Premature Baby Weights

c) 55 %

103. a)

Pie Chart
Homework Time

b) 38%;
c) 67%

105. a) 18   **b)** 20%   **c)** 20%   **d)** 36%   **e)** 36%   **f)** yes
g) 4%

CHAPTER 3

1. mean, median, mode
3. resistant
5. **a)** 45
    b) 3
    c) 5
    d) 20
7. −5
9. mode
11. mode
13. true
15. b
17. c
19. resistant
21. false
23. **a)** 4
    b) 4
    c) no mode
    d) 0
    e) 190

f) 1600

g) 30

h) 0

i) 174

25. mean = \$220; median & mode = \$215; all illustrate a fair price

27. a) 140; 50

b) median

c) 50; 50

d) equally good

e) median

f) mean

29. mean = \$42.38

31. b

33. 1) skewed left, median

2) symmetric bell-shaped, mean = median

3) skewed right, mean

4) skewed right, mean

5) symmetric bell-shaped, mean = median

35. dispersion or spread

37. 5

39. a) s   **b)** σ (sigma)

41. 1) below   2) above   3) μ

43. b

45. a

47. b

49. false

51. false

53. Sarabella: μ = \$159,000; σ = \$139,685

20th Century: μ = \$184,500; σ = \$124,878

Sarabella

55. Ms. Sue

57. a) & b)

stock	$\bar{x}$	s
x	68	1.83
y	68	2.71
z	68	5.31

c) stock z is more speculative

stock x is more conservative

59.

	Drug companies		Cosmetic companies	
	R & D	Marketing	R & D	Marketing
a)	$\bar{x} = 3.11$	$\bar{x} = 2.40$	$\bar{x} = 1.39$	$\bar{x} = 3.68$
b)	s = 0.88	s = 0.61	s = 0.53	s = 0.75

c) The drug companies spend more on R & D relative to the cosmetic companies. While, the cosmetic companies spend more on marketing than the drug companies.

61. Chebyshev's; Empirical

63. a) 68%   **b)** 95%   **c)** all; 99%; 100%

65. a

67. a

69. b

71. c

73. false

75. true

77. false

79. a) 95%   **b)** 68%   **c)** 81.5%   **d)** approx 97.5%

e) 150 is unusual   **f)** yes

81. Although officer B has more absolute variability (standard deviation = 15) than officer A (standard deviation = 5), the relative variation for officer B (coefficient of variation = 10%) is less than the relative variation for officer A (coefficient of variation = 12.5%).

83. approx. 11%

85. sample: $z = \dfrac{x - \bar{x}}{s}$;

population: $z = \dfrac{x - \mu}{\sigma}$

87. a

89. a) 0

b) –2.5

c) 108

d) 106

91. less; equal; distribution

93. whole

95. 90; 10

97. 50

99. false

101. false

103. true

105. a)

x	z
45	–1.67
165	4.50
590	1.27
830	0.80
1470	0

b) 165

107. a) mean = 86.5;   **b)** s = 10.93;

c)

x	z
90	0.32
100	1.24
79	–0.69
70	–1.51
95	0.78
85	–0.14

109. a) Steven's writing score is better than 85% of the all the scores. Steven's math score is better than 90% of the all the scores. Steven's history score is better than 75% of the all the scores.

b) 15%; 10%; 25%

c) 3rd quartile = history; 9th decile = math

111. a) 112   **b)** 114   **c)** 40%   **d)** 4
     e) 102   **f)** 110   **g)** 120

113. minimum, Q1, median, Q3 & maximum

115. first; third

117. first; third; box; 50%

119. a

121. e

123. 1.5; 3.0

125. false

127. false

129. a) 19, 64, 81, 89, 98
    b)

    c) skewed left
    d) IQR = 25
    e) outlier = 19
    f) z of 19 = –3.20
    g) lowers mean & no effect on median

131. male sample results:
    a)

    b) symmetric
    c) Q1=23; med = 30; Q3 = 37
    d) yes: 0 & 60
    e) z of 0 = -2.05; z of 60 = 2.00
    f) very little effect on the mean and no effect on median

female sample results:
    a)

b) skewed right
c) Q1=15.5; med = 20; Q3 = 28.5
d) yes: 69
e) z of 69 = 3.63
f) raises the mean and no effect on median

133. b

135. bimodal

137. sample mean: $\bar{x} = \dfrac{\Sigma x}{n}$

    population mean: $\mu = \dfrac{\Sigma x}{N}$

139. sample

141. 75

143. false

145. a

147. a) 10
    b) 34
    c) 340
    d) 100
    e) 1156
    f) 30
    g) 294
    h) 90
    i) 1

149. a) μ = 26; median = 26.5; mode = 28
    b) mode, it best supports the ad campaign

151. a) mean = 65.1; median = 80.5; mode = 82
    b) μ
    c) median b/c it is not influenced by the extreme data values

153. a) mean = $3.30 million; median = $450,000; mode = $200,000
    b) mode

155. a) 6.41
    b) 6.25
    c) 5½
    d) mode

157. a) 24
    b) if the sample is representative of the class then one can see that very few of the students are 24 or older.

159. No! This logic is not correct, since he doesn't take into consideration that each semester's avg is for a different number of credits.

161. a) 1) Brown
       2) Brown
       3) Brown Hair; Brown Eyes
       4) Brown Hair; Blue Eyes
    b) Mode, because the data is categorical

163. a) 888.5
    b) 0.25 lbs
    c) 7.5 lbs

165. ask your instructor

167. i) skewed right; mean
  ii) bell shaped; mean=median
  iii) bell shaped; mean=median
  iv) bell shaped; mean=median

169. s

171. a) 18   **b)** 52   **c)** 7.21   **d)** 7.21   **e)** 6.45

173. true

175. b

177. $\sigma_x = 6.68$; $\sigma_y = 4.12$; team y has the more consistent defense

179. a) range = 40, s = 13.46
  b) range = 40, s = 13.46
  c) range = 160, s = 215.34

181. a) $\bar{x} = 14$; s = 4.32
  b) 18.32
  c) 18.32
  d) 9.68
  e) 9.68
  f) 10, 12, 14, 16, 18
  g) same as part f
  h) 0%
  i) 0%
  j) approx. 86%

183. a) $\bar{x} = 0.083$ (8.3%)
  b) s = 0.013 (1.3%)
  c) 11
  d) 73.3%
  e) 100%

185. a) $\bar{x} = 16.82$ ppm; s = 0.90 ppm
  b) none exceeded the standard of 18.62 ppm

187. false

189. false

191. c

193. a) $\bar{x} = \$67.84$; s = \$41.28   **b)** 93.33%   **c)** 93.33%
  (in billion dollars)

195. a) the percentage can vary from 0% to 25%
  b) 2.5%

197. a) Fund C
  b) Fund A
  c) Fund C

199. a) $\bar{x} = 71.08$; s = 19.37
  b) 96%
  c) 100%
  d) discuss with instructor
  e) no

201. 9.17

203. b

205. d

207. false

209. c

211. z score

213. 25

215. c

217. false

219. i) 42.55   **ii)** 40.1   **iii)** 124.25   **iv)** 267   **v)** 129.2

221. a) Condo A
  b) Condo M

223. Lorenzo's grade = 94
  Michael's grade = 87
  Lorenzo had the higher grade

225. a) $\bar{x} = 6.04$, s = 0.13
  b) z = -1.5, x = 5.85
    z = 1.5, x = 6.24
  c) Yes, the parts do meet the conditions.

227. a) 115
  b) 119
  c) 105
  d) 87
  e) 105
  f) 91

229. a) 20 seconds
  b) 28 seconds
  c) 8 seconds
  d) 85%
  e) 16 seconds
  f) 12 seconds
  g) 36 seconds

231. Barbara ; Mike ; Alice

233. Jim

235. b

237. 25

239. c

241. skewed left

243. a) 65, 137.5, 173, 182, 205
  b)

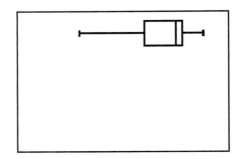

  c) skewed left
  d) IQR = 44.5
  e) outlier = 65
  f) z of 65 = -2.53
  g) lowers mean & no effect on median

245. a) A:51 B:67
  b) A:67 B:87
  c) A:57 B:79

d) A:43,93; B:45,95

e) A:16 B:20

f) A:skewed to the right B:skewed to the left

g) 75

h) 50

i) 50

k) A: minimum knowledge; A: top students; B: easier test

247. a) 106,142,175,186,272

b) MINITAB output for Boxplot:

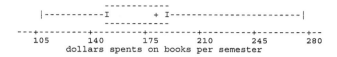

c) skewed left

d) IQR = 44 (1) 272 (2) none

e) 272; student may have needed to buy technical texts that are often very expensive relative to other standard texts.

249. a) & b)

c) answers vary

251. answers can vary

253.

a) cereal:

whole-grain:

all-bran:

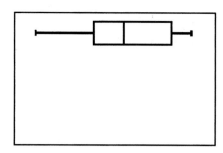

b) answers will vary

c) 5-number summary for cereal: 1.6, 2, 2, 2.1, 3
5-number summary for whole-grain cereal: 2.9, 3.1, 4, 4, 5
5-number summary for all-bran cereal: 5, 8, 9.5, 12, 13

d) potential outliers:
cereal: 1.6 & 3.0

e) answers vary

CHAPTER 4

1. experiment

3. true

5. event

7. c

9. d

11. a) R, Y, B

b) BB ** AA
B* *B A*
BA *A AB

c) HHH
HHT
HTH
HTT
THH
THT
TTH
TTT

d) same as answer 1c

e) BYE
BEY
EBY
EYB
YBE
YEB

f) GOOD OGOD
GDOO OGDO
OODG ODOG
OOGD ODGO
DOOG DOGO
DGOO GODO

13. a) 1   **b)** 49   **c)** 343   **d)** 2401

15. factorial; 4; 3; 2; 1; 24

17. 720

19. a

21. 24

23. 120

25. **a)** 2   **b)** 24   **c)** 12   **d)** 24   **e)** 210
f) 1,663,200   **g)** 95,040

27. **b)** $\dfrac{4}{16}$ **c)** $\dfrac{4}{16}$ **d)** $\dfrac{8}{16}$

29. c

31. 420

33. **a)** 453,600   **b)** 840   **c)** 1680   **d)** 3360

35. $_nC_s$; $\dfrac{_nP_s}{s!}$ or $\dfrac{n!}{(n-s)!s!}$

37. 35

39. 56

41. $75{,}287{,}520 = {_{100}}C_5$

43. $280 = {_4}C_3\,{_8}C_4$

45. **a)** 240   **b)** 11,520

47. **a)** $40{,}320 = 8!$ **b)** $24 = 4!$ **c)** $384 = (4! \cdot 2)$
d) $1152 = (4!4! \cdot 2)$

49. $21 = {_7}C_2$

51. long run

53. Law of Large Numbers

55. a

57. true

59. **a)** relative frequency;
b) relative frequency;
c) relative frequency or subjective;
d) relative frequency;

61. *number of outcomes satisfying event E;*
total number of outcomes in the sample space

63. **a)** ½₂   **b)** ⅙₉₉₉   **c)** ½₂   **d)** ⅖   **e)** ⅞

65. **a)** $\dfrac{6}{24}$ **b)** $\dfrac{2}{24}$ **c)** $\dfrac{1}{24}$

67. **a)** $\dfrac{3}{8}$ **b)** $\dfrac{3}{8}$ **c)** $\dfrac{4}{8}$

69. 0; 1

71. false

73. true

75. queen; red card; queen and a red card; queen; red card; queen and a red card

77. mutually exclusive

79. false

81. false

83. mutually exclusive; same; ace; king; ½₂; ½₂; ⁸⁄₅₂

85. not mutually exclusive; 4; even number; 4

87. P(getting 4 heads)

89. independent; and; times; A and B; A; B

91.

outcome	2	3	4	5	6	7	8	9	10	11	12
probability	$\dfrac{1}{36}$	$\dfrac{2}{36}$	$\dfrac{3}{36}$	$\dfrac{4}{36}$	$\dfrac{5}{36}$	$\dfrac{6}{36}$	$\dfrac{5}{36}$	$\dfrac{4}{36}$	$\dfrac{3}{36}$	$\dfrac{2}{36}$	$\dfrac{1}{36}$

b) $\dfrac{8}{36}$ **c)** $\dfrac{28}{36}$ **d)** $\dfrac{26}{36}$ **c)** $\dfrac{18}{36}$

93. **a)** 120 **b)** 60 **c)** $\dfrac{1}{120}$

95. **a)** $\dfrac{3744}{2{,}598{,}960} = ({_{13}}C_1\,{_4}C_2\,{_{12}}C_1\,{_4}C_3) \,/\, {_{52}}C_5$

b) $\dfrac{624}{2{,}598{,}960} = ({_{13}}C_1\,{_4}C_4\,{_{12}}C_1\,{_4}C_1) \,/\, {_{52}}C_5$

c) $\dfrac{68{,}640}{2{,}598{,}960} = ({_{13}}C_1\,{_4}C_2\,{_{12}}C_3\,{_4}C_1) \,/\, {_{52}}C_5$

d) $\dfrac{247{,}104}{2{,}598{,}960} = ({_{13}}C_1\,{_4}C_2\,{_{12}}C_1\,{_{11}}C_1\,{_4}C_1) \,/\, {_{52}}C_5$

e) $\dfrac{5{,}148}{2{,}598{,}960} = ({_{13}}C_5\,{_4}C_1) \,/\, {_{52}}C_5$

97. $\dfrac{4}{10}$

99. dependent; B; occurred; A and B; B | A

101. **a)** P(B | A)
b) probability of B, given that event A has occurred
c) P(A | B)
d) probability of A, given that event B has occurred

103. conditional; first shot is a blank; ²⁰⁄₃₀; ⅔

105. without replacement; with replacement

107. $\dfrac{64}{1326} = ({_4}C_1\,{_{16}}C_1) \,/\, {_{52}}C_5$

109. **a)** $\dfrac{120}{1001} = ({_5}C_1\,{_3}C_1\,{_4}C_1\,{_2}C_1) \,/\, {_{14}}C_4$

b) $\dfrac{90}{1001} = ({_5}C_3\,{_9}C_1) \,/\, {_{14}}C_4$

c) $\dfrac{270}{1001} = ({_4}C_2\,{_{10}}C_2) \,/\, {_{14}}C_4$

111. **a)** $\dfrac{1}{31}$ **b)** $\dfrac{812}{900}$ **c)** $\dfrac{88}{900}$

113. **a)** $\dfrac{5}{90}$ **b)** $\dfrac{20}{25}$

115. **a)** 0.10   **b)** 0.68   **c)** 0.22

117. **a)** ⅟₁₃   **b)** ¹⁰⁰⁰⁄₉₉₉₉   **c)** ½₂   **d)** ⅟₃₆₅   **e)** ⅕   **f)** ⅛

119. **a)** ¹⁴⁴⁄₂₇₀₄   **b)** ¹³²⁄₂₆₅₂   **c)** ⁴⁰⁰⁄₂₇₀₄   **d)** ³⁸⁰⁄₂₆₅₂

121. **a)** $\dfrac{21}{26}$ **b)** $\dfrac{5}{26}$ **c)** $\dfrac{15}{26}$ **d)** $\dfrac{2}{26}$ **e)** $\dfrac{18}{26}$
f) $\dfrac{5}{26}$ **g)** $\dfrac{21}{26}$ **h)** $\dfrac{6}{26}$ **i)** $\dfrac{4}{26}$ **j)** $\dfrac{1}{26}$

123. **a)** classical
b) subjective

c) subjective
d) relative frequency
f) relative frequency
125. 40,320
127. 840
129. 60
131. a) 676   **b)** 650   **c)** 6760   **d)** 20280

133. $378,378,000 = \dfrac{15!}{2!\,4!\,3!\,2!\,3!}$

135. ⅟₁₀₀

137. $\dfrac{6}{21}$

139. $99,884,400 = {}_{50}C_7$
141. a) $4 = {}_4C_3$
       b) $60 = {}_4C_1\,{}_6C_2$
       c) $36 = {}_4C_2\,{}_6C_1$
       d) $120 = {}_{10}C_3$

143. a) $\dfrac{8}{36}$ **b)** $\dfrac{4}{36}$ **c)** $\dfrac{3}{9}$ **d)** $\dfrac{4}{10}$ **e)** $\dfrac{5}{11}$ **f)** 0.49293

CHAPTER 5

1. chance
3. any value; uncountable number
5. b
7. a) continuous
    b) discrete
    c) discrete
    d) discrete
9. probability distribution; horizontal; vertical
11. d
13. true
15. a) probability distributions A & D
     b) probability distributions B: the sum of all the
        probabilities should equal 1
        probability distribution C: the probability of an
        event must be a non-negative value
17. probability distribution I:
     a) X: 0, 1, 2, 3
     b) shape: uniform

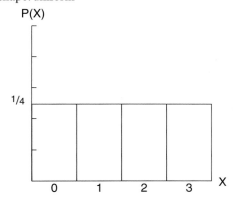

c) 1; yes
d) mean = 1.5
e) sd = 1.12
f) 0.5
g) 1
probability distribution II:
a) X: 1, 2, 3, 4
b) shape: skewed right

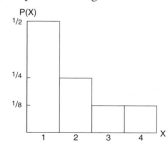

c) 1; yes
d) mean = 1.88
e) sd = 1.05
f) ¾
g) ⅞
probability distribution III:
a) X: −1, 0, 1
b) shape: symmetric

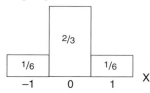

c) 1; yes
d) mean = 0
e) sd = 0.58
f) ⅔
g) 1
probability distribution IV:
a) X: 2, 4, 6
b) shape: skewed left

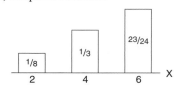

c) 1; yes
d) mean = 4.83
e) sd = 1.4
f) ⅞
g) ⅞
19. a) $P(X \le 250) = 0.07 + 0.13 + 0.26 + 0.19 + 0.05 = 0.87$
    b) $1 - 0.87 = 0.13$
    c) 0.82
    d) 0.20

21. $\mu;$ $\displaystyle\sum_{\substack{\text{all possible} \\ \text{x values}}}(X \text{ value}) \cdot (\text{probability of } X);$ $\displaystyle\sum_{\substack{\text{all possible} \\ \text{x values}}}X \cdot P(X)$

23. d

25. true

27. **a)** mean = 38.8
b) 0.25
c) sd = 10.66
d) 0.47
e) 0.96

29. **a)** plan #2   **b)** plan #2   **c)** plan #1

31. **a)** identical
b) independent
c) success; failure
d) success

33. true

35. 4

37. 7; 5; ¼; ¾; 21; 5; 21

39. binomial probability formula

41. μ_s; $\mu_s = np$

43. acceptance sampling

45. e

47. false

49. true

51. **a)** $\dfrac{256}{10,000} = 0.0256$ **b)** $\dfrac{1296}{10,000} = 0.1296$ **c)** $\dfrac{1792}{10,000} = 0.1792$

53. $\dfrac{1}{1024} = 0.001$

55. **a)** 0.0308 **b)** 0.5282 **c)** 0.1681

57. **a)** 0.01   **b)** yes, it was helpful.

59. **a)** $\dfrac{1}{625} = 0.0016$ **b)** $\dfrac{512}{625} = 0.8192$

c) $\dfrac{608}{625} = 9728$ **d)** $\dfrac{81}{625} = 0.1296$

61. 0.1488

63. **a)**

X	P(X)
0	0.2373
1	0.3955
2	0.2637
3	0.0879
4	0.0146
5	0.0010

b) skewed right

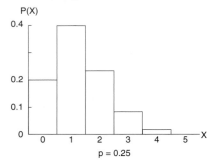

p = 0.25

c) mean = 1.25; sd = 0.9682

65. **a)**

X	P(X)
0	0.000
1	0.000
2	0.003
3	0.016
4	0.057
5	0.137
6	0.228
7	0.260
8	0.195
9	0.087
10	0.071

b) skewed left

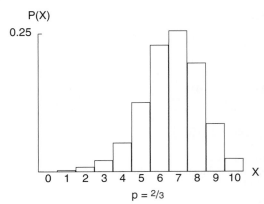

p = 2/3

c) mean = 6.667; sd = 1.491

67. **a)**

X	P(X)
0	0.0751
1	0.2253
2	0.3003
3	0.2336
4	0.1168
5	0.0389
6	0.0087
7	0.0012
8	0.0001
9	0.0000

b) skewed right

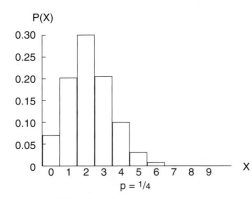

p = 1/4

c) mean = 2.25; sd = 1.3

69. **a)**
X	P(X)
0	0.6983
1	0.2573
2	0.0406
3	0.0036
4	0.0002
5	0.0000
6	0.0000
7	0.0000

b) skewed right

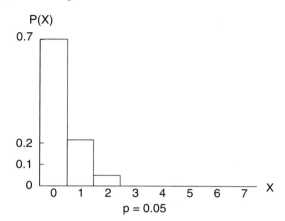

c) mean = 0.35; sd = 0.5766

71. **a)**
X	P(X)
0	0.7738
1	0.2036
2	0.0214
3	0.0011
4	0.0000
5	0.0000

b) skewed right

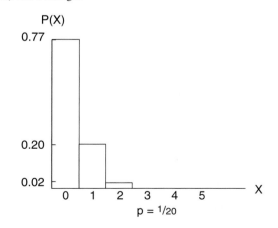

c) mean = 0.25; sd = 0.4873

73. **a)**
X	P(X)
0	0.0003
1	0.0064
2	0.0512
3	0.2048
4	0.4096
5	0.3277

b) skewed left

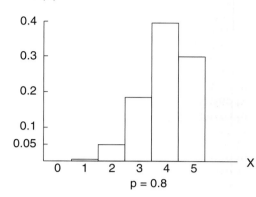

c) mean = 4; sd = 0.8944

75. **a)**
X	P(X)
0	0.0000
1	0.0000
2	0.0000
3	0.0021
4	0.0305
5	0.2321
6	0.7351

b) skewed left

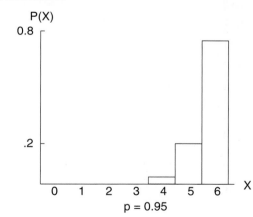

c) mean = 5.7; sd = 0.5339

77. **a)** 0.0003; 0.9997
b) 0.0371; 0.9629
c) 0.7358; 0.2642
d) as the chance of a defective tile decreases within the shipment, the probability of the shipment will be rejected will decrease also. The quality control should be satisfied with this relationship since he would only want to reject shipments that have a greater percentage of defective tiles.

79. discrete; continuous
81. **a)** continuous;
b) discrete;

c) discrete;
d) continuous;
e) discrete;
f) continuous;
g) discrete;
h) discrete;
i) discrete;
j) continuous;
k) discrete;
l) discrete;
m) continuous;
n) discrete;
o) continous

83. 1
85. a) 0.98
    b) 0.005
    c) 0.003
    d) yes
    e) check the process
87. false
89. a)

X	P(X)
0	0.5
1	0.25
2	0.125
3	0.0625
4	0.0625

b) 0.875   c) 0.9375   d) 0.125   e) 0.0625
f) 0.5   g) 0.5   h) 0.0625
i & j) prob. dist. for number of tosses is:

X	P(X)
1	0.5
2	0.25
3	0.125
4	0.125

i) mean = 1.875   j) sd = 1.05

91. a) X: 1, 2, 3
    b) aspirin: shape = skewed right;

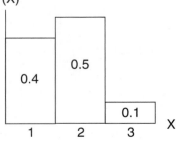

P(X)

0.4   0.5   0.1

1   2   3   X

ibuprofen: shape = skewed right

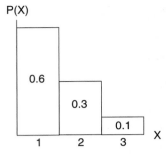

P(X)

0.6

0.3

0.1

1   2   3   X

c) aspirin: 1; ibuprofen: 1
d) aspirin: 1.7 tablets; ibuprofen: 1.5 tablets
e) aspirin: 0.64 tablets; ibuprofen: 0.67 tablets
f) same since the probs are equal

93. a) X: 0, 1, 2, 3
    b) shape: skewed right

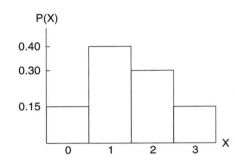

P(X)

0.40
0.30
0.15

0   1   2   3   X

c) 1
d) mean = 1.45 donuts
e) sd = 0.92 donuts
f) 0.15; likely

95. a)

Probability Dist. for Craig

X	P(X)
0	0.3277
1	0.4096
2	0.2048
3	0.0512
4	0.0064
5	0.0003

Probability Dist. for Matthew

X	P(X)
0	0.0313
1	0.1562
2	0.3125
3	0.3125
4	0.1562
5	0.0313

Probability Distribution for Debbie

X	P(X)
0	0.0003
1	0.0064
2	0.0512
3	0.2048
4	0.4096
5	0.3277

b) Probability histogram for Craig

Probability histogram for Matthew

Probability histogram for Debbie

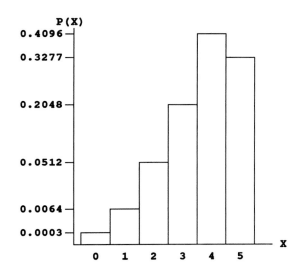

c) Craig: skewed to the right; Matthew: symmetric;
Debbie: skewed to the left.
For 0.3, the shape of the histogram is skewed to the right.
For 0.7, the shape of the histogram is skewed to the left.

d) Craig: 1; Mathew: 2.5; Debbie: 4

e) Craig: $\mu_s = 1$; Matthew: $\mu_s = 2.5$; Debbie: $\mu_s = 4$.

f) Craig: $\sigma_s = 0.89$; Matthew: $\sigma_s = 1.12$; Debbie: $\sigma_s = 0.89$.

g) The sum of all the probabilities of each binomial probability distribution is one. These results are expected since this is a characteristic of a probability distribution.

97. c

99. ⅓

101. e

103. e

105. a) $\dfrac{1}{243} = 0.0041$ **b)** $\dfrac{51}{243} = 0.2099$ **c)** $\dfrac{11}{243} = 0.0453$

107. a) $\dfrac{625}{1296} = 0.4823$ **b)** $\dfrac{1}{1296} = 0.0008$ **c)** $\dfrac{1125}{1296} = 0.8681$

109. a)   **b)** 17%

0	0.0388
1	0.1368
2	0.2293
3	0.2428
4	0.1821
total:	0.8298 or 83%

CHAPTER 6

1. true

3. true

5. true

7. b

9. answers vary

11. normal distribution properties are:
- The normal curve is bell-shaped and has a single peak which is located at the center.
- The mean, median and mode all have the same numerical value and are located at the center of the distribution.
- The normal curve is symmetric about the mean.
- The data values in the normal distribution are clustered about the mean.
- In theory, the normal curve extends infinitely in both directions, always getting closer to the horizontal axis but never touching it.
- The total area under the normal curve is 1 which can also be interpreted as probability.

13. a) 0.0013   **b)** 0.1586   **c)** 0.5   **d)** 0.9772
    e) 1   **f)** 0.5   **g)** 0.8413   **h)** 0.0227

i) 0.9986 **j)** 0 **k)** 0.6827 **l)** 0.9545
m) 0.9973 **n)** 0.9999 or approx. 1

15. center

17. 100

19. 15.87; 84.13

21. false

23. false

25. false

27. **a)** 0.9938
b) 0.5997
c) 0.9032

29. **a)** 0.9500 **b)** 0.9902

31. **a)** −0.25 **b)** 2.33 **c)** −1.65 to 1.65

33. **a)** 0.8577
b) 0.6589
c) 0.2514

35. **a)** 0.9962
b) 0.9525
c) 0.0229

37. approx. 730 tax returns

39. 10.26 months

41. 727 hours

43. P_{16}

45. **a)** P_{98}
b) P_{16}
c) P_{69}

47. 85.2

49. **a)** X = 341.6
b) X = 284.4
c) X = 320.8
d) X = 248.8
e) X = 326.8
f) X = 310

51. **a)** 12.3%
b) 14.98%
c) 4.01%

53. 0.1056

55. **a)** 0.1587
b) 0.0228
c) 0.3072

57. **a)** 0.0808
b) 0.0047
c) 0.0752

59. 5

61. normal

63. **a)** 50
b) 5

65. c

67. **a) 1.** 0.0179
2. 0.0108
3. 0.0287
4. 0.9892

b) 1. 0.1350
2. 0.1210
3. 0.8790
4. 1

69. a

71. **a)** 0.0055
b) 0.0436

73. **a)** 0.0359
b) 0.5342
c) 0.0001

75. **a)** 0.0089
b) 0.0606

77. **a)** 0.0003
b) 0.1210

79. **a)** approx. 0
b) 0.0227
c) 0.5
d) 0.8413
e) 0.9986
f) 1
g) 0.6828
h) 0.9445
i) 0.9973

81. true

83. 0; 2

85. **a)** z = 0.99 **b)** z = 1.28 **c)** z = −0.67 to z = 0.67

87. c

89. **a)** 0.0494 **b)** 0.1490 **c)** 0.3821

91. **a)** 9.68%
b) approx. 27 games
c) 0.3446

93. **a)** 0.62%
b) apprx. 1543 students
c) 0.7262

95. Tina; Michael; Allison; Meow

97. b

99. **a)** 360 **b)** 14.07

101. c

103. **a)** 0.0035
b) 0.0007

105. **a)** 0.0301
b) 0.1292
c) 0.0838

107. **a)** 0.1003
b) 0.9932

CHAPTER 7

1. nonsampling

3. μ

5. $\mu_{\bar{x}}$

7. c

9. **a)** $\mu = 121.2$
 b) i) 122   ii) 0.8
 c) i) 119.67   ii) −1.53
 d) i) 119   ii) −2.2

11. **a)** MA, MT, MH, ME, MW, AT, AH, AE, AW, TH, TE, TW, HE, HW, EW
 b) ⅟₁₅
 c) HM & WT

13. **a)** $\bar{x}$ **b)** μ **c)** σ **d)** $\mu_{\bar{x}}$ **e)** $\sigma_{\bar{x}}$

15. $\mu_{\bar{x}}$; population; μ

17. standard deviation; $\sigma_{\bar{x}}$; sample size; $\dfrac{\sigma}{\sqrt{n}}$

19. a

21.
	$\mu_{\bar{x}}$	$\sigma_{\bar{x}}$
a)	100	3
b)	100	1
c)	100	0.9
d)	100	0.45

23.
	$\mu_{\bar{x}}$	$\sigma_{\bar{x}}$
a)	470	5
b)	470	4.17
c)	470	2.28
d)	470	1.77
e)	470	0.97

25. finite correction;

$$\dfrac{\sigma}{\sqrt{n}}\sqrt{\dfrac{N-n}{N-1}}$$

27. **a)** 1.5   **b)** 0.98   **c)** 0.04; yes—approx. equal to 1

29. normal; large; 30

31. **a)** normal; central limit
 b) 130; 130
 c) 1; 1

33.
	$\mu_{\bar{x}}$	$\sigma_{\bar{x}}$	shape
a)	110	5	normal
b)	110	2	normal
c)	110	1	normal

35. d

37. d

39.
	1)	2)	3)
a)	normal	160	1
b)	normal	16	1/3
c)	unknown	4000	40
d)	normal	12000	100
e)	normal	32	0.5
f)	normal	500	5
g)	normal	20000	300
h)	unknown	8	0.4
i)	normal	1000	50
j)	unknown	24000	200

41. $\dfrac{\bar{x} - \mu_{\bar{x}}}{\sigma_{\bar{x}}}$

43. **a)** 0.9772 **b)** 0.5 **c)** 0

45. 0.9332

47. 0.0348

59. 0.0227

51. 0.0086

53. 1

55. 0.9044

57. **a)** 0.0013
 b) maybe; the EPA rating doesn't indicate whether it is estimated based on highway or city driving conditions.

59. **a)** 106.71 to 113.29
 b) 106.08 to 113.92
 c) 104.85 to 115.15

61. **a)** 0.3085 **b)** 0.1336

63. a

65. b

67. c

69. large; np; n(1 − p)

71. proportion

73. x/n

75. $\sigma_{\hat{p}}$

77. $\sqrt{\dfrac{p(1-p)}{n}}$

79. d

81. a

83. **a)** 0.3   **b)** 0.9   **c)** 0.1081

85. **a)** 0.25
 b) 56
 c) the 56 possible samples are:
   BBR, BBY, BBL, BBG, BBO, BBR, BRY, BRL, BRG, BRO, BRY, BRL, BRG, BRO, BRY, BRL, BRG, BRO, BRY, BRL, BRG, BRO, RRO, RRB, RRB, RRL, RRG, RRY, RYO, RYG, RYL, RYO, RYG, RYL, BYO, BYG, BYL, BYO, BYG, BYL, YOG, YOL, GOL, OGB, OGB, OGR, OGR, GLB, GLB, GLR, GLR, GLY, YLG, OYG, ROL, ROL

proportion of red m&m's per sample	frequency
0/3 = 0	20
1/3 = 0.3333	30
2/3 = 0.6667	6

 d) mean of all the proportions = 0.25
   std deviation of the proportions = 0.2113

 e) $\mu_{\hat{p}} = p = 0.25$; $\sigma_{\hat{p}} = \sqrt{\dfrac{p(1-p)}{n}}\sqrt{\dfrac{N-n}{N-1}} = 0.2113$
   where p = 0.25, n = 3 & N = 8

87. **a)** 0.1462
 b) 0.0397
 c) 0.9753

89. b

91. a

93. **a)** mean; μ

b) size; $\dfrac{\sigma}{\sqrt{n}}$

95. 120; 3.75

97. true

99. **a)** $\mu = 78.75$

    b) i) 80   ii) 1.25

    c) i) 82   ii) 3.25

    d) i) 74.33   ii) –4.42

101. **a)** 197; 2.96

    b) 197; 1

    c) no effect on mean; smaller standard deviation

103. **a)** 0.6667   **b)** 0.37

105. **a)** 0.9117

    b) 0.7279

    c) 0.0121

    d) 0.03 or 3%

    e) –0.05 or –5%

    f) yes, if $\hat{p} < p$

107. **a)** 0.1727

    b) 0.0973

    c) 0.9532

    d) -0.01 or –1%

    e) –0.09 or–9%

    f) yes, if $\hat{p} < p$

CHAPTER 8

1. parameter

3. estimation

5. sample proportion, $\hat{p}$

7. d

9. true

11. sampling

13. point

15. unbiasedness; efficiency; consistency; sufficiency

17. 1960

19. $\overline{X} - (2.58)\dfrac{\sigma}{\sqrt{n}}$; $\overline{X} + (2.58)\dfrac{\sigma}{\sqrt{n}}$

21. $\overline{X} - (t_{99.5\%})\dfrac{s}{\sqrt{n}}$; $\overline{X} + (t_{99.5\%})\dfrac{s}{\sqrt{n}}$

23. unknown; sample standard deviation, s; normal

25. d

27. true

29. d

31. 30.51 to 32.89 mpg

33. 10.93 to 14.07 years

35. 2379.5 to 2470.5 hours

37. $\sqrt{\dfrac{\hat{p}(1-\hat{p})}{n}}$

39. c

41. **a)** 90%:0.2244 to 0.3756; margin of error = 0.0756

        95%:0.2102 to 0.3898; margin of error = 0.0898

        99%:0.1818 to 0.4182; margin of error = 0.1182

    b) 90%:0.2810 to 0.3190; margin of error = 0.0190

        95%:0.2775 to 0.3225; margin of error = 0.0225

        99%:0.2703 to 0.3297; margin of error = 0.0297

    c) 90%:0.2977 to 0.3023; margin of error = 0.0023

        95%:0.2973 to 0.3027; margin of error = 0.0027

        99%:0.2964 to 0.3036; margin of error = 0.0036

    d) The width of each confidence interval and the margin of error at each confidence level decreases.

43. 0.6824 to 0.7376

45. **a)** 0.5648 to 0.6150

    b) 0.5569 to 0.6229

47. Either the true population proportion will be within 45% –/+ 3 percentage points or not, thus the chance is either 0% or 100%.

49. population parameter; margin

51. E; width

53. increased

55. $\left[\dfrac{z\sigma}{E}\right]^2$

57. false

59. n=1849

61. 167

63. point

65. true

67. false

69. $\overline{X} - (1.65)\dfrac{\sigma}{\sqrt{n}}$; $\overline{X} + (1.65)\dfrac{\sigma}{\sqrt{n}}$

71. interval; all; 95%

73. false

75. 35.47 to 37.13 hours

77. **a)** full-time students

    b) population mean

    c) sample mean

    d) $247

    e) 90%: margin of error = $2.31

        95%: margin of error = $2.74

        99%: margin of error = $3.61

    f) 90%: 244.69 to 249.31 dollars

    g) 95%: 244.26 to 249.74 dollars

    h) 99%: 243.39 to 250.61 dollars

79. **a)** symmetric bell-shape

    b) mean

    c) normal

    d) sample; freedom; n – 1

    e) normal; 30

81. $\hat{p} - (1.65)\, s_{\hat{p}}$; $\hat{p} + (1.65)\, s_{\hat{p}}$

83. **a)** potential buyers of shavers

    b) population proportion

   c) sample proportion
   d) 0.0201
   e) 90%: margin of error = 0.0026
      95%: margin of error = 0.0031
      99%: margin of error = 0.0041
   f) 90%: 0.0175 to 0.0227
      95%: 0.0170 to 0.0232
      99%: 0.0160 to 0.0242

85. **a)** nation's WP market
   b) population proportion
   c) sample proportion
   d) 0.24
   e) 1) 90%: margin of error = 0.0705
      0.1695 to 0.3105
   e) 2) 90%: margin of error = 0.0353
      0.2047 to 0.2753
   e) 3) 90%: margin of error = 0.0219
      0.2181 to 0.2619
   f) 1) 95%: margin of error = 0.0837
      0.1563 to 0.3237
   f) 2) 95%: margin of error = 0.0419
      0.1981 to 0.2819
   f) 3) 95%: margin of error = 0.0261
      0.2139 to 0.2661
   g) 1) 99%: margin of error = 0.1102
      0.1298 to 0.3502
   g) 2) 99%: margin of error = 0.0552
      0.1848 to 0.2952
   g) 3) 99%: margin of error = 0.0343
      0.2057 to 0.2743

87. **a)** 0.3757 to 0.4243
   b) 0.3262 to 0.3938

89. **a)** 77.4
   b) 154.8
   c) 77.4

91. (z) $(\sqrt{\frac{\hat{p}(1-\hat{p})}{n}})$

93. **a)** 426
   b) 401

CHAPTER 9

1. true; reject H_0; H_0
3. II
5. true
7. a
9. I
11. one
13. −1.65; 1.65
15. fail to reject
17. c
19. true
21. H_0: The population mean weight loss is 12 lbs for the first ten days.

H_a: The population mean weight loss is less than 12 lbs for the first ten days.

directional test.

23. H_0: The population proportion of asthmatic children whose mothers smoked during pregnancy is 10%.

H_a: The population proportion of asthmatic children whose mothers smoked during pregnancy is not 10%.

nondirectional test.

25. H_0: The population mean consumption of electricity per day of the energy saving refrigerator is 4.9 k.w.h.

H_a: The population mean consumption of electricity per day of the energy saving refrigerator is more than 4.9 k.w.h.

directional test.

27. **a)** Reject H_0 if the test statistic is either less than −1.96 or greater than 1.96
   b) Yes
   c) Yes

29. **a)** Reject H_0 if the test statistic is less than −2.33.
   b) No
   c) No
   d) Yes
   e) Yes

31. **a)**

   b) Reject H_0, accept H_a
   c) Yes

33. **a)** For z = 2.33, chance of Type I error = 1%
   b) 1%

35. **a)** For z = −1.65, chance of Type I error = 5%

37.

Decision rule: Reject H_0 if the test statistic is less than −2.33

a) 1) Fail to reject H$_o$
2) Fail to reject H$_o$
3) Reject H$_o$, accept H$_a$
4) Fail to reject H$_o$

b) −2.35

39.

Decision rule: Reject H$_o$ if the test statistic is less than −1.96 or greater than 1.96.

a) 1) Fail to reject H$_o$
2) Reject H$_o$, accept H$_a$
3) Reject H$_o$, accept H$_a$
4) Fail to reject H$_o$

b) 2.36; −2.49

41. very; significant; marginally or not; not

43. true

45. **a)** H$_o$: The population mean age of recipients of unemployment benefits is 37 years.

H$_a$: The population mean age of recipients of unemployment benefits is not 37 years.

b)

c) p-value=0.0000 or 0%
d) Reject H$_o$, accept H$_a$.

47. **a)** H$_o$: The population proportion of the babies delivered by Cesarean Section is 20%.

H$_a$: The population proportion of the babies delivered by Cesarean Section is more than 20%.

b) Z$_c$ = 1.65
Decision rule: Reject H$_o$ if the test statistic is more than Z$_c$ = 1.65.

c)

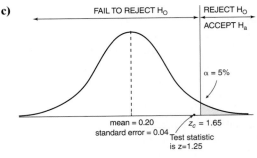

d) p-value = 0.1057 or 10.57%
e) *Conclusion*: Fail to reject H$_o$.
f) The test statistic is not statistically significant.
g) The research group cannot conclude that C-Sections have increased.

49. **a)** H$_o$: The population mean achievement test score for fifth graders is 88.

H$_a$: The population mean achievement test score for fifth graders is higher than 88.

b) Z$_c$ = 2.33
Decision Rule: Reject H$_o$ if the test statistic is more than the Z$_c$ = 2.33

c)

d) p-value 0.1210 or 12.10%
e) *Conclusion*: Fail to reject H$_o$.
f) The test statistic is not statistically significant.
g) The district superintendent cannot conclude that her fifth graders are above the norm.

51. H$_o$: The population proportion of US airline flights delayed at least 15 minutes is 10%.

H$_a$: The population proportion of US airline flights delayed at least 15 minutes is less than 10%

Z$_c$ = −2.33
Decision rule: Reject H$_o$ if the test statistic is less Z$_c$ = −2.33.

Conclusion: Fail to reject H$_o$.
The test statistic is not statistically significant.
a) p-value = 0.4165 or 41.65%
b) The null hypothesis cannot be rejected at $\alpha = 1\%$

53. true

55. b

57. α

59. $\dfrac{sample\ result - mean}{std\ error}$

61. −2.33; +2.33

63. b

65. false

67. **a)** yes; **b)** 3%

69. H$_o$: The population proportion of wives who hold full-time jobs earn more than their husbands is 20%.

H$_a$: The population proportion of wives who hold full-time jobs earn more than their husbands is less than 20%

directional test.

71. **a)** Reject H$_o$ if the test statistic is less than −1.65.
b) Yes
c) Yes
d) No
e) No

73. For z = −1.65, chance of Type I error = 5%

75.

Decision rule: Reject H$_o$ if the test statistic is greater $Z_c = 1.65$.
a) 1) Fail to reject H$_o$
2) Fail to reject H$_o$
3) Fail to reject H$_o$
4) Fail to reject H$_o$
b) none

77. **a)** H$_o$: The population mean reaction time is 0.20 seconds.

H$_a$: The population mean reaction time is less than 0.20 seconds.

b) $Z_c = -2.33$
Decision rule: Reject H$_o$ if the test statistic is less $Z_c = -2.33$.

c)

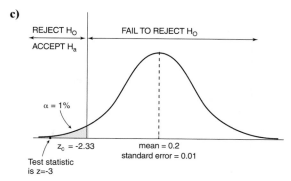

d) p-value = 0.0013 or 0.13%
e) *Conclusion*: Reject H$_o$, accept H$_a$.
f) The test statistic is statistically significant.
g) The sample result supports the psychiatrist's hypothesis.

CHAPTER 10

1. population

3. **a)** 0.30
b) 0.67
c) 0.90
d) 0.37
e) 0.11

5. **a)** p
b) $\sqrt{\dfrac{p(1-p)}{n}}$
c) np; n(1 − p)

7. false

9. **a)** 0.0197
b) 0.8485
c) 0.9345
d) 0.0049
e) 0.3015

11. proportion

13. **a)** p; >
b) population; <
c) proportion; ≠

15. d

17. c

19. **a)** H$_o$: population proportion of cars with major defective parts is 10%: p = 0.1

H$_a$: population proportion of cars with major defective parts is greater than 10%: p > 0.1

b) $\mu_{\hat{p}} = 0.1$; $\sigma_{\hat{p}} = 0.03$; distribution of the test statistic is a normal distribution

c) Reject H$_o$ if the test statistic is greater than 1.65
d) $\hat{p} = 0.16$ and z = 2
e) Reject H$_o$, accept H$_a$ at $\alpha = 5\%$; Yes

21. **a)** H$_o$: population proportion of American people who say life in the U.S. is getting worse is 40%: p = 0.40

H_a: population proportion of American people who say life in the U.S. is getting worse is not 40%: $p \neq 0.40$

b) $\mu_{\hat{p}} = 0.40$; $\sigma_{\hat{p}} = 0.0245$; distribution of the test statistic is a normal distribution

c) Reject H_o, if the test statistic is either less than -1.96 or greater than 1,96

d) $\hat{p} = 0.4375$ and $z = 1.53$

e) Fail to reject H_o at $\alpha = 5\%$; No

23. a) H_o: population proportion of LI shoppers being charged sales tax on non-taxable items in supermarkets is 25%: $p = 0.25$

H_a: population proportion of LI shoppers being charged sales tax on non-taxable items in supermarkets is more than 25%: $p > 0.25$

b) $\mu_{\hat{p}} = 0.25$; $\sigma_{\hat{p}} = 0.0306$; distribution of the test statistic is a normal distribution

c) Reject H_o, if the test statistic is greater than 2.33

d) $\hat{p} = 0.325$ and $z = 2.45$

e) Reject H_o, accept H_a at $\alpha = 1\%$; Yes

25. a) H_o: population proportion of men who wed before age 22 were divorced within 20 years is 68%: $p = 0.68$

H_a: population proportion of men who wed before age 22 were divorced within 20 years is not 68%: $p \neq 0.68$

b) $\mu_{\hat{p}} = 0.68$ $\sigma_{\hat{p}} = 0.0295$, distribution of the test statistic is a normal distribution

c) Reject H_o, if the test statistic is either less than -1.96 or greater than 1.96

d) $\hat{p} = 0.744$ and $z = 2.17$

e) Reject H_o, accept H_a at $\alpha = 5\%$; Yes

27. a) H_o: population proportion of women who fear walking alone at night in their neighborhoods is 75%: $p = 0.75$

H_a: population proportion of women who fear walking alone at night in their neighborhoods is less than 75%: $p < 0.75$

b) $\mu_{\hat{p}} = 0.75$; $\sigma_{\hat{p}} = 0.0274$; distribution of the test statistic is a normal distribution

c) Reject H_o, if the test statistic is less than -1.65

d) $\hat{p} = 0.648$ and $z = -3.72$

e) Reject H_o, accept H_a at $\alpha = 5\%$; Yes

29. a) H_o: population proportion of cars with major defective parts is 10%: $p = 0.1$

H_a: population proportion of cars with major defective parts is greater than 10%: $p > 0.1$

b) $\mu_{\hat{p}} = 0.1$; $\sigma_{\hat{p}} = 0.03$; The distribution of the test statistic is a normal distribution

c) reject H_0 if the p-value of the test statistic is less than 5%.

d) $\hat{p} = 0.16$, $z = 2$ and p-value $= 0.0228$

e) reject H_0, accept H_a at a p-value of 0.0228; The manufacturer's claim is correct.

f) smallest alpha level $= 2.28\%$

31. a) H_o: population proportion of American people who say life in the U.S. is getting worse is 40%: $p = 0.40$

H_a: population proportion of American people who say life in the U.S. is getting worse is not 40%: $p \neq 0.40$

b) $\mu_{\hat{p}} = 0.40$; $\sigma_{\hat{p}} = 0.0245$; The distribution of the test statistic is a normal distribution

c) reject H_0, if the p-value of the test statistic is less than 5%.

d) $\hat{p} = 0.4375$, $z = 1.53$ and p-value $= 0.1258$

e) fail to reject H_0 at a p-value of 0.1258; You should agree with the Institute's claim.

f) smallest alpha level $= 12.58\%$

33. a) H_o: population proportion of LI shoppers being charged sales tax on non-taxable items in supermarkets is 25%: $p = 0.25$

H_a: population proportion of LI shoppers being charged sales tax on non-taxable items in supermarkets is more than 25%: $p > 0.25$

b) $\mu_{\hat{p}} = 0.25$; $\sigma_{\hat{p}} = 0.0306$; The distribution of the test statistic is a normal distribution

c) reject H_0, if the p-value of the test statistic is less than 1%.

d) $\hat{p} = 0.325$, $z = 2.45$ and p-value $= 0.0072$

e) reject H_0, accept H_a at a p-value of 0.0072; The sample data support's Mr. Jessel's claim.

f) smallest alpha level $= 0.72\%$

35. a) H_o: population proportion of men who wed before age 22 were divorced within 20 years is 68%: $p = 0.68$

H_a: population proportion of men who wed before age 22 were divorced within 20 years is not 68%: $p \neq 0.68$

b) $\mu_{\hat{p}} = 0.68$ $\sigma_{\hat{p}} = 0.0295$, The distribution of the test statistic is a normal distribution

c) reject H_0, if the p-value of the test statistic less than 5%.

d) $\hat{p} = 0.744$, $z = 2.17$ and p-value $= 0.0301$

e) reject H_0, accept H_a at a p-value of 0.0301; The Institute can conclude that the Census Bureau's claim is incorrect.

f) smallest alpha level $= 3.01\%$

37. a) H_o: population proportion of women who fear walking alone at night in their neighborhoods is 75%: $p = 0.75$

H_a: population proportion of women who fear walking alone at night in their neighborhoods is less than 75%: $p < 0.75$

b) $\mu_{\hat{p}} = 0.75$; $\sigma_{\hat{p}} = 0.0274$; The distribution of the test statistic is a normal distribution

c) reject H_0, if the p-value of the test statistic is less than 5%.

d) $\hat{p} = 0.648$, $z = -3.72$ and p-value $= 9.79$ E -5

e) reject H_0, accept H_a at a p-value of 9.79 E-5; The sample data support's the sociologist's claim.

f) smallest alpha level $= 9.79$ E -5

39. false

41. d

43. false

45. c

47. proportion

49. true

51. H_o is true

53. true

55. **a)** H_o: population proportion of defective parts manufactured under the new process is 10%: $p = 0.1$

   H_a: population proportion of defective parts manufactured under the new process is less than 10%: $p < 0.1$

   b) $\mu_{\hat{p}} = 0.1$; $\sigma_{\hat{p}} = 0.0106$; distribution of the test statistic is a normal distribution

   c) Reject H_o if the test statistic is less than -1.65

   d) $\hat{p} = 0.0875$ and $z = -1.18$

   e) Fail to reject H_o at $\alpha = 5\%$; No

57. **a)** H_o: population proportion of employees retained for more than 6 months under the new hiring procedure is 60%: $p = 0.6$

   H_a: population proportion of employees retained for more than 6 months under the new hiring procedure is more than 60%: $p > 0.6$

   b) $\mu_{\hat{p}} = 0.6$; $\sigma_{\hat{p}} = 0.0346$, distribution of the test statistic is a normal distribution

   c) Reject H_o, if the test statistic is greater than 1.65

   d) $\hat{p} = 0.63$ and $z = 0.87$

   e) Fail to reject H_o at $\alpha = 5\%$; No

CHAPTER 11

1. directional

3. true

5. **a)** μ_o ; $>$
   b) mean; μ_o; $<$
   c) population; $\neq$

7. b

9. a

11. false

13. **a)** H_o: The population mean breaking strength is 90 lbs using the new manufacturing process: $\mu = 90$

   H_a: The population mean breaking strength is greater than 90 lbs using the new manufacturing process: $\mu > 90$

   b) $\mu_{\bar{x}} = 90$; $\sigma_{\bar{x}} = 0.75$; the distribution of the test statistic is a normal distribution.

   c) reject H_o if the test statistic is greater than 2.33.

   d) $\bar{x} = 93$ and $z = 4$

   e) reject H_o, accept H_a at $\alpha = 1\%$; yes

15. **a)** H_o: The population mean number of daily passengers is 125,000 during snow storms: $\mu = 125,000$

   H_a: The population mean number of daily passengers is greater than 125,000 during snow storms: $\mu > 125,000$

   b) $\mu_{\bar{x}} = 125,000$; $\sigma_{\bar{x}} = 666.67$; the distribution of the test statistic is a normal distribution.

   c) reject H_o if the test statistic is greater than 1.65

   d) $\bar{x} = 126,000$ and $z = 1.5$

   e) fail to reject H_o at $\alpha = 5\%$; no

17. **a)** H_o: The population mean time to harvest 1 acre of oranges is 5 hours under the new method: $\mu = 5$

   H_a: The population mean time to harvest 1 acre of oranges is less than 5 hours under the new method: $\mu < 5$

   b) $\mu_{\bar{x}} = 5$; $\sigma_{\bar{x}} = 0.075$ hours, the distribution of the test statistic is a normal distribution.

   c) reject H_o if the test statistic is less than -2.33.

   d) $\bar{x} = 4.75$ and $z = -3.33$

   e) reject H_o, accept H_a at $\alpha = 1\%$; yes

19. **a)** H_o: The population mean saving passbook account balance is \$1236.45: $\mu = 1236.45$

   H_a: The population mean saving passbook account balance is less than \$1236.45: $\mu < 1236.45$

   b) $\mu_{\bar{x}} = 1236.45$; $\sigma_{\bar{x}} = 15.88$; the distribution of the test statistic is a normal distribution.

   c) reject H_o if the test statistic is less than -1.65.

   d) $\bar{x} = 1217.69$ and $z = 1.18$

   e) fail to reject H_o at $\alpha = 5\%$; no

21. estimate

23. population; normal

25. d

27. false

29. **a)** -1.71
   b) -2.72
   c) 1.72
   d) 2.57
   e) -2.02; 2.02
   f) -2.66; 2.66

31. **a)** H_o: The population mean amount of the expectorant drug DOKE for every milliliter of the suppressant is 25 milligrams: $\mu = 25$

   H_a: The population mean amount of the expectorant drug DOKE for every milliliter of the suppressant is not equal to 25 milligrams: $\mu \neq 25$

   b) $\mu_{\bar{x}} = 25$; $s_{\bar{x}} = 0.1$; the distribution of the test statistic is a t distribution.

   c) reject H_o if the test statistic is either less than -2.02 or greater than 2.02.

   d) $\bar{x} = 25.4$ and $t = 4$

   e) reject H_o, accept H_a at $\alpha = 5\%$; yes

33. **a)** H_o: The population mean non-stop travel time from NY City to Washington, D.C. is 4.5 hours: $\mu = 4.5$

   H_a: The population mean non-stop travel time from NY City to Washington, D.C. is not 4.5 hours: $\mu \neq 4.5$

b) $\mu_{\bar{x}} = 4.5$; $s_{\bar{x}} = 0.05$; the distribution of the test statistic is a t distribution.

c) reject H_o if the test statistic is either less than -2.68 or greater than 2.68.

d) $\bar{x} = 4.3$ and $t = -4$

e) reject H_o, accept H_a at $\alpha = 1\%$; yes

35. a) H_o: The population mean life of the Louisiana shellfish is 27 months: $\mu = 27$

H_a: The population mean life of the Louisiana shellfish is greater than 27 months: $\mu > 27$

b) $\mu_{\bar{x}} = 27$; $s_{\bar{x}} = 0.7$; the distribution of the test statistic is a t distribution.

c) reject H_o if the test statistic is greater than 1.75 months.

d) $\bar{x} = 28.05$ and $t = 1.5$

e) fail to reject H_o at $\alpha = 5\%$; no

37. a) H_o: The population mean effective period for the muscle relaxing tablets is 4.4 hours: $\mu = 4.4$

H_a: The population mean effective period for the muscle relaxing tablets is less than 4.4 hours: $\mu < 4.4$

b) $\mu_{\bar{x}} = 4.4$; $s_{\bar{x}} = 0.1$; the distribution of the test statistic is a t distribution.

c) reject H_o if the test statistic is less than -2.36.

d) $\bar{x} = 4.2$ and $t = -2$

e) fail to reject H_o at $\alpha = 1\%$; no

39. a) H_o: The population mean decrease in blood pressure over a three week period is 20 points: $\mu = 20$

H_a: The population mean decrease in blood pressure over a three week period is less than 20 points: $\mu < 20$

b) $\mu_{\bar{x}} = 20$; $s_{\bar{x}} = 0.5$; the distribution of the test statistic is a t distribution.

c) reject H_o if the test statistic is less than -1.68.

d) $\bar{x} = 19.14$ and $t = -1.72$

e) reject H_o, accept H_a at $\alpha = 5\%$; yes

41. a) H_o: Population mean systolic blood pressure for 25 yr old females living in southwestern USA is 124: $\mu = 124$
H_a: Population mean systolic blood pressure for 25 yr old females living in southwestern USA is less than 124: $\mu < 124$

b) $\mu_{\bar{x}} = 124$; $\sigma_{\bar{x}} = 2$; distribution of the test statistic is a normal distribution

c) reject H_0 if the p-value of the test statistic is less than 5%

d) $\bar{X} = 120$, $z = -2$ and p-value $= 0.0228$

e) reject H_0, accept H_a at a p-value of 0.0228
Sociologist can conclude 25 yr old females in the southwestern USA have significantly lower blood pressures

f) smallest alpha level $= 2.28\%$

43. a) H_o: Population mean age of recipients of unemployment benefits is 37 yrs: $\mu = 37$ years
H_a: Population mean age of recipients of unemployment benefits is not 37 yrs: $\mu \neq 37$ years

b) $\mu_{\bar{x}} = 37$; $\sigma_{\bar{x}} = 0.35$; distribution of the test statistic is a normal distribution

c) reject H_0 if the p-value of the test statistic is less than 1%

d) $\bar{X} = 36$, $z = -2.83$ and p-value $= 0.0047$

e) reject H_0, accept H_a at a p-value of 0.0047
The trade union can reject the agency's claim.

f) smallest alpha level $= 0.47\%$

45. a) H_o: Population average age of 1st time brides is 23.9 yrs: $\mu = 23.9$ years
H_a: Population average age of 1st time brides is greater than 23.9 yrs: $\mu > 23.9$ years

b) $\mu_{\bar{x}} = 23.9$; $\sigma_{\bar{x}} = 4.2$; distribution of the test statistic is a normal distribution

c) reject H_0 if the p-value of the test statistic is less than 5%

d) $\bar{X} = 24.9$, $z = 2.38$ and p-value $= 0.0086$

e) reject H_0, accept H_a at a p-value of 0.0086
There is sufficient evidence to support sociologist's claim.

f) smallest alpha level $= 0.86\%$

47. a) H_o: Population mean time to travel from downtown to the suburbs is 45 minutes: $\mu = 45$ minutes
H_a: Population mean time to travel from downtown to the suburbs is less than 45 minutes: $\mu < 45$ minutes

b) $\mu_{\bar{x}} = 44$; $\sigma_{\bar{x}} = 1$; distribution of the test statistic is a normal distribution

c) reject H_0 if the p-value of the test statistic is less than 5%

d) $\bar{X} = 42$, $z = -3$ and p-value $= 0.0013$

e) reject H_0, accept H_a at a p-value of 0.0013
The data supports the traffic engineer.

f) smallest alpha level $= 0.13\%$

49. a) H_o: The population mean amount of the expectorant drug DOKE for every milliliter of the suppressant is 25 milligrams: $\mu = 25$ milliliters
H_a: The population mean amount of the expectorant drug DOKE for every milliliter of the suppressant is not equal to 25 milligrams: $\mu \neq 25$ milliliters

b) $\mu_{\bar{x}} = 25$; $s_{\bar{x}} = 0.1$; the distribution of the test statistic is a t distribution.

c) reject H_0 if the p-value of the test statistic is less than 5%.

d) $\bar{x} = 25.4$, $t = 4$ and p-value $= 3.12$ E -4

e) reject H_0, accept H_a at p-value of 3.12 E -4; the product is not meeting the manufacturer's specifications.

f) smallest alpha level $= 3.12$ E -4

51. a) H_o: The population mean non-stop travel time from NY City to Washington, D.C. is 4.5 hours: $\mu = 4.5$ hours
H_a: The population mean non-stop travel time from NY City to Washington, D.C. is not 4.5 hours: $\mu \neq 4.5$ hours

b) $\mu_{\bar{x}} = 4.5$; $s_{\bar{x}} = 0.05$; the distribution of the test statistic is a t distribution.

c) reject H_0 if the p-value of the test statistic less than 1% .

d) $\bar{x} = 4.3$, $t = -4$ and p-value = 2.18 E -4

e) reject H_0, accept H_a at a p-value of 2.18 E -4; The sample results refute the automobile club's claim.

f) smallest alpha level = 2.18 E -4

53. a) H_o: The population mean life of the Louisiana shellfish is 27 months: $\mu = 27$ months

H_a: The population mean life of the Louisiana shellfish is greater than 27 months: $\mu > 27$ months

b) $\mu_{\bar{x}} = 27$; $s_{\bar{x}} = 0.7$; the distribution of the test statistic is a t distribution.

c) reject H_0 if the p-value of the test statistic is less than 5%

d) $\bar{x} = 28.05$, $t = 1.5$ and p-value = 0.0772

e) fail to reject H_0 at a p-value of 0.0772; The ecologist's claim is not too low.

f) smallest alpha level = 7.72%

55. a) H_o: The population mean effective period for the muscle relaxing tablets is 4.4 hours: $\mu = 4.4$ hours

H_a: The population mean effective period for the muscle relaxing tablets is less than 4.4 hours: $\mu < 4.4$ hours

b) $\mu_{\bar{x}} = 4.4$; $s_{\bar{x}} = 0.1$; the distribution of the test statistic is a t distribution.

c) reject H_0 if the p-value of the test statistic is less than 1%.

d) $\bar{x} = 4.2$, $t = -2$ and p-value = 0.0239

e) fail to reject H_0 at a p-value of 0.0239; The sample results do not support the researcher's suspicions.

f) smallest alpha level = 2.39%

57. a) H_o: The population mean decrease in blood pressure over a three week period is 20 points: $\mu = 20$ points

H_a: The population mean decrease in blood pressure over a three week period is less than 20 points: $\mu < 20$ points

b) $\mu_{\bar{x}} = 20$; $s_{\bar{x}} = 0.5$; the distribution of the test statistic is a t distribution.

c) reject H_0 if the p-value of the test statistic is less than 5%.

d) $\bar{x} = 19.14$, $t = -1.72$ and p-value = 0.0468

e) reject H_0, accept H_a at a p-value of 0.0468; The sample data indicate that the pharmaceutical company's claim is supported.

f) smallest alpha level = 4.68%

59. directional

61. equal; =

63. true

65. false

67. d

69. false

71. a) H_o: The population mean norm for the mathematics anxiety test is 6 for the students at her school: $\mu = 6$

H_a: The population mean norm for the mathematics anxiety test is not 6 for the students at her school: $\mu \neq 6$

b) $\mu_{\bar{x}} = 6$; $\sigma_{\bar{x}} = 0.16$; the distribution of the test statistic is a normal distribution.

c) reject H_o if the test statistic is either less than -1.96 or greater than 1.96.

d) $\bar{x} = 5.73$ and $z = -1.69$.

e) fail to reject H_o at $\alpha = 5\%$; no

73. a) H_o: The population mean registration time is 90 minutes under the new system: $\mu = 90$

H_a: The population mean registration time is less than 90 minutes under the new system: $\mu < 90$

b) $\mu_{\bar{x}} = 90$; $\sigma_{\bar{x}} = 2$; the distribution of the test statistic is a normal distribution.

c) reject H_o if the test statistic is less than -2.33.

d) $\bar{x} = 84$ and $z = -3$.

e) reject H_o, accept H_a at $\alpha = 1\%$; yes

75. a) H_o: The population mean passenger's luggage weight is 35 pounds: $\mu = 35$

H_a: The population mean pasenger's luggage weight is not 35 pounds: $\mu \neq 35$

b) $\mu_{\bar{x}} = 35$; $s_{\bar{x}} = 0.8$; the distribution of the test statistic is a t distribution.

c) reject H_o if the test statistic is either less than -2.80 or greater than 2.80.

d) $\bar{x} = 36$ and $t = 1.25$

e) fail to reject H_o at $\alpha = 1\%$; no

77. a) H_o: The population mean time children aged 6 to 10 within the upper-middle class neighborhood watch TV is 21 hours per week: $\mu = 21$

H_a: The population mean time children aged 6 to 10 within the upper-middle class neighborhood watch TV is less than 21 hours per week: $\mu < 21$

b) $\mu_{\bar{x}} = 21$; $s_{\bar{x}} = 0.69$; the distribution of the test statistic is a t distribution.

c) reject H_o if the test statistic is less than -1.71.

d) $\bar{x} = 20$ and $t = -1.67$.

e) fail to reject H_o at $\alpha = 5\%$; no

CHAPTER 12

1. counts

3. p_2

5. proportion for population 1; size of sample 1; count possessing a particular characteristic for sample 1

7. $\hat{p}_1 - \hat{p}_2$

9. $p_1 - p_2$

11. normal distribution

13.
$$s_{\hat{p}_1 - \hat{p}_2}; \sqrt{\frac{\hat{p}_1(1-\hat{p}_1)}{n_1} + \frac{\hat{p}_2(1-\hat{p}_2)}{n_2}}$$

15. sample proportion of men who never eat breakfast;
$$\hat{p}_1 = \frac{389}{1450} = 0.2683;$$
sample proportion of women who never eat breakfast;
$$\hat{p}_2 = \frac{327}{1500} = 0.218;$$

17. a) the mean is denoted $\mu_{\hat{p}_1-\hat{p}}$ and the formula is

$$\mu_{\hat{p}_1-\hat{p}_2} = p_1 - p_2$$

b) $\sigma_{\hat{p}_1-\hat{p}_2} = \sqrt{\dfrac{p_1(1-p_1)}{n_1} + \dfrac{p_2(1-p_2)}{n_2}}$

c) the standard error is denoted $\sigma_{\hat{p}_1-\hat{p}_2}$ and the formula is

$$\sigma_{\hat{p}_1-\hat{p}_2} = \sqrt{\dfrac{p_1(1-p_1)}{n_1} + \dfrac{p_2(1-p_2)}{n_2}}$$

d) the estimate of the standard error is denoted $s_{\hat{p}_1-\hat{p}_2}$ and the formula is

$$s_{\hat{p}_1-\hat{p}_2} = \sqrt{\dfrac{\hat{p}_1(1-\hat{p}_1)}{n_1} + \dfrac{\hat{p}_2(1-\hat{p}_2)}{n_2}}$$

19. a) the estimate of the standard error is denoted $s_{\hat{p}_1-\hat{p}_2}$; and the formula is

$$s_{\hat{p}_1-\hat{p}_2} = \sqrt{\dfrac{\hat{p}_1(1-\hat{p}_1)}{n_1} + \dfrac{\hat{p}_2(1-\hat{p}_2)}{n_2}}$$

b) when the independent sample selected from each population is a large sample

c) the estimate of the population standard deviation is denoted $s_{\hat{p}_1-\hat{p}_2}$, and the formula is

$$s_{\hat{p}_1-\hat{p}_2} = \sqrt{\dfrac{\hat{p}_1(1-\hat{p}_1)}{n_1} + \dfrac{\hat{p}_2(1-\hat{p}_2)}{n_2}}$$

21. a) $\hat{p}_1 = 0.24; \hat{p}_2 = 0.3104$
b) $s_{\hat{p}_1-\hat{p}_2} \approx 0.0170$
c) $s_{\hat{p}_1-\hat{p}_2} \approx 0.0170$

23. a) p_1 = proportion of all households watching the TV networks in 2001; p_2 = proportion of all households watching the TV networks in 2000
b) $\hat{p}_1$ = proportion of all households surveyed watching the TV networks in 2001; $\hat{p}_2$ = proportion of all households surveyed watching the TV networks in 2000
c) $\hat{p}_1 \approx 0.61; \hat{p}_2 \approx 0.70$
d) $\sigma_{\hat{p}_1-\hat{p}_2} \approx 0.0163$
e) $\sigma_{\hat{p}_1-\hat{p}_2} \approx 0.0163$

25. a) p_1 = proportion of all men who admit to dozing off at their workplace; p_2 = proportion of all women who admit to dozing off at their workplace
b) $\hat{p}_1$ = proportion of all men surveyed who admit to dozing off at their workplace; $\hat{p}_2$ = proportion of all women surveyed who admit to dozing off at their workplace
c) $\hat{p}_1 \approx 0.26; \hat{p}_2 \approx 0.13$
d) $\sigma_{\hat{p}_1-\hat{p}_2} \approx 0.0184$
e) $\sigma_{\hat{p}_1-\hat{p}_2} \approx 0.0184$

27. b
29. true
31. true

33. a) 0.4008
b) 0.7189
c) 0.5992
d) 0.2811

35. a) 0.7325
b) 0.6299
c) yes
d) 0.1026
e) normal
f) 0.11
g) 0.0178
h) 0.0178

37. a) p_1 = proportion of all people in the 25–34 age group who believe Nixon will be remembered as a great president
p_2 = proportion of all people in the 65 and over age group who believe Nixon will be remembered as a great president
b) $\hat{p}_1$ = proportion of people within the poll who are in the 24–34 age group who believe Nixon will be remembered as a great president
$\hat{p}_2$ = proportion of people within the poll who are in the 65 and over age group who believe Nixon will be remembered as a great president
c) $\hat{p}_1 \approx 0.3; \hat{p}_2 \approx 0.37$
d) $\sigma_{\hat{p}_1-\hat{p}_2} \approx 0.0196$
e) $\sigma_{\hat{p}_1-\hat{p}_2} \approx 0.0196$

39. $\hat{p} = \dfrac{X_1 + X_2}{n_1 + n_2}$; $\hat{p} = \dfrac{n_1\hat{p}_1 + n_2\hat{p}_2}{n_1 + n_2}$

41. two proportions
43. no; proportion; proportion; $p_1 - p_2$

45. $\dfrac{(\hat{p}_1 - \hat{p}_2) - \mu_{\hat{p}_1-\hat{p}_2}}{\sigma_{\hat{p}_1-\hat{p}_2}}$

47. c
49. d
51. a
53. true
55. true
57. false
59. true
61. the best estimate for the common population proportion value, p, is called the pooled sample proportion, $\hat{p}$, and the formulas to compute $\hat{p}$ are $\hat{p} = \dfrac{X_1 + X_2}{n_1 + n_2}$ and

$$\hat{p} = \dfrac{n_1\hat{p}_1 + n_2\hat{p}_2}{n_1 + n_2}$$

63. $s_{\hat{p}_1-\hat{p}_2} = \sqrt{\dfrac{\hat{p}_1(1-\hat{p}_1)}{n_1} + \dfrac{\hat{p}_2(1-\hat{p}_2)}{n_2}}$

65.
a) 0.0217
b) 0.0223
c) 0.0212
d) 0.0239
e) 0.0192
f) 0.0191
g) 0.014
h) 0.0229

67.
a) H_0: There is no difference between the population proportion of high school seniors who have smoked daily during 1999 and 1994: $p_1 - p_2 = 0$
H_a: The population proportion of high school seniors who smoked daily during 1999 is greater than the population proportion of high school seniors who smoked daily during 1994: $p_1 - p_2 > 0$
b) the distribution of the test statistic is approximately a normal distribution; $\mu_{\hat{p}_1 - \hat{p}_2} = 0$ and $s_{\hat{p}_1 - \hat{p}_2} = 0.0154$
c) Reject H_0 if the test statistic of the difference between the sample proportions is greater than $z_c = 1.65$
d) The test statistic z = 1.30
e) Fail to Reject H_0 at $\alpha = 5\%$. There is no difference between the population proportion of high school seniors who have smoked daily during 1999 and 1994.

69.
a) H_0: There is no difference between the population proportion of males and females who sleep in the nude: $p_1 - p_2 = 0$
H_a: There is a difference between the population proportion of males and females who sleep in the nude: $p_1 - p_2 \neq 0$
b) the distribution of the test statistic is approximately a normal distribution; $\mu_{\hat{p}_1 - \hat{p}_2} = 0$ and $s_{\hat{p}_1 - \hat{p}_2} = 0.0180$
c) Reject H_0 if the test statistic of the difference between the sample proportions is either less than $z_{LC} = -1.96$ or greater than $z_{RC} = 1.96$
d) The test statistic z = 3.89
e) Reject H_0 and accept H_a at $\alpha = 5\%$. There a difference between the population proportion of males and females who sleep in the nude

71.
a) H_0: There is no difference between the population proportion of unemployment in the New England states and the Mid-Atlantic states in 1994: $p_1 - p_2 = 0$
H_a: There is a difference between the population proportion of unemployment in the New England states and the Mid-Atlantic states in 1994: $p_1 - p_2 \neq 0$
b) the distribution of the test statistic is approximately a normal distribution; $\mu_{\hat{p}_1 - \hat{p}_2} = 0$ and $s_{\hat{p}_1 - \hat{p}_2} = 0.0107$
c) Reject H_0 if the test statistic of the difference between the sample proportions is either less than $z_{LC} = -2.58$ or greater than $z_{RC} = 2.58$
d) The test statistic z = -0.75

e) Fail to Reject H_0 at $\alpha = 1\%$. There is no difference between the population proportion of unemployment in the New England states and the Mid-Atlantic states in 1994.

73.
a) H_0: There is no difference between the population proportion of women in the Northwest and women in the Midwest who say they are attractive without makeup: $p_1 - p_2 = 0$
H_a: The population proportion of women from the Northwest who say they are attractive without makeup is greater than the population proportion from the Midwest: $p_1 - p_2 > 0$
b) the distribution of the test statistic is approximately a normal distribution; $\mu_{\hat{p}_1 - \hat{p}_2} = 0$ and $s_{\hat{p}_1 - \hat{p}_2} = 0.0203$
c) Reject H_0 if the test statistic of the difference between the sample proportions is greater than $z_c = 1.65$.
d) The test statistic z = 6.90
e) Reject H_0 and accept H_a at $\alpha = 5\%$. The population proportion of women from the Northwest who say they are attractive without makeup is greater than the proportion from the Midwest.

75.
a) H_0: There is no difference between the population proportion of people who wear seatbelts and those who do not wear seatbelts that are uninjured in passenger car crashed: $p_1 - p_2 = 0$
H_a: The population proportion of people who wear seatbelts and are uninjured is greater than those who do not wear seatbelts and are uninjured in car crashes: $p_1 - p_2 > 0$
b) the distribution of the test statistic is approximately a normal distribution; $\mu_{\hat{p}_1 - \hat{p}_2} = 0$ and $s_{\hat{p}_1 - \hat{p}_2} = 0.0208$
c) Reject H_0 if the test statistic of the difference between the sample proportions is greater than $z_c = 2.33$.
d) The test statistic z = 18.13
e) Reject H_0 and accept H_a at $\alpha = 1\%$. The population proportion of people who wear seatbelts and are uninjured is greater than those who do not wear seatbelts and are uninjured in car crashes.

77.
a) H_0: There is no difference between the population proportion of households having 1 or more computers in 2000 and the population proportion of households having 1 or more computers in 1998: $p_1 - p_2 = 0$
H_a: The population proportion of households having 1 or more computers in 2000 is greater than the population proportion of households having 1 or more computers in 1998: $p_1 - p_2 > 0$
b) the distribution of the test statistic is approximately a normal distribution; $\mu_{\hat{p}_1 - \hat{p}_2} = 0$ and $s_{\hat{p}_1 - \hat{p}_2} = 0.0200$
c) Reject H_0 if the test statistic of the difference between the sample proportions is greater than $z_c = 1.65$.
d) The test statistic z = 2.48
e) Reject H_0 and accept H_a at $\alpha = 5\%$. The population proportion of households having 1 or more computers

in 2000 is greater than the population proportion of households having 1 or more computers in 1998.

79. i) a) H_0: There is no difference between the population proportion of home team victories and visitor team victories for basketball: $p_1 - p_2 = 0$

   H_a: The population proportion of home team victories is greater than the proportion of visitor team victories for basketball: $p_1 - p_2 > 0$

   b) the distribution of the test statistic is approximately a normal distribution; $\mu_{\hat{p}_1 - \hat{p}_2} = 0$ and $s_{\hat{p}_1 - \hat{p}_2} = 0.0503$

   c) Reject H_0 if the test statistic of the difference between the sample proportions is reater than $z_c = 1.65$.

   d) The test statistic z = 5.62

   e) Reject H_0 and accept H_a at $\alpha = 5\%$. The population proportion of home team victories is greater than the population proportion of visitor team victories for basketball.

ii) a) H_0: There is no difference between the population proportion of home team victories and visitor team victories for baseball: $p_1 - p_2 = 0$

   H_a: The population proportion of home team victories is greater than the population proportion of visitor team victories for baseball: $p_1 - p_2 > 0$

   b) the distribution of the test statistic is approximately a normal distribution; $\mu_{\hat{p}_1 - \hat{p}_2} = 0$ and $s_{\hat{p}_1 - \hat{p}_2} = 0.0707$

   c) Reject H_0 if the test statistic of the difference between the sample proportions is greater than $z_c = 1.65$.

   d) The test statistic z = 0.85

   e) Fail to Reject H_0 at $\alpha = 5\%$. There is no difference between the population proportion of home team victories and visitor team victories for baseball.

iii) a) H_0: There is no difference between the population proportion of home team victories and visitor team victories for hockey: $p_1 - p_2 = 0$

   H_a: The population proportion of home team victories is greater than the population proportion of visitor team victories for hockey: $p_1 - p_2 > 0$

   b) the distribution of the test statistic is approximately a normal distribution; $\mu_{\hat{p}_1 - \hat{p}_2} = 0$ and $s_{\hat{p}_1 - \hat{p}_2} = 0.0703$

   c) Reject H_0 if the test statistic of the difference between the sample proportions is greater than $z_c = 1.65$.

   d) The test statistic z = 1.07

   e) Fail to Reject H_0 at $\alpha = 5\%$. There is no difference between the population proportion of home team victories and visitor team victories for hockey.

iv) a) H_0: There is no difference between the population proportion of home team victories and visitor team victories for football: $p_1 - p_2 = 0$

   H_a: The population proportion of home team victories is greater than the population proportion of visitor team victories for football: $p_1 - p_2 > 0$

   b) the distribution of the test statistic is approximately a normal distribution; $\mu_{\hat{p}_1 - \hat{p}_2} = 0$ and $s_{\hat{p}_1 - \hat{p}_2} = 0.0711$

   c) Reject H_0 if the test statistic of the difference between the sample proportions is greater than $z_c = 1.65$.

   d) The test statistic z = 2.13

   e) Reject H_0 and Accept H_a at $\alpha = 5\%$. The population proportion of home team victories is greater than the population proportion of visitor team victories for football.

v) a) H_0: There is no difference between the population proportion of home team victories and visitor team victories for all sports: $p_1 - p_2 = 0$

   H_a: The population proportion of home team victories is greater than the population proportion of visitor team victories for all sports: $p_1 - p_2 > 0$

   b) the distribution of the test statistic is approximately a normal distribution; $\mu_{\hat{p}_1 - \hat{p}_2} = 0$ and $s_{\hat{p}_1 - \hat{p}_2} = 0.0319$

   c) Reject H_0 if the test statistic of the difference between the sample proportions is greater than $z_c = 1.65$.

   d) The test statistic z = 5.37

   e) Reject H_0 and Accept H_a at $\alpha = 5\%$. The population proportion of home team victories is greater than the population proportion of visitor team victories for all sports.

81. a) H_0: There is no difference between the population proportion of Maymark dishwashers that need repairs within the first 5 years and the population proportion of Whirlstream dishwashers that need repairs within the first 5 years: $p_1 - p_2 = 0$

   H_a: The population proportion of Maymark dishwashers that need repairs within the first 5 years is less than the population proportion of Whirlstream dishwashers that need repairs within the first 5 years: $p_1 - p_2 < 0$

   b) the distribution of the test statistic is approximately a normal distribution; $\mu_{\hat{p}_1 - \hat{p}_2} = 0$ and $s_{\hat{p}_1 - \hat{p}_2} = 0.0384$

   c) Reject H_0 if the test statistic of the difference between the sample proportions is less than $z_c = -2.33$.

   d) The test statistic z = -1.43

   e) Fail to Reject H_0 at $\alpha = 1\%$. There is no difference between the population proportion of Maymark dishwashers that need repairs within the first 5 years and the population proportion of Whirlstream dishwashers that need repairs within the first 5 years.

83. a) H_0: There is no difference between the population proportion of women who are aware of being overweight and the population proportion of men who are aware of being overweight: $p_1 - p_2 = 0$

   H_a: The population proportion of women who are aware of being overweight is greater than the population proportion of men who are aware of being overweight: $p_1 - p_2 > 0$

   b) the distribution of the test statistic is approximately a normal distribution; $\mu_{\hat{p}_1 - \hat{p}_2} = 0$ and $s_{\hat{p}_1 - \hat{p}_2} = 0.0417$

   c) Reject H_0 if the test statistic of the difference between the sample proportions is greater than $z_c = 2.33$.

   d) The test statistic $z = 0.96$.

   e) Fail to Reject H_0 at $\alpha = 1\%$. There is no difference between the population proportion of women who are aware of being overweight and the population proportion of men who are aware of being overweight.

85. a) H_0: There is no difference between the population proportion of defective computer chips manufactured under the new process and the population proportion of defective computer chips manufactured under the present process: $p_1 - p_2 = 0$

   H_a: The population proportion of defective computer chips manufactured under the new process is less than the population proportion of defective computer chips manufactured under the present process: $p_1 - p_2 < 0$

   b) the distribution of the test statistic is approximately a normal distribution; $\mu_{\hat{p}_1 - \hat{p}_2} = 0$ and $s_{\hat{p}_1 - \hat{p}_2} = 0.0210$

   c) Reject H_0 if the test statistic of the difference between the sample proportions is less than $z_c = -1.65$.

   d) The test statistic $z = -1.90$.

   e) Reject H_0 and Accept H_a at $\alpha = 5\%$. The population proportion of defective computer chips manufactured under the new process is less than the population proportion of defective computer chips manufactured under the present process.

87. a) H_0: There is no difference between the population proportion of Americans who are concerned about their privacy for the years 1991 and 1993: $p_1 - p_2 = 0$

   H_a: There is a difference between the population proportion of Americans who are concerned about their privacy for the years 1991 and 1993: $p_1 - p_2 \neq 0$

   b) the distribution of the test statistic is approximately a normal distribution; $\mu_{\hat{p}_1 - \hat{p}_2} = 0$ and $s_{\hat{p}_1 - \hat{p}_2} = 0.0184$

   c) Reject H_0 if the test statistic of the difference between the sample proportions is either less than $z_{LC} = -1.96$ or greater than $z_{RC} = 1.96$.

   d) The test statistic $z = -2.72$.

   e) Reject H_0 and Accept H_a at $\alpha = 5\%$. There is a difference between the population proportion of Americans who are concerned about their privacy for the years 1991 and 1993.

89. placebo

91. double-blind; experiment

93. An experimental study involves a treatment group and a control group. The only difference between the treatment and control groups is that the subjects of the treatment group are administered the treatment drug and the subjects of the control group are administered the placebo.

95. A treatment effect is the psychological effect of the treatment group feeling better not because of the actual treatment they received but because they feel they were selected for some special treatment.

97. a) treatment group = group receiving the surgery and the cancer vaccine treatment

   b) control group = group receiving the surgery and the placebo vaccine

   c) H_0: There is no difference between the population proportion of patients receiving the surgery and the cancer vaccine treatment and the population proportion of patients receiving the surgery and the placebo vaccine who remain disease-free after 3 years: $p_1 - p_2 = 0$.

   H_a: The population proportion of patients receiving the surgery and the cancer vaccine treatment who remain disease-free after 3 years is greater than the population proportion of patients receiving the surgery and the placebo vaccine who remain disease-free after 3 years: $p_1 - p_2 > 0$.

99. a) H_0: There is no difference between the population proportion of patients receiving the experimental drug CentroRx and angioplasty and the population proportion of patients receiving the placebo drug and angioplasty after 1 year: $p_1 - p_2 = 0$.

   H_a: The population proportion of patients receiving the experimental drug CentroRx and angioplasty is greater than the population proportion of patients receiving the placebo drug and angioplasty after 1 year: $p_1 - p_2 > 0$.

   b) the distribution of the test statistic is approximately a normal distribution; $\mu_{\hat{p}_1 - \hat{p}_2} = 0$ and $s_{\hat{p}_1 - \hat{p}_2} = 0.0588$

   c) Reject H_0 if the test statistic of the difference between the sample proportions is greater than $z_c = 2.33$.

   d) The test statistic $z = 2.83$.

   e) Reject H_0 and Accept H_a at $\alpha = 1\%$. The population proportion of patients receiving the experimental drug CentroRx and angioplasty is greater than the population proportion of patients receiving the placebo drug and angioplasty after 1 year.

101. **a)** H_0: There is no difference between the population proportion of thighs which were administered the treatment cream that lost an average of 0.5" of fat and the population proportion of thighs which were administered the placebo cream and lost an average of 0.5" of fat: $p_1 - p_2 = 0$.

    H_a: The population proportion of thighs which were administered the treatment cream that lost an average of 0.5" of fat is greater than the population proportion of thighs which were administered the placebo cream and lost an average of 0.5" of fat: $p_1 - p_2 > 0$.

b) the distribution of the test statistic is approximately a normal distribution; $\mu_{\hat{p}_1 - \hat{p}_2} = 0$ and $s_{\hat{p}_1 - \hat{p}_2} = 0.0434$

c) Reject H_0 if the test statistic of the difference between the sample proportions is greater than $z_c = 2.33$.

d) The test statistic z = 6.35.

e) Reject H_0 and Accept H_a at $\alpha = 1\%$. The population proportion of thighs which were administered the treatment cream that lost an average of 0.5" of fat is greater than the population proportion of thighs which were administered the placebo cream and lost an average of 0.5" of fat.

103. **a)** H_0: There is no difference between the population proportion of people administered Hismanal contracting a headache and the population proportion of people administered a placebo contracting a headache: $p_1 - p_2 = 0$.

    H_a: There is a difference between the population proportion of people administered Hismanal contracting a headache and the population proportion of people administered a placebo contracting a headache: $p_1 - p_2 \neq 0$.

b) the distribution of the test statistic is approximately a normal distribution; $\mu_{\hat{p}_1 - \hat{p}_2} = 0$ and $s_{\hat{p}_1 - \hat{p}_2} = 0.0104$

c) Reject H_0 if the test statistic of the difference between the sample proportions is either less than $z_{LC} = -2.58$ or greater than $z_{RC} = 2.58$.

d) The test statistic z = 1.98.

e) Fail to Reject H_0 at $\alpha = 1\%$. There is no difference between the population proportion of people administered Hismanal contracting a headache and the population proportion of people administered a placebo contracting a headache.

105. **a)** H_0: There is no difference between the population proportion of people administered Hismanal gaining weight and the population proportion of people administered a placebo gaining weight: $p_1 - p_2 = 0$.

    H_a: There is a difference between the population proportion of people administered Hismanal gaining weight and the population proportion of people administered a placebo gaining weight: $p_1 - p_2 \neq 0$.

b) the distribution of the test statistic is approximately a normal distribution; $\mu_{\hat{p}_1 - \hat{p}_2} = 0$ and $s_{\hat{p}_1 - \hat{p}_2} = 0.0060$

c) Reject H_0 if the test statistic of the difference between the sample proportions is either less than $z_{LC} = -2.58$ or greater than $z_{RC} = 2.58$.

d) The test statistic z = -37.03.

e) Reject H_0 and Accept H_a at $\alpha = 1\%$. There is a difference between the population proportion of people administered Hismanal gaining weight and the population proportion of people administered a placebo gaining weight.

107. **a)** H_0: There is no difference between the population proportion of people administered Hismanal getting nervous and the population proportion of people administered a placebo getting nervous: $p_1 - p_2 = 0$.

    H_a: There is a difference between the population proportion of people administered Hismanal getting nervous and the population proportion of people administered a placebo getting nervous: $p_1 - p_2 \neq 0$.

b) the distribution of the test statistic is approximately a normal distribution; $\mu_{\hat{p}_1 - \hat{p}_2} = 0$ and $s_{\hat{p}_1 - \hat{p}_2} = 0.0302$

c) Reject H_0 if the test statistic of the difference between the sample proportions is either less than $z_{lc} = -2.58$ or greater than $z_{rc} = 2.58$.

d) The test statistic z = 1.81.

e) Fail to Reject H_0 at $\alpha = 1\%$. There is no difference between the population proportion of people administered Hismanal getting nervous and the population proportion of people administered a placebo getting nervous.

109. Yes, since from the hypothesis test of problem 108 we can conclude that the population proportion of people administered Hismanal getting drowsy is not significantly different than the population proportion of people administered the placebo getting drowsy.

111. **a)** H_0: There is no difference between the population proportion of females and the population proportion of males who take chances: $p_1 - p_2 = 0$

    H_a: There is a difference between the population proportions of females and the population proportion of males who take chances: $p_1 - p_2 \neq 0$

b) the distribution of the test statistic is approximately a normal distribution; $\mu_{\hat{p}_1 - \hat{p}_2} = 0$ and $s_{\hat{p}_1 - \hat{p}_2} = 0.0242$

c) Reject H_0 if the p-value of the test statistic is less than 1%.

d) Test statistic: z = -2.48 and p-value = 0.0134

e) Fail to reject H_0 at a p-value of 0.0134. There is no difference between the population proportions of females and males who take chances.

f) Smallest alpha = 1.34%

113. **a)** H_0: There is no difference between the population proportion of nonsmokers and smokers in their opinion regarding should smoking be banned in all public places.: $p_1 - p_2 = 0$

H_a: The difference between the population proportion of nonsmokers and the population proportion of smokers who believe smoking should be banned in all public places is greater than zero: $p_1 - p_2 > 0$

b) the distribution of the test statistic is approximately a normal distribution; $\mu_{\hat{p}_1 - \hat{p}_2} = 0$ and $s_{\hat{p}_1 - \hat{p}_2} = 0.0215$

c) Reject H_0 if the p-value of the test statistic is less than 1%.

d) Test statistic: z = 10.71 and p-value = 4.69 E-27

e) Reject H_0 and accept H_a at a p-value of 4.69 E-27. The population proportion of nonsmokers who believe smoking should be banned in all public places is greater than the population proportion of smokers who believe smoking should be banned in all public places.

f) Smallest alpha = 4.69 E-27

115. a) H_0: There is no difference between the population proportion of black children in 2000 and the population proportion of black children in 1979 who dropped out of high school: $p_1 - p_2 = 0$

H_a: The difference between the population proportion of black children who dropped out of high school in 2000 and the population proportion of black children who dropped out of high school in 1970 is less than zero: $p_1 - p_2 < 0$

b) the distribution of the test statistic is approximately a normal distribution; $\mu_{\hat{p}_1 - \hat{p}_2} = 0$ and $s_{\hat{p}_1 - \hat{p}_2} = 0.0106$

c) Reject H_0 if the p-value of the test statistic is less than 5%.

d) Test statistic: z = –5.66 and p-value = 7.38 E-9

e) Reject H_0 and accept H_a at a p-value of 7.38 E-9 The population proportion of black children who dropped out of high school in 2000 is less than the population proportion of black children who dropped out of high school in 1970.

f) Smallest alpha = 7.38 E-9

117. a) H_0: There is no difference between the population proportion success rate of the two point conversion for passing and running: $p_1 - p_2 = 0$

H_a: There is difference between the population proportion success rate of the two point conversion for passing and running: $p_1 - p_2 \neq 0$

b) the distribution of the test statistic is approximately a normal distribution; $\mu_{\hat{p}_1 - \hat{p}_2} = 0$ and $s_{\hat{p}_1 - \hat{p}_2} = 0.0654$

c) Reject H_0 if the p-value of the test statistic is less than 5%.

d) Test statistic: z = 0.83 and p-value = 0.4068

e) Fail to reject H_0 at a p-value of 0. 4068. There is no difference between the population proportion success rate of the two point conversion for passing and running.

f) Smallest alpha = 40.68 %

119. a) H_0: There is no difference between the population proportion of parents in 2000 and the population proportion of parents in 1995 who helped their children eat less fat : $p_1 - p_2 = 0$

H_a: The difference between the population proportion of parents in 2000 and the population proportion of parents in 1995 who helped their children eat less fat is less than zero: $p_1 - p_2 < 0$

b) the distribution of the test statistic is approximately a normal distribution; $\mu_{\hat{p}_1 - \hat{p}_2} = 0$ and $s_{\hat{p}_1 - \hat{p}_2} = 0.0316$

c) Reject H_0 if the p-value of the test statistic is less than 5%.

d) Test statistic: z = –4.43 and p-value = 4.67 E-6

e) Reject H_0 and accept H_a at a p-value of 4.67 E-6 The population proportion of parents who helped their children eat less fat in 2000 is less than the population proportion of parents helped their children eat less fat in 1995.

f) Smallest alpha = 4.67 E-6

121. a) H_0: There is no difference between the population proportion of nonsmokers and the population proportion of smokers who strongly believe that nicotine is an addictive substance: $p_1 - p_2 = 0$

H_a: The difference between the population proportion of nonsmokers who strongly believe that nicotine is an addictive substance and the population proportion of smokers who strongly believe that nicotine is an addictive substance is less than zero: $p_1 - p_2 < 0$

b) the distribution of the test statistic is approximately a normal distribution; $\mu_{\hat{p}_1 - \hat{p}_2} = 0$ and $s_{\hat{p}_1 - \hat{p}_2} = 0.0174$

c) Reject H_0 if the p-value of the test statistic is less than 5%.

d) Test statistic: z = –2.29 and p-value = 0.0109

e) Reject H_0 and accept H_a at a p-value of 0.0109 The population proportion of nonsmokers who strongly believe that nicotine is an addictive substance is less than the population proportion of smokers who strongly believe that nicotine is an addictive substance.

f) Smallest alpha = 1.09%

123. i) a) H_0: There is no difference between the population proportion of MCL sprains on Astro Turf and natural grass: $p_1 - p_2 = 0$

H_a: The difference between the population proportion of MCL sprains on Astro Turf and the population proportion of MCL sprains on natural grass is greater than zero: $p_1 - p_2 > 0$

b) the distribution of the test statistic is approximately a normal distribution; $\mu_{\hat{p}_1 - \hat{p}_2} = 0$ and $s_{\hat{p}_1 - \hat{p}_2} = 0.026$

c) Reject H_0 if the p-value of the test statistic is less than 5%.

d) Test statistic: z = 2.76 and p-value = 0.0029

e) Reject H_0 and accept H_a at a p-value of 0.0029. The population proportion of MCL sprains on Astro

Turf is greater than the population proportion of MCL sprains on natural grass.

f) Smallest alpha = 0.29%

ii) a) H_0: There is no difference between the population proportion of ACL sprains on Astro Turf and natural grass: $p_1 - p_2 = 0$

H_a: The difference between the population proportion of ACL sprains on Astro Turf and the population proportion of ACL sprains on natural grass is greater than zero: $p_1 - p_2 > 0$

b) the distribution of the test statistic is approximately a normal distribution; $\mu_{\hat{p}_1 - \hat{p}_2} = 0$ and $s_{\hat{p}_1 - \hat{p}_2} = 0.0139$

c) Reject H_0 if the p-value of the test statistic is less than 5%.

d) Test statistic: z = 0.39 and p-value = 0.3483

e) Fail to reject H_0 at a p-value of 0.3483.
The population proportion of MCL sprains on Astro Turf is greater than the population proportion of MCL sprains on natural grass.

f) Smallest alpha = 34.83%

iii) H_0: There is no difference between the population proportion of total injuries on Astro Turf and natural grass: $p_1 - p_2 = 0$

H_a: The difference between the population proportion of total injuries on Astro Turf and the population proportion of total injuries on natural grass is greater than zero: $p_1 - p_2 > 0$

a) the distribution of the test statistic is approximately a normal distribution; $\mu_{\hat{p}_1 - \hat{p}_2} = 0$ and $s_{\hat{p}_1 - \hat{p}_2} = 0.0215$

b) Reject H_0 if the p-value of the test statistic is less than 5%.

c) Test statistic: z = 3.14 and p-value = 8.45 E-4

d) Reject H_0 and accept H_a at a p-value of 8.45 E-4.
The population proportion of MCL sprains on Astro Turf is greater than the population proportion of MCL sprains on natural grass.

e) Smallest alpha = 8.45 E-4

125. a) H_0: There is no difference between the population proportion of coronary heart disease for Society A and Society B: $p_1 - p_2 = 0$

H_a: There is difference between the population proportion of coronary heart disease for Society A and Society B: $p_1 - p_2 \neq 0$

b) the distribution of the test statistic is approximately a normal distribution; $\mu_{\hat{p}_1 - \hat{p}_2} = 0$ and $s_{\hat{p}_1 - \hat{p}_2} = 0.03$

c) Reject H_0 if the p-value of the test statistic is less than 1%.

d) Test statistic: z = 2 and p-value = 0.0455

e) Fail to reject H_0 at a p-value of 0.0455.
There is no difference between the population proportion of coronary heart disease for Society A and Society B.

f) Smallest alpha = 4.55 %

127. a) H_0: There is no difference between the population proportion of State University grads and the

population proportion of private college grads who find jobs within their fields in six months of graduation: $p_1 - p_2 = 0$

H_a: There is difference between the population proportion of State University grads and the population proportion of private college grads who find jobs within their fields in six months of graduation: $p_1 - p_2 \neq 0$

b) the distribution of the test statistic is approximately a normal distribution; $\mu_{\hat{p}_1 - \hat{p}_2} = 0$ and $s_{\hat{p}_1 - \hat{p}_2} = 0.0365$

c) Reject H_0 if the p-value of the test statistic is less than 5%.

d) Test statistic: z = –0.76 and p-value = 0.4468

e) Fail to reject H_0 at a p-value of 0.4468.
There is no difference between the population proportion of State University grads and the population proportion of private college grads who find jobs within their fields in six months of graduation.

f) Smallest alpha = 44.68 %

129. a) H_0: There is no difference between the population proportion of men and the population proportion of women who approve of mothers working when their children are less than five years old: $p_1 - p_2 = 0$

H_a: There is difference between the population proportion of men and the population proportion of women who approve of mothers working when their children are less than five years old: $p_1 - p_2 \neq 0$

b) the distribution of the test statistic is approximately a normal distribution; $\mu_{\hat{p}_1 - \hat{p}_2} = 0$ and $s_{\hat{p}_1 - \hat{p}_2} = 0.0451$

c) Reject H_0 if the p-value of the test statistic is less than 5%.

d) Test statistic: z = –1.11 and p-value = 0.2671

e) Fail to reject H_0 at a p-value of 0.2671.
There is no difference between the population proportion of men and the population proportion of women who approve of mothers working when their children are less than five years old.

f) Smallest alpha = 26.51 %

131. a) H_0: There is no difference between the population proportion of people cured using drug A and the population proportion of people cured using drug B: $p_1 - p_2 = 0$

H_a: The difference between the population proportion people cured using drug A and the population proportion of people cured using drug B is less than zero: $p_1 - p_2 < 0$

b) the distribution of the test statistic is approximately a normal distribution; $\mu_{\hat{p}_1 - \hat{p}_2} = 0$ and $s_{\hat{p}_1 - \hat{p}_2} = 0.0671$

c) Reject H_0 if the p-value of the test statistic is less than 1%.

d) Test statistic: z = –0.55 and p-value = 0.2900

e) Fail to reject H_0 at a p-value of 0.2900
There is no difference between the population pro-

portion of people cured using drug A and the population proportion of people cured using drug B.

f) Smallest alpha = 29%

133. a) H_0: There is no difference between the population proportion of patients who received angioplasty and the drug CentroRx and population proportion of patients who received angioplasty and a placebo that didn't have life-threatening blockages one year later: $p_1 - p_2 = 0$

H_a: The difference between the population proportion of patients who received angioplasty and the drug CentroRx that didn't have life-threatening blockages one year later and the population proportion of patients who received angioplasty and a placebo is greater than zero: $p_1 - p_2 > 0$

b) the distribution of the test statistic is approximately a normal distribution; $\mu_{\hat{p}_1 - \hat{p}_2} = 0$ and $s_{\hat{p}_1 - \hat{p}_2} = 0.0588$

c) Reject H_0 if the p-value of the test statistic is less than 1%.

d) Test statistic: z = 2.83 and p-value = 0.0023

e) Reject H_0 and accept H_a at a p-value of 0.0023. The population proportion of patients who received angioplasty and the drug CentroRx that didn't have life-threatening blockages one year later is greater than the population proportion of patients who received angioplasty and a placebo.

f) Smallest alpha = 0.23%

135. a) H_0: There is no difference between the population proportion of thighs which were administered the treated cream that lost half an inch of fat and population proportion of thighs which were administered the placebo cream: $p_1 - p_2 = 0$

H_a: The difference between the population proportion of thighs which were administered the treated cream that lost half an inch of fat and the population proportion of thighs which were administered the placebo cream is greater than zero: $p_1 - p_2 > 0$

b) the distribution of the test statistic is approximately a normal distribution; $\mu_{\hat{p}_1 - \hat{p}_2} = 0$ and $s_{\hat{p}_1 - \hat{p}_2} = 0.0434$

c) Reject H_0 if the p-value of the test statistic is less than 1%.

d) Test statistic: z = 6.35 and p-value = 1.14 E-10

e) Reject H_0 and accept H_a at a p-value of 1.14 E-10. The population proportion of patients who received angioplasty and the drug CentroRx that didn't have life-threatening blockages one year later is greater than the population proportion of patients who received angioplasty and a placebo.

f) Smallest alpha = 1.14 E-10

137. normal; np; n(1-p)

139. a) n_1 = size of sample selected from population 1

b) n_2 = size of sample selected from population 2

c) $\hat{p}_1$ = proportion for sample selected from population 1

d) $\hat{p}_2$ = proportion for sample selected from population 2

e) p_1 = proportion for population 1

f) p_2 = proportion for population 2

141. c

143. Sample proportion of:

a) men drivers who wear seatbelts = 376/625 = 0.6016

b) women drivers who wear seatbelts = 492/758 = 0.6491

c) men drivers who do not wear seatbelts = 249/625 = 0.3984

d) women drivers who do not wear seatbelts = 266/758 = 0.3509

145. a) 0.6301

b) 0.7903

c) yes

d) –0.1602

e) approximately normal

f) –0.26

g) 0.1447

h) 0.1447

147. a) p_1 = proportion of college graduates who listen to sports on the radio;

p_2 = proportion of college graduates who watch sports on TV

b) $\hat{p}_1$ = proportion of college graduates surveyed who listen to sports on the radio;

$\hat{p}_2$ = proportion of college graduates surveyed who watch sports on TV

c) $\hat{p}_1 \approx 0.33$; $\hat{p}_2 \approx 0.27$

d) $\sigma_{\hat{p}_1 - \hat{p}_2} \approx 0.220$

e) $\sigma_{\hat{p}_1 - \hat{p}_2} \approx 0.220$

149. d

151. H_0

153. true; = ; $\hat{p}(1 - \hat{p})$

155. a) $\hat{p} = 0.5259$ **b)** $\hat{p} = 0.8071$

157. a) H_0: There is no difference between the population proportion of people in 2004 and in 2000 that said "US-made goods have improved in the last few years": $p_1 - p_2 = 0$.

H_a: The population proportion of people in 2004 that said "US-made goods have improved in the last few years" is greater than the population proportion of people in 2000 that said "US-made goods have improved in the last few years": $p_1 - p_2 > 0$.

b) the distribution of the test statistic is approximately a normal distribution; $\mu_{\hat{p}_1 - \hat{p}_2} = 0$ and $s_{\hat{p}_1 - \hat{p}_2} = 0.0165$

c) Reject H_0 if the test statistic of the difference between the sample proportions is greater than $z_c = 2.33$

d) The test statistic z = 10.91, p-value = 5.30 E–28

e) Reject H_0 and accept H_a at α = 1%. The population proportion of people in 2004 who said "US-made goods have improved in the last few years" is greater than the population proportion in 2000.

159. a) H_0: There is no difference between the population proportion of grades of A's and B's for small classes and the population proportion of A's and B's for large classes: $p_1 - p_2 = 0$.

  H_a: The population proportion of grades of A's and B's for small classes is greater than the population proportion of A's and B's for large classes: $p_1 - p_2 > 0$.

  b) the distribution of the test statistic is approximately a normal distribution; $\mu_{\hat{p}_1 - \hat{p}_2} = 0$ and $s_{\hat{p}_1 - \hat{p}_2} = 0.0335$

  c) Reject H_0 if the test statistic of the difference between the sample proportions is greater than $z_c = 1.65$

  d) The test statistic $z = 4.79$, p-value $= 8.28\text{E-}07$

  e) Reject H_0 and accept H_a at $\alpha = 5\%$. The population proportion of grades of A's and B's for small classes is greater than the population proportion of A's and B's for large classes.

161. a) H_0: There is no difference between the population proportion of women having a heart attack and taking at least 100 units of vitamin E daily and the population proportion of women having a heart attack and not taking any vitamin E daily: $p_1 - p_2 = 0$.

  H_a: There is a difference between the population proportion of women having a heart attack and taking at least 100 units of vitamin E daily and the population proportion of women having a heart attack and not taking any vitamin E daily: $p_1 - p_2 \neq 0$.

  b) the distribution of the test statistic is approximately a normal distribution; $\mu_{\hat{p}_1 - \hat{p}_2} = 0$ and $s_{\hat{p}_1 - \hat{p}_2} = 0.0167$

  c) Reject H_0 if the test statistic of the difference between the sample proportions is either less than $z_{LC} = -1.96$ or greater than $z_{RC} = 1.96$

  d) The test statistic $z = -2.12$, p-value $= 0.0341$

  e) Yes, Reject H_0 and accept H_a at $\alpha = 5\%$. There is a difference between the population proportion of women having a heart attack and taking at least 100 units of vitamin E daily and the population proportion of women having a heart attack and not taking any vitamin E daily.

CHAPTER 13

1. Two means

3. a) $\mu_{\bar{x}_1 - \bar{x}_2}$; μ_1; μ_2; population; population

  b) $\sqrt{\dfrac{(n_1 - 1)s_1^{\,2} + (n_2 - 1)s_2^{\,2}}{n_1 + n_2 - 2} \cdot \left(\dfrac{1}{n_1} + \dfrac{1}{n_2}\right)}$

  c) t; $n_1 + n_2 - 2$

5. No; mean; mean; $\mu_1 - \mu_2$

7. true

9. test statistic

11. c

13. false

15. a) Pop 1: manufacturer's new light bulbs.
  Pop 2: competitor's light bulbs.

  b) *Hypotheses:*
  H_0: There is no difference between the population mean life of the new light bulbs and the population mean life of the competitor's light bulbs: $\mu_1 - \mu_2 = 0$.
  H_a: The difference between population mean life of the new light bulbs and the population mean life of the competitor's light bulbs is greater than zero: $\mu_1 - \mu_2 > 0$.

  c) *Expected Results:*
  $\mu_{\bar{x}_1 - \bar{x}_2} = 0$
  $s_{\bar{x}_1 - \bar{x}_2} \approx 19.03$
  Hypothesis test model: the distribution of the test statistic is a t distribution.

  d) *Decision rule:*
  Reject H_0 if the test statistic is greater than $t_c = 1.66$.

  e) *test statistic:* $t = 2.63$

  f) *Conclusion:*
  Reject H_0, Accept H_a at $\alpha = 5\%$.
  Question:
  Sample results support the manufacturer's claim.

17. a) Pop 1: typing speeds of the community college graduates.
  Pop 2: typing speeds of the secretarial student graduates.

  b) *Hypotheses:*
  H_0: There is no difference in the population mean typing speed of the community college graduates and the secretarial student graduates: $\mu_1 - \mu_2 = 0$.
  H_a: The difference between the population mean typing speed of the community college graduates and the secretarial student graduates is not equal to zero: $\mu_1 - \mu_2 \neq 0$.

  c) *Expected Results:*
  $\mu_{\bar{x}_1 - \bar{x}_2} = 0$
  $s_{\bar{x}_1 - \bar{x}_2} \approx 3.10$
  Hypothesis test model: the distribution of the test statistic is a t distribution.

  d) *Decision Rule:*
  Reject H_0 if the test statistic is either less than $t_{LC} = -1.99$ or greater than $t_{RC} = 1.99$.

  e) *test statistic:* $t = 1.29$

  f) *Conclusion:*
  Fail to reject H_0 at $\alpha = 5\%$.
  Answer:
  The personnel director cannot conclude that there is

a significant difference in the population mean typing speed of the community college graduate and secretarial school graduates.

19. **a)** Pop 1: married graduate students

Pop 2: unmarried graduate students

b) *Hypotheses:*

H_o: There is no difference between the population mean cumulative average of married and unmarried graduate students: $\mu_1 - \mu_2 = 0$

H_a: The difference between population mean cumulative average of married graduate students and the population mean cumulative average of unmarred graduate students is less than zero:

$\mu_1 - \mu_2 < 0$

c) *Expected Results:*

$\mu_{\bar{x}_1 - \bar{x}_2} = 0$

$s_{\bar{x}_1 - \bar{x}_2} \approx 0.16$

Hypothesis test model: the distribution of the test statistic is a *t* distribution.

d) *Decision rule:*

Reject H_o if the test statistic is less than $t_c = -2.50$.

e) *test statistic:* t = –1.32

f) *Conclusion:*

Fail to reject H_o at $\alpha = 1\%$

Answer:

We cannot agree with the sociologist's claim.

21. B:A

23. **a)** Pop 1: control group

Pop 2: treatment group

b) *Hypotheses:*

H_o: There is no difference between the population mean amount of Vitamin A stored in mice between the control and treatment groups: $\mu_1 - \mu_2 = 0$

H_a: The difference between population mean amount of Vitamin A stored in the mice of the treatment group and the population mean amount of Vitamin A stored in the mice of the control group is less than zero: $\mu_1 - \mu_2 < 0$

c) *Expected Results:*

$\mu_{\bar{x}_1 - \bar{x}_2} = 0$

$s_{\bar{x}_1 - \bar{x}_2} \approx 139.63$

Hypothesis test model: the distribution of the test statistic is a *t* distribution.

d) *Decision rule:*

Reject H_o if the test statistic is less than $t_c = -2.47$.

e) *test statistic:* t = –6.40

f) *Conclusion:*

Reject H_o, Accept H_a at $\alpha = 1\%$

Answer:

The researcher can conclude that the population mean amount of Vitamin A stored in mice on the diet deficient diet is significantly less.

25. **a)** H_0: There is no difference between the population mean life of the new light bulbs and the population mean life of the competitor's light bulbs: $\mu_1 - \mu_2 = 0$

H_a: The difference between the population mean life of the new light bulbs and the population mean life of the competitor's light bulbs is greater than zero: $\mu_1 - \mu_2 > 0$

b) The distribution of the test statistic is a t distribution, $\mu_{\bar{x}_1 - \bar{x}_2} = 0$ and $s_{\bar{x}_1 - \bar{x}_2} = 19.03$

c) Reject H_0 if the p-value of the test statistic is less than 5%.

d) Test statistic: t = 2.63 and p-value = 0.0050

e) Reject H_0 and accept H_a at a p-value of 0.0050. The sample results support the manufacturer's claim.

f) smallest alpha = 0.5%

27. **a)** H_0: There is no difference between the population mean typing speed of the community college graduates and the population mean typing speed of the secretarial student graduates: $\mu_1 - \mu_2 = 0$

H_a: The difference between the population mean typing speed of the community college graduates and the population mean typing speed of the secretarial student graduates is not equal to zero: $\mu_1 - \mu_2 \neq 0$

b) The distribution of the test statistic is a t distribution, $\mu_{\bar{x}_1 - \bar{x}_2} = 0$ and $s_{\bar{x}_1 - \bar{x}_2} = 3.10$

c) Reject H_0 if the p-value of the test statistic is less than 5%.

d) Test statistic: t = 1.29 and p-value = 0.2012

e) Fail to Reject H_0 at a p-value of 0.2012

The personnel director cannot conclude that there is a significant difference in the mean typing speed of these graduates.

f) Smallest alpha = 20.12%

29. **a)** H_0: There is no difference between the population mean cumulative average of married graduate students and the population mean cumulative average of unmarried graduate students: $\mu_1 - \mu_2 = 0$

H_a: The difference between the population mean cumulative average of married graduate students and the population mean cumulative average of unmarried graduate students is less than zero: $\mu_1 - \mu_2 = < 0$

b) The distribution of the test statistic is a t distribution, $\mu_{\bar{x}_1 - \bar{x}_2} = 0$ and $s_{\bar{x}_1 - \bar{x}_2} = 0.16$

c) Reject H_0 if the p-value of the test statistic is less than 1%.

d) Test statistic: t = –1.32 and p-value = 0.0998

e) Fail to Reject H_0 at a p-value of 0.0998

I don't agree with the sociologist's claim.

f) Smallest alpha = 9.98%

31. **a)** H_0: There is no difference between the population mean stamina level of the treatment group and

the population mean stamina level of the control group: $\mu_1 - \mu_2 = 0$

H_a: The difference between the population mean stamina level of the treatment group and the population mean stamina level of the control group is greater than zero: $\mu_1 - \mu_2 > 0$

b) The distribution of the test statistic is a t distribution, $\mu_{\bar{x}_1 - \bar{x}_2} = 0$ and $s_{\bar{x}_1 - \bar{x}_2} = 2.78$

c) Reject H_0 if the p-value of the test statistic is less than 5%.

d) Test statistic: t = 2.88 and p-value = 0.0038

e) Reject H_0 and accept H_a at a p-value of 0.0038. The sample results support the nutritionist's belief.

f) smallest alpha = 0.38%

33. false

35. b

37. 1.09

39. false

41. H_o

43. d

45. true

47. a) Pop 1: urban sixth grade students

Pop 2: rural sixth grade students

b) *Hypotheses:*

H_0: There is no difference between the population mean score of the urban sixth grade students and the population mean score of the rural sixth grade students on the standardized reading comprehension test: $\mu_1 - \mu_2 = 0$.

H_a: The difference between the population mean score of the urban sixth grade students and the population mean score of the rural sixth grade students on the standardized reading comprehension test is greater than zero: $\mu_1 - \mu_2 > 0$.

c) *Expected Results:*

$\mu_{\bar{x}_1 - \bar{x}_2} = 0$

$\sigma_{\bar{x}_1 - \bar{x}_2} \approx 2.08$

Hypothesis test model: the distribution of the test statistic is a normal distribution.

d) *Decision rule:*

Reject H_0 if the test statistic is greater than $z_c = 1.65$.

e) *test statistic:* z = 2.16; p-value = 0.0154

f) *Conclusion:*

Reject H_0, Accept H_a at $\alpha = 5\%$.

Question:

The educational researcher can conclude that the urban sixth grade students performed significantly better on the standardized test at $\alpha = 5\%$.

49. a) Pop 1: American League Pitchers

Pop 2: National League Pitchers

b) *Hypotheses:*

H_0: There is no difference between the population

mean E.R.A of American League pitchers and National League pitchers: $\mu_1 - \mu_2 = 0$

H_a: The difference between the population mean E.R.A of American League pitchers and the population mean E.R.A of National League pitchers is less than zero: $\mu_1 - \mu_2 < 0$

c) *Expected Results:*

$\mu_{\bar{x}_1 - \bar{x}_2} = 0$

$s_{\bar{x}_1 - \bar{x}_2} \approx 0.07$

Hypothesis test model: the distribution of the test statistic is a *t* distribution.

d) *Decision rule:*

Reject H_o if the test statistic is less than $t_c = -2.46$.

e) *test statistic:* t = –1.49; p-value: 0.0730

f) *Conclusion:*

Fail to reject H_o at $\alpha = 1\%$

Answer:

The sportswriter's claim is not justified.

51. Part I.

a) Pop 1: Ivy League College

Pop 2: Military Academy

b) *Hypotheses:*

H_o: There is no difference between the population mean verbal S.A.T score of the IVY League College and the Military Academy: $\mu_1 - \mu_2 = 0$

H_a: The difference between the population mean verbal S.A.T score of the IVY League College and the population mean verbal S.A.T score of the Military Academy is greater than zero: $\mu_1 - \mu_2 > 0$

c) *Expected Results:*

$\mu_{\bar{x}_1 - \bar{x}_2} = 0$

$s_{\bar{x}_1 - \bar{x}_2} \approx 11.05$

Hypothesis test model: the distribution of the test statistic is a *t* distribution.

d) *Decision rule:*

Reject H_o if the test statistic is greater than $t_c = 1.66$.

e) *test statistic:* t = 3.62; p-value: 2.33 E –4

f) *Conclusion:*

Reject H_o, Accept H_a at $\alpha = 5\%$

Answer:

The educational researcher can conclude that the IVY League College has a higher mean verbal S.A.T.

51. Part II.

a) Pop 1: IVY League College

Pop 2: Military Academy

b) *Hypotheses:*

H_o: There is no difference between the population mean mathematics S.A.T score of the IVY League College and the Military Academy: $\mu_1 - \mu_2 = 0$

H_a: The difference between the population mean mathematics S.A.T score of the IVY League

College and the population mean mathematics S.A.T score of the Military Academy is less than zero: $\mu_1 - \mu_2 < 0$

c) *Expected Results:*

$\mu_{\bar{x}_1 - \bar{x}_2} = 0$

$s_{\bar{x}_1 - \bar{x}_2} \approx 12.17$

Hypothesis test model: the distribution of the test statistic is a t distribution.

d) *Decision rule:*

Reject H_o if the test statistic is less than $t_c = -1.66$.

e) *test statistic:* $t = -2.88$; p-value: 0.0025

f) *Conclusion:*

Reject H_o, Accept H_a at $\alpha = 5\%$

Answer:

The educational researcher can conclude the mean math S.A.T score is greater for the Military Academy.

51. Part III.

a) Pop 1: IVY League College

Pop 2: Military Academy

b) *Hypotheses:*

H_o: There is no difference between the population mean combined S.A.T score of the IVY League College and the Military Academy: $\mu_1 - \mu_2 = 0$

H_a: The difference between the population mean combined S.A.T score of the IVY League College and the Military Academy is not equal to zero: $\mu_1 - \mu_2 \neq 0$

c) *Expected Results:*

$\mu_{\bar{x}_1 - \bar{x}_2} = 0$

$s_{\bar{x}_1 - \bar{x}_2} \approx 16.42$

Hypothesis test model: the distribution of the test statistic is a t distribution.

d) *Decision rule:*

Reject H_o if the test statistic is less than $t_{LC} = -1.66$ or greater than $t_{RC} = 1.66$.

e) *test statistic:* $t = 0.30$; p-value: 0.7614

f) *Conclusion:*

Fail to reject H_o at $\alpha = 5\%$

Answer:

The educational researcher can't conclude that the combined mean S.A.T score is significantly different for the IVY League College and the Military Academy.

CHAPTER 14

1. classifications

3. 4; 3

5. c

7. non-negative

9. false

11. a) $X^2 = \sum \dfrac{(O - E)^2}{E}$

b) $X^2 = \sum \dfrac{O^2}{E} - n$

13. total; column; sample size

15. a

17. c

19. false

21. a) *Formulate the two hypotheses H_o and H_a.*

H_o: The population classifications gender and movie preference are independent.

H_a: The population classifications gender and movie preference are dependent.

b) For $\alpha = 5\%$ and $df = 4$, $\chi^2_\alpha = 9.49$.

Decision Rule: reject H_o if X^2 is greater than 9.49.

c) $X^2 = 36.96$

d) *Conclusion:* reject H_o and accept H_a at $\alpha = 5\%$. Yes, we can conclude that there is a relationship between gender and movie preference.

23. a) Formulate the two hypotheses H_o and H_a.

H_o: The population classifications drug treatment and result of the treatment are independent.

H_a: The population classifications drug treatment and result of the treatment are dependent.

b) For $\alpha = 5\%$ and $df = 4$, $\chi^2_\alpha = 9.49$.

Decision Rule: reject H_o if X^2 is greater than 9.49.

c) $X^2 = 1.01$

d) *Conclusion:* fail to reject H_o at $\alpha = 5\%$. Yes, Drug treatment and relief from pain are independent at $\alpha = 5\%$.

25. a) Formulate the two hypotheses H_o and H_a.

H_o: The population classifications math anxiety and the successful completion of the introductory math course are independent.

H_a: The population classifications math anxiety and the successful completion of the introductory math course are dependent.

b) For $\alpha = 1\%$ and $df = 2$, $\chi^2_\alpha = 9.21$.

Decision Rule: reject H_o if X^2 is greater than 9.21.

c) $X^2 = 37.77$

d) *Conclusion:* reject H_o and accept H_a at $\alpha = 1\%$. No, Math anxiety and the successful completion of the introductory math course are not independent at $\alpha = 1\%$.

27. a) Formulate the two hypotheses H_o and H_a.

H_o: The populaiton classifications age and music category are independent.

H_a: The populaiton classifications age and music category are dependent.

b) For $\alpha = 5\%$ and $df = 16$, $\chi^2_\alpha = 26.30$.
Decision Rule: reject H_o if X^2 is greater than 26.30.
c) $X^2 = 91.66$
d) *Conclusion:* reject H_o and accept H_a at $\alpha = 5\%$.
Yes, age and music category are dependent at $\alpha = 5\%$.

29. **a)** independent
   b) cell
   c) five

31. theoretical

33. $k - 1$

35. false

37. **a)** Formulate the two hypotheses H_o and H_a.
   H_o: sample data fits a uniform distribution.
   H_a: sample data doesn't fit a uniform distribution.
   b) For $\alpha = 1\%$ and $df = 4$, $\chi^2_\alpha = 13.28$.
   Decision Rule: reject H_o if X^2 is greater than 13.28.
   c) $X^2 = 14.37$
   d) *Conclusion:* reject H_o and accept H_a at $\alpha = 1\%$.
   We can conclude that there is a preference for packaging shape.

39. **a)** Formulate the two hypotheses H_o and H_a.
   H_o: sample data fits a uniform distribution.
   H_a: sample data doesn't fit a uniform distribution.
   b) For $\alpha = 5\%$ and $df = 5$, $\chi^2_\alpha = 11.07$.
   Decision Rule: reject H_o if X^2 is greater than 11.07.
   c) $X^2 = 10.30$
   d) *Conclusion:* fail to reject H_o at $\alpha = 5\%$.
   The quality control engineer can conclude that the production of defective parts is evenly distributed throughout the workweek.

41. **a)** Formulate the two hypotheses H_o and H_a.
   H_o: The number of hours worked per week fits a normal distribution.
   H_a: The number of hours worked per week doesn't fit a normal distribution.
   b)

Interval Boundaries	z score	Probability	Expected Frequency
below 12.32	below −1.40	8.08%	48.48
12.32 – 17.01	−1.40 to −0.70	16.12%	96.72
17.01 – 21.70	−0.70 to 0.0	25.80%	154.80
21.70 – 26.39	0.0 to 0.70	25.80%	154.80
26.39 – 31.08	0.70 to 1.40	16.12%	96.72
above 31.08	above 1.40	8.08%	48.48

   c) For $\alpha = 5\%$ and $df = 3$, $\chi^2_\alpha = 7.82$
   Decision Rule: reject H_o if X^2 is greater than 7.82
   d) $X^2 = 12.36$
   e) reject H_o and accept H_a at $\alpha = 5\%$. The number of hours worked per week doesn't fit a normal distribution.

43. **a)** *Formulate the two hypotheses H_0 and H_a.*
   H_0: The population classifications gender and movie preference are independent.

   H_a: The population classifications gender and movie preference are dependent.
   b) *Decision Rule:* reject H_0 if the p-value of χ^2 test statistics is less than 5%
   c) $\chi^2 = 36.96$; p-value = 1.84 E-7
   d) *Conclusion:* reject H_0 and accept H_a at a p-value = 1.84 E-7.
   Yes, we can conclude that there is a relationship between gender and movie preference.
   e) Smallest alpha = 1.84 E-7

45. **a)** *Formulate the two hypotheses H_0 and H_a.*
   H_0: The population classifications drug treatment and result of the treatment are independent.
   H_a: The population classifications drug treatment and result of the treatment are dependent.
   b) *Decision Rule:* reject H_0 if the p-value of χ^2 test statistics is less than 5%.
   c) $\chi^2 = 1.01$; p-value = 0.9078
   d) *Conclusion:* fail to reject H_0 at a p-value = 0.9078
   Yes, Drug treatment and relief from pain are independent at $\alpha = 5\%$.
   e) Smallest alpha = 90.78%

47. **a)** *Formulate the two hypotheses H_0 and H_a*
   H_0: The population classifications math anxiety and the successful completion of the introductory math course are independent.
   H_a: The population classifications math anxiety and the successful completion of the introductory math course are dependent.
   b) *Decision Rule:* reject H_0 if the p-value of χ^2 test statistics is less than 1%.
   c) $\chi^2 = 37.77$; p-value = 6.30 E-9
   d) *Conclusion:* reject H_0 and accept H_a at a p-value = 6.30 E-9.
   No, Math anxiety and the successful completion of the introductory math course are not independent at $\alpha = 1\%$.
   e) Smallest alpha = 6.30 E-9

49. **a)** *Formulate the two hypotheses H_0 and H_a.*
   H_0: The population classifications age and music category are independent.
   H_a: The population classifications age and music category are dependent.
   b) *Decision Rule:* reject H_0 if the p-value of χ^2 test statistics is less than 5%.
   c) $\chi^2 = 91.66$; p-value = 1.23 E-12
   d) *Conclusion:* reject H_0 and accept H_a at a p-value = 1.23 E-12.
   Yes, age and music category are dependent at $\alpha = 5\%$.
   e) Smallest alpha = 1.23 E-12

51. false

53. cell

55. count

57. true

59. true

61. false

63. a) Formulate the two hypotheses H_o and H_a.

H_o: The population classifications the Dow Jones average and the prime interest rate are independent.

H_a: The population classifications the Dow Jones average and the prime interest rate are dependent.

b) For $\alpha = 1\%$ and $df = 4$, $\chi^2_\alpha = 13.28$.
Decision Rule: reject H_o if X^2 is greater than 13.28.

c) test statistic: $X^2 = 1.01$; p-value $= 0.9078$

d) *Conclusion:* fail to reject H_o at $\alpha = 1\%$.
No, the Dow Jones average and the Prime Interest Rate are not dependent at $\alpha = 1\%$.

65. a) Formulate the two hypotheses H_o and H_a.

H_o: The population classifications educational background and the frequency of movie attendance per year are independent.

H_a: The population classifications educational background and the frequency of movie attendance are dependent.

b) For $\alpha = 5\%$ and $df = 6$, $\chi^2_\alpha = 12.59$.
Decision Rule: reject H_o if X^2 is greater than 12.59.

c) test statistic: $X^2 = 54.32$; p-value $= 6.37\,E-10$

d) *Conclusion:* reject H_o and accept H_a at $\alpha = 5\%$.
Yes, educational background and the frequency of movie attendance per year are dependent at $\alpha = 5\%$.

67. a) Formulate the two hypotheses H_o and H_a.

H_o: sample data fits the population proportions.

H_a: sample data doesn't fit the population proportions.

b) For $\alpha = 5\%$ and $df = 1$, $\chi^2_\alpha = 3.84$.
Decision Rule: reject H_o if X^2 is greater than 3.84.

c) $X^2 = 2.62$

d) *Conclusion:* fail to reject H_o at $\alpha = 5\%$.
The sample data is consistent with the population proportions.

CHAPTER 15

1. measurements

3. scatter diagram

5. linear correlation

7. b

9. false

11. a) negative
b) positive
c) positive
d) no linear correlation

13. Pearson's correlation coefficient, r.

15. strongest; perfect; upward

17. -1; $+1$; weak

19. true

21. false

23. a) r = 0.87 is a stronger positive linear correlation
b) although the r values represent a different type of relationship they have the same strength
c) r = 0.95 represents a very strong relationship, whereas, r = 0.05 represents a very weak relationship

25. rho: ρ

27. a) zero; no; 0
b) positive; >; negative; <; significant; ≠

29. r_α; $n-2$

31. false

33. b

35. a) yes
b) 23.04%

37. $y' = a + bx$; $\dfrac{n\Sigma(xy) - \Sigma x \Sigma y}{n(\Sigma x^2) - (\Sigma x)^2}$; $\dfrac{\Sigma y - b\Sigma x}{n}$; dependent;

independent

39. a)

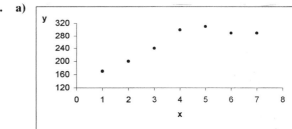

b) r = 0.86
c) yes
d) 74.06% of the variance in grass density that can be accounted for by the variance in seed density.
e) $y' = 21.79x + 170$
f) $y' \approx 246$ seedlings/ft^2

41. a)

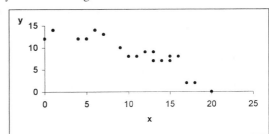

b) r = −0.89
c) yes
d) 78.83% of the variance in percent of yearly salary increase that can be accounted for by the variance in the number of sick days per year.
e) $y' = -0.62x + 15.22$
f) $y' = 10.29\%$ increase in yearly salary.

43. a) *Formulate the two hypotheses H_0 and H_a*

H_0: The population linear correlation coefficient between advertising expenditures and beer sales is 0, $\rho = 0$.

H_a: The population linear correlation coefficient between advertising expenditures and beer sales is greater than zero, $\rho > 0$.

b) Hypothesis testing model is the sampling distribution of the correlation coefficients where $\rho = 0$.

c) *Decision Rule:* reject H_0 if the p-value of correlation coefficient test statistic is less than 1%

d) $r = 0.94$; p-value = 6.93 E-4

e) *Conclusion:* reject H_0 and accept H_a at a p-value of 6.93 E-4.
There is a positive linear correlation between advertising expenditures and beer sales.

f) Smallest alpha = 6.93 E-4

45. a) *Formulate the two hypotheses H_0 and H_a*
H_0: The population linear correlation coefficient between the amount of rainfall in May and the number of mosquitoes is $0, \rho = 0$.
H_a: The population linear correlation coefficient between the amount of rainfall in May and the number of mosquitoes is not equal to zero, $\rho \neq 0$.

b) Hypothesis testing model is the sampling distribution of the correlation coefficients where $\rho = 0$.

c) *Decision Rule:* reject H_0 if the p-value of the correlation coefficient test statistic is less than 1%

d) $r = 0.90$; p-value = 0.0153.

e) *Conclusion:* Fail to reject H_0 at a p-value of 0.0153. There is no linear correlation between the amount of rainfall in May and the number of mosquitoes.

f) Smallest alpha = 1.53%.

47. a) *Formulate the two hypotheses H_0 and H_a*
H_0: The population linear correlation coefficient between the midterm grades and final exam grades for students taking Prof DePorto's introduction to statistics class is $0, \rho = 0$.
H_a: The population linear correlation coefficient between the midterm grades and final exam grades for students taking Prof DePorto's introduction to statistics class is greater than zero, $\rho > 0$.

b) Hypothesis testing model is the sampling distribution of the correlation coefficients where $\rho = 0$.

c) *Decision Rule:* reject H_0 if the p-value of the correlation coefficient test statistic is less than 5%

d) $r = 0.27$; p-value = 0.094

e) *Conclusion:* Fail to reject H_0 at a p-value = 0.094. There is no linear correlation coefficient amount of rainfall in May and the number of mosquitoes.

f) Smallest alpha = 9.4%

49. negative

51. strongest; negative; downward

53. positive; negative

55. a) 2
b) 1
c) 1
d) 3
e) 3

57. c

59.

	r_α	significant (Yes, No)
a)	0.59	no
b)	0.44	yes
c)	–0.42	yes
d)	0.43	yes
e)	–0.32	yes
f)	0.44	no

61. true

63. a)

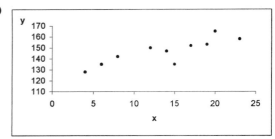

b) $r = 0.85$

c) yes

d) 71.44% of the variance in blood pressure that can be accounted for by the variance in pounds above ideal weight.

e) $y' = 1.54x + 125.19$

f) $y' \approx 141$(lbs)

CHAPTER 16

1. Analysis of Variance

3. s_2^2

5. 1.53

7. $F = 1$

9. $F_{0.01}(10,20) = 3.37$

11. false

13. $F_{0.01}(8,9) = 5.47$

15. $F_{0.01}(13,20) = 3.23$

17. a) $F_{0.10}(30,40) = 1.54$
b) $F_{0.05}(30,40) = 1.74$
c) $F_{0.025}(30,40) = 1.94$
d) $F_{0.01}(30,40) = 2.20$

19. $\dfrac{(LARGER\ VARIANCE)}{(SMALLER\ VARIANCE)}$

21. a

23. c

25. a

27. false

29. a) $F = 1.58$

b) H_0: $\sigma_1^2 = \sigma_2^2$; H_a: $\sigma_1^2 \neq \sigma_2^2$; test statistic: $F = 1.58$; $F_{0.05}(49,49) = 1.69$ (use closest degrees of freedom)
Conclusion: Since the calculated F, test statistic, 1.58, is not greater than the critical F-value, 1.69, then

the population variances are assumed equal at $\alpha = 0.10$.

31. a) F = 2.72

b) H_0: $\sigma_1^2 = \sigma_2^2$; H_a: $\sigma_1^2 \neq \sigma_2^2$; test statistic: F = 2.72; $F_{0.025}$ (20,21) = 2.42 (use c closest degrees of freedom)
Conclusion: Since the calculated F, test statistic, 2.72, is greater than the critical F-value, 2.42, then the population variances are assumed unequal at $\alpha = 0.05$.

33. a) F = 2.38

b) H_0: $\sigma_1^2 = \sigma_2^2$; H_a: $\sigma_1^2 \neq \sigma_2^2$; test statistic: F = 2.38; $F_{0.05}$ (99,99) = 1.35 (use closest degrees of freedom)
Conclusion: Since the calculated F, test statistic, 2.38, is greater than the critical F-value, 1.35, then the population variances are assumed unequal at $\alpha = 0.10$.

35. a) $s_1^2 = 306.6$ $s_2^2 = 620.51$; F = 2.02

b) H_0: $\sigma_1^2 = \sigma_2^2$; H_a: $\sigma_1^2 \neq \sigma_2^2$; test statistic: F = 2.02; $F_{0.01}$ (7,5) = 10.46
Conclusion: Since the calculated F, test statistic, 2.02, is not greater than the critical F-value, 10.46, then the population variances are assumed equal at $\alpha = 0.02$.

37. H_0: $\sigma_1^2 = \sigma_2^2$; H_a: $\sigma_1^2 \neq \sigma_2^2$; test statistic: F = 1.98; $F_{0.05}$ (30,40) = 1.74
Conclusion: Since the calculated F, test statistic, 1.98, is greater than the critical F-value, 1.74, then the sample variances are assumed unequal at $\alpha = 0.10$. No, Kathleen cannot pool the sample variances.

39. $s_1^2 = 71.4$ $s_2^2 = 37.7$; H_0: $\sigma_1^2 = \sigma_2^2$; H_a: $\sigma_1^2 \neq \sigma_2^2$ test statistic: F = 1.89; $F_{0.01}$ (9,10) = 4.94:
Conclusion: Since the calculated F, test statistic, 1.89, is less than the critical F-value, 4.94, then the sample variances are assumed equal at $\alpha = 0.02$. The results support the use of the two sample t-test with a pooled standard deviation.

41. between variance

43. within variance

45. sums of squares; $\sum (x - \bar{x})^2$

47. b

49. true

51. a) $\sigma_1^2 = 4$; $\sigma_2^2 = 4$ $\sigma_3^2 = 4$
b) 4
c) 40.82
d) 44.82
e) No, the total group variance is the sum of the within group variance, 4, and between group variance, 40.82.

53. a) 336
b) 2744
c) 3080

d) yes
e) 16;16; 16
f) 16
g) 130.67
h) 146.67
i) No, the total variance is due to within variance, 16, and between variance, 130.67.

55. a) 270
b) 208544
c) 208824
d) yes
e) 18; 18; 18
f) 18
g) 14
h) 32
i) No, the total variance is due to within variance, 18, and between variance, 14.

57. a) Each sample selected from a normal population
b) Each sample is selected from a population that has the same population variance, σ_2.
c) When samples are drawn from different populations the samples must be random and independent.

59. true

61. false

63. false

65. increase; decrease

67. number of groups; total number of data values

69. population; equal; one population; group; different

71. d

73. a

75. reject the null hypothesis

77. $\left[\dfrac{\left(\sum T_1\right)^2}{n_1} + \dfrac{\left(\sum T_2\right)^2}{n_2} + \dfrac{\left(\sum T_3\right)^2}{n_3} + \dfrac{\left(\sum T_4\right)^2}{n_4} \right]; \dfrac{\left(\sum x\right)^2}{N}$

79. sample size of group 4; total number of data values; data values in group 3

81. 34; 36; 13.25; 0.94; 14.10

83. 2.98

85. 2.40

87. 2.12

89. 2.86

91. a) $F_{0.10}$ (20,20) = 1.79
b) $F_{0.05}$ (20,20) = 2.12
c) $F_{0.025}$ (20,20) = 2.46
d) $F_{0.01}$ (20,20) = 2.94

93.

Source Of Variation	Sums Of Squares	Degrees Of Freedom	Mean Square	Test Statistic F
Between	39.2	1	39.2	1.80
Within	392.6	18	21.81	
Total	**431.8**	19		

$F_{0.01}$ (1,18) = 8.29 No, since F, the test statistic, 1.80, is less than the critical F, 8.29, the test statistic is not statistically significant at $\alpha = 0.01$.

95. a) 596
   b) 9
   c) 228
   d) 15.56
   e) 14.65
   f) $F_{0.05}$ (2,9) = 4.26 Yes, since F, the test statistic, 14.65, is greater than the critical F, 4.26, the test statistic is significantly significant at $\alpha = 0.05$.

97. a) H_0: $\mu_1 = \mu_2 = \mu_3$ There is no difference between population treatment means

   H_a: $\mu_1 \neq \mu_2 \neq \mu_3$ There is a difference between population treatment means
   b) F-distribution
   c) If the test statistic, F, is greater than the critical $F_{0.05}$ (2,9) = 4.26, then Reject the Null Hypothesis
   d,e) Sums of Squares and df are indicated in the table.

Source Of Variation	Sums Of Squares	Degrees Of Freedom	Mean Square	Test Statistic F
Between	72.67	2	36.34	36.34
Within	9	9	1	
Total	81.67	11		

   f) Reject H_0 and accept H_a, there is a difference between the population treatment means at $\alpha = 0.05$.

99. a) H_0: $\mu_1 = \mu_2 = \mu_3$ There is no difference between population mean playing weights of female athletes in basketball, track and soccer.

   H_a: $\mu_1 \neq \mu_2 \neq \mu_3$ There is a difference between population mean playing weights of female athletes in basketball, track and soccer.
   b) F-statistic = 5.29
   c) The $F_{0.01}$ (2,27) = 5.49.
   d) Since the test statistic, F = 5.29, is less than the critical F, 5.49, the results are not significant at $\alpha = 0.01$. There is no difference between population mean playing weights of female athletes in basketball, track and soccer.

101. a) H_0: $\mu_1 = \mu_2 = \mu_3$ There is no difference between population mean water holding properties of the three brands of diapers.

   H_a: $\mu_1 \neq \mu_2 \neq \mu_3$ There is a difference between population mean water holding properties of the three brands of diapers.
   b) F-distribution
   c) If the test statistic, F, is greater than the critical $F_{0.05}$ (2,12) = 3.89, then Reject the Null Hypothesis
   d,e) Sums of Squares and df are indicated in the table.

Source Of Variation	Sums Of Squares	Degrees Of Freedom	Mean Square	Test Statistic F
Between	2.70	2	1.35	13.5
Within	1.22	12	0.10	
Total	3.92	14		

   f) Reject H_0 and accept H_a, there is a difference between population mean water holding properties of the three brands of diapers at $\alpha = 0.05$.

103. a) H_0: $\mu_1 = \mu_2 = \mu_3$ There is no difference between population mean mercury levels for the three age groups of loons.

   H_a: $\mu_1 \neq \mu_2 \neq \mu_3$ There is a difference between population mean mercury levels for the three age groups of loons.
   b) F-distribution
   c) If the test statistic, F, is greater than the critical $F_{0.01}$ (2,9) = 8.02, then Reject the Null Hypothesis
   d,e) Sums of Squares and df are indicated in the table. *NOTE: Since the data values are small, the calculations in the source table use 5 decimal places.

Source Of Variation	Sums Of Squares	Degrees Of Freedom	Mean Square	Test Statistic F
Between	0.2665	2	0.13325	17.17139
Within	0.06984	9	0.00776	
Total	0.33634	11		

   f) Reject H_0 and accept H_a, there is a difference between population mean mercury levels for the three age groups of loons at $\alpha = 0.01$.

105. 1.86
107. false
109. c
111. $F_{0.05}$ (7,10) = 3.01
113. $F_{0.025}$ (15,17) = 2.72
115. c
117. c
119. a) F = 2.69
   b) $F_{0.025}$ (18,21) = 2.42
121. a) F = 3.21
   b) H_0: $\sigma_1^2 = \sigma_2^2$; H_a: $\sigma_1^2 \neq \sigma_2^2$; test statistic F = 3.21; $F_{0.025}$ (5,5) = 7.15
   Conclusion: Since the calculated F, test statistic, 3.21, is not greater than the critical F-value, 7.15, then the population variances are assumed equal at $\alpha = 0.05$
123. between group variance
125. SS_{TOTAL}; $SS_{BETWEEN TREATMENTS}$; $SS_{WITHIN TREATMENTS}$
127. a) Population variances Within are the same for each group, 25
   b) Average Within group variance = 25
   c) Between group variance = 0

d) Total group variance = 25

e) Total group variance is due entirely to Within group variance

129. a) 336

    b) 2744

    c) 3080

    d) yes

    e) 16

    f) 16

    g) 130.65

    h) 146.65

    i) No, total group variance is the sum of Within and Between group variance

131. sample size of group 6; total number of data values of all groups;   data values for group 5

133. a)

Source Of Variation	Sums Of Squares	Degrees Of Freedom	Mean Square	Test Statistic F
Between	150.51	4	**37.63**	**11.19**
Within	87.43	26	**3.36**	
Total	**237.94**	**31**		

    b) $F_{0.01}$ (4,26) = 2.74 Yes, since the test statistic, F = 11.19, is greater than the critical F, 2.74 at $\alpha = 0.05$.

135. a) H_0: $\mu_1 = \mu_2 = \mu_3$ There is no difference between population mean number of hours worked P/T by students from the three regions.

        H_a: $\mu_1 \neq \mu_2 \neq \mu_3$ There is a difference between population mean number of hours worked P/T by students from the three regions.

    b) F-distribution

    c) If the test statistic, F, is greater than the critical $F_{0.05}$ (2,12) = 3.89, then Reject the Null Hypothesis

    d,e) Sums of Squares and df are indicated in the table.

Source Of Variation	Sums Of Squares	Degrees Of Freedom	Mean Square	Test Statistic F
Between	7.09	2	3.55	12.24
Within	3.51	12	0.29	
Total	10.6	14		

    f) Reject H_0 and accept H_a, there is a difference between population mean number of hours worked P/T by students from the three regions at $\alpha = 0.05$.

CHAPTER 17

1. parametric

3. distribution free

5. false

7. Statistics test that require few assumptions about the population from which sample data is collected.

9. $1/2$

11. $np; \sqrt{np(1-p)}$

13. negative; plus

15. d

17. a) 65

    b) 32

    c) 3

    d) 33

    e) 42

    f) 1. H_0: Population median = 26

        H_a: Population median $\neq$ 26

      2. Binomial distribution is the hypothesis testing model. Since np and n(1-p) are both greater than 5, the normal distribution is used to approximate the binomial distribution. $\mu_s = 32.5$ and $\sigma_s = 4.03$.

      3. Reject H_0 if the test statistic, z, is either less than –1.96 or greater than 1.96.

      4. Test statistic, z = –0.25

      5. Fail to Reject H_0, at $\alpha = 0.05$. No, although there is a difference between the hypothesized population median, 26, and the sample median, 32.5, the difference is not statistically significant at $\alpha = 0.05$.

    g) p-value = 0.40

19. 1. H_0: Population median = 8340

        Population median time for VCRs to fail is 8,340 hours.

        H_a: Population median $\neq$ 8340

        Population median time for VCRs to fail is not 8,340 hours.

    2. Binomial distribution is the hypothesis testing model. Since np and n(1-p) are both greater than 5, the normal distribution is used to approximate the binomial distribution. $\mu_s = 15$ and $\sigma_s = 2.74$.

    3. Reject H_0 if the test statistic, z, is either less than –1.96 or greater than 1.96.

    4. Test statistic, z = 2.01 p-value = 0.02

    5. Reject H_0 and Accept H_a at $\alpha = 0.05$. Yes, the median time for VCRs to fail is not 8,340.

21. 1. H_0: Population median = 600

        Population median number of calories from fat is 600.

        H_a: Population median < 600

        Population median number of calories from fat is less than 600.

    2. Binomial distribution is the hypothesis testing model. Since np and n(1-p) are both greater than 5, the normal distribution is used to approximate the binomial distribution. $\mu_s = 7$ and $\sigma_s = 1.87$.

    3. Reject H_0 if the test statistic, z, is greater than 1.65.

    4. Test statistic, z = 1.87 p-value = 0.03

    5. Reject H_0 and Accept H_a at $\alpha = 0.05$. Yes, the population median number of calories from fat is less than 600.

23. If either (or both) of the following is/are NOT met:
   a) The population(s) from which the samples are drawn is/are not normal
   b) The populations' variances are not equal

25. The Mann-Whitney Rank Sum Test

27. mean

29. W

31. c

33. true

35. H_0: The two populations are the same. The median of population 1 = median of population 2.
   H_a: The two populations are different. The median of population 1 < median of population 2.
   a) $n_1 = 10; n_2 = 12$
   b) median sample 1 = 28.5; median sample 2 = 39.5
   c) W = 94.5
   d) No, since the test statistic, z = –1.35, is not less than –1.65
   e) p = 0.09

37. a) H_0: Treatment A and Treatment B are the same (or There is no difference between Treatments A and B)
   H_a: Treatment A and Treatment B are not the same (or There is a difference between Treatments A and B)
   b) W = 129.5
   c) z = 1.85
   d) No, since the test statistic, z = 1.65, is not less than z_{cl} = –1.96 or greater than z_{cr}= 1.96 where α = 0.05.

39. No, since the test statistics, z = –0.93, is not less than z_c = –1.65. The difference is not statistically significant at α = 0.05.

41. No, since the test statistics, z = 1.08, is not less than z_{cl} = –1.96 or greater than z_{cr} = 1.96.
   There is no significant difference between the two distributions at α = 0.05.

43. H_0: The two populations are the same.
   H_a: The two populations are different.

45. Kruskal-Wallis H test

47. H; $\dfrac{12}{N(N+1)}\left[\dfrac{\left(\sum R_1\right)^2}{n_1} + \dfrac{\left(\sum R_2\right)^2}{n_2} + \ldots + \dfrac{\left(\sum R_k\right)^2}{n_k}\right] - 3(N+1)$

49. H statistic; χ_a^2

51. false

53. true

55. a) H_0: The populations are the same.
   H_a: The populations are different Chi-Square distribution is used as the hypothesis testing mode
   Reject H_0 if the test statistic, Kruskal-Wallis H statistic, is greater than χ_a^2
   b) H = 8.46
   c) df = 2

   d) At α = 0.05, H, 8.46, is significant since it exceeds $\chi_{0.05}^2$ = 5.99.; At α = 0.01, H, 8.46, is not significant since it is less than $\chi_{0.01}^2$ = 9.21.
   e) Since the test statistic H, 8.46, is greater than 5.99, reject H_0 and accept H_a at α = 0.05. The distributions are not the same.
   f) p-value = 0.01

57. 1. H_0: The populations are the same. Population annual income for police officers at the Patrolmen Rank in NYC, LA, and Boston is the same.
   H_a: The populations are not the same. Population annual income for police officers at the Patrolmen Rank in NYC, LA, and Boston is not the same.
   2. Chi-Square distribution is used as the hypothesis testing model
   3. Reject H_0 if the test statistic, Kruskal-Wallis H statistic, is greater than $\chi_{0.05}^2$, which equals 5.99.
   4. H = 4.13
   5. Fail to Reject H_0, since the test statistic H, 4.13, is less than 5.99 at α = 0.05. The data do not indicate a significant difference between annual income for police officers at the Patrolmen Rank in NYC, LA and Boston.

59. 1. H_0: The populations are the same. There is no difference in the number of patients treated in the emergency room at Mercy, Nassau, and Helpme Hospitals.
   H_a: The populations are not the same. There is a difference in the number of patients treated in the emergency room at Mercy, Nassau, and Helpme Hospitals.
   2. Chi-Square distribution is used as the hypothesis testing model.
   3. Reject H_0 if the test statistic, Kruskal-Wallis H statistic, is greater than $\chi_{0.01}^2$, which equals 9.21.
   4. H = 1.37
   5. Fail to Reject H_0, since the test statistic H, 1.37, is less than 9.21 at α = 0.01. The data do not indicate a significant difference between the number of patients treated in the emergency room at Mercy, Nassau, and Helpme Hospitals.

61. less powerful; do not all sample data; difficult to use for large samples

63. g

65. c

67. tests whether 3 or more populations are the same; uses χ^2 distribution if each sample has at least 5 observations

69. d

71. 1. H_0: Population median = 12
   H_a: Population median > 12
   2. Binomial distribution is the hypothesis testing model. Since np and n(1-p) are both greater than 5, the normal distribution is used to approximate the binomial distribution. μ_s = 9 and σ_s = 2.21.

3. Reject H_0 if the test statistic, z, is greater than 1.65.

4. Test statistic, z = 0.23, p-value = 0.41

5. Fail to Reject H_0, at $\alpha = 0.05$. There is no reason to believe that the number of days in which the effects of the drug will appear is more than 12.

73. **1.** H_0: Population median = $2000

The population median cost for automobile insurance is $2000.

H_a: Population median > $2000

The population median cost for automobile insurance is greater than $2000.

2. Binomial distribution is the hypothesis testing model. Since np and n(1-p) are both greater than 5, the normal distribution is used to approximate the binomial distribution. $\mu_s = 7$ and $\sigma_s = 1.87$.

3. Reject H_0 if the test statistic, z, is greater than 1.65.

4. Test statistic, z = 0.27, p-value = 0.39

5. Fail to Reject H_0, at $\alpha = 0.05$. There is no reason to believe that the median cost for automobile insurance is greater than $2000.

75. **1.** H_0: The two populations are the same. The population mean time for learning each procedure is the same.

H_a: The two populations are different. The population mean time for learning each procedure is different.

2. Normal distribution is used as the hypothesis testing model.

3. Reject H_0 if the test statistic, z, is either less than $z_{cl} = -2.58$ or greater than $z_{cr} = 2.58$

4. Test statistic z = 2.82, p-value = 3.49E-05

5. Reject H_0, Accept H_a at $\alpha = 0.01$. The mean time for learning the procedures is significantly different between the groups of nursing students.

77. **1.** H_0: The populations are the same. There is no difference in the population sexual awareness scores of the groups.

H_a: The populations are not the same. There is a difference in the population sexual awareness scores of the groups.

2. Chi-Square distribution is used as the hypothesis testing model.

3. Reject H_0 if the test statistic, Kruskal-Wallis H statistic, is greater than $\chi^2_{0.01}$, which equals 11.34.

4. H = 13.11

5. Reject H_0, Accept H_a at $\alpha = 0.01$. There is a difference in the population sexual awareness scores of the groups.

APPENDICES

Contents

APPENDIX A: DATABASE

The following database, DATABASE, represents a sample of 75 student records. The record layout for each student is as follows:

Column Label	Variable Name	Variable Description
C1	ID	identification number
C2	AGE	age in years
C3	SEX	gender
C4	MAJ	academic area of concentration
C5	AVE	high school average
C6	HR	hair color
C7	EYE	eye color
C8	WRK	hours worked per week
C9	STY	hours studied per week
C10	MAT	matriculation status
C11	GPA	grade point average
C12	NAP	hour of the day a nap is taken
C13	SHT	student height in inches
C14	PHT	same sex parent's height in inches
C15	AM	ideal age to marry
C16	MOB	month of birth
C17	LK	preference of softdrink: Coke, Pepsi or neither
C18	HND	handedness
C19	GFT	amount in dollars spent on gift
C20	PH	number of hours spent on phone per week
C21	NB	response to question: Choose a number: 1, 2, 3, 4.
C22	AST	response to question: Do you believe in astrology?

Data Variable Values

Variable Name	Variable Value
ID	4 digit numeric
AGE	2 digit numeric
SEX	0=male, 1=female
MAJ	1=bus, 2=cmp, 3=fpa, 4=hth, 5=lib, 6=sci
AVE	2 digit numeric
HR	1=blonde, 2=black, 3=brown, 4=red
EYE	1=blue, 2=brown, 3=green
WRK	2 digit numeric
STY	2 digit numeric
MAT	0=yes, 1=no
GPA	3 digit 2 decimal numeric
NAP	standard military hours
SHT	2 digit numeric
PHT	2 digit numeric
AM	2 digit numeric
MOB	2 digit numeric, 01-12, month
LK	1=n , 2=p 3=c
HND	0=left, 1=right
GFT	3 digit numeric
PH	2 digit numeric
NB	1 digit numeric
AST	0=yes, 1=no

C1	C2	C3	C4	C5	C6	C7	C8	C9	C10	C11	C12	C13	C14	C15	C16	C17	C18	C19	C20	C21	C22
1618	19	0	5	81	3	1	16	11	0	1.87	1300	74	71	25	06	2	1	100	02	4	0
7290	20	1	5	87	1	1	12	19	0	3.05	2000	60	65	25	04	3	1	120	04	2	1
5506	21	0	1	85	3	3	15	10	1	3.62	1500	74	72	33	08	1	1	050	01	4	1
8496	19	1	2	88	3	3	14	09	0	3.67	1700	61	63	25	06	3	0	050	10	3	1
2832	18	1	1	72	3	3	08	23	0	2.25	0700	69	64	23	07	1	1	200	10	3	0
3407	22	0	5	83	3	1	14	20	0	2.70	1400	74	72	30	12	2	1	025	01	4	1
8573	19	1	5	78	3	2	15	17	1	2.30	1500	60	62	25	04	2	1	150	05	4	0
6265	20	0	6	76	3	2	22	16	1	2.51	0900	67	67	26	03	1	0	100	02	4	0
4821	19	0	1	74	1	1	18	22	1	2.10	2200	74	68	30	03	3	1	100	01	4	1
9029	19	0	1	79	1	1	10	12	0	1.92	1600	69	71	25	10	3	1	200	01	1	0
3001	19	1	5	83	3	1	10	20	1	3.15	1500	64	66	24	02	2	1	050	10	2	1
8010	23	1	1	78	3	2	20	11	0	2.00	1700	65	66	30	07	3	1	025	02	3	1
4699	19	1	5	74	1	3	26	09	0	1.95	1400	65	64	25	12	3	1	050	07	2	1
8298	24	0	1	88	3	3	12	19	1	2.88	1600	70	75	24	03	2	1	100	10	4	1
1896	18	1	5	81	3	1	18	09	1	2.65	1800	68	66	26	01	2	1	050	10	2	0
4789	19	1	5	84	3	1	17	08	0	1.98	0900	65	65	25	12	3	1	050	05	3	0
3592	27	1	1	83	3	1	15	19	1	3.21	2200	65	63	25	11	3	1	050	02	4	0
7679	21	0	1	87	1	1	16	07	0	1.95	1600	76	74	30	02	3	1	035	03	2	0
0209	18	1	6	80	3	1	22	10	1	2.96	1400	66	66	24	10	3	1	070	10	4	0
4489	21	0	5	84	1	3	14	08	0	2.95	1000	71	69	24	07	3	1	050	02	4	1
0880	18	0	1	90	3	2	08	18	0	2.00	1500	71	75	26	03	3	1	075	02	4	1
7168	37	1	5	87	3	2	11	16	1	2.82	2100	61	60	30	04	3	1	050	02	1	0
5709	28	1	1	85	2	2	07	10	1	1.95	1700	65	67	32	01	3	1	100	25	4	0
7520	20	1	5	77	2	2	25	12	1	3.01	1400	62	65	23	01	3	1	040	07	3	0
2757	20	1	4	72	1	1	27	15	0	2.70	1300	63	62	25	08	2	1	100	03	2	1
3016	19	1	5	83	3	3	20	11	0	2.67	1100	60	65	28	04	3	0	175	07	4	0
7298	21	0	2	77	3	3	12	09	0	2.81	1500	68	68	26	11	3	1	100	02	4	1
5677	18	0	6	85	3	1	16	27	1	3.76	1600	66	65	25	10	2	1	040	04	4	0
0406	21	1	2	70	3	2	14	10	1	2.67	1200	62	64	23	03	1	1	050	07	3	1
7673	19	1	4	77	3	2	16	07	0	2.32	1500	67	66	26	04	3	1	125	04	3	0
3480	20	1	1	83	4	3	24	08	0	2.09	1600	64	63	23	04	3	1	100	05	2	1
6994	18	1	5	86	3	3	19	09	1	2.42	1700	65	61	27	01	2	1	100	02	3	0
4009	18	1	5	84	3	2	10	10	1	1.90	1300	62	64	26	01	1	1	075	02	4	0
7879	20	0	6	77	2	2	08	07	1	1.98	1900	69	68	26	02	3	1	090	02	1	1
2021	19	1	5	82	1	3	20	12	0	3.15	1000	65	64	26	01	2	1	100	10	1	0
0044	19	1	4	90	1	2	00	14	0	3.40	1600	67	70	24	02	3	1	050	09	3	0
4508	19	1	1	84	1	3	15	10	1	2.87	2100	65	65	24	07	3	1	075	06	2	1
1085	23	1	5	91	3	2	10	28	1	3.51	1700	67	64	26	07	2	1	040	10	2	0
8289	20	1	1	78	2	2	22	08	1	1.95	1700	63	62	26	09	3	1	050	15	1	0
5664	18	0	5	75	3	1	26	06	0	2.43	1600	71	67	25	10	2	1	050	01	3	1
1284	19	1	5	81	2	2	12	08	0	2.47	1500	66	63	23	07	1	1	100	20	2	0
9406	19	0	6	79	2	2	14	10	0	2.66	1300	68	69	25	06	3	1	100	03	1	1
8022	19	0	1	88	1	3	00	12	1	3.28	1600	71	69	28	09	3	1	050	01	2	1
0954	25	1	5	87	3	2	09	15	1	3.41	1600	63	63	27	04	1	1	050	01	4	1
5012	20	0	5	75	2	2	10	21	1	2.20	2100	77	71	35	03	2	0	150	02	3	0
0013	19	1	5	80	3	1	30	11	1	2.32	1700	63	61	25	08	2	1	175	25	3	0
8809	22	1	4	88	1	2	08	20	1	2.97	1600	65	69	25	09	3	1	100	05	2	0
3697	20	1	1	93	3	2	16	29	1	3.75	1500	62	66	26	08	3	1	075	12	2	1
7807	18	1	5	77	3	2	18	20	0	2.78	1300	64	62	25	10	3	1	050	15	4	1
2058	30	1	4	82	3	2	20	15	1	2.84	1600	61	62	28	06	2	1	030	03	3	0
9801	18	1	4	79	3	2	08	10	1	3.10	1400	65	64	28	04	1	1	040	15	3	1
5464	18	1	5	75	1	1	24	06	0	2.49	1500	65	67	30	07	3	0	075	10	1	1
8002	24	1	4	88	3	2	10	10	1	3.24	1300	69	67	28	09	1	1	100	05	3	0
1919	18	0	1	81	3	1	09	21	1	2.95	1100	69	66	28	04	3	1	050	08	3	1
6728	19	0	1	86	3	2	17	23	1	2.81	1900	72	69	23	01	3	1	150	20	2	1
9603	26	1	4	79	2	2	16	10	0	2.36	1600	70	66	24	10	3	1	100	02	4	1
8871	22	0	2	88	3	2	08	17	1	3.10	2000	67	67	27	03	3	1	200	01	3	1
6587	19	1	5	86	3	2	15	28	1	3.78	2200	61	59	25	03	3	1	100	03	3	1
0250	19	0	5	90	3	2	12	15	0	3.08	1900	71	70	28	10	3	1	100	13	2	0

1010	19	0	1	81	3	2	20	11	1	3.07	1100	69	70	25	12	2	1	150	03	4	1
2721	22	1	5	92	1	2	17	12	0	3.15	1600	60	63	25	07	1	1	040	03	2	0
5256	18	1	5	95	1	2	12	15	1	3.65	1500	63	64	26	01	3	1	050	06	3	1
9847	18	0	1	89	3	2	08	14	1	3.70	1000	66	66	24	09	2	1	200	20	2	1
1617	20	1	5	81	2	1	16	21	1	2.73	1500	65	64	24	03	3	1	075	01	2	0
8077	20	0	6	88	3	1	10	17	1	3.75	1300	73	75	27	01	3	1	050	09	4	1
0001	19	1	5	90	3	2	10	20	1	3.17	1600	68	65	26	06	3	1	040	02	4	0
7755	31	0	1	87	3	2	37	25	0	3.56	1300	67	67	40	09	3	1	075	07	4	0
4607	18	1	3	84	3	2	16	30	0	3.75	1700	65	63	25	04	1	1	075	05	4	0
6930	20	1	1	76	3	2	28	23	1	2.05	1600	65	64	27	09	2	1	030	10	1	0
9788	19	0	5	89	3	2	17	28	1	3.85	1500	69	68	24	02	3	1	050	01	3	0
4697	22	0	5	74	3	2	16	09	0	2.74	1600	70	65	25	03	3	1	100	10	1	0
6796	18	1	1	86	3	2	17	09	0	2.64	1300	68	65	26	11	2	1	075	01	3	1
3529	23	1	3	73	3	2	15	12	0	2.93	1700	64	63	26	09	1	1	070	10	3	1
9244	19	0	5	79	1	1	12	24	0	2.47	1500	72	68	26	03	2	1	100	01	2	1
2581	24	0	3	82	3	2	25	08	1	2.18	1800	71	70	28	09	2	0	025	01	2	1

APPENDIX B: CHAPTER FORMULAS

CHAPTER 2

Class Width = Range/(# of classes) and roundup

CHAPTER 3

Population Mean: $\mu = \dfrac{\Sigma x}{N}$

Median is the middle value (after the data values have been arranged in numerical order)

$\underset{\text{median}}{\text{position of}} = \dfrac{N+1}{2}$ th data value

Mode is most frequent data value

Sample Mean: $\overline{x} = \dfrac{\Sigma x}{n}$

Range=largest value - smallest value

Population Variance $= \dfrac{\Sigma(x-\mu)^2}{N}$

OR

$\sigma^2 = \dfrac{\Sigma(x-\mu)^2}{N}$

Definition Formula for the Population Standard Deviation:

$\sigma = \sqrt{variance}$

OR

$\sigma = \sqrt{\dfrac{\Sigma(x-\mu)^2}{N}}$

Computational Formula for the Population Standard Deviation:

$\sigma = \sqrt{\dfrac{\Sigma x^2 - \dfrac{(\Sigma x)^2}{N}}{N}}$

Definition Formula for the Sample Standard Deviation:

$s = \sqrt{\dfrac{\Sigma(x-\overline{x})^2}{n-1}}$

Computational Formula for the Sample Standard Deviation:

$s = \sqrt{\dfrac{\Sigma x^2 - \dfrac{(\Sigma x)^2}{n}}{n-1}}$

z Score Formula:
Population: $z = \dfrac{x - \mu}{\sigma}$

Sample: $z = \dfrac{x - \overline{x}}{s}$

Raw Score Formula:
Population:

$x = \mu + z\,\sigma$

Sample: $x = \overline{x} + zs$

Percentile Rank Formula:

PR of $x = \dfrac{[B + (\frac{1}{2})E]}{N}$ (100)

CHAPTER 4

Counting Rule 1: Permutation Rule.
The number of permutations (arrangements) of n different objects taken altogether, denoted $_nP_n$, is:

$$_nP_n = n!$$

COUNTING RULE 2: Permutation Rule for n objects taken *s* at a time.
The number of permutations of *n* **different** objects taken *s* at a time, denoted $_nP_s$, is:

$$_nP_s = n(n-1)(n-2)\cdots(n-s+1)$$

COUNTING RULE 3: Permutation Rule of N objects with k alike objects
Given N objects where n_1 are alike, n_2 are alike, ... ,n_k are alike, then the number of permutations of these N objects is:

$$\dfrac{N!}{(n_1!)(n_2!)\cdots(n_k!)}$$

COUNTING RULE 4: Number of Combinations of n objects taken s at a time
The number of combinations of n objects taken s at a time, is:

$$_nC_s = \dfrac{_nP_s}{s!}$$

The formula for $_nC_s$ in factorial notation is written as:

$$nC_s = \frac{n!}{s!\,(n-s)!}$$

Classical Probability Definition for Equally Likely Outcomes:

$$P(\text{Event } E) = \frac{\text{number of outcomes satisfying event E}}{\text{total \# of outcomes in sample space}}$$

Relative Frequency Approach to Calculating Probability:

$$P(\text{Event } A) = \frac{\text{number of times event A occurred}}{\text{total \# of times the experiment was repeated}}$$

The Addition Rule:
P(A or B) = P(A) + P(B) - P(A and B)

The Complement Rule:
P(E) + P(E') = 1

Multiplication Rule for Independent Events:
$P(A \text{ and } B) = P(A) \cdot P(B)$

Multiplication Rule for Dependent Events:
$P(A \text{ and } B) = P(A) \cdot P(B \mid A)$

Conditional Probability Formula
$$P(A \mid B) = \frac{P(A \text{ and } B)}{P(B)}$$

CHAPTER 5

The Mean of a Discrete Random Variable X

$$\mu = \sum_{\substack{all\ possible \\ X\ values}} X \cdot P(X)$$

Standard Deviation of a Discrete Random Variable

$$\sigma = \sqrt{\sum_{\substack{all\ possible \\ X\ values}} (X-\mu)^2 \cdot P(X)}$$

Binomial Probability Formula
P(s successes in n trials) = $nC_s\, p^s\, q^{(n-s)}$

Mean of a Binomial Distribution

$$\mu_s = np$$

Standard Deviation of a Binomial Distribution

$$\sigma_s = \sqrt{n \cdot p \cdot (1-p)}$$

CHAPTER 6

z Score Formula:
$$z = \frac{x - \mu}{\sigma}$$

Raw Score Formula:
$$X = \mu + (z)\sigma$$

Mean of a Binomial Distribution
$$\mu_s = np$$

Standard Deviation of a Binomial Distribution
$$\sigma_s = \sqrt{np(1-p)}$$

CHAPTER 7

Mean of the Sampling Distribution of the Mean:
$$\mu_{\bar{x}} = \mu$$

Standard Error or Standard Deviation of the Sampling Distribution of the Mean:
$$\sigma_{\bar{x}} = \frac{\sigma}{\sqrt{n}}$$

The population proportion is:
$$p = \frac{X}{N}$$

The sample proportion is:
$$\hat{p} = \frac{x}{n}$$

Mean of the Sampling Distribution of The Proportion is: $\mu_{\hat{p}} = p$

Standard Error or Standard Deviation of the Sampling Distribution of The Proportion is:

$$\sigma_{\hat{p}} = \sqrt{\frac{p(1-p)}{n}}$$

CHAPTER 8

A 90% Confidence Interval for the population mean, μ , (with known population standard deviation) is:

$$\bar{X} - (1.65)\frac{\sigma}{\sqrt{n}} \text{ to } \bar{X} + (1.65)\frac{\sigma}{\sqrt{n}}$$

A 95% Confidence Interval for the population mean, μ , (with known population standard deviation) is:

$$\overline{X}-(1.96)\frac{\sigma}{\sqrt{n}} \quad to \quad \overline{X}+(1.96)\frac{\sigma}{\sqrt{n}}$$

A 99% Confidence Interval for the population mean, μ , (with known population standard deviation) is:

$$\overline{X}-(2.58)\frac{\sigma}{\sqrt{n}} \quad to \quad \overline{X}+(2.58)\frac{\sigma}{\sqrt{n}}$$

A 90% Confidence Interval for the population mean, μ , when the population standard deviation is *unknown*, is:

$$\overline{X}-(t_{95\%})\frac{s}{\sqrt{n}} \quad to \quad \overline{X}+(t_{95\%})\frac{s}{\sqrt{n}}$$

A 95% Confidence Interval for the population mean, μ , when the population standard deviation is *unknown*, is:

$$\overline{X}-(t_{97.5\%})\frac{s}{\sqrt{n}} \quad to \quad \overline{X}+(t_{97.5\%})\frac{s}{\sqrt{n}}$$

A 99% Confidence Interval for the population mean, μ , when the population standard deviation is *unknown*, is:

$$\overline{X}-(t_{99.5\%})\frac{s}{\sqrt{n}} \quad to \quad \overline{X}+(t_{99.5\%})\frac{s}{\sqrt{n}}$$

A 90% Confidence Interval for the Population Proportion, p, is:

$$\hat{p}-(1.65)\,s_{\hat{p}} \quad to \quad \hat{p}+(1.65)\,s_{\hat{p}}$$

A 95% Confidence Interval for the Population Proportion, p, is:

$$\hat{p}-(1.96)\,s_{\hat{p}} \quad to \quad \hat{p}+(1.96)\,s_{\hat{p}}$$

A 99% Confidence Interval for the Population Proportion, p, is:

$$\hat{p}-(2.58)\,s_{\hat{p}} \quad to \quad \hat{p}+(2.58)\,s_{\hat{p}}$$

The margin of error for estimating a population mean, where the population standard deviation is known, is:

$$E = (z)\left(\frac{\sigma}{\sqrt{n}}\right)$$

The sample size formula when estimating the population mean is:

$$n = \left[\frac{z\sigma}{E}\right]^2$$

The margin of error for estimating a population proportion is:

$$E = (z)\left(\sqrt{\frac{\hat{p}(1-\hat{p})}{n}}\right)$$

The sample size formula when estimating the population proportion using $\hat{p}$, a point estimate of the population proportion, is:

$$n = \frac{z^2(\hat{p})(1-\hat{p})}{E^2}$$

The conservative sample size formula in estimating the population proportion is:

$$n = \frac{z^2(0.25)}{E^2}$$

CHAPTER 9

z SCORE Formula:

$$z = \frac{x-\mu}{\sigma}$$

Test Statistic Formula:

$$z = \frac{sample\_population}{proportion\ proportion}{standard\,error}$$

$$z = \frac{sample\,mean - population\,mean}{standard\,error}$$

CHAPTER 10

Population proportion is:

$$p = \frac{X}{N}$$

Sample proportion is:

$$\hat{p} = \frac{x}{n}$$

Mean of the Sampling Distribution of The Proportion is: $\mu_{\hat{p}} = p$

Standard error or standard deviation of the Sampling Distribution of The Proportion is:

$$\sigma_{\hat{p}} = \sqrt{\frac{p(1-p)}{n}}$$

Test Statistic Formula is:

$$z = \frac{\hat{p} - \mu_{\hat{p}}}{\sigma_{\hat{p}}}$$

CHAPTER 11

Mean of the sampling distribution of the mean is:

$$\mu_{\bar{x}} = \mu$$

Standard error or standard deviation of the sampling distribution of the mean is:

$$\sigma_{\bar{x}} = \frac{\sigma}{\sqrt{n}}$$

Estimate of the standard error or standard deviation of the sampling distribution of the mean is:

$$s_{\bar{x}} = \frac{s}{\sqrt{n}}$$

Test Statistic Formula:
a) for normal distribution:

$$z = \frac{\bar{x} - \mu_{\bar{x}}}{\sigma_{\bar{x}}}$$

b) for t distribution:

$$t = \frac{\bar{x} - \mu_{\bar{x}}}{s_{\bar{x}}}$$

To find t_c, need to determine degrees of freedom using formula:

$$df = n-1$$

CHAPTER 12

Sampling Distributions of the Difference Between Two Proportions

Mean: $\mu_{\hat{p}_1 - \hat{p}_2} = p_1 - p_2$

Standard Error:

$$s_{\hat{p}_1 - \hat{p}_2} = \sqrt{\frac{\hat{p}(1-\hat{p})}{n_1} + \frac{\hat{p}(1-\hat{p})}{n_2}} \qquad \text{or}$$

$$s_{\hat{p}_1 - \hat{p}_2} = \sqrt{\hat{p}(1-\hat{p})\left(\frac{1}{n_1} + \frac{1}{n_2}\right)}$$

where $\hat{p} = \dfrac{x_1 + x_2}{n_1 + n_2}$ or $\hat{p} = \dfrac{n_1\hat{p}_1 + n_2\hat{p}_2}{n_1 + n_2}$

Test Statistic Formula is: $z = \dfrac{(\hat{p}_1 - \hat{p}_2) - \mu_{\hat{p}_1 - \hat{p}_2}}{s_{\hat{p}_1 - \hat{p}_2}}$

CHAPTER 13

Mean of the Sampling Distribution of the Difference Between Two Means is:

$$\mu_{\bar{x}_1 - \bar{x}_2} = \mu_1 - \mu_2$$

Standard error or standard deviation of the Sampling Distribution of the Difference Between Two Means is:

$$\sigma_{\bar{x}_1 - \bar{x}_2} = \sqrt{\frac{\sigma_1^2}{n_1} + \frac{\sigma_2^2}{n_2}}$$

Estimate of the standard error or standard deviation of the Sampling Distribution of The Difference Between Two Means is:

$$s_{\bar{x}_1 - \bar{x}_2} = \sqrt{\frac{(n_1-1)s_1^2 + (n_2-1)s_2^2}{n_1 + n_2 - 2} \cdot \left(\frac{1}{n_1} + \frac{1}{n_2}\right)}$$

The Sampling Distribution of The Difference Between Two Means is approximated by a t distribution with degrees of freedom which is given by:

$$df = n_1 + n_2 - 2.$$

Test Statistic Formula is:

$$t = \frac{(\bar{x}_1 - \bar{x}_2) - \mu_{\bar{x}_1 - \bar{x}_2}}{s_{\bar{x}_1 - \bar{x}_2}}$$

Difference between the two sample means is: $d = \overline{X}_1 - \overline{X}_2$

CHAPTER 14

Pearson's Chi-Square Test Statistic is:

$$X^2 = \sum_{all\ cells} \frac{(O-E)^2}{E}$$

or

$$X^2 = \sum_{all\ cells} \left(\frac{O^2}{E}\right) - n$$

Chi-Square Distribution: degrees of freedom:

$$df = (r-1)(c-1)$$

$$\text{expected cell frequency} = \frac{(RT)(CT)}{n}$$

CHAPTER 15

Pearson's or Sample Correlation Coefficient, r (test statistic).

$$r = \frac{n\Sigma(xy) - (\Sigma x)(\Sigma y)}{\sqrt{n(\Sigma x^2) - (\Sigma x)^2}\sqrt{n(\Sigma y^2) - (\Sigma y)^2}}$$

degrees of freedom, df, for testing the correlation coefficient is:

$$df = n - 2$$

Coefficient of Determination = r^2

Regression Line Formula: $y' = a + bx$

where:
y' is the predicted value of y, the dependent variable, given the value of x, the independent variable,

and

a and b are the regression coefficients obtained by the formulas:

$$b = \frac{n\Sigma(xy) - \Sigma x \Sigma y}{n(\Sigma x^2) - (\Sigma x)^2}$$

$$a = \frac{\Sigma y - b\Sigma x}{n}$$

CHAPTER 16
ANOVA

Sums of Squares $SS = \Sigma(x - \bar{x})^2$

$SS_{(between\ treatments)} + SS_{(within\ treatments)} = SS_{(total)}$

$$SS_{(total)} = \Sigma x^2 - \frac{(\Sigma x)^2}{N}$$

$SS_{(between\ treatments)} =$

$$\left(\frac{(\Sigma T_1)^2}{n_1} \frac{+(\Sigma T_2)^2}{n_2} + ... + \frac{(\Sigma T_i)^2}{n_1}\right) - \frac{(\Sigma x)^2}{N}$$

$$SS_{(within\ treatments)} = \Sigma x^2 - \left(\frac{(\Sigma T_1)^2}{n_1} \frac{+(\Sigma T_2)^2}{n_2} + ... + \frac{(\Sigma T_i)^2}{n_1}\right)$$

Degrees of Freedom: $df_{(Between)} + df_{(within)} = df_{(Total)}$

Where: $df_{(Between)} = k - 1$
$df_{(within)} = N - k$
$df_{(Total)} = N - 1$

Mean Square, (denoted MS), formulas:

$$MS_{(Between)} = \frac{SS_{bet}}{df_{bet}}$$

$$MS_{(within)} = \frac{SS_{within}}{df_{within}}$$

Test statistic formula: $F = \dfrac{s_1^2}{s_2^2}$

test statistic: F-statistic

$$F = \frac{treatment\ sample\ variance}{within\ sample\ variance}$$

CHAPTER 17

NONPARAMETRIC TESTS

SIGN TEST for MEDIANS

binomial mean: $\mu_s = np$

binomial std dev: $\sigma_s = \sqrt{np(1-p)}$

If the statistical result O, is less than n/2,

then test statistic is: $z = \dfrac{(O + \frac{1}{2}) - \mu_s}{\sigma_s}$

If the statistical result O, is greater than n/2,

then the test statistic is: $z = \dfrac{(O - \frac{1}{2}) - \mu_s}{\sigma_s}$

MANN-WHITNEY RANK-SUM TEST

When normal distribution can be applied, then test statistic, z, is:

$$z = \frac{w - \dfrac{n_1(n_1 + n_2 + 1)}{2}}{\sqrt{\dfrac{n_1 n_2 (n_1 + n_2 + 1)}{12}}}$$

KRUSKAL-WALLIS H TEST

Kruskal-Wallis H test statistic formula:

$$H = \frac{12}{N(N+1)}\left[\frac{(\sum R_1)^2}{n_1} + \frac{(\sum R_2)^2}{n_2} + \ldots + \frac{(\sum R_k)^2}{n_k}\right] - 3(N+1)$$

APPENDIX C: SUMMARY OF HYPOTHESIS TESTS

SUMMARY OF HYPOTHESIS TESTS FOR TESTING THE VALUE OF A POPULATION PARAMETER			
FORM OF THE NULL HYPOTHESIS	CONDITIONS OF TEST	TEST STATISTIC FORMULA	TEST STATISTIC DISTRIBUTION IS A:
$\mu = \mu_0$	KNOWN σ and $n > 30$	$z = \dfrac{\bar{x} - \mu_{\bar{x}}}{\sigma_{\bar{x}}}$ where: $\sigma_{\bar{x}} = \dfrac{\sigma}{\sqrt{n}}$	Normal Distribution
$\mu = \mu_0$	UNKNOWN σ	$t = \dfrac{\bar{x} - \mu_{\bar{x}}}{s_{\bar{x}}}$ where: $s_{\bar{x}} = \dfrac{s}{\sqrt{n}}$	t Distribution where: $df = n - 1$
$p = p_0$	$np > 5$ and $n(1 - p) > 5$	$z = \dfrac{\hat{p} - \mu_{\hat{p}}}{\sigma_{\hat{p}}}$ where: $\sigma_{\hat{p}} = \sqrt{\dfrac{p(1-p)}{n}}$	Normal Distribution

SUMMARY OF HYPOTHESIS TESTS INVOLVING TWO POPULATION MEANS			
FORM OF THE NULL HYPOTHESIS	CONDITIONS OF TEST	TEST STATISTIC FORMULA	TEST STATISTIC DISTRIBUTION IS A:
$\mu_1 - \mu_2 = 0$	KNOWN: σ_1 and σ_2 and n_1 and n_2 are both greater than 30	$z = \dfrac{\bar{x}_1 - \bar{x}_2}{\sigma_{\bar{x}_1 - \bar{x}_2}}$ where: $\sigma_{\bar{x}_1 - \bar{x}_2} = \sqrt{\dfrac{\sigma_1^{\,2}}{n_1} + \dfrac{\sigma_2^{\,2}}{n_2}}$	Normal Distribution
$\mu_1 - \mu_2 = 0$	UNKNOWN: σ_1 and σ_2 and $\sigma_1 \approx \sigma_2$	$t = \dfrac{\bar{x}_1 - \bar{x}_2}{s_{\bar{x}_1 - \bar{x}_2}}$ where: $s_{\bar{x}_1 - \bar{x}_2} = \sqrt{\dfrac{(n_1 - 1)\,s_1^{\,2} + (n_2 - 1)\,s_2^{\,2}}{n_1 + n_2 - 2} \cdot \left(\dfrac{1}{n_1} + \dfrac{1}{n_2}\right)}$	t Distribution where: $df = n_1 + n_2 - 2$

SUMMARY OF CONFIDENCE INTERVALS

CONFIDENCE INTERVALS FORMULAS AND CONDITIONS				
PARAMETER BEING ESTIMATED	CONDITIONS OF ESTIMATE	POINT ESTIMATE	CONFIDENCE INTERVAL	SAMPLING DISTRIBUTION IS A:
μ	Known σ	$\bar{x}$	$\bar{x} - (z)\left(\dfrac{\sigma}{\sqrt{n}}\right)$ to $\bar{x} + (z)\left(\dfrac{\sigma}{\sqrt{n}}\right)$ where: z = 1.65 for 90% z = 1.96 for 95% z = 2.58 for 99%	Normal Distribution
μ	Unknown σ	$\bar{x}$	$\bar{x} - (t)\left(\dfrac{s}{\sqrt{n}}\right)$ to $\bar{x} + (t)\left(\dfrac{s}{\sqrt{n}}\right)$ where: $t = t_{95\%}$ for 90% $t = t_{97.5\%}$ for 95% $t = t_{99.5\%}$ for 99%	t Distribution with: df = n - 1
p	$n\hat{p} > 5$ and $n(1 - \hat{p}) > 5$	$\hat{p}$	$\hat{p} - (z)(s_{\hat{p}})$ to $\hat{p} + (z)(s_{\hat{p}})$ where: z = 1.65 for 90% z = 1.96 for 95% z = 2.58 for 99%	Normal Distribution

APPENDIX D: STATISTICAL TABLES

TABLE I: THE SUCCESS OCCURRENCE TABLE, $_nC_s$[1]

The entries in the table give the number of ways to get s successes in n trials, which is represented by $_nC_s$[1]

n\s	0	1	2	3	4	5	6	7	8	9	10	11	12	13	14	15	16	17	18	19	20
0	1																				
1	1	1																			
2	1	2	1																		
3	1	3	3	1																	
4	1	4	6	4	1																
5	1	5	10	10	5	1															
6	1	6	15	20	15	6	1														
7	1	7	21	35	35	21	7	1													
8	1	8	28	56	70	56	28	8	1												
9	1	9	36	84	126	126	84	36	9	1											
10	1	10	45	120	210	252	210	120	45	10	1										
11	1	11	55	165	330	462	462	330	165	55	11	1									
12	1	12	66	220	495	792	924	792	495	220	66	12	1								
13	1	13	78	286	715	1287	1716	1716	1287	715	286	78	13	1							
14	1	14	91	364	1001	2002	3003	3432	3003	2002	1001	364	91	14	1						
15	1	15	105	455	1365	3003	5005	6435	6435	5005	3003	1365	455	105	15	1					
16	1	16	120	560	1820	4368	8008	12870	11440	8008	4368	1820	560	120	16	1					
17	1	17	136	680	2380	6188	12376	24310	24310	19448	12376	6188	2380	680	136	17	1				
18	1	18	153	816	3060	8568	18564	43758	43758	48620	31824	18564	8568	3060	816	153	18	1			
19	1	19	171	969	3876	11628	27132	75582	75582	92378	92378	50388	27132	11628	3876	969	171	19	1		
20	1	20	190	1140	4845	15504	38760	125970	125970	167960	184756	125970	77520	38760	15504	4845	1140	190	20	1	

[1] The values for $_nC_s$ can also be obtained by using the formula: $_nC_s = \dfrac{n!}{s!\,(n-s)!}$.

This formula was discussed in Section 4.3 as Counting Rule 4.

TABLE II: THE STANDARD NORMAL CURVE AREA TABLES

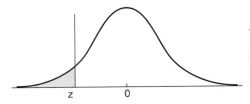

The entries in TABLE II represent the area under the Standard Normal Distribution to the left of the z score.

z	0	1	2	3	4	5	6	7	8	9
−3.	.0013	.0009	.0007	.0005	.0003	.0002	.0001	.0001	.0001	.0000[2]
−2.9	.0018	.0018	.0017	.0017	.0016	.0016	.0015	.0015	.0014	.0014
−2.8	.0025	.0024	.0024	.0023	.0023	.0022	.0021	.0021	.0020	.0019
−2.7	.0035	.0034	.0033	.0032	.0031	.0030	.0029	.0028	.0027	.0026
−2.6	.0047	.0045	.0044	.0043	.0041	.0040	.0039	.0038	.0037	.0036
−2.5	.0062	.0060	.0059	.0057	.0055	.0054	.0052	.0051	.0049	.0048
−2.4	.0082	.0080	.0078	.0075	.0073	.0071	.0069	.0068	.0066	.0064
−2.3	.0107	.0104	.0102	.0099	.0096	.0094	.0091	.0089	.0087	.0084
−2.2	.0139	.0136	.0132	.0129	.0125	.0122	.0119	.0116	.0113	.0110
−2.1	.0179	.0174	.0170	.0166	.0162	.0158	.0154	.0150	.0146	.0143
−2.0	.0228	.0222	.0217	.0212	.0207	.0202	.0197	.0192	.0188	.0183
−1.9	.0287	.0281	.0274	.0268	.0262	.0256	.0250	.0244	.0239	.0233
−1.8	.0359	.0352	.0344	.0336	.0329	.0322	.0314	.0307	.0301	.0294
−1.7	.0446	.0436	.0427	.0418	.0409	.0401	.0392	.0384	.0375	.0367
−1.6	.0548	.0537	.0526	.0516	.0505	.0495	.0485	.0475	.0465	.0455
−1.5	.0668	.0655	.0643	.0630	.0618	.0606	.0594	.0582	.0571	.0559
−1.4	.0808	.0793	.0778	.0764	.0749	.0735	.0722	.0708	.0694	.0681
−1.3	.0968	.0951	.0934	.0918	.0901	.0885	.0869	.0853	.0838	.0823
−1.2	.1151	.1131	.1112	.1093	.1075	.1056	.1038	.1020	.1003	.0985
−1.1	.1357	.1335	.1314	.1292	.1271	.1251	.1230	.1210	.1190	.1170
−1.0	.1587	.1562	.1539	.1515	.1492	.1469	.1446	.1423	.1401	.1379
−0.9	.1841	.1814	.1788	.1762	.1736	.1711	.1685	.1660	.1635	.1611
−0.8	.2119	.2090	.2061	.2033	.2005	.1977	.1949	.1922	.1894	.1867
−0.7	.2420	.2389	.2358	.2327	.2296	.2266	.2236	.2206	.2177	.2148
−0.6	.2743	.2709	.2676	.2643	.2611	.2578	.2546	.2514	.2483	.2451
−0.5	.3085	.3050	.3015	.2981	.2946	.2912	.2877	.2843	.2810	.2776
−0.4	.3446	.3409	.3372	.3337	.3300	.3264	.3228	.3192	.3156	.3121
−0.3	.3821	.3783	.3745	.3707	.3669	.3632	.3594	.3557	.3520	.3483
−0.2	.4207	.4168	.4129	.4090	.4052	.4013	.3974	.3936	.3897	.3859
−0.1	.4602	.4562	.4522	.4483	.4443	.4404	.4364	.4325	.4286	.4247
−0.0	.5000	.4960	.4920	.4880	.4840	.4801	.4761	.4721	.4681	.4641

[2]Please note: to four decimal places, the area to the left of z = −3.9 is *approximately* zero.

TABLE II: THE STANDARD NORMAL CURVE AREA TABLE

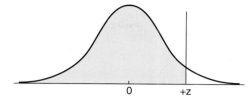

The entries in TABLE II represent the area under the Standard Normal Distribution to the left of the z score.

z	0	1	2	3	4	5	6	7	8	9
0.0	.5000	.5040	.5080	.5120	.5160	.5199	.5239	.5279	.5319	.5359
0.1	.5398	.5438	.5478	.5517	.5557	.5596	.5636	.5675	.5714	.5753
0.2	.5793	.5832	.5871	.5910	.5948	.5987	.6026	.6064	.6103	.6141
0.3	.6179	.6217	.6255	.6293	.6331	.6368	.6406	.6443	.6480	.6517
0.4	.6554	.6591	.6628	.6664	.6700	.6736	.6772	.6808	.6844	.6879
0.5	.6915	.6950	.6985	.7019	.7054	.7088	.7123	.7157	.7190	.7224
0.6	.7257	.7291	.7324	.7357	.7389	.7422	.7454	.7486	.7517	.7549
0.7	.7580	.7611	.7642	.7673	.7704	.7734	.7764	.7794	.7823	.7852
0.8	.7881	.7910	.7939	.7967	.7995	.8023	.8051	.8078	.8106	.8133
0.9	.8159	.8186	.8212	.8238	.8264	.8289	.8315	.8340	.8365	.8389
1.0	.8413	.8438	.8461	.8485	.8508	.8531	.8554	.8577	.8599	.8621
1.1	.8643	.8665	.8686	.8708	.8729	.8749	.8770	.8790	.8810	.8830
1.2	.8849	.8869	.8888	.8907	.8925	.8944	.8962	.8980	.8997	.9015
1.3	.9032	.9049	.9066	.9082	.9099	.9115	.9131	.9147	.9162	.9177
1.4	.9192	.9207	.9222	.9236	.9251	.9265	.9278	.9292	.9306	.9319
1.5	.9332	.9345	.9357	.9370	.9382	.9394	.9406	.9418	.9429	.9441
1.6	.9452	.9463	.9474	.9484	.9495	.9505	.9515	.9525	.9535	.9545
1.7	.9554	.9564	.9573	.9582	.9591	.9599	.9608	.9616	.9625	.9633
1.8	.9641	.9649	.9656	.9664	.9671	.9678	.9686	.9693	.9699	.9706
1.9	.9713	.9719	.9726	.9732	.9738	.9744	.9750	.9756	.9761	.9767
2.0	.9772	.9778	.9783	.9788	.9793	.9798	.9803	.9808	.9812	.9817
2.1	.9821	.9826	.9830	.9834	.9838	.9842	.9846	.9850	.9854	.9857
2.2	.9861	.9864	.9868	.9871	.9875	.9878	.9881	.9884	.9887	.9890
2.3	.9893	.9896	.9898	.9901	.9904	.9906	.9909	.9911	.9913	.9916
2.4	.9918	.9920	.9922	.9925	.9927	.9929	.9931	.9932	.9934	.9936
2.5	.9938	.9940	.9941	.9943	.9945	.9946	.9948	.9949	.9951	.9952
2.6	.9953	.9955	.9956	.9957	.9959	.9960	.9961	.9962	.9963	.9964
2.7	.9965	.9966	.9967	.9968	.9969	.9970	.9971	.9972	.9973	.9974
2.8	.9974	.9975	.9976	.9977	.9977	.9978	.9979	.9979	.9980	.9981
2.9	.9981	.9982	.9982	.9983	.9984	.9984	.9985	.9985	.9986	.9986
3.	.9987	.9990	.9993	.9995	.9997	.9998	.9998	.9999	.9999	1.0000[3]

[3]Please note: to four decimal places, the area to the left of z = 3.9 is *approximately* 1.

TABLE III: CRITICAL VALUES FOR THE *t* DISTRIBUTIONS

FOR HYPOTHESIS TESTING

The entries in the table give the critical *t* values for the specified number of degrees of freedom *(df)* and the level of significance (α) for a one tailed or a two tailed test.

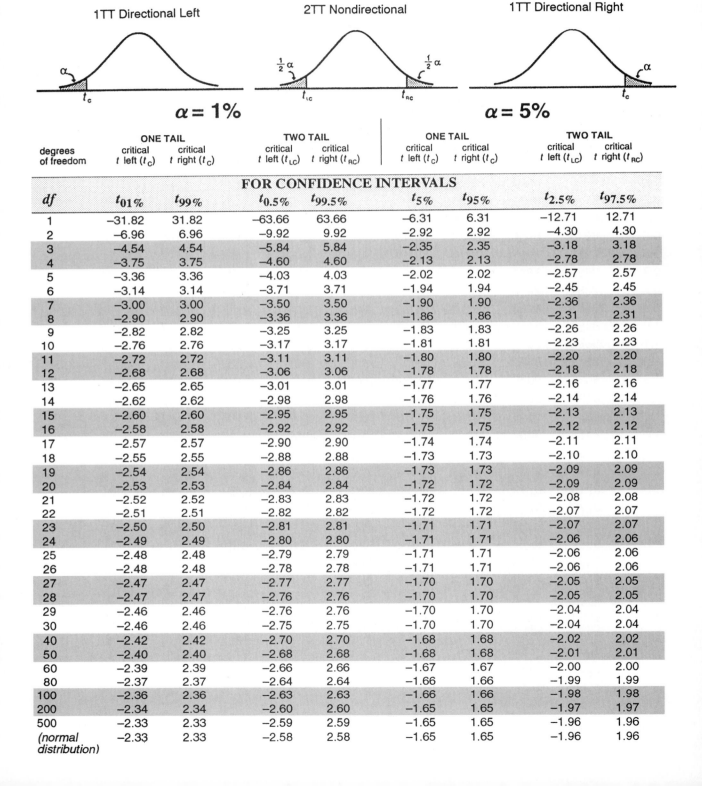

degrees of freedom	ONE TAIL critical *t* left (t_c)	ONE TAIL critical *t* right (t_c)	TWO TAIL critical *t* left (t_{LC})	TWO TAIL critical *t* right (t_{RC})	ONE TAIL critical *t* left (t_c)	ONE TAIL critical *t* right (t_c)	TWO TAIL critical *t* left (t_{LC})	TWO TAIL critical *t* right (t_{RC})
FOR CONFIDENCE INTERVALS								
df	$t_{01\%}$	$t_{99\%}$	$t_{0.5\%}$	$t_{99.5\%}$	$t_{5\%}$	$t_{95\%}$	$t_{2.5\%}$	$t_{97.5\%}$
1	−31.82	31.82	−63.66	63.66	−6.31	6.31	−12.71	12.71
2	−6.96	6.96	−9.92	9.92	−2.92	2.92	−4.30	4.30
3	−4.54	4.54	−5.84	5.84	−2.35	2.35	−3.18	3.18
4	−3.75	3.75	−4.60	4.60	−2.13	2.13	−2.78	2.78
5	−3.36	3.36	−4.03	4.03	−2.02	2.02	−2.57	2.57
6	−3.14	3.14	−3.71	3.71	−1.94	1.94	−2.45	2.45
7	−3.00	3.00	−3.50	3.50	−1.90	1.90	−2.36	2.36
8	−2.90	2.90	−3.36	3.36	−1.86	1.86	−2.31	2.31
9	−2.82	2.82	−3.25	3.25	−1.83	1.83	−2.26	2.26
10	−2.76	2.76	−3.17	3.17	−1.81	1.81	−2.23	2.23
11	−2.72	2.72	−3.11	3.11	−1.80	1.80	−2.20	2.20
12	−2.68	2.68	−3.06	3.06	−1.78	1.78	−2.18	2.18
13	−2.65	2.65	−3.01	3.01	−1.77	1.77	−2.16	2.16
14	−2.62	2.62	−2.98	2.98	−1.76	1.76	−2.14	2.14
15	−2.60	2.60	−2.95	2.95	−1.75	1.75	−2.13	2.13
16	−2.58	2.58	−2.92	2.92	−1.75	1.75	−2.12	2.12
17	−2.57	2.57	−2.90	2.90	−1.74	1.74	−2.11	2.11
18	−2.55	2.55	−2.88	2.88	−1.73	1.73	−2.10	2.10
19	−2.54	2.54	−2.86	2.86	−1.73	1.73	−2.09	2.09
20	−2.53	2.53	−2.84	2.84	−1.72	1.72	−2.09	2.09
21	−2.52	2.52	−2.83	2.83	−1.72	1.72	−2.08	2.08
22	−2.51	2.51	−2.82	2.82	−1.72	1.72	−2.07	2.07
23	−2.50	2.50	−2.81	2.81	−1.71	1.71	−2.07	2.07
24	−2.49	2.49	−2.80	2.80	−1.71	1.71	−2.06	2.06
25	−2.48	2.48	−2.79	2.79	−1.71	1.71	−2.06	2.06
26	−2.48	2.48	−2.78	2.78	−1.71	1.71	−2.06	2.06
27	−2.47	2.47	−2.77	2.77	−1.70	1.70	−2.05	2.05
28	−2.47	2.47	−2.76	2.76	−1.70	1.70	−2.05	2.05
29	−2.46	2.46	−2.76	2.76	−1.70	1.70	−2.04	2.04
30	−2.46	2.46	−2.75	2.75	−1.70	1.70	−2.04	2.04
40	−2.42	2.42	−2.70	2.70	−1.68	1.68	−2.02	2.02
50	−2.40	2.40	−2.68	2.68	−1.68	1.68	−2.01	2.01
60	−2.39	2.39	−2.66	2.66	−1.67	1.67	−2.00	2.00
80	−2.37	2.37	−2.64	2.64	−1.66	1.66	−1.99	1.99
100	−2.36	2.36	−2.63	2.63	−1.66	1.66	−1.98	1.98
200	−2.34	2.34	−2.60	2.60	−1.65	1.65	−1.97	1.97
500	−2.33	2.33	−2.59	2.59	−1.65	1.65	−1.96	1.96
(normal distribution)	−2.33	2.33	−2.58	2.58	−1.65	1.65	−1.96	1.96

TABLE IV: CRITICAL VALUES FOR THE CHI-SQUARE DISTRIBUTIONS, χ^2_α

The entries in the table give the critical chi-square values (χ^2_α) for the specified number of degrees of freedom (*df*) and the level of significance (α).

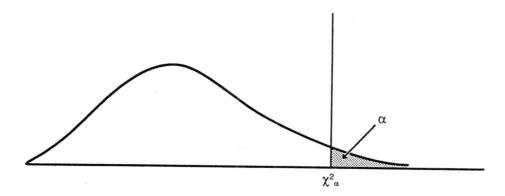

degrees of freedom	significance level	
df	α = 5%	α = 1%
1	3.84	6.64
2	5.99	9.21
3	7.82	11.34
4	9.49	13.28
5	11.07	15.09
6	12.59	16.81
7	14.07	18.48
8	15.51	20.09
9	16.92	21.67
10	18.31	23.21
11	19.68	24.72
12	21.03	26.22
13	22.36	27.69
14	23.68	29.14
15	25.00	30.58
16	26.30	32.00
17	27.59	33.41
18	28.87	34.80
19	30.14	36.19
20	31.41	37.57

TABLE V: CRITICAL VALUES OF THE CORRELATION COEFFICIENT, r_α

1TT Directional Left
use a negative critical r value, $-r_\alpha$

2TT Nondirectional
use a positive critical r value, r_α
and a negative critical r value, $-r_\alpha$

1TT Directional Right
use a positive critical r value, r_α

| | $\alpha = 5\%$ | | $\alpha = 1\%$ | |
df	one tail	two tail	one tail	two tail
1	0.99	1.00	1.00	1.00
2	0.90	0.95	0.98	0.99
3	0.81	0.88	0.93	0.96
4	0.73	0.81	0.88	0.92
5	0.67	0.75	0.83	0.87
6	0.62	0.71	0.79	0.83
7	0.58	0.67	0.75	0.80
8	0.54	0.63	0.72	0.76
9	0.52	0.60	0.69	0.73
10	0.50	0.58	0.66	0.71
11	0.48	0.53	0.63	0.68
12	0.46	0.53	0.61	0.66
13	0.44	0.51	0.59	0.64
14	0.42	0.50	0.57	0.61
15	0.41	0.48	0.56	0.61
16	0.40	0.47	0.54	0.59
17	0.39	0.46	0.53	0.58
18	0.38	0.44	0.52	0.56
19	0.37	0.43	0.50	0.55
20	0.36	0.42	0.49	0.54
21	0.35	0.41	0.48	0.53
22	0.34	0.40	0.47	0.52
23	0.34	0.40	0.46	0.51
24	0.33	0.39	0.45	0.50
25	0.32	0.38	0.45	0.49
26	0.32	0.37	0.44	0.48
27	0.31	0.37	0.43	0.47
28	0.31	0.36	0.42	0.46

To determine the critical value of the correlation coefficient, r_α, when the *df* is greater than 28, use the formula:

$$r_\alpha = \frac{t_c}{\sqrt{t_c^2 + (n-2)}}$$

where:

t_c is the corresponding critical value of t for $(n-2)$ degrees of freedom

TABLE VI: RANDOM NUMBER TABLE

63271	59986	71744	51102	15141	80714	58683	93108	13554	79945
88547	09896	95436	79115	08303	01041	20030	63754	08459	28364
55957	57243	83865	09911	19761	66535	40102	26646	60147	15702
46276	87453	44790	67122	45573	84358	21625	16999	13385	22782
55363	07449	34835	15290	76616	67191	12777	21861	68689	03263
69393	92785	49902	58447	42048	30378	87618	26933	40640	16281
13186	29431	88190	04588	38733	81290	89541	70290	40113	08243
17726	28652	56836	78351	47327	18518	92222	55201	27340	10493
36520	64465	05550	30157	82242	29520	69753	72602	23756	54935
81628	36100	39254	56835	37636	02421	98063	89641	64953	99337
84649	48968	75215	75498	49539	74240	03466	49292	36401	45525
63291	11618	12613	75055	43915	26488	41116	64531	56827	30825
70502	53225	03655	05915	37140	57051	48393	91322	25653	06543
06426	24771	59935	49801	11082	66762	94477	02494	88215	27191
20711	55609	29430	70165	45406	78484	31639	52009	18873	96927
41990	70538	77191	25860	55204	73417	83920	69468	74972	38712
72452	36618	76298	26678	89334	33938	95567	29380	75906	91807
37042	40318	57099	10528	09925	89773	41335	96244	29002	46453
53766	52875	15987	46962	67342	77592	57651	95508	80033	69828
90585	58955	53122	16025	84299	53310	67380	84249	25348	04332
32001	96293	37203	64516	51530	37069	40261	61374	05815	06714
62606	64324	46354	72157	67248	20135	49804	09226	64419	29457
10078	28073	85389	50324	14500	15562	64165	06125	71353	77669
91561	46145	24177	15294	10061	98124	75732	00815	83452	97355
13091	98112	53959	79607	52244	63303	10413	63839	74762	50289
73864	83014	72457	22682	03033	61714	88173	90835	00634	85169
66668	25467	48894	51043	02365	91726	09365	63167	95264	45643
84745	41042	29493	01836	09044	51926	43630	63470	76508	14194
48068	26805	94595	47907	13357	38412	33318	26098	82782	42851
54310	96175	97594	88616	42035	38093	36745	56702	40644	83514
14877	33095	10924	58013	61439	21882	42059	24177	58739	60170
78295	23179	02771	43464	59061	71411	05697	67194	30495	21157
67524	02865	39593	54278	04237	92441	26602	63835	38032	94770
58268	57219	68124	73455	83236	08710	04284	55005	84171	42596
97158	28672	50685	01181	24262	19427	52106	34308	73685	74246
04230	16831	69085	30802	65559	09205	71829	06489	85650	38707
94879	56606	30401	02602	57658	70091	54986	41394	60437	03195
71446	15232	66715	26385	91518	70566	02888	79941	39684	54315
32886	05644	79316	09819	00813	88407	17461	73925	53037	91904
62048	33711	25290	21526	02223	75947	66466	06232	10913	75336
84534	42351	21628	53669	81352	95152	08107	98814	72743	12849
84707	15885	84710	35866	06446	86311	32648	88141	73902	69981
19409	40868	64220	80861	13860	68493	52908	26374	63297	45052
57978	48015	25973	66777	45924	56144	24742	96702	88200	66162
57295	98298	11199	96510	75228	41600	47192	43267	35973	23152
94044	83785	93388	07833	38216	31413	70555	03023	54147	06647
30,014	25879	71763	96679	90603	99396	74557	74224	18211	91637
07265	69563	64268	88802	72264	66540	01782	08396	19251	83613
84404	88642	30263	80310	11522	57810	27627	78376	36240	48952
21778	02085	27762	46097	43324	34354	09369	14966	10158	76089

TABLE VII   Critical Values of the *F*-Distribution, F_α (dfs$_1^2$, dfs$_2^2$), For α = 0.10

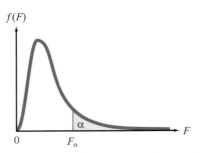

s_2^2 \ s_1^2	NUMERATOR DEGREES OF FREEDOM								
	1	**2**	**3**	**4**	**5**	**6**	**7**	**8**	**9**
1	39.86	49.50	53.59	55.83	57.24	58.20	58.91	59.44	59.86
2	8.53	9.00	9.16	9.24	9.29	9.33	9.35	9.37	9.38
3	5.54	5.46	5.39	5.34	5.31	5.28	5.27	5.25	5.24
4	4.54	4.32	4.19	4.11	4.05	4.01	3.98	3.95	3.94
5	4.06	3.78	3.62	3.52	3.45	3.40	3.37	3.34	3.32
6	3.78	3.46	3.29	3.18	3.11	3.05	3.01	2.98	2.96
7	3.59	3.26	3.07	2.96	2.88	2.83	2.78	2.75	2.72
8	3.46	3.11	2.92	2.81	2.73	2.67	2.62	2.59	2.56
9	3.36	3.01	2.81	2.69	2.61	2.55	2.51	2.47	2.44
10	3.29	2.92	2.73	2.61	2.52	2.46	2.41	2.38	2.35
11	3.23	2.86	2.66	2.54	2.45	2.39	2.34	2.30	2.27
12	3.18	2.81	2.61	2.48	2.39	2.33	2.28	2.24	2.21
13	3.14	2.76	2.56	2.43	2.35	2.28	2.23	2.20	2.16
14	3.10	2.73	2.52	2.39	2.31	2.24	2.19	2.15	2.12
15	3.07	2.70	2.49	2.36	2.27	2.21	2.16	2.12	2.09
16	3.05	2.67	2.46	2.33	2.24	2.18	2.13	2.09	2.06
17	3.03	2.64	2.44	2.31	2.22	2.15	2.10	2.06	2.03
18	3.01	2.62	2.42	2.29	2.20	2.13	2.08	2.04	2.00
19	2.99	2.61	2.40	2.27	2.18	2.11	2.06	2.02	1.98
20	2.97	2.59	2.38	2.25	2.16	2.09	2.04	2.00	1.96
21	2.96	2.57	2.36	2.23	2.14	2.08	2.02	1.98	1.95
22	2.95	2.56	2.35	2.22	2.13	2.06	2.01	1.97	1.93
23	2.94	2.55	2.34	2.21	2.11	2.05	1.99	1.95	1.92
24	2.93	2.54	2.33	2.19	2.10	2.04	1.98	1.94	1.91
25	2.92	2.53	2.32	2.18	2.09	2.02	1.97	1.93	1.89
26	2.91	2.52	2.31	2.17	2.08	2.01	1.96	1.92	1.88
27	2.90	2.51	2.30	2.17	2.07	2.00	1.95	1.91	1.87
28	2.89	2.50	2.29	2.16	2.06	2.00	1.94	1.90	1.87
29	2.89	2.50	2.28	2.15	2.06	1.99	1.93	1.89	1.86
30	2.88	2.49	2.28	2.14	2.05	1.98	1.93	1.88	1.85
40	2.84	2.44	2.23	2.09	2.00	1.93	1.87	1.83	1.79
60	2.79	2.39	2.18	2.04	1.95	1.87	1.82	1.77	1.74
120	2.75	2.35	2.13	1.99	1.90	1.82	1.77	1.72	1.68
∞	2.71	2.30	2.08	1.94	1.85	1.77	1.72	1.67	1.63

Denominator Degrees of Freedom

Source: From M. Merrington and C. M. Thompson, "Tables of Percentage Points of the Inverted Beta (*F*)-Distribution," *Biometrika*, 1943, 33, 73–88.

(continued)

TABLE VII (continued)

s_2^2	NUMERATOR DEGREES OF FREEDOM									
s_1^2	10	12	15	20	24	30	40	60	120	∞
1	60.19	60.71	61.22	61.74	62.00	62.26	62.53	62.79	63.06	63.33
2	9.39	9.41	9.42	9.44	9.45	9.46	9.47	9.47	9.48	9.49
3	5.23	5.22	5.20	5.18	5.18	5.17	5.16	5.15	5.14	5.13
4	3.92	3.90	3.87	3.84	3.83	3.82	3.80	3.79	3.78	3.76
5	3.30	3.27	3.24	3.21	3.19	3.17	3.16	3.14	3.12	3.10
6	2.94	2.90	2.87	2.84	2.82	2.80	2.78	2.76	2.74	2.72
7	2.70	2.67	2.63	2.59	2.58	2.56	2.54	2.51	2.49	2.47
8	2.54	2.50	2.46	2.42	2.40	2.38	2.36	2.34	2.32	2.29
9	2.42	2.38	2.34	2.30	2.28	2.25	2.23	2.21	2.18	2.16
10	2.32	2.28	2.24	2.20	2.18	2.16	2.13	2.11	2.08	2.06
11	2.25	2.21	2.17	2.12	2.10	2.08	2.05	2.03	2.00	1.97
12	2.19	2.15	2.10	2.06	2.04	2.01	1.99	1.96	1.93	1.90
13	2.14	2.10	2.05	2.01	1.98	1.96	1.93	1.90	1.88	1.85
14	2.10	2.05	2.01	1.96	1.94	1.91	1.89	1.86	1.83	1.80
15	2.06	2.02	1.97	1.92	1.90	1.87	1.85	1.82	1.79	1.76
16	2.03	1.99	1.94	1.89	1.87	1.84	1.81	1.78	1.75	1.72
17	2.00	1.96	1.91	1.86	1.84	1.81	1.78	1.75	1.72	1.69
18	1.98	1.93	1.89	1.84	1.81	1.78	1.75	1.72	1.69	1.66
19	1.96	1.91	1.86	1.81	1.79	1.76	1.73	1.70	1.67	1.63
20	1.94	1.89	1.84	1.79	1.77	1.74	1.71	1.68	1.64	1.61
21	1.92	1.87	1.83	1.78	1.75	1.72	1.69	1.66	1.62	1.59
22	1.90	1.86	1.81	1.76	1.73	1.70	1.67	1.64	1.60	1.57
23	1.89	1.84	1.80	1.74	1.72	1.69	1.66	1.62	1.59	1.55
24	1.88	1.83	1.78	1.73	1.70	1.67	1.64	1.61	1.57	1.53
25	1.87	1.82	1.77	1.72	1.69	1.66	1.63	1.59	1.56	1.52
26	1.86	1.81	1.76	1.71	1.68	1.65	1.61	1.58	1.54	1.50
27	1.85	1.80	1.75	1.70	1.67	1.64	1.60	1.57	1.53	1.49
28	1.84	1.79	1.74	1.69	1.66	1.63	1.59	1.56	1.52	1.48
29	1.83	1.78	1.73	1.68	1.65	1.62	1.58	1.55	1.51	1.47
30	1.82	1.77	1.72	1.67	1.64	1.61	1.57	1.54	1.50	1.46
40	1.76	1.71	1.66	1.61	1.57	1.54	1.51	1.47	1.42	1.38
60	1.71	1.66	1.60	1.54	1.51	1.48	1.44	1.40	1.35	1.29
120	1.65	1.60	1.55	1.48	1.45	1.41	1.37	1.32	1.26	1.19
∞	1.60	1.55	1.49	1.42	1.38	1.34	1.30	1.24	1.17	1.00

Denominator Degrees of Freedom

TABLE VIII   Critical Values of the F-Distribution, F_α (dfs$_1^2$, dfs$_2^2$), For $\alpha = 0.05$

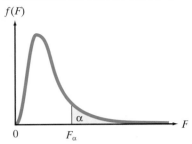

s_2^2	\multicolumn{9}{c}{NUMERATOR DEGREES OF FREEDOM (s_1^2)}
	1	2	3	4	5	6	7	8	9
1	161.4	199.5	215.7	224.6	230.2	234.0	236.8	238.9	240.5
2	18.51	19.00	19.16	19.25	19.30	19.33	19.35	19.37	19.38
3	10.13	9.55	9.28	9.12	9.01	8.94	8.89	8.85	8.81
4	7.71	6.94	6.59	6.39	6.26	6.16	6.09	6.04	6.00
5	6.61	5.79	5.41	5.19	5.05	4.95	4.88	4.82	4.77
6	5.99	5.14	4.76	4.53	4.39	4.28	4.21	4.15	4.10
7	5.59	4.74	4.35	4.12	3.97	3.87	3.79	3.73	3.68
8	5.32	4.46	4.07	3.84	3.69	3.58	3.50	3.44	3.39
9	5.12	4.26	3.86	3.63	3.48	3.37	3.29	3.23	3.18
10	4.96	4.10	3.71	3.48	3.33	3.22	3.14	3.07	3.02
11	4.84	3.98	3.59	3.36	3.20	3.09	3.01	2.95	2.90
12	4.75	3.89	3.49	3.26	3.11	3.00	2.91	2.85	2.80
13	4.67	3.81	3.41	3.18	3.03	2.92	2.83	2.77	2.71
14	4.60	3.74	3.34	3.11	2.96	2.85	2.76	2.70	2.65
15	4.54	3.68	3.29	3.06	2.90	2.79	2.71	2.64	2.59
16	4.49	3.63	3.24	3.01	2.85	2.74	2.66	2.59	2.54
17	4.45	3.59	3.20	2.96	2.81	2.70	2.61	2.55	2.49
18	4.41	3.55	3.16	2.93	2.77	2.66	2.58	2.51	2.46
19	4.38	3.52	3.13	2.90	2.74	2.63	2.54	2.48	2.42
20	4.35	3.49	3.10	2.87	2.71	2.60	2.51	2.45	2.39
21	4.32	3.47	3.07	2.84	2.68	2.57	2.49	2.42	2.37
22	4.30	3.44	3.05	2.82	2.66	2.55	2.46	2.40	2.34
23	4.28	3.42	3.03	2.80	2.64	2.53	2.44	2.37	2.32
24	4.26	3.40	3.01	2.78	2.62	2.51	2.42	2.36	2.30
25	4.24	3.39	2.99	2.76	2.60	2.49	2.40	2.34	2.28
26	4.23	3.37	2.98	2.74	2.59	2.47	2.39	2.32	2.77
27	4.21	3.35	2.96	2.73	2.57	2.46	2.37	2.31	2.25
28	4.20	3.34	2.95	2.71	2.56	2.45	2.36	2.29	2.24
29	4.18	3.33	2.93	2.70	2.55	2.43	2.35	2.28	2.22
30	4.17	3.32	2.92	2.69	2.53	2.42	2.33	2.27	2.21
40	4.08	3.23	2.84	2.61	2.45	2.34	2.25	2.18	2.12
60	4.00	3.15	2.76	2.53	2.37	2.25	2.17	2.10	2.04
120	3.92	3.07	2.68	2.45	2.29	2.17	2.09	2.02	1.96
∞	3.84	3.00	2.60	2.37	2.21	2.10	2.01	1.94	1.88

Denominator Degrees of Freedom

Source: From M. Merrington and C. M. Thompson, "Tables of Percentage Points of the Inverted Beta (*F*)-Distribution." *Biometrika*, 1943, 33, 73–88.

(continued)

TABLE VIII   *(continued)*

s_2^2	s_1^2	NUMERATOR DEGREES OF FREEDOM									
		10	12	15	20	24	30	40	60	120	∞
	1	241.9	243.9	245.9	248.0	249.1	250.1	251.1	252.2	253.3	254.3
	2	19.40	19.41	19.43	19.45	19.45	19.46	19.47	19.48	19.49	19.50
	3	8.79	8.74	8.70	8.66	8.64	8.62	8.59	8.57	8.55	8.53
	4	5.96	5.91	5.86	5.80	5.77	5.75	5.72	5.69	5.66	5.63
	5	4.74	4.68	4.62	4.56	4.53	4.50	4.46	4.43	4.40	4.36
	6	4.06	4.00	3.94	3.87	3.84	3.81	3.77	3.74	3.70	3.67
	7	3.64	3.57	3.51	3.44	3.41	3.38	3.34	3.30	3.27	3.23
	8	3.35	3.28	3.22	3.15	3.12	3.08	3.04	3.01	2.97	2.93
	9	3.14	3.07	3.01	2.94	2.90	2.86	2.83	2.79	2.75	2.71
Denominator Degrees of Freedom	10	2.98	2.91	2.85	2.77	2.74	2.70	2.66	2.62	2.58	2.54
	11	2.85	2.79	2.72	2.65	2.61	2.57	2.53	2.49	2.45	2.40
	12	2.75	2.69	2.62	2.54	2.51	2.47	2.43	2.38	2.34	2.30
	13	2.67	2.60	2.53	2.46	2.42	2.38	2.34	2.30	2.25	2.21
	14	2.60	2.53	2.46	2.39	2.35	2.31	2.27	2.22	2.18	2.13
	15	2.54	2.48	2.40	2.33	2.29	2.25	2.20	2.16	2.11	2.07
	16	2.49	2.42	2.35	2.28	2.24	2.19	2.15	2.11	2.06	2.01
	17	2.45	2.38	2.31	2.23	2.19	2.15	2.10	2.06	2.01	1.96
	18	2.41	2.34	2.27	2.19	2.15	2.11	2.06	2.02	1.97	1.92
	19	2.38	2.31	2.23	2.16	2.11	2.07	2.03	1.98	1.93	1.88
	20	2.35	2.28	2.20	2.12	2.08	2.04	1.99	1.95	1.90	1.84
	21	2.32	2.25	2.18	2.10	2.05	2.01	1.96	1.92	1.87	1.81
	22	2.30	2.23	2.15	2.07	2.03	1.98	1.94	1.89	1.84	1.78
	23	2.27	2.20	2.13	2.05	2.01	1.96	1.91	1.86	1.81	1.76
	24	2.25	2.18	2.11	2.03	1.98	1.94	1.89	1.84	1.79	1.73
	25	2.24	2.16	2.09	2.01	1.96	1.92	1.87	1.82	1.77	1.71
	26	2.22	2.15	2.07	1.99	1.95	1.90	1.85	1.80	1.75	1.69
	27	2.20	2.13	2.06	1.97	1.93	1.88	1.84	1.79	1.73	1.67
	28	2.19	2.12	2.04	1.96	1.91	1.87	1.82	1.77	1.71	1.65
	29	2.18	2.10	2.03	1.94	1.90	1.85	1.81	1.75	1.70	1.64
	30	2.16	2.09	2.01	1.93	1.89	1.84	1.79	1.74	1.68	1.62
	40	2.08	2.00	1.92	1.84	1.79	1.74	1.69	1.64	1.58	1.51
	60	1.99	1.92	1.84	1.75	1.70	1.65	1.59	1.53	1.47	1.39
	120	1.91	1.83	1.75	1.66	1.61	1.55	1.50	1.43	1.35	1.25
	∞	1.83	1.75	1.67	1.57	1.52	1.46	1.39	1.32	1.22	1.00

TABLE IX   Critical Values of the *F*-Distribution, F_α (dfs$_1^2$, dfs$_2^2$), For α = 0.025

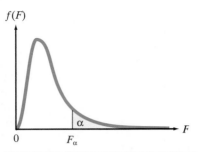

s_2^2 \ s_1^2	NUMERATOR DEGREES OF FREEDOM								
	1	2	3	4	5	6	7	8	9
1	647.8	799.5	864.2	899.6	921.8	937.1	948.2	956.7	963.3
2	38.51	39.00	39.17	39.25	39.30	39.33	39.36	39.37	39.39
3	17.44	16.04	15.44	15.10	14.88	14.73	14.62	14.54	14.47
4	12.22	10.65	9.98	9.60	9.36	9.20	9.07	8.98	8.90
5	10.01	8.43	7.76	7.39	7.15	6.98	6.85	6.76	6.68
6	8.81	7.26	6.60	6.23	5.99	5.82	5.70	5.60	5.52
7	8.07	6.54	5.89	5.52	5.29	5.12	4.99	4.90	4.82
8	7.57	6.06	5.42	5.05	4.82	4.65	4.53	4.43	4.36
9	7.21	5.71	5.08	4.72	4.48	4.32	4.20	4.10	4.03
10	6.94	5.46	4.83	4.47	4.24	4.07	3.95	3.85	3.78
11	6.72	5.26	4.63	4.28	4.04	3.88	3.76	3.66	3.59
12	6.55	5.10	4.47	4.12	3.89	3.73	3.61	3.51	3.44
13	6.41	4.97	4.35	4.00	3.77	3.60	3.48	3.39	3.31
14	6.30	4.86	4.24	3.89	3.66	3.50	3.38	3.29	3.21
15	6.20	4.77	4.15	3.80	3.58	3.41	3.29	3.20	3.12
16	6.12	4.69	4.08	3.73	3.50	3.34	3.22	3.12	3.05
17	6.04	4.62	4.01	3.66	3.44	3.28	3.16	3.06	2.98
18	5.98	4.56	3.95	3.61	3.38	3.22	3.10	3.01	2.93
19	5.92	4.51	3.90	3.56	3.33	3.17	3.05	2.96	2.88
20	5.87	4.46	3.86	3.51	3.29	3.13	3.01	2.91	2.84
21	5.83	4.42	3.82	3.48	3.25	3.09	2.97	2.87	2.80
22	5.79	4.38	3.78	3.44	3.22	3.05	2.93	2.84	2.76
23	5.75	4.35	3.75	3.41	3.18	3.02	2.90	2.81	2.73
24	5.72	4.32	3.72	3.38	3.15	2.99	2.87	2.78	2.70
25	5.69	4.29	3.69	3.35	3.13	2.97	2.85	2.75	2.68
26	5.66	4.27	3.67	3.33	3.10	2.94	2.82	2.73	2.65
27	5.63	4.24	3.65	3.31	3.08	2.92	2.80	2.71	2.63
28	5.61	4.22	3.63	3.29	3.06	2.90	2.78	2.69	2.61
29	5.59	4.20	3.61	3.27	3.04	2.88	2.76	2.67	2.59
30	5.57	4.18	3.59	3.25	3.03	2.87	2.75	2.65	2.57
40	5.42	4.05	3.46	3.13	2.90	2.74	2.62	2.53	2.45
60	5.29	3.93	3.34	3.01	2.79	2.63	2.51	2.41	2.33
120	5.15	3.80	3.23	2.89	2.67	2.52	2.39	2.30	2.22
∞	5.02	3.69	3.12	2.79	2.57	2.41	2.29	2.19	2.11

Denominator Degrees of Freedom

Source: From M. Merrington and C. M. Thompson, "Tables of Percentage Points of the Inverted Beta (*F*)-Distribution," *Biometrika*, 1943, 33, 73–88.

(continued)

TABLE IX   *(continued)*

s_2^2 \ s_1^2	NUMERATOR DEGREES OF FREEDOM									
	10	**12**	**15**	**20**	**24**	**30**	**40**	**60**	**120**	**∞**
1	968.6	976.7	984.9	993.1	997.2	1,001	1,006	1,010	1,014	1,018
2	39.40	39.41	39.43	39.45	39.46	39.46	39.47	39.48	39.49	39.50
3	14.42	14.34	14.25	14.17	14.12	14.08	14.04	13.99	13.95	13.90
4	8.84	8.75	8.66	8.56	8.51	8.46	8.41	8.36	8.31	8.26
5	6.62	6.52	6.43	6.33	6.28	6.23	6.18	6.12	6.07	6.02
6	5.46	5.37	5.27	5.17	5.12	5.07	5.01	4.96	4.90	4.85
7	4.76	4.67	4.57	4.47	4.42	4.36	4.31	4.25	4.20	4.14
8	4.30	4.20	4.10	4.00	3.95	3.89	3.84	3.78	3.73	3.67
9	3.96	3.87	3.77	3.67	3.61	3.56	3.51	3.45	3.39	3.33
10	3.72	3.62	3.52	3.42	3.37	3.31	3.26	3.20	3.14	3.08
11	3.53	3.43	3.33	3.23	3.17	3.12	3.06	3.00	2.94	2.88
12	3.37	3.28	3.18	3.07	3.02	2.96	2.91	2.85	2.79	2.72
13	3.25	3.15	3.05	2.95	2.89	2.84	2.78	2.72	2.66	2.60
14	3.15	3.05	2.95	2.84	2.79	2.73	2.67	2.61	2.55	2.49
15	3.06	2.96	2.86	2.76	2.70	2.64	2.59	2.52	2.46	2.40
16	2.99	2.89	2.79	2.68	2.63	2.57	2.51	2.45	2.38	2.32
17	2.92	2.82	2.72	2.62	2.56	2.50	2.44	2.38	2.32	2.25
18	2.87	2.77	2.67	2.56	2.50	2.44	2.38	2.32	2.26	2.19
19	2.82	2.72	2.62	2.51	2.45	2.39	2.33	2.27	2.20	2.13
20	2.77	2.68	2.57	2.46	2.41	2.35	2.29	2.22	2.16	2.09
21	2.73	2.64	2.53	2.42	2.37	2.31	2.25	2.18	2.11	2.04
22	2.70	2.60	2.50	2.39	2.33	2.27	2.21	2.14	2.08	2.00
23	2.67	2.57	2.47	2.36	2.30	2.24	2.18	2.11	2.04	1.97
24	2.64	2.54	2.44	2.33	2.27	2.21	2.15	2.08	2.01	1.94
25	2.61	2.51	2.41	2.30	2.24	2.18	2.12	2.05	1.98	1.91
26	2.59	2.49	2.39	2.28	2.22	2.16	2.09	2.03	1.95	1.88
27	2.57	2.47	2.36	2.25	2.19	2.13	2.07	2.00	1.93	1.85
28	2.55	2.45	2.34	2.23	2.17	2.11	2.05	1.98	1.91	1.83
29	2.53	2.43	2.32	2.21	2.15	2.09	2.03	1.96	1.89	1.81
30	2.51	2.41	2.31	2.20	2.14	2.07	2.01	1.94	1.87	1.79
40	2.39	2.29	2.18	2.07	2.01	1.94	1.88	1.80	1.72	1.64
60	2.27	2.17	2.06	1.94	1.88	1.82	1.74	1.67	1.58	1.48
120	2.16	2.05	1.94	1.82	1.76	1.69	1.61	1.53	1.43	1.31
∞	2.05	1.94	1.83	1.71	1.64	1.57	1.48	1.39	1.27	1.00

Denominator Degrees of Freedom

TABLE X   Critical Values of the *F*-Distribution, F_α (dfs_1^2, dfs_2^2), For $\alpha = 0.01$

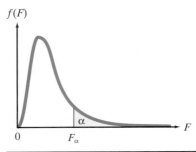

s_2^2	s_1^2 NUMERATOR DEGREES OF FREEDOM								
	1	2	3	4	5	6	7	8	9
1	4,052	4,999.5	5,403	5,625	5,764	5,859	5,928	5,982	6,022
2	98.50	99.00	99.17	99.25	99.30	99.33	99.36	99.37	99.39
3	34.12	30.82	29.46	28.71	28.24	27.91	27.67	27.49	27.35
4	21.20	18.00	16.69	15.98	15.52	15.21	14.98	14.80	14.66
5	16.26	13.27	12.06	11.39	10.97	10.67	10.46	10.29	10.16
6	13.75	10.92	9.78	9.15	8.75	8.47	8.26	8.10	7.98
7	12.25	9.55	8.45	7.85	7.46	7.19	6.99	6.84	6.72
8	11.26	8.65	7.59	7.01	6.63	6.37	6.18	6.03	5.91
9	10.56	8.02	6.99	6.42	6.06	5.80	5.61	5.47	5.35
10	10.04	7.56	6.55	5.99	5.64	5.39	5.20	5.06	4.94
11	9.65	7.21	6.22	5.67	5.32	5.07	4.89	4.74	4.63
12	9.33	6.93	5.95	5.41	5.06	4.82	4.64	4.50	4.39
13	9.07	6.70	5.74	5.21	4.86	4.62	4.44	4.30	4.19
14	8.86	6.51	5.56	5.04	4.69	4.46	4.28	4.14	4.03
15	8.68	6.36	5.42	4.89	4.56	4.32	4.14	4.00	3.89
16	8.53	6.23	5.29	4.77	4.44	4.20	4.03	3.89	3.78
17	8.40	6.11	5.18	4.67	4.34	4.10	3.93	3.79	3.68
18	8.29	6.01	5.09	4.58	4.25	4.01	3.84	3.71	3.60
19	8.18	5.93	5.01	4.50	4.17	3.94	3.77	3.63	3.52
20	8.10	5.85	4.94	4.43	4.10	3.87	3.70	3.56	3.46
21	8.02	5.78	4.87	4.37	4.04	3.81	3.64	3.51	3.40
22	7.95	5.72	4.82	4.31	3.99	3.76	3.59	3.45	3.35
23	7.88	5.66	4.76	4.26	3.94	3.71	3.54	3.41	3.30
24	7.82	5.61	4.72	4.22	3.90	3.67	3.50	3.36	3.26
25	7.77	5.57	4.68	4.18	3.85	3.63	3.46	3.32	3.22
26	7.72	5.53	4.64	4.14	3.82	3.59	3.42	3.29	3.18
27	7.68	5.49	4.60	4.11	3.78	3.56	3.39	3.26	3.15
28	7.64	5.45	4.57	4.07	3.75	3.53	3.36	3.23	3.12
29	7.60	5.42	4.54	4.04	3.73	3.50	3.33	3.20	3.09
30	7.56	5.39	4.51	4.02	3.70	3.47	3.30	3.17	3.07
40	7.31	5.18	4.31	3.83	3.51	3.29	3.12	2.99	2.89
60	7.08	4.98	4.13	3.65	3.34	3.12	2.95	2.82	2.72
120	6.85	4.79	3.95	3.48	3.17	2.96	2.79	2.66	2.56
∞	6.63	4.61	3.78	3.32	3.02	2.80	2.64	2.51	2.41

Denominator Degrees of Freedom

Source: From M. Merrington and C. M. Thompson, "Tables of Percentage Points of the Inverted Beta (*F*)-Distribution," *Biometrika*, 1943, 33, 73–88.

(continued)

TABLE XI *(continued)*

s_2^2 \\ s_1^2	10	12	15	20	24	30	40	60	120	∞
	NUMERATOR DEGREES OF FREEDOM									
1	6,056	6,106	6,157	6,209	6,235	6,261	6,287	6,313	6,339	6,366
2	99.40	99.42	99.43	99.45	99.46	99.47	99.47	99.48	99.49	99.50
3	27.23	27.05	26.87	26.69	26.60	26.50	26.41	26.32	26.22	26.13
4	14.55	14.37	14.20	14.02	13.93	13.84	13.75	13.65	13.56	13.46
5	10.05	9.89	9.72	9.55	9.47	9.38	9.29	9.20	9.11	9.02
6	7.87	7.72	7.56	7.40	7.31	7.23	7.14	7.06	6.97	6.88
7	6.62	6.47	6.31	6.16	6.07	5.99	5.91	5.82	5.74	5.65
8	5.81	5.67	5.52	5.36	5.28	5.20	5.12	5.03	4.95	4.86
9	5.26	5.11	4.96	4.81	4.73	4.65	4.57	4.48	4.40	4.31
10	4.85	4.71	4.56	4.41	4.33	4.25	4.17	4.08	4.00	3.91
11	4.54	4.40	4.25	4.10	4.02	3.94	3.86	3.78	3.69	3.60
12	4.30	4.16	4.01	3.86	3.78	3.70	3.62	3.54	3.45	3.36
13	4.10	3.96	3.82	3.66	3.59	3.51	3.43	3.34	3.25	3.17
14	3.94	3.80	3.66	3.51	3.43	3.35	3.27	3.18	3.09	3.00
15	3.80	3.67	3.52	3.37	3.29	3.21	3.13	3.05	2.96	2.87
16	3.69	3.55	3.41	3.26	3.18	3.10	3.02	2.93	2.84	2.75
17	3.59	3.46	3.31	3.16	3.08	3.00	2.92	2.83	2.75	2.65
18	3.51	3.37	3.23	3.08	3.00	2.92	2.84	2.75	2.66	2.57
19	3.43	3.30	3.15	3.00	2.92	2.84	2.76	2.67	2.58	2.49
20	3.37	3.23	3.09	2.94	2.86	2.78	2.69	2.61	2.52	2.42
21	3.31	3.17	3.03	2.88	2.80	2.72	2.64	2.55	2.46	2.36
22	3.26	3.12	2.98	2.83	2.75	2.67	2.58	2.50	2.40	2.31
23	3.21	3.07	2.93	2.78	2.70	2.62	2.54	2.45	2.35	2.26
24	3.17	3.03	2.89	2.74	2.66	2.58	2.49	2.40	2.31	2.21
25	3.13	2.99	2.85	2.70	2.62	2.54	2.45	2.36	2.27	2.17
26	3.09	2.96	2.81	2.66	2.58	2.50	2.42	2.33	2.23	2.13
27	3.06	2.93	2.78	2.63	2.55	2.47	2.38	2.29	2.20	2.10
28	3.03	2.90	2.75	2.60	2.52	2.44	2.35	2.26	2.17	2.06
29	3.00	2.87	2.73	2.57	2.49	2.41	2.33	2.23	2.14	2.03
30	2.98	2.84	2.70	2.55	2.47	2.39	2.30	2.21	2.11	2.01
40	2.80	2.66	2.52	2.37	2.29	2.20	2.11	2.02	1.92	1.80
60	2.63	2.50	2.35	2.20	2.12	2.03	1.94	1.84	1.73	1.60
120	2.47	2.34	2.19	2.03	1.95	1.86	1.76	1.66	1.53	1.38
∞	2.32	2.18	2.04	1.88	1.79	1.70	1.59	1.47	1.32	1.00

Denominator Degrees of Freedom

APPENDIX E: TI-83 Plus INSTRUCTIONS

Instructions To Enter Data, Sort Data And Insert a New LIST.

TO ENTER DATA INTO A STAT LIST:

1) Press STAT to display EDIT menu shown in VIEW SCREEN 1.

VIEW SCREEN 1

2) Press ENTER to select 1:EDIT
This displays Lists L1, L2, and L3 shown in VIEW SCREEN 2.

VIEW SCREEN 2

ENTERING DATA INTO L1:

1) Move cursor into List L1

2) Key data value & press ENTER
Repeat until all data are entered

EXAMPLE:

Enter: 19, 16, 48, 42, 33 into L1. Notice the highlighted value of L1 is displayed on the bottom of the screen. Observe in VIEW SCREEN 3, the data value 33 is represented as $L1(5) = 33$.

VIEW SCREEN 3

SORTING A LIST IN ASCENDING ORDER:

1) Press STAT to display EDIT menu shown in VIEW SCREEN 4.

VIEW SCREEN 4

2) Select 2 for 2:SORTA(
SORTA(appears on home screen

3) Press 2nd & 1 for List L1

4) Press ENTER & **DONE** appears on home screen indicating L1 has been sorted in ascending order.

To VIEW List L1:

1) Press STAT & ENTER to select 1:EDIT. List L1 appears in ascending order shown in VIEW SCREEN 5.

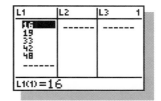

VIEW SCREEN 5

SORTING A LIST IN DESCENDING ORDER:

1) Press STAT

2) Select 3 for 3:SORTD(to sort data in descending order. SORTD(appears on home screen

3) Press 2nd & 1 for List L1

4) Press ENTER & **DONE** appears indicating L1 has been sorted in descending order.

To VIEW List L1:

Press STAT & ENTER to select 1:EDIT. List L1 appears in descending order shown in VIEW SCREEN 6.

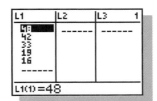

VIEW SCREEN 6

TO EDIT A VALUE WITHIN A LIST:

1) Press STAT & ENTER to select 1:EDIT
2) Highlight data value within List to be changed.
3) Key new value over old value and press ENTER

DELETING A VALUE FROM A LIST:

1) Highlight data value
2) Press DEL **NOTE: CLEAR KEY WILL NOT DEL-ETE A DATA VALUE!**

TO CREATE A NEW LIST NAMED AVG:
EXAMPLE: To create a new List called *AVG between L1 and L2*:

1) Press STAT & ENTER to select 1:EDIT
2) Use up cursor ▲ to highlight List L2
3) Press 2nd & INS (DEL key) keys
   A blank List will be displayed between L1 and L2 and at the bottom of the screen the NAME= prompt appears shown in VIEW SCREEN 7.

VIEW SCREEN 7

4) Input the name AVG
   (Reminder: the first character of a List name must be a letter and cannot be more than 5 characters long)

5) Press ENTER
   A new List named AVG will appear between Lists L1 and L2 as shown in VIEW SCREEN 8.

VIEW SCREEN 8

USING THE TI-83 Plus TO PLOT A HISTOGRAM

GRAPHS FOR ONE VARIABLE STATS:
I: HISTOGRAMS

TO CONSTRUCT A HISTOGRAM:

1) ENTER data values in L1

2) Press WINDOW to display the **WINDOW** variable values.
VIEW SCREEN 9 shows the default values for: Xmin, Xmax, Xscl, Ymin, Ymax, Yscl, Xres.

VIEW SCREEN 9

3) Set values for each window variable using the following guide for a **HISTOGRAM.**

For a HISTOGRAM:
set XMIN = **smallest data value**
set XMAX > **largest data value**
set XSCL = **class width**
set YMIN = **0**
set YMAX >   **greatest class freq.**
set YSCL = **1 OR appropriate frequency scale**
set Xres = **1**

4) Press 2nd & STAT PLOT (Y = key)
The **STAT PLOTS Menu** is displayed with 1:PLOT1 . . . highlighted.

5) Press ENTER to display **stat plot editor** screen for Plot 1. This is shown in VIEW SCREEN 10.

VIEW SCREEN 10

6) Highlight ON & press ENTER

7) Highlight **HISTOGRAM:** 3rd graph to right of TYPE and press ENTER

8) For Xlist: : key in the name of data List. For this example, key in L1 and press ENTER

9) For Freq: press ENTER for 1

The previous inputs to generate a Histogram are shown in VIEW SCREEN 11.

VIEW SCREEN 11

10) Press GRAPH to display the HISTOGRAM.

A HISTOGRAM for the data set in CHAPTER 2 PROBLEM #132 USING SIX CLASSES is shown in VIEW SCREEN 12 using the following WINDOW variable settings:

Xmin =   40
Xmax = 101
Xscl =   10
Ymin =   0
Ymax =   12
Yscl =   1
Xres =   1

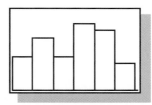

VIEW SCREEN 12

TO DISPLAY THE CLASS LIMITS AND CLASS FREQUENCIES OF A HISTOGRAM

1) Press TRACE : a blinking cursor appears at top center of first bar of the histogram. In lower left corner of the screen appear the quantities: Min, Max and n.
These quantities represent:

Min = lower class limit of bar highlighted by cursor
Max < lower class limit of bar to the right of cursor
n = frequency of bar highlighted by cursor

VIEW SCREEN 13 shows **TRACE information of 1st bar of HISTOGRAM** for data set in **CHAPTER 2: PROBLEM #132.**

VIEW SCREEN 13

P1:L1 in the upper left corner identifies the HISTOGRAM as **STAT PLOT P1** where **L1** contains the data. Notice in the lower left screen are the values for the first bar: **Min = 40, Max < 50 & n = 5.** These values indicate that the *FIRST class* has a lower limit of 40 **(Mn = 40)** with a class frequency of 5 **(n = 5)** while the *SECOND class* has a lower limit of 50 **(Max < 50)**.

2) Use cursor to display the class marks and frequencies of the other bars of the Histogram.

DISPLAYING CLASS BOUNDARIES

To display the class boundaries, you need to change only the Xmin value of the Window variables to the lower class boundary of the 1st class. For this problem, we ONLY change the Xmin value to 39.5. To accomplished this:

1) Press   WINDOW

2) Key 39.5 (lower boundary of 1st class) for Xmin & press   ENTER

3) Press   GRAPH   to display HISTOGRAM

4) Press   TRACE   to display the boundaries and frequency of the 1st class.

The values **Min = 39.5, Max < 49.5,** and **n = 5** for the 1st class are displayed in VIEW SCREEN 14.

VIEW SCREEN 14

In VIEW SCREEN 14, the boundaries for the 1st class are 39.5 **(inclusive since Min = 39.5)** to 49.5 **(not inclusive since Max < 49.5)**. Use right cursor to display the remaining class boundaries.

USING THE TI-83 Plus TO PLOT A FREQUENCY POLYGON

GRAPHS FOR ONE VARIABLE STATS:
II: FREQUENCY POLYGONS

TO CONSTRUCT A FREQUENCY POLYGON

1) ENTER class marks in L1

2) ENTER corresponding frequencies in L2

REMEMBER TO INCLUDE AN ADDITIONAL CLASS MARK TO THE LEFT OF THE LOWEST CLASS AND TO THE RIGHT OF THE HIGHEST CLASS. THE FREQUENCY FOR EACH OF THESE ADDITIONAL CLASS MARKS IS ZERO!

3) Press WINDOW to set the **WINDOW** variable values using following guide for a Frequency Polygon.

For a FREQUENCY POLYGON:
set Xmin < smallest class mark
set Xmax > largest class mark set Xscl = class width
   OR appropriate scale
set Ymin = 0
set Ymax > greatest class freq.
 set Yscl = 1 OR appropriate frequency scale
 set Xres = 1

4) Press 2nd & STAT PLOT (Y = key) **1:PLOT1. . . . of the STAT PLOTS Menu** is displayed

5) Press ENTER to display **stat plot editor** screen for Stat Plot 1 as shown in VIEW SCREEN 15.

VIEW SCREEN 15

6) Select ON & press ENTER

7) Select **xyLine** graph: 2nd graph to right of TYPE and press ENTER . THIS GRAPH TYPE WILL PRODUCE A FREQUENCY POLYGON.

8) For Xlist: Input **L1** which contains the class marks and press ENTER . **THIS INDICATES THAT LIST L1 CONTAINS THE CLASS MARKS**.

9) For Ylist: Input **L2** which contains the frequencies and press ENTER . **THIS INDICATES THAT List L2 CONTAINS THE FREQUENCIES**.

10) Select + for MARK: and press ENTER .

The selections to generate a Frequency Polygon are shown in VIEW SCREEN 16.

VIEW SCREEN 16

11) Press GRAPH to display FREQUENCY POLYGON. A FREQUENCY POLYGON for the data in Table 2.19 is shown in VIEW SCREEN 17 using the following WINDOW variable settings:

Xmin =   2
Xmax = 45
 Xscl =   5
 Ymin =   0
Ymax = 40
 Yscl =   1
 Xres =   1

VIEW SCREEN 17

TO VERIFY THE CLASS MARKS AND THE CORRESPONDING FREQUENCIES

1) Press TRACE : a blinking cursor appears at the 1st class mark with its frequency as shown in VIEW SCREEN 18.

VIEW SCREEN 18

In the lower left corner of SCREEN 18 appears X = 3 & Y = 0.

FOR A FREQUENCY POLYGON, the X value is the class mark and the Y value is the class frequency. For this frequency polygon, the 1st class has a class mark of : X = 3 with a frequency of: Y = 0.

The **P1:L1,L2** in the upper left corner identifies the graph as Stat Plot 1 where L1 contains the class marks and L2 contains the frequencies.

2) Use cursor keys to identify the class marks and frequencies of the other classes.

USING THE TI-83 Plus TO PLOT AN OGIVE

GRAPHS FOR ONE VARIABLE STATS:
III: OGIVE

TO CONSTRUCT AN OGIVE:

1) ENTER class values in L1
2) ENTER cumulative freq into L2
3) Press WINDOW to set the **WINDOW** variable values using the following guide for an Ogive.

   For an OGIVE:
   set Xmin < smallest class value
   set Xmax > largest class value
   ** set Xscl = class width OR appropriate scale**
   set Ymin = 0
   set Ymax > greatest freq
   ** set Yscl = 1 OR appropriate frequency scale**
   ** set Xres = 1**

4) Press 2nd & STAT PLOT (Y = key) **1:PLOT1 . . .** of the **STAT PLOTS Menu** is displayed.
5) Press ENTER
6) Select ON & press ENTER
7) Select **xyLine** graph: 2nd graph to right of TYPE and press ENTER .
8) For Xlist : Input **L1 which indicates that L1 contains the class values** and press ENTER .
9) For Ylist : Input **L2 which indicates that L2 contains the cumulative frequencies and press** ENTER .
10) Select + for MARK : and press ENTER .

The selections to generate an ogive are shown in VIEW SCREEN 19.

VIEW SCREEN 19

11) Press GRAPH to display OGIVE. An OGIVE for the data in Table 2.21 is shown in VIEW SCREEN 20 with the following WINDOW variable settings:

$$Xmin = 40$$
$$Xmax = 250$$
$$Xscl = 30$$
$$Ymin = 0$$
$$Ymax = 55$$
$$Yscl = 1$$
$$Xres = 1$$

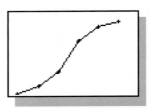

VIEW SCREEN 20

TO VERIFY THE CLASS VALUES AND THE CORRE-SPONDING CUMULATIVE FREQUENCIES

1) Press TRACE : a blinking cursor appears at the 1st class value with its cumulative frequency displayed in VIEW SCREEN 21.

VIEW SCREEN 21

Notice in the lower left corner of VIEW SCREEN 21 appears X = 52 and Y = 0.

FOR AN OGIVE, the X value is the class value and the Y value is the cumulative frequency.
FOR THIS OGIVE, the 1st class has a class value of X = 52 with a cumulative frequency of Y = 0.
The P1:L1,L2 in the upper left corner identifies the graph as Stat Plot 1 where the class values are in List L1 and the cumulative frequencies are in List L2.

2) Use cursor key to identify the class values and cumulative frequencies of the other classes.

USING THE TI-83 Plus TO COMPUTE Σ EXPRESSIONS, MEAN, STANDARD DEVIATION AND 5–NUMBER SUMMARY

STAT ANALYSIS FOR 1-VARIABLE

1-VARIABLE STAT ANALYSIS THE MEAN, Σx^2, Σx, POPULATION and SAMPLE STANDARD DEVIATIONS, n, and the 5-Number Summary: MinX, Q_1, Median, Q_3 & MaxX

1) Press STAT

2) Highlight CALC & 1:1-VAR STATS as shown in VIEW SCREEN 22.

VIEW SCREEN 22

3) Press ENTER & **1-VAR STATS** will appear on the home screen

4) Input List name that contains the data values.
   For **L1:** Press 2nd and 1 as displayed in VIEW SCREEN 23.

VIEW SCREEN 23

5) Press ENTER for 1-VAR STATS results

EXAMPLE:

The 1-VAR STATS results for: *16, 19, 33, 42, 48* are displayed in VIEW SCREENs 24a & 24b.

VIEW SCREEN 24a   VIEW SCREEN 24b

In VIEW SCREEN 24a, the **1-VAR STATS** results shown are:

mean: $\bar{x} = 31.6$

sum of data values: $\Sigma x = 158$

sum of squared values: $\Sigma x^2 = 5774$

sample std dev: $Sx = 13.97497764$

pop std dev: $\sigma x = 12.49959999$

number of data values: $n = 5$

In VIEW SCREEN 24a, the downward arrow appearing next to n = 5 indicates there are additional **1-VAR STATS** results. **To obtain the remaining results shown in VIEW SCREEN 24b, press the down cursor ▾ five times to display these results.** An upward arrow appears at the top of the VIEW SCREEN when you reached the final result of VIEW SCREEN 24b.

The results are:

number of data values: $n = 5$

minimum data value: $minX = 16$

1st quartile: $Q_1 = 17.5$

median: $med = 33$

3rd quartile: $Q_3 = 45$

maximum data value: $maxX = 48$

The last five results of VIEW SCREEN 24b:

MinX, Q_1, Median, Q_3 & MaxX are called the **5-Number Summary**.

USING THE TI-83 Plus TO COMPUTE
POPULATION AND SAMPLE STANDARD DEVIATIONS

After computing the **1-VAR STATS** analysis, you can also retrieve the value of any one of these statistical variables: $\bar{x}$, Σx, Σx^2, **Sx**, σx, **n, minX, Q₁, med, Q₃,** and **maxX** using the VARS key.

One use of the VARS key is to compute the **variance of a sample and a population.**

PROCEDURE TO COMPUTE THE SAMPLE AND POPULATION VARIANCES

Before you can compute the VARIANCES OF A SAMPLE OR A POPULATION, you must first compute 1-VAR STATS on the List containing the sample or population data values. This step will store the appropriate values within the stat variables needed to compute the variance.

Computing the sample variance

1) Press VARS to display the VARS menu shown in VIEW SCREEN 25.

VIEW SCREEN 25

2) Press 5 for 5: STATISTICS to display the STATISTICS MENU shown in VIEW SCREEN 26.

VIEW SCREEN 26

3) Press 3 to select 3: Sx The sample std deviation **Sx** appears on the home screen.

To compute the sample variance, square the sample deviation.

4) Press x^2 key and Enter

The sample variance Sx^2 is computed.

The sample variance for the data: *16, 19, 33, 42, 48* is shown in VIEW SCREEN 27.

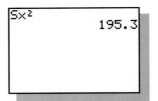

VIEW SCREEN 27

Computing the population variance

1) Press VARS

2) Press 5 for 5: STATISTICS to display the STATISTICS MENU shown in VIEW SCREEN 26.

3) Press 4 to select 4: σx

The population standard deviation σx appears on home screen.

To compute the population variance, square the population standard deviation.

4) Press x^2 key and Enter

The value of the population variance σx^2 is computed.

The population variance for the data: *16, 19, 33, 42, 48* is shown in VIEW SCREEN 28.

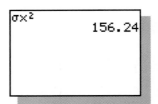

VIEW SCREEN 28

USING THE TI-83 Plus TO DETERMINE THE MODE

The TI-83 plus doesn't compute the mode directly for you. However you can use the sort feature to arrange the data values in numerical order and then scan the data set to identify the mode, if any.

Enter the following data into L1:

19, 18, 21, 20, 19, 20, 23, 21, 22, 18, 23,

21, 22, 23, 21, 19, 19, 21, 22, 23, 18

To sort L1:

1) Press STAT & Select 2 for 2: SortA(. SORTA(appears on home screen.

2) Press 2nd & 1 for List L1 containing data values to be sorted.

This is shown in VIEW SCREEN 29.

VIEW SCREEN 29

3) Press Enter & **Done** appears indicating List L1 has been sorted in ascending order.

4) Press STAT & Enter to display L1 in ascending order shown in VIEW SCREEN 30.

VIEW SCREEN 30

To determine the mode, scan L1 using the down cursor ▼ key to identify the most frequent data value. For this data set, the data value 21 is the mode since it has the greatest frequency.

USING THE TI-83 Plus TO CALCULATE 1-VAR STATS USING TWO LISTS

CALCULATING 1-VAR STATS USING TWO LISTS: L1 & L2 WHERE L1 CONTAINS THE DATA VALUES AND L2 HAS THE CORRESPONDING FREQUENCIES.

Enter the following data values into L1 and the corresponding frequencies into L2.

data values	frequency
90	6
87	4
83	2
79	5
76	6
73	6
69	9

1) Enter data values into L1.
2) Enter corresponding frequencies into L2.
   This is shown in VIEW SCREEN 31.

VIEW SCREEN 31

3) Press STAT
4) Highlight CALC & 1:1-VAR STATS

5) Press ENTER and **1-VAR STATS** appears on home screen
6) Key in **L1,L2**
   where **L1** represents the List containing the data values followed by a comma(the key directly above the 7 key) and L2 which is the List containing the corresponding frequencies.
   This is shown in VIEW SCREEN 32.

VIEW SCREEN 32

8) Press ENTER to display some 1-VAR STATS results shown in VIEW SCREEN 33.

VIEW SCREEN 33

USING STAT LISTS TO COMPUTE THE SUM OF THE DEVIATIONS FROM THE MEAN: $\Sigma(x - \mu)$ or $\Sigma(x - \bar{x})$

TO COMPUTE THE SUM OF THE DEVIATIONS FROM THE MEAN:

$$\Sigma(x - \mu) \text{ or } \Sigma(x - \bar{x})$$

EXAMPLE:
Enter the data values into L1:
6, 2, 4, 5, 3, 1, 7

1) Enter data values into L1
   To compute mean using 1-VAR STATS

2) Press STAT & Highlight CALC

3) Highlight 1:1-VAR STATS & ENTER
   1-VAR STATS appears on home screen

4) Input L1 for List name containing the data values and press ENTER

   Notice, the **mean = 4**.
   Now input the formula to compute the sum of the deviations from the mean. This is accomplished by the steps:

5) Press STAT & ENTER

6) Move cursor to L2

7) Press the up cursor ▲ key to highlight L2 as shown in VIEW SCREEN 34.

VIEW SCREEN 34
Notice at the bottom of the screen, **L2** = is displayed. Once the name of a List is highlighted as shown in VIEW SCREEN 34, a formula can be inserted for the highlighted List.
We need to enter the formula for the deviations from the mean:

(x – mean)

Instead of the letter x, we will input **L1** where the x or data values are listed followed by a minus then a 4 for the mean to obtain the expression:

L2 = (L1-4)

The exact key strokes to obtain this formula as shown at the bottom of VIEW SCREEN 35 are:

Press (key
Press 2nd & 1 to obtain **L1**
Press – (subtraction key)
Press 4 for the mean
Press) key
Press ENTER key

VIEW SCREEN 35
The deviations from the mean are now displayed in L2 shown in VIEW SCREEN 36.

VIEW SCREEN 36
To compute the sum of the deviations in L2:

1) Press 2nd & QUIT (MODE key)

2) Press 2nd & List (STAT key)

3) Highlight MATH.
   This is shown in VIEW SCREEN 37.

```
NAMES OPS MATH
1■min(
2:max(
3:mean(
4:median(
5:sum(
6:prod(
7↓stdDev(
```

VIEW SCREEN 37

4) Press 5 for 5:SUM

5) Input L2 : the name of List to be summed.

6) Press ENTER to obtain the sum of L2.
   Notice, the **SUM** of **L2** is **zero** as shown in VIEW SCREEN 38 which represents the sum of the deviations from the mean.

VIEW SCREEN 38

USING THE TI-83 Plus TO CONSTRUCT BOX PLOTS AND TRACING THE 5-NUMBER SUMMARY

GRAPHS FOR ONE VARIABLE STATS:

I. BOXPLOTS

To create a box plot:

1) ENTER data values into L1

2) Press WINDOW to set the **WINDOW** variable values using the following guide for a Box Plot.

For a BOX PLOT:

set Xmin < smallest data value
set Xmax > largest data value
The values for Xscl, Ymin, Ymax, Yscl and Xres are not used to construct a Boxplot so you can disregard these variables.

3) Press 2nd & STAT PLOT (Y = key) **1:PLOT1** . . . of the **STAT PLOTS Menu** is displayed.

4) Press ENTER to display **stat plot editor** screen for Stat Plot 1 as shown in VIEW SCREEN 39.

VIEW SCREEN 39

5) Select ON & press ENTER

6) For TYPE : select 5th graph:
BOXPLOT to right of TYPE and press ENTER

7) Input **L1**: List name containing the data values and press ENTER

8) Press ENTER to select **1** for Freq:
The selections to generate a BOXPLOT are shown in VIEW SCREEN 40.

VIEW SCREEN 40

9) Press GRAPH
BOXPLOT appears on display.
A BOXPLOT for the data set:
0, 10, 10, 20, 40, 54, 55,

60, 65, 66, 66, 66, 67, 67,
68, 68, 69, 70, 71, 71, 72,
73, 75, 88, 96, 100

is shown in VIEW SCREEN 41 using the following WINDOW variable settings:

Xmin =   0
Xmax = 105
Xscl =   1
Ymin =   0
Ymax =   10
Yscl =   1
Xres =   1

VIEW SCREEN 41

Tracing the 5-NUMBER SUMMARY

The 5-number summary values: minX, Q_1, Med, Q_3, & maxX can be traced from the BOXPLOT:

1) Press TRACE : a blinking cursor appears on the BOX-PLOT.

2) Use cursor keys to trace the values of the 5-Number Summary:
minX, Q_1, Med, Q_3, & maxX on the BOXPLOT. Each value is displayed in the lower left corner of the screen.
In the upper left corner of the screen appears **P1:L1** which indicates this BOXPLOT graph is STAT PLOT 1 and the data values are in LIST L1.
VIEW SCREEN 42 displays the BOXPLOT with the TRACE positioned at the MEDIAN value: Med = 67. Verify the 5-Number Summary is:
minX = 0, Q_1 = 55, Med = 67, Q_3 = 71, & maxX = 100.

VIEW SCREEN 42

USING THE MODBOXPLOT TO DETECT OUTLIERS

GRAPHS FOR ONE VARIABLE STATS:

II. MODIFIED BOXPLOTS

A modified BOXPLOT (or ModBoxplot) graphs all the data values of a List that are within *1.5*IQR of the first (Q1) and third quartile (Q3)* like a typical BOXPLOT. Any data value **BEYOND** these **FENCES** is plotted individually using one of the Marks: □ **or + or** * you select and is defined as an **OUTLIER**. These **outliers** can be identified using the TRACE key and are prompted by: **x = .**

Using the SAME DATA SET, let's construct a ModBoxplot.

To Create a ModBoxplot:

1) ENTER the data into L1.
   Use the following data set:
   0, 10, 10, 20, 40, 54, 55, 60,
   65, 66, 66, 66, 67, 67, 68, 68,
   69, 70, 71, 71, 72, 73, 75, 88,
   96, 100

2) Press WINDOW to set the **WINDOW** variable values using the following guide for ModBoxplot.

For a BOXPLOT or MODBOXPLOT:
set Xmin < smallest data value
set Xmax > largest data value
The values for Xscl, Ymin, Ymax, Yscl and Xres are not used to construct a ModBoxplot so you can disregard these variables.

3) Press 2nd & STAT PLOT (Y = key) **1:PLOT1** . . . of the **STAT PLOTS Menu** is displayed.

4) Press ENTER to display the **stat plot editor** screen for **Stat Plot 1**.

5) Select ON & press ENTER

6) For TYPE : select 4th graph MODBOXPLOT to right of TYPE and press ENTER

7) For Xlist : Input **L1**, the List containing the data values, and press ENTER

8) For Freq : press ENTER to select **1** for Frequency

9) For Mark : select one symbol: □ **or + or** * to use to identify any outliers. For this example, select □ for the mark.

The selections to generate a MODBOXPLOT are shown in VIEW SCREEN 43.

VIEW SCREEN 43

A MODBOXPLOT for the data set in L1 is shown in VIEW SCREEN 44 with the following WINDOW variable settings:

Xmin =	0
Xmax =	105
Xscl =	1
Ymin =	0
Ymax =	10
Yscl =	1
Xres =	1

VIEW SCREEN 44

Notice in VIEW SCREEN 44 there are 5 outliers marked by 5 □ (boxes) beyond the whiskers of the MODBOXPLOT.

IDENTIFYING THE OUTLIERS

1) Press TRACE : a blinking cursor appears on MOD-BOXPLOT.

2) Use cursor keys to identify the **5 number summary** values: **minX, Q1, Med, Q3, maxX and the outliers**.

Notice in VIEW SCREEN 45, the value x = 20 is represented by a **box** □ beyond the left whisker indicating that 20 is an outlier.

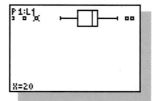

VIEW SCREEN 45

Notice if you move the cursor to the left you should verify that there are additional outliers. These outlier values are: x = 10(twice) and x = 0 (shown as minX = 0). Moving the cursor beyond the right whisker, you should verify that the value x = 96 is also an outlier. This is shown in VIEW SCREEN 46.

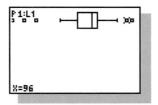

VIEW SCREEN 46

Move the cursor to the last box □ on the right to verify that x = 100 (shown as maxX = 100) is an outlier.

PLOTTING MORE THAN ONE BOXPLOT

The TI-83 Plus can plot 3 BOXPLOTS at once using the three STAT PLOTS. When 3 boxplots are displayed at once, PLOT 1 displays the boxplot on the top of the screen while the boxplot of PLOT 2 is shown in the middle and the boxplot of PLOT 3 is displayed at the bottom.

1) ENTER the data into L1.
    Use the following data set:
     **0, 10, 10, 20, 40, 54, 55, 60,
     65, 66, 66, 66, 67, 67, 68, 68,
     69, 70, 71, 71, 72, 73, 75, 88,
     96, 100**

2) Press WINDOW to set the **WINDOW** variable values using the following guide for BoxPlot and ModBoxplot.

For a BOXPLOT or MODBOXPLOT:
set Xmin < smallest data value
set Xmax > largest data value
Remember, the values for Xscl, Ymin, Ymax, Yscl and Xres are not used to construct a ModBoxplot so you can disregard these variables.

3) Press 2nd & STAT PLOT (Y = key) 1:PLOT1 . . . of the **STAT PLOTS Menu** is displayed.

4) Press ENTER to display stat plot editor screen.
    Input the following to set up the **stat plot editor** screen for **Stat Plot 1**.

5) Select ON & press ENTER

6) For TYPE : select 4th graph:
    MODBOXPLOT to right of TYPE and press ENTER

7) Input **L1** and press ENTER

8) Press ENTER to select 1 for Freq:

9) For Mark : select □ for the mark.

The STAT PLOT 1 selections to generate a MODBOX-PLOT are shown in VIEW SCREEN 47.

VIEW SCREEN 47
Now we will use STAT PLOT 2 and the same data in L1 to graph a BOXPLOT by performing the following steps:

10) Press 2nd & STAT PLOT (Y = key) 1:PLOT1 . . . of the **STAT PLOTS Menu** is displayed.

11) Press 2 & ENTER to display the **stat plot editor** screen for **STAT PLOT 2**.

12) Select ON & press ENTER

13) For TYPE : highlight 5th graph to right of TYPE for BOXPLOT and press ENTER

14) For Xlist : Input **L1** for List name and press ENTER

15) For Freq : press ENTER to select **1** for Frequency
     VIEW SCREEN 48 shows the Stat Plot 2 selections to generate a BOXPLOT using List L1.

VIEW SCREEN 48

16) Press Graph to display two BOXPLOTS as shown in VIEW SCREEN 49.

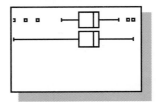

VIEW SCREEN 49
Notice MODBOXPLOT is on the top while the BOX-PLOT is below.

17) Press TRACE to verify the MODBOXPLOT is STAT PLOT 1.
     VIEW SCREEN 50 shows STAT PLOT 1 as the MOD-BOXPLOT with Med = 67 highlighted by a blinking cursor.

VIEW SCREEN 50
The **P1:L1** in the upper left corner indicates MODBOX-PLOT as STAT PLOT 1 using LIST L1.

18) Press down cursor ▾ to highlight the BOXPLOT of STAT PLOT 2 with a blinking cursor at the Med = 67. This is shown in VIEW SCREEN 51.

VIEW SCREEN 51
The **P2:L1** in the upper left corner identifies the BOXPLOT as STAT PLOT 2 using List L1.
Verify that the values for Q_1, Med, and Q_3 are the same for both BOXPLOTS. Explain why this is true and why the values at the end of the whiskers for both boxplots are not the same.

PROCEDURE TO COMPUTE BINOMIAL PROBABILITIES

There are two TI-83 Plus functions to compute binomial probabilities. They are: binompdf(and binomcdf(. We will first illustrate binompdf(. binompdf(n,p,s) computes the binomial probability for a specified success value, **s,** for **n** trials & prob of a success, **p.**

To illustrate binompdf(n,p,s) consider **EXAMPLE 5.18.**

For Example 5.18(a): we use: n = 5, p = 1/4 & s = 3 to compute P(3 correct answers) as follows:

1) Press 2nd & VARS for DISTR to display the Distribution Menu shown in VIEW SCREEN 52.

VIEW SCREEN 52

2) Select **0** for 0:binompdf

(0:binompdf(appears on the home screen shown in VIEW SCREEN 53.

VIEW SCREEN 53

3) Input **5, 1/4, 3** for n, p, s to obtain binompdf (5, 1/4, 3) as shown in VIEW SCREEN 54.

VIEW SCREEN 54

4) Press ENTER to obtain the result shown in VIEW SCREEN 55. Rounding off to 4 decimal places, **P(3 correct answers) ≈ .0879**

VIEW SCREEN 55

For Example 5.18(b): use: n = 5, p = 1/4 & s = 5 to compute P(5 correct answers) as follows:

1) Press 2nd & VARS for DISTR
2) Select **0** for 0:binompdf(
3) Input **5, 1/4, 5** for n,p,s to obtain binompdf(5, 1/4, 5) as shown in VIEW SCREEN 56.

VIEW SCREEN 56

4) Press ENTER to obtain the result shown in VIEW SCREEN 57. Rounding off to 4 decimal places, **P(5 correct answers) ≈ .0010**

VIEW SCREEN 57

For Example 5.18(c): we need to compute: P(at most 2 correct). Remember P(at most 2 correct) equals the **sum** of the binomial probabilities for s = 0 to s = 2.
P(at most 2) = P(s = 0)+P(s = 1)+ P(s = 2)

The function: binomcdf (n, p, s) computes a **cumulative** probability at a specified "s" value. That is **binomcdf(n, p, s) = P(at most s)**. So, **binomcdf (5, 1/4, 2) = P(at most 2)**.
To compute this result:

1) Press 2nd & VARS for DISTR
2) Press ALPHA & **A** (MATH key) for A:binomcdf(
3) Input **5, 1/4, 2** for n, p, s to obtain binomcdf(5, 1/4, 2) as shown in VIEW SCREEN 58.

VIEW SCREEN 58

4) Press ENTER to obtain the result shown in VIEW SCREEN 59. Rounding off to 4 decimal places, **P(at most 2 correct) ≈ .8965**

```
binomcdf(5,1/4,2
)
       .896484375
```

VIEW SCREEN 59

```
binompdf(5,1/4,4
)+binompdf(5,1/4
,5)
         .015625
```

VIEW SCREEN 60

For Example 5.18(d): use binompdf(twice to compute the:
P(at least 4 correct) as shown in VIEW SCREEN 60 to verify:
P(at least 4 correct) ≈ .0156.

PROCEDURE TO COMPUTE PROBABILITIES FOR THE NORMAL DISTRIBUTION

The **TI-83Plus** function normalcdf(**can be used to compute normal distribution probabilities between two z scores.**

normalcdf(z_1,z_2) computes the probability between the z scores, z_1 and z_2, where z_1 represents the lowerbound and z_2 represents the upperbound.

To illustrate normalcdf(consider **EXAMPLE 6.3.**

For Example 6.3(a): to find the area between z = 0 & z = 1.5, then z = 0 is the lowerbound of the area and z = 1.5 is the upperbound.

To compute this area:

1) Press 2nd & VARS for DISTR to display the Distribution Menu shown in VIEW SCREEN 61.

VIEW SCREEN 61

2) Select **2** for 2:normalcdf

(2:normalcdf(appears on the home screen shown in VIEW SCREEN 62.

VIEW SCREEN 62

3) Input 0,1.5 for z_1,z_2 to obtain normalcdf(0,1.5) as shown in VIEW SCREEN 63.

VIEW SCREEN 63

4) Press ENTER to obtain the result shown in VIEW SCREEN 64. Rounding off to 4 decimal places, **area between z = 0 & z = 1.5 ≈ .4332**

VIEW SCREEN 64

Consider EXAMPLE 6.1(a): we need to compute the area to the left of z = −0.53. Whenever we want to compute the area to the LEFT of a z score we will use −4 as the z score representing the LOWER bound.

For area to the left of -0.53:

1) Press 2nd & VARS for DISTR

2) Select **2** for 2:normalcdf(

3) Input -4,-.53 for z_1,z_2 to obtain normalcdf(-4,-.53) as shown in VIEW SCREEN 65.

VIEW SCREEN 65

4) Press ENTER to obtain the result shown in VIEW SCREEN 66. Rounding off to 4 decimal places, **area to LEFT of z = −.53 ≈ .2980**

VIEW SCREEN 66

Notice this result is slightly different from the textbook. This difference is due to the roundoff errors associated with Table II which was used to compute the textbook answer.

Now consider EXAMPLE 6.2(a): we need to compute the area to the right of z = −1.37. To compute the area to the RIGHT of a z score we will use 4 as the z score representing the UPPER bound.

For area to the right of -1.37:

1) Press 2nd & VARS for DISTR

2) Select **2** for 2:normalcdf(

3) Input -1.37,4 for $z_1 z_2$ to obtain normalcdf(-1.37,4) as shown in VIEW SCREEN 67.

VIEW SCREEN 67

4) Press ENTER to obtain the result shown in VIEW SCREEN 68. Rounding off to 4 decimal places, **area to RIGHT of $z = -1.37 \approx .9146$**

VIEW SCREEN 68

Again you will notice a slight discrepancy with the textbook result due to roundoff errors of Table II.

PROCEDURE TO DETERMINE THE Z SCORE GIVEN THE AREA TO THE LEFT OF A NORMAL DISTRIBUTION

The TI-83Plus function invNorm(determines the z score associated with a specified area to the left of the z score
invNorm(area to left as decimal) computes the z score associated given the **area to left** as a **DECIMAL**.

To illustrate invNorm(consider **EXAMPLE 6.5**.

For Example 6.5(a), we need to determine the z score that cuts off the lowest 20% of area. **To determine this z score:**

1) Press 2nd & VARS for DISTR to display the Distribution Menu shown in VIEW SCREEN 69.

VIEW SCREEN 69

2) Select 3 for 3:invNorm(

3:invNorm(appears on the home screen shown in VIEW SCREEN 70.

VIEW SCREEN 70

3) Input **.20** which represents 20% as a decimal to get invNorm(.20) as shown in VIEW SCREEN 71.

VIEW SCREEN 71

4) Press ENTER to obtain the result shown in VIEW SCREEN 72. Rounding off to 2 decimal places, **the z score that cuts off the lowest 20% of area is z ≈ -.84.**

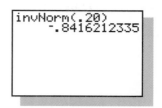

VIEW SCREEN 72

For Example 6.5(b), we need to determine the z score that cuts off the highest 10% of area.

REMEMBER: to use the invNorm(function we need to input the area to the **LEFT** of the z score. The area to the left is 90% or 0.90. **So we need to determine the z score that cuts off the lowest 90%. To determine this z score:**

1) Press 2nd & VARS for DISTR

2) Select **3** for 3:invNorm(

3) Input **.90** which represents 90% as a decimal to get invNorm(.90) as shown in VIEW SCREEN 73.

VIEW SCREEN 73

4) Press ENTER to obtain the result shown in VIEW SCREEN 74. Rounding off to 2 decimal places, **the z score that cuts off the highest 10% of area is z ≈ 1.28.**

VIEW SCREEN 74

For Example 6.5(c), we need to determine the z scores that cutoff the middle 90% of the area. The middle 90% is between two z scores. The smaller z score has 5% of the area to its left. **To determine this z score:**

1) Press 2nd & VARS for DISTR
2) Select 3 for 3:invNorm(
3) Input **.05 which represents the area to the left of the lower z score to obtain** invNorm(.05) as shown in **VIEW SCREEN 75**.

VIEW SCREEN 75

4) Press ENTER to obtain the result shown in VIEW SCREEN 76. Rounding off to 2 decimal places, **the z score that cuts off the lowest 5% of area is z ≈ -1.64**.

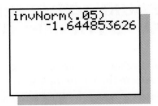

VIEW SCREEN 76

Using the symmetry of the normal curve, the z scores that cutoff the middle 90% are:

z ≈ -1.64 and z ≈ 1.64.

Again you will notice a slight discrepancy with the textbook result due to roundoff errors of Table II.

PROCEDURE TO CONSTRUCT A CONFIDENCE INTERVAL FOR A POPULATION MEAN USING NORMAL DISTRIBUTION WITH STATS INPUT

Confidence Interval For Pop Mean Where Pop Std Dev is KNOWN and Sample Size is greater than 30

1) Press STAT & HIGHLIGHT TESTS

2) Select 7 for **7:ZInterval . . .** input screen for Z confidence interval for a population mean is displayed in VIEW SCREEN 77.

VIEW SCREEN 77

3) **INPUT FOR A ZInterval USING SAMPLE RESULTS:**

   a) at **Inpt:**highlight Stats & ENTER

   b) at σ:input **pop std dev** & ENTER

   c) at $\bar{x}$:input **sample mean** & ENTER

   d) at n:input **sample size** & ENTER

   e) at **C-Level:**input **confidence level (as a decimal)** & ENTER

   f) highlight Calculate & ENTER to determine confidence interval

TO CONSTRUCT A 95% CONFIDENCE INTERVAL FOR THE POP MEAN WHERE:
$\sigma = 18$; $\bar{x} = 114$ & n = 36.

The ZINTERVAL INPUT is:

   a) **Highlight** STATS & ENTER

   b) for σ: INPUT **18** & ENTER

   c) for $\bar{x}$: INPUT **114** & ENTER

   d) for **n:** INPUT **36** & ENTER

   e) for **C-Level:** INPUT .95 & ENTER The **ZInterval** input screen should contain the info shown in VIEW SCREEN 78.

VIEW SCREEN 78

   f) Highlight Calculate & ENTER
   The 95% ZInterval results are shown in VIEW SCREEN 79

VIEW SCREEN 79

The ZInterval results are:

(108.12,119.88) *is the 95% confidence interval for the population mean*

$\bar{x} = 114$ is the sample mean

n = 36 is the sample size

TO CONSTRUCT A 99% CONFIDENCE INTERVAL FOR THE POP MEAN WHERE:

$\sigma = 18$; $\bar{x} = 114$ & n = 36.

1) Press STAT & HIGHLIGHT TESTS

2) Select 7 for **7:ZInterval . . .**

The ZINTERVAL INPUT is:

   a) **Highlight** STATS & ENTER

   b) for σ: INPUT **18** & ENTER

   c) for $\bar{x}$: INPUT **114** & ENTER

   d) for **n:** INPUT **36** & ENTER

   e) for **C-Level:** INPUT .99 & ENTER

   f) Highlight Calculate & ENTER
   The 99% ZInterval results are shown in VIEW SCREEN 80

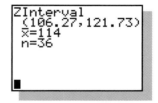

VIEW SCREEN 80

The ZInterval results are:
ZInterval: (106.27,121.73) is the 99% confidence interval for the population mean

$\bar{x} = 114$ *is the **sample mean***

n = 36 *is the **sample size***

PROCEDURE TO CONSTRUCT A CONFIDENCE INTERVAL FOR A POPULATION MEAN USING NORMAL DISTRIBUTION WITH DATA INPUT

Confidence Interval For Pop Mean Where Pop Std Dev is KNOWN and Sample Size is greater than 30

1) Press STAT & HIGHLIGHT TESTS

2) Select 7 for **7:ZInterval** . . . input screen for Z confidence interval for a population mean is displayed in VIEW SCREEN 81.

VIEW SCREEN 81

3) **INPUT FOR A ZInterval USING SAMPLE DATA:**
   a) at **Inpt:**highlight Data & ENTER
   b) at **σ:**input **pop std dev** & ENTER
   c) at **List:**input List name containing **sample data** & ENTER
   d) at **Freq:**input 1 or name of list containing frequencies & ENTER
   e) at **C-Level:**input **confidence level (as a decimal)** & ENTER
   f) highlight Calculate & ENTER to determine confidence interval

TO CONSTRUCT A 95% CONFIDENCE INTERVAL FOR THE POP MEAN WHERE $\sigma = 9$ **AND THE SAMPLE DATA IS ENTERED INTO LIST L1.**

   SAMPLE DATA:
   80 68 91 87 73 90 66 79 80 81
   79 65 94 69 81 77 78 92 81 74
   69 96 78 85 89 76 82 86 79 77 91
   80 92 79 85 79 86 83 76 84

The ZINTERVAL INPUT is:
   a) **Highlight** DATA & ENTER
   b) for **σ:** INPUT **9** & ENTER
   c) for **List:** INPUT **L1** & ENTER
   d) for **Freq:** INPUT **1** & ENTER
   e) for **C-Level:** INPUT .95 & ENTER The **ZInterval** input screen should contain the info shown in VIEW SCREEN 82.

VIEW SCREEN 82

f) Highlight Calculate & ENTER
The 95% ZInterval results are shown in VIEW SCREEN 83

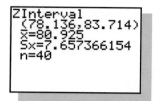

VIEW SCREEN 83
The ZInterval results are:
(78.136,83.714) *is the 95% confidence interval for the population mean*
$\bar{x} = 80.925$ *is the sample mean*
Sx = 7.657366154 *is the sample standard deviation*
n = 40 is the *sample size*

TO CONSTRUCT A 99% CONFIDENCE INTERVAL FOR THE POPULATION MEAN USING THE SAME SAMPLE DATA IN LIST L1, PERFORM THE STEPS.

1) Press STAT & HIGHLIGHT TESTS
2) Select 7 for **7:ZInterval** . . .

The ZINTERVAL INPUT is:
   a) **Highlight** DATA & ENTER
   b) for **σ:** INPUT **9** & ENTER
   c) for **List:** INPUT **L1** & ENTER
   d) for **Freq:** INPUT **1** & ENTER
   e) for **C-Level:** INPUT .99 & ENTER
   f) Highlight Calculate & ENTER
   The 99% ZInterval results are shown in VIEW SCREEN 84

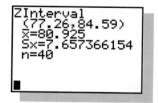

VIEW SCREEN 84
The ZInterval results are:
(77.26,84.59) *is the 99% confidence interval for the population mean*
$\bar{x} = 80.925$ *is the sample mean*
Sx = 7.657366154 *is the sample std deviation*
n = 40 *is the sample size*

PROCEDURE TO CONSTRUCT A CONFIDENCE INTERVAL FOR A POPULATION MEAN USING *t* DISTRIBUTION WITH STATS INPUT

Confidence Interval For Pop Mean Where Pop Std Dev is UNKNOWN

1) Press STAT & HIGHLIGHT TESTS

2) Select 8 for **8:TInterval . . .** input screen for T confidence interval for a population mean is displayed in VIEW SCREEN 85.

VIEW SCREEN 85

3) INPUT FOR A TInterval USING SAMPLE RESULTS:
 a) at **Inpt:**highlight Stats & ENTER
 b) at **$\bar{x}$:input sample mean** & ENTER
 c) at **Sx:**input **sample std dev, s,** and ENTER
 d) at **n:** input **sample size** & ENTER
 e) at **C-Level:**input **confidence level (as a decimal)** & ENTER
 f) highlight Calculate & ENTER to determine confidence interval

TO CONSTRUCT A 95% CONFIDENCE INTERVAL FOR THE POP MEAN WHERE
 $\bar{x}$ = 120, s = 8 & n = 16.

FOR THIS 95% CONFIDENCE INTERVAL, INPUT THE RESULTS TO TInterval SCREEN:

1) Press STAT & HIGHLIGHT TESTS

2) Select 8 for 8:TInterval . . .

The TINTERVAL INPUT is:
 a) Highlight STATS & ENTER
 b) at **$\bar{x}$:input 120** & ENTER
 c) at **Sx:**input **8** & ENTER
 d) at **n:** input **16** & ENTER
 e) at **C-Level:**input **.95** & ENTER

The **TInterval** input screen should contain the info shown in VIEW SCREEN 86.

VIEW SCREEN 86
 f) Highlight Calculate & ENTER

The 95% TInterval results are shown in VIEW SCREEN 87

VIEW SCREEN 87

The TInterval results are:

(115.74,124.26) *is the 95% confidence interval for the population mean*

$\bar{x}$ = 120 *is the sample mean*

Sx = 8 *is the sample std dev*

n = 16 is the *sample size*

TO CONSTRUCT A 99% CONFIDENCE INTERVAL FOR THE POP MEAN WHERE:

$\bar{x}$ = 120, s = 8 and n = 16

1) Press STAT & HIGHLIGHT TESTS

2) Select 8 for **8:TInterval . . .**

The TINTERVAL INPUT is:
 a) Highlight STATS & ENTER
 b) at **$\bar{x}$:input 120** & ENTER
 c) at **Sx:**input **8** & ENTER
 d) at **n:** input **16** & ENTER
 e) for **C-Level:** INPUT .99 & ENTER
 f) Highlight Calculate & ENTER

The TInterval results are shown in VIEW SCREEN 88

VIEW SCREEN 88

The TInterval results are:

(114.11,125.89) – this is the 99% confidence interval for the population mean

$\bar{x}$ = 120 *is the sample mean*

Sx = 8 *is the sample std dev*

n = 16 *is the sample size*

PROCEDURE TO CONSTRUCT A CONFIDENCE INTERVAL FOR A POPULATION MEAN USING *t* DISTRIBUTION WITH DATA INPUT

Confidence Interval For Pop Mean Where Pop Std Dev is UNKNOWN

1) Press STAT & HIGHLIGHT TESTS

2) Select 8 for **8:TInterval . . .** input screen for T confidence interval for a population mean is displayed in VIEW SCREEN 89.

VIEW SCREEN 89

3) **INPUT FOR A TInterval USING SAMPLE RESULTS:**

   a) at **Inpt:**highlight **Data** & ENTER

   b) at **LIST:** input List name containing sample data & ENTER

   c) at **Freq:input 1 or name of list containing frequencies** & ENTER

   d) at **C-Level:**input **confidence level (as a decimal)** & ENTER

   e) highlight **Calculate** & ENTER to determine confidence interval

TO CONSTRUCT A 95% CONFIDENCE INTERVAL FOR THE POP MEAN WHERE THE SAMPLE DATA IS ENTERED INTO LIST L1.

   SAMPLE DATA:

   80 68 91 87 73 90 66 79 80 81
   79 65 94 69 81 77 78 92 81 74

The TINTERVAL INPUT is:

   a) **Highlight** DATA & ENTER

   b) for **List:** INPUT **L1** & ENTER

   c) for **Freq:** INPUT **1** & ENTER

   d) for **C-Level:** INPUT .95 & ENTER

The **TInterval** input screen should contain the info shown in VIEW SCREEN 90.

VIEW SCREEN 90

   f) Highlight Calculate & ENTER

The 95% TInterval results are shown in VIEW SCREEN 91

VIEW SCREEN 91

The TInterval results are:

(75.25,83.25) *is the 95% confidence interval for the population mean*

$\bar{x} = 79.25$ *is the* **sample mean**

Sx = 8.546313456 *is the sample std dev*

n = 20 *is the sample size*

TO CONSTRUCT A 99% CONFIDENCE INTERVAL FOR THE POP MEAN USING THE SAME SAMPLE DATA IN LIST L1 , PERFORM THE STEPS.

1) Press DATA & HIGHLIGHT TESTS

2) Select 8 for **8:ZInterval . . .**

The TINTERVAL INPUT is:

   a) **Highlight** DATA & ENTER

   b) for **List:** INPUT **L1** & ENTER

   c) for **Freq:** INPUT **1** & ENTER

   d) for **C-Level:** INPUT .99 & ENTER

   f) Highlight Calculate & ENTER

The **TInterval** results are shown in VIEW SCREEN 92.

VIEW SCREEN 92

The TInterval results are:

(73.783,84.717) *is the 99% confidence interval for the population mean*

$\bar{x} = 79.25$ *is the sample mean*

Sx = 8.546313456 *is the sample std dev*

n = 20 *is the sample size*

PROCEDURE TO CONSTRUCT A CONFIDENCE INTERVAL FOR A POPULATION PROPORTION USING NORMAL DISTRIBUTION

Confidence Interval For a Population Proportion

1) Press STAT & HIGHLIGHT TESTS

2) Select A for A: **1-PropZInt . . .** input screen for Z confidence interval for a pop proportion is displayed in VIEW SCREEN 93.

VIEW SCREEN 93

3) **INPUT FOR 1-PropZInt USING SAMPLE RESULTS:**
   a) at **x:** input **number of successes** and ENTER
   b) at **n:** input **sample size and** ENTER
   c) at **C-Level:**input **confidence level (as a decimal)** & ENTER
   d) highlight Calculate & ENTER to determine confidence interval

TO CONSTRUCT A 95% CONFIDENCE INTERVAL FOR THE POPULATION PROPORTION WHERE:

$x = 918$ and **n = 1360**

FOR THIS 95% CONFIDENCE INTERVAL, INPUT THE SAMPLE RESULTS TO 1-PropZInt SCREEN:

1) **Press STAT & HIGHLIGHT TESTS**

2) **Select A for A: 1-PropZInt . . .**

The 1-PropZINT INPUT is:
   a) for **x:** INPUT **918** & ENTER
   b) for **n:** INPUT **1360** & ENTER
   c) for **C-Level:** INPUT **.95** & ENTER

The **1-PropZINT** input screen should contain the info shown in VIEW SCREEN 94.

VIEW SCREEN 94
f) Highlight Calculate & ENTER
The 95% 1-PropZInt results are shown in VIEW SCREEN 95

VIEW SCREEN 95

The 1-PropZInt results are:

(.65011,.69989) *is the 95% confidence interval for the population proportion*

$\hat{p} = .675$ *is the **sample proportion***

n = 1360 *is the **sample size***

TO CONSTRUCT A 99% CONFIDENCE INTERVAL FOR THE POPULATION PROPORTION WHERE:

$x = 918$ and **n = 1360**

1) Press STAT & HIGHLIGHT TESTS

2) Select A for A: 1-PropZInt . . .

The 1-PropZINT INPUT is:
   a) for **x:** INPUT **918** & ENTER
   b) for **n:** INPUT **1360** & ENTER
   c) for **C-Level:** INPUT **.99** & ENTER
   d) highlight Calculate & ENTER
The 99% 1-PropZInt results are shown in VIEW SCREEN 96

VIEW SCREEN 96

The 1-PropZInt results are:

(.64229,.70771) *is the 99% confidence interval for the population proportion*

$\hat{p} = .675$ *is the **sample proportion***
n = 1360 *is the **sample size***

PROCEDURE TO PERFORM A HYPOTHESIS TEST INVOLVING A POPULATION PROPORTION USING A NORMAL DISTRIBUTION

ONE POP PROPORTION TEST USING THE NORMAL DISTRIBUTION

1) Press STAT & Highlight TESTS shown in VIEW SCREEN 97.

VIEW SCREEN 97

2) Press 5 for **5:1-PropZTest . . .** input screen as shown in VIEW SCREEN 98.

VIEW SCREEN 98

3) For a **1-PropZTEST, INPUT:**
   a) at p_0:input **pop proportion** as stated in H_0 & ENTER
   b) at **x:**input **number of successes for the sample** & ENTER
   c) at **n:**input **sample size** & ENTER
   d) at **prop:**highlight **form of H_a, alternative hypothesis,** & ENTER
   e) highlight Calculate & ENTER

LET'S PERFORM A TEST WHERE:

H_0:p = .20; H_a:p>.20; x = 222; n = 1016 and α = 5%.

For this 1-PropZTest, INPUT:
   a) at p_0:INPUT **.2** & ENTER
   b) at **x:** INPUT **222** & ENTER
   c) at **n:** INPUT **1016** & ENTER
   d) at **prop:** HIGHLIGHT **> p_0** & ENTER

The 1-PropZTest input screen should contain the info shown in VIEW SCREEN 99.

VIEW SCREEN 99

e) highlight Calculate & ENTER
The test results are shown in VIEW SCREEN 100.

VIEW SCREEN 100

The **1-PropZTest** test results are:

prop>.2 *is* H_a

z = 1.474521142 *is the z score of the sample proportion*

p = .0701706992 *is the p-value*

$\hat{p}$ **= .218503937** *is the sample proportion*

n = 1016 *is the sample size*

We *FAIL TO REJECT* H_0 at α = 5% since the p-value > 5%.

What is the conclusion if $\alpha = 1\%$?

FOR A GRAPH OF THE TEST RESULTS:

1) press STAT & highlight TESTS
2) press 5 for **5:1-PropZTEST . . .**
3) highlight DRAW & ENTER
   VIEW SCREEN 101 is displayed.

VIEW SCREEN 101

In VIEW SCREEN 101, the z score and the p-value are displayed. Since this is a 1TT where H_a is prop>.2, the right tail is shaded. This shaded area represents the p-value.

PROCEDURE TO PERFORM A HYPOTHESIS TEST INVOLVING A POPULATION MEAN USING NORMAL DISTRIBUTION WITH STATS INPUT

ONE POP MEAN HYPOTHESIS TEST USING THE NORMAL DISTRIBUTION WITH KNOWN POPULATION STD DEV

1) Press STAT & Highlight TESTS shown in VIEW SCREEN 102.

VIEW SCREEN 102

2) Press 1 for **1:Z-Test . . .** input screen as shown in VIEW SCREEN 103.

VIEW SCREEN 103

3) **INPUT** for a **Z-TEST USING SAMPLE RESULTS:**
   a) at **Inpt:**highlight Stats & ENTER
   b) at μ_0:input **population mean** as stated in null hypothesis & ENTER
   c) at σ:input **pop std dev** & ENTER
   d) at $\bar{x}$:input **sample mean** & ENTER
   e) at **n:**input **sample size** & ENTER
   f) at μ:highlight **form of H_a, alternative hypothesis,** & ENTER
   g) highlight Calculate & ENTER

LET'S PERFORM A TEST WHERE:

$H_0: \mu = 120; H_a: \mu < 120$

$\sigma = 18, \bar{x} = 114, n = 36 \ \& \ \alpha = 1\%$.

For this Z-TEST, INPUT:
   a) Highlight **STATS** & **ENTER**
   b) for μ_0: INPUT **120** & ENTER
   c) for σ: INPUT **18** & ENTER
   d) for $\bar{x}$: INPUT **114** & ENTER
   e) for **n**: INPUT **36** & ENTER
   f) for μ: HIGHLIGHT **< μ_0** & ENTER

The Z-TEST input screen should contain the info shown in VIEW SCREEN 104.

VIEW SCREEN 104

g) Highlight Calculate & ENTER

The test results are shown in VIEW SCREEN 105.

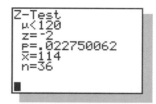

VIEW SCREEN 105

The Z-TEST results are:

$\mu < 120$: *is* H_a

z = –2: *is z score of sample mean*

p = .022750062: *is p-value of test*

$\bar{x} = 114$: *is sample mean*

n = 36: *is sample size*

We *FAIL TO REJECT H_0* at $\alpha = 1\%$ since the **p-value > 1%**.

What is the conclusion if $\alpha = 5\%$?

FOR A GRAPH OF THE TEST RESULTS:

1) press STAT
2) highlight TESTS
3) press 1 for **1:Z-Test . . .**
   VIEW SCREEN 103 is displayed.
4) highlight Draw & ENTER
   VIEW SCREEN 106 is displayed.

VIEW SCREEN 106

In VIEW SCREEN 106, the z score and the p-value are displayed. Since this is a 1TT where H_a is $\mu < 120$, the left tail is shaded. This shaded area represents the p-value of the test.

PROCEDURE TO PERFORM A HYPOTHESIS TEST INVOLVING A POPULATION MEAN USING NORMAL DISTRIBUTION WITH DATA INPUT

ONE POP MEAN HYPOTHESIS TEST USING THE NORMAL DISTRIBUTION WITH KNOWN POP STD DEVIATION

1) Press STAT & Highlight TESTS shown in VIEW SCREEN 107.

VIEW SCREEN 107

2) Press 1 for **1:Z-Test . . .** input screen as shown in VIEW SCREEN 108

VIEW SCREEN 108

3) **INPUT for a Z-TEST USING SAMPLE DATA:**
   a) at Inpt:highlight **Data** & ENTER
   b) at μ_0:input **population mean** as stated in null hypothesis & ENTER
   c) at σ:input **population std deviation** & ENTER
   d) at List:input List name containing **sample data** & ENTER
   e) at Freq:input 1 or name of list containing frequencies & ENTER
   f) at μ:highlight **form of Ha, alternative hypothesis,** & ENTER
   g) highlight Calculate & ENTER

LET'S PERFORM A Z-TEST WHERE THE FOLLOWING SAMPLE DATA HAS BEEN ENTERED INTO LIST L1:

SAMPLE DATA

750 765 780 710 720 715 730 735
740 745 750 760 680 675 690 695
650 600 615 620 630 640 590 585
560 555 490 485 475 465 460 695
650 610 575 450

AND WHERE:

H_0: $\mu = 610$; Ha: $\mu > 610$
$\sigma = 120$ and $\alpha = 5\%$.

For this Z-TEST, INPUT:
   a) Highlight DATA & ENTER
   b) for μ_0: INPUT **610** & ENTER
   c) for σ: INPUT **120** & ENTER

d) for **List:** INPUT **L1** & ENTER
e) for **Freq:** INPUT **1** & ENTER
f) for μ: HIGHLIGHT > μ_0 & ENTER

The Z-TEST input screen contains the info shown in VIEW SCREEN 109.

VIEW SCREEN 109

g) highlight Calculate & ENTER

The test results are shown in VIEW SCREEN 110.

VIEW SCREEN 110

The Z-TEST results are:

$\mu > 610$ *is* H_a

z = 1.5 is **z score** *of sample mean*

p = .0668072287 *is the p-value*

$\bar{x} = 640$ *is sample mean of L1*

Sx = 98.61179298 *is sample std dev. of List L1*

n = 36 *is the sample size*

We FAIL TO REJECT H_0 *at* $\alpha = 5\%$ *since the p-value > 5%.*
What is the conclusion if $\alpha = 1\%$?

FOR A GRAPH OF THE TEST RESULTS:

1) press STAT & highlight TESTS
2) press 1 for **1:Z-Test . . .**
3) highlight Draw & ENTER

   VIEW SCREEN 111 is displayed.

VIEW SCREEN 111

In VIEW SCREEN 111, the z score and the p-value are displayed. Since this is a 1TT where Ha is $\mu > 610$, the right tail is shaded. This shaded area represents the p-value of the test.

PROCEDURE TO PERFORM A HYPOTHESIS TEST INVOLVING A POPULATION MEAN USING t DISTRIBUTION WITH STATS INPUT

ONE POPULATION MEAN HYPOTHESIS TEST USING THE t DISTRIBUTION WITH UNKNOWN POP STD DEVIATION

1) Press STAT & Highlight TESTS shown in VIEW SCREEN 112.

VIEW SCREEN 112

2) Press 2 for **2:T-Test . . .** input screen as shown in VIEW SCREEN 113

VIEW SCREEN 113

3) **INPUT for a T-TEST USING SAMPLE RESULTS:**
   a) at **Inpt:**highlight Stats & ENTER
   b) at μ_0:input **population mean** as stated in null hypothesis & ENTER
   c) at $\bar{x}$: input **sample mean** & ENTER
   d) at Sx:input **sample std dev, s,** and ENTER
   e) at n:input **sample size** & ENTER
   f) at μ:highlight **form of H$_a$, alternative hypothesis,** & ENTER
   g) highlight Calculate & ENTER

LET'S PERFORM A T-TEST WHERE:
$H_0: \mu = 45,000; Ha: \mu < 45,000$
$\bar{x} = 42,900; s = 3,590; n = 16 \& \alpha = 5\%$

For this T-TEST, INPUT:
   a) **Highlight STATS & ENTER**
   b) for μ_0: INPUT **45000** & ENTER
   c) for $\bar{x}$: INPUT **42900** & ENTER
   d) for Sx: INPUT **3590** & ENTER
   e) for **n:** INPUT **16** & ENTER
   f) for μ: HIGHLIGHT $< \mu_0$ & ENTER
The T-TEST input screen should contain the info shown in VIEW SCREEN 114.

VIEW SCREEN 114

g) highlight Calculate & ENTER
The test results are shown in VIEW SCREEN 115.

VIEW SCREEN 115
The **T-TEST** results are:

$\mu < 45000$ *is* **H$_a$**

t = −2.339832869 *is the t score*

p = .0167670406 *is the p-value*

$\bar{x}$ **= 42900** *is the sample mean*

Sx = 3590 *is the sample std dev*

n = 16 *is the sample size*

We REJECT **H$_0$** at $\alpha = 5\%$ since the p-value < 5%.
What is the conclusion if $\alpha = 1\%$?

FOR A GRAPH OF THE TEST RESULTS:

1) press STAT & highlight TESTS
2) press 2 for **2:T-Test . . .**
3) highlight Draw & ENTER
   VIEW SCREEN 116 is displayed.

VIEW SCREEN 116

In VIEW SCREEN 116, the t score and the p-value are displayed. Since this is a 1TT where H$_a$ is $\mu < 45000$, the left tail is shaded. This shaded area represents the p-value.

PROCEDURE TO PERFORM A HYPOTHESIS TEST INVOLVING TWO POPULATION PROPORTIONS USING A NORMAL DISTRIBUTION

1) Press STAT & Highlight TESTS shown in VIEW SCREEN 117.

VIEW SCREEN 117

2) press 6 for **6:2-PropZTest . . .** input screen for a two sample proportion hypothesis test as displayed in VIEW SCREEN 118.

VIEW SCREEN 118

3) INPUT for a 2-PropZTEST USING SAMPLE RESULTS:
 a) for x1: input **the number of successes for sample one** & ENTER
 b) for n1: input the **sample size** for sample one & ENTER
 c) for x2: input **the number of successes for sample two** & ENTER
 d) for n2: input the **sample size** for sample two & ENTER
 e) for p1: highlight **form of Ha, alternative hypothesis,** & ENTER
 f) Highlight Calculate & ENTER

LET'S PERFORM A 2-PropZTEST WHERE
 $\alpha = 5\%$, $H_0: p_1 - p_2 = 0$; $H_a: p_1 - p_2 > 0$
 For sample 1: $x_1 = 870$ & $n_1 = 1500$
 For sample 2: $x_2 = 702$ & $n_2 = 1300$

For this 2-PropZTEST, INPUT:
 a) For x1: INPUT **870** & ENTER
 b) For n1: INPUT **1500** & ENTER
 c) For x2: INPUT **702** & ENTER
 d) For n2: INPUT **1300** & ENTER
 e) For p1: HIGHLIGHT **> p2** & ENTER
The 2-PropZTEST input screen should contain the info shown in VIEW SCREEN 119.

VIEW SCREEN 119

f) Highlight Calculate & ENTER
The test results are shown in VIEW SCREENS 120a & 120b.

VIEW SCREEN 120a   VIEW SCREEN 120b

The **2-PropZTEST** results are:

p1 > p2 *is* **H**$_a$

z = 2.127310376 *is the* **z score** *of the difference between two sample proportions*

p = .0166970917 *is the p-value*

$\hat{p}_1 = $ **.58** *is the* **proportion of sample 1**

$\hat{p}_2 = $ **.54** *is the* **proportion of sample 2**

$\hat{p} = $ **.5614285714** *is the* **pooled sample proportion**

n1 = 1500 *is the* **size of sample 1**

n2 = 1300 *is the* **size of sample 2**

We *REJECT* **H**$_0$ and *ACCEPT* **H**$_a$ at $\alpha = 5\%$ since the p-value < 5%.

What is the conclusion if $\alpha = 1\%$?

FOR A GRAPH OF THE TEST RESULTS:
1) press STAT & highlight TESTS
2) press 2 for **2:PropZTest . . .**
3) highlight Draw & ENTER
VIEW SCREEN 121 is displayed.

VIEW SCREEN 121

In VIEW SCREEN 121, the z score and the p-value are displayed. Since this is a 1TT where Ha is p1 > p2, the right tail is shaded. This shaded area represents the p-value.

PROCEDURE TO PERFORM A HYPOTHESIS TEST INVOLVING TWO POPULATION MEANS USING NORMAL DISTRIBUTION WITH STATS INPUT

TWO POP MEAN TEST WITH KNOWN POPULATION STD DEVIATIONS

1) Press STAT & Highlight TESTS shown in VIEW SCREEN 122.

VIEW SCREEN 122

2) press 3 for **3:2-SampZTest. . . .** input screen for a 2 sample mean test with pop std deviations KNOWN as shown in VIEW SCREEN 123.

VIEW SCREEN 123

3) **INPUT for a 2-SampZTEST USING SAMPLE RESULTS:**
   a) **at Inpt:Highlight Stats** & ENTER
   b) **at σ_1:key pop1 std dev** & ENTER
   c) **at σ_2:key pop2 std dev** & ENTER
   d) **at $\bar{x}$:key sample mean1** & ENTER
   e) **ar n_1:key sample size1** & ENTER
   f) **at $\bar{x}_2$:key sample mean2** & ENTER
   g) **at n_2:key sample size2** & ENTER
   h) **for $\mu 1$: highlight** the **form Ha, alternative hypothesis,** & ENTER
   i) **Highlight** Calculate & ENTER

LET'S PERFORM A 2-SampZTEST WHERE

$\alpha = 1\%, H_0: \mu_1 - \mu_2 = 0; H_a: \mu_1 - \mu_2 > 0$
For pop 1: $\sigma_1 = 20; \bar{x}_1 = 120$ & $n_1 = 81$
For pop 2: $\sigma_2 = 30; \bar{x}_2 = 112$ & $n_2 = 64$

For this 2-SampZTEST, INPUT:
   a) **at Inpt:Highlight Stats** & ENTER
   b) **for σ_1:** INPUT **20** & ENTER
   c) **for σ_2:** INPUT **30** & ENTER
   d) **for $\bar{x}1$:** INPUT **120** & ENTER
   e) **for n1:** INPUT **81** & ENTER
   f) **for $\bar{x}2$:** INPUT **112** & ENTER
   g) **for n2:** INPUT **64** & ENTER
   h) **for $\mu 1$:** HIGHLIGHT **$> \mu 2$** & ENTER

The 2-SampZTest input screens should contain the info shown in VIEW SCREENS 124a and 124b.

VIEW SCREEN 124a   VIEW SCREEN 124b

i) **Highlight** Calculate & ENTER

The 2-SampZTest results are shown in VIEW SCREENS 125a and 125b.

VIEW SCREEN 125a   VIEW SCREEN 125b

The 2-SampZTest test results are:

$\mu 1 > \mu 2$ *is* $H_a: \mu_1 - \mu_2 > 0$

z = 1.835288605 *is the **z-score** of the difference between the two sample means:* $\bar{x}_1 - \bar{x}_2$

p = .0332314098 *is the **p-value***

$\bar{x}_1$ **= 120** *is the **mean of sample 1***

$\bar{x}_2$ **= 112** *is the **mean of sample 2***

n1 = 81 *is the **size of sample 1***

n2 = 64 *is the **size of sample 2***

We *FAIL TO REJECT H$_0$* at $\alpha = 1\%$ since the p-value > 1%. *What is the conclusion if* $\alpha = 5\%$?

FOR A GRAPH OF THE TEST RESULTS:

1) press STAT & highlight TESTS
2) press 3 for **3:2-SampZTest. . . .**
3) highlight Draw & ENTER

VIEW SCREEN 126

In VIEW SCREEN 126, the z score and the p-value are displayed. Since this is a 1TT where H$_a$ is $\mu 1 > \mu 2$, the right tail is shaded. This shaded area represents the p-value.

PROCEDURE TO PERFORM A HYPOTHESIS TEST INVOLVING TWO POPULATION MEANS USING NORMAL DISTRIBUTION WITH DATA INPUT

TWO POP MEAN TEST WITH KNOWN POPULATION STD DEVIATIONS

1) Press STAT & Highlight TESTS shown in VIEW SCREEN 127.

VIEW SCREEN 127

2) press 3 for **3:2-SampZTest**. . . . input screen for a 2 sample z test as shown in VIEW SCREEN 128.

VIEW SCREEN 128

3) **INPUT for a 2-SampZTEST USING DATA:**
   a) **at Inpt:Highlight Data** & ENTER
   b) **at σ_1:key pop1 std dev** & ENTER
   c) **at σ_2:key pop2 std dev** & ENTER
   d) **at List1: key List containing data for sample 1** & ENTER
   e) **at List2: key List containing data for sample 2** & ENTER
   f) **at Freq1: key 1 or List name containing frequencies for sample1** & ENTER
   g) **at Freq2: key 1 or List name containing frequencies for sample2** & ENTER
   h) **for $\mu 1$: highlight the form Ha, alternative hypothesis,** & ENTER
   i) **Highlight** Calculate & ENTER

LET'S PERFORM A 2-SampZTEST WHERE $\alpha = 5\%$ & THE SAMPLE DATA BELOW.
Enter Samples Into LISTS

INPUT SAMPLE 1 INTO L1
113 117 112 115 112 116 119
113 121 123 124 119 117 123
111 112 115 114 118 119 115
123 127 119 117 124 126 129
118 125 126 128 119 127 125
117 119 125 124 128 121 125

INPUT SAMPLE 2 INTO L2
124 126 128 113 118 117 114
117 113 120 125 120 127 125
121 115 117 117 128 124 126
127 129 129 127 126 122 126
128 129 123 129 126 128 127
127 129 122 123 126 123 126

LET'S PERFORM 2-SampZTEST USING THE SAMPLE DATA IN LISTS L1 & L2,
$H_0: \mu_1 - \mu_2 = 0; H_a: \mu_1 - \mu_2 < 0$ and
for pop 1: $\sigma_1 = 7$ & **for pop 2:** $\sigma_2 = 6$

For this 2-SampZTEST, INPUT:
   a) **Highlight DATA & ENTER**
   b) **for σ_1:** INPUT **7** & ENTER
   c) **for σ_2:** INPUT **6** & ENTER
   d) **for List1:** INPUT **L1** & ENTER
   e) **for List2:** INPUT **L2** & ENTER
   f) **for Freq1:** INPUT **1** & ENTER
   g) **for Freq2:** INPUT **1** & ENTER
   h) **for $\mu 1$:** HIGHLIGHT **< $\mu 2$** & ENTER

The 2-SampZTest input screens should contain the info shown in VIEW SCREENS 129a and 129b.

VIEW SCREEN 129a   VIEW SCREEN 129b

   i) **Highlight** Calculate & ENTER **2-SampZTest** results are shown in VIEW SCREENS 130a & 130b.

VIEW SCREEN 130a   VIEW SCREEN 130b

The 2-SampZTest test results are:

$\mu 1 > \mu 2$ is H$_a$:$\mu_1 - \mu_2 < 0$

z = –2.460272582 *is the z-score of the difference between the two sample means:* $\bar{x}_1 - \bar{x}_2$

p = .0069415825 *is the p-value*

$\bar{x}_1 = 120$ *is the mean of sample 1*

$\bar{x}_2 = 123.5$ *is mean of sample 2*

Sx1 = 5.1890679 *is the std dev of sample 1*

Sx2 = 4.84012699 *is the std dev of sample 2*

n1 = 42 *is the size of sample 1*

n2 = 42 *is the size of sample 2*

We *REJECT* H_0 *and ACCEPT* H_a at $\alpha = 5\%$ since the p-value $< 5\%$.

What is the conclusion if $\alpha = 1\%$?

FOR A GRAPH OF THE TEST RESULTS:

1) press STAT & highlight **TESTS**

2) press 3 for **3:2-SampZTest. . . .**

3) highlight Draw & ENTER

VIEW SCREEN 131 is displayed.

VIEW SCREEN 131

In VIEW SCREEN 131, the z score and the p-value are displayed. Since this is a 1TT where H_a is $\mu 1 < \mu 2$, the left tail is shaded. This shaded area represents the p-value. Note: since the p-value is very small, the shaded area is not noticeable.

PROCEDURE TO PERFORM A HYPOTHESIS TEST INVOLVING TWO POPULATION MEANS USING t DISTRIBUTION WITH STATS INPUT

TWO POP MEAN t TEST WITH UNKNOWN POPULATION STD DEVIATIONS

1) Press STAT & Highlight TESTS shown in VIEW SCREEN 132.

VIEW SCREEN 132

2) press 4 for **4:2-SampTTest. . . .** input screen for a 2 sample t test as shown in VIEW SCREEN 133.

VIEW SCREEN 133

3) **INPUT for a 2-SampTTEST USING SAMPLE RESULTS:**
   a) at **Inpt:**Highlight Stats & ENTER
   b) at $\bar{x}_1$:mean of sample1 & ENTER
   c) at **Sx1:**std dev of sample1, s_1, & ENTER
   d) at n_1:size of sample1 & ENTER
   e) at $\bar{x}_2$:mean of sample2 & ENTER
   f) at **Sx2:**std dev of sample2, s_2, & ENTER
   g) at n_2:size of sample2 & ENTER
   h) at $\mu1$: highlight the **form H**a, alternative hypothesis, & ENTER
   i) at **Pooled:**Highlight YES & ENTER
   j) Highlight Calculate & ENTER

LET'S PERFORM A 2-SampTTEST WHERE

$\alpha = 1\%$ & $H_0: \mu_1 - \mu_2 = 0$ & $H_a:\mu_1 - \mu_2 < 0$

For sample1: $\bar{x}_1 = 116$; $s_1 = 6.7$ & $n_1 = 16$

For sample2: $\bar{x}_2 = 120$; $s_2 = 5.6$ & $n_2 = 20$

For this 2-SampTTEST, INPUT:
   a) **at Inpt:Highlight** Stats & ENTER
   b) at $\bar{x}1$: INPUT **116** & ENTER
   c) at **Sx1:** INPUT **6.7** & ENTER
   d) at **n1:** INPUT **16** & ENTER
   e) at $\bar{x}2$: INPUT **120** & ENTER
   f) at **Sx2:** INPUT **5.6** & ENTER
   g) at **n2:** INPUT **20** & ENTER
   h) at $\mu1$: HIGHLIGHT $< \mu2$ & ENTER
   i) at **Pooled:**HIGHLIGHT Yes & ENTER

The 2-SampTTest input screens should contain the info shown in VIEW SCREENS 134a and 134b.

VIEW SCREEN 134a   VIEW SCREEN 134b

   j) **Highlight** Calculate & ENTER **2-SampTTest** results are shown in VIEW SCREENS 135a and 135b.

VIEW SCREEN 135a   VIEW SCREEN 135b

The 2-SampTTest results are:

$\mu1 < \mu2$ is $H_a: \mu_1 - \mu_2 < 0$

t = –1.951910354 *is the **t-score** of the difference between the two sample means:* $\bar{x}_1 - \bar{x}_2$

p = .0296123491 *is the **p-value***

df = 34 *is the degrees of freedom*

$\bar{x}1 = $ **116** *is the **mean of sample1***

$\bar{x}2 = $ **120** *is the **mean of sample2***

Sx1 = 6.7 *is the **std dev of sample1***

Sx2 = 5.6 *is the std dev of sample2*

Sxp = 6.10975594 *is the pooled std deviation of both samples*

n1 = 16 *is the size of sample 1*

n2 = 20 *is the size of sample 2*

We *FAIL TO REJECT* H_0 $\alpha = 1\%$ since the p-value $> 1\%$.
What is the conclusion if $\alpha = 5\%$?

FOR A GRAPH OF THE TEST RESULTS:

1) press STAT & highlight TESTS
2) press 4 for **4:2-SampTTest. . . .**
3) highlight Draw & ENTER
   VIEW SCREEN 136 is displayed.

VIEW SCREEN 136

In VIEW SCREEN 136, the t score and the p-value are displayed. Since this is a 1TT where H_a is $\mu 1 < \mu 2$, the left tail is shaded. This shaded area represents the p-value.

PROCEDURE TO PERFORM A HYPOTHESIS TEST INVOLVING TWO POPULATION MEANS USING *t* DISTRIBUTION WITH DATA INPUT

TWO POP MEAN *t* TEST WITH UNKNOWN POPULATION STD DEVIATIONS

1) Press STAT & Highlight TESTS shown in VIEW SCREEN 137.

VIEW SCREEN 137

2) press 4 for **4:2-SampTTest. . . .** input screen for a 2 sample *t* test as shown in VIEW SCREEN 138.

VIEW SCREEN 138

3) **INPUT for a 2-SampTTEST USING SAMPLE DATA:**
   a) **at Inpt:Highlight** Data & ENTER
   b) **at List1: key List containing data for sample 1 &** ENTER
   c) **at List2: key List containing data for sample 2 &** ENTER
   d) **at Freq1: key 1 or List name containing frequencies for sample1 &** ENTER
   e) **at Freq2: key 1 or List name containing frequencies for sample2 &** ENTER
   f) **for $\mu 1$: highlight the form Ha, alternative hypothesis,** & ENTER
   g) **at Pooled:Highlight** YES & ENTER
   h) **Highlight** Calculate & ENTER

LET'S PERFORM A 2-SampTTEST WHERE
$\alpha = 5\%$ & H$_0$: $\mu_1 - \mu_2 = 0$ & H$_a$: $\mu_1 - \mu_2 > 0$
AND THE GIVEN SAMPLE DATA.
Enter Samples Into LISTS
INPUT SAMPLE 1 INTO L1
SAMPLE DATA FOR SAMPLE 1:
83 87 92 85 92 86 89 93
81 92 95 94 88 93 85

INPUT SAMPLE 2 INTO L2
SAMPLE DATA FOR SAMPLE 2:
74 96 78 83 86 87 94 77 83 80

For this 2-SampTTEST, INPUT:
   a) **at Inpt:Highlight** Data & ENTER
   b) **at List1: INPUT L1 &** ENTER
   c) **at List2: INPUT L2 &** ENTER
   d) **at Freq1: INPUT 1 &** ENTER
   e) **at Freq2: INPUT 1 &** ENTER
   f) **at $\mu 1$: HIGHLIGHT** > μ_2 & ENTER
   g) **at Pooled:Highlight** YES & ENTER

The 2-SampTTest input screen should contain the info shown in VIEW SCREEN 139.

VIEW SCREEN 139
   h) **Highlight** Calculate & ENTER

The 2-SampTTest results are shown in VIEW SCREENS 140a and 140b.

VIEW SCREEN 140a   VIEW SCREEN 140b

The 2-SampTTest results are:
   $\mu 1 > \mu 2$ is H$_a$: $\mu_1 - \mu_2 > 0$
   t = 2.267745166 *is the **t-score** of the difference between the two sample means:* $\bar{x}_1 - \bar{x}_2$
   p = .0165253764 *is the **p-value***
   df = 23 *is the **degrees of freedom***
   $\bar{x}1 = 89$ *is the **mean of sample 1***
   $\bar{x}2 = 83.8$ *is the **mean of sample 2***
   Sx1 = 4.35889894 *is the **std dev of sample 1***
   Sx2 = 7.1460945 *is the **std dev of sample 2***
   Sxp = 5.61674515 *is the **pooled std dev of both samples***

n1 = 15 *is the size of sample 1*

n2 = 10 *is the size of sample 2*

We *REJECT H_0* and ACCEPT H_a α = 5% since the p-value < 5%.

What is the conclusion if $\alpha = 1\%$?

FOR A GRAPH OF THE TEST RESULTS:

1) press STAT & highlight TESTS

2) press 4 for **4:2-SampTTest. . . .**

3) highlight Draw & ENTER

   VIEW SCREEN 141 is displayed.

VIEW SCREEN 141

In VIEW SCREEN 141, the t score and the p-value are displayed. Since this is a 1TT with H_a is $\mu1 > \mu2$, the right tail is shaded. This shaded area represents the p-value.

PROCEDURE TO INPUT OBSERVED VALUES OF A CHI-SQUARE TEST OF INDEPENDENCE INTO MATRIX A

1) INPUT OBSERVED VALUES INTO MATRIX A AS FOLLOWS.

a) Press 2nd & MATRIX (x^{-1} key) to display matrix name menu as shown in VIEW SCREEN 142.

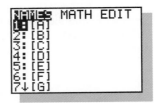

VIEW SCREEN 142

The first name: **1:[A]** refers to **MATRIX A** and is written **[A]**.

b) HIGHLIGHT EDIT as shown in VIEW SCREEN 143.

VIEW SCREEN 143

c) Select **1:[A]** for MATRIX[A] and its *size appears* as displayed in VIEW SCREEN 144.

VIEW SCREEN 144

To define the size of MATRIX[A]:

d) Input number of rows & ENTER

e) Input number of columns & ENTER

After **MATRIX[A] is defined,** you can enter the values of **[A]**.

WE WILL EXPLAIN HOW TO INPUT THE FOLLOWING OBSERVED VALUES LISTED IN THE 4x2 CONTINGENCY TABLE INTO MATRIX A.

Education Level	Grand Jury Selected		Not Selected	
Elementary	a	24	b	36
Secondary	c	98	d	102
Some College	e	16	f	44
College Degree	g	42	h	38

TO INPUT THESE OBSERVED VALUES INTO A 4x2 MATRIX[A]:

a) Press 2nd & MATRIX (x^{-1} key)

b) HIGHLIGHT EDIT

c) Press 1 to select **1:[A]**

d) Press 4 ENTER 2 ENTER to define a 4x2 Matrix for **[A]**.

The cursor highlights the first element of the 4x2 MATRIX [A] as displayed in VIEW SCREEN 145.

VIEW SCREEN 145

e) Input the first observed value **24** of **cell a** into [A] & ENTER.

f) Input the second observed value **36** of **cell b** into [A] & ENTER.

CONTINUE THIS PROCESS UNTIL ALL THE OBSERVED VALUES ARE ENTERED INTO MATRIX[A].

VIEW SCREEN 146 displays the final input screen for MATRIX[A].

VIEW SCREEN 146

Notice the last cell value **38** in MATRIX[A] is highlighted. Its position within [A] is 4th row & 2nd column and is written at the bottom of the screen as 4,2 = 38. After all the observed results are entered into [A], you can conduct a chi-square test of independence.

PROCEDURE TO PERFORM A CHI-SQUARE HYPOTHESIS TEST OF INDEPENDENCE

TO PERFORM A CHI-SQUARE TEST AT α = 5% TO DETERMINE IF A PERSON'S SELECTION TO SERVE ON THE GRAND JURY IS INDEPENDENT OF THEIR EDUCATIONAL LEVEL, WE WILL USE THE 4x2 CONTINGENCY TABLE.

Education Level	Grand Jury Selected		Not Selected	
Elementary	a	24	b	36
Secondary	c	98	d	102
Some College	e	16	f	44
College Degree	g	42	h	38

To perform this chi-square test, input these observed values into a 4x2 matrix [A]:

a) Press 2nd & MATRIX (x^{-1} key)

b) HIGHLIGHT EDIT

c) Press 1 to select **1:[A]**

d) Press 4 ENTER 2 ENTER to define a 4x2 Matrix for **[A]** shown in VIEW SCREEN 147.

VIEW SCREEN 147

e) Input all observed values into MATRIX [A]. VIEW SCREEN 148 shows the input screen for MATRIX[A].

VIEW SCREEN 148

Notice the last cell value **38** in MATRIX[A] is highlighted. Its position is the 4th row & 2nd column of [A] and is written as 4,2 = 38 at the bottom of screen.

TO PERFORM THE CHI-SQUARE TEST:

1) Press STAT & Highlight TESTS

2) Highlight **C: χ^2-Test** & ENTER

The χ^2- Test screen appears as shown in VIEW SCREEN 149.

VIEW SCREEN 149

3) at **Observed:[A]** press ENTER to indicate the observed results are in MATRIX[A].

4) at **Expected:[B]** press ENTER to designate MATRIX[B] as the matrix where the expected results of the chi-square test will be stored.

5) HIGHLIGHT Calculate & ENTER

The χ^2-Test results are shown in VIEW SCREEN 150.

VIEW SCREEN 150

The χ^2-Test results are:

χ^2 = **11.86531987** *is Pearson's chi-square statistic,* X^2

p = .0078590496 *is the p-value*

df = 3 *is the degrees of freedom*

We *REJECT H_0 & ACCEPT H_a at α = 5% since the p-value < 5%.*

What is the conclusion if α = 1%?

TO RETRIEVE THE EXPECTED RESULTS:

1) Press 2nd & MATRIX (x^{-1} key)

2) press 2 for **2:[B]** & ENTER to obtain the expected values of MATRIX[B] shown in VIEW SCREEN 151.

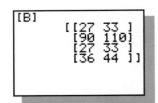

VIEW SCREEN 151

Notice the expected value in the 4th row & 1st column is 36.

FOR A GRAPH OF THE TEST RESULTS:

1) Press **STAT** & highlight **TESTS**
2) Highlight **C: χ^2 -Test** & **ENTER**
3) Highlight **Draw** & **ENTER**
   VIEW SCREEN 152 is displayed.

VIEW SCREEN 152

In **VIEW SCREEN 152**, *Pearson's chi-square statistic,* X^2 and the p-value are displayed. The right shaded tail area represents the p-value. Note: since the p-value is very small, the shaded area is not noticeable.

PROCEDURE TO CONSTRUCT A SCATTER DIAGRAM

CONSTRUCTING A SCATTER DIAGRAM

1) Enter the data values for each variable X and Y into a separate stat list.

   For this example, enter the X and Y values into **L1** and **L2** respectively.

   X: 23 24 25 26 27 28

   Y: 161 166 164 170 167 169

2) Press WINDOW to display the **window variables values.**

3) Set the window variables using the following guide for a **SCATTER DIAGRAM**.

For a SCATTER DIAGRAM:

set **XMIN**   **< smallest data value**

set **XMAX**   **> largest data value**

set **XSCL**   **= 1 OR appropriate frequency scale**

set **YMIN**   **= < smallest data value**

set **YMAX**   **> largest data value**

set **YSCL**   **= 1 OR appropriate frequency scale**

set **Xres**   **= 1**

For this example, set the **window variables to:**

Xmin = 20   *:less than the smallest X value*

Xmax = 30   *:greater than the largest X value*

Xscl = 1   *:set to one*

Ymin = 155   *:less than the smallest Y value*

Ymax = 175   *:greater than the largest Y value*

Yscl = 1   *:set to one*

Xres = 1   *:set to one*

VIEW SCREEN 153 displays the WINDOW values for this scatter diagram.

VIEW SCREEN 153

4) Press 2nd & STAT PLOT (Y = key)

   The **STAT PLOTS Menu** is displayed with **1:PLOT1 . . . .** highlighted.

5) Press ENTER to display **stat plot editor** screen for Plot 1.

6) Highlight ON & press ENTER

7) Highlight **SCATTER DIAGRAM**: 1st graph to right of TYPE & ENTER

8) For Xlist: : key in the name of data List. For this example, key in **L1** and press ENTER

9) For Ylist: : key in the name of data List. For this example, key in **L2** and press ENTER

10) For MARK: **select** □ **(1st item: box:** □**)** to designate how the points in the scatter diagram will be displayed & ENTER

   The input screen for defining this scatter plot is shown in VIEW SCREEN 154.

VIEW SCREEN 154

11) Press GRAPH to display the **scatter diagram** shown in VIEW SCREEN 155.

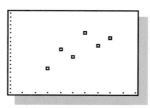

VIEW SCREEN 155

12) Press TRACE to identify the X and Y values of the points in the scatter diagram.

   The X and Y values of the first point of the scatter diagram: **X = 23 and Y = 161** are displayed at the bottom of the screen as shown in VIEW SCREEN 156.

VIEW SCREEN 156

   The **P1:L1,L2** in the upper left corner refers to stat plot P1 while the **L1,L2** indicates that the data values are stored in **Lists L1 and L2**.

13) Press cursor ▶ key to move to the next point on scatter diagram. This second point is identified by: **X = 24 and Y = 166.**

   The 3rd point is **X = 25 and Y = 164.** And so on.

PROCEDURE TO PERFORM STATISTICAL ANALYSIS FOR 2-VARIABLES: TO DETERMINE THE REGRESSION COEFFICIENTS: a & b OF THE REGRESSION LINE y' = a + bx, PEARSON'S CORRELATION COEFFICIENT, r, AND THE COEFFICIENT OF DETERMINATION, r₂

To display the values of r and **r²**, it is necessary to set the *Diagnostic display mode on.*

To set DiagnosticOn:

1) Press 2nd & CATALOG (0 KEY) and scroll to **DiagnosticOn** shown in VIEW SCREEN 157.

VIEW SCREEN 157

2) Press ENTER twice. DONE appears indicating mode is set to **DiagnosticOn**.

TO DISPLAY THE VALUES OF r, r² AND THE REGRESSION COEFFICIENTS

1) Input the X and Y values into **L1** and **L2** respectively.

   X: 23 24 25 26 27 28
   Y: 161 166 164 170 167 169

2) Press STAT & Highlight CALC

3) Press **8** for 8:LinReg(a+bx)

4) Input: XList name , YList name and press ENTER
   For this example, input: L1,L2
   The values of: **a, b, r and r²** are displayed shown in VIEW SCREEN 158.

VIEW SCREEN 158

The **LinReg** results are:

y = a+bx

a = 130.4666667 *is the intercept of the regression line*

b = 1.4 *is the slope of the regression line*

r² = .6255319149 *is the coefficient of determination*

r = .790905756 *is Pearson's correlation coefficient*

PROCEDURE TO DISPLAY REGRESSION LINE AND TO
COMPUTE THE PREDICTED Y VALUE FROM THE REGRESSION LINE

TO DISPLAY THE REGRESSION LINE

1) Input the X and Y values into **L1** and **L2** respectively.

   X: 23 24 25 26 27 28

   Y: 161 166 164 170 167 169

2) Press **STAT** & Highlight **CALC**
3) Press **8** for **8:LinReg(a+bx)**
4) Input L1,L2 & **ENTER**

   These 4 steps compute & store the regression variables required for the regression equation.

5) Press **Y =** . A blinking cursor appears to next to **\Y1 =** shown in VIEW SCREEN 159.

VIEW SCREEN 159

6) Press **VARS** & press **5** for **5:Statistics. . . .** . The **statistics vars menu** is displayed as shown in VIEW SCREEN 160.

VIEW SCREEN 160

7) HIGHLIGHT **EQ** (3rd COLUMN) shown in VIEW SCREEN 161.

VIEW SCREEN 161

8) Press **ENTER** to select **1:RegEQ** . The **RegEQ:** **130.4666666667 + 1.4X** appears next to **\Y1 =** shown in VIEW SCREEN 162.

VIEW SCREEN 162

9) Press **GRAPH** to draw regression line as shown in VIEW SCREEN 163.

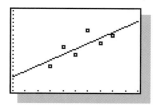

VIEW SCREEN 163

10) Press **TRACE** to identify the X & Y values of the points on the REGRESSION LINE. Note the 1st point is: **X = 23 & Y = 161**. **P1:L1,L2** appears in left upper corner of the screen.

11) Press up cursor ▲ to place cursor ON THE REGRESSION LINE as shown in VIEW SCREEN 164.

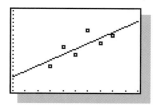

VIEW SCREEN 164

The regression equation **Y1 = 130.46666666667 + 1.4X**

appears in the upper left corner of the screen. Notice **THE POINT X = 25 and Y = 165.46667 IS DISPLAYED** at the bottom of the screen as shown in VIEW SCREEN 164. As the cursor moves along the regression line, the points of the regression line will be displayed at the bottom of the screen.

WHY IS THE Y VALUE: Y = 165.47 FOR X = 25 ON THE REGRESSION LINE DIFFERENT THAN THE Y VALUE: Y = 164 FOR X = 25 ON THE SCATTER DIAGRAM? EXPLAIN.

TO PREDICT THE Y VALUE FOR A SPECIFIED X VALUE USING THE REGRESSION LINE

With the regression line graphed as shown in VIEW SCREEN 164, we can use the regression line to calculate a predicted y value(y') for a specified X value. To calculate a predicted y value for X = 26:

1) Press 2nd & CALC (TRACE key) to display the **CALCULATE menu** as shown in VIEW SCREEN 165.

VIEW SCREEN 165

2) press ENTER to select 1:value . **X =** and a **blinking cursor** appears.

3) Input 26 for X value & **ENTER** The *predicted y value (y'): Y = 166.86667 for X = 26* appears as shown in VIEW SCREEN 166.

VIEW SCREEN 166

WHAT IS THE PREDICTED y VALUE (y') FOR x = 27?

PROCEDURE TO PERFORM A TWO-SAMPLE F-TEST

TO PERFORM A TWO-SAMPLE F-TEST

The TI–83 Plus 2-SampFTest performs an F-Test to compare two normal population standard deviations, σ_1 and σ_2.

Let's perform a TWO-SAMPLE F-TEST using the sample results of Example 16.4.

1) Press STAT & Highlight TESTS shown in VIEW SCREEN 167.

VIEW SCREEN 167

2) Press ALPHA & D (x⁻¹ key) for **D:2-SampFTest.** . . . input screen for a 2 sample F test as shown in VIEW SCREEN 168.

VIEW SCREEN 168

3) **INPUT for a 2-SampFTEST USING SAMPLE RESULTS:**
   a) **at Inpt:Highlight** Stats & ENTER
   b) **at Sx1:std dev of sample1, s_1,** & ENTER
   c) **at n_1:size of sample1** & ENTER
   d) **at Sx2:std dev of sample2, s_2,** & ENTER
   e) **at n_2:size of sample2** & ENTER
   h) **at σ1: highlight** the **form Ha, alternative hypothesis,** & ENTER
   i) **Highlight** Calculate & ENTER

LET'S PERFORM A 2-SampFTEST USING THE INFO FROM EXAMPLE 16.4 WHERE

$\alpha = 0.10$ & **H$_0$:** $\sigma_1^2 = \sigma_2^2$ & **H$_a$:** $\sigma_1^2 \neq \sigma_2^2$

For sample1: $s_1 = 3.74$ & $n_1 = 10$

For sample2: $s_2 = 2$ & $n_2 = 11$

For this 2-SampFTEST, INPUT:
   a) **at Inpt:Highlight** Stats & ENTER
   b) **Sx1:** INPUT **3.74** & ENTER

   c) at **n1:** INPUT **10** & ENTER
   d) at **Sx2:** INPUT **2** & ENTER
   e) at **n2:** INPUT **11** & ENTER
   h) at **σ1:** HIGHLIGHT $\neq \sigma_2$ & ENTER

The 2-SampFTest input screen should contain the info shown in VIEW SCREEN 169.

VIEW SCREEN 169

j) Highlight Calculate & ENTER

2-SampTTest results are shown in VIEW SCREENS 170a and 170b.

VIEW SCREEN 170a   VIEW SCREEN 170b

The 2-SampFTest results are:

2-SampFTest

$\sigma_1 \neq \sigma_2$

F = 3.4969 *is the test statistic F*

p = .0640582526 *is the p-value*

Sx1 = 3.74 *is std dev of sample 1*

Sx2 = 2 *is std dev of sample 2*

$n_1 = 10$ *is size of sample 1*

$n_2 = 11$ *is size of sample 2*

Since this 2-SampFTEST is being conducted at $\alpha = 0.10$ where **H$_a$:** $\sigma_1^2 \neq \sigma_2^2$, then using Table VII critical F-value is: **$F_{0.05}(9,10) = 3.02$.**

Since the test statistic, F = 3.5 (to 2 decimal places), is greater than the critical

F-value, $F_{0.05}(9,10) = 3.02$, reject **H$_0$** and accept **H$_a$**. Thus, the population variances are significantly different at $\alpha = 0.10$.

PROCEDURE TO PERFORM ONE-WAY ANOVA

TO PERFORM A ONE-WAY ANALYSIS OF VARIANCE, ANOVA

The TI–83 Plus test function ANOVA(computes a one-way analysis of variance for comparing the means of 2 to 20 populations. The null hypothesis H_0:the population means are equal is tested against the alternative H_a: the population means are not all equal. To perform an ANOVA test, you must enter each sample data into a List.

Let's perform an ANOVA test using the information of Example 16.6.

1) INPUT the data of the 4 samples into Lists L1 , L2 , L3 & L4 .

2) Press STAT & Highlight TESTS shown in VIEW SCREEN 171.

VIEW SCREEN 171

3) Select F : for F:ANOVA(
   ANOVA(appears on the home screen.

4) Input the 4 List names containing the sample data separating each List name by a comma to get: ANOVA(L1,L2,L3,L4) as shown in VIEW SCREEN 172.

VIEW SCREEN 172

5) Press ENTER
   The ANOVA test results are shown in VIEW SCREENS 173a & 173b.

VIEW SCREEN 173a   VIEW SCREEN 173b

The One-way ANOVA results are:

F = 4.942842833 *is the test statistic*

p = .0105502285 *is the p-value*

Factor

df = 3 *is the degrees of freedom for the between treatments*

SS = 20.3258152 *is the sum of squares for between treatments*

MS = 6.77527174 *is the mean square for between treatments*

Error

df = 19 *is the degrees of freedom for within treatments*

SS = 26.04375 *is the sum of squares for within treatments*

MS = 1.37072368 *is the mean square for within treatments*

SXp = 1.17077909 *is the pooled standard deviation*

Since this ANOVA test is being conducted at $\alpha = 0.05$, we need to look up the critical F-value, $F_{0.05}(3,19)$ in Table VII.

From Table VII, the critical F-value: $F_{0.05}(3,19) = 3.13$.

Since the calculated test statistic F, 4.94, is **greater than** the critical F-value (3.13), we **reject the null hypothesis, H_0, and accept the alternative hypothesis H_a** at $\alpha = 0.05$. Therefore, we conclude that the population means are **not** all equal.

INDEX